2019–2020

FORTY-SECOND EDITION

Florida
School Directory

A State Guide to K-12 Districts, Dioceses, and Schools...

Powered by the Industry's Best Data

- **NEW...8 Additional Administrator Titles!**
- Charter Management Organization Index
- Facebook and Twitter Indicators
- Email Address Availability Highlighted
- Detailed School and District Listings
- Names and Job Titles of Key Personnel
- New Schools and Personnel Index

MDR

A Dun & Bradstreet Division

Copyright 2019 Market Data Retrieval | 6 Armstrong Road, Shelton, CT 06484

Copyright 2019 Market Data Retrieval, a D&B Company. All Rights Reserved. No information furnished hereby may be reproduced or transmitted in any form or by any means, electronic or mechanical, including photocopying and recording, or by any information storage or retrieval system, except as may be expressly permitted by MDR, 6 Armstrong Road, Shelton, CT 06484.

The information in this directory is licensed with the express understanding and agreement that the information will be solely for internal use and will not be used for the creation and/or updating of databases, electronic or otherwise, that are sold or provided to any third party without the express written permission of MDR.

51-Volume National Set	ISBN# 978-1-951295-51-6

Individual Bound State Editions

	ISSN#	ISBN#		ISSN#	ISBN#
Alabama	1077-7393	978-1-947802-68-1	Montana	1077-7652	978-1-951295-25-7
Alaska	1077-7407	978-1-951295-00-4	Nebraska	1077-7660	978-1-951295-26-4
Arizona	1077-7415	978-1-951295-01-1	Nevada	1077-7679	978-1-951295-27-1
Arkansas	1077-7423	978-1-951295-02-8	New Hampshire	1077-7687	978-1-951295-28-8
California	1077-7431	978-1-951295-03-5	New Jersey	1077-7695	978-1-951295-29-5
Colorado	1077-744X	978-1-951295-04-2	New Mexico	1077-7709	978-1-951295-30-1
Connecticut	1077-7458	978-1-951295-05-9	New York	1077-7717	978-1-951295-31-8
Delaware	1077-7466	978-1-951295-06-6	North Carolina	1077-7725	978-1-951295-32-5
District of Columbia	1077-7474	978-1-951295-07-3	North Dakota	1077-7733	978-1-951295-33-2
Florida	1077-7482	978-1-951295-08-0	Ohio	1077-7741	978-1-951295-34-9
Georgia	1077-7490	978-1-951295-09-7	Oklahoma	1077-775X	978-1-951295-35-6
Hawaii	1077-7504	978-1-951295-10-3	Oregon	1077-7768	978-1-951295-36-3
Idaho	1077-7512	978-1-951295-11-0	Pennsylvania	1077-7776	978-1-951295-37-0
Illinois	1077-7520	978-1-951295-12-7	Rhode Island	1077-7784	978-1-951295-38-7
Indiana	1077-7539	978-1-951295-13-4	South Carolina	1077-7792	978-1-951295-39-4
Iowa	1077-7547	978-1-951295-14-1	South Dakota	1077-7806	978-1-951295-40-0
Kansas	1077-7555	978-1-951295-15-8	Tennessee	1077-7814	978-1-951295-41-7
Kentucky	1077-7563	978-1-951295-16-5	Texas	1077-7822	978-1-951295-42-4
Louisiana	1077-7571	978-1-951295-17-2	Utah	1077-7830	978-1-951295-43-1
Maine	1077-758X	978-1-951295-18-9	Vermont	1077-7849	978-1-951295-44-8
Maryland	1077-7598	978-1-951295-19-6	Virginia	1077-7857	978-1-951295-45-5
Massachusetts	1077-7601	978-1-951295-20-2	Washington	1077-7865	978-1-951295-46-2
Michigan	1077-761X	978-1-951295-21-9	West Virginia	1077-7873	978-1-951295-47-9
Minnesota	1077-7628	978-1-951295-22-6	Wisconsin	1077-7881	978-1-951295-48-6
Mississippi	1077-7636	978-1-951295-23-3	Wyoming	1077-789X	978-1-951295-49-3
Missouri	1077-7644	978-1-951295-24-0	Sales Manager's Guide	2150-2021	978-1-951295-50-9

If you have any questions or comments concerning this directory, please write to MDR, 6 Armstrong Road, Shelton, CT 06484, or call us toll-free at 800-333-8802 or collect at 203-926-4800.

MDR's School Directory

TABLE OF CONTENTS

Sample Directory Listings

MDR's School Directories are your complete reference source, providing comprehensive data on public school districts and schools, Catholic and other independent schools, and regional and county centers in all 50 states and the District of Columbia. Every public school district and school entry in MDR's School Directories is updated each year through telephone interviews conducted with school district personnel. These interviews take place from July to September, capturing the most current school year data available. In addition, information obtained from state, district and school directories is used to verify information contained in MDR's School Directories.

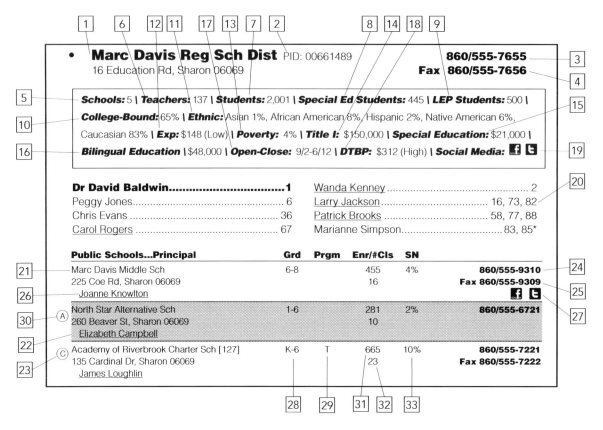

Each directory listing is uniformly organized to reflect the following data as applicable.

Definitions of Codes and Data:

DISTRICT DATA

1 District Name and Address
The physical location address for the superintendent's office is listed. MDR also maintains the mailing address, if different, for each district office. For this alternative mailing address, contact MDR directly at 800-333-8802.

2 District PID Number
Personal Identification Number of the district. Helps identify specific institutions when speaking to an MDR Representative or searching in Education MarketView.

3 Telephone Number
The telephone number of the district's central administration office.

4 Fax Number
The fax number of the district's central administration office. Please use the fax numbers in the directory appropriately.

> The FCC prohibits the use of a telephone facsimile machine to send unsolicited advertisements. If you need further clarification of the laws that exist, you can contact the FCC directly at 888-225-5322, or you can visit their website at http://www.fcc.gov.

5 Number of Schools
The number of schools reporting directly to the district. In the case of decentralized large districts (such as Chicago Public Schools), the number of schools reflects those reporting directly to the central school district in addition to those administered directly by each of the subdistrict offices.

6 Number of Teachers
The number of full-time equivalent teachers throughout the district as reported by the U.S. Department of Education.

7 District Enrollment
The projected number of students enrolled in the district for fall 2019.

8 Special Ed Students
The number of students having a written Individualized Education Plan (IEP) indicating their participation in a Special Education Program.

9 LEP Students
The number of Limited-English Proficient students being served in appropriate programs of language assistance (i.e., English as a second language, high-intensity language training, bilingual education).

10 College-Bound Students
The percentage of the district's 12th grade enrollment planning to attend two- or four-year colleges.

11 Student Ethnic Percentages
The student enrollment percentage by ethnic group: Asian, African American, Hispanic, Native American and Caucasian. This information is reported annually by the U.S. Department of Education. Due to rounding, the percentages may not add up to 100%.

12 District Expenditure
The district's expenditure per student for instructional materials. In addition to the actual dollar amount, a level of expenditure is provided as follows:
> High = $300+
> Med = $200-299
> Low = Under $200

13 Poverty Level
This census data reflects the percentage of school-age children in the district from families below the poverty line. Poverty levels are as follows:
> Low = 0-5%
> Med-Low = 6-15%
> Med-High = 16-29%
> High = 30%+

14 Title I
The district's Title I dollar allocation is for the 2018 fiscal year. Funding levels are as follows:
> Highest = $2.5 Million+
> High = $500,000-2.49 Million
> Medium = $150,000-499,999
> Low = Under $150,000

15 Special Education
The sum of federal and state dollars earmarked for special education programs in the district.

16 Bilingual Education
The sum of federal and state dollars earmarked for English Language Acquisition programs in the district.

17 District Opening/Closing Dates
The month and day of the official opening and closing dates of the school district.

18 District Tech Budget Per Pupil
The district's total IT technology budget dollars per pupil. DTBP levels are as follows:
> High = $100+
> Med = $80-99
> Low = $1-79

19 Social Media
The use of Facebook 🅵 and/or Twitter 🅣 for information communication, messaging and other content.

20 District-Level Administrators and Job Title Codes
The names of administrative staff with district-wide responsibilities are listed, followed by numeric codes representing their specific areas of responsibility. A full list of job title codes and their descriptions can be found on the bottom of the directory pages.

The names are listed, from left to right, in numeric job title sequence to facilitate identification of individuals responsible for specific administrative areas. In cases where an individual has multiple responsibilities, the job title with the lowest code number is used for sequencing.

An asterisk (*) denotes district administrators who maintain offices at one of the schools in the district rather than at the district office.

Superintendents who are new to the district are printed in **bold** type. Also see our index of new personnel on page NEW1.

An underscore of a district-level administrator indicates an email address at that institution in our database and in Education MarketView.

SCHOOL DATA

21 School Name and Address
The physical location address of the school is listed. MDR also maintains the mailing address, if different, for every school. For this alternative address, contact MDR directly at 800-333-8802.

22 New Schools
The listings of public schools opening for the first time during this school year are shaded for easy identification. Also see our index of new public schools on page NEW1.

23 Charter Management Organization (CMO)
Indicates the CMO number from the CMO Index to which this school reports.

24 Telephone Number
The telephone number of the school's central administration office. Note that in some cases a school district may require that all calls to schools must first go through a central switchboard to be routed to individual schools. In these cases, the central switchboard number is given for all schools affected.

25 Fax Number
The fax number of the school's administration office. Please use the fax numbers in the directory appropriately.

> The FCC prohibits the use of a telephone facsimile machine to send unsolicited advertisements. If you need further clarification of the laws that exist, you can contact the FCC directly at 888-225-5322, or you can visit their website at http://www.fcc.gov.

26 Principal Name

The name of the school principal. When a school has both an elementary and secondary principal, both names are given. The elementary principal is listed first, with the secondary principal listed below.

Principals who are new to their public school are printed in **bold** type. Also see our index of new personnel on page NEW1.

All principals printed with an underscore have an email address at that institution in our database and in Education MarketView.

27 Social Media

The use of Facebook and/or Twitter for information communication, messaging and other content.

28 School Grade Span/Voc, Special, Adult Schools

The lowest and highest grades taught in the school. Schools with dedicated programs in the areas of vocational, special and adult education are designated as Voc, Spec and Adult, respectively.

29 School Program Codes

In addition to the grades taught within the school, schools that have special curriculum programs are indicated with these codes following the school grade span.

A = Alternative Program: Identifies traditional schools that also provide a special setting/curriculum for students who do not function well in traditional classroom settings.

G = Adult Classes: Identifies schools that offer adult education classes.

M = Magnet Program: Identifies traditional schools that also offer an enriched curricula in a special subject area to qualified students.

T = Title I Schoolwide: Identifies public schools that have a Title I Schoolwide program, allowing greater spending flexibility.

V = Career & Technical Education Programs: Identifies schools that offer Career & Technical Education programs.

30 Other School Types

Schools that are unique in the curriculum they offer or in the way they operate are indicated to the left of the school name.

(A) = Alternative School: Identifies schools that provide instruction exclusively for students who do not function well in traditional classroom settings.

(C) = Charter School: Public schools that have certain freedoms from state and local regulations and policies, having more administrative independence.

(M) = Magnet School: Identifies schools where all students are offered enriched curricula. Students qualify for admission by competitive exams.

(Y) = Year-Round School: Schools that operate 12 months a year.

31 Student Enrollment

The projected number of students enrolled for fall 2019.

32 Number of Classrooms

The number of classrooms within a school. The number of classrooms prints below student enrollment when known.

33 Student Need

Percentage of students eligible for the free and reduced-price lunch program at the school.

Florida

A Dun & Bradstreet Division

STATE STATISTICS

DISTRICT PERSONNEL BY JOB FUNCTION

Job Code	Job Description	Total	Under 2,500	Enrollment 2,500-9,000	10,000+
1	SUPERINTENDENT	119	10	19	49
2	BUS/FINANCE/PURCHASING	175	10	27	125
3	BUILDINGS AND GROUNDS	182	7	21	145
4	FOOD SERVICE	108	9	17	79
5	TRANSPORTATION	123	9	19	91
6	ATHLETIC	39	7	9	21
7	HEALTH SERVICES	46	2	10	31
8	CURRIC/INSTRUCT K-12	83	7	21	44
9	CURRIC/INSTRUCT ELEM	34	0	7	25
10	CURRIC/INSTRUCT SEC	34	1	6	25
11	FEDERAL PROGRAM	79	7	17	39
12	TITLE I	37	1	6	26
13	TITLE V	9	1	6	2
15	ASST SUPERINTENDENT	183	5	11	141
16	INSTRUCTIONAL MEDIA SERVICES	53	4	16	30
17	CHIEF OPERATIONS OFFICER	12	0	1	8
18	CHIEF ACADEMIC OFFICER	16	0	0	13
19	CHIEF FINANCIAL OFFICER	33	1	5	24
20	ART K-12	11	0	0	9
21	ART ELEM	2	0	0	2
22	ART SEC	1	0	0	1
23	MUSIC K-12	11	0	0	9
24	MUSIC ELEM	1	0	0	1
25	MUSIC SEC	1	0	0	1
26	BUSINESS EDUCATION	1	0	1	0
27	CAREER & TECH ED	46	3	9	30
28	TECHNOLOGY EDUCATION	4	1	0	3
29	FAMILY/CONSUMER SCIENCE	1	1	0	0
30	ADULT EDUCATION	36	2	8	23
31	CAREER/SCH-TO-WORK K-12	34	2	5	25
32	CAREER/SCH-TO-WORK ELEM	0	0	0	0
33	CAREER/SCH-TO-WORK SEC	1	0	0	1
34	EARLY CHILDHOOD ED	49	3	10	34
35	HEALTH/PHYS EDUCATION	22	1	3	15
36	GUIDANCE SERVICES K-12	29	3	8	17
37	GUIDANCE SERVICES ELEM	5	0	0	4
38	GUIDANCE SERVICES SEC	6	1	0	4
39	SOCIAL STUDIES K-12	11	0	0	9
40	SOCIAL STUDIES ELEM	0	0	0	0
41	SOCIAL STUDIES SEC	2	0	0	2
42	SCIENCE K-12	12	1	2	7
43	SCIENCE ELEM	1	0	0	0
44	SCIENCE SEC	3	0	0	3
45	MATH K-12	15	0	4	9
46	MATH ELEM	5	0	0	4
47	MATH SEC	4	0	0	3
48	ENGLISH/LANG ARTS K-12	3	0	0	3
49	ENGLISH/LANG ARTS ELEM	5	0	0	5
50	ENGLISH/LANG ARTS SEC	4	0	0	4
51	READING K-12	11	0	4	6
52	READING ELEM	3	0	0	2
53	READING SEC	1	0	0	1
54	REMEDIAL READING K-12	7	1	3	3
55	REMEDIAL READING ELEM	0	0	0	0
56	REMEDIAL READING SEC	1	0	1	0

DISTRICT PERSONNEL BY JOB FUNCTION

Job Code	Job Description	Total	Under 2,500	Enrollment 2,500-9,000	10,000+
57	BILINGUAL/ELL	58	6	15	32
58	SPECIAL EDUCATION K-12	101	8	20	66
59	SPECIAL EDUCATION ELEM	2	0	1	1
60	SPECIAL EDUCATION SEC	1	0	0	1
61	FOREIGN/WORLD LANG K-12	9	0	0	9
62	FOREIGN/WORLD LANG ELEM	0	0	0	0
63	FOREIGN/WORLD LANG SEC	0	0	0	0
64	RELIGIOUS EDUCATION K-12	3	0	0	0
65	RELIGIOUS EDUCATION ELEM	0	0	0	0
66	RELIGIOUS EDUCATION SEC	0	0	0	0
67	SCHOOL BOARD PRESIDENT	68	9	18	36
68	TEACHER PERSONNEL	130	7	23	94
69	ACADEMIC ASSESSMENT	77	7	19	44
70	RESEARCH/DEVELOPMENT	29	0	0	23
71	PUBLIC INFORMATION	62	1	7	47
72	SUMMER SCHOOL	6	0	1	5
73	INSTRUCTIONAL TECH	110	11	25	57
74	INSERVICE TRAINING	63	2	9	45
75	MARKETING/DISTRIBUTIVE	2	0	0	2
76	INFO SYSTEMS	83	6	23	52
77	PSYCHOLOGICAL ASSESSMENT	34	2	9	21
78	AFFIRMATIVE ACTION	25	0	2	20
79	STUDENT PERSONNEL	67	5	13	47
80	DRIVER ED/SAFETY	11	0	1	9
81	GIFTED/TALENTED	44	2	9	26
82	VIDEO SERVICES	14	2	3	9
83	SUBSTANCE ABUSE PREVENTION	44	4	15	23
84	ERATE	30	5	6	18
85	AIDS EDUCATION	17	2	6	7
88	ALTERNATIVE/AT RISK	46	4	11	28
89	MULTI-CULTURAL CURRICULUM	10	0	1	9
90	SOCIAL WORK	22	0	8	12
91	SAFETY/SECURITY	68	4	17	43
92	MAGNET SCHOOL	10	0	2	7
93	PARENTAL INVOLVEMENT	21	0	4	14
95	TECH PREP PROGRAM	8	0	3	5
97	CHIEF INFORMATION OFFICER	10	0	0	7
98	CHIEF TECHNOLOGY OFFICER	6	0	1	4
270	CHARACTER EDUCATION	9	1	3	5
271	MIGRANT EDUCATION	30	3	6	16
273	TEACHER MENTOR	21	2	8	11
274	BEFORE/AFTER SCH	22	0	4	17
275	RESPONSE TO INTERVENTION	30	5	7	17
277	REMEDIAL MATH K-12	4	0	1	3
280	LITERACY COACH	19	1	6	10
285	STEM	33	3	9	19
286	DIGITAL LEARNING	37	4	9	23
288	COMMON CORE STANDARDS	28	4	11	12
294	ACCOUNTABILITY	60	4	18	31
295	NETWORK SYSTEM	78	7	21	49
296	TITLE II PROGRAMS	42	7	14	20
297	WEBMASTER	13	2	4	7
298	GRANT WRITER/PTNRSHIPS	50	5	12	28
750	CHIEF INNOVATION OFFICER	3	0	0	2
751	CHIEF OF STAFF	8	0	0	4
752	SOCIAL EMOTIONAL LEARNING	9	0	3	5

DISTRICTS BY EXPENDITURE AND ENROLLMENT

Expenditure	Total	Under 2500	2500-9999	10,000+
Low (Under $200)	45	3	9	33
Medium ($200 - 299)	20	7	8	5
High ($300+)	2	0	1	1
TOTAL DISTRICTS	67	10	18	39

SCHOOLS BY LEVEL AND TYPE

School Level	Total	Public	Private	Catholic
Elementary	2,770	2,197	403	170
Middle/Junior	593	581	12	0
Senior	613	561	21	31
K-12 (Combined)	747	266	478	3
Adult/Special/Voc Ed	263	198	59	6
TOTAL SCHOOLS	4,986	3,803	973	210

COUNTY STATISTICS

COUNTY		DISTRICTS	SCHOOLS	ELEM ENROLL[1]	MIDDLE/JHS ENROLL[2]	SENIOR ENROLL[3]	TOTAL ENROLL[4]	% OF STATE	K-5[5]	K-6	K-8	5-8[6]	7-9[7]	7-12[8]	K-12[9]	OTHER[10]
ALACHUA	PUBLIC	1	57	14,868	6,152	8,267	26,179		30	1	2	9	0	8	6	1
	NONPUBLIC	0	21	3,613	0	937	4,550		3	0	5	0	0	1	12	0
	TOTAL	**1**	**78**	**18,481**	**6,152**	**9,204**	**30,729**	**1.0**	**33**	**1**	**7**	**9**	**0**	**9**	**18**	**1**
BAKER	PUBLIC	1	8	2,479	1,193	1,385	5,000		4	0	0	1	0	1	1	1
	NONPUBLIC	0	0	0	0	0	0		0	0	0	0	0	0	0	0
	TOTAL	**1**	**8**	**2,479**	**1,193**	**1,385**	**5,000**	**0.2**	**4**	**0**	**0**	**1**	**0**	**1**	**1**	**1**
BAY	PUBLIC	1	47	14,678	4,720	7,653	27,390		20	0	4	7	0	7	5	4
	NONPUBLIC	0	6	778	0	89	867		0	0	2	0	0	0	3	1
	TOTAL	**1**	**53**	**15,456**	**4,720**	**7,742**	**28,257**	**0.9**	**20**	**0**	**6**	**7**	**0**	**7**	**8**	**5**
BRADFORD	PUBLIC	1	11	1,655	723	860	3,300		6	0	0	1	0	1	2	1
	NONPUBLIC	0	5	528	0	191	719		0	0	1	0	0	0	4	0
	TOTAL	**1**	**16**	**2,183**	**723**	**1,051**	**4,019**	**0.1**	**6**	**0**	**1**	**1**	**0**	**1**	**6**	**1**
BREVARD	PUBLIC	1	107	40,667	7,985	24,122	77,214		4	60	4	1	11	16	5	6
	NONPUBLIC	0	37	6,019	0	1,815	7,834		1	2	15	0	0	2	15	2
	TOTAL	**1**	**144**	**46,686**	**7,985**	**25,937**	**85,048**	**2.7**	**5**	**62**	**19**	**1**	**11**	**18**	**20**	**8**
BROWARD	PUBLIC	1	311	134,383	53,652	80,437	270,550		162	1	30	48	0	44	16	10
	NONPUBLIC	0	106	29,941	0	10,627	40,568		16	4	49	0	0	4	29	4
	TOTAL	**1**	**417**	**164,324**	**53,652**	**91,064**	**311,118**	**9.9**	**178**	**5**	**79**	**48**	**0**	**48**	**45**	**14**
CALHOUN	PUBLIC	1	6	1,247	314	602	2,100		1	0	1	1	0	1	0	1
	NONPUBLIC	0	0	0	0	0	0		0	0	0	0	0	0	0	0
	TOTAL	**1**	**6**	**1,247**	**314**	**602**	**2,100**	**0.1**	**1**	**0**	**1**	**1**	**0**	**1**	**1**	**1**
CHARLOTTE	PUBLIC	1	26	7,214	3,335	5,520	16,300		11	0	1	4	0	5	2	3
	NONPUBLIC	0	7	948	0	98	1,046		1	0	4	0	0	0	2	0
	TOTAL	**1**	**33**	**8,162**	**3,335**	**5,618**	**17,346**	**0.6**	**12**	**0**	**5**	**4**	**0**	**5**	**4**	**3**
CITRUS	PUBLIC	1	23	7,268	3,608	4,652	15,000		11	0	0	4	0	4	2	2
	NONPUBLIC	0	6	850	0	201	1,051		0	0	3	0	0	0	3	0
	TOTAL	**1**	**29**	**8,118**	**3,608**	**4,853**	**16,051**	**0.5**	**11**	**0**	**3**	**4**	**0**	**4**	**5**	**2**
CLAY	PUBLIC	1	48	20,198	5,849	12,460	35,609		3	24	2	1	5	8	4	1
	NONPUBLIC	0	15	1,835	0	444	2,279		1	0	4	0	0	0	9	1
	TOTAL	**1**	**63**	**22,033**	**5,849**	**12,904**	**37,888**	**1.2**	**4**	**24**	**6**	**1**	**5**	**8**	**13**	**2**
COLLIER	PUBLIC	1	62	22,052	10,212	14,730	47,816		27	4	2	10	1	10	6	2
	NONPUBLIC	0	16	3,234	0	1,134	4,368		1	0	5	0	0	1	9	0
	TOTAL	**1**	**78**	**25,286**	**10,212**	**15,864**	**52,184**	**1.7**	**28**	**4**	**7**	**10**	**1**	**11**	**15**	**2**

[1] **Elem Enroll** is the school by school total of enrollments in K-4, K-5, K-6, K-8 schools, elementary and middle/JHS students in K-12 schools and students in special ed schools. Public enrollments include public and county-operated schools.

[2] **Middle/JHS Enroll** is the school by school total of enrollments in 5-8 and 7-9 public schools. Public enrollments include public and county-operated schools. Private middle/JHS enrollments are included in Senior Enroll.

[3] **Senior Enroll** is the school by school total of enrollments in 7-12 and 9-12 schools; the secondary students in K-12 schools and students in vocational ed schools. Public enrollments include public and county-operated schools. For private schools, Senior Enroll includes middle/JHS enrollment plus senior enrollment.

[4] **Public Total Enroll** columns are not the sum of school building enrollments. They are projected district-wide Fall enrollments provided to MDR by each school district office, plus county-operated school enrollments.

[5] **K-5** includes pre-kindergarten, kindergarten, K-3, K-4, K-5 schools.

[6] **5-8** includes schools with low grades of 4, 5, 6 and high grades of 7, 8, 9 (e.g., 4-8, 5-8, 6-8, 6-9).

[7] **7-9** includes schools with low grades of 7, 8 and high grades of 7, 8, 9 (e.g., 7-7, 7-8, 7-9, 8-9).

[8] **7-12** includes 7-12, 8-12, 9-12, 10-12, etc.

[9] **K-12** includes schools with both elementary and secondary grades.

[10] **Other** includes special ed, vocational ed and adult schools.

***Public State Totals** for all columns can exceed the sum of the counties because state totals include state-operated schools and their enrollments.

COUNTY		DISTRICTS	SCHOOLS	ELEM ENROLL[1]	MIDDLE/JHS ENROLL[2]	SENIOR ENROLL[3]	TOTAL ENROLL[4]	% OF STATE	K-5[5]	K-6	K-8	5-8[6]	7-9[7]	7-12[8]	K-12[9]	OTHER[10]
COLUMBIA	PUBLIC	1	16	5,855	1,513	2,750	10,000		9	1	0	1	0	0	3	1
	NONPUBLIC	0	7	493	0	69	562		0	0	3	0	0	0	4	0
	TOTAL	1	23	6,348	1,513	2,819	10,562	0.3	9	1	3	1	0	1	7	1
DE SOTO	PUBLIC	1	5	2,484	1,031	1,292	5,238		3	0	0	1	0	1	0	0
	NONPUBLIC	0	0	0	0	0	0		0	0	0	0	0	0	0	0
	TOTAL	1	5	2,484	1,031	1,292	5,238	0.2	3	0	0	1	0	1	0	0
DIXIE	PUBLIC	1	5	1,230	465	531	2,149		3	0	0	1	0	1	0	0
	NONPUBLIC	0	1	6	0	4	10		0	0	0	0	0	0	1	0
	TOTAL	1	6	1,236	465	535	2,159	0.1	3	0	0	1	0	1	1	0
DUVAL	PUBLIC	1	193	69,127	24,159	34,024	129,000		107	2	15	31	0	24	7	7
	NONPUBLIC	0	93	17,580	0	7,685	25,265		5	5	25	1	0	4	43	10
	TOTAL	1	286	86,707	24,159	41,709	154,265	4.9	112	7	40	32	0	28	50	17
ESCAMBIA	PUBLIC	1	62	19,553	9,096	11,011	42,211		36	0	0	10	0	8	4	4
	NONPUBLIC	0	24	4,167	0	978	5,145		2	0	15	0	0	2	5	0
	TOTAL	1	86	23,720	9,096	11,989	47,356	1.5	38	0	15	10	0	10	9	4
FLAGLER	PUBLIC	1	12	6,742	1,834	4,344	12,904		0	5	1	0	2	3	0	1
	NONPUBLIC	0	4	517	0	14	531		0	0	3	0	0	0	1	0
	TOTAL	1	16	7,259	1,834	4,358	13,435	0.4	0	5	4	0	2	3	1	1
FRANKLIN	PUBLIC	1	2	947	0	266	1,000		0	0	1	0	0	0	1	0
	NONPUBLIC	0	1	36	0	14	50		0	0	0	0	0	0	1	0
	TOTAL	1	3	983	0	280	1,050	0.1	0	0	1	0	0	0	2	0
GADSDEN	PUBLIC	1	14	2,842	963	1,244	5,000		4	0	2	2	0	1	4	1
	NONPUBLIC	0	2	286	0	114	400		0	0	0	0	0	0	2	0
	TOTAL	1	16	3,128	963	1,358	5,400	0.2	4	0	2	2	0	1	6	1
GILCHRIST	PUBLIC	1	4	1,431	562	748	2,741		2	0	0	0	0	0	2	0
	NONPUBLIC	0	0	0	0	0	0		0	0	0	0	0	0	0	0
	TOTAL	1	4	1,431	562	748	2,741	0.1	2	0	0	0	0	0	2	0
GLADES	PUBLIC	1	4	1,178	0	441	1,650		0	1	2	0	0	1	0	0
	NONPUBLIC	0	0	0	0	0	0		0	0	0	0	0	0	0	0
	TOTAL	1	4	1,178	0	441	1,650	0.1	0	1	2	0	0	1	0	0
GULF	PUBLIC	1	5	1,088	0	854	1,924		0	2	0	0	0	2	0	0
	NONPUBLIC	0	1	90	0	0	90		0	0	1	0	0	0	0	1
	TOTAL	1	6	1,178	0	854	2,014	0.1	0	2	1	0	0	2	0	1
HAMILTON	PUBLIC	1	2	946	0	633	1,650		0	1	0	0	0	1	0	0
	NONPUBLIC	0	2	101	0	44	145		0	0	0	0	0	0	2	0
	TOTAL	1	4	1,047	0	677	1,795	0.1	0	1	0	0	0	1	2	0

[1] **Elem Enroll** is the school by school total of enrollments in K-4, K-5, K-6, K-8 schools, elementary and middle/JHS students in K-12 schools and students in special ed schools. Public enrollments include public and county-operated schools.

[2] **Middle/JHS Enroll** is the school by school total of enrollments in 5-8 and 7-9 public schools. Public enrollments include public and county-operated schools. Private middle/JHS enrollments are included in Senior Enroll.

[3] **Senior Enroll** is the school by school total of enrollments in 7-12 and 9-12 schools, the secondary students in K-12 schools and students in vocational ed schools. Public enrollments include public and county-operated schools. For private schools, Senior Enroll includes middle/JHS enrollment plus senior enrollment.

[4] **Public Total Enroll** columns are not the sum of school building enrollments. They are projected district-wide Fall enrollments provided to MDR by each school district office, plus county-operated school enrollments.

[5] **K-5** includes pre-kindergarten, kindergarten, K-3, K-4, K-5 schools.

[6] **5-8** includes schools with low grades of 4, 5, 6 and high grades of 7, 8, 9 (e.g., 4-8, 5-8, 6-8, 6-9).

[7] **7-9** includes schools with low grades of 7, 8 and high grades of 7, 8, 9 (e.g., 7-7, 7-8, 7-9, 8-9).

[8] **7-12** includes 7-12, 8-12, 9-12, 10-12, etc.

[9] **K-12** includes schools with both elementary and secondary grades.

[10] **Other** includes special ed, vocational ed and adult schools.

*Public State Totals for all columns can exceed the sum of the counties because state totals include state-operated schools and their enrollments

COUNTY		DISTRICTS	SCHOOLS	ELEM ENROLL[1]	MIDDLE/JHS ENROLL[2]	SENIOR ENROLL[3]	TOTAL ENROLL[4]	% OF STATE	K-5[5]	K-6	K-8	5-8[6]	7-9[7]	7-12[8]	K-12[9]	OTHER[10]
HARDEE	PUBLIC	1	8	2,441	1,178	1,395	5,276		5	0	0	1	0	1	1	0
	NONPUBLIC	0	1	10			10		0	0	0	0	0	0	0	1
	TOTAL	**1**	**9**	**2,451**	**1,178**	**1,395**	**5,286**	**0.2**	**5**	**0**	**0**	**1**	**0**	**1**	**1**	**1**
HENDRY	PUBLIC	1	15	3,432	1,602	2,205	7,500		7	0	0	2	0	2	2	2
	NONPUBLIC	0	1	122	0	0	122		0	1	0	0	0	0	0	0
	TOTAL	**1**	**16**	**3,554**	**1,602**	**2,205**	**7,622**	**0.2**	**7**	**1**	**0**	**2**	**0**	**2**	**2**	**2**
HERNANDO	PUBLIC	1	27	12,234	3,674	6,963	21,790		10	0	3	7	0	4	2	1
	NONPUBLIC	0	8	1,248	0	325	1,573		1	0	2	0	0	0	5	0
	TOTAL	**1**	**35**	**13,482**	**3,674**	**7,288**	**23,363**	**0.7**	**11**	**0**	**5**	**7**	**0**	**4**	**7**	**1**
HIGHLANDS	PUBLIC	1	19	5,907	2,803	3,502	12,300		10	0	0	4	0	3	2	0
	NONPUBLIC	0	5	696	0	117	813		2	0	1	0	0	0	2	0
	TOTAL	**1**	**24**	**6,603**	**2,803**	**3,619**	**13,113**	**0.4**	**12**	**0**	**1**	**4**	**0**	**3**	**4**	**0**
HILLSBOROUGH	PUBLIC	1	292	117,605	40,849	62,856	220,287		150	2	30	48	0	34	10	18
	NONPUBLIC	0	84	14,577	0	5,537	20,114		12	2	23	2	0	4	35	6
	TOTAL	**1**	**376**	**132,182**	**40,849**	**68,393**	**240,401**	**7.6**	**162**	**4**	**53**	**50**	**0**	**38**	**45**	**24**
HOLMES	PUBLIC	1	7	2,191	142	901	3,500		1	0	1	0	0	1	4	0
	NONPUBLIC	0	1	0	0	65	65		0	0	0	0	0	0	1	0
	TOTAL	**1**	**8**	**2,191**	**142**	**966**	**3,565**	**0.1**	**1**	**0**	**1**	**0**	**0**	**1**	**5**	**0**
INDIAN RIVER	PUBLIC	1	29	8,470	3,837	6,343	17,500		14	1	1	5	0	4	2	2
	NONPUBLIC	0	8	1,065	0	257	1,322		0	0	4	0	0	0	4	0
	TOTAL	**1**	**37**	**9,535**	**3,837**	**6,600**	**18,822**	**0.6**	**14**	**1**	**5**	**5**	**0**	**4**	**6**	**2**
JACKSON	PUBLIC	1	17	3,942	919	1,800	6,500		5	0	1	1	0	2	5	3
	NONPUBLIC	0	3	161	0	88	249		0	0	0	0	0	0	2	1
	TOTAL	**1**	**20**	**4,103**	**919**	**1,888**	**6,749**	**0.2**	**5**	**0**	**1**	**1**	**0**	**2**	**7**	**4**
JEFFERSON	PUBLIC	1	1	549	0	220	769		0	0	0	0	0	0	1	0
	NONPUBLIC	0	1	236	0	94	330		0	0	0	0	0	0	1	0
	TOTAL	**1**	**2**	**785**	**0**	**314**	**1,099**		**0**	**0**	**0**	**0**	**0**	**0**	**2**	**0**
LAFAYETTE	PUBLIC	1	3	601	269	360	1,300		1	0	0	0	0	0	2	0
	NONPUBLIC	0	1	76	0	34	110		0	0	0	0	0	0	1	0
	TOTAL	**1**	**4**	**677**	**269**	**394**	**1,410**		**1**	**0**	**0**	**0**	**0**	**0**	**3**	**0**
LAKE	PUBLIC	1	54	21,823	9,015	13,030	41,590		25	0	4	10	0	11	2	2
	NONPUBLIC	0	23	4,264	0	1,133	5,397		2	1	3	0	0	0	14	3
	TOTAL	**1**	**77**	**26,087**	**9,015**	**14,163**	**46,987**	**1.5**	**27**	**1**	**7**	**10**	**0**	**11**	**16**	**5**
LEE	PUBLIC	1	113	47,177	18,578	28,222	94,405		50	0	10	18	0	24	4	7
	NONPUBLIC	0	23	4,208	0	1,639	5,847		1	1	7	0	0	1	13	0
	TOTAL	**1**	**136**	**51,385**	**18,578**	**29,861**	**100,252**	**3.2**	**51**	**1**	**17**	**18**	**0**	**25**	**17**	**7**

[1] **Elem Enroll** is the school by school total of enrollments in K-4, K-5, K-6, K-8 schools, elementary and middle/JHS students in K-12 schools and students in special ed schools. Public enrollments include public and county-operated schools.

[2] **Middle/JHS Enroll** is the school by school total of enrollments in 5-8 and 7-9 public schools. Public enrollments include public and county-operated schools. Private middle/JHS enrollments are included in Senior Enroll.

[3] **Senior Enroll** is the school by school total of enrollments in 7-12 and 9-12 schools, the secondary students in K-12 schools and students in vocational ed schools. Public enrollments include public and county-operated schools. For private schools, Senior Enroll includes middle/JHS enrollment plus senior enrollment.

[4] **Public Total Enroll** columns are not the sum of school building enrollments. They are projected district-wide Fall enrollments provided to MDR by each school district office, plus county-operated school enrollments.

[5] **K-5** includes pre-kindergarten, kindergarten, K-3, K-4, K-5 schools.

[6] **5-8** includes schools with low grades of 4, 5, 6 and high grades of 7, 8, 9 (e.g., 4-8, 5-8, 6-8, 6-9).

[7] **7-9** includes schools with low grades of 7, 8 and high grades of 7, 8, 9 (e.g., 7-7, 7-8, 7-9, 8-9).

[8] **7-12** includes 7-12, 8-12, 9-12, 10-12, etc.

[9] **K-12** includes schools with both elementary and secondary grades.

[10] **Other** includes special ed, vocational and adult schools.

*Public State Totals for all columns can exceed the sum of the counties because state totals include state-operated schools and their enrollments

COUNTY		DISTRICTS	SCHOOLS	ELEM ENROLL[1]	MIDDLE/JHS ENROLL[2]	SENIOR ENROLL[3]	TOTAL ENROLL[4]	% OF STATE	K-5[5]	K-6	K-8	5-8[6]	7-9[7]	7-12[8]	K-12[9]	OTHER[10]
LEON	PUBLIC	1	51	17,804	6,965	9,601	34,500		24	0	5	9	0	6	4	3
	NONPUBLIC	0	21	3,914	0	1,033	4,947		1	1	6	0	0	1	11	1
	TOTAL	**1**	**72**	**21,718**	**6,965**	**10,634**	**39,447**	**1.3**	**25**	**1**	**11**	**9**	**0**	**7**	**15**	**4**
LEVY	PUBLIC	1	12	2,958	1,109	1,435	6,100		5	0	1	1	0	0	5	0
	NONPUBLIC	0	2	129	0	46	175		0	0	0	0	0	0	2	0
	TOTAL	**1**	**14**	**3,087**	**1,109**	**1,481**	**6,275**	**0.2**	**5**	**0**	**1**	**1**	**0**	**0**	**7**	**0**
LIBERTY	PUBLIC	1	5	854	16	372	1,373		0	0	2	0	0	2	1	0
	NONPUBLIC	0	1	150	0	0	150		0	0	0	0	0	0	0	1
	TOTAL	**1**	**6**	**1,004**	**16**	**372**	**1,523**	**0.1**	**0**	**0**	**2**	**0**	**0**	**2**	**1**	**1**
MADISON	PUBLIC	1	7	1,831	0	707	2,500		3	0	2	0	0	2	0	0
	NONPUBLIC	0	0	0	0	0	0		0	0	0	0	0	0	0	0
	TOTAL	**1**	**7**	**1,831**	**0**	**707**	**2,500**	**0.1**	**3**	**0**	**2**	**0**	**0**	**2**	**0**	**0**
MANATEE	PUBLIC	1	68	25,279	10,938	14,762	49,200		35	2	5	11	0	7	7	1
	NONPUBLIC	0	16	2,204	0	1,290	3,494		3	0	6	0	0	0	7	0
	TOTAL	**1**	**84**	**27,483**	**10,938**	**16,052**	**52,694**	**1.7**	**38**	**2**	**11**	**11**	**0**	**7**	**14**	**1**
MARION	PUBLIC	1	57	20,806	9,369	12,604	42,624		32	0	1	10	0	9	3	2
	NONPUBLIC	0	21	3,836	0	1,212	5,048		3	0	7	0	0	1	9	1
	TOTAL	**1**	**78**	**24,642**	**9,369**	**13,816**	**47,672**	**1.5**	**35**	**0**	**8**	**10**	**0**	**10**	**12**	**3**
MARTIN	PUBLIC	1	29	8,526	4,351	6,070	19,244		12	1	0	5	0	6	1	4
	NONPUBLIC	0	9	1,615	0	259	1,874		1	1	4	0	0	0	3	0
	TOTAL	**1**	**38**	**10,141**	**4,351**	**6,329**	**21,118**	**0.7**	**13**	**2**	**4**	**5**	**0**	**6**	**4**	**4**
MIAMI-DADE	PUBLIC	1	467	183,158	54,068	104,920	350,101		197	9	78	63	1	73	28	18
	NONPUBLIC	0	178	38,649	0	17,097	55,746		34	8	63	3	1	12	46	11
	TOTAL	**1**	**645**	**221,807**	**54,068**	**122,017**	**405,847**	**12.9**	**231**	**17**	**141**	**66**	**2**	**85**	**74**	**29**
MONROE	PUBLIC	1	19	5,989	286	2,452	8,849		4	0	8	0	0	4	3	0
	NONPUBLIC	0	3	497	0	63	560		0	0	2	0	0	0	1	0
	TOTAL	**1**	**22**	**6,486**	**286**	**2,515**	**9,409**	**0.3**	**4**	**0**	**10**	**0**	**0**	**4**	**4**	**0**
NASSAU	PUBLIC	1	18	5,569	2,806	3,697	12,000		9	0	0	3	0	3	2	1
	NONPUBLIC	0	5	1,060	0	71	1,131		0	1	3	0	0	0	1	0
	TOTAL	**1**	**23**	**6,629**	**2,806**	**3,768**	**13,131**	**0.4**	**9**	**1**	**3**	**3**	**0**	**3**	**3**	**1**
OKALOOSA	PUBLIC	1	46	16,575	6,377	9,017	30,638		19	0	3	8	0	6	7	3
	NONPUBLIC	0	3	1,056	0	284	1,340		0	0	1	0	0	0	2	0
	TOTAL	**1**	**49**	**17,631**	**6,377**	**9,301**	**31,978**	**1.0**	**19**	**0**	**4**	**8**	**0**	**6**	**9**	**3**
OKEECHOBEE	PUBLIC	1	11	3,061	1,497	1,737	6,200		5	0	0	2	0	2	2	0
	NONPUBLIC	0	4	387	0	151	538		0	0	2	0	0	0	2	0
	TOTAL	**1**	**15**	**3,448**	**1,497**	**1,888**	**6,738**	**0.2**	**5**	**0**	**2**	**2**	**0**	**2**	**4**	**0**

[1] **Elem Enroll** is the school by school total of enrollments in K-4, K-5, K-6, K-8 schools, elementary and middle/JHS students in K-12 schools and students in special ed schools. Public enrollments include public and county-operated schools.

[2] **Middle/JHS Enroll** is the school by school total of enrollments in 5-8 and 7-9 public schools. Public enrollments include public and county-operated schools. Private middle/JHS enrollments are included in Senior Enroll.

[3] **Senior Enroll** is the school by school total of enrollments in 7-12 and 9-12 schools, the secondary students in K-12 schools and students in vocational ed schools. Public enrollments include public and county-operated schools. For private schools, Senior Enroll includes middle/JHS enrollment plus senior enrollment.

[4] **Public Total Enroll** columns are not the sum of school building enrollments. They are projected district-twice Fall enrollments provided to MDR by each school district office, plus county-operated school enrollments.

[5] **K-5** includes pre-kindergarten, kindergarten, K-3, K-4, K-5 schools.

[6] **5-8** includes schools with low grades of 4, 5, 6 and high grades of 7, 8, 9 (e.g., 4-8, 5-8, 6-8, 6-9).

[7] **7-9** includes schools with low grades of 7, 8 and high grades of 7, 8, 9 (e.g., 7-7, 7-8, 7-9, 8-9).

[8] **7-12** includes 7-12, 8-12, 9-12, 10-12, etc.

[9] **K-12** includes schools with both elementary and secondary grades.

[10] **Other** includes special ed, vocational and adult schools.

*Public State Totals for all columns can exceed the sum of the counties because state totals include state-operated schools and their enrollments

COUNTY		DISTRICTS	SCHOOLS	ELEM ENROLL[1]	MIDDLE/JHS ENROLL[2]	SENIOR ENROLL[3]	TOTAL ENROLL[4]	% OF STATE	SCHOOLS BY GRADE SPAN							
									K-5[5]	K-6	K-8	5-8[6]	7-9[7]	7-12[8]	K-12[9]	OTHER[10]
ORANGE	PUBLIC	2	254	104,676	44,807	65,278	221,243		134	1	19	41	0	36	7	16
	NONPUBLIC	0	83	18,647		6,643	25,290		4	4	25	0	0	3	42	5
	TOTAL	**2**	**337**	**123,323**	**44,807**	**71,921**	**246,533**	**7.8**	**138**	**5**	**44**	**41**	**0**	**39**	**49**	**21**
OSCEOLA	PUBLIC	1	77	35,745	11,862	21,582	67,709		27	1	16	10	0	12	7	4
	NONPUBLIC	0	12	2,614	0	595	3,209		0	0	5	0	0	0	6	1
	TOTAL	**1**	**89**	**38,359**	**11,862**	**22,177**	**70,918**	**2.3**	**27**	**1**	**21**	**10**	**0**	**12**	**13**	**5**
PALM BEACH	PUBLIC	1	223	94,542	39,640	59,265	195,455		109	2	20	35	0	36	8	13
	NONPUBLIC	0	76	19,889	0	6,023	25,912		8	2	32	1	0	5	26	2
	TOTAL	**1**	**299**	**114,431**	**39,640**	**65,288**	**221,367**	**7.0**	**117**	**4**	**52**	**36**	**0**	**41**	**34**	**15**
PASCO	PUBLIC	1	97	36,095	16,213	22,112	75,001		51	1	5	15	0	12	9	4
	NONPUBLIC	0	23	2,918	0	960	3,878		4	0	6	0	0	1	11	1
	TOTAL	**1**	**120**	**39,013**	**16,213**	**23,072**	**78,879**	**2.5**	**55**	**1**	**11**	**15**	**0**	**13**	**20**	**5**
PINELLAS	PUBLIC	1	152	49,614	19,931	29,688	101,427		80	1	10	22	0	22	4	13
	NONPUBLIC	0	70	12,231	0	3,506	15,737		11	0	27	3	0	4	20	5
	TOTAL	**1**	**222**	**61,845**	**19,931**	**33,194**	**117,164**	**3.7**	**91**	**1**	**37**	**25**	**0**	**26**	**24**	**18**
POLK	PUBLIC	1	156	53,262	21,548	30,848	105,000		74	1	8	25	1	23	12	12
	NONPUBLIC	0	31	4,885	0	2,201	7,086		1	1	9	0	0	2	16	2
	TOTAL	**1**	**187**	**58,147**	**21,548**	**33,049**	**112,086**	**3.6**	**75**	**2**	**17**	**25**	**1**	**25**	**28**	**14**
PUTNAM	PUBLIC	1	21	6,121	2,445	2,409	11,000		8	3	0	3	2	3	1	1
	NONPUBLIC	0	2	350	0	150	500		0	0	0	0	0	0	2	0
	TOTAL	**1**	**23**	**6,471**	**2,445**	**2,559**	**11,500**	**0.4**	**8**	**3**	**0**	**3**	**2**	**3**	**3**	**1**
SANTA ROSA	PUBLIC	1	37	13,211	6,422	8,768	29,089		15	2	0	7	0	6	4	3
	NONPUBLIC	0	6	814	0	220	1,034		3	0	0	0	0	0	3	0
	TOTAL	**1**	**43**	**14,025**	**6,422**	**8,988**	**30,123**	**1.0**	**18**	**2**	**0**	**7**	**0**	**6**	**7**	**3**
SARASOTA	PUBLIC	1	59	21,760	8,672	13,928	43,150		26	1	4	13	0	6	6	3
	NONPUBLIC	0	23	2,733	0	1,263	3,996		1	0	5	0	0	1	13	3
	TOTAL	**1**	**82**	**24,493**	**8,672**	**15,191**	**47,146**	**1.5**	**27**	**1**	**9**	**13**	**0**	**7**	**19**	**6**
SEMINOLE	PUBLIC	1	68	30,778	15,298	21,135	68,000		40	1	0	12	0	9	3	3
	NONPUBLIC	0	18	5,650	0	809	6,459		1	0	8	0	0	0	7	2
	TOTAL	**1**	**86**	**36,428**	**15,298**	**21,944**	**74,459**	**2.4**	**41**	**1**	**8**	**12**	**0**	**9**	**10**	**5**
ST JOHNS	PUBLIC	1	44	21,582	7,714	12,875	42,222		18	1	6	7	0	6	3	3
	NONPUBLIC	0	14	2,668	0	389	3,057		4	0	6	1	0	1	2	0
	TOTAL	**1**	**58**	**24,250**	**7,714**	**13,264**	**45,279**	**1.4**	**22**	**1**	**12**	**8**	**0**	**7**	**5**	**3**
ST LUCIE	PUBLIC	1	45	24,724	4,205	13,011	44,210		18	0	11	4	0	7	4	1
	NONPUBLIC	0	11	2,066	0	1,109	3,175		0	0	3	0	0	1	7	0
	TOTAL	**1**	**56**	**26,790**	**4,205**	**14,120**	**47,385**	**1.5**	**18**	**0**	**14**	**4**	**0**	**8**	**11**	**1**

[1] **Elem Enroll** is the school by school total of enrollments in K-4, K-5, K-6, K-8 schools, elementary and middle/JHS students in K-12 schools and students in special ed schools. Public enrollments include public and county-operated schools.

[2] **Middle/JHS Enroll** is the school by school total of enrollments in 5-8 and 7-9 public schools. Public enrollments include public and county-operated schools. Private middle/JHS enrollments are included in Senior Enroll.

[3] **Senior Enroll** is the school by school total of enrollments in 7-12 and 9-12 schools, the secondary students in K-12 schools and students in vocational ed schools. Public enrollments include public and county-operated schools. For private schools, Senior Enroll includes middle/JHS enrollment plus senior enrollment.

[4] **Public Total Enroll** columns are not the sum of school building enrollments. They are projected district-wide Fall enrollments provided to MDR by each school district office, plus county-operated school enrollments.

[5] **K-5** includes pre-kindergarten, kindergarten, K-3, K-4, K-5 schools.

[6] **5-8** includes schools with low grades of 4, 5, 6 and high grades of 7, 8, 9 (e.g., 4-8, 5-8, 6-8, 6-9).

[7] **7-9** includes schools with low grades of 7, 8 and high grades of 7, 8, 9 (e.g., 7-7, 7-8, 7-9, 8-9).

[8] **7-12** includes 7-12, 8-12, 9-12, 10-12, etc.

[9] **K-12** includes schools with both elementary and secondary grades.

[10] **Other** includes special ed, vocational ed and adult schools.

***Public State Totals** for all columns can exceed the sum of the counties because state totals include state-operated schools and their enrollments

SCHOOLS BY GRADE SPAN

COUNTY		DISTRICTS	SCHOOLS	ELEM ENROLL[1]	MIDDLE/JHS ENROLL[2]	SENIOR ENROLL[3]	TOTAL ENROLL[4]	% OF STATE	K-5[5]	K-6	K-8	5-8[6]	7-9[7]	7-12[8]	K-12[9]	OTHER[10]
SUMTER	PUBLIC	1	10	5,129	1,181	2,388	8,500		4	0	0	1	0	1	3	1
	NONPUBLIC	0	1	12	0	5	17		0	0	0	0	0	0	1	0
	TOTAL	1	11	5,141	1,181	2,393	8,517	0.3	4	0	0	1	0	1	4	1
SUWANNEE	PUBLIC	1	9	2,924	1,385	1,642	5,776		4	0	0	1	0	1	2	1
	NONPUBLIC	0	4	306	0	167	473		0	0	0	0	0	0	4	0
	TOTAL	1	13	3,230	1,385	1,809	6,249	0.2	4	0	0	1	0	1	6	1
TAYLOR	PUBLIC	1	6	1,612	559	643	2,900		2	1	0	1	0	2	0	0
	NONPUBLIC	0	1	131	0	44	175		0	0	0	0	0	0	1	0
	TOTAL	1	7	1,743	559	687	3,075	0.1	2	1	0	1	0	2	1	0
UNION	PUBLIC	1	6	979	765	601	2,300		1	0	0	0	0	1	2	1
	NONPUBLIC	0	0	0	0	0	0		0	0	0	0	0	0	0	0
	TOTAL	1	6	979	765	601	2,300	0.1	1	0	0	0	0	1	2	1
VOLUSIA	PUBLIC	1	83	30,026	13,587	19,439	64,000		47	0	3	12	0	14	6	1
	NONPUBLIC	0	28	4,542	0	1,243	5,785		1	1	13	0	0	0	11	1
	TOTAL	1	111	34,568	13,587	20,682	69,785	2.2	48	1	16	12	0	15	17	2
WAKULLA	PUBLIC	1	11	2,522	1,067	1,544	5,255		5	0	1	2	0	1	2	0
	NONPUBLIC	0	1	125	0	0	125		0	0	1	0	0	0	0	0
	TOTAL	1	12	2,647	1,067	1,544	5,380	0.2	5	0	2	2	0	1	2	0
WALTON	PUBLIC	1	21	5,277	2,505	2,846	10,201		7	0	0	3	0	5	5	1
	NONPUBLIC	0	2	68	0	17	85		1	0	0	0	0	0	1	0
	TOTAL	1	23	5,345	2,505	2,863	10,286	0.3	8	0	0	3	0	5	6	1
WASHINGTON	PUBLIC	1	9	1,593	714	904	3,400		2	0	0	2	0	2	2	1
	NONPUBLIC	0	1	104	0	41	145		0	0	0	0	0	0	1	0
	TOTAL	1	10	1,697	714	945	3,545	0.1	2	0	0	2	0	2	3	1
STATE TOTAL	PUBLIC*	68	3,803	1,441,086	538,534	844,903	2,849,978		1,738	133	325	558	23	559	261	196
	NONPUBLIC	0	1,183	231,935	0	80,638	312,573		129	35	409	11	1	52	481	65
	TOTAL	68	4,986	1,673,021	538,534	925,541	3,162,551		1,867	168	734	569	24	611	742	261

[1] **Elem Enroll** is the school by school total of enrollments in K-4, K-5, K-6, K-8 schools, elementary and middle/JHS students in K-12 schools and students in special ed schools. Public enrollments include public and county-operated schools.

[2] **Middle/JHS Enroll** is the school by school total of enrollments in 5-8 and 7-9 public schools. Public enrollments include public and county-operated schools. Private middle/JHS enrollments are included in Senior Enroll.

[3] **Senior Enroll** is the school by school total of enrollments in 7-12 and 9-12 schools, the secondary students in K-12 schools and students in vocational schools. Public enrollments include public and county-operated schools. For private schools, Senior Enroll includes middle/JHS enrollment plus senior enrollment.

[4] **Public Total Enroll** columns are not the sum of school building enrollments. They are projected district-wide Fall enrollments provided to MDR by each school district office, plus county-operated school enrollments.

[5] **K-5** includes pre-kindergarten, kindergarten, K-3, K-4, K-5 schools.

[6] **5-8** includes schools with low grades of 4, 5, 6 and high grades of 7, 8, 9 (e.g., 4-8, 5-8, 6-8, 6-9).

[7] **7-9** includes schools with low grades of 7, 8 and high grades of 7, 8, 9 (e.g., 7-7, 7-8, 7-9, 8-9).

[8] **7-12** includes 7-12, 8-12, 9-12, 10-12, etc.

[9] **K-12** includes schools with both elementary and secondary grades.

[10] **Other** includes special ed, vocational and adult schools.

*Public State Totals for all columns can exceed the sum of the counties because state totals include state-operated schools and their enrollments.

DISTRICT BUYING POWER INDEX
COUNTIES RANKED BY PERCENTAGE OF STATE SPENDING

COUNTY DISTRICT	PID	COUNTY % OF STATE	DISTRICT % OF COUNTY	DISTRICT % OF STATE	NUMBER OF SCHOOLS	ENROLL	EXP	POV
MIAMI-DADE		12.90						
Miami-Dade Co Public Sch Dist	00185155		100.00	12.90	467	350,101	LOW	MED-HIGH
BROWARD		9.49						
Broward Co Public Schools	00182725		100.00	9.49	311	270,550	LOW	MED-HIGH
ORANGE		9.17						
Orange Co Public School Dist	00196568		100.00	9.17	251	215,703	MED	MED-HIGH
HILLSBOROUGH		7.58						
Hillsborough Co Pub Sch Dist	00191805		100.00	7.58	292	220,287	LOW	MED-HIGH
PALM BEACH		6.02						
Palm Beach Co School Dist	00198073		100.00	6.02	223	195,455	LOW	MED-LOW
DUVAL		4.37						
Duval Co Public School Dist	00188779		100.00	4.37	193	129,000	LOW	MED-HIGH
POLK		3.87						
Polk Co School Dist	00201187		100.00	3.87	156	105,000	LOW	MED-HIGH
PINELLAS		3.56						
Pinellas Co School Dist	00199429		100.00	3.56	152	101,427	LOW	MED-HIGH
LEE		2.91						
Lee Co School Dist	00194089		100.00	2.91	113	94,405	LOW	MED-HIGH
BREVARD		2.81						
Brevard Co School Dist	00181965		100.00	2.81	107	77,214	LOW	MED-HIGH
COLLIER		2.58						
Collier Co Public School Dist	00184814		100.00	2.58	62	47,816	MED	MED-HIGH
PASCO		2.34						
Pasco Co School Dist	00199156		100.00	2.34	97	75,001	LOW	MED-HIGH
ESCAMBIA		2.13						
Escambia Co School Dist	00190265		100.00	2.13	62	42,211	MED	MED-HIGH
OSCEOLA		1.80						
Osceola Co School Dist	00197964		100.00	1.80	77	67,709	LOW	MED-HIGH
VOLUSIA		1.60						
Volusia Co School Dist	00204294		100.00	1.60	83	64,000	LOW	MED-HIGH
CLAY		1.57						
Clay Co School Dist	00184656		100.00	1.57	48	35,609	MED	MED-LOW
SEMINOLE		1.57						
Seminole Co Public School Dist	00203575		100.00	1.57	68	68,000	LOW	MED-LOW
MANATEE		1.49						
Manatee Co School Dist	00195033		100.00	1.49	68	49,200	LOW	MED-HIGH
ST JOHNS		1.43						
St Johns Co School Dist	00202363		100.00	1.43	44	42,222	LOW	MED-LOW
SARASOTA		1.41						
Sarasota Co School Dist	00203238		100.00	1.41	59	43,150	LOW	MED-LOW
ST LUCIE		1.33						
St Lucie Co School Dist	00202844		100.00	1.33	45	44,210	LOW	MED-HIGH
LEON		1.24						
Leon Co School Dist	00194479		100.00	1.24	51	34,500	LOW	MED-HIGH
ALACHUA		1.19						
Alachua Co School Dist	00181094		100.00	1.19	57	26,179	LOW	MED-HIGH
BAY		1.09						
Bay Co School Dist	00181537		100.00	1.09	47	27,390	LOW	MED-HIGH
MARION		1.09						
Marion Co Public Schools	00195344		100.00	1.09	57	42,624	LOW	MED-HIGH
OKALOOSA		1.06						
Okaloosa Co School Dist	00196128		100.00	1.06	46	30,638	LOW	MED-LOW
LAKE		1.02						
Lake Co School Dist	00193700		100.00	1.02	54	41,590	LOW	MED-HIGH
SANTA ROSA		0.91						
Santa Rosa Co School Dist	00203006		100.00	0.91	37	29,089	LOW	MED-LOW

DISTRICT BUYING POWER INDEX

COUNTIES RANKED BY PERCENTAGE OF STATE SPENDING

COUNTY DISTRICT	PID	COUNTY % OF STATE	DISTRICT % OF COUNTY	DISTRICT % OF STATES	NUMBER OF SCHOOLS	ENROLL	EXP	POV
MARTIN Martin Co School Dist	00195710	0.84	100.00	0.84	29	19,244	LOW	MED-LOW
HERNANDO Hernando Co School Dist	00191611	0.71	100.00	0.71	27	21,790	LOW	MED-HIGH
INDIAN RIVER School Dist of Indian River Co	00193334	0.68	100.00	0.68	29	17,500	LOW	MED-HIGH
WALTON Walton Co School Dist	00204907	0.56	100.00	0.56	21	10,201	HIGH	MED-HIGH
CITRUS Citrus Co School Dist	00184527	0.53	100.00	0.53	23	15,000	LOW	MED-HIGH
COLUMBIA Columbia Co School Dist	00185040	0.49	100.00	0.49	16	10,000	MED	MED-HIGH
OKEECHOBEE Okeechobee Co School Dist	00196506	0.47	100.00	0.47	11	6,200	HIGH	MED-HIGH
HENDRY Hendry Co School Dist	00191544	0.46	100.00	0.46	15	7,500	MED	HIGH
PUTNAM Putnam Co School Dist	00202193	0.45	100.00	0.45	21	11,000	LOW	HIGH
CHARLOTTE Charlotte Co Public Sch Dist	00184412	0.40	100.00	0.40	26	16,300	LOW	MED-HIGH
HIGHLANDS Highlands Co School Dist	00191702	0.38	100.00	0.38	19	12,300	LOW	HIGH
NASSAU Nassau Co School Dist	00196013	0.38	100.00	0.38	18	12,000	LOW	MED-LOW
MONROE Monroe Co School Dist	00195849	0.31	100.00	0.31	19	8,849	LOW	MED-HIGH
HARDEE Hardee Co School Dist	00191477	0.30	100.00	0.30	8	5,276	MED	HIGH
DE SOTO DeSoto Co School Dist	00188664	0.29	100.00	0.29	5	5,238	MED	HIGH
FLAGLER Flagler Co School Dist	00191001	0.28	100.00	0.28	12	12,904	LOW	MED-HIGH
GADSDEN Gadsden Co School Dist	00191087	0.23	100.00	0.23	14	5,000	LOW	HIGH
JACKSON Jackson Co School Dist	00193499	0.23	100.00	0.23	17	6,500	LOW	MED-HIGH
SUMTER Sumter Co School Dist	00203989	0.22	100.00	0.22	10	8,500	LOW	MED-HIGH
LEVY Levy Co School Dist	00194807	0.21	100.00	0.21	12	6,100	LOW	MED-HIGH
WAKULLA Wakulla Co School Dist	00204854	0.20	100.00	0.20	11	5,255	LOW	MED-HIGH
SUWANNEE Suwannee Co School Dist	00204098	0.18	100.00	0.18	9	5,776	LOW	MED-HIGH
GILCHRIST Gilchrist Co School Dist	00191269	0.17	100.00	0.17	4	2,741	MED	MED-HIGH
BRADFORD Bradford Co School Dist	00181874	0.15	100.00	0.15	11	3,300	MED	MED-HIGH
MADISON Madison Co School Dist	00194948	0.15	100.00	0.15	7	2,500	MED	HIGH
WASHINGTON Washington Co School Dist	00205004	0.14	100.00	0.14	9	3,400	MED	MED-HIGH
BAKER Baker Co School Dist	00181484	0.13	100.00	0.13	8	5,000	LOW	MED-HIGH
TAYLOR Taylor Co School Dist	00204165	0.12	100.00	0.12	6	2,900	MED	HIGH

DISTRICT BUYING POWER INDEX

COUNTIES RANKED BY PERCENTAGE OF STATE SPENDING

COUNTY DISTRICT	PID	COUNTY % OF STATE	DISTRICT % OF COUNTY	DISTRICT % OF STATES	NUMBER OF SCHOOLS	ENROLL	EXP	POV
HOLMES		0.11						
Holmes Co School Dist	00193255		100.00	0.11	7	3,500	LOW	MED-HIGH
UNION		0.11						
Union Co School Dist	00204244		100.00	0.11	6	2,300	MED	MED-HIGH
HAMILTON		0.10						
Hamilton Co School Dist	00191403		100.00	0.10	2	1,650	MED	HIGH
CALHOUN		0.09						
Calhoun Co School Dist	00184357		100.00	0.09	6	2,100	MED	MED-HIGH
GLADES		0.09						
Glades Co School Dist	00191300		100.00	0.09	4	1,650	MED	MED-HIGH
GULF		0.09						
Gulf Co School Dist	00191336		100.00	0.09	5	1,924	MED	MED-HIGH
DIXIE		0.08						
Dixie Co School Dist	00188731		100.00	0.08	5	2,149	LOW	HIGH
FRANKLIN		0.06						
Franklin Co School Dist	00191037		100.00	0.06	2	1,000	MED	HIGH
LAFAYETTE		0.05						
Lafayette Co School Dist	00193683		100.00	0.05	3	1,300	MED	MED-HIGH
LIBERTY		0.05						
Liberty Co School Dist	00194895		100.00	0.05	5	1,373	LOW	MED-HIGH
JEFFERSON		0.00						
Jefferson Co School Dist	00193619		100.00	0.00	1	769	LOW	MED-HIGH

NEW SCHOOLS/NEW PRINCIPALS

SCHOOL	PRINCIPAL	GRADES	ENROLLMENT	COUNTY	PAGE
Lake Success Academy	Byfield, Porsha, Dr	9-12	80	Lake	59
Barbara Harvey Elem Sch	Rio, Hayley	K-5	401	Manatee	68
Dr Mona Jain Middle Sch	Hodges-Lindsay, Angela	6-8	600	Manatee	68
Parrish Cmty High Sch	Little, Craig	9-12	560	Manatee	69
Mater Virtual Acad Chart MS HS	Alvarez, Ofelia	6-12	43	Miami-Dade	80
Phoenix Acad of Excellence N	Robinson, Latoya	6-8	401	Miami-Dade	74
Somerset Academy Palms	Ruiz, Suzette	K-8	120	Miami-Dade	84
Lower Keys Ace	Henriquez, Michael	6-12	18	Monroe	89
Castleview Elem Sch	Helton, Julie	K-5	722	Orange	98
Horizon West Middle Sch	Thomas, Michelle	6-8	401	Orange	99
Water Spring Elem Sch	Klaber, Amy	K-5	864	Orange	100
Harmony Middle Sch	Telemko, Frank	6-8	1,050	Osceola	103
Elisa Nelson Elem Sch	Adhia, Hema	1-5	401	Pinellas	117

NEW PRINCIPALS

SCHOOL	PRINCIPAL	GRADES	ENROLLMENT	COUNTY	PAGE
Duval Early Learning Academy	Robbins, Christiana	PK-K	291	Alachua	2
F W Buchholz High Sch	Tenbieg, James	9-12	2,285	Alachua	2
Fearnside Family Services Ctr	Strappy, Natalie	PK-PK	93	Alachua	2
Ft Clarke Middle Sch	Taber, Jared	6-8	1,029	Alachua	2
J J Finley Elem Sch	Jones, Kelly	K-5	687	Alachua	2
Kimball Wiles Elem Sch	Munn, Katherine	K-5	937	Alachua	2
Meadowbrook Elem Sch	Burklew, Brad	K-5	831	Alachua	2
Newberry Elem Sch	McAlhany, Vicki	PK-4	633	Alachua	2
Professional Acad Mag-Loften	McElroy, Bill	9-12	263	Alachua	2
W W Irby Elem Sch	Floyd, Tanya	PK-2	432	Alachua	3
Bay Haven Charter Academy	Bolinger, Larry	K-8	696	Bay	4
Jinks Middle Sch	Carpenter, Blythe	6-8	558	Bay	4
Merriam Cherry Street Elem Sch	Eckles, Stacie	PK-5	330	Bay	4
North Bay Haven Charter MS	Bolinger, Larry	6-8	524	Bay	4
Atlantis Elem Sch	Clarke, Jennifer	PK-6	713	Brevard	7
Bayside High Sch	Zander, Holli	9-12	1,706	Brevard	8
Cambridge Elem Sch	Tagye, Gina	PK-6	661	Brevard	7
Central Middle Sch	Scheuerer, Todd	7-8	1,193	Brevard	8
Cocoa Beach Jr Sr High Sch	Rendell, Mark, Dr	7-12	1,013	Brevard	8
Cocoa Jr Sr High Sch	Rendell, Mark, Dr	7-12	1,451	Brevard	8
Enterprise Elem Sch	Dufresne, Kelli	PK-6	599	Brevard	7
Fieldston Preparatory Sch	Colletti, Cindy	Spec	62	Brevard	6
Freedom 7 Elem Sch	Lott, Kathryn	K-6	387	Brevard	7
Imperial Estates Elem Sch	Adams, Cynthia	PK-6	639	Brevard	7
Melbourne High Sch	Kirk, Chad	9-12	2,113	Brevard	9
Mila Elem Sch	O'Brien, Dawna, Dr	PK-6	465	Brevard	8
Odyssey Preparatory Academy	Knight, Monica	K-12	319	Brevard	7
R L Stevenson School-Arts	Fleeger, Tiffiny	K-6	506	Brevard	8
Stone Middle Sch	Poole, Hilary	7-8	791	Brevard	9
Sunrise Elem Sch	Jost, Janene	PK-6	820	Brevard	8
Titusville High Sch	Gonzalez, Jennifer	9-12	1,377	Brevard	9
Viera Charter Sch [132]	Robinson, Sarah	K-8	1,054	Brevard	7
Viera High Sch	Robinson, Sarah	9-12	1,990	Brevard	9
Avant Garde Academy	Clermont, Fred	K-12	1,200	Broward	16
Avant Garde Academy	Valdes, Arlene, Dr	K-12	1,200	Broward	16
Avant Garde Academy	Valdes, Arlene, Dr	K-12	1,200	Broward	16
Ben Gamla CS-South Broward [130]	Berman, Gur, Dr	K-8	432	Broward	16
Ben Gamla Preparatory Chtr Sch	Iacono, Gayle	7-12	492	Broward	16
Boyd H Anderson High Sch	Griffin, James	9-12	1,712	Broward	11
Championship Acad-Davie	Dupell, Todd	K-8	559	Broward	16
Chapel Trail Elem Sch	Suarez, Susan	PK-5	813	Broward	11
Charles W Flanagan High Sch	Peters, Paula	9-12	2,519	Broward	11
Coconut Creek Elem Sch	Ray, Roberta	K-5	639	Broward	11
Coral Glades High Sch	Kaplan, Mark, Dr	9-12	2,454	Broward	11
Coral Springs High Sch	Suarez, Vivian	9-12	2,811	Broward	11
Crystal Lake Cmty Middle Sch	Toliver, Earnest	6-8	1,413	Broward	11
CS of Excellence-Ft Lauderdale	Azor, Nadine	K-5	303	Broward	16
Dave Thomas Educ Ctr-East	Williams, Jonathan	Adult	200	Broward	11
Davie Elem Sch	Anderson, Erik	PK-5	745	Broward	11
Driftwood Elem Sch	Ringler, Christine	PK-5	634	Broward	12
Eagles Nest Charter Middle Sch	Hope, B	6-8	56	Broward	16
Everest Charter Sch	Reynolds, Cristina	K-8	102	Broward	16
Excelsior Charter Sch Broward	Codling, Janett, Dr	K-5	150	Broward	16
Fairway Elem Sch	Good, Katherine	PK-5	715	Broward	12

School	Key Personnel	Grades	Enrollment	County	
Falcon Cove Middle Sch	Carruth, Steven	6-8	2,299	Broward	12
Flamingo Elem Sch	Bullock, Philip	PK-5	670	Broward	12
Franklin Acad Pembroke Pines	Nadal, Jennifer	6-12	120	Broward	16
Franklin Academy Cooper City	Fox, Alexandra	K-8	1,336	Broward	16
Franklin Academy K-12	Showalter, Diane	K-12	691	Broward	16
Ft Lauderdale High Sch	Brown, Erin	9-12	2,133	Broward	12
Griffin Elem Sch	Jones, Angie	PK-5	624	Broward	12
Imagine ES-N Lauderdle CS [137]	Standley, Stephanie	K-5	623	Broward	16
Imagine Weston [137]	Sorokin, Kristin	K-8	938	Broward	16
J P Taravella High Sch	DeArmas, Mary	9-12	3,107	Broward	12
James S Hunt Elem Sch	Amaker, Rendolyn	PK-5	627	Broward	12
Lanier James Education Center	Clemon, Bonnie	K-12	125	Broward	12
Lauderdale Lakes Middle Sch	Slesinski, Jill	6-8	866	Broward	12
Liberty Elem Sch	Whaley, Matthew	PK-5	989	Broward	13
Margate Middle Sch	Phillips, Sabine	6-8	1,211	Broward	13
Marjory Stoneman Douglas HS	Kefford, Michelle	9-12	3,303	Broward	13
McArthur High Sch	Broomfield, Alfred	9-12	2,069	Broward	13
Meadowbrook Elem Sch	Levine, David	PK-5	708	Broward	13
Miramar High Sch	Formoso, Loli	9-12	2,415	Broward	13
N Broward MS Acad-Excellence	Sandler, Robin	K-8	340	Broward	16
Norcrest Elem Sch	Charpentier, Marc	PK-5	775	Broward	13
North Fork Elem Sch	Robinson, Lavina	PK-5	439	Broward	13
Nova High Sch	Awofadeju, Olayemi	9-12	2,222	Broward	13
Park Trails Elem Sch	Manville, Arlene	PK-5	1,226	Broward	14
Pembroke Pines ES-East Campus	Augustin, Channale	K-5	1,919	Broward	17
Peters Elem Sch	Deutsch, Susanna	PK-5	725	Broward	14
Pinewood Elem Sch	Daniel, Kicia	PK-5	591	Broward	14
Piper High Sch	Hautigan, Marie	9-12	2,411	Broward	14
Renaissance CS University [133]	Guillen, Athena	K-8	1,427	Broward	17
Renaissance CS-Cooper City [133]	Self, Jackson	K-8	1,199	Broward	17
Renaissance CS-Coral Springs [133]	Self, Lynette	K-8	1,509	Broward	17
Riverside Elem Sch	Sheib, Sabrina	K-5	736	Broward	14
Somerset Acad ES South Campus	Montero, Bernardo	K-5	860	Broward	17
Somerset Academy-Riverside	Rivas, Michelle	K-5	475	Broward	17
South Broward High Sch	Brown, Patricia	9-12	2,316	Broward	15
South Broward Mont Charter Sch	Kpenkaan, Elizabeth	K-5	150	Broward	17
Sunset Lakes Elem Sch	Goulette, Janice	PK-5	900	Broward	15
Tamarac Elem Sch	Garrick, Richard	PK-5	734	Broward	15
Tropical Elem Sch	Schneider, Robert	PK-5	1,004	Broward	15
Walker Elem Sch	Eligon, Tauri	PK-5	811	Broward	15
West Broward Academy [132]	Pickens, Will	K-8	549	Broward	17
Blountstown Elem Sch	Brogden, Stephanie	PK-5	581	Calhoun	20
Deep Creek Elem Sch	Vernon, James	PK-5	691	Charlotte	21
Charles E Bennett Elem Sch	Cagle, Sheree	PK-6	690	Clay	23
Clay Virtual Academy	Amburgey, Steve	K-12	212	Clay	23
Flcca Clay Co	Roache, Lindsay	K-12	83	Clay	23
Grove Park Elem Sch	Jackson, Stephanie	K-6	498	Clay	23
Lake Asbury Junior High Sch	McConnell, Mallory	7-8	1,109	Clay	23
Lakeside Junior High Sch	Gunder, Ivin	7-8	834	Clay	23
R C Bannerman Learning Center	Aftuck, Martin	6-12	175	Clay	24
Ridgeview High Sch	Murphy, Becky	9-12	1,575	Clay	24
S Bryan Jennings Elem Sch	Love, Elise	PK-6	529	Clay	24
Wilkinson Elem Sch	Terrell, Rachael	PK-6	802	Clay	24
Barron G Collier High Sch	Bremseth, Jon	9-12	1,727	Collier	25
Cypress Palm Middle Sch	Cox, D, Dr	6-8	715	Collier	25
Everglade City Sch	Allison, Cheri, Dr	PK-12	159	Collier	25
Golden Gate Middle Sch	Bergey, Kelly	6-8	1,096	Collier	25
Highlands Elem Sch	Horne, Margaux	PK-5	624	Collier	26
Lely Elem Sch	Crehan, Christa	PK-5	611	Collier	26
Mike Davis Elem Sch	Stewart, Tamie	K-5	645	Collier	26
Naples Park Elem Sch	Auger, Michelle	PK-5	418	Collier	26
North Naples Middle Sch	Lonergan, Kimberly	6-8	902	Collier	26
Oakridge Middle Sch	Duda, Joseph	6-8	1,201	Collier	26
Palmetto Ridge High Sch	Ragusa, James	9-12	1,971	Collier	26
Parkside Elem Sch	Fike, Melanie	PK-5	741	Collier	26
Village Oaks Elem Sch	Budzynski, Beverly	PK-6	600	Collier	26
Five Points Elem Sch	Lashley, Thomas	PK-5	465	Columbia	27
Fort White Elem Sch	Christie, Michael	PK-5	650	Columbia	27
DeSoto Middle Sch	Derpich, Michelle	6-8	1,031	De Soto	28
West Elem Sch	Bruck, Ryan	PK-5	854	De Soto	28
Annie R Morgan Elem Sch	Johnson, Laquitrice	K-5	360	Duval	30
Arlington Elem Sch	Gomez, Jasmin	K-5	236	Duval	30
Arlington Heights Elem Sch	Scott, Vondeira	PK-5	328	Duval	33
Bayview Elem Sch	Metz, Melissa	K-5	369	Duval	30
Beauclerc Elem Sch	Walker, A Matt	K-5	774	Duval	30
Bridge to Success Acad HS	Foster, Vincent	9-12	50	Duval	32

School	Personnel	Grades	Enrollment	County	
Bridge to Success Acad MS	Prier, Aleya	4-8	80	Duval	33
Chimney Lakes Elem Sch	Gilley, Bill	K-5	1,038	Duval	30
Crystal Springs Elem Sch	Simpson, Todd	PK-5	1,044	Duval	30
Duncan U Fletcher Middle Sch	Matthews, Chelsea	6-8	1,324	Duval	32
Duval Charter Scholars Academy [133]	Cross, Adam	K-8	583	Duval	29
Enterprise Learning Academy	Collins, Jeffrey	PK-5	823	Duval	30
First Coast High Sch	Fluent, Justin	9-12	2,077	Duval	32
George W Carver Elem Sch	Ray, La'Tatia	PK-5	352	Duval	33
Grasp Academy	Powell, Annessia	2-7	250	Duval	30
Greenfield Elem Sch	Anderson, Tangia	PK-5	613	Duval	30
Greenland Pines Elem Sch	Walker, Beverly	PK-5	765	Duval	30
Highlands Elem Sch	Sanders, Tavianna	PK-5	453	Duval	33
Highlands Middle Sch	Wilcox, Kenyannya	6-8	906	Duval	33
Hyde Grove Elem Sch	Little, Erica	PK-2	594	Duval	33
Jefferson Davis Middle Sch	Talley, Andrea	6-8	1,000	Duval	33
John Love Elem Sch	Embry, Sylvia	PK-2	198	Duval	33
Joseph Finegan Elem Sch	Connor, Lindsey	PK-5	392	Duval	31
Joseph Stilwell Middle Sch	Tuschhoff, Tamara	6-8	801	Duval	33
Landmark Middle Sch	Tyson-White, Cicely	6-8	1,430	Duval	33
Long Branch Elem Sch	Graham, Wayman, Dr	3-5	166	Duval	33
Marine Science Education Ctr	Ledford, Dean	12-12	38	Duval	32
Mayport Middle Sch	Koek, Chris	6-8	814	Duval	33
Normandy Village Elem Sch	Guthrie, Jessica	PK-5	526	Duval	33
Pace Ctr for Girls-Jacksonvlle	Reed, Kimberly	6-12	61	Duval	32
Ramona Boulevard Elem Sch	Lampkin, Devonne	K-5	379	Duval	33
Richard Brown Gifted Talented	Kincaid, Kristi	K-5	324	Duval	31
Robert E Lee High Sch	Feagins, Timothy	9-12	1,723	Duval	32
Rutledge H Pearson Elem Sch	Davis, Carolyn	PK-5	276	Duval	33
Sadie Tillis Elem Sch	Dunbar, Helen	K-5	486	Duval	31
San Jose Academy	Knapp, Michelle	6-8	111	Duval	30
Timucuan Elem Sch	Brown, Kimberly	PK-5	591	Duval	31
Waverly Academy	Jewell, Virgina, Dr	6-8	100	Duval	30
Westside High Sch	Raulerson, J Rebecca	9-12	1,579	Duval	32
Whitehouse Elem Sch	Jordan-Long, Angela	PK-5	491	Duval	32
Northview High Sch	Munoz, Aaron	9-12	499	Escambia	37
Pine Meadow Elem Sch	Greenberg, Elizabeth	K-5	615	Escambia	38
Pleasant Grove Elem Sch	Mullen, Rs	K-5	599	Escambia	38
Reinhart Holm Elem Sch	Fina, Teri	PK-5	440	Escambia	38
Scenic Heights Elem Sch	Cox, Ms	K-5	823	Escambia	38
Gadsden Central Academy	Galvin-Wells, Carla	3-12	19	Gadsden	40
Gulf Coast Acad Science Tech	Fieserg, Nevian	6-8	236	Hernando	44
Gulf Coast Middle Sch	Gatti, Joe	6-8	110	Hernando	44
Pine Grove Elem Sch	Kalament, Thomas	PK-5	916	Hernando	44
Park Elem Sch	Conner, Carey	PK-5	533	Highlands	45
Adams Middle Sch	Mitchell, Nishira	6-8	829	Hillsborough	50
Bell Creek Academy [132]	Hammill, Chris	6-12	643	Hillsborough	46
Beth Shields Middle Sch	Carr, Colleen	6-8	1,579	Hillsborough	47
Brewster Tech & Adult Center	Robbins, Shirley	Adult	400	Hillsborough	46
Carrollwood Elem Sch	Stover, Maryjo	PK-5	748	Hillsborough	50
Channelside Academy Middle Sch	Fuentes, Cristina	6-8	138	Hillsborough	46
Davidsen Middle Sch	Arena, Stacy	6-8	1,079	Hillsborough	49
Deer Park Elem Sch	Lefler, Edith	K-5	913	Hillsborough	49
Don Giunta Middle Sch	Land, Cindy	6-8	824	Hillsborough	52
Dowdell Middle Sch	Boyd, James	6-8	637	Hillsborough	51
Dr Kiran C Patel High Sch	Strawn, Marlee, Dr	9-9	300	Hillsborough	46
Durant High Sch	Graham, Gary	9-12	2,398	Hillsborough	52
E L Bing Elem Sch	Hill-Anderson, Melanie	PK-5	504	Hillsborough	47
East Tampa Academy	Jones, Frankie	K-1	37	Hillsborough	46
Edison Elem Sch	Dodd, Candice	PK-5	399	Hillsborough	47
Eisenhower Middle Sch	Stingone, Robert	6-8	1,270	Hillsborough	52
Erwin Technical Center	Goode, James, Dr	Adult	1,000	Hillsborough	46
Excelsior Prep Charter Sch	Mullings, Stephanie	K-3	109	Hillsborough	46
Farnell Middle Sch	Binder, Tim	6-8	1,229	Hillsborough	49
Fishhawk Creek Elem Sch	Sims, Steven	K-5	1,022	Hillsborough	52
Florida Autism Ctr Excellence	Maklary, Sherry	Spec	104	Hillsborough	46
Florida Connections Academy	Trombino, Marcie	K-10	1,300	Hillsborough	46
Focus Academy	Kraft, Elisabeth	Spec	75	Hillsborough	46
Frost Elem Sch	Mikell, Tiffaney	PK-5	605	Hillsborough	48
Gordon Burnett Middle Sch	Newton, Valerie	6-8	795	Hillsborough	51
Henderson Hammock Charter Sch [133]	Griffin, James	K-8	1,147	Hillsborough	46
Heritage Elem Sch	Booth, Mary	PK-5	556	Hillsborough	50
Hillsborough Virtual Sch	Russell, Christina	K-12	369	Hillsborough	46
Ican Charter Academy	Cann, Zenobia, Dr	K-8	401	Hillsborough	46
Jack R Lamb Elem Sch	Angeletti, Chantel	PK-5	727	Hillsborough	52
Jackson Elem Sch	Haneline, Jarrod	PK-5	523	Hillsborough	48
Jennings Middle Sch	Anderson, Latonya	6-8	823	Hillsborough	48

School	Key Personnel	Grades	Enroll	County	Code
Just Elem Sch	McDonald, Kevin	PK-5	267	Hillsborough	48
Kenly Elem Sch	Wallace, Russell	PK-5	509	Hillsborough	48
Leto High Sch	McCoy, Larissa	9-12	2,115	Hillsborough	49
Lincoln Magnet Sch	Rushing, Ann	PK-5	488	Hillsborough	52
Mann Middle Sch	Jones, Dante	6-8	957	Hillsborough	51
Mendez Exceptional Center	Bell, Marvin	Spec	21	Hillsborough	51
Middleton High Sch	Brown, Tiatasha	9-12	1,595	Hillsborough	51
Mitchell Elem Sch	Best, Renee	K-5	771	Hillsborough	49
Morgan Woods Elem Sch	Kepa, Jessica	PK-5	453	Hillsborough	50
Mort Elem Sch	Hailey-Brown, Latiecea	PK-5	889	Hillsborough	48
Muller Elem Sch	Bottini, Melanie	PK-5	407	Hillsborough	50
Navigator Acad of Leadership	Clark, Shane	K-8	401	Hillsborough	47
Nelson Elem Sch	Hewitt, Mary Lou	PK-5	802	Hillsborough	52
Oak Park Elem Sch	Moody, Ryan	PK-5	572	Hillsborough	48
Pizzo K-8 Patel Lower Campus	Cronin, Amber	PK-8	745	Hillsborough	48
Riverview Acad Math & Science	Ringdahl, Marcy	K-8	401	Hillsborough	47
Rodgers Middle Sch	New, David	6-8	749	Hillsborough	52
Seminole Heights Charter HS [131]	Washington, Franca	9-12	254	Hillsborough	47
Sgt Paul R Smith Middle Sch	Kleesattel, Robert	6-8	745	Hillsborough	50
Slam Apollo	Williamson, M	K-8	401	Hillsborough	47
Southshore Charter Academy [133]	Garcia, Cecilia, Dr	K-8	1,160	Hillsborough	47
Sports Ldrshp Management Acad [130]	Mielke, Aimee	6-12	532	Hillsborough	47
Spoto High Sch	Haggins, Jazrick	9-12	1,679	Hillsborough	48
Springhead Elem Sch	McClellan, Michelle	PK-5	882	Hillsborough	52
Sulphur Springs K-8 Cmty Sch	Gaillard, Marc	PK-5	778	Hillsborough	48
Tampa Bay Blvd Elem Sch	Vinueza, Glenda	PK-5	687	Hillsborough	49
Thonotosassa Elem Sch	Montoto, Anthony	PK-5	430	Hillsborough	48
Turner-Bartels K-8 STEM	Buggs, Robert	PK-8	1,861	Hillsborough	50
Twin Lakes Elem Sch	Batista, Kilsys	K-5	724	Hillsborough	50
West Tampa Elem Sch	Kastner, Kevin	PK-5	424	Hillsborough	49
West University Charter HS [131]	Smith, Bobby	9-12	287	Hillsborough	47
Woodmont Charter Sch [133]	Caldwell, Rasheema	K-8	739	Hillsborough	47
Yates Elem Sch	Varnum, Lisa	PK-5	696	Hillsborough	51
Ponce De Leon Elem Sch	Jones, Rodd	PK-5	315	Holmes	55
Ponce De Leon High Sch	Locke, Anissa	6-12	301	Holmes	55
Poplar Springs Sch	Morgan, Brian	PK-12	386	Holmes	55
Grand Ridge Sch	Pender, Laurence	PK-8	592	Jackson	57
Beverly Shores Elem Sch	Christidis, Cindy	PK-5	736	Lake	58
Hope Forest Academy	Cantrell, Mike	3-12	20	Lake	59
Lake Co Virtual Sch	Miller, Donald	6-12	90	Lake	59
Leesburg Elem Sch	Jordan, Susan	K-5	771	Lake	59
Mt Dora Middle Sch	Frazier, Chad	6-8	851	Lake	59
Pinecrest Academy Four Corners	Rivas, Jorge	K-8	245	Lake	59
Rimes Early Learning Center	Dudley, Greggory	PK-2	280	Lake	59
Seminole Springs Elem Sch	Work, Michelle	PK-5	531	Lake	59
Tavares High Sch	Stein, Jacob	9-12	1,423	Lake	59
Triangle Elem Sch	Straughan, Marlene	PK-5	768	Lake	59
Caloosa Elem Sch	Lamar, Ashley	PK-5	964	Lee	61
Cape Coral Charter Sch [133]	Trotter, Jamie	PK-8	636	Lee	61
Cape Coral High Sch	Engelhart, Christian	9-12	1,608	Lee	61
Coronado High Sch [131]	Morris, Janet	9-12	178	Lee	61
Dunbar Cmty Sch	Mitchell, Samone, Dr	Adult	300	Lee	61
Edgewood Academy Sch	Frink, Carol	PK-5	583	Lee	61
Franklin Park Elem Sch	Freeman, Michelle	PK-5	467	Lee	61
Ft Myers Technical College	Johnson, Judy	Voc	125	Lee	61
G Weaver Hipps Elem Sch	Nauss, Deborah, Dr	PK-5	817	Lee	61
Gateway Charter Interm Sch [133]	Carter, Angela	6-8	956	Lee	61
Island Coast High Sch	Cort-Mora, Michelle, Dr	9-12	1,693	Lee	62
Lamp Sch	LaFountain, Jeanne	6-12	150	Lee	62
Lehigh Acres Middle Sch	Gibson, Brian	6-8	1,356	Lee	62
Oasis Charter Elem Sch	Grecsek, Marybeth	PK-5	895	Lee	62
Six Mile Charter Academy [133]	Thompson, Michelle	PK-8	951	Lee	63
Treeline Elem Sch	Wilcken, Jennifer	PK-5	1,056	Lee	63
Tropic Isles Elem Sch	Mazzoli, Rob	PK-5	907	Lee	63
Astoria Park Elem Sch	Solz, David	PK-5	591	Leon	64
Bond Elem Sch	Jackson, Delshuana	PK-5	687	Leon	64
Conley Elem Sch	Koerner, Jason	PK-5	765	Leon	64
Fairview Middle Sch	Edwards, Rusty	6-8	837	Leon	64
Gilchrist Elem Sch	Crowe, Scotty	PK-5	981	Leon	64
John G Riley Elem Sch	Knight, April	PK-5	615	Leon	65
Lively Technical Center	Bell, Shelly	Voc	50	Leon	65
R Frank Nims Middle Sch	Bolden, Benny, Dr	6-8	503	Leon	65
SAS on Thomasville	Lombardo, Eirin	K-8	446	Leon	65
Springwood Elem Sch	Myers, Sylvia	PK-5	592	Leon	65
Success Acad-Ghazvini Lrng Ctr	Lowe, Jessica	6-8	283	Leon	65
Tallahassee Classical Sch	Wright, Stephen	K-8	401	Leon	65

School	Key Personnel	Grades	Enrollment	County	#
Chiefland Middle High Sch	McLelland, Matt	6-12	815	Levy	66
James Madison Prep Chtr HS	Akerman, Mark	9-10	197	Madison	67
Bayshore Elem Sch	Pletcher, Bernadette	PK-5	733	Manatee	68
Braden River Elem Sch	Bennett, Joshua	PK-5	621	Manatee	68
Buffalo Creek Middle Sch	Scarbrough, Bradley	6-8	1,221	Manatee	68
Daughtrey Prep Sch Arts & Sci	Bench, Shelby	PK-5	737	Manatee	68
Imagine Schools North Manatee [137]	Kelly, Erin	PK-8	607	Manatee	68
Lakewood Ranch High Sch	Dahlquist, Dustin	9-12	2,340	Manatee	69
Lincoln Memorial Middle Sch	King, Ronnie	6-8	468	Manatee	69
Louise R Johnson K-8 Sch Int'l	Losada, Anthony	K-8	975	Manatee	69
Louise R Johnson K-8 Sch Int'l	Losada, Anthony	K-8	975	Manatee	69
Manatee School for the Arts	Jones, Bill, Dr	6-12	2,135	Manatee	69
Martha B King Middle Sch	Kreiling, Kristin	6-8	1,111	Manatee	69
Myakka Elem Sch	Ricks, Carol	PK-5	266	Manatee	69
Oneco Elem Sch	Organek, Kimberly	PK-5	615	Manatee	69
Pace Center for Girls-Manatee	Wick Mavis, Amy	5-12	52	Manatee	69
Palmetto Elem Sch	Mealor, Michelle, Dr	PK-5	732	Manatee	69
Parrish Charter Academy [136]	Patterson, Dawn	K-3	360	Manatee	69
Robert E Willis Elem Sch	Price, Kathy	K-5	774	Manatee	69
William H Bashaw Elem Sch	Mendoza, Mario	PK-5	624	Manatee	69
Belleview Elem Sch	Reece, Stacey, Dr	PK-5	701	Marion	70
Belleview-Santos Elem Sch	White, Kimberly	PK-5	509	Marion	70
East Marion Elem Sch	Hamby, Kendra	PK-5	669	Marion	71
Evergreen Elem Sch	Kemp, Ashley	K-5	458	Marion	71
Ft McCoy Sch	Fisher, Jennifer	PK-8	1,004	Marion	71
Lake Weir High Sch	Wade, Colleen	9-12	1,475	Marion	71
Marion Oaks Elem Sch	Dreher, Lisa	PK-5	892	Marion	71
Marion Technical Institute	Beasley, Jennifer	9-12	231	Marion	71
McIntosh Area Sch	Roach, Cindy	K-5	75	Marion	71
Oakcrest Elem Sch	Balius, Catherine	PK-5	592	Marion	71
Ocala Springs Elem Sch	Cino, Michelle	PK-5	648	Marion	71
Reddick-Collier Elem Sch	Sandy, Christine	PK-5	413	Marion	71
Romeo Elem Sch	Parker, Suzette	PK-5	752	Marion	71
Martin Co Acceleration Academy	Sharp, Margaret	9-12	120	Martin	73
Treasure Coast Classical Acad	Swearingin, Janine	K-6	550	Martin	73
American Senior High Sch	Papp, Stephen	9-12	2,010	Miami-Dade	78
Andover Middle Sch	Turner, Rennina	6-8	494	Miami-Dade	78
Archimedean Middle Conserv Sch	Mirhaj, Afshin	6-8	327	Miami-Dade	81
Archimedean Upper Conserv Sch	Mirhaj, Afshin	9-12	328	Miami-Dade	81
Arvida Middle Sch	Holbrook, Angela	K-8	337	Miami-Dade	81
Banyan Elem Sch	Faraldo, Vanessa	PK-5	332	Miami-Dade	75
Ben Gamla Charter Sch [130]	Frometa, Tina	K-8	251	Miami-Dade	81
Benjamin Franklin K-8 Ctr	Loubeau, Diana	PK-8	557	Miami-Dade	75
Brentwood Elem Sch	Jackson, Sharon, Dr	PK-5	552	Miami-Dade	78
Charles R Hadley Elem Sch	Jordan, Reandra	PK-5	874	Miami-Dade	75
Charter HS of the Americas	Sanchez, Ms	9-12	90	Miami-Dade	75
Coconut Grove Elem Sch	Schneider, J Ordana	PK-5	449	Miami-Dade	75
Coral Way K-8 Center	Martin, Barbara	PK-8	1,252	Miami-Dade	75
Country Club Middle Sch	Crespo, Rafael	6-8	660	Miami-Dade	79
Doctors CS of Miami Shores	Jackson, C Edward, Dr	6-12	585	Miami-Dade	79
Don Soffer Aventura High Sch	McKnight, David	9-9	401	Miami-Dade	74
Doral Academy Charter High Sch [130]	Jimenez, Francisco	9-12	1,800	Miami-Dade	75
Downtown Doral Chart Upper Sch	Lapica, Wilhelm	6-10	1,200	Miami-Dade	75
Dr Michael M Krop Sr High Sch	Kosnitzky, Adam, Dr	9-12	2,561	Miami-Dade	79
Early Beginnings Acad-Civic CT	Pauline, Tiffanie	Spec	117	Miami-Dade	75
Emerson Elem Sch	Hayes, Kristin	PK-5	357	Miami-Dade	76
Ethel Beckford-Richmond Plc	Coffey, Crystal	PK-PK	100	Miami-Dade	74
Everglades Preparatory Academy [132]	Marrero, Aida	6-12	820	Miami-Dade	82
Georgia Jones-Ayers Mid Sch	Edwards, Bernard	6-8	423	Miami-Dade	76
Golden Glades Elem Sch	Spence, Crystal	PK-5	211	Miami-Dade	79
Hialeah Gardens Middle Sch	Lima, Cynthia	6-8	1,685	Miami-Dade	79
Homestead Senior High Sch	Galardi, John	9-12	2,050	Miami-Dade	82
International Studies Chart HS [130]	Rodriguez, Vitoriano	6-12	413	Miami-Dade	76
Juvenile Justice Center Sch	Iber, Alberto	6-12	107	Miami-Dade	74
Kelsey Pharr Elem Sch	Jordan, Reandra	PK-5	354	Miami-Dade	76
Kenwood K-8 Center	Rodriguez, Rudy	PK-8	1,096	Miami-Dade	83
Kinloch Park Middle Sch	Coto-Gonzalez, Sylvia	6-8	716	Miami-Dade	76
KIPP Sunrise Academy	Kress, Monica	K-5	171	Miami-Dade	76
Lake Stevens Elem Sch	Schwam, Marc	PK-5	275	Miami-Dade	79
Lake Stevens Middle Sch	Chardon, Elizabeth	6-8	536	Miami-Dade	79
Mae Walters Elem Sch	Torrens, Mileydis	PK-5	523	Miami-Dade	80
Mater Academy Charter Mid Sch [130]	Nunez, Jose	6-8	1,344	Miami-Dade	80
Mater International Prep Acad	Melian, Ileana	6-9	170	Miami-Dade	77
Mater Perform Arts & Ent Acad [130]	Nunez, Jose	6-12	193	Miami-Dade	80
Mater Perform Arts & Ent Acad [130]	Nunez, Jose	6-12	193	Miami-Dade	80
Mater Preparatory Academy	Marty, Judith	K-8	401	Miami-Dade	77

School	Personnel	Grades	Enrollment	County	Code
Meadowlane Elem Sch	Garcia, Maritza	PK-5	738	Miami-Dade	80
Miami Coral Park Sr High Sch	Weiner, Scott	9-12	2,451	Miami-Dade	77
Miami Norland Sr High Sch	Redmon, Ronald	9-12	1,813	Miami-Dade	80
N Edelcup-Sunny Isles Bch K-8	Mesa, Melissa	K-8	2,097	Miami-Dade	80
North Miami Elem Sch	Darbonne, Deborah, Dr	PK-5	502	Miami-Dade	80
Palm Glades Preparatory Acad [132]	Ferreira, Laura	6-12	200	Miami-Dade	83
Palm Lakes Elem Sch	Arias-Gonzalez, Jacqueline	PK-5	622	Miami-Dade	81
Riviera Middle Sch	Bulnes, Jorge	6-8	501	Miami-Dade	84
Ruth Owens Kruse Center	Abreu, Cathay	Spec	180	Miami-Dade	84
Santa Clara Elem Sch	Ancheta, Ramses	PK-5	631	Miami-Dade	77
Silver Bluff Elem Sch	Barreira, Mayra	PK-5	459	Miami-Dade	78
Somerset Academy Soho MS [130]	Morales, Layda	6-8	590	Miami-Dade	84
Somerset Virtual Acad Mid HS	Lopez, Alina	6-12	100	Miami-Dade	78
South Dade Middle Sch	Munoz, Guillermo	4-8	1,286	Miami-Dade	84
Spanish Lake Elem Sch	Brito, Milko	PK-5	1,530	Miami-Dade	81
Tropical Elem Sch	Bouza Debs, Viviana	PK-5	429	Miami-Dade	84
Big Pine Academy	Williams, Sarah	PK-8	175	Monroe	89
Addie R Lewis Elem Sch	Driver, Jason	K-8	760	Okaloosa	91
Choctawhatchee Senior High Sch	Heck, Michelle	9-12	1,638	Okaloosa	92
Choice High & Tech Center	Sansom, Jerry	Voc	300	Okaloosa	92
Clifford Meigs Middle Sch	Lamb, Tracey	6-8	561	Okaloosa	92
Liza Jackson Preparatory Sch	McKinley, Kaye	K-8	848	Okaloosa	92
Longwood Elem Sch	Michna, Yvonne	PK-5	584	Okaloosa	92
Max Bruner Jr Middle Sch	Massey, Gary	6-8	801	Okaloosa	92
Okaloosa Stemm Academy	Martin, Scheree	6-8	239	Okaloosa	92
Plew Elem Sch	Matz, Tammy	K-5	793	Okaloosa	92
Richbourg Sch	Anderson, Amy	Spec	79	Okaloosa	92
Shoal River Middle Sch	Miller, Craig	6-8	842	Okaloosa	92
Silver Sands Sch	Wheat, Stephanie	Spec	148	Okaloosa	92
Okeechobee Virtual Sch	Myers, Lauren	6-12	26	Okeechobee	93
AMI Kids-Orlando Sch	Tovine, William	6-12	38	Orange	94
Apopka Elem Sch	Pinder, Latricia	PK-5	791	Orange	97
Chancery Charter High Sch [131]	Villanueva, Isabel	9-12	388	Orange	94
Colonial High 9th Grade Ctr	Maestre, Hector, Dr	9-9	1,000	Orange	97
Colonial High Sch	Maestre, Hector, Dr	9-12	3,403	Orange	97
Corner Lake Middle Sch	Browning, Paul	6-8	943	Orange	96
Dillard Street Elem Sch	Smid, Tiffany	PK-5	530	Orange	99
Dr Phillips Elem Sch	Rogers, Christine	PK-5	729	Orange	99
Eagle's Nest Elem Sch	Adams, Lisa	PK-5	710	Orange	99
East Lake Elem Sch	Brown, Latonya	PK-5	602	Orange	96
East River High Sch	Campbell, Nikki	9-12	2,043	Orange	97
Eccleston Elem Sch	Bittick, Janet	K-5	541	Orange	99
Florida Virtual Middle Sch	Henson, Kenneth	6-8	1,575	Orange	93
Freedom Middle Sch	Leavitt, Cheri	6-8	1,255	Orange	99
Innovation Mont High Sch	Cherico, Patrice	9-10	24	Orange	94
Killarney Elem Sch	Vereen, Debra	PK-5	419	Orange	97
Lake George Elem Sch	Watson, Lauren	PK-5	604	Orange	98
Lovell Elem Sch	Sarasty, Melissa	PK-5	713	Orange	97
Magnolia Sch	Green, Latonia	Spec	117	Orange	99
Meadowbrook Middle Sch	Hardrick, David	6-8	994	Orange	95
MetroWest Elem Sch	Gjini, Xhuljeta	K-5	649	Orange	99
Millennia Elem Sch	Pena, Dyanira	PK-5	1,031	Orange	99
Millennia Gardens Elem Sch	Carralero, Michelle	PK-5	997	Orange	99
Ocoee Elem Sch	Goshe, Kandace	PK-5	778	Orange	99
Odyssey Middle Sch	Smith, Beatriz	6-8	876	Orange	98
Orange Co Preparatory Academy [132]	Graham, Chentella	K-8	336	Orange	94
Orange Youth Academy	Tovine, William	6-12	52	Orange	94
Orlando Gifted Academy	Wright, John	2-5	172	Orange	96
Pinecrest Preparatory Academy [130]	Lumpuy, Desiree	K-8	239	Orange	95
Pinewood Elem Sch	Steinke, Kelly	PK-5	583	Orange	97
Positive Pathways Ctr	Tovine, William	6-12	291	Orange	95
Renaissance CS-Hunters Creek [133]	Knowles, Patrice	K-8	1,238	Orange	95
Rock Lake Elem Sch	Atkinson, Linton	PK-5	370	Orange	95
Sun Blaze Elem Sch	Szymanski, Christine	K-5	1,160	Orange	98
Sunset Park Elem Sch	Gangwisch, Jay	K-5	933	Orange	99
Sunshine Charter High Sch [131]	Rugraff, Don	9-12	301	Orange	95
UCP Charter School-Downtown	Shea, Jodi	Spec	284	Orange	95
Union Park Elem Sch	Ramirez, Ashlynn	PK-5	493	Orange	96
Ventura Elem Sch	Gonzalez, Ana	PK-5	726	Orange	98
Westpointe Elem Sch	Grubbs-Holmes, Atresa	K-5	715	Orange	100
Wheatley Elem Sch	Miller, Lukeshia	PK-5	472	Orange	95
Winter Park 9th Grade Center	White, Paul, Dr	9-9	800	Orange	97
Adult Lrng Center Osceola	Combs, Karen	Adult	460	Osceola	102
Canoe Creek Charter Academy [133]	Ramos, Alan	K-8	491	Osceola	103
Creative Inspiration Journey	Marquis, Patricia	K-5	401	Osceola	103
Flora Ridge Elem Sch	Dwyer, William	PK-5	1,075	Osceola	103

School	Principal	Grades	Enrollment	County	Page
Kissimmee Middle Sch	Rolando, Eugenia	6-8	1,341	Osceola	103
Koa Elem Sch	Terry, Ashton	PK-5	653	Osceola	103
Liberty High Sch	Misty, Cruz	9-12	2,020	Osceola	103
Mater Acad St Cloud	Singh, Victoria	K-7	90	Osceola	103
Narcoossee Middle Sch	Weeden, Gary	6-8	1,295	Osceola	103
Osceola Virtual Sch	Hodges, Pete	K-12	52	Osceola	104
Renaissance CS at Tapestry [133]	Owens, Sandy	K-8	1,396	Osceola	104
Renaissance CS-Poinciana [133]	Gomez, Maria	K-8	860	Osceola	104
Acreage Pines Elem Sch	Karbowski, Darline	PK-5	529	Palm Beach	108
Adult Education Center	Mears, Stuart	Adult	600	Palm Beach	105
Citrus Cove Elem Sch	Cromwell, Natalie, Dr	PK-5	1,128	Palm Beach	109
Crystal Lakes Elem Sch	Green, Laura	PK-5	791	Palm Beach	109
Egret Lake Elem Sch	Napier, Dionne	K-5	632	Palm Beach	106
Equestrian Trails Elem Sch	Johnson, Michele	PK-5	879	Palm Beach	106
Forest Hill Cmty High Sch	Rivera, Esther	9-12	2,458	Palm Beach	107
Glade View Elem Sch	Dowers, Shundra	K-5	273	Palm Beach	107
Glades Academy	Jones, Vincynthia	K-8	279	Palm Beach	105
Hagen Road Elem Sch	Standish, Bernadette	PK-5	748	Palm Beach	109
Highland Elem Sch	Villani, Elena	PK-5	1,224	Palm Beach	107
Hope-Centennial Elem Sch	Nathan, Lakeisha	PK-5	652	Palm Beach	107
Howell L Watkins Middle Sch	Tomas-Andres, Awilda	6-8	912	Palm Beach	108
Independence Middle Sch	Lundman, E	6-8	1,378	Palm Beach	108
Indian Ridge Sch	Ford, Eugene	Spec	110	Palm Beach	107
Loggers Run Cmty Middle Sch	Hierholzer, Krista	6-8	1,206	Palm Beach	110
New Horizons Elem Sch	Pallaria, Dana	PK-5	684	Palm Beach	107
Olympus International Academy	Swenson, Nancy	K-8	199	Palm Beach	105
Omni Middle Sch	DeLuz, Nikkia	6-8	1,473	Palm Beach	110
Pace Ctr for Girls-Palm Beach	Pappas, Aggie	5-12	42	Palm Beach	105
Pahokee High Sch	Dennard, Dwayne	9-12	424	Palm Beach	108
Palm Beach Gardens Cmty HS	Hoffman, Donald, Dr	9-12	2,736	Palm Beach	108
Palm Beach Virtual Sch	Henry, Bradley	K-12	108	Palm Beach	105
Palm Springs Elem Sch	Fox, Bonnie	PK-5	846	Palm Beach	107
Panther Run Elem Sch	De La Vega, Edilia	PK-5	883	Palm Beach	107
Rosenwald Elem Sch	Hightower, Bruce	K-5	283	Palm Beach	108
Slam High School Palm Beach	Duvo, Clint	9-12	401	Palm Beach	106
Somerset Academy of the Arts	Sauri, Elizabeth	K-8	401	Palm Beach	106
Southtech Siccess Center	Harvey, Maynard	9-10	25	Palm Beach	106
Spanish River Cmty High Sch	Castellano, Allison	9-12	2,343	Palm Beach	110
Waters Edge Elem Sch	Walker, Juliann	K-5	819	Palm Beach	110
West Boca Raton Cmty High Sch	Capitano, Edmund	9-12	2,217	Palm Beach	110
West Riviera Elem Sch	McKnight, Alisha, Dr	PK-5	609	Palm Beach	109
Western Academy Charter Sch	Manriquez, Jessica	K-8	523	Palm Beach	106
Athenian Acad-Tech & Arts	Markowitz, Evan	K-8	359	Pasco	112
Calusa Elem Sch	Hartman, Trudy	K-5	510	Pasco	113
Connerton Elem Sch	Edwards, Kelly	PK-5	921	Pasco	113
Countryside Montessori Academy	Picone, Michael	1-8	344	Pasco	112
Cypress Elem Sch	Berryhill, Tammy	PK-5	722	Pasco	113
Double Branch Elem Sch	Wiggins, Lori	PK-5	751	Pasco	113
Fivay High Sch	Joens, Jason	9-12	1,763	Pasco	114
Gulf High Sch	Morgenstein, Jeff	9-12	1,561	Pasco	114
Gulf Trace Elem Sch	Scilex, Dawn	PK-5	633	Pasco	113
Longleaf Elem Sch	McCormack, Jennifer	PK-5	678	Pasco	113
Rodney B Cox Elem Sch	Natal, Kimberly	PK-5	510	Pasco	114
Trinity Elem Sch	Wolin, Adam	K-5	616	Pasco	114
Zephyrhills High Sch	Stanley, Christina, Dr	9-12	1,477	Pasco	114
Bauder Elem Sch	Leichman, Jodi	PK-5	769	Pinellas	118
Bay Vista Fundamental Sch	Hall, Ms	K-5	647	Pinellas	118
Belcher Elem Sch	Moody, Kristy	PK-5	685	Pinellas	117
Belleair Elem Sch	Austin, Kelly	PK-5	552	Pinellas	117
Blanton Elem Sch	Roth, Lisa	PK-5	523	Pinellas	119
Carwise Middle Sch	Eiben, Chad	6-8	1,273	Pinellas	116
Countryside High Sch	Vicari, Mr	9-12	2,103	Pinellas	116
Dunedin Highland Middle Sch	Vasallo, Michael	6-8	1,024	Pinellas	117
Fairmount Park Elem Sch	Lawson, Lakisha	PK-5	565	Pinellas	119
Forest Lakes Elem Sch	McHugh, Michael	PK-5	510	Pinellas	117
Gulfport Elem Montessori Acad	Bryan, Wendy	PK-5	643	Pinellas	118
High Point Elem Sch	Mendoza, Melody	PK-5	671	Pinellas	118
Highland Lakes Elem Sch	Gehringer, Donna	PK-5	584	Pinellas	117
James B Sanderlin IB World Sch	Armstrong, Ms	PK-8	573	Pinellas	118
Lakeview Fundamental Elem Sch	Baker, Tijuana	K-5	345	Pinellas	118
Lakewood Elem Sch	Woodford, Stephanie	PK-5	379	Pinellas	118
Lealman Avenue Elem Sch	Duffy, Kim	PK-5	451	Pinellas	119
Maximo Elem Sch	Moses, Tekoa	PK-5	517	Pinellas	118
Midtown Academy	Victor, Keila	K-5	306	Pinellas	119
Oldsmar Elem Sch	Bauman, Kristina	PK-5	600	Pinellas	117
Osceola Middle Sch	Lowery, Solomon, Dr	6-8	1,207	Pinellas	118

School	Personnel	Grades	Enrollment	County	Code
Pace Center for Girls-Pinellas	Hollis, Tanya	6-12	38	Pinellas	116
Pinellas Park Elem Sch	Frodine, Lori	PK-5	557	Pinellas	119
Pinellas Park Middle Sch	Shedrick, Jason, Dr	6-8	1,183	Pinellas	119
Plumb Elem Sch	Delduca, Holly	PK-5	735	Pinellas	118
Sandy Lane Elem Sch	Moss, Jeff, Dr	K-5	346	Pinellas	118
Seventy-Fourth St Elem Sch	Hathaway, Jessley	PK-5	519	Pinellas	119
Shore Acres Elem Sch	Sulte, Kris	PK-5	636	Pinellas	119
Skycrest Elem Sch	Defant, Eliza	PK-5	618	Pinellas	118
Tarpon Springs Middle Sch	Phelps, E	6-8	809	Pinellas	117
Thurgood Marshall Fundmntl MS	Wilson, Nicole	6-8	940	Pinellas	119
Bartow Int'l Baccalaureat HS	Andrews, Brian	9-12	227	Polk	122
Chain of Lakes Collegiate HS	Bonney, Keith	11-12	313	Polk	123
Cypress Junction Mont Sch	Romey, Curtis	K-8	193	Polk	123
Davenport School of the Arts	Braaten, Cynthia	K-8	1,157	Polk	122
Doris A Sanders Learning Ctr	Bruno, Polly	Spec	109	Polk	123
Edward W Bok Academy North	Moses, Damien	6-7	160	Polk	123
Frostproof Elem Sch	Meyers, Dart	PK-2	428	Polk	124
Garden Grove Elem Sch	Bergwall, Shauna	PK-5	512	Polk	124
Gibbons St Pre-Sch Center	Kent, Gregory	PK-PK	228	Polk	124
James E Stephens Elem Sch	Bracey, James	PK-5	426	Polk	124
Janie Howard Wilson Elem Sch [140]	Ray, Linda, Dr	K-5	409	Polk	123
Lakeland Highlands Middle Sch	Santiago, Edgar	6-8	1,278	Polk	122
Lawton Chiles Middle Academy	Kendrick, Telay	6-8	649	Polk	122
Lena Vista Elem Sch	Sharp, Deneece	PK-5	892	Polk	125
McKeel Central Academy	Massung, Angela	K-5	570	Polk	123
McLaughlin Mid Fine Art Acad	Wright, Debra	6-8	832	Polk	125
Mulberry High Sch	Chipman, Sharon	9-12	1,193	Polk	122
Navigator Acad of Leadership	Clark, Shane	K-8	401	Polk	123
New Beginnings High Sch	Nelson, Terri	6-12	500	Polk	123
Pace Center for Girls-Polk	Katzman, Ellen	6-12	55	Polk	123
Palmetto Elem Sch	Short, Jessica	PK-4	551	Polk	124
Philip O'Brien Elem Sch	Huntley, Charlie	PK-5	695	Polk	125
Shelley S Boone Middle Sch	Sears, Michael	6-8	1,180	Polk	125
Sleepy Hill Middle Sch	Selph, Wallace	6-8	1,051	Polk	122
South McKeel Academy	Powell, Mrs	K-8	1,164	Polk	124
Summerlin Academy	Downing, Cynthia	9-12	511	Polk	122
Eleanor H Miller Sch	Symonds, Rodney	Spec	133	Putnam	127
Kelley Smith Elem Sch	Taylor, Tracy	PK-5	474	Putnam	127
Cranberry Elem Sch	Porinchak, Brad	PK-5	681	Sarasota	129
Sarasota Co Technical Inst	Dipillo, Ronald	Voc	702	Sarasota	130
State Clg of FL Collegiate Sch	Monod, Kelly	6-12	401	Sarasota	130
Suncoast Polytechnical HS	Turgeon, John	Voc	565	Sarasota	130
YMCA Triad Alt Sch-North	Ritter, Melanie	6-12	61	Sarasota	130
Bear Lake Elem Sch	Ramkissoon, Kristen	PK-5	1,080	Seminole	132
Crystal Lake Elem Sch	Carver, Rick	PK-5	768	Seminole	132
Eastbrook Elem Sch	Dunaye, Rod	PK-5	787	Seminole	132
Goldsboro Elem Magnet Sch	Mulholland, Chris	PK-5	886	Seminole	132
Hagerty High Sch	Frasca, Rob	9-12	2,417	Seminole	132
Keeth Elem Sch	Kramperth, Joanne	PK-5	643	Seminole	132
Lake Mary High Sch	Reynolds, Mickey	9-12	2,914	Seminole	132
Rainbow Elem Sch	Marshall, Mrs	PK-5	778	Seminole	133
Red Bug Elem Sch	Sharpe, Christine	PK-5	853	Seminole	133
Rock Lake Middle Sch	Dunlop, Martin	6-8	943	Seminole	133
Seminole High Sch	Rodriguez, Jordan	9-12	3,189	Seminole	133
Wekiva Elem Sch	Schreiner, Keaton	PK-5	830	Seminole	133
John A Crookshank Elem Sch	Jackson, Mr	PK-5	812	St Johns	134
Palencia Elem Sch	Goodrich, Catherine	K-5	841	St Johns	135
Pvpv/Rawlings Elem Sch	Gates, Dr	K-5	1,020	St Johns	135
R J Murray Middle Sch	Steele, Paula	6-8	765	St Johns	135
Sebastian Middle Sch	Gabaldon, Kirstie	6-8	727	St Johns	135
St Johns Technical High Sch	Force, Ms	Voc	1,250	St Johns	135
Switzerland Point Middle Sch	Brunet, Ms	6-8	1,313	St Johns	135
Valley Ridge Academy	McMandon, Sandra	K-8	1,406	St Johns	135
Creative Arts Acad of St Lucie	Reid, Lori Anne, Dr	K-8	329	St Lucie	136
Fairlawn Elem Sch	Ricksecker, Heather	K-5	618	St Lucie	136
Forest Grove Middle Sch	Jamison, Arthur, Dr	6-8	870	St Lucie	136
Ft Pierce Central High Sch	Buchanon, Monarae	9-12	2,602	St Lucie	136
Lakewood Park Elem Sch	Walukiewicz, Kerri	PK-5	732	St Lucie	136
Oak Hammock K-8 Sch	Galloway, Patricia	K-8	1,460	St Lucie	136
Pace Ctr for Girls-Treasure	Colter, Vickie	6-12	47	St Lucie	136
Performance Based Prep Academy	Seal, Susan	9-12	114	St Lucie	136
Port St Lucie High Sch	Wigginton, Brooke	9-12	1,754	St Lucie	136
Renaissance CS-Tradition [133]	Wilson, Amanda	K-8	1,145	St Lucie	136
River's Edge Elem Sch	Ingersoll, Mrs	K-5	631	St Lucie	136
Treasure Coast High Sch	Smith, Todd	9-12	2,823	St Lucie	137
White City Elem Sch	Laoutas, Alexandra	PK-5	586	St Lucie	137

School	Key Personnel	Grades	Enrollment	County	Page
Suwannee Virtual Sch	Barr, Jennifer	6-12	93	Suwannee	138
Champion Elem Sch	Inge, Richard	PK-5	630	Volusia	140
Deland Middle Sch	DeVito, John	6-8	1,179	Volusia	140
Deltona Middle Sch	Feltner, Kimberly	6-8	1,159	Volusia	140
Discovery Elem Sch	McLean, Leslie	K-5	602	Volusia	140
Edith I Starke Elem Sch	Ahr, Eilene	PK-5	417	Volusia	140
Enterprise Elem Sch	Douglas, Alicia	PK-5	580	Volusia	140
Forest Lake Elem Sch	Freeman, Virginia	PK-5	634	Volusia	140
Highbanks Learning Center	Johns, Dale	8-12	30	Volusia	141
Louise S McInnis Elem Sch	Lavallee, Sharon, Dr	PK-5	402	Volusia	141
Mainland High Sch	Huth, Timothy	9-12	1,870	Volusia	141
Osceola Elem Sch	Bruner, Lynn	K-5	405	Volusia	141
Pace Center for Girls-Volusia	McCurdy, Georgia	6-12	39	Volusia	141
Pine Ridge High Sch	Nehrig, Paul	9-12	1,725	Volusia	141
Port Orange Elem Sch	Polite, Angela	K-5	408	Volusia	141
Pride Elem Sch	Johnson, Libby	PK-5	590	Volusia	141
South Daytona Elem Sch	Wallace, Tennille	K-5	852	Volusia	141
Southwestern Middle Sch	Copeland, Jacquese	6-8	783	Volusia	141
Spirit Elem Sch	DeVaney, Carrie	PK-5	693	Volusia	141
Timbercrest Elem Sch	Tidmarsh, Lonnie	PK-5	784	Volusia	142
Westside Elem Sch	Copeland, Dwayne	PK-5	586	Volusia	142
Dune Lakes Elem Sch	Spence, Meredith	K-5	700	Walton	143
Seaside Neighborhood Sch	Mixson, Kim	5-12	357	Walton	144
Walton Learning Center	Sansom, Ray	6-12	38	Walton	144

NEW SUPERINTENDENTS

DISTRICT	SUPERINTENDENT	GRADES	ENROLLMENT	COUNTY	PAGE
School Dist of Indian River Co	Moxley, Susan, Dr	PK-12	17,500	Indian River	55
Madison Co School Dist	Joseph, Shirley	PK-12	2,500	Madison	67
Florida Virtual School Dist	Algazi, Louis, Dr	K-12	5,540	Orange	93
Orange Co PSD-Transformation	Brown-Cannon, Tashanda	K-8		Orange	95
Orange Co Public SD-Dep Supt	Wright, John	K-8		Orange	95
Orange Co Public SD-High Sch	Border, Harold	9-12		Orange	97
Orange Co Public SD-North	Jones, Rahin	PK-8		Orange	97
Orange Co Public SD-Southeast	Bohn, William	PK-8		Orange	98
Orange Co Public SD-West	Fritzler, Patricia	PK-8		Orange	99
Palm Beach Co SD-Ctl Region	Zuloaga-Haines, Valerie	PK-12		Palm Beach	106
Palm Beach Co SD-South Region	Licata, Peter	PK-12		Palm Beach	109
Volusia Co School Dist	Egnor, Timothy	PK-12	64,000	Volusia	140

FLORIDA

- **Florida Dept of Education** PID: 00181082   850/245-0505
  325 W Gaines St Ste 1514, Tallahassee 32399   Fax 850/245-9667

Schools: 10

STATE-OPERATED SCHOOLS

State Schs..Principal	Grd	Prgm	Enr/#Cls	SN
A D Henderson Univ Sch 777 Glades Rd, Boca Raton 33431 Sherry Bees	K-12		1,148 25	561/297-3970 Fax 561/297-3939
© Advanced Technology College 1770 Technology Blvd, Daytona Beach 32117 Dr Amy Locklear	Voc		226	386/506-4100 Fax 386/506-4191
Famud Research Sch 400 W Orange Ave, Tallahassee 32305 Pink Hightower \ G Starr Swain	K-12		484	850/412-5930
Ⓐ FL HS Accelerated Lrng-North © 428 SW Pine Island Rd, Cape Coral 33991 Janet Morris	9-12		300	239/242-4230 Fax 239/242-4231
Ⓐ FL HS Accelerated Lrng-South © 3057 Cleveland Ave, Fort Myers 33901 Charles Pease	9-12		300	239/337-9140 Fax 239/337-9141
Florida A & M Dev Research Sch 400 W Orange Ave, Tallahassee 32305 Joan McGlockton	K-12	TV	630 24	74% 850/412-5930 Fax 850/412-5895
Florida School-Deaf & Blind 207 San Marco Ave, St Augustine 32084 Carol Bogue	Spec	T	81	73% 904/827-2200 Fax 904/827-2714
Florida State Univ Sch 3000 School House Rd, Tallahassee 32311 Suzanne Wilkinson \ Megan Brink	K-12	TV	1,744 90	28% 850/245-3700 Fax 850/245-3721
P K Yonge Dev Research Sch 1080 SW 11th St, Gainesville 32601 Carrie Geiger	K-12		1,157 48	28% 352/392-1554 Fax 352/392-9559
© Pembroke Pines-Fsu Charter ES 601 SW 172nd Ave, Pembroke Pnes 33029 Dr Lisa Libidinsky	K-5		699 33	34% 954/499-4244 Fax 954/499-3016

ALACHUA COUNTY

ALACHUA PUBLIC SCHOOLS

- **Alachua Co School Dist** PID: 00181094   352/955-7300
  620 E University Ave, Gainesville 32601   Fax 352/955-6700

Schools: 57 \ *Teachers:* 1,506 \ *Students:* 26,179 \
Special Ed Students: 3,808 \ *LEP Students:* 770 \ *College-Bound:* 60%
\ *Ethnic:* Asian 6%, African American 37%, Hispanic 10%, Caucasian
47% \ *Exp:* $194 (Low) \ *Poverty:* 18% \ *Title I:* $8,399,718 \
Special Education: $17,485,000 \ *Bilingual Education:* $1,611,000 \
Open-Close: 08/12 - 05/29 \ *DTBP:* $203 (High)

Public Schs..Principal	Grd	Prgm	Enr/#Cls	SN
A L Mebane Middle Sch 16401 NW County Road 241, Alachua 32615 Manda Bessner	6-8	TV	363 30	52% 386/462-1648 Fax 386/273-4632
Ⓐ A Quinn Jones Center 1108 NW 7th Ave, Gainesville 32601 Darin Jones	6-12	T	93 16	82% 352/955-6840 Fax 844/350-6308
Abraham Lincoln Middle Sch 1001 SE 12th St, Gainesville 32641 Latroy Strappy	6-8	TV	647 70	45% 352/955-6711 Fax 844/270-6772
Alachua Elem Sch 13800 NW 152nd Pl, Alachua 32615 Heather Harbour	3-5	GT	334 29	58% 386/462-1841 Fax 844/273-4585
Alachua Eschool 2802 NE 8th Ave, Gainesville 32641 Edwin Stefansen	K-12		41	352/955-7584 Fax 352/363-5184
© Alachua Learning Academy ES 11100 W State Road 235, Alachua 32615 Krishna Rivera	K-5	T	112 9	52% 386/418-2080 Fax 386/418-4116
© Alachua Learning Academy MS 11100 W State Road 235, Alachua 32615 Krishna Rivera	6-8	T	52	72% 386/418-2080 Fax 386/418-4116
Archer Elem Sch 14533 SW 170th St, Archer 32618 Stella Arduser	PK-5	GT	545 15	50% 352/495-2111 Fax 844/567-8852
© Boulware Springs Charter Sch 1303 NE 23rd Ave, Gainesville 32609 Kay Abbitt	K-5	T	159	67% 352/244-9732

School	Grades		Enrollment	%	Phone/Fax
C W Norton Elem Sch 2200 NW 45th Ave, Gainesville 32605 Elena Mayo	PK-5	T	687	45%	352/955-6765 Fax 352/700-1298
© Caring & Sharing Learning Sch 1951 SE 4th St, Gainesville 32641 Curtiss Peterson	PK-6	T	223 6	78%	352/372-1004 Fax 352/372-0894
Chester Shell Elem Sch 21633 SE 65th Ave, Hawthorne 32640 Holly Burton	PK-5	T	365 11	75%	352/481-1901 Fax 888/519-3199
Duval Early Learning Academy 2106 NE 8th Ave, Gainesville 32641 **Christiana Robbins**	PK-K		291 25		352/955-6703 Fax 844/567-8853
Eastside High Sch 1201 SE 43rd St, Gainesville 32641 Shane Andrew	9-12	TV	1,323 90	50%	352/955-6704 Fax 844/667-1773
© Einstein Sch 5910 SW Archer Rd, Gainesville 32608 Aurelio Holds	2-8	T	107 8	48%	352/335-4321 Fax 352/335-1575
© Expressions Lrng Arts Academy 5408 SW 13th St, Gainesville 32608 Juniper DiGiovanni	K-5		85 4	16%	352/373-5223 Fax 352/373-6327
F W Buchholz High Sch 5510 NW 27th Ave, Gainesville 32606 **James Tenbieg**	9-12	V	2,285 118	29%	352/955-6702 Fax 844/770-0225
Fearnside Family Services Ctr 3600 NE 15th St, Gainesville 32609 **Natalie Strappy**	PK-PK		93	100%	352/955-6875 Fax 844/273-4664
© Florida Sia Tech Charter Sch 7022 NW 10th Pl, Gainesville 32605 Dr William Scott	9-12	TV	219 7	41%	352/333-7952 Fax 352/371-4426
Ft Clarke Middle Sch 9301 NW 23rd Ave, Gainesville 32606 **Jared Taber**	6-8	TV	1,029 70	45%	352/333-2800 Fax 352/868-6660
Gainesville High Sch 1900 NW 13th St, Gainesville 32609 David Shelnutt	9-12	TV	1,888	43%	352/955-6707 Fax 844/607-5796
© Genesis Preparatory Sch 207 NW 23rd Ave, Gainesville 32609 Cynthia Tennell	K-3	T	72 4	79%	352/379-1188 Fax 352/379-1142
Glen Springs Elem Sch 2826 NW 31st Ave, Gainesville 32605 Deanna Feagin	K-5	T	494 24	53%	352/955-6708 Fax 844/700-1291
Hawthorne Middle/High Sch 21403 SE 69th Ave, Hawthorne 32640 Daniel Ferguson	6-12	GTV	354 31	61%	352/481-1900 Fax 844/567-8854
© Healthy Learning Academy 13505 W Newberry Rd, Jonesville 32669 Suzanne Borganelli	K-5		99	13%	352/372-2279 Fax 352/372-1665
Hidden Oak Elem Sch 2100 Fort Clarke Blvd, Gainesville 32606 James Kuhn	PK-5		777	33%	352/333-2801 Fax 352/333-2805
High Springs Community Sch 19559 High Springs Main St, High Springs 32643 Lynn McNeill	PK-8	T	952 40	47%	386/454-1958 Fax 844/273-4472
Howard W Bishop Middle Sch 1901 NE 9th St, Gainesville 32609 Michael Gamble	6-8	TV	692 65	47%	352/955-6701 Fax 352/316-7370
Idylwild Elem Sch 4601 SW 20th Ter, Gainesville 32608 Wanza Wakeley	K-5	T	687 40	73%	352/955-6709 Fax 844/567-8855
J J Finley Elem Sch 1912 NW 5th Ave, Gainesville 32603 **Kelly Jones**	K-5	T	687 25	38%	352/955-6705 Fax 844/585-9513
Joseph Williams Elem Sch 1245 SE 7th Ave, Gainesville 32641 Anyana Stokes	K-5	T	569 32	70%	352/955-6719 Fax 888/519-5261
Kanapaha Middle Sch 5005 SW 75th St, Gainesville 32608 Sherry Estes	6-8	TV	1,056 50	48%	352/955-6960 Fax 844/567-8856
Kimball Wiles Elem Sch 4601 SW 75th St, Gainesville 32608 **Katherine Munn**	K-5	G	937 47	35%	352/955-6955 Fax 844/576-2606
Lake Forest Elem Sch 4401 SE 4th Ave, Gainesville 32641 Karla Hutchinson	PK-5	T	420 26	89%	352/955-6710 Fax 855/313-5069
Lawton M Chiles Elem Sch 2525 School House Rd, Gainesville 32608 Cory Tomlinson	K-5		795 35	39%	352/333-2825 Fax 352/585-9512
Littlewood Elem Sch 812 NW 34th St, Gainesville 32605 Justin Russell	PK-5	T	706 32	48%	352/955-6712 Fax 844/700-1292
Marjorie K Rawlings Elem Sch 3500 NE 15th St, Gainesville 32609 Laura Creamer	1-5	T	264 25	87%	352/955-6715 Fax 844/272-5206
Meadowbrook Elem Sch 11525 NW 39th Ave, Gainesville 32606 **Brad Burklew**	K-5		831	36%	352/333-2828 Fax 844/567-8857
© Micanopy Academy 708 NW Okehumkee St, Micanopy 32667 Tara Lowe	6-10	T	58 6	67%	352/466-1090 Fax 352/466-1030
© Micanopy Area Co-op Sch 802 NW Seminary Ave, Micanopy 32667 Anne Thomson	K-5	T	212 6	49%	352/466-0990
Myra Terwilliger Elem Sch 301 NW 62nd St, Gainesville 32607 Ashlea Zeller	PK-5	T	558 40	75%	352/955-6717 Fax 352/726-2917
Ⓐ N Central Florida Public Chart © 2209 NW 13th St, Gainesville 32609 Randy Starling	9-12	T	206	50%	352/379-2902 Fax 352/379-2956
Newberry Elem Sch 25705 SW 15th Ave, Newberry 32669 **Vicki McAlhany**	PK-4	T	633 25	45%	352/472-1100 Fax 352/576-2605
Newberry High Sch 400 SW 258th St, Newberry 32669 James Sheppard	9-12	TV	653 40	45%	352/472-1101 Fax 844/700-1294
Oak View Middle Sch 1203 SW 250th St, Newberry 32669 Kelly Armstrong	5-8	TV	899 40	42%	352/472-1102 Fax 844/726-2914
© One Room Elem School House 4180 NE 15th St, Gainesville 32609 Sarah Sonberg	K-5	T	40 8	76%	352/376-4014 Fax 352/376-3345
© One Room Middle Sch 3930 NE 15th St, Gainesville 32609 Sarah Sonberg	6-8		35		352/727-4373 Fax 352/727-4372
Ⓐ Pace Center for Girls-Alachua 1010 SE 4th Ave, Gainesville 32601 Kathie Southwick	6-12		43	28%	352/374-8799 Fax 352/378-6602
Professional Acad Mag-Loften 3000 E University Ave, Gainesville 32641 **Bill McElroy**	9-12	GTV	263 30	53%	352/955-6839 Fax 844/772-7672
© Resilience Charter Sch 1717 NE 9th St, Gainesville 32609 Leah Fox	6-10		69	48%	352/226-8675 Fax 352/505-3158
Santa Fe High Sch 16213 NW US Highway 441, Alachua 32615 Dr Beth Leclear	9-12	GTV	1,086 40	37%	386/462-1125 Fax 352/448-1691
Sidney Lanier Center 312 NW 16th Ave, Gainesville 32601 Royce Kamman	Spec	T	163 15	53%	352/955-6841 Fax 352/955-6885
Stephen Foster Elem Sch 3800 NW 6th St, Gainesville 32609 Lisa Peterson	K-5	T	539 20	55%	352/955-6706 Fax 844/585-9514

1	Superintendent	8	Curric/Instruct K-12	19	Chief Financial Officer	29	Family/Consumer Science	39	Social Studies K-12	49	English/Lang Arts Elem	59	Special Education Elem	69	Academic Assessment
2	Bus/Finance/Purchasing	9	Curric/Instruct Elem	20	Art K-12	30	Adult Education	40	Social Studies Elem	50	English/Lang Arts Sec	60	Special Education Sec	70	Research/Development
3	Buildings And Grounds	10	Curric/Instruct Sec	21	Art Elem	31	Career/Sch-to-Work K-12	41	Social Studies Sec	51	Reading K-12	61	Foreign/World Lang K-12	71	Public Information
4	Food Service	11	Federal Program	22	Art Sec	32	Career/Sch-to-Work Elem	42	Science K-12	52	Reading Elem	62	Foreign/World Lang Elem	72	Summer School
5	Transportation	12	Title I	23	Music K-12	33	Career/Sch-to-Work Sec	43	Science Elem	53	Reading Sec	63	Foreign/World Lang Sec	73	Instructional Tech
6	Athletic	13	Title V	24	Music Elem	34	Early Childhood Ed	44	Science Sec	54	Remedial Reading K-12	64	Religious Education K-12	74	Inservice Training
7	Health Services	14	Asst Superintendent	25	Music Sec	35	Health/Phys Education	45	Math K-12	55	Remedial Reading Elem	65	Religious Education Elem	75	Marketing/Distributive
		15	Asst Superintendent	26	Business Education	36	Guidance Services K-12	46	Math Elem	56	Remedial Reading Sec	66	Religious Education Sec	76	Info Systems
		16	Instructional Media Svcs	27	Career & Tech Ed	37	Guidance Services Elem	47	Math Sec	57	Bilingual/ELL	67	School Board President	77	Psychological Assess
		17	Chief Operations Officer	28	Technology Education	38	Guidance Services Sec	48	English/Lang Arts K-12	58	Special Education K-12	68	Teacher Personnel	78	Affirmative Action
		18	Chief Academic Officer												

	Grd	Prgm	Enr/#Cls	SN	
W A Metcalfe Elem Sch 1250 NE 18th Ave, Gainesville 32609 Jacquatte Rolle	1-5	T	208 37	84%	352/955-6713 Fax 855/313-5369
W W Irby Elem Sch 13505 NW 140th St, Alachua 32615 **Tanya Floyd**	PK-2	T	432 28	59%	386/462-5002 Fax 888/527-8215
Westwood Middle Sch 3215 NW 15th Ave, Gainesville 32605 Daniel Burney	6-8	TV	1,093 60	42%	352/955-6718 Fax 844/770-0224
William S Talbot Elem Sch 5701 NW 43rd St, Gainesville 32653 Nannette Dell	PK-5		764 60	31%	352/955-6716 Fax 352/726-2916

ALACHUA CATHOLIC SCHOOLS

● **Diocese St Augustine Ed Office** PID: 00202533
Listing includes only schools located in this county. See District Index for location of Diocesan Offices.

Catholic Schs..Principal	Grd	Prgm	Enr/#Cls	SN	
Queen of Peace Catholic Acad 10900 SW 24th Ave, Gainesville 32607 Tammie Vassou	PK-8		200		352/332-8808 Fax 352/448-4560
St Francis Catholic Academy 4100 NW 115th Ter, Gainesville 32606 Jason Acosta	9-12		206 18		352/376-6545 Fax 352/248-0418
St Patrick Interparish Sch 550 NE 16th Ave, Gainesville 32601 Frank Mackritis	PK-8		385 21		352/376-9878 Fax 352/371-6177 [t]

ALACHUA PRIVATE SCHOOLS

Private Schs..Principal	Grd	Prgm	Enr/#Cls	SN	
Brentwood Sch 1111 NW 55th St, Gainesville 32605 Robert Schackow	PK-5		242 11		352/373-3222 Fax 352/378-7848
Christian Life Academy 12000 SW Archer Rd, Gainesville 32608 Robin Roberts	PK-12		40 2		352/495-3040 Fax 352/495-3046
Cornerstone Academy 1520 NW 34th St, Gainesville 32605 Doug Lawson	PK-12		190 21		352/378-9337 Fax 352/378-7708
Countryside Christian Sch 10926 NW 39th Ave, Gainesville 32606 Jody Robertson	K-12	G	114 5		352/332-9731 Fax 352/332-4153
Eastside Baptist Church Sch 1501 E University Ave, Gainesville 32641 Tim Keyes	K-12		10 3		352/373-5639
Family Life Academy 17259 SW Archer Rd, Archer 32618 Glenn Pigpen	K-12		40 5		352/495-3409 Fax 352/495-0445
First Christian Academy 24530 NW 199th Ln, High Springs 32643 Stan Stone	PK-12		460		386/454-1641 Fax 386/454-9727
Gainesville Country Day Sch 6801 SW 24th Ave, Gainesville 32607 Dr Nancye Childers	PK-5		258 10		352/332-7783 Fax 352/331-7613
Jordan Glen Sch 12425 SW 154th St, Archer 32618 Jeff Davis	PK-8		99 6		352/495-2728 Fax 352/495-1539

	Grd	Prgm	Enr/#Cls	SN	
Living Springs Academy 23901 NW 212th Ave, High Springs 32643 Aileen Valenzuela	K-8		25 3		386/454-2777
Millhopper Montessori Sch 8505 NW 39th Ave, Gainesville 32606 Christina Miller	PK-8		225 9		352/375-6773
Newberry Christian Cmty Sch 3536 NW 8th Ave, Gainesville 32605 Mr Schrader	PK-12		190		352/363-6322
Oak Hall Sch 1700 SW 75th St, Gainesville 32607 Dr James Hutchins	PK-12		800 25		352/332-3609 Fax 352/332-4975
Oakhall Lower Sch 7715 SW 14th Ave, Gainesville 32607 Kathryn Sheffey	PK-5		420 23		352/332-1452 Fax 352/332-4945
Ⓐ Reichert House Youth Academy 1704 SE 2nd Ave, Gainesville 32641 Steven Belk	3-12		121		352/334-2320 Fax 352/334-2166
The Rock Sch 9818 SW 24th Ave Ste B, Gainesville 32607 Erica Heise	PK-12		420 20		352/331-7625 Fax 352/331-9760
Trilogy Sch 8700 NW 23rd Ave, Gainesville 32606 Quinn Wiggins	1-12		95		352/332-8802 Fax 352/332-2456
Z L Sung Adventist Sch 2115 NW 39th Ave, Gainesville 32605 Manuel Barajas	K-10		10 2		352/376-6040 Fax 352/373-5678

BAKER COUNTY

BAKER PUBLIC SCHOOLS

● **Baker Co School Dist** PID: 00181484
392 South Blvd E, Macclenny 32063

904/259-6251
Fax 904/259-2825

> **Schools:** 8 \ **Teachers:** 302 \ **Students:** 5,000 \ **Special Ed Students:** 627 \ **LEP Students:** 16 \ **College-Bound:** 60% \ **Ethnic:** Asian 1%, African American 12%, Hispanic 2%, Caucasian 85% \ **Exp:** $125 (Low) \ **Poverty:** 21% \ **Title I:** $1,236,635 \ **Special Education:** $4,563,000 \ **Bilingual Education:** $54,000 \ **Open-Close:** 08/12 - 05/27 \ **DTBP:** $179 (High)

Sherrie Raulerson 1	Julia Richardson 2,71,73
Marybeth Windham 2	Denny Wells 3
Tonya Tarte 4	Johnnie Jacobs 5
John Staples 6	Tina Bradley 7*
David Davis 8,74,285	Susan Voorhees 11,54,57,69,294
Robin Mobley 15,68,78,273	Carrie Dobson 27,30,31,80
Mike Green 36,58,81,83,85,90	Dean Griffin 67
Anne Lewis 83	David Crawford 91
Pam Williams 274*	Wayne Howell 295,297

Public Schs..Principal	Grd	Prgm	Enr/#Cls	SN	
Baker Co Adult Ed Center 523 W Minnesota Ave, Macclenny 32063 Rejeania Watts	Adult		100		904/259-0403 Fax 904/259-0378
Baker Co High Sch 1 Wildcat Dr, Glen St Mary 32040 Allen Murphy	9-12	TV	1,385	36%	904/259-6286 Fax 904/259-5617

79 Student Personnel	91 Safety/Security	275 Response To Intervention	298 Grant Writer/Ptnrships
80 Driver Ed/Safety	92 Magnet School	277 Remedial Math K-12	750 Chief Innovation Officer
81 Gifted/Talented	93 Parental Involvement	280 Literacy Coach	751 Chief of Staff
82 Video Services	95 Tech Prep Program	285 STEM	752 Social Emotional Learning
83 Substance Abuse Prev	97 Chief Infomation Officer	286 Digital Learning	
84 Erate	98 Chief Technology Officer	288 Common Core Standards	**Other School Types**
85 AIDS Education	270 Character Education	294 Accountability	Ⓐ = Alternative School
88 Alternative/At Risk	271 Migrant Education	295 Network System	Ⓒ = Charter School
89 Multi-Cultural Curriculum	273 Teacher Mentor	296 Title II Programs	Ⓜ = Magnet School
90 Social Work	274 Before/After Sch	297 Webmaster	Ⓨ = Year-Round School

School Programs
A = Alternative Program
G = Adult Classes
M = Magnet Program
T = Title I Schoolwide
V = Career & Tech Ed Programs

Social Media
[f] = Facebook
[t] = Twitter

New Schools are shaded
New Superintendents and Principals are bold
Personnel with email addresses are underscored

FL-3

Baker Co Middle Sch 211 E Jonathan St, Macclenny 32063 Sherry Barrett	6-8	TV	1,193 60	46%	904/259-2226 Fax 904/259-0459

Baker Co PK & Kindergarten Ctr — PK-K — T — 550 — 45% — 904/259-0405 / Fax 904/259-6520
362 South Blvd E, Macclenny 32063
Bonnie Jones

Baker Co Virtual Sch — K-12 — 10 — 904/259-7825
290 E Jonathan St, Macclenny 32063
Debra Melvin

J Franklin Keller Interm Sch — 4-5 — T — 769 / 37 — 49% — 904/259-4244 / Fax 904/259-3771
420 S 8th St, Macclenny 32063
David Davis

MacClenny Elem Sch — 1-3 — T — 592 / 50 — 45% — 904/259-2551 / Fax 904/259-5171
1 Wild Kitten Dr, Macclenny 32063
Debbie Fraser

Westside Elem Sch — 1-3 — T — 568 — 55% — 904/259-2216 / Fax 904/259-5172
1 Panther Cir, Glen St Mary 32040
Lynne Fort

BAY COUNTY

BAY PUBLIC SCHOOLS

• **Bay Co School Dist** PID: 00181537   850/767-4100
1311 Balboa Ave, Panama City 32401   Fax 850/747-5367

Schools: 47 \ *Teachers:* 1,786 \ *Students:* 27,390 \
Special Ed Students: 5,024 \ *LEP Students:* 851 \ *College-Bound:* 76%
\ *Ethnic:* Asian 2%, African American 17%, Hispanic 8%, Caucasian
72% \ *Exp:* $184 (Low) \ *Poverty:* 20% \ *Title I:* $7,581,642 \
Special Education: $23,657,000 \ *Bilingual Education:* $1,159,000 \
Open-Close: 08/12 - 05/27 \ *DTBP:* $194 (High)

William Husfelt	1	Dan Fuller	2
Jim Loyed	2,19	Douglas Lee	3,15
Lee Walters	3	Julio Narvaez	4
Michael Carter	5	Kirk Harrell	6*
Denise Kelley	9,15,30,77,90	Suzanne Farrar	10
Eugenia Robinson	11,93	Sandy Davis	15,74,273
Tamra Hogue	16,73,82	Jennifer Lathem-Walters	34
Kara Mulkusky	36,79	Katie McCurdy	42
Cylle Rowell	45	Sally Gentilli	57
Kimberley Edwards	58	Ginger Littleton	67
Shirley Baker	68,78	Camilla Hudson	69,294
Sharon Michalik	71	Leon Faircloth	73,286
Chip Shows	76,295	Michael Jones	91
Linda Pitts	280	Lisa Churchwell	296

Public Schs..Principal	Grd	Prgm	Enr/#Cls	SN	
A Crawford Mosley High Sch 501 Mosley Dr, Lynn Haven 32444 Brian Bullock	9-12	TV	1,802 100	32%	850/767-4400 Fax 850/872-4453
© Bay Haven Charter Academy 2501 Hawks Landing Blvd, Panama City 32405 **Larry Bolinger**	K-8		696 24	31%	850/248-3500 Fax 850/248-3514
Bay High Sch 1200 Harrison Ave, Panama City 32401 Billy May	9-12	TV	1,223 85	51%	850/767-4600 Fax 850/872-4651
Bay Virtual Sch 1515 June Ave Bldg 5, Panama City 32405 Shelly Rouse	K-12		69		850/767-4377 Fax 850/767-4244

Breakfast Point Academy 601 N Richard Jackson Blvd, P C Beach 32407 Clinton Whitfield	K-8	T	1,143	40%	850/767-1190 Fax 850/767-1195

C C Washington Academy — 6-8 — T — 91 — 85% — 850/767-5576 / Fax 850/914-6429
1310 E 11th St, Panama City 32401
Michael Harless

Callaway Elem Sch — PK-5 — T — 557 / 37 — 59% — 850/767-1241 / Fax 850/871-2865
7115 E Highway 22, Panama City 32404
Tim Keiffer

Cedar Grove Elem Sch — PK-5 — T — 506 / 35 — 70% — 850/767-4550 / Fax 850/747-5649
2826 E 15th St, Panama City 32405
Sheila Wojnowski

Ⓐ Central High Sch — 9-10 — 151 — 37% — 850/866-4148 / Fax 850/615-0552
© 1250 W 17th St, Panama City 32405
Jeremy Knapp

© Chautauqua Lrn & Srv Chtr Sch — Spec — 51 — 25% — 850/785-5056 / Fax 850/785-5051
1118 Magnolia Ave, Panama City 32401
Cynthia McCauley

Deane Bozeman Sch — PK-12 — TV — 1,265 / 48 — 52% — 850/767-1300 / Fax 850/265-5377
13410 Highway 77, Panama City 32409
Josh Balkom

Deer Point Elem Sch — PK-5 — T — 736 — 34% — 850/767-5462 / Fax 850/767-3669
4800 Highway 2321, Panama City 32404
Rebecca Reeder

Everitt Middle Sch — 6-8 — TV — 689 / 50 — 81% — 850/767-3776 / Fax 850/872-7721
608 School Ave, Panama City 32401
Phillip Mullins

Hiland Park Elem Sch — PK-5 — T — 736 — 52% — 850/767-4685 / Fax 850/747-5307
2507 E Baldwin Rd, Panama City 32405
Rhonda Woodward

Hutchison Beach Elem Sch — K-5 — T — 619 / 25 — 42% — 850/767-5195 / Fax 850/233-5178
12900 Hutchison Blvd, P C Beach 32407
Glenda Nouskhajian

J R Arnold High Sch — 9-12 — GTV — 1,756 — 33% — 850/767-3700 / Fax 850/236-3068
550 N Alf Coleman Rd, P C Beach 32407
Samuel Bland

Jinks Middle Sch — 6-8 — TV — 558 / 40 — 82% — 850/767-4695 / Fax 850/872-7612
600 W 11th St, Panama City 32401
Blythe Carpenter

Lucille Moore Elem Sch — PK-5 — T — 449 / 45 — 72% — 850/767-1428 / Fax 850/747-5686
1900 Michigan Ave, Panama City 32405
Keri Weatherly

Lynn Haven Elem Sch — PK-5 — T — 697 / 50 — 40% — 850/767-1454 / Fax 850/271-3685
301 W 9th St, Lynn Haven 32444
John Cannon

M K Lewis School-Millville — Spec — T — 158 / 18 — 52% — 850/767-1792 / Fax 850/872-4727
203 N East Ave, Panama City 32401
Lori Hast

Merriam Cherry Street Elem Sch — PK-5 — T — 330 / 25 — 70% — 850/767-1480 / Fax 850/747-5499
1125 Cherry St, Panama City 32401
Stacie Eckles

Merritt Brown Middle Sch — 6-8 — TV — 762 / 60 — 54% — 850/767-3976 / Fax 850/767-4008
5044 Merritt Brown Way, Panama City 32404
Charlotte Marshall

Mowat Middle Sch — 6-8 — TV — 1,097 / 57 — 46% — 850/767-4040 / Fax 850/265-2179
1903 W Highway 390, Lynn Haven 32444
Ed Sheffield

Ⓐ New Horizons Learning Center — 6-12 — T — 145 / 22 — 88% — 850/767-1110 / Fax 850/767-1111
3200 Minnesota Ave, Panama City 32405
Gordon Pongratz

© North Bay Haven Charter ES — K-5 — 696 — 850/248-0205 / Fax 850/215-0644
1 Buccaneer Dr, Panama City 32404
Mike McLaughlin

© North Bay Haven Charter MS — 6-8 — 524 — 37% — 850/248-0801 / Fax 850/248-1201
1 Buccaneer Dr, Panama City 32404
Larry Bolinger

© North Bay Haven Chrtr Acad HS 1 Buccaneer Dr, Panama City 32404 Michael McLaughlin	9-12		847	26%	850/248-0801 Fax 850/248-1201
Northside Elem Sch 2001 Northside Dr, Panama City 32405 Amy Harvey	PK-5	T	601 41	55%	850/767-1506 Fax 850/747-5315
Ⓜ Oakland Terrace Elem Sch 2010 W 12th St, Panama City 32401 Bryan Long	PK-5	T	328 25	76%	850/767-4565 Fax 850/872-7613
Ⓜ Oscar Patterson Elem Sch 1025 Redwood Ave, Panama City 32401 Crystal McNeal	K-5	T	254 28	80%	850/767-4675 Fax 850/747-5478
© Palm Bay Prep Academy 1104 Balboa Ave, Panama City 32401 Kathleen Fontaine	6-12		355		850/215-0770 Fax 850/818-0486
Ⓐ Panama City Marine Institute 200 E Beach Dr, Panama City 32401 Cindy Surber	6-12		71 7	42%	850/872-4715 Fax 850/785-6880
Parker Elem Sch 640 S Highway 22 A, Panama City 32404 Christopher Coan	PK-5	T	547 39	71%	850/767-4570 Fax 850/767-1581 🅕
Patronis Elem Sch 7400 Patronis Dr, P C Beach 32408 Ellie Spivey	K-5	T	742 44	36%	850/767-5075 Fax 850/233-5077
© Rising Leaders Academy 1527 Lincoln Ave, Panama City 32405 Dr Soha Abdel-Jaber	K-8		187	15%	850/215-0844 Fax 850/215-1711
Rosenwald High Sch 924 Bay Ave, Panama City 32401 Chaundra Tyson	9-12	ATV	161 60	79%	850/767-4580 Fax 850/872-7615
Rutherford High Sch 1000 School Ave, Panama City 32401 L Coy Pilson	9-12	TV	1,004 90	52%	850/767-4500 Fax 850/872-4827
Southport Elem Sch 1835 Bridge St, Southport 32409 Holly Buchanan	PK-5	T	422 26	49%	850/767-1636 Fax 850/265-3703
Springfield Elem Sch 520 School Ave, Panama City 32401 Ilea Faircloth	PK-5	T	409 40	75%	850/767-4575 Fax 850/747-5386
St Andrew Sch 3001 W 15th St, Panama City 32401 Janie Branstetter	Spec	T	112 11	86%	850/767-4595 Fax 850/747-5317
Surfside Middle Sch 300 Nautilus St, P C Beach 32413 Dr Sue Harrell	6-8	TV	755	42%	850/767-5180 Fax 850/233-5193
Tom P Haney Technical Center 3016 Highway 77, Panama City 32405 Ann Leonard	Voc	G	1,000		850/767-5500 Fax 850/747-5555
Tommy Smith Elem Sch 5044 Tommy Smith Dr, Panama City 32404 Debra Spradley	PK-5	T	678 48	52%	850/767-1688 Fax 850/747-5339
Tyndall Elem Sch 7800 Tyndall Pkwy, Panama City 32403 Kimberly Kirkman	PK-5	T	737 47	26%	850/767-1714 Fax 850/286-6484
© University Academy 1980 Discovery Loop, Panama City 32405 Wesley Smith	K-7		534	18%	850/481-4410
Waller Elem Sch 11332 E Highway 388, Youngstown 32466 Gina McNally	PK-5	T	486 37	73%	850/767-4341 Fax 850/722-0988
West Bay Elem Sch 14813 School Dr, Panama City 32413 Deniece Moss	K-5	T	315	52%	850/767-1850 Fax 850/767-1851

BAY CATHOLIC SCHOOLS

- **Diocese Pensacola-Tallahassee** PID: 01483467
  Listing includes only schools located in this county. See District Index for location of Diocesan Offices.

Catholic Schs..Principal	Grd	Prgm	Enr/#Cls	SN
St John-Evangelist Cath Sch 1005 Fortune Ave, Panama City 32401 Dr Vicki Parks	PK-8		262 13	850/763-1775 Fax 850/784-4461

BAY PRIVATE SCHOOLS

Private Schs..Principal	Grd	Prgm	Enr/#Cls	SN
Bacot Academy 2211 Saint Andrews Blvd, Panama City 32405 Cindy Bacot	Spec		30	850/215-2614
Covenant Christian Sch 2350 Frankford Ave, Panama City 32405 Michael Sabo	PK-12		140 18	850/769-7448 Fax 850/763-2104
Holy Nativity Episcopal Sch 205 Hamilton Ave, Panama City 32401 Judy Hughes	PK-8		265 24	850/747-0060 Fax 850/747-7447 🅕
Kaleidoscope Sch of Disc 2420 Jenks Ave Unit C4, Panama City 32405 Pam Williams	K-12		50	850/785-7157 Fax 850/785-0811
Panama City Advanced Sch 3332 Token Rd, Panama City 32405 Rashid Karaman	PK-12		120 12	850/784-2520 Fax 850/784-2575 🅕

BRADFORD COUNTY

BRADFORD PUBLIC SCHOOLS

- **Bradford Co School Dist** PID: 00181874   904/966-6800
  501 W Washington St, Starke 32091   Fax 904/966-6030

> **Schools:** 11 \ **Teachers:** 240 \ **Students:** 3,300 \ **Special Ed Students:** 719 \ **LEP Students:** 5 \ **College-Bound:** 57% \ **Ethnic:** Asian 1%, African American 23%, Hispanic 3%, Caucasian 73% \ **Exp:** $217 (Med) \ **Poverty:** 25% \ **Title I:** $1,184,987 \ **Special Education:** $4,653,000 \ **Bilingual Education:** $4,000 \ **Open-Close:** 08/12 - 05/22 \ **DTBP:** $159 (High) 🅕 🅣

Stacey Creighton	1,11,288	John Valinski	2
Joe Cox	3	Chris Wilder	4
Louetie Smith	5	Sherree Alvarez	8,12,296
Evelyn Chastain	9	Dr Rob Charles	10
David Harris	15	Cynthia Devalerio	34
Barbara Johns	57,58,79	Cheryl Canova	67
Emilee Mecusker	68,273	Brenda Little	73,286
Brenda Leto	76	Shawn Burgin	91
Linda Niles	295	Amanda Futch	752

79	Student Personnel	91	Safety/Security	275	Response To Intervention	298	Grant Writer/Ptnrships	School Programs	Social Media
80	Driver Ed/Safety	92	Magnet School	277	Remedial Math K-12	750	Chief Innovation Officer	A = Alternative Program	
81	Gifted/Talented	93	Parental Involvement	280	Literacy Coach	751	Chief of Staff	G = Adult Classes	🅕 = Facebook
82	Video Services	95	Tech Prep Program	285	STEM	752	Social Emotional Learning	M = Magnet Program	
83	Substance Abuse Prev	97	Chief Infomation Officer	286	Digital Learning			T = Title I Schoolwide	🅣 = Twitter
84	Erate	98	Chief Technology Officer	288	Common Core Standards	Other School Types	V = Career & Tech Ed Programs	
85	AIDS Education	270	Character Education	294	Accountability	Ⓐ = Alternative School		
88	Alternative/At Risk	271	Migrant Education	295	Network System	© = Charter School	New Schools are shaded	
89	Multi-Cultural Curriculum	273	Teacher Mentor	296	Title II Programs	Ⓜ = Magnet School	New Superintendents and Principals are bold	
90	Social Work	274	Before/After Sch	297	Webmaster	Ⓨ = Year-Round School	Personnel with email addresses are underscored	

Public Schs..Principal	Grd	Prgm	Enr/#Cls	SN
Bradford High Sch 581 N Temple Ave, Starke 32091 James Simpson	9-12	T	787	49% 904/966-6075 Fax 904/966-6020
Ⓐ Bradford Intervention Center 501 W Washington St, Starke 32091 Shawn Jenkins	6-12	T	111	84% 904/966-6004 Fax 904/966-6038
Bradford Middle Sch 527 N Orange St, Starke 32091 John Green	6-8	T	667 45	61% 904/966-6705 Fax 904/966-6714
Bradford Virtual Elem Sch 501 W Washington St, Starke 32091 Lisa Prevatt	K-5		2	904/966-6010 Fax 904/966-6826
Bradford Virtual High Sch 501 W Washington St, Starke 32091 Bryan Boyer	6-12		18	904/966-6860 Fax 904/966-6826
Brooker Elem Sch 18551 Charlotte Ave, Brooker 32622 Debbie Parmenter	PK-5	T	126 10	68% 352/485-1812 Fax 352/485-2036
Hampton Elem Sch 10501 Hampton Ave, Starke 32091 Denise Schultz	PK-5	T	207 12	70% 352/468-1212 Fax 352/468-1659
Lawtey Elem Sch 22703 Park St, Lawtey 32058 Lisa Prevatt	PK-5	T	222 30	66% 904/966-6795 Fax 904/966-6748
North Technical College 609 N Orange St, Starke 32091 Patricia Nobles	Voc	AG	200 30	904/966-6764 Fax 904/966-6786
Southside Elem Sch 823 Stansbury St, Starke 32091 Earnest Williams	PK-5	T	571 48	72% 904/966-6061 Fax 904/964-8881
Starke Elem Sch 1000 W Weldon St, Starke 32091 Jennifer Vaughan	PK-5	T	527 31	60% 904/966-6045 Fax 904/966-6868

BRADFORD PRIVATE SCHOOLS

Private Schs..Principal	Grd	Prgm	Enr/#Cls	SN
Bradford Christian Academy 2324 NE State Road 16, Starke 32091 Ronnie King	K-12		20 3	904/964-9619 Fax 904/964-9372
Cassels Christian Academy 202 W Market Rd Ste 1, Starke 32091 Staci Griffis	PK-12		200	904/368-9907 f
Hope Christian Academy 3900 SE State Road 100, Starke 32091 Michelle Lewshon	PK-12		250	352/473-4040
Northside Christian Academy 7415 NW County Road 225, Starke 32091 Tyler Hildebran	PK-12		200	904/964-7124
Starke Christian Sch 507 W Call St, Starke 32091 Deana Thornton	PK-8		49	904/964-6100 Fax 904/964-6109 f

BREVARD PUBLIC SCHOOLS

- **Brevard Co School Dist** PID: 00181965   321/633-1000
  2700 Judge Fran Jamieson Way, Viera 32940

> **Schools:** 107 \ **Teachers:** 4,850 \ **Students:** 77,214 \
> **Special Ed Students:** 12,977 \ **LEP Students:** 2,624 \ **College-Bound:** 82%
> \ **Ethnic:** Asian 2%, African American 16%, Hispanic 15%, Caucasian
> 67% \ **Exp:** $182 (Low) \ **Poverty:** 17% \ **Title I:** $21,537,721 \
> **Special Education:** $65,923,000 \ **Bilingual Education:** $4,660,000 \
> **Open-Close:** 08/12 - 05/28 \ **DTBP:** $186 (High)

Dr Mark Mullins	1	Pennie Zuercher	2,11,19
Susan Hann	3,15	Cynthia Barrett	4
Kevin Thornton	4	Robin Novelli	5,7,15,36
Jane Cline	9,12,15,16,34,93,280	Dr Stephanie Soliven	10,15,79,90,752
Lena Wiebelt	11	Dr Carol Mela	12
Christine Moore	12,15,34,271	Dr Beth Thedy	15,68
Matt Reed	15,71	Russell Cheatham	15,73,76,95,97,295
Stephanie Archer	15	Janice Scholz	27
Jeff Arnott	30	Marilyn Sylvester	34
Rachel Winsten	35,80	Judith Magloire	57,89
Tina Descovich	67	Dr Dawna Bobersky	79
Nancy Howser	81	Gina Clark	82
Dr Kimberly Rogers	88	Andrew Walters	91
Debi Embry	274	Virginia Gleason	275
Pamela Aulakh	286	Andrea Young	297
Pamela Gunthorpe	298		

- **Brevard Co Schs-Choice** PID: 12234885   321/633-1000
  2700 Judge Fran Jamieson Way, Melbourne 32940   Fax 321/632-1508

Stephanie Archer 15

Public Schs..Principal	Grd	Prgm	Enr/#Cls	SN
Brevard Adult Education Cocoa 1225 Clearlake Rd, Cocoa 32922 Jeff Arnott	Adult	V	300 11	321/633-3575 Fax 321/633-3488
Brevard Co Adult Sch-Titusville 1311 N US Highway 1 Bldg 6, Titusville 32796 Jeff Arinott	Adult	V	200 14	321/264-3088 Fax 321/264-3042
Brevard Virtual Elem Sch 1225 Clearlake Rd, Cocoa 32922 Heather Price	K-5		67	321/633-3660 Fax 321/633-3663
Brevard Virtual High Sch 1225 Clearlake Rd, Cocoa 32922 Heather Price	6-12		148	321/633-3660 Fax 321/633-3663
© Educational Horizons Chtr Sch 1281 S Wickham Rd, W Melbourne 32904 Cheryl Turner	K-6		117 4	32% 321/729-0786 Fax 321/729-8403
© Emma Jewel Charter Sch 705 Blake Ave Ste A, Cocoa 32922 Thomas Cole	K-8	T	357	91% 321/634-5462 Fax 321/634-5465
Fieldston Preparatory Sch 2940 Columbia Blvd, Titusville 32780 **Cindy Colletti**	Spec	T	62 8	86% 321/268-3664 Fax 321/268-3643
© Imagine Schools W Melbourne [138] 3355 Imagine Way, W Melbourne 32904 Brian Degonzague	K-6	T	438 22	96% 321/768-6200 Fax 321/768-6300

1	Superintendent	8	Curric/Instruct K-12	19	Chief Financial Officer	29	Family/Consumer Science
2	Bus/Finance/Purchasing	9	Curric/Instruct Elem	20	Art K-12	30	Adult Education
3	Buildings And Grounds	10	Curric/Instruct Sec	21	Art Elem	31	Career/Sch-to-Work K-12
4	Food Service	11	Federal Program	22	Art Sec	32	Career/Sch-to-Work Elem
5	Transportation	12	Title I	23	Music K-12	33	Career/Sch-to-Work Sec
6	Athletic	13	Title V	24	Music Elem	34	Early Childhood Ed
7	Health Services	15	Asst Superintendent	25	Music Sec	35	Health/Phys Education
		16	Instructional Media Svcs	26	Business Education	36	Guidance Services K-12
		17	Chief Operations Officer	27	Career & Tech Ed	37	Guidance Services Elem
		18	Chief Academic Officer	28	Technology Education	38	Guidance Services Sec

39	Social Studies K-12	49	English/Lang Arts Elem	59	Special Education Elem
40	Social Studies Elem	50	English/Lang Arts Sec	60	Special Education Sec
41	Social Studies Sec	51	Reading K-12	61	Foreign/World Lang K-12
42	Science K-12	52	Reading Elem	62	Foreign/World Lang Elem
43	Science Elem	53	Reading Sec	63	Foreign/World Lang Sec
44	Science Sec	54	Remedial Reading K-12	64	Religious Education K-12
45	Math K-12	55	Remedial Reading Elem	65	Religious Education Elem
46	Math Elem	56	Remedial Reading Sec	66	Religious Education Sec
47	Math Sec	57	Bilingual/ELL	67	School Board President
48	English/Lang Arts K-12	58	Special Education K-12	68	Teacher Personnel

69	Academic Assessment
70	Research/Development
71	Public Information
72	Summer School
73	Instructional Tech
74	Inservice Training
75	Marketing/Distributive
76	Info Systems
77	Psychological Assess
78	Affirmative Action

School	Grd	Prgm	Enr/#Cls	SN	Phone
© Legacy Academy Charter Sch 3815 Curtis Blvd, Cocoa 32927 Tiffany Ward	K-6		234		321/362-5601 Fax 321/338-7715
Ⓐ NC ALC Pathways Gardendale 301 Grove Blvd, Merritt Is 32953 Ronald Bove	5-12		99 6		321/633-3489 Fax 321/633-3515
© Odyssey Charter Sch 1755 Eldron Blvd SE, Palm Bay 32909 Wendi Nolder \ Dr Monica Knight	K-6	T	1,000 7	71%	321/733-0442 Fax 321/733-1178
© Odyssey Preparatory Academy 1350 Wyoming Dr SE, Palm Bay 32909 **Monica Knight**	K-12	T	319	100%	321/345-4117 Fax 321/327-7261
© Palm Bay Acad Charter Lang Imm 1464 Troutman Blvd NE, Palm Bay 32905 Madhu Longani	K-3		100		321/723-4218 Fax 321/953-5160
© Palm Bay Academy Charter ES 2112 Palm Bay Rd NE, Palm Bay 32905 Madhu Longani	K-5	T	340 6	100%	321/984-2710 Fax 321/984-0799
© Palm Bay Academy Charter MS 635 Community College Pkwy SE, Palm Bay 32909 Jerry Runnersmith	6-8		185		321/726-9005 Fax 321/726-3938
Palm Bay High Adult Ed 101 Pirate Ln, Melbourne 32901 John Thomas	Adult		200		321/952-5914 Fax 321/676-2891 f
Ⓐ Pathways at Pine Grove 2175 N Wickham Rd, Melbourne 32935 Michael Smith	6-12		34	74%	321/242-4770 Fax 321/242-4772
© Pineapple Cove Classical Acad 3555 Norfolk Pkwy, W Melbourne 32904 Dr Ashley Cook	K-6		474		321/499-2585 Fax 321/768-9830
© Pineapple Cove Classical Acad 6162 Minton Rd NW, Palm Bay 32907 Lisa Wheeler	K-10		850	31%	321/802-9500 Fax 321/802-9933
Riverdale Country Sch 1975 Palm Bay Rd NE, Palm Bay 32905 Richard Maust	Spec	AT	87	92%	321/728-2856 Fax 321/728-2623
© Royal Palm Charter Sch 7145 Babcock St SE, Palm Bay 32909 Shannon Shupe	K-7	T	335 8	71%	321/723-0650 Fax 321/722-1117
© Sculptor Charter Sch 1301 Armstrong Dr, Titusville 32780 Renee Bernhard	K-8		553 31	25%	321/264-4000 Fax 321/264-4011
South Area Cmty Adult Sch 1362 S Babcock St, Melbourne 32901 Rebecca Camp	Adult	V	200 17		321/952-5977 Fax 321/952-5831
© Viera Charter Sch [132] 6206 Breslay Dr, Viera 32940 **Sarah Robinson**	K-8		1,054	13%	321/541-1434 Fax 321/608-2322

● **Brevard Co Schs-Elementary** PID: 12234861 321/633-1000
2700 Judge Fran Jamieson Way, Melbourne 32940 Fax 321/632-6139

Jane Cline 15

Public Schs..Principal	Grd	Prgm	Enr/#Cls	SN	
Anderson Elem Sch 3011 S Fiske Blvd, Rockledge 32955 Denise Johnson	K-6	T	717 45	49%	321/633-3610 Fax 321/633-3619
Apollo Elem Sch 3085 Knox McRae Dr, Titusville 32780 Francis O'Leary	K-6	T	840 42	69%	321/267-7890 Fax 321/269-3838
Atlantis Elem Sch 7300 Briggs Ave, Cocoa 32927 **Jennifer Clarke**	PK-6	T	713 37	56%	321/633-6143 Fax 321/633-6038
Audubon Elem Sch 1201 N Banana River Dr, Merritt Is 32952 Elia Lea	PK-6	T	536 46	52%	321/452-2085 Fax 321/454-1055

School	Grd	Prgm	Enr/#Cls	SN	Phone
Ⓜ Cambridge Elem Sch 2000 Cambridge Dr, Cocoa 32922 **Gina Tagye**	PK-6	T	661 30	83%	321/633-3550 Fax 321/633-3420
Cape View Elem Sch 8440 Rosalind Ave, Cpe Canaveral 32920 Jill Keane	PK-6	T	380 32	68%	321/784-0284 Fax 321/868-6690
Ⓨ Challenger 7 Elem Sch 6135 Rena Ave, Cocoa 32927 Magali Rassel	K-6	MT	563 44	63%	321/636-5801 Fax 321/631-3208
Christa McAuliffe Elem Sch 155 Del Mundo St NW, Palm Bay 32907 Victoria Finsted	PK-6	T	776 45	73%	321/768-0465 Fax 321/952-5985
Columbia Elem Sch 1225 Waco Blvd SE, Palm Bay 32909 Rachel Roberts	PK-6	T	478 45	76%	321/676-1319 Fax 321/952-5854
Coquina Elem Sch 850 Knox McRae Dr, Titusville 32780 Blair Lovelace	PK-6	T	516 30	80%	321/264-3060 Fax 321/264-3062
Croton Elem Sch 1449 Croton Rd, Melbourne 32935 Roseann Bennett	PK-6	T	552 40	71%	321/259-3818 Fax 321/242-6477
Discovery Elem Sch 1275 Glendale Ave NW, Palm Bay 32907 Karry Castillo	PK-6	T	644	79%	321/951-4920 Fax 321/952-5870
Dr W J Creel Elem Sch 2000 Glenwood Dr, Melbourne 32935 Nicole Gaumond	PK-6	T	844 80	69%	321/259-3233 Fax 321/259-3844 f t
Ⓜ Endeavour Elem Sch 905 Pineda St, Cocoa 32922 Christopher Reed	PK-6	T	662 44	88%	321/633-3545 Fax 321/633-3546
Enterprise Elem Sch 7000 Enterprise Rd, Cocoa 32927 **Kelli Dufresne**	PK-6	T	599 40	50%	321/633-3434 Fax 321/633-3438
Fairglen Elem Sch 201 Indian Trl, Cocoa 32927 Catherine Murphy	PK-6	T	680 39	71%	321/631-1993 Fax 321/631-3011
© Freedom 7 Elem Sch Ⓜ 400 S 4th St, Cocoa Beach 32931 **Kathryn Lott**	K-6		387 21	11%	321/868-6610 Fax 321/868-6615
Gemini Elem Sch 2100 Oak St, Melbourne Bch 32951 Jennifer Julian	K-6		465 36	17%	321/727-3090 Fax 321/725-7481
Ⓜ Golfview Elem Sch 1530 S Fiske Blvd, Rockledge 32955 Katrina Hudson	PK-6	T	555 24	69%	321/633-3570 Fax 321/633-3579
Harbor City Elem Sch 1377 Sarno Rd, Melbourne 32935 Joy Salamone	PK-6	T	371 43	73%	321/254-5534 Fax 321/242-6468
Imperial Estates Elem Sch 900 Imperial Estates Ln, Titusville 32780 **Cynthia Adams**	PK-6	T	639 26	62%	321/267-1773 Fax 321/264-3038
Indialantic Elem Sch 1050 N Palm Ave, Indialantic 32903 Lori Braga	K-6		735 34	23%	321/723-2811 Fax 321/952-5848
John F Turner Sr Elem Sch 3175 Jupiter Blvd SE, Palm Bay 32909 Ashley Toll	PK-6	T	562 42	78%	321/676-5700 Fax 321/952-5964
Jupiter Elem Sch 950 Tupelo Rd SW, Palm Bay 32908 Sherie Troisi	PK-6	T	728 65	76%	321/952-5990 Fax 321/952-5992
Lewis Carroll Elem Sch 1 Skyline Blvd, Merritt Is 32953 Jenifer Born	K-6		659 37	37%	321/452-1234 Fax 321/454-1064
Lockmar Elem Sch 525 Pepper St NE, Palm Bay 32907 Norma Hostetler	K-6	T	690 50	54%	321/676-3730 Fax 321/952-5879

79 Student Personnel	**91** Safety/Security	**275** Response To Intervention	**298** Grant Writer/Ptnrships	**School Programs**	**Social Media**
80 Driver Ed/Safety	**92** Magnet School	**277** Remedial Math K-12	**750** Chief Innovation Officer	A = Alternative Program	
81 Gifted/Talented	**93** Parental Involvement	**280** Literacy Coach	**751** Chief of Staff	G = Adult Classes	f = Facebook
82 Video Services	**95** Tech Prep Program	**285** STEM	**752** Social Emotional Learning	M = Magnet Program	
83 Substance Abuse Prev	**97** Chief Infomation Officer	**286** Digital Learning		T = Title I Schoolwide	t = Twitter
84 Erate	**98** Chief Technology Officer	**288** Common Core Standards	**Other School Types**	V = Career & Tech Ed Programs	
85 AIDS Education	**270** Character Education	**294** Accountability	Ⓐ = Alternative School	
88 Alternative/At Risk	**271** Migrant Education	**295** Network System	© = Charter School	New Schools are shaded
89 Multi-Cultural Curriculum	**273** Teacher Mentor	**296** Title II Programs	Ⓜ = Magnet School	New Superintendents and Principals are bold
90 Social Work	**274** Before/After Sch	**297** Webmaster	Ⓨ = Year-Round School	Personnel with email addresses are underscored

FL-7

Longleaf Elem Sch 4290 N Wickham Rd, Melbourne 32935 Kimberly Bias	PK-6		646 56	22%	321/242-4700 Fax 321/242-4708	
Manatee Elem Sch 3425 Viera Blvd, Viera 32940 Shannon Daly	K-6		940	14%	321/433-0050 Fax 321/433-9927	
Meadowlane Interm Elem Sch 2700 Wingate Blvd, W Melbourne 32904 Adrienne Schwab	3-6	T	868	43%	321/722-5539 Fax 321/722-4719	
Meadowlane Primary Elem Sch 2800 Wingate Blvd, W Melbourne 32904 Susan Schroeder	PK-2	T	625 45	43%	321/723-6354 Fax 321/952-5948	
Mila Elem Sch 288 W Merritt Ave, Merritt Is 32953 **Dr Dawna O'Brien**	PK-6	T	465 36	70%	321/454-1070 Fax 321/454-1071	
Mims Elem Sch 2582 US Highway 1, Mims 32754 Sheryl Haskins	PK-6	T	479 36	85%	321/264-3020 Fax 321/264-3026	
Oak Park Elem Sch 3395 Dairy Rd, Titusville 32796 Susan Mulchrone	PK-6	T	723	70%	321/269-3252 Fax 321/264-3080	
Ocean Breeze Elem Sch 1101 Cheyenne Dr, Indn HBR Bch 32937 Shelley Michaud	PK-6		532 35	31%	321/779-2040 Fax 321/779-2045	
Palm Bay Elem Sch 1200 Alamanda Rd NE, Palm Bay 32905 Michael Mahl	PK-6	T	613 55	85%	321/723-1055 Fax 321/952-5924	
Pinewood Elem Sch 3757 Old Dixie Hwy, Mims 32754 Mitzi Robinson	PK-6	T	519 27	65%	321/269-4530 Fax 321/264-3030	
Port Malabar Elem Sch 301 Pioneer Ave NE, Palm Bay 32907 Cindy Whalin	PK-6	T	688 48	72%	321/725-0070 Fax 321/952-5949	
Quest Elem Sch 8751 Trafford Dr, Melbourne 32940 Christine Boyd	PK-6		1,088 50	18%	321/242-1411 Fax 321/242-1719	
© R L Stevenson School-Arts Ⓜ 1450 Martin Blvd, Merritt Is 32952 **Tiffiny Fleeger**	K-6		506 15	18%	321/454-3550 Fax 321/454-3553	
Ralph Williams Elem Sch 1700 Clubhouse Dr, Rockledge 32955 Wesley Herold	PK-6		584 65	33%	321/617-7700 Fax 321/617-7703	
Riviera Elem Sch 351 Riviera Dr NE, Palm Bay 32905 Kori Hurst	PK-6	T	692 40	81%	321/676-4237 Fax 321/952-5957	
Roy Allen Elem Sch 2601 Fountainhead Blvd, Melbourne 32935 Lori Migliore	PK-6	T	711 33	61%	321/242-6450 Fax 321/242-6453	
Sabal Elem Sch 1401 N Wickham Rd, Melbourne 32935 Stephanie Hall	PK-6	T	536 36	68%	321/254-7261 Fax 321/242-6475	
Saturn Elem Sch 880 N Range Rd, Cocoa 32926 Janice Rutherford	PK-6	T	852	73%	321/633-3535 Fax 321/633-3539	
Sea Park Elem Sch 300 Sea Park Blvd, Satellite Bch 32937 Ena Leiba	PK-6		321 28	36%	321/779-2050 Fax 321/779-2052	
Sherwood Elem Sch 2541 Post Rd, Melbourne 32935 Karen Ivery	PK-6	T	457 50	61%	321/254-6424 Fax 321/242-6478	
South Lake Elem Sch 3755 Garden St, Titusville 32796 Jennifer Brockwell	K-6		311		321/264-1137	
Spessard L Holland Elem Sch 50 Holland Ct, Satellite Bch 32937 Samantha Alison	K-6		490 27	27%	321/773-7591 Fax 321/773-6315	

Sunrise Elem Sch 1651 Mara Loma Blvd SE, Palm Bay 32909 **Janene Jost**	PK-6	T	820 34	59%	321/674-6145 Fax 321/674-6147	
Suntree Elem Sch 900 Jordan Blass Dr, Melbourne 32940 Shari Tressler	K-6		668 40	23%	321/242-6480 Fax 321/242-6485	
Surfside Elem Sch 475 Cassia Blvd, Satellite Bch 32937 Lori Masterson	K-6		457 32	22%	321/773-2818 Fax 321/777-1841	
T Roosevelt Elem Sch 1400 Minutemen Cswy, Cocoa Beach 32931 Kimberly Humphrey	K-6	T	377 30	36%	321/868-6660 Fax 321/783-2331	
Tropical Elem Sch 885 S Courtenay Pkwy, Merritt Is 32952 Kristin Sorokin	K-6	T	818 42	47%	321/454-1080 Fax 321/454-1087	
Ⓜ University Park Elem Sch 500 W University Blvd, Melbourne 32901 Ana Diaz	PK-6		473 32	88%	321/723-2566 Fax 321/952-5971 f	
Ⓜ West Melbourne ES -Science 2255 Meadowlane Ave, W Melbourne 32904 Dr Neleffra Marshall	K-6		553 22	19%	321/956-5040 Fax 321/956-5043	
Westside Elem Sch 2175 Degroodt Rd SW, Palm Bay 32908 Darlene Rogers	PK-6	T	769 49	60%	321/956-5050 Fax 321/956-5053	

- • **Brevard Co Schs-Secondary** PID: 12234873 321/633-1000
  2700 Judge Fran Jamieson Way, Melbourne 32940 Fax 321/633-3447

Dr Stephanie Soliven 15

Public Schs..Principal	Grd	Prgm	Enr/#Cls	SN
Andrew Jackson Middle Sch 1515 Knox McRae Dr, Titusville 32780 Tina Susin	7-8	V	549 37	61% 321/269-1812 Fax 321/269-7811
Astronaut High Sch 800 War Eagle Blvd, Titusville 32796 Krista Miller	9-12	AV	1,073 50	51% 321/264-3000 Fax 321/264-3013
Bayside High Sch 1901 Degroodt Rd SW, Palm Bay 32908 **Holli Zander**	9-12	V	1,706 100	50% 321/956-5000 Fax 321/956-5021
Central Middle Sch 2600 Wingate Blvd, W Melbourne 32904 **Todd Scheuerer**	7-8	V	1,193 78	52% 321/722-4150 Fax 321/722-4165
Cocoa Beach Jr Sr High Sch 1500 Minutemen Cswy, Cocoa Beach 32931 **Dr Mark Rendell**	7-12	V	1,013 35	29% 321/783-1776 Fax 321/868-6602
Cocoa Jr Sr High Sch 2000 Tiger Trl, Cocoa 32926 **Dr Mark Rendell**	7-12	TV	1,451 85	76% 321/632-5300 Fax 321/636-1218
DeLaura Middle Sch 300 Jackson Ave, Satellite Bch 32937 Jeremy LeBrun	7-8	V	819 50	24% 321/773-7581 Fax 321/773-0702
Eau Gallie High Sch 1400 Commodore Blvd, Melbourne 32935 Jeremy Salmon	9-12	AV	1,700 120	46% 321/242-6400 Fax 321/242-6427
Edgewood Jr Sr High Sch 180 E Merritt Ave, Merritt Is 32953 Jacqueline Ingratta	7-12	V	948 36	14% 321/454-1030 Fax 321/452-1176
Herbert C Hoover Middle Sch 2000 Hawk Haven Dr, Indialantic 32903 Burt Clark	7-8	AGV	506 36	37% 321/727-1611 Fax 321/725-0076
Heritage High Sch 2351 Malabar Rd NW, Palm Bay 32907 John Harris	9-12		1,830	63% 321/722-4178 Fax 321/722-4198
James Madison Middle Sch 3375 Dairy Rd, Titusville 32796 Joseph Flora	7-8	V	495 45	67% 321/264-3120 Fax 321/264-3124

1 Superintendent	19 Chief Financial Officer	39 Social Studies K-12	59 Special Education Elem	69 Academic Assessment
2 Bus/Finance/Purchasing	8 Curric/Instruct K-12	20 Art K-12	30 Adult Education	40 Social Studies Elem	50 English/Lang Arts Sec	60 Special Education Sec	70 Research/Development
3 Buildings And Grounds	9 Curric/Instruct Elem	21 Art Elem	31 Career/Sch-to-Work K-12	41 Social Studies Sec	51 Reading K-12	61 Foreign/World Lang K-12	71 Public Information
4 Food Service	10 Curric/Instruct Sec	22 Art Sec	32 Career/Sch-to-Work Elem	42 Science K-12	52 Reading Elem	62 Foreign/World Lang Elem	72 Summer School
5 Transportation	11 Federal Program	23 Music K-12	33 Career/Sch-to-Work Sec	43 Science Elem	53 Reading Sec	63 Foreign/World Lang Sec	73 Instructional Tech
6 Athletic	12 Title I	24 Music Elem	34 Early Childhood Ed	44 Science Sec	54 Remedial Reading K-12	64 Religious Education K-12	74 Inservice Training
7 Health Services	13 Title V	25 Music Sec	35 Health/Phys Education	45 Math K-12	55 Remedial Reading Elem	65 Religious Education Elem	75 Marketing/Distributive
	16 Instructional Media Svcs	26 Business Education	36 Guidance Services K-12	46 Math Elem	56 Remedial Reading Sec	66 Religious Education Sec	76 Info Systems
	17 Chief Operations Officer	27 Career & Tech Ed	37 Guidance Services Elem	47 Math Sec	57 Bilingual/ELL	67 School Board President	77 Psychological Assess
	18 Chief Academic Officer	28 Technology Education	38 Guidance Services Sec	48 English/Lang Arts K-12	58 Special Education K-12	68 Teacher Personnel	78 Affirmative Action
	15 Asst Superintendent			49 English/Lang Arts Elem			

John F Kennedy Middle Sch 2100 S Fiske Blvd, Rockledge 32955 Sherry Tomlinson	7-8	V	611 45	39%	321/633-3500 Fax 321/633-3509
Lyndon B Johnson Middle Sch 2155 Croton Rd, Melbourne 32935 Marina Middleto	7-8	AV	736	59%	321/242-6430 Fax 321/242-6436
Ⓜ McNair Magnet Sch 1 Challenger Dr, Cocoa 32922 Jasmine Delaughter	7-8		479 35		321/633-3630 Fax 321/633-3639
Melbourne High Sch 74 Bulldog Blvd, Melbourne 32901 **Chad Kirk**	9-12	V	2,113	30%	321/952-5880 Fax 321/952-5898
Merritt Island High Sch 100 Mustang Way, Merritt Is 32953 James Rehmer	9-12	V	1,538 75	32%	321/454-1000 Fax 321/454-1014
Ⓜ Palm Bay Magnet High Sch 101 Pirate Ln, Melbourne 32901 Karl Kaminski	9-12	GV	1,570 108	63%	321/952-5900 Fax 321/676-2891
Rockledge High Sch 220 Rockledge Ave, Rockledge 32955 Bradley Merrill	9-12	GV	1,516 65	42%	321/636-3711 Fax 321/632-6064
Satellite High Sch 300 Scorpion Ct, Satellite Bch 32937 Robert Pruett	9-12	V	1,352 61	20%	321/779-2000 Fax 321/773-0703
Southwest Middle Sch 451 Eldron Blvd SE, Palm Bay 32909 Ronald Shaw	7-8	V	833 84	68%	321/952-5800 Fax 321/952-5819
Space Coast Jr Sr High Sch 6150 Banyan St, Cocoa 32927 Sylvia Mijuskovic	7-12	V	1,586 65	46%	321/638-0750 Fax 321/638-0766
Stone Middle Sch 1101 E University Blvd, Melbourne 32901 **Hilary Poole**	7-8	V	791 60	69%	321/723-0741 Fax 321/951-1497
Thomas Jefferson Middle Sch 1275 S Courtenay Pkwy, Merritt Is 32952 Meara Trine	7-8	V	660 48	43%	321/453-5154 Fax 321/459-2854
Titusville High Sch 150 Terrier Trl S, Titusville 32780 **Jennifer Gonzalez**	9-12	AV	1,377	47%	321/264-3100 Fax 321/264-3130
Viera High Sch 6103 Stadium Pkwy, Viera 32940 **Sarah Robinson**	9-12	V	1,990	17%	321/632-1770 Fax 321/433-4338
West Shore Jr Sr High Sch 250 Wildcat Aly, Melbourne 32935 Eric Fleming	7-12		953	11%	321/242-4730 Fax 321/242-4740

BREVARD CATHOLIC SCHOOLS

● **Diocese of Orlando Ed Office** PID: 00197639
Listing includes only schools located in this county. See District Index for location of Diocesan Offices.

Catholic Schs..Principal	Grd	Prgm	Enr/#Cls	SN	
Ascension Catholic Sch 2950 N Harbor City Blvd, Melbourne 32935 Anita Brady	PK-8		472 24		321/254-5495
Divine Mercy Catholic Sch 1940 N Courtenay Pkwy, Merritt Is 32953 Dave Parker	PK-8		240 12		321/452-0263 Fax 321/453-7573
Holy Name of Jesus Sch 3060 N Highway A1A, Indialantic 32903 Kathleen Falk	PK-8		300 26		321/773-1630 Fax 321/773-7148

Melbourne Central Catholic HS 154 E Florida Ave, Melbourne 32901 Ernie Herrington	9-12		500 40		321/727-0793 Fax 321/952-0798 🔵🟦
Our Lady of Lourdes Sch 420 E Fee Ave, Melbourne 32901 Donna Witherspoon	PK-8		200 15		321/723-3631 Fax 321/723-7408 🔵🟦
Our Saviours Catholic Sch 5301 N Atlantic Ave, Cocoa Beach 32931 Janet Peddecord	PK-8		200 11		321/783-2330 Fax 321/784-6330 🔵
St Joseph Catholic Sch 5320 Babcock St NE, Palm Bay 32905 Claudia Stokes	PK-8		220 14		321/723-8866 Fax 321/727-1181
St Mary's Sch 1152 Seminole Dr, Rockledge 32955 Sandra Basinger	PK-8		250 20		321/636-4208 Fax 321/636-0591 🔵
St Teresa Catholic Sch 207 Ojibway Ave, Titusville 32780 Jacqueline Zackel	PK-8		150 11		321/267-1643 Fax 321/268-5124 🔵

BREVARD PRIVATE SCHOOLS

Private Schs..Principal	Grd	Prgm	Enr/#Cls	SN	
Ambassador Christian Sch 175 Cone Rd, Merritt Is 32952 Joyce Wichmann	K-12		70		321/305-6931
Assurance Christian Academy 1009 S Fiske Blvd, Rockledge 32955 Dr Sylvester Jones	K-12		45		321/638-0985
Bethany Christian Sch 1100 Dorchester Ave, W Melbourne 32904 Sue Schwanda	PK-12	V	220 30		321/727-2038 Fax 321/729-4212 🔵
Brevard Adventist Chrn Acad 1500 Cox Rd, Cocoa 32926 Rose Grant	PK-8		40		321/636-2551 Fax 321/305-6943
Brevard Private Academy 508 S Plumosa St Ste A, Merritt Is 32952 Cheree Shaykhian	7-12		125		321/459-3466 Fax 321/459-9899
Calvary Chapel Academy 2955 Minton Rd, Melbourne 32904 Tim Flay	PK-8		450		321/729-9922 Fax 321/215-9478
Community Christian Sch 3550 W Eau Gallie Blvd, Melbourne 32934 Shelley Willms \ Julie Austin	K-12		130 15		321/259-1590 Fax 321/259-5301
Covenant Christian Sch 720 Emerson Dr NE, Palm Bay 32907 Randy Down	PK-12		340 15		321/727-2661 Fax 321/728-9574
Creative Learning Sch 453 King St, Cocoa 32922 Dr Kathryn Mendoza	Spec		25		321/633-5511
Devereux Sch 8000 Devereux Dr, Viera 32940 Matthew Dugan	Spec		134 15		321/242-9100 Fax 866/416-2057
Einstein Montessori Academy 5650 King St, Cocoa 32926 Denise Osbrach	2-12		86 9		321/631-9876 Fax 321/631-8009
Florida Preparatory Academy 1950 Academy Dr, Melbourne 32901 Lisa Gray	5-12		200 42		321/723-3211 Fax 321/676-0422
Holy Trinity Episcopal Academy 50 W Strawbridge Ave, Melbourne 32901 Dr Jessica Kelce \ Nancy Giangrisostomi	PK-12		950 34		321/723-8323 Fax 321/723-2553
Indian Harbour Montessori Sch 1230 Banana River Dr, Indn HBR Bch 32937 Denise Johnson	PK-6		120 10		321/777-1480 Fax 321/777-1198

79 Student Personnel	**91** Safety/Security	**275** Response To Intervention	**298** Grant Writer/Ptnrships	**School Programs**
80 Driver Ed/Safety	**92** Magnet School	**277** Remedial Math K-12	**750** Chief Innovation Officer	A = Alternative Program
81 Gifted/Talented	**93** Parental Involvement	**280** Literacy Coach	**751** Chief of Staff	G = Adult Classes
82 Video Services	**95** Tech Prep Program	**285** STEM	**752** Social Emotional Learning	M = Magnet Program
83 Substance Abuse Prev	**97** Chief Infomation Officer	**286** Digital Learning		T = Title I Schoolwide
84 Erate	**98** Chief Technology Officer	**288** Common Core Standards	**Other School Types**	V = Career & Tech Ed Programs
85 AIDS Education	**270** Character Education	**294** Accountability	Ⓐ = Alternative School	
88 Alternative/At Risk	**271** Migrant Education	**295** Network System	Ⓒ = Charter School	**New Schools are shaded**
89 Multi-Cultural Curriculum	**273** Teacher Mentor	**296** Title II Programs	Ⓜ = Magnet School	**New Superintendents and Principals are bold**
90 Social Work	**274** Before/After Sch	**297** Webmaster	Ⓨ = Year-Round School	**Personnel with email addresses are underscored**

Social Media
🔵 = Facebook
🟦 = Twitter

Lake Fern Montessori Academy 257 Aguinaldo Ave, Titusville 32780 Tyka Price	PK-8	102 4	321/268-3365 Fax 321/268-3397
Merritt Island Christian Sch 140 Magnolia Ave, Merritt Is 32952 Amy Twigg	PK-12	500 42	321/453-2710 Fax 321/452-6580
Palm Bay SDA Sch 3507 Carriage Gate Dr, Melbourne 32904 Doris Brown	K-8	20	321/733-4551 Fax 321/768-1949
Park Avenue Christian Academy 2600 S Park Ave, Titusville 32780 Kraig Ricksecker	PK-8	250 40	321/267-1871 Fax 321/268-4057
Patterson Private Sch 1803 N Wickham Rd Ste 6, Melbourne 32935 Carolyn Clark	K-12	40	321/254-9525 Fax 321/723-4492
Rockledge Christian Sch 2175 S Fiske Blvd, Rockledge 32955 Ric Speigner	PK-8	175 14	321/632-1053 Fax 321/632-8951
Sancta Familia Academy 1204 N Harbor City Blvd, Melbourne 32935 Dorothy Noonan	K-12	401	321/259-6464
Space Coast Christian Academy 1950 Michigan Ave, Cocoa 32922 Deana Clark	PK-12	135 7	321/636-0883 Fax 321/634-5318
Space Coast Early Intervention 3790 Dairy Rd, Melbourne 32904 Terri Clark	PK-1	97	321/729-6858
St Mark's Academy 2 Church St, Cocoa 32922 Joi Robertson	PK-6	120 8	321/639-5771 Fax 321/639-5774
Temple Christian Sch 1400 N Washington Ave, Titusville 32796 Ronda Gordon	K-12	215 15	321/269-2837 Fax 321/383-9101
Verdi Ecoschool 1851 Highland Ave, Melbourne 32935 Ayana Verdi	PK-9	80	321/298-2501
Wade Christian Academy 4300 N Wickham Rd, Melbourne 32935 Ed Buchanan	PK-12	105 16	321/259-6788 Fax 321/259-0399
West Melbourne Christian Acad 3150 Milwaukee Ave, Melbourne 32904 Mark Siler	K-12	127 14	321/725-3743 Fax 321/725-6661

BREVARD REGIONAL CENTERS

● **FDLRS-East Brevard** PID: 04496188　　　321/633-1000
2700 Judge Fran Jamieson Way, Melbourne 32940　　Fax 321/633-3533

Mark Mullins ....1　Patricia Fontan 11
Dawna Bobersky 81

BROWARD COUNTY

BROWARD PUBLIC SCHOOLS

● **Broward Co Public Schools** PID: 00182725　　　754/321-0000
600 SE 3rd Ave, Ft Lauderdale 33301　　　　　　Fax 754/321-2318

Schools: 311 \ **Teachers:** 16,391 \
Students: 270,550 \ **Special Ed Students:** 35,428 \ **LEP Students:** 33,834
\ **College-Bound:** 77% \ **Ethnic:** Asian 4%, African American 39%, Hispanic
34%, Caucasian 22% \ **Exp:** $168 (Low) \ **Poverty:** 17% \ **Title I:** $83,613,881
\ **Special Education:** $161,944,000 \ **Bilingual Education:** $46,989,000 \
Open-Close: 08/14 - 06/02 \ **DTBP:** $193 (High) \ 🅕 🅣

Robert Runcie 1	Ivan Perrone 2
Judith Marte 2,19	Oleg Gorokhovsky 2
Leo Bobadilla 3	Dr Maryann May 3
Maurice Woods 3,17	Mary Mulder 4
John Lyles 5	Shawn Cerra 6
Marcia Bynoe 7,83,85	Dan Gohl 8,18
Dr Nicole Mancini 9	Guy Barmoha 10
Stephanie Williams 11	Luwando Wright-Hines 12,271
Jeffrey Moquin 15,751	Enid Valdez 27,30
Robert Crawford 27,31	Dr Lori Canning 34,57
Dr Daniel Shapiro 37	Danny Tritto 38
Victoria Saldaia 57	Dr Antoine Hickman 58,81
Heather Brinkworth 67	Alan Strauss 68,78
Richard Baum 69,70	Kathy Koch 71
Dr Laurel Thompson 79	Matthew Schroeder 80
Dr Daryl Diamond 81	Zuzel Rodriguez 81
Brian Katz 91	Phillip Dunn 97
Dr Deborah Gavilan 274	Mildred Grimaldo 280
Dr Lisa Milenkovic 285	Dr Valerie Wanza 294

Public Schs..Principal	Grd	Prgm	Enr/#Cls	SN
Annabel C Perry Elem Sch 6850 SW 34th St, Miramar 33023 Thomas Correll	PK-8	T	733 37	91% 754/323-7050 Fax 754/323-7090 🅕 🅣
Apollo Middle Sch 6800 Arthur St, Hollywood 33024 Shawn Aycock	6-8	TV	1,399 75	81% 754/323-2900 Fax 754/323-2985
Atlantic Technical High Sch 4700 Coconut Creek Pkwy, Coconut Creek 33063 Robert Crawford	Voc	GT	674	59% 754/321-5100 Fax 754/321-5380
Atlantic West Elem Sch 301 NW 69th Ter, Margate 33063 Diane Eagan	PK-5	T	719 39	85% 754/322-5300 Fax 754/322-5340
Attucks Middle Sch 3500 N 22nd Ave, Hollywood 33020 Errol Evans	6-8	TV	806 62	85% 754/323-3000 Fax 754/323-3085
Bair Middle Sch 9100 NW 21st Mnr, Sunrise 33322 Keietta Givens	6-8	GTV	902	75% 754/322-2900 Fax 754/322-2985
Banyan Elem Sch 8800 NW 50th St, Sunrise 33351 Dr Eric Miller	PK-5	T	612 52	83% 754/322-5350 Fax 754/322-5390
Bayview Elem Sch 1175 Middle River Dr, Ft Lauderdale 33304 Tonya Frost	K-5		578 30	21% 754/322-5400 Fax 754/322-5440
Ⓜ Beachside Montessori Vlg Sch 2230 Lincoln St, Hollywood 33020 Vered Roberts	PK-8		787	28% 754/323-8050 Fax 754/323-8090

1	Superintendent	8	Curric/Instruct K-12	19	Chief Financial Officer	29	Family/Consumer Science
2	Bus/Finance/Purchasing	9	Curric/Instruct Elem	20	Art K-12	30	Adult Education
3	Buildings And Grounds	10	Curric/Instruct Sec	21	Art Elem	31	Career/Sch-to-Work K-12
4	Food Service	11	Federal Program	22	Art Sec	32	Career/Sch-to-Work Elem
5	Transportation	12	Title I	23	Music K-12	33	Career/Sch-to-Work Sec
6	Athletic	13	Title V	24	Music Elem	34	Early Childhood Ed
7	Health Services	15	Asst Superintendent	25	Music Sec	35	Health/Phys Education
		16	Instructional Media Svcs	26	Business Education	36	Guidance Services K-12
		17	Chief Operations Officer	27	Career & Tech Ed	37	Guidance Services Elem
		18	Chief Academic Officer	28	Technology Education	38	Guidance Services Sec

39	Social Studies K-12	49	English/Lang Arts Elem	59	Special Education Elem	69	Academic Assessment
40	Social Studies Elem	50	English/Lang Arts Sec	60	Special Education Sec	70	Research/Development
41	Social Studies Sec	51	Reading K-12	61	Foreign/World Lang K-12	71	Public Information
42	Science K-12	52	Reading Elem	62	Foreign/World Lang Elem	72	Summer School
43	Science Elem	53	Reading Sec	63	Foreign/World Lang Sec	73	Instructional Tech
44	Science Sec	54	Remedial Reading K-12	64	Religious Education K-12	74	Inservice Training
45	Math K-12	55	Remedial Reading Elem	65	Religious Education Elem	75	Marketing/Distributive
46	Math Elem	56	Remedial Reading Sec	66	Religious Education Sec	76	Info Systems
47	Math Sec	57	Bilingual/ELL	67	School Board President	77	Psychological Assess
48	English/Lang Arts K-12	58	Special Education K-12	68	Teacher Personnel	78	Affirmative Action

School	Grades	Prog	Enroll / Staff	%	Phone / Fax	Social
Bennett Elem Sch 1755 NE 14th St, Ft Lauderdale 33304 Danielle Smith	PK-5	T	376 30	88%	754/322-5450 Fax 754/322-5490	
Blanche Ely High Sch 1201 NW 6th Ave, Pompano Beach 33060 Karlton Johnson	9-12	TV	2,036 100	86%	754/322-0950 Fax 754/322-1080	f t
Boulevard Heights Elem Sch 7201 Johnson St, Hollywood 33024 Juan Alejo	PK-5	T	672 45	81%	754/323-4950 Fax 754/323-4990	f t
Boyd H Anderson High Sch 3050 NW 41st St, Laud Lakes 33309 **James Griffin**	9-12	ATV	1,712 108	85%	754/322-0200 Fax 754/322-0330	
Bright Horizons Sch 3901 NE 1st Ter, Pompano Beach 33064 Ann Kowalski	Spec	T	147 18	60%	754/321-6400 Fax 754/321-6440	
Broadview Elem Sch 1800 SW 62nd Ave, N Lauderdale 33068 Dr Josh Kisten	PK-5	T	808 25	89%	754/322-5500 Fax 754/322-5540	f t
Broward Estates Elem Sch 441 NW 35th Ave, Lauderhill 33311 Cyntheria Hunt	PK-5	T	391 40	96%	754/322-5550 Fax 754/322-5590	
Broward Virtual Sch 1400 NW 44th Ave, Coconut Creek 33066 Christopher McGuire	6-12		273	29%	754/321-6050 Fax 754/321-6065	
Castle Hill Elem Sch 2640 NW 46th Ave, Lauderhill 33313 Letitia Phillips	PK-5	T	618 38	95%	754/322-5600 Fax 754/322-5640	f t
Central Park Elem Sch 777 N Nob Hill Rd, Plantation 33324 Cherise Coleman	K-5		872 43	38%	754/322-5700 Fax 754/322-5740	
Challenger Elem Sch 5703 NW 94th Ave, Tamarac 33321 Tara Zdanowicz	PK-5	T	1,037 49	70%	754/322-5750 Fax 754/322-5790	f t
Chapel Trail Elem Sch 19595 Taft St, Pembroke Pnes 33029 **Susan Suarez**	PK-5	T	813 57	41%	754/323-5000 Fax 754/323-5040	f t
Ⓜ **Charles Drew Elem Sch** 1000 NW 31st Ave, Pompano Beach 33069 Angeline Flowers	PK-5	T	526 38	96%	754/322-6250 Fax 754/322-6290	f t
Charles W Flanagan High Sch 12800 Taft St, Pembroke Pnes 33028 **Paula Peters**	9-12		2,519	56%	754/323-0650 Fax 754/323-0780	
Coconut Creek Elem Sch 500 NW 45th Ave, Coconut Creek 33066 **Roberta Ray**	K-5	T	639 38	72%	754/322-5800 Fax 754/322-5840	f t
Coconut Creek High Sch 1400 NW 44th Ave, Coconut Creek 33066 Scott Fiske	9-12	TV	1,524 100	79%	754/322-0350 Fax 754/322-0481	
Coconut Palm Elem Sch 13601 Monarch Lakes Blvd, Miramar 33027 Teresa Thelmas	K-5	T	741	63%	754/323-5050 Fax 754/323-5090	
Ⓨ **Colbert Museum Magnet** 2702 Funston St, Hollywood 33020 Dorsett McLeod	PK-5	MT	690 40	92%	754/323-5100 Fax 754/323-5140	
College Academy at BC 3501 Davie Rd, Davie 33314 Deborah Davey	11-12		441 20	34%	754/321-6900 Fax 754/321-6940	
Collins Elem Sch 1050 NW 2nd St, Dania Beach 33004 Dr Tracy Jackson	PK-5	T	370	92%	754/323-5150 Fax 754/323-5175	
Cooper City Elem Sch 5080 SW 92nd Ave, Cooper City 33328 Monica Schlosser	K-5	T	745 40	43%	754/323-5200 Fax 754/323-5240	
Cooper City High Sch 9401 Stirling Rd, Cooper City 33328 Wendy Doll	9-12	GV	2,341 90	31%	754/323-0200 Fax 754/323-0330	
Coral Cove Elem Sch 5100 SW 148th Ave, Miramar 33027 Stephanie Saban	PK-5	T	668 44	52%	754/323-7950 Fax 754/323-7990	
Coral Glades High Sch 2700 Sportsplex Dr, Coral Springs 33065 **Dr Mark Kaplan**	9-12	TV	2,454	57%	754/322-1250 Fax 754/322-1380	t
Coral Park Elem Sch 8401 Westview Dr, Coral Springs 33067 Camille Pontillo	PK-5	T	608 45	53%	754/322-5850 Fax 754/322-5890	f t
Coral Springs Elem Sch 3601 NW 110th Ave, Coral Springs 33065 Vonda Oliver	PK-8	T	667 38	83%	754/322-5900 Fax 754/322-5940	f t
Coral Springs High Sch 7201 W Sample Rd, Coral Springs 33065 **Vivian Suarez**	9-12	TV	2,811	63%	754/322-0500 Fax 754/322-0630	t
Coral Springs Middle Sch 10300 Wiles Rd, Coral Springs 33076 Sara La Rosa	6-8	GTV	1,155 52	53%	754/322-3000 Fax 754/322-3085	
Country Hills Elem Sch 10550 Westview Dr, Coral Springs 33076 Nicole Ortega	K-5		854 50	38%	754/322-5950 Fax 754/322-5990	f t
Country Isles Elem Sch 2300 Country Isles Rd, Weston 33326 Mindy Morgan	PK-5		986 49	32%	754/323-5250 Fax 754/323-5290	
Cresthaven Elem Sch 801 NE 25th St, Pompano Beach 33064 Donald Lee	PK-5	T	588 35	91%	754/322-6000 Fax 754/322-6040	f t
Croissant Park Elem Sch 1800 SW 4th Ave, Ft Lauderdale 33315 Michelle-Ann Allison	PK-5	T	773 42	89%	754/323-5300 Fax 754/323-5340	
Cross Creek Sch 1010 NW 31st Ave, Pompano Beach 33069 Colleen Stearn	Spec	T	125 20	80%	754/321-6450 Fax 754/321-6490	
Ⓜ **Crystal Lake Cmty Middle Sch** 3551 NE 3rd Ave, Pompano Beach 33064 **Earnest Toliver**	6-8	GTV	1,413 70	84%	754/322-3100 Fax 754/322-3185	f t
Cypress Bay High Sch 18600 Vista Park Blvd, Weston 33332 Charles Neely	9-12	V	4,797	18%	754/323-0350 Fax 754/323-0363	
Ⓨ **Cypress Elem Sch** 851 SW 3rd Ave, Pompano Beach 33060 Vanessa Schnur	PK-5	MT	762 42	90%	754/322-6050 Fax 754/322-6090	
Cypress Run Education Center 2800 NW 30th Ave, Pompano Beach 33069 Gastrid Harrigan	Spec	T	115 10	84%	754/321-6500 Fax 754/321-6540	
Dania Elem Sch 300 SE 2nd Ave, Dania Beach 33004 Lewis Jackson	PK-5	T	472 68	82%	754/323-5350 Fax 754/323-5390	f t
Dave Thomas Educ Ctr-East 180 SW 2nd St, Pompano Beach 33060 **Jonathan Williams**	Adult		200		754/321-6750 Fax 754/321-6790	
Ⓐ **Dave Thomas Educ Ctr-W** 4690 Coconut Creek Pkwy, Coconut Creek 33063 Tracy Talley	6-12	GV	669 32	81%	754/321-6800 Fax 754/321-6840	
Davie Elem Sch 7025 SW 39th St, Davie 33314 **Erik Anderson**	PK-5	T	745 46	82%	754/323-5400 Fax 754/323-5440	
Deerfield Beach Elem Sch 650 NE 1st St, Deerfield Bch 33441 Drew Gerlach	PK-5	T	588 37	74%	754/322-6100 Fax 754/322-6140	f t
Deerfield Beach High Sch 910 SW 15th St, Deerfield Bch 33441 Jon Marlow	9-12	GTV	2,439 95	72%	754/322-0650 Fax 754/322-0780	
Deerfield Beach Middle Sch 701 SE 6th Ave, Deerfield Bch 33441 Latori Fulton	6-8	TV	1,176 55	82%	754/322-3300 Fax 754/322-3385	

---

79 Student Personnel	**91** Safety/Security	**275** Response To Intervention	**298** Grant Writer/Ptnrships	**School Programs**	**Social Media**		
80 Driver Ed/Safety	**92** Magnet School	**277** Remedial Math K-12	**750** Chief Innovation Officer	A = Alternative Program			
81 Gifted/Talented	**93** Parental Involvement	**280** Literacy Coach	**751** Chief of Staff	G = Adult Classes	f = Facebook		
82 Video Services	**95** Tech Prep Program	**285** STEM	**752** Social Emotional Learning	M = Magnet Program			
83 Substance Abuse Prev	**97** Chief Infomation Officer	**286** Digital Learning		T = Title I Schoolwide	t = Twitter		
84 Erate	**98** Chief Technology Officer	**288** Common Core Standards	**Other School Types**	V = Career & Tech Ed Programs			
85 AIDS Education	**270** Character Education	**294** Accountability	Ⓐ = Alternative School				
88 Alternative/At Risk	**271** Migrant Education	**295** Network System	Ⓒ = Charter School	New Schools are shaded			
89 Multi-Cultural Curriculum	**273** Teacher Mentor	**296** Title II Programs	Ⓜ = Magnet School	New Superintendents and Principals are bold			
90 Social Work	**274** Before/After Sch	**297** Webmaster	Ⓨ = Year-Round School	Personnel with email addresses are underscored			

School / Address / Contact	Grades	Codes	Enroll / Staff	%	Phone / Fax
Ⓜ Deerfield Park Elem Sch, 650 SW 3rd Ave, Deerfield Bch 33441, Jocelyn Reid	PK-5	T	631 / 40	95%	754/322-6150 Fax 754/322-6190
Dillard Elem Sch, 2330 NW 12th Ct, Ft Lauderdale 33311, Gretchen Atkins	PK-5	T	857 / 31	98%	754/322-6200 Fax 754/322-6240
Dillard High Sch, 2501 NW 11th St, Ft Lauderdale 33311, Cassandra Robinson	6-12	AGV	2,258 / 150		754/322-0800 Fax 754/322-0930
Discovery Elem Sch, 8800 NW 54th Ct, Sunrise 33351, Julie De Greeff	PK-5	T	972	70%	754/322-9100 Fax 754/322-9140
Ⓨ Dolphin Bay Elem Sch, 16450 Miramar Pkwy, Miramar 33027, Sandra Nelson	PK-5	MT	690	55%	754/323-8000 Fax 754/323-8040
Driftwood Elem Sch, 2700 N 69th Ave, Hollywood 33024, **Christine Ringler**	PK-5	T	634 / 37	80%	754/323-5450 Fax 754/323-5490 🅕🅣
Driftwood Middle Sch, 2751 N 70th Ter, Hollywood 33024, Steven Williams	6-8	TV	1,384 / 100	80%	754/323-3100 Fax 754/323-3160
Eagle Point Elem Sch, 100 Indian Trce, Weston 33326, Christine Fernandez	PK-5		1,406 / 46	36%	754/323-5500 Fax 754/323-5540 🅕🅣
Ⓜ Eagle Ridge Elem Sch, 11500 Westview Dr, Coral Springs 33076, Thomas Redshaw	PK-5		857 / 47	29%	754/322-6300 Fax 754/322-6340 🅕🅣
Embassy Creek Elem Sch, 10905 SE Lake Blvd, Hollywood 33026, Robert Becker	K-5		1,241 / 42	21%	754/323-5550 Fax 754/323-5590
Endeavour Prim Learning Center, 2701 NW 56th Ave, Lauderhill 33313, Denise Lawrence	PK-3	T	384 / 23	97%	754/321-6600 Fax 754/321-6640
Everglades Elem Sch, 2900 Bonaventure Blvd, Weston 33331, Eliot Tillinger	PK-5		1,028 / 47	18%	754/323-5600 Fax 754/323-5640
Everglades High Sch, 17100 SW 48th Ct, Miramar 33027, Haleh Darbar	9-12	V	2,338	51%	754/323-0500 Fax 754/323-0640
Fairway Elem Sch, 7850 Fairway Blvd, Miramar 33023, **Katherine Good**	PK-5	T	715 / 38	89%	754/323-5650 Fax 754/323-5690
Falcon Cove Middle Sch, 4251 Bonaventure Blvd, Weston 33332, **Steven Carruth**	6-8		2,299	16%	754/323-3200 Fax 754/323-3285
Flamingo Elem Sch, 1130 SW 133rd Ave, Davie 33325, **Philip Bullock**	PK-5	T	670 / 38	62%	754/323-5700 Fax 754/323-5740
Floranada Elem Sch, 5251 NE 14th Way, Ft Lauderdale 33334, John Vetter	PK-5	T	751 / 37	54%	754/322-6350 Fax 754/322-6390
Forest Glen Middle Sch, 6501 Turtle Run Blvd, Coral Springs 33067, Ronald Forsman	6-8	GTV	1,354	62%	754/322-3400 Fax 754/322-3485 🅕🅣
Forest Hills Elem Sch, 3100 NW 85th Ave, Coral Springs 33065, Barbara Rothman	PK-5	T	722 / 35	83%	754/322-6400 Fax 754/322-6440 🅕
Fox Trail Elem Sch, 1250 S Nob Hill Rd, Davie 33324, Lynn Burgess	PK-5	T	1,208 / 50	50%	754/323-5800 Fax 754/323-5840
Ft Lauderdale High Sch, 1600 NE 4th Ave, Ft Lauderdale 33305, **Erin Brown**	9-12	AGTV	2,133	66%	754/322-1100 Fax 754/322-1230
Gator Run Elem Sch, 1101 Glades Pkwy, Weston 33327, Keith Peters	PK-5		1,320 / 65	16%	754/323-5850 Fax 754/323-5890
Glades Middle Sch, 16700 SW 48th Ct, Miramar 33027, Ricardo Reyes	6-8	T	1,392	52%	754/323-4600 Fax 754/323-4685
Griffin Elem Sch, 5050 SW 116th Ave, Cooper City 33330, **Angie Jones**	PK-5		624 / 32	37%	754/323-5900 Fax 754/323-5940
Ⓨ Gulfstream Acad Hallandale Bch, 1000 SW 3rd St, Hallandale 33009, Robert Pappas	PK-8	MT	1,591 / 59	89%	754/323-5950 Fax 754/323-5990
Ⓨ Hallandale High Sch, 720 NW 9th Ave, Hallandale 33009, Mark Howard	9-12	MTV	1,233	84%	754/323-0900 Fax 754/323-1030
Harbordale Elem Sch, 900 SE 15th St, Ft Lauderdale 33316, Theresa Bucolo	K-5	T	499 / 19	42%	754/323-6050 Fax 754/323-6090 🅕🅣
Hawkes Bluff Elem Sch, 5900 SW 160th Ave, Davie 33331, Melinda Cunningham	PK-5		859 / 45	29%	754/323-6100 Fax 754/323-6140
Heron Heights Elem Sch, 11010 Nob Hill Rd, Parkland 33076, Merideth Weiss Schnur	K-5		1,137 / 46	10%	754/322-9150 Fax 754/322-9190 🅕🅣
Hollywood Central Elem Sch, 1700 Monroe St, Hollywood 33020, Delicia December	PK-5	T	438 / 32	78%	754/323-6150 Fax 754/323-6190 🅕🅣
Hollywood Hills Elem Sch, 3501 Taft St, Hollywood 33021, John Fossas	K-5	T	752 / 40	50%	754/323-6200 Fax 754/323-6240 🅕🅣
Hollywood Hills High Sch, 5400 Stirling Rd, Hollywood 33021, Lourdes Gonzalez	9-12	GTV	1,912	74%	754/323-1050 Fax 754/323-1180
Hollywood Park Elem Sch, 901 N 69th Way, Hollywood 33024, Maria Menendez	PK-5	T	506 / 34	87%	754/323-6250 Fax 754/323-6290 🅕🅣
Horizon Elem Sch, 2101 N Pine Island Rd, Sunrise 33322, Thaddeus Smith	PK-5	T	592 / 40	79%	754/322-6450 Fax 754/322-6490
Indian Ridge Middle Sch, 1355 S Nob Hill Rd, Davie 33324, Ian Murray	6-8	T	1,985 / 94	41%	754/323-3300 Fax 754/323-3385
Indian Trace Elem Sch, 400 Indian Trce, Weston 33326, Amy Winder	PK-5		716 / 45	22%	754/323-6300 Fax 754/323-6340 🅕🅣
J P Taravella High Sch, 10600 Riverside Dr, Coral Springs 33071, **Mary DeArmas**	9-12	AGTV	3,107 / 105	56%	754/322-2300 Fax 754/322-2430
James Rickards Middle Sch, 6000 NE 9th Ave, Oakland Park 33334, Washington Collado	6-8	T	888 / 58	84%	754/322-4400 Fax 754/322-4485 🅕🅣
James S Hunt Elem Sch, 7800 NW 35th Ct, Coral Springs 33065, **Rendolyn Amaker**	PK-5	T	627 / 51	90%	754/322-6500 Fax 754/322-6540
Ⓨ Lake Forest Elem Sch, 3550 SW 48th Ave, Pembroke Park 33023, Sharon Boyd	PK-5	MT	732 / 36	94%	754/323-6350 Fax 754/323-6390 🅕🅣
Lakeside Elem Sch, 900 NW 136th Ave, Pembroke Pnes 33028, Kathryne May	PK-6	T	800	51%	754/323-6400 Fax 754/323-6440
Ⓐ Lanier James Education Center, 1050 NW 7th Ct, Hallandale 33009, **Bonnie Clemon**	K-12	TV	125 / 18	86%	754/321-7350 Fax 754/321-7390
Larkdale Elem Sch, 3250 NW 12th Pl, Ft Lauderdale 33311, Carla Hart	PK-5		424 / 26	96%	754/322-6600 Fax 754/322-6640
Lauderdale Lakes Middle Sch, 3911 NW 30th Ave, Laud Lakes 33309, **Jill Slesinski**	6-8	TV	866	91%	754/322-3500 Fax 754/322-3585

#		#		#		#		#		#	
1	Superintendent	8	Curric/Instruct K-12	19	Chief Financial Officer	29	Family/Consumer Science	39	Social Studies K-12	49	English/Lang Arts Elem	59	Special Education Elem	69	Academic Assessment
2	Bus/Finance/Purchasing	9	Curric/Instruct Elem	20	Art K-12	30	Adult Education	40	Social Studies Elem	50	English/Lang Arts Sec	60	Special Education Sec	70	Research/Development
3	Buildings & Grounds	10	Curric/Instruct Sec	21	Art Elem	31	Career/Sch-to-Work K-12	41	Social Studies Sec	51	Reading K-12	61	Foreign/World Lang K-12	71	Public Information
4	Food Service	11	Federal Program	22	Art Sec	32	Career/Sch-to-Work Elem	42	Science K-12	52	Reading Elem	62	Foreign/World Lang Elem	72	Summer School
5	Transportation	12	Title I	23	Music K-12	33	Career/Sch-to-Work Sec	43	Science Elem	53	Reading Sec	63	Foreign/World Lang Sec	73	Instructional Tech
6	Athletic	13	Title V	24	Music Elem	34	Early Childhood Ed	44	Science Sec	54	Remedial Reading K-12	64	Religious Education K-12	74	Inservice Training
7	Health Services	15	Asst Superintendent	25	Music Sec	35	Health/Phys Education	45	Math K-12	55	Remedial Reading Elem	65	Religious Education Elem	75	Marketing/Distributive
		16	Instructional Media Svcs	26	Business Education	36	Guidance Services K-12	46	Math Elem	56	Remedial Reading Sec	66	Religious Education Sec	76	Info Systems
		17	Chief Operations Officer	27	Career & Tech Ed	37	Guidance Services Elem	47	Math Sec	57	Bilingual/ELL	67	School Board President	77	Psychological Assess
		18	Chief Academic Officer	28	Technology Education	38	Guidance Services Sec	48	English/Lang Arts K-12	58	Special Education K-12	68	Teacher Personnel	78	Affirmative Action

School / Address / Principal	Grades	Programs	Enroll	%	Phone	Fax
Ⓜ Lauderhill 6-12 Magnet Sch 1901 NW 49th Ave, Lauderhill 33313 Dr Ryan Reardon	6-12	AGTV	864	93%	754/322-3600	Fax 754/322-3685
Lauderhill P Turner Elem Sch 1500 NW 49th Ave, Lauderhill 33313 Richard Garrick f	PK-5	T	678 / 52	96%	754/322-6700	Fax 754/322-6740
Liberty Elem Sch 2450 Banks Rd, Margate 33063 **Matthew Whaley**	PK-5	T	989 / 44	80%	754/322-6750	Fax 754/322-6790
Lloyd Estates Elem Sch 750 NW 41st St, Oakland Park 33309 Shawn Allen	PK-5	T	540 / 34	94%	754/322-6800	Fax 754/322-6840
Lyons Creek Middle Sch 4333 Sol Press Blvd, Coconut Creek 33073 Vernicca Wynter	6-8	T	1,952 / 72	57%	754/322-3700	Fax 754/322-3785
Manatee Bay Elem Sch 19200 Manatee Isles Dr, Weston 33332 Heather DeVaughn t	K-5		1,207	16%	754/323-6450	Fax 754/323-6490
Maplewood Elem Sch 9850 Ramblewood Dr, Coral Springs 33071 Leena Itty	PK-5	T	749 / 40	59%	754/322-6850	Fax 754/322-6890
Margate Elem Sch 6300 NW 18th St, Margate 33063 Thomas Schroeder t	PK-5	T	1,023 / 40	71%	754/322-6900	Fax 754/322-6940
Margate Middle Sch 500 NW 65th Ave, Margate 33063 **Sabine Phillips**	6-8	AGTV	1,211 / 60	82%	754/322-3800	Fax 754/322-3885
Marjory Stoneman Douglas HS 5901 Pine Island Rd, Parkland 33076 **Michelle Kefford** t	9-12	V	3,303	24%	754/322-2150	Fax 754/322-2280
Martin Luther King Elem Sch 591 NW 31st Ave, Ft Lauderdale 33311 Mitshuca Moreau f t	PK-5	T	503	97%	754/322-6550	Fax 754/322-6590
Ⓜ Mary M Bethune Elem Sch 2400 Meade St, Hollywood 33020 Latosha Williams f t	PK-5	T	445 / 51	94%	754/323-4900	Fax 754/323-4940
McArthur High Sch 6501 Hollywood Blvd, Hollywood 33024 **Alfred Broomfield**	9-12	TV	2,069 / 70	77%	754/323-1200	Fax 754/323-1330
McNab Elem Sch 1350 SE 9th Ave, Pompano Beach 33060 Dorys Palacio f t	PK-5	T	623 / 35	54%	754/322-7050	Fax 754/322-7090
Ⓨ McNicol Middle Sch 1602 S 27th Ave, Hollywood 33020 Melissa Gurreonero f t	6-8	MTV	743 / 70	90%	754/323-3400	Fax 754/323-3485
Meadowbrook Elem Sch 2300 SW 46th Ave, Ft Lauderdale 33317 **David Levine**	PK-5	T	708 / 41	91%	754/323-6500	Fax 754/323-6540
Millennium Collegiate Academy 5803 NW 94th Ave, Tamarac 33321 Francine Baugh	6-12	T	1,452	74%	754/322-3900	Fax 754/322-3985
Miramar Elem Sch 6831 SW 26th St, Miramar 33023 Joanne Schlissel	PK-5	T	620 / 42	92%	754/323-6550	Fax 754/323-6590
Miramar High Sch 3601 SW 89th Ave, Miramar 33025 **Loli Formoso**	9-12	GTV	2,415 / 85	75%	754/323-1350	Fax 754/323-1480
Mirror Lake Elem Sch 1200 NW 72nd Ave, Plantation 33313 Marlen Veliz	PK-5	T	678 / 30	73%	754/322-7100	Fax 754/322-7140
Monarch High Sch 5050 Wiles Rd, Coconut Creek 33073 James Neer	9-12	V	2,443	54%	754/322-1400	Fax 754/322-1530
Morrow Elem Sch 408 SW 76th Ter, N Lauderdale 33068 Laurel Crowle	PK-5	T	530	93%	754/322-7150	Fax 754/322-7190
New Renaissance Middle Sch 10701 Miramar Blvd, Miramar 33025 Janet Morales	6-8	T	1,193	86%	754/323-3500	Fax 754/323-3585
New River Middle Sch 3100 Riverland Rd, Ft Lauderdale 33312 Melinda Wessinger	6-8	T	1,591	83%	754/323-3600	Fax 754/323-3685
Nob Hill Elem Sch 2100 NW 104th Ave, Sunrise 33322 Jeannie Floyd	PK-5	T	636 / 38	59%	754/322-7200	Fax 754/322-7240
Norcrest Elem Sch 3951 NE 16th Ave, Pompano Beach 33064 **Marc Charpentier** f t	PK-5	T	775 / 30	76%	754/322-7250	Fax 754/322-7290
Ⓜ North Andrews Gardens Elem Sch 345 NE 56th St, Oakland Park 33334 Catrice Duhart f t	K-5	T	865 / 52	78%	754/322-7300	Fax 754/322-7340
Ⓜ North Fork Elem Sch 101 NW 15th Ave, Ft Lauderdale 33311 **Lavina Robinson** f t	PK-5	T	439 / 35	99%	754/322-7350	Fax 754/322-7390
North Lauderdale Elem Sch 7500 Kimberly Blvd, N Lauderdale 33068 Nichele Williams f t	PK-8	T	750 / 37	93%	754/322-7400	Fax 754/322-7440
North Side Elem Sch 120 NE 11th St, Ft Lauderdale 33304 Heilange Porcena	PK-5	T	369 / 30	97%	754/322-7450	Fax 754/322-7490
Northeast High Sch 700 NE 56th St, Oakland Park 33334 Anthony Valachovic	9-12	GTV	1,672 / 100	74%	754/322-1550	Fax 754/322-1686
Nova Blanche Forman Elem Sch 3521 Davie Rd, Davie 33314 Russell Schwartz f t	K-5	T	768 / 55	66%	754/323-6600	Fax 754/323-6640
Nova Eisenhower Elem Sch 6501 SW 39th St, Davie 33314 Angine Tyghter f t	K-5	T	769 / 37	70%	754/323-6650	Fax 754/323-6690
Nova High Sch 3600 College Ave, Davie 33314 **Olayemi Awofadeju**	9-12	GTV	2,222	60%	754/323-1650	Fax 754/323-1780
Nova Middle Sch 3602 College Ave, Davie 33314 Rayner Garranchan	6-8	TV	1,292 / 65	63%	754/323-3700	Fax 754/323-3785
Oakland Park Elem Sch 936 NE 33rd St, Oakland Park 33334 Michelle Garcia	PK-5	T	603 / 32	92%	754/322-7500	Fax 754/322-7540
Oakridge Elem Sch 1507 N 28th Ave, Hollywood 33020 Eduardo Aguilar	PK-5	T	533 / 36	90%	754/323-6700	Fax 754/323-6740
Olsen Middle Sch 330 SE 11th Ter, Dania Beach 33004 Valerie Harris	6-8		665	81%	754/323-3800	Fax 754/323-3885
Orange Brook Elem Sch 715 S 46th Ave, Hollywood 33021 Devon O'Neal f t	PK-5	T	699 / 43	91%	754/323-6750	Fax 754/323-6790
Oriole Elem Sch 3081 NW 39th St, Laud Lakes 33309 Sheneka Blue f t	PK-5	T	663 / 40	96%	754/322-7550	Fax 754/322-7590
Pace Center for Girls-Broward 2225 N Andrews Ave, Wilton Manors 33311 Aggie Pappas	6-12		93 / 12	99%	954/561-6939	Fax 954/561-7317
Palm Cove Elem Sch 11601 Washington St, Pembroke Pnes 33025 Davida Johnson	K-5	T	596 / 72	75%	754/323-6800	Fax 754/323-6840
Palmview Elem Sch 2601 N Cypress Rd, Pompano Beach 33064 Robert Gibson	PK-5	T	617 / 37	94%	754/322-7600	Fax 754/322-7640
Panther Run Elem Sch 801 NW 172nd Ave, Pembroke Pnes 33029 Elaine Saef f t	K-5		551 / 46	36%	754/323-6850	Fax 754/323-6890

---

79 Student Personnel
80 Driver Ed/Safety
81 Gifted/Talented
82 Video Services
83 Substance Abuse Prev
84 Erate
85 AIDS Education
88 Alternative/At Risk
89 Multi-Cultural Curriculum
90 Social Work

91 Safety/Security
92 Magnet School
93 Parental Involvement
95 Tech Prep Program
97 Chief Infomation Officer
98 Chief Technology Officer
270 Character Education
271 Migrant Education
273 Teacher Mentor
274 Before/After Sch

275 Response To Intervention
277 Remedial Math K-12
280 Literacy Coach
285 STEM
286 Digital Learning
288 Common Core Standards
294 Accountability
295 Network System
296 Title II Programs
297 Webmaster

298 Grant Writer/Ptnrships
750 Chief Innovation Officer
751 Chief of Staff
752 Social Emotional Learning

Other School Types
Ⓐ = Alternative School
Ⓒ = Charter School
Ⓜ = Magnet School
Ⓨ = Year-Round School

School Programs
A = Alternative Program
G = Adult Classes
M = Magnet Program
T = Title I Schoolwide
V = Career & Tech Ed Programs

New Schools are shaded
New Superintendents and Principals are bold
Personnel with email addresses are underscored

Social Media
f = Facebook
t = Twitter

School	Grades		Enrollment	%	Phone
Park Lakes Elem Sch 3925 N State Road 7, Laud Lakes 33319 Rhonda Parris	PK-5	T	995 16	94%	754/322-7650 Fax 754/322-7690
Park Ridge Elem Sch 5200 NE 9th Ave, Pompano Beach 33064 Joseph Balchunas	PK-5	T	586 44	96%	754/322-7700 Fax 754/322-7740
Park Springs Elem Sch 5800 NW 66th Ter, Coral Springs 33067 Katherine Policastro	PK-5	T	1,005 35	38%	754/322-7750 Fax 754/322-7790
Park Trails Elem Sch 10700 Trails End, Parkland 33076 **Arlene Manville**	PK-5	T	1,226 45	13%	754/322-7800 Fax 754/322-7840
Parkside Elem Sch 10257 NW 29th St, Coral Springs 33065 Laneia Hall	PK-5	T	868 45	71%	754/322-7850 Fax 754/322-7890
Ⓜ Parkway Middle Sch 3600 NW 5th Ct, Ft Lauderdale 33311 Bradford Mattair	6-8	AGTV	1,470	83%	754/322-4000 Fax 754/322-4085
Pasadena Lakes Elem Sch 8801 Pasadena Blvd, Pembroke Pnes 33024 Janet Phelps	PK-5	T	555 40	75%	754/323-6900 Fax 754/323-6940
Pembroke Lakes Elem Sch 11251 Taft St, Pembroke Pnes 33026 Marsha Wagner	K-5	T	719 43	56%	754/323-6950 Fax 754/323-6990
Pembroke Pines Elem Sch 6700 SW 9th St, Pembroke Pnes 33023 Natasha Bell	PK-5	T	590 40	82%	754/323-7000 Fax 754/323-7040
Peters Elem Sch 851 NW 68th Ave, Plantation 33317 **Susanna Deutsch**	PK-5	T	725 42	65%	754/322-7900 Fax 754/322-7940
Ⓐ Pine Ridge Education Center 1251 SW 42nd Ave, Ft Lauderdale 33317 Dr Henry Brown	K-12	T	70 15	96%	754/321-7250 Fax 754/321-7290
Pines Lakes Elem Sch 10300 Johnson St, Pembroke Pnes 33026 Susan Sasse	PK-5	T	539 29	74%	754/323-7100 Fax 754/323-7140
Pines Middle Sch 200 N Douglas Rd, Pembroke Pnes 33024 Carlton Campbell	6-8	GTV	846 72	79%	754/323-4000 Fax 754/323-4085
Pinewood Elem Sch 1600 SW 83rd Ave, N Lauderdale 33068 **Kicia Daniel**	PK-5	T	591 40	81%	754/322-7950 Fax 754/322-7990
Pioneer Middle Sch 5350 SW 90th Ave, Cooper City 33328 Michael Consaul	6-8	V	1,494 45	31%	754/323-4100 Fax 754/323-4185
Piper High Sch 8000 NW 44th St, Sunrise 33351 **Marie Hautigan**	9-12	AGTV	2,411 130	71%	754/322-1700 Fax 754/322-1830
Plantation Elem Sch 651 NW 42nd Ave, Plantation 33317 Judith Pitter	PK-5	T	646 40	93%	754/322-8000 Fax 754/322-8040
Plantation High Sch 6901 NW 16th St, Plantation 33313 Parinaz Bristol	9-12	AGTV	2,025 100	73%	754/322-1850 Fax 754/322-1980
Plantation Middle Sch 6600 W Sunrise Blvd, Plantation 33313 Sherri Wilson	6-8	TV	701	78%	754/322-4100 Fax 754/322-4185
Plantation Park Elem Sch 875 SW 54th Ave, Plantation 33317 Julie Gittelman	PK-5	T	541 22	57%	754/323-7150 Fax 754/323-7190
Pompano Beach Elem Sch 700 NE 13th Ave, Pompano Beach 33060 Shezette Blue-Small	PK-5	T	504 38	94%	754/322-8050 Fax 754/322-8090
Ⓜ Pompano Beach High Sch 600 NE 13th Ave, Pompano Beach 33060 Hudson Thomas	9-12		1,205 18	45%	754/322-2000 Fax 754/322-2130
Pompano Beach Middle Sch 310 NE 6th St, Pompano Beach 33060 Sonja Smith-Braziel	6-8	TV	1,078	85%	754/322-4200 Fax 754/322-4285
Quiet Waters Elem Sch 4150 W Hillsboro Blvd, Deerfield Bch 33442 W Henning	PK-5	T	1,210 46	65%	754/322-8100 Fax 754/322-8140
Ramblewood Elem Sch 8950 Shadow Wood Blvd, Coral Springs 33071 Maria Perez	PK-5	T	877 36	63%	754/322-8150 Fax 754/322-8190
Ramblewood Middle Sch 8505 W Atlantic Blvd, Coral Springs 33071 Cory Smith	6-8	TV	1,239 85	58%	754/322-4300 Fax 754/322-4388
Riverglades Elem Sch 7400 Parkside Dr, Parkland 33067 Joanne Seltzer	PK-5		1,069 32	18%	754/322-8200 Fax 754/322-8240
Riverland Elem Sch 2600 SW 11th Ct, Ft Lauderdale 33312 Oslay Gil	PK-5	T	562 40	94%	754/323-7200 Fax 754/323-7240
Riverside Elem Sch 11450 Riverside Dr, Coral Springs 33071 **Sabrina Sheib**	K-5		736	39%	754/322-8250 Fax 754/322-8290
Ⓜ Robert C Markham Elem Sch 1501 NW 15th Ave, Pompano Beach 33069 Shedrick Dukes	PK-5	T	599 30	97%	754/322-6950 Fax 754/322-6990
Rock Island Elem Sch 2350 NW 19th St, Ft Lauderdale 33311 Cormic Priester	PK-5	T	585 25	94%	754/322-8300 Fax 754/322-8340
Royal Palm Elem Sch 1951 NW 56th Ave, Lauderhill 33313 Thomas Darby	PK-5	T	841 70	95%	754/322-8350 Fax 754/322-8390
Sanders Park Elem Sch 800 NW 16th St, Pompano Beach 33060 Karen Bennett	PK-5	T	522 25	96%	754/322-8400 Fax 754/322-8440
Sandpiper Elem Sch 3700 N Hiatus Rd, Sunrise 33351 Camille LaChance	PK-5	T	619 45	69%	754/322-8450 Fax 754/322-8490
Sawgrass Elem Sch 12655 NW 8th St, Sunrise 33325 Stephen Decotis	PK-5	T	1,033 44	53%	754/322-8500 Fax 754/322-8540
Ⓜ Sawgrass Springs Middle Sch 12500 W Sample Rd, Coral Springs 33065 James Cecil	6-8	TV	1,202 85	54%	754/322-4500 Fax 754/322-4585
Sea Castle Elem Sch 9600 Miramar Blvd, Miramar 33025 Rick Rodriguez	PK-5	T	844 34	82%	754/323-7250 Fax 754/323-7290
Ⓐ Seagull Alternative High Sch 425 SW 28th St, Ft Lauderdale 33315 Bonnie Clemon	9-12		341 57	78%	754/321-7300 Fax 754/321-7340
Seminole Middle Sch 6200 SW 16th St, Plantation 33317 Kathryn Marlow	6-8	TV	1,122 70	55%	754/323-4200 Fax 754/323-4285
Sheridan Hills Elem Sch 5001 Thomas St, Hollywood 33021 Josetta Campbell	PK-5	T	512 45	76%	754/323-7300 Fax 754/323-7340
Sheridan Park Elem Sch 2310 N 70th Ter, Hollywood 33024 Jacqueline Carro	PK-5	T	692 45	76%	754/323-7350 Fax 754/323-7390
Ⓥ Sheridan Tech High Sch 3775 SW 16th St, Ft Lauderdale 33312 Thomas Moncilovich	Voc	GM	567		754/321-7450 Fax 754/321-7490
Silver Lakes Elem Sch 2300 SW 173rd Ave, Miramar 33029 Tammy Gilbert	PK-5	T	413 44	50%	754/323-7400 Fax 754/323-7440
Silver Lakes Middle Sch 7600 Tam Oshanter Blvd, N Lauderdale 33068 Alison Trautmann	6-8	TV	700 70	85%	754/322-4600 Fax 754/322-4685

1 Superintendent	8 Curric/Instruct K-12	19 Chief Financial Officer	29 Family/Consumer Science	39 Social Studies K-12	49 English/Lang Arts Elem	59 Special Education Elem	69 Academic Assessment
2 Bus/Finance/Purchasing	9 Curric/Instruct Elem	20 Art K-12	30 Adult Education	40 Social Studies Elem	50 English/Lang Arts Sec	60 Special Education Sec	70 Research/Development
3 Buildings And Grounds	10 Curric/Instruct Sec	21 Art Elem	31 Career/Sch-to-Work K-12	41 Social Studies Sec	51 Reading K-12	61 Foreign/World Lang K-12	71 Public Information
4 Food Service	11 Federal Program	22 Art Sec	32 Career/Sch-to-Work Elem	42 Science K-12	52 Reading Elem	62 Foreign/World Lang Elem	72 Summer School
5 Transportation	12 Title I	23 Music K-12	33 Career/Sch-to-Work Sec	43 Science Elem	53 Reading Sec	63 Foreign/World Lang Sec	73 Instructional Tech
6 Athletic	13 Title V	24 Music Elem	34 Early Childhood Ed	44 Science Sec	54 Remedial Reading K-12	64 Religious Education K-12	74 Inservice Training
7 Health Services	15 Asst Superintendent	25 Music Sec	35 Health/Phys Education	45 Math K-12	55 Remedial Reading Elem	65 Religious Education Elem	75 Marketing/Distributive
	16 Instructional Media Svcs	26 Business Education	36 Guidance Services K-12	46 Math Elem	56 Remedial Reading Sec	66 Religious Education Sec	76 Info Systems
	17 Chief Operations Officer	27 Career & Tech Ed	37 Guidance Services Elem	47 Math Sec	57 Bilingual/ELL	67 School Board President	77 Psychological Assess
	18 Chief Academic Officer	28 Technology Education	38 Guidance Services Sec	48 English/Lang Arts K-12	58 Special Education K-12	68 Teacher Personnel	78 Affirmative Action

FL—14

School	Grd	Prgm	Enr/#Cls	%SN	Phone
Silver Palms Elem Sch 1209 NW 155th Ave, Pembroke Pnes 33028 Irina Shearer	PK-5		638 70	40%	754/323-7450 Fax 754/323-7490 🔵🔵
Silver Ridge Elem Sch 9100 SW 36th St, Davie 33328 Wendy Borowski	PK-5		1,035 45	41%	754/323-7500 Fax 754/323-7540
Silver Shores Elem Sch 1701 SW 160th Ave, Miramar 33027 Jonathan Leff	PK-5	T	440	52%	754/323-7550 Fax 754/323-7590
Silver Trail Middle Sch 18300 Sheridan St, Ft Lauderdale 33331 Stephen Frazier	6-8		1,467 100	33%	754/323-4300 Fax 754/323-4385 🔵🔵
South Broward High Sch 1901 N Federal Hwy, Hollywood 33020 **Patricia Brown**	9-12	AGTV	2,316 80	69%	754/323-1800 Fax 754/323-1930 🔵🔵
South Plantation High Sch 1300 SW 54th Ave, Plantation 33317 Christine Henschel	9-12	ATV	2,262	65%	754/323-1950 Fax 754/323-2080
Stephen Foster Elem Sch 3471 SW 22nd St, Ft Lauderdale 33312 Ricardo Grimaldo	PK-5	T	675 36	83%	754/323-5750 Fax 754/323-5790
Stirling Elem Sch 5500 Stirling Rd, Hollywood 33021 Jacqueline Arnaez	K-5	T	607 33	79%	754/323-7600 Fax 754/323-7640 🔵🔵
Stranahan High Sch 1800 SW 5th Pl, Ft Lauderdale 33312 Michelle Padura	9-12	ATV	1,403 107	82%	754/323-2100 Fax 754/323-2230
Sunland Park Elem Sch 919 NW 13th Ave, Ft Lauderdale 33311 Sharonda Bailey	PK-5	T	515 29	93%	754/322-8550 Fax 754/322-8590
Sunrise Middle Sch 1750 NE 14th St, Ft Lauderdale 33304 Michael Walker	6-8	TV	1,341 60	70%	754/322-4700 Fax 754/322-4385
Sunset Lakes Elem Sch 18400 SW 25th St, Miramar 33029 **Janice Goulette**	PK-5		900	34%	754/323-7650 Fax 754/323-7690
Sunshine Elem Sch 7737 LaSalle Blvd, Miramar 33023 Donna Aaron	K-5	T	592 45	89%	754/323-7700 Fax 754/323-7740
Tamarac Elem Sch 7601 N University Dr, Tamarac 33321 **Richard Garrick**	PK-5	T	734 60	77%	754/322-8600 Fax 754/322-8640 🔵
Tedder Elem Sch 4157 NE 1st Ter, Pompano Beach 33064 Shinita Beavers	PK-5	T	592 42	92%	754/322-8650 Fax 754/322-8690
Tequesta Trace Middle Sch 1800 Indian Trce, Weston 33326 Paul Micensky	6-8	AGV	1,615	31%	754/323-4400 Fax 754/323-4485
The Quest Center 6401 Charleston St, Hollywood 33024 Leo Nesmith	Spec	T	200	56%	754/321-7500 Fax 754/321-7540
Thurgood Marshall Elem Sch 800 NW 13th St, Ft Lauderdale 33311 Michael Billins	PK-5	T	433 45	97%	754/322-7000 Fax 754/322-7040
Tradewinds Elem Sch 5400 Johnson Rd, Coconut Creek 33073 Michael Breslaw	PK-5	T	1,249	54%	754/322-8700 Fax 754/322-8740
Tropical Elem Sch 1500 SW 66th Ave, Plantation 33317 **Robert Schneider**	PK-5	T	1,004 33	48%	754/323-7750 Fax 754/323-7790
Village Elem Sch 2100 NW 70th Ave, Sunrise 33313 Wanda Haynes	PK-5	T	703 42	95%	754/322-8750 Fax 754/322-8790 🔵🔵
Ⓜ Virginia Shuman Young Elem Sch 101 NE 11th Ave, Ft Lauderdale 33301 Cynthia Felton	PK-5		684 31	31%	754/322-9050 Fax 754/322-9090
Ⓜ Walker Elem Sch 1001 NW 4th St, Ft Lauderdale 33311 **Tauri Eligon**	PK-5	GT	811 30	98%	754/322-8800 Fax 754/322-8840
Walter C Young Middle Sch 901 NW 129th Ave, Pembroke Pnes 33028 Harold Osborn	6-8	GT	1,113 74	48%	754/323-4500 Fax 754/323-4585 🔵🔵
Ⓨ Watkins Elem Sch 3520 SW 52nd Ave, Pembroke Park 33023 Lori Mendez	PK-5	MT	540 35	95%	754/323-7800 Fax 754/323-7840 🔵🔵
Welleby Elem Sch 3230 N Nob Hill Rd, Sunrise 33351 Frances Ollivierre	PK-5	T	802 37	71%	754/322-8850 Fax 754/322-8890
West Broward High Sch 500 NW 209th Ave, Pembroke Pnes 33029 Brad Fatout	9-12	V	2,682	30%	754/323-2600 Fax 754/323-2730
West Hollywood Elem Sch 6301 Hollywood Blvd, Hollywood 33024 Lina Palacios	PK-5	T	547 35	93%	754/323-7850 Fax 754/323-7890 🔵🔵
Westchester Elem Sch 12405 Royal Palm Blvd, Coral Springs 33065 Melissa Frame-Geraine	K-5	T	1,140 54	53%	754/322-8900 Fax 754/322-8940
Western High Sch 1200 SW 136th Ave, Davie 33325 Jimmy Arrojo	9-12	V	3,384	43%	754/323-2400 Fax 754/323-2530
Westglades Middle Sch 11000 Holmberg Rd, Parkland 33076 Matthew Bianchi	6-8	V	1,794	15%	754/322-4800 Fax 754/322-4885
Westpine Middle Sch 9393 NW 50th St, Sunrise 33351 Christopher Johnson	6-8	T	1,024	73%	754/322-4900 Fax 754/322-4985
Westwood Heights Elem Sch 2861 SW 9th St, Ft Lauderdale 33312 Jodi Washington	PK-5	T	728	95%	754/323-7900 Fax 754/323-7940 🔵🔵
Ⓐ Whiddon-Rogers Education Ctr 700 SW 26th St, Ft Lauderdale 33315 Wylie Howard	6-12	G	1,024 35	72%	754/321-7550 Fax 754/321-7590 🔵🔵
Whispering Pines Sch 3609 S Douglas Rd, Miramar 33025 Michael Gleason	Spec	T	204 20	63%	754/321-7650 Fax 754/321-7690 🔵🔵
William Dandy Middle Sch 2400 NW 26th St, Ft Lauderdale 33311 Felice Winston	6-8	TV	967 89	93%	754/322-3200 Fax 754/322-3285
William McFatter Tech High Sch 6500 Nova Dr, Davie 33317 Jeanette Johnson	Voc	G	605	50%	754/321-5700 Fax 754/321-5980
Wilton Manors Elem Sch 2401 NE 3rd Ave, Ft Lauderdale 33305 Melissa Holtz	PK-5	T	617 20	76%	754/322-8950 Fax 754/322-8990
WinGate Oaks Center 1211 NW 33rd Ter, Ft Lauderdale 33311 Donald Cottrell	Spec	G	47 30	77%	754/321-6850 Fax 754/321-6868
Winston Park Elem Sch 4000 Winston Park Blvd, Coconut Creek 33073 Carolyn Eggelletion	PK-5	T	1,211 46	55%	754/322-9000 Fax 754/322-9040

● **Broward Co Public Charter Schs** PID: 11818828
600 SE 3rd Ave, Ft Lauderdale 33301
754/321-2135
Fax 754/321-2138

Donte Fulton-Collins 15

Public Schs..Principal	Grd	Prgm	Enr/#Cls	SN	
© Academic Solutions Academy-A 2000 W Commercial Blvd Ste 100, Ft Lauderdale 33309 Andrew Kinlock	9-12		147		954/572-6600 Fax 954/572-6444
© Academic Solutions High Sch 2000 W Commercial Blvd, Ft Lauderdale 33309 Andrew Kinlock	9-12		249	68%	954/572-6600 Fax 954/572-6444

79 Student Personnel	**91** Safety/Security	**275** Response To Intervention	**298** Grant Writer/Ptnrships	**School Programs**	**Social Media**
80 Driver Ed/Safety	**92** Magnet School	**277** Remedial Math K-12	**750** Chief Innovation Officer	A = Alternative Program	
81 Gifted/Talented	**93** Parental Involvement	**280** Literacy Coach	**751** Chief of Staff	G = Adult Classes	🔵 = Facebook
82 Video Services	**95** Tech Prep Program	**285** STEM	**752** Social Emotional Learning	M = Magnet Program	
83 Substance Abuse Prev	**97** Chief Infomation Officer	**286** Digital Learning		T = Title I Schoolwide	🔵 = Twitter
84 Erate	**98** Chief Technology Officer	**288** Common Core Standards	**Other School Types**	V = Career & Tech Ed Programs	
85 AIDS Education	**270** Character Education	**294** Accountability	Ⓐ = Alternative School		
88 Alternative/At Risk	**271** Migrant Education	**295** Network System	© = Charter School	New Schools are shaded	
89 Multi-Cultural Curriculum	**273** Teacher Mentor	**296** Title II Programs	Ⓜ = Magnet School	New Superintendents and Principals are bold	
90 Social Work	**274** Before/After Sch	**297** Webmaster	Ⓨ = Year-Round School	Personnel with email addresses are underscored	

© Alpha International Academy 121 S 24th Ave, Hollywood 33020 Wayne Neunie	K-5	T	90	88%	954/505-7974 Fax 954/505-7076
© Andrews High School-N Broward 3500 N Andrews Ave, Pompano Beach 33064 Eunice Casey	9-12		302	68%	954/944-4123 Fax 954/784-3850
© Ascend Career Academy 5251 Coconut Creek Pkwy, Pompano Beach 33063 Vincent Alessi	9-12		228	76%	954/978-4555
© Atlantic Mont Chtr Sch West 2550 S Flamingo Rd, Ft Lauderdale 33325 Juana Garcia	K-5		150	19%	954/423-9704 Fax 954/399-9787
© Atlantic Montessori Chtr Sch 9893 Pines Blvd, Pembroke Pnes 33024 Juana Garcia	K-3		137	18%	754/263-2700 Fax 754/263-2596
© Avant Garde Academy 2025 McKinley St, Hollywood 33020 Fred Clermont \ Dr Arlene Valdes \ Dr Arlene Valdes	K-12		1,200		754/816-6153 Fax 754/800-2715
© Ben Gamla Charter -N Broward [130] 2620 Hollywood Blvd, Hollywood 33020 Sharon Miller	K-8		500	50%	954/342-4064 Fax 954/342-4107
© Ben Gamla CS-South Broward [130] 6511 W Sunrise Blvd, Sunrise 33313 Dr Gur Berman	K-8	T	432	81%	954/587-8348 Fax 954/587-8347
© Ben Gamla Preparatory Chtr Sch 2650 Van Buren St, Hollywood 33020 Gayle Iacono	7-12		492		954/924-6495 Fax 954/924-6496
© Bridgeprep Acad Broward Co 7595 NW 61st St, Tamarac 33321 Ruth Kalinsky	K-8		317		954/271-0090
© Bridgeprep Acad Hollywd Hills 1400 N 46th Ave, Hollywood 33021 Ronald Marcelo	K-5	T	307	45%	954/362-8268 Fax 954/362-8271
© Broward Math & Science Schools 6101 NW 31st St, Margate 33063 Ali Gumus	K-12		190	49%	954/969-8488 Fax 954/756-8053
© Central Charter Sch 4525 N State Road 7, Ft Lauderdale 33319 Tonya Dix	K-8	T	900 24	63%	954/735-6295 Fax 954/735-6232
© Championship Acad W Broward 7100 W Oakland Park Blvd, Sunrise 33313 Pauline Reyna	K-8		309		954/514-7323
© Championship Acad-Davie 3367 N University Dr, Hollywood 33024 Todd Dupell	K-8	T	559	74%	954/362-3415 Fax 954/640-9678
© Championship Academy-Hollywood 1100 Hillcrest Dr, Hollywood 33021 Savitra Guthrie	K-5	T	417 5	79%	954/924-8006 Fax 954/924-8044
© Championship Distinction HS 3020 NW 33rd Ave, Ft Lauderdale 33311 Savitria Guthrie	9-12		800	67%	954/924-8006 Fax 954/924-8044
© Championship Distinction MS 1100 Hillcrest Dr, Hollywood 33021 Savitria Guthrie	6-8		228	79%	954/924-8006 Fax 954/924-8044
© City of Pembroke Pines MS-West 18500 Pembroke Rd, Pembroke Pnes 33029 Michael Castellano	6-8		1,332	25%	954/443-4847 Fax 954/447-1691
© Coral Springs Charter Sch [133] 3205 N University Dr, Coral Springs 33065 Gary Springer	6-12		1,664 100	39%	954/340-4100 Fax 954/340-4111
© CS of Excellence-Davie 2801 N University Dr, Pembroke Pnes 33024 Rosa Dyer	K-5	T	328	74%	954/433-8838 Fax 954/433-8636
© CS of Excellence-Ft Lauderdale 1217 SE 3rd Ave, Ft Lauderdale 33316 Nadine Azor	K-5	T	303 12	76%	954/522-2997 Fax 954/522-3159
© Eagles Nest Charter Academy 3698 NW 15th St, Lauderhill 33311 Christine Mentis	K-8	T	381 9	81%	954/635-2308 Fax 954/990-6921
© Eagles Nest Charter Middle Sch 201 N University Dr, Coral Springs 33071 B Hope	6-8	T	56 3	52%	954/341-5550 Fax 954/341-5557
© Everest Charter Sch 10044 W McNab Rd, Tamarac 33321 Cristina Reynolds	K-8		102	75%	954/532-3015 Fax 754/307-1912
© Excelsior Charter Sch Broward 2099 W Prospect Rd, Ft Lauderdale 33309 Dr Janett Codling	K-5		150		754/701-1192
© Franklin Acad Pembroke Pines 5000 SW 207th Ter, Ft Lauderdale 33332 Jennifer Nadal	6-12		120	54%	954/315-0770 Fax 954/315-0769
© Franklin Acad Pembroke Pines 18800 Pines Blvd, Pembroke Pnes 33029 Elena Diaz	K-8		1,392	21%	954/703-2294 Fax 954/436-2861
© Franklin Academy Cooper City 6301 S Flamingo Rd, Cooper City 33330 Alexandra Fox	K-8		1,336	15%	954/780-5533 Fax 954/252-8147
© Franklin Academy K-12 5000 SW 207th Ter, Ft Lauderdale 33332 Diane Showalter	K-12		691	50%	954/315-0770
© Franklin Academy Sunrise 4500 NW 103rd Ave, Sunrise 33351 Sergio DelGado	K-8		1,374	61%	754/206-0850 Fax 954/572-9544 f
© Greentree Prep Charter Sch 6301 SW 160th Ave, Ft Lauderdale 33331 Rosa Pou	K-5		155		954/780-8733 Fax 954/430-7707
© Hollywood Acad Arts & Sciences [133] 1705 Van Buren St, Hollywood 33020 Mark Hage	K-8	T	434 28	55%	954/925-6404 Fax 954/925-8123
© Imagine ES-N Lauderdle CS [137] 1395 S State Road 7, N Lauderdale 33068 Stephanie Standley	K-5	T	623 30	96%	954/973-8900 Fax 954/974-5588
© Imagine School at Broward [137] 9001 Westview Dr, Coral Springs 33067 Debra Darling	K-8		838	43%	954/255-0020 Fax 954/255-1336
© Imagine Schools Plantation [137] 8200 Peters Rd, Plantation 33324 Ethiel Calvo-Torres	K-8		364	18%	954/358-4200 Fax 954/472-1994
© Imagine Weston [137] 2500 Glades Cir, Weston 33327 Kristin Sorokin	K-8		938 40	15%	954/659-3600 Fax 954/659-3620
© Innovation Charter Sch 600 SW 3rd St Ste 1400, Pompano Beach 33060 Susan Alexander	K-5	T	242	93%	954/715-1777
© International Sch of Broward 3100 N 75th Ave, Hollywood 33024 Calogero Pantano	6-12	T	90	51%	954/987-2026 Fax 954/987-7261
© N Broward MS Acad-Excellence 8200 SW 17th St, N Lauderdale 33068 Robin Sandler	K-8		340 28	77%	954/718-2211 Fax 954/718-2215
© New Life Charter Academy 3550 Davie Blvd, Ft Lauderdale 33312 Shirley Brunache	K-5		158		954/381-5199 Fax 954/734-6408
© North Broward Acad Excellence [133] 8200 SW 17th St, N Lauderdale 33068 Robin Sandler	K-5	T	684 48	71%	954/718-2211 Fax 954/718-2215
© Panacea Prep Charter Sch 201 N University Dr, Coral Springs 33071 Belinda Hope	K-5	T	125	73%	954/341-5550 Fax 954/341-5557
© Paragon Academy of Technology 502 N 28th Ave, Hollywood 33020 Dr Steven Montes	6-8	T	141 12	59%	954/925-0155 Fax 954/925-0209

1	Superintendent	8	Curric/Instruct K-12	19	Chief Financial Officer	29	Family/Consumer Science	39 Social Studies K-12	49 English/Lang Arts Elem	59 Special Education Elem	69 Academic Assessment

1	Superintendent	8	Curric/Instruct K-12	19	Chief Financial Officer	29	Family/Consumer Science	39	Social Studies K-12	49	English/Lang Arts Elem	59	Special Education Elem	69	Academic Assessment
2	Bus/Finance/Purchasing	9	Curric/Instruct Elem	20	Art K-12	30	Adult Education	40	Social Studies Elem	50	English/Lang Arts Sec	60	Special Education Sec	70	Research/Development
3	Buildings And Grounds	10	Curric/Instruct Sec	21	Art Elem	31	Career/Sch-to-Work K-12	41	Social Studies Sec	51	Reading K-12	61	Foreign/World Lang K-12	71	Public Information
4	Food Service	11	Federal Program	22	Art Sec	32	Career/Sch-to-Work Elem	42	Science K-12	52	Reading Elem	62	Foreign/World Lang Elem	72	Summer School
5	Transportation	12	Title I	23	Music K-12	33	Career/Sch-to-Work Sec	43	Science Elem	53	Reading Sec	63	Foreign/World Lang Sec	73	Instructional Tech
6	Athletic	13	Title V	24	Music Elem	34	Early Childhood Ed	44	Science Sec	54	Remedial Reading K-12	64	Religious Education K-12	74	Inservice Training
7	Health Services	14	Instructional Media Svcs	25	Music Sec	35	Health/Phys Education	45	Math K-12	55	Remedial Reading Elem	65	Religious Education Elem	75	Marketing/Distributive
		15	Asst Superintendent	26	Business Education	36	Guidance Services K-12	46	Math Elem	56	Remedial Reading Sec	66	Religious Education Sec	76	Info Systems
		16	Instructional Media Svcs	27	Career & Tech Ed	37	Guidance Services Elem	47	Math Sec	57	Bilingual/ELL	67	School Board President	77	Psychological Assess
		17	Chief Operations Officer	28	Technology Education	38	Guidance Services Sec	48	English/Lang Arts K-12	58	Special Education K-12	68	Teacher Personnel	78	Affirmative Action

FL—16

School	Grades	Prog	Enroll	%	Phone / Fax
© Pembroke Pines ES-Central 12350 Sheridan St, Pembroke Pnes 33026 Sean Chance	K-8		624 48		954/322-3300 Fax 954/322-3383
© Pembroke Pines ES-East Campus 10801 Pembroke Rd, Pembroke Pnes 33025 **Channale Augustin**	K-5		1,919 35	26%	954/443-4800 Fax 954/443-4811
© Pembroke Pines ES-West 1680 SW 184th Ave, Pembroke Pnes 33029 Michael Castellano	K-8		624 24		954/450-6990 Fax 954/443-4820
© Pembroke Pines High Sch 17189 Sheridan St, Ft Lauderdale 33331 Peter Bayer	9-12		2,032	26%	954/538-3700 Fax 954/538-3715
© Pembroke Pines MS-Central 12350 Sheridan St, Pembroke Pnes 33026 Sean Chance	6-8		679		954/322-3300 Fax 954/322-3383
© Renaissance Charter ES-Pines [133] 10501 Pines Blvd, Pembroke Pnes 33026 Daniel Verdier	K-5	T	961	55%	954/862-1283 Fax 954/862-1284
© Renaissance Charter MS-Pines [133] 10501 Pines Blvd, Pembroke Pnes 33026 Daniel Verdier	6-8	T	453	63%	954/862-1283 Fax 954/862-1284
© Renaissance CS Plantation [133] 6701 W Sunrise Blvd, Plantation 33313 Sheriffee Humphrey	K-8	T	864	83%	954/556-9700 Fax 954/556-9701
© Renaissance CS University [133] 8399 N University Dr, Tamarac 33321 **Athena Guillen**	K-8	T	1,427	62%	954/414-0996 Fax 954/414-0998
© Renaissance CS-Cooper City [133] 2800 N Palm Ave, Hollywood 33026 **Jackson Self**	K-8		1,199	53%	954/668-2500 Fax 954/668-2980
© Renaissance CS-Coral Springs [133] 6250 W Sample Rd, Coral Springs 33067 **Lynette Self**	K-8	T	1,509	53%	954/369-1179 Fax 954/780-5411
© Rise Academy Sch-Sci & Tech 6101 NW 31st St, Margate 33063 Carmella Morton	K-8	T	313	75%	954/968-7977 Fax 954/968-8386
© Somerset Acad -Miramar South [130] 12425 SW 53rd St, Miramar 33027 Alexandra Prieto	K-5	T	212	39%	305/829-2406 Fax 305/829-4477
© Somerset Acad CS-Neighborhood [130] 9300 Pembroke Rd, Miramar 33025 Athena Guillen	K-5	T	522	73%	954/435-1570 Fax 954/435-1571
© Somerset Acad ES South Campus 19620 Pines Blvd, Hollywood 33029 **Bernardo Montero**	K-5		860		954/404-7775
© Somerset Acad Key Charter HS [130] 959 SE 6th Ave, Deerfield Bch 33441 Dennis Mulrooney	9-12		227	43%	954/481-0602 Fax 954/481-0603
© Somerset Acad Key Charter MS [130] 959 SE 6th Ave, Deerfield Bch 33441 Dennis Mulrooney	6-8		425		954/481-0602
© Somerset Acad-Riverside MS [130] 2251 Riverside Dr, Coral Springs 33065 **Dr Mary Stuart**	6-8	T	19	74%	954/255-9740 Fax 954/987-7891
© Somerset Academy Charter HS [130] 20805 Johnson St, Pembroke Pnes 33029 Bernardo Montero	9-12		1,034	42%	954/442-0233 Fax 954/442-1762
© Somerset Academy CS-Davie [130] 3788 Davie Rd, Davie 33314 **Dina Miller**	K-5	T	150	61%	954/584-5528 Fax 954/584-5598
© Somerset Academy East Prep [130] 2000 S State Road 7, Miramar 33023 **Dr Mary Stuart**	K-5	T	237	69%	954/987-7890 Fax 954/987-7891
© Somerset Academy ES Pemb Pines [130] 20801 Johnson St, Pembroke Pnes 33029 Bernardo Montero	K-5		941	37%	954/442-0233 Fax 954/442-0813
© Somerset Academy Middle Sch [130] 20803 Johnson St, Pembroke Pnes 33029 Bernardo Montero	6-8		892	42%	954/442-0233 Fax 954/442-1762
© Somerset Academy Miramar HS [130] 9300 Pembroke Rd, Miramar 33025 Athena Guillen	9-12	T	285	69%	954/435-1570 Fax 954/435-1571
© Somerset Academy Miramar MS [130] 12425 SW 53rd St, Miramar 33027 Alexandra Prieto	5-8		440		305/829-2406 Fax 305/829-4477
© Somerset Academy Pompano [130] 1101 NW 33rd St, Pompano Beach 33064 Dr Donna Kaye	K-5	T	138	86%	954/946-4144 Fax 954/946-4005
© Somerset Academy-Miramar [130] 12601 Somerset Blvd, Miramar 33027 **Alexandra Prieto**	K-5	T	518 25	64%	305/829-2406 Fax 305/829-4477
© Somerset Academy-Riverside 2251 Riverside Dr, Coral Springs 33065 **Michelle Rivas**	K-5		475		954/255-9740
© Somerset Arts Conservatory HS [130] 20803 Johnson St, Pembroke Pnes 33029 Bernardo Montero	9-12		164	31%	954/442-0233 Fax 954/442-1762
© Somerset Pines Academy [130] 901 NE 33rd St, Pompano Beach 33064 Dr Donna Kaye	K-8	T	514	70%	954/786-5980 Fax 954/786-5981
© Somerset Prep CS Middle [130] 9300 Pembroke Rd, Miramar 33025 Athena Guillen	6-8	T	351	71%	954/435-1570 Fax 954/435-1571
© Somerset Prep CS-N Lauderdale [130] 7101 Kimberly Blvd, N Lauderdale 33068 Donyale McGhee	K-12		247		954/718-5065 Fax 954/718-5066
© Somerset Village Academy [130] 225 NW 29th St, Wilton Manors 33311 Anthony Marucci	K-5	T	246	93%	954/390-0971 Fax 954/390-0972
© Somerset Village MS Acad [130] 225 NW 29th St, Wilton Manors 33311 Anthony Marucci	6-8	T	151	95%	954/390-0971 Fax 954/390-0972
© South Broward Mont Charter Sch 520 NW 5th St, Hallandale 33009 **Elizabeth Kpenkaan**	K-5		150	70%	954/251-1443 Fax 954/251-1820
© Suned High School-Margate 1117 Banks Rd, Margate 33063 Tammy Lara	9-12		254	93%	954/246-4004 Fax 954/379-2722
© Sunfire High Sch 2360 W Oakland Park Blvd, Oakland Park 33311 Deeette Naukana	9-12		367	75%	954/678-3939 Fax 954/485-6243
© Sunrise High Sch 424 W Sunrise Blvd, Ft Lauderdale 33311 Martie Lovely	9-12	AG	423	80%	954/446-9234 Fax 954/522-1539
© Sunshine Elem Chtr Sch 502 N 28th Ave, Hollywood 33020 Dr Steven Montes	K-5	T	313	66%	954/925-0155 Fax 954/925-0209
© West Broward Academy [132] 5281 Coconut Creek Pkwy, Margate 33063 **Will Pickens**	K-8		549	69%	754/702-2320 Fax 754/263-5900

BROWARD CATHOLIC SCHOOLS

- **Archdiocese of Miami Ed Office**   PID: 00187854
  Listing includes only schools located in this county. See District Index for location of Diocesan Offices.

79 Student Personnel	91 Safety/Security	275 Response To Intervention
80 Driver Ed/Safety	92 Magnet School	277 Remedial Math K-12
81 Gifted/Talented	93 Parental Involvement	280 Literacy Coach
82 Video Services	95 Tech Prep Program	285 STEM
83 Substance Abuse Prev	97 Chief Infomation Officer	286 Digital Learning
84 Erate	98 Chief Technology Officer	288 Common Core Standards
85 AIDS Education	270 Character Education	294 Accountability
88 Alternative/At Risk	271 Migrant Education	295 Network System
89 Multi-Cultural Curriculum	273 Teacher Mentor	296 Title II Programs
90 Social Work	274 Before/After Sch	297 Webmaster

298 Grant Writer/Ptnrships	**School Programs**	**Social Media**
750 Chief Innovation Officer	A = Alternative Program	
751 Chief of Staff	G = Adult Classes	🅕 = Facebook
752 Social Emotional Learning	M = Magnet Program	
	T = Title I Schoolwide	🅣 = Twitter
Other School Types	V = Career & Tech Ed Programs	
Ⓐ = Alternative School		
Ⓒ = Charter School	New Schools are shaded	
Ⓜ = Magnet School	New Superintendents and Principals are bold	
Ⓨ = Year-Round School	Personnel with email addresses are underscored	

Catholic Schs..Principal	Grd	Prgm	Enr/#Cls	SN
All Saints Catholic Sch 10900 W Oakland Park Blvd, Sunrise 33351 Kristen Whiting	K-8		261	954/742-4842 Fax 954/742-4871
Annunciation Catholic Sch 3751 SW 39th St, Hollywood 33023 Jennifer Nicholson	PK-8		300 18	954/989-8287 Fax 954/989-0660
Archbishop Edward McCarthy HS 5451 S Flamingo Rd, Sw Ranches 33330 Richard Jean	9-12		1,600 42	954/434-8820 Fax 954/680-4835
Cardinal Gibbons High Sch 2900 NE 47th St, Ft Lauderdale 33308 Oscar Cedeno	9-12		1,300 50	954/491-2900 Fax 954/772-1025
Chaminade Madonna College Prep 500 E Chaminade Dr, Hollywood 33021 Dr Judith Mucheck	9-12		600 50	954/989-5150 Fax 954/983-4663
Little Flower Sch 1843 Pierce St, Hollywood 33020 Maureen McNulty	PK-8		260 14	954/922-1217 Fax 954/927-8962
Mary Help of Christians Sch 6000 N University Dr, Parkland 33067 Dr Alexandra Fernandez	PK-8		280 20	954/323-8006 Fax 954/323-8010
Nativity Sch 5200 Johnson St, Hollywood 33021 Elena Ortiz	PK-8		870 30	954/983-4981 Fax 954/987-6368
Our Lady Queen of Martyrs Sch 2785 Happy Hoyer St, Ft Lauderdale 33312 Althea Mossop	PK-8		280 13	954/583-8112 Fax 954/797-4984
St Ambrose Sch 363 SE 12th Ave, Deerfield Bch 33441 Lisa Dodge	PK-8		220 20	954/427-2226 Fax 954/427-2293
St Andrew Sch 9990 NW 29th St, Coral Springs 33065 Kristen Hughes	PK-8		500 20	954/753-1280 Fax 954/753-1933
St Anthony Sch 820 NE 3rd St, Ft Lauderdale 33301 Terry Maus	PK-8		450 15	954/467-7747 Fax 954/901-2601
St Bartholomew Sch 8003 Miramar Pkwy, Miramar 33025 Christine Gonzales	PK-8		175 13	954/431-5253 Fax 954/431-3385
St Bernadette Catholic Sch 7450 Stirling Rd, Hollywood 33024 Maria Wagner	PK-8		204 12	954/432-7022
St Bonaventure Catholic Sch 1301 SW 136th Ave, Davie 33325 Lisa Kempinski	PK-8		650 20	954/476-5200 Fax 954/476-5203
St Coleman Sch 2250 SE 12th St, Pompano Beach 33062 Dr Lori St Thomas	PK-8		650 29	954/942-3500 Fax 954/785-0603
St David Catholic Sch 3900 S University Dr, Davie 33328 Jane Broder	PK-8		550 21	954/472-7086 Fax 954/452-8243
St Gregory Sch 200 N University Dr, Plantation 33324 Cari Canino	PK-8		820 30	954/473-8169 Fax 954/472-1638
St Helen Sch 3340 W Oakland Park Blvd, Ft Lauderdale 33311 Stephanie Tascillo	PK-8		220 11	954/739-7094 Fax 954/739-0797
St Jerome Catholic Sch 2601 SW 9th Ave, Ft Lauderdale 33315 Stephanie Murphy	PK-8		250 13	954/524-1990 Fax 954/524-7439
St Mark Catholic Sch 5601 S Flamingo Rd, Sw Ranches 33330 Teresita Wardlaw	PK-8		650	954/434-3887 Fax 954/434-3595
St Thomas Aquinas High Sch 2801 SW 12th St, Ft Lauderdale 33312 Denise Aloma	9-12		2,000	954/581-0700 Fax 954/581-8263

BROWARD PRIVATE SCHOOLS

Private Schs..Principal	Grd	Prgm	Enr/#Cls	SN
Abundant Life Chrn Academy 1494 Banks Rd, Margate 33063 Stacy Angier	PK-10		420 20	954/979-2665 Fax 954/979-1983
Alazhar Sch 7201 W McNab Rd, Tamarac 33321 Dina Ibrahim	PK-8		240	954/722-1555
American Heritage Sch 12200 W Broward Blvd, Plantation 33325 Lauren Johnston \ Anita Latorre \ Elise Blum	PK-12		2,400 122	954/472-0022 Fax 954/473-4917
American Preparatory Academy 4850 S Pine Island Rd, Davie 33328 Soraya Matos	K-12		150	954/434-8936 Fax 954/434-8956
AMI Kids Greater Ft Lauderdale 3220 SW 4th Ave, Ft Lauderdale 33315 Felix Collazo	6-12		55 3	954/764-2733
Ann Storck Center 1790 SW 43rd Way, Ft Lauderdale 33317 Lori Mandke	Spec		50	954/584-8000 Fax 954/321-8863
Apple Tree Montessori Sch 6301 SW 160th Ave, Sw Ranches 33331 Susan Levine	PK-8		250 20	954/252-9250 Fax 954/252-9230
Atlantis Academy 11411 NW 56th Dr, Coral Springs 33076 Donna Bussiere	K-12		146 10	954/752-7571 Fax 954/752-1963
Aukela Christian Military Acad 2835 Madison St, Hollywood 33020 Audrey Rodriguez	PK-12		90 10	954/929-7010 Fax 954/927-2523
Baldwin Academy 2540 NW 21st St, Ft Lauderdale 33311	PK-5		190	954/730-7855
Baldwin Academy South 1161 SW 30th Ave, Ft Lauderdale 33312	PK-5		79	954/909-5906
Baudhuin Pre-School 3301 College Ave, Ft Lauderdale 33314 Nancy Lieberman	Spec		145 15	954/262-7100 Fax 954/262-3936
Beacon Hill Sch 7600 Davie Road Ext, Hollywood 33024 Dr Tara Fiore	PK-8		100 30	954/963-2600 Fax 954/963-2878
Beth Emet Elem Sch 4807 S Flamingo Rd, Cooper City 33330 Noemi Gozlan	K-5		140	954/680-1882 Fax 954/680-4717
Bethany Christian Sch 615 SE 9th St, Ft Lauderdale 33316 Dede Hunter	PK-8		230 15	954/522-2554 Fax 954/522-3406
Blake Sch 7011 W Sunrise Blvd, Plantation 33313 Alene Padgett	PK-8		168 10	954/584-6816 Fax 954/584-6820
Brauser Maimonides Academy 5300 SW 40th Ave, Ft Lauderdale 33314 Yosefah Berkowitz	PK-8		533 18	954/989-6886 Fax 954/989-4548
Broward Children's Ctr North 25 SE 20th Ave, Pompano Beach 33060	Spec		70	954/946-7503 Fax 954/580-0461
Broward Jr Academy 201 NW 46th Ave, Plantation 33317 George Aristide	K-10		300 5	954/316-8301 Fax 954/316-8308
Calvary Christian Academy 1708 N State Road 7, Hollywood 33021 Jason Rachels	K-12		230	954/322-4375
Calvary Christian Academy 2401 W Cypress Creek Rd, Ft Lauderdale 33309 Irene Contento \ Joseph Wilson \ Aaron Mills	PK-12		1,700	954/905-5100 Fax 954/653-2991

1 Superintendent	19 Chief Financial Officer	39 Social Studies K-12	59 Special Education Elem	69 Academic Assessment
2 Bus/Finance/Purchasing	8 Curric/Instruct K-12	20 Art K-12	29 Family/Consumer Science	40 Social Studies Elem	49 English/Lang Arts Elem	60 Special Education Sec	70 Research/Development
3 Buildings And Grounds	9 Curric/Instruct Elem	21 Art Elem	30 Adult Education	41 Social Studies Sec	50 English/Lang Arts Sec	61 Foreign/World Lang K-12	71 Public Information
4 Food Service	10 Curric/Instruct Sec	22 Art Sec	31 Career/Sch-to-Work K-12	42 Science K-12	51 Reading K-12	62 Foreign/World Lang Elem	72 Summer School
5 Transportation	11 Federal Program	23 Music K-12	32 Career/Sch-to-Work Elem	43 Science Elem	52 Reading Elem	63 Foreign/World Lang Sec	73 Instructional Tech
6 Athletic	12 Title I	24 Music Elem	33 Career/Sch-to-Work Sec	44 Science Sec	53 Reading Sec	64 Religious Education K-12	74 Inservice Training
7 Health Services	13 Title V	25 Music Sec	34 Early Childhood Ed	45 Math K-12	54 Remedial Reading K-12	65 Religious Education Elem	75 Marketing/Distributive
	15 Asst Superintendent	26 Business Education	35 Health/Phys Education	46 Math Elem	55 Remedial Reading Elem	66 Religious Education Sec	76 Info Systems
	16 Instructional Media Svcs	27 Career & Tech Ed	36 Guidance Services K-12	47 Math Sec	56 Remedial Reading Sec	67 School Board President	77 Psychological Assess
	17 Chief Operations Officer	28 Technology Education	37 Guidance Services Elem	48 English/Lang Arts K-12	57 Bilingual/ELL	68 Teacher Personnel	78 Affirmative Action
	18 Chief Academic Officer		38 Guidance Services Sec		58 Special Education K-12		

School	Grades		Enroll/Staff	Phone
Center Academy 4700 Riverside Dr Ste 100, Coral Springs 33067 Barbara Cooper	6-12		86	954/575-1231
Christ Church Sch 4845 NE 25th Ave, Ft Lauderdale 33308 Tane Bonham	PK-5		320 17	954/771-7700 Fax 954/776-4553
Clever Oaks Montesorri Sch 8250 Peters Rd, Plantation 33324 Jackie Adorna	PK-2		150	954/473-4400 Fax 954/473-4433
Danul-Uloom Islamic Inst 7050 Hollywood Blvd, Pembroke Pnes 33024 Shaikh Mohamed	K-5		38	954/963-9514 Fax 954/963-0902
David Posnack Jewish Day Sch 5810 S Pine Island Rd, Davie 33328 Brenda Stein \ Pamera Zaslow \ Gayle Green	K-12		700 12	954/583-6100 Fax 954/791-5463
Emerald Hills Private Sch 3270 Stirling Rd, Hollywood 33021 Robin Levin	K-2		62	954/964-9163
Ft Lauderdale Preparatory Sch 3275 W Oakland Park Blvd, Ft Lauderdale 33311 Kelly Lonsteia	PK-12		200 15	954/485-7500
Gateway Christian Academy 2130 NW 26th St, Ft Lauderdale 33311 Gracelyn Farquharson	K-5		145	954/485-7012 Fax 954/485-6929
Glades Christian Academy 400 Lakeview Dr, Coral Springs 33071 Lorene Hall	K-7		107	954/755-6405 Fax 954/825-0872
Gloria Dei Lutheran Academy 7601 SW 39th St, Davie 33328 Sharon Vonada	PK-8		212 17	954/475-8584 Fax 954/475-2232 f
God Little Creation Preschool 6400 NW 31st Ave, Ft Lauderdale 33309 Brandy Andrews	PK-PK		100	954/973-1129
Grace Christian Academy 3301 N 72nd Ave, Hollywood 33024 Richard Risi	K-12		40 4	954/983-6497
Guidepost Mont-Hollywood Beach 2230 Hollywood Blvd, Hollywood 33020 Vivian Castellisi	PK-8		155	954/923-7100
Hebrew Academy Community Sch 1500 N State Road 7, Margate 33063 Chaim Botwinick	PK-8		335 45	954/978-6341 Fax 954/333-3913
Highlands Christian Academy 501 NE 48th St, Pompano Beach 33064 Larry Smith \ Dawn Utz	PK-12		650 50	954/421-1747 Fax 954/421-2429 t
Holy Temple Christian Academy 1800 NW 9th Ave, Ft Lauderdale 33311 Margaret Johnson	K-12		160 8	954/467-0758 Fax 954/467-0748
Lighthouse Christian Sch 2331 NE 26th Ave, Pompano Beach 33062 Rita O'Leary	K-8		135	954/941-7501 Fax 954/933-4033 f
Little Flower Montessori 519 NE 26th St, Wilton Manors 33305 Kathleen Dzura	PK-6		85 3	954/565-8205 Fax 954/256-9141
Lycee Franco-American Sch 8900 Stirling Rd, Hollywood 33024 Antonio Rodrigues	PK-5		100 8	954/237-0356 Fax 954/237-0366
Masoret Yehudit Day Sch 640 E Hallandale Beach Blvd, Hallandale 33009 Ainat Sharon	PK-6		210	954/457-3899
Master's Academy 13900 Griffin Rd, Ft Lauderdale 33330 Cesar Rodriquez	PK-8		255 10	954/434-2960 Fax 954/434-4719
Montessori Academy-East 19200 Pines Blvd, Pembroke Pnes 33029 Monica Benitez	PK-8		650	954/435-4622 Fax 954/435-4768
Montessori Institute-Broward 12425 Orange Dr, Davie 33330 Melissa Lafuent	PK-6		208	954/472-9620
Mt Bethel Christian Academy 901 NW 11th Ave, Ft Lauderdale 33311 David Harvin	PK-8		150 10	954/462-0255 Fax 954/462-0355
Mt Olivet Junior Academy 3013 NW 11th St, Ft Lauderdale 33311 Cynthia Murray	PK-8		70 5	954/792-6010 Fax 954/792-2248 f t
New Hope Christian Sch 6400 NW 31st Ave, Ft Lauderdale 33309 Brandy Andrews	K-6		100	954/973-1129
New Mirawood Academy 5820 Hallandale Beach Blvd, Hollywood 33023 Ray Gordon	PK-PK		401 9	954/983-5531 Fax 954/983-4403
North Broward Prep Sch 7600 Lyons Rd, Coconut Creek 33073 Kathleen Malanowski \ Genevieve Hoppe \ Jamie Otis	PK-12		2,100 100	954/247-0011 Fax 954/247-0042
Nur Ul Islam Academy 10600 SW 59th St, Cooper City 33328 Judy Mohammed \ Magda Emara \ Rafman Twahir	PK-12		400 15	954/434-3288 Fax 954/434-9333
Our Savior Lutheran Sch 8001 NW 5th St, Plantation 33324 Linda Root	PK-8		158 16	954/370-2161 Fax 954/473-0395
Paladin Academy 14900 NW 20th St, Pembroke Pnes 33028 Jodi Miller	Spec		80 13	954/431-4224 Fax 954/437-0283
Parkridge Christian Academy 5600 Coral Ridge Dr, Coral Springs 33076 Josh Halulko	PK-8		250	954/346-0236 Fax 954/346-0013
Parkway Christian Sch 1200 S Flamingo Rd, Davie 33325 Nicole Koski	PK-8		300	954/424-6425 Fax 954/424-6761
Phyl's Academy 3205 Royal Palm Blvd, Margate 33063 Dr Marjorie Freedman	PK-8		700	954/731-7524 Fax 954/777-9960
Pine Crest Sch 1501 NE 62nd St, Ft Lauderdale 33334 Dr Kristin Shealy \ Amy Varo-Haub \ Joseph Walters	PK-12		1,673	954/492-4100 Fax 954/492-4550
Pine Island Montessori Sch 5499 SW 82nd Ave, Davie 33328 Sherrie Sens	PK-5		120	954/434-6337 Fax 954/434-2289
Potential Christian Academy 12401 Stirling Rd, Cooper City 33330 Julia Elliott	PK-7		240 17	954/434-1550 Fax 954/318-0077
Questa-Summit Mont Middle Sch 5451 SW 64th Ave, Ft Lauderdale 33314 Judy Dempsey	PK-8		475	954/584-3466 Fax 954/584-7816
Randazzo Sch 2251 NW 36th Ave, Coconut Creek 33066 Franchon Thompson \ Diana Fundora	PK-12		200 8	954/968-1750 Fax 954/968-1857
Redeeming Word Pre-Sch Academy 2800 W Prospect Rd, Ft Lauderdale 33309 Jacqueline Francis	PK-8		152	954/485-1435 Fax 954/485-6023
Sagemont Lower Sch 1570 Sagemont Way, Weston 33326 Monica Vigna	PK-5		300 20	954/384-5454 Fax 954/384-0053
Sagemont Upper Sch 2585 Glades Cir, Weston 33327 Mellesia Nelson	6-12	G	468	954/389-2454
Salah-Tawfik Elem Mid Sch 5455 NW 108th Ave, Sunrise 33351 Rabeena Khan	PK-8		180 13	954/741-8130
Sawgrass Adventist Sch 11701 NW 4th St, Plantation 33325 Robert Stevenson	K-8		160 6	954/473-4622 Fax 954/370-8041

79	Student Personnel	91	Safety/Security	275	Response To Intervention	298	Grant Writer/Ptnrships
80	Driver Ed/Safety	92	Magnet School	277	Remedial Math K-12	750	Chief Innovation Officer
81	Gifted/Talented	93	Parental Involvement	280	Literacy Coach	751	Chief of Staff
82	Video Services	95	Tech Prep Program	285	STEM	752	Social Emotional Learning
83	Substance Abuse Prev	97	Chief Infomation Officer	286	Digital Learning		
84	Erate	98	Chief Technology Officer	288	Common Core Standards		Other School Types
85	AIDS Education	270	Character Education	294	Accountability	Ⓐ	= Alternative School
88	Alternative/At Risk	271	Migrant Education	295	Network System	Ⓒ	= Charter School
89	Multi-Cultural Curriculum	273	Teacher Mentor	296	Title II Programs	Ⓜ	= Magnet School
90	Social Work	274	Before/After Sch	297	Webmaster	Ⓨ	= Year-Round School

School Programs
A = Alternative Program
G = Adult Classes
M = Magnet Program
T = Title I Schoolwide
V = Career & Tech Ed Programs

Social Media
f = Facebook
t = Twitter

New Schools are shaded
New Superintendents and Principals are bold
Personnel with email addresses are underscored

School of Islamic Studies 5455 NW 108th Ave, Sunrise 33351 Rabia Khan	PK-8	220	954/741-8130 Fax 954/741-8788
Sha'Arei Bina Torah Acad-Girls 2907 Taylor St, Hollywood 33020 Dr Rochelle Brand	6-12	110	954/927-5544 Fax 954/927-3444
Shepherd of the Coast Chri Sch 1901 E Commercial Blvd, Ft Lauderdale 33308 Meghan Smith	K-8	100 8	954/772-5468 Fax 954/772-2232
Sheridan Hills Christian Sch 3751 Sheridan St, Hollywood 33021 Tiffany Gilbreath \ Christy Chipman	PK-12	450 40	954/966-7995 Fax 954/961-1359
South Florida Acad of Learning 3700 Coconut Creek Pkwy, Coconut Creek 33066 Baila Gansburg	K-12	65 7	954/532-9110 Fax 954/633-4961
St Mark's Episcopal Sch 1750 E Oakland Park Blvd, Ft Lauderdale 33334 Kathleen Rotella	PK-8	380 30	954/563-4508 Fax 954/563-0504
Summit Questa Montessori ES 5451 SW 64th Ave, Davie 33314 Judy Dempsey	PK-8	425	954/584-3466 Fax 954/584-7816
Tabernacle Christian Ctr Acad 4101 SW 61st Ave, Davie 33314 Loren Terrelonge	K-8	120	954/583-4718 Fax 954/581-0569
Tanglewood Academy 9860 Pines Blvd, Pembroke Pnes 33024 Kelly Lennon	PK-1	176	954/431-8805 Fax 954/431-3840
Trinity Christian Sch 3901 NE 22nd Ave, Pompano Beach 33064 Debbie Galup	K-5	100	954/941-8033 Fax 954/941-3240
Trinity Lutheran Sch 11 SW 11th Ct, Ft Lauderdale 33315 Candace Church	K-8	125 7	954/463-7471 Fax 954/463-3928
University School-Nova SE Univ 3375 SW 75th Ave, Ft Lauderdale 33314 William Kopas	PK-12	1,800 91	954/262-4400 Fax 954/262-3971 🟦🟦
Westlake Preparatory Sch 8950 Stirling Rd, Hollywood 33024 D Dustin Rolin	K-12	120 13	954/236-2300 Fax 954/473-0770
Westminster Academy 5601 N Federal Hwy, Ft Lauderdale 33308 Tracey Wood \ Mike Critch	PK-12 G	1,000 68	954/771-4600 Fax 954/334-6131
Weston Christian Academy 1420 Indian Trce, Weston 33326 Bobby McCann	K-8	314 15	954/349-9224 Fax 954/349-0678
Xceed Prep Acad Coral Springs 3301 N University Dr Ste 110, Coral Springs 33065 Betty Norton	6-12	23	954/361-3405
Xceed Preparatory Acad Weston 2900 Glades Cir Ste 1600, Ft Lauderdale 33327 Kenneth Bass	6-12	23	954/866-0248
Youth Under Construction Ctr 231 S Dixie Hwy W, Pompano Beach 33060 Devin King	K-12	401	954/951-6588
Zion Early Learning Center 959 SE 6th Ave, Deerfield Bch 33441	PK-PK	60 50	954/421-3146

BROWARD REGIONAL CENTERS

● **FDLRS-Reach** PID: 04498265 754/321-2205
600 SE 3rd Ave, Ft Lauderdale 33301 Fax 754/321-2715

Gwen Lipscomb ....1,11 Gladys Martinez 16
Joanne Brustad 73

CALHOUN COUNTY

CALHOUN PUBLIC SCHOOLS

● **Calhoun Co School Dist** PID: 00184357 850/674-5927
20859 Central Ave E Ste G20, Blountstown 32424 Fax 850/674-5814

Schools: 6 \ *Teachers:* 176 \ *Students:* 2,100 \ *Special Ed Students:* 440 \ *LEP Students:* 14 \ *College-Bound:* 71% \ *Ethnic:* African American 11%, Hispanic 7%, Caucasian 81% \ *Exp:* $214 (Med) \ *Poverty:* 27% \ *Title I:* $747,975 \ *Special Education:* $3,689,000 \ *Bilingual Education:* $42,000 \ *Open-Close:* 08/12 - 05/27 \ *DTBP:* $350 (High)

Ralph Yoder 1	Elaine Barber 2
Willy Pitts 3,5	Belle Stewart 4
Tracie Taylor 8,69,74,271,273,294	Stacy Willams 13,34,58,77,275
Danny Ryals 67	Neva Miller 68,91*
David Simpson 73,76,295	Renee Harrell 84

Public Schs..Principal	Grd	Prgm	Enr/#Cls	SN
Altha Public Sch 25820 NE Fuqua Cir, Altha 32421 **Sue Price**	K-12	TV	634 50	58% 850/762-3121 Fax 850/762-9502
Blountstown Elem Sch 20883 NE Fuller Warren Dr, Blountstown 32424 **Stephanie Brogden**	PK-5	T	581 35	64% 850/674-8169 Fax 850/674-8844
Blountstown Middle Sch 17586 Main St N, Blountstown 32424 Stephanie Brogden	6-8	T	314 20	55% 850/674-8234 Fax 850/674-6480
Blountstown Senior High Sch 18597 NE State Road 69, Blountstown 32424 Debbie Williams	9-12	AT	407 31	45% 850/674-5724 Fax 850/674-8865
Calhoun Co Adult Sch 17283 NW Charlie Johns St, Blountstown 32424 Vicky Davis	Adult		50 4	850/674-8734 Fax 850/674-6490
Carr Elem & Middle Sch 18987 NW Sr73, Clarksville 32430 Darryl Taylor	K-8	T	227 17	60% 850/674-5395 Fax 850/674-5421

CHARLOTTE COUNTY

CHARLOTTE PUBLIC SCHOOLS

● **Charlotte Co Public Sch Dist** PID: 00184412 941/255-0808
1445 Education Way, Pt Charlotte 33948 Fax 941/255-7569

Schools: 26 \ *Teachers:* 1,406 \ *Students:* 16,300 \ *Special Ed Students:* 3,072 \ *LEP Students:* 408 \ *College-Bound:* 65% \ *Ethnic:* Asian 2%, African American 9%, Hispanic 16%, Caucasian 73% \ *Exp:* $115 (Low) \ *Poverty:* 16% \ *Title I:* $3,835,876 \ *Special Education:* $7,883,000 \ *Bilingual Education:* $225,000 \ *Open-Close:* 08/12 - 05/28 \ *DTBP:* $185 (High)

1	Superintendent	8	Curric/Instruct K-12	19	Chief Financial Officer	29	Family/Consumer Science
2	Bus/Finance/Purchasing	9	Curric/Instruct Elem	20	Art K-12	30	Adult Education
3	Buildings And Grounds	10	Curric/Instruct Sec	21	Art Elem	31	Career/Sch-to-Work K-12
4	Food Service	11	Federal Program	22	Art Sec	32	Career/Sch-to-Work Elem
5	Transportation	12	Title I	23	Music K-12	33	Career/Sch-to-Work Sec
6	Athletic	13	Title V	24	Music Elem	34	Early Childhood Ed
7	Health Services	14	Asst Superintendent	25	Music Sec	35	Health/Phys Education
		15	Instructional Media Svcs	26	Business Education	36	Guidance Services K-12
		16	Instructional Media Svcs	27	Career & Tech Ed	37	Guidance Services Elem
FL—20		17	Chief Operations Officer	28	Technology Education	38	Guidance Services Sec
		18	Chief Academic Officer				

39	Social Studies K-12	49	English/Lang Arts Elem	59	Special Education Elem
40	Social Studies Elem	50	English/Lang Arts Sec	60	Special Education Sec
41	Social Studies Sec	51	Reading K-12	61	Foreign/World Lang K-12
42	Science K-12	52	Reading Elem	62	Foreign/World Lang Elem
43	Science Elem	53	Reading Sec	63	Foreign/World Lang Sec
44	Science Sec	54	Remedial Reading K-12	64	Religious Education K-12
45	Math K-12	55	Remedial Reading Elem	65	Religious Education Elem
46	Math Elem	56	Remedial Reading Sec	66	Religious Education Sec
47	Math Sec	57	Bilingual/ELL	67	School Board President
48	English/Lang Arts K-12	58	Special Education K-12	68	Teacher Personnel

69	Academic Assessment
70	Research/Development
71	Public Information
72	Summer School
73	Instructional Tech
74	Inservice Training
75	Marketing/Distributive
76	Info Systems
77	Psychological Assess
78	Affirmative Action

Public Schs..Principal	Grd	Prgm	Enr/#Cls	SN	
ⒶⒸ AMI Kids Crossroads Hope Acad 45991 Bermont Rd, Punta Gorda 33982 Cynthia Kusha	6-12		22	86%	941/575-5790
Ⓒ Babcock Neighborhood Sch 42891 Lake Babcock Dr, Punta Gorda 33982 **Shannon Treece**	K-7		340		850/727-4985
Baker Head Start 311 E Charlotte Ave, Punta Gorda 33950 Maureen Watts	PK-PK		189 17	66%	941/575-5470 Fax 941/575-5474
Career Quest Ed Center 1441 Tamiami Trl Unit 365, Pt Charlotte 33948 Jack Ham	Adult		200 3		941/255-7614 Fax 941/255-7433
Charlotte Harbor Sch 22450 Hancock Ave, Pt Charlotte 33980 Herb Bennett	Spec	GTV	151 22	55%	941/255-7440 Fax 941/255-7446
Charlotte High Sch 1250 Cooper St, Punta Gorda 33950 Cathy Corsaletti	9-12	TV	1,929 87	51%	941/575-5450 Fax 941/575-5464
Charlotte Technical College 18150 Murdock Cir, Pt Charlotte 33948 Barney Duffy	Voc	GT	800 45		941/255-7500 Fax 941/255-7509
Charlotte Virtual Sch 18300 Cochran Blvd, Pt Charlotte 33948 Jack Han	6-12	A	105		941/255-7545 Fax 941/255-7548
Deep Creek Elem Sch 26900 Harbor View Rd, Punta Gorda 33983 **James Vernon**	PK-5	T	691 29	44%	941/255-7535 Fax 941/255-7541
Ⓨ East Elem Sch 27050 Fairway Dr, Punta Gorda 33982 Dr Lori Carr	PK-5	MT	703 38	52%	941/575-5475 Fax 941/575-5482
Ⓒ Fsw Collegiate High Sch 26300 Airport Rd, Punta Gorda 33950 Matthew Catanzarite	9-12	T	372	25%	941/637-5673 Fax 941/637-3508
Kingsway Elem Sch 23300 Quasar Blvd, Pt Charlotte 33980 Ron Rogala	PK-5	T	620 50	42%	941/255-7590 Fax 941/255-7591
L A Ainger Middle Sch 245 Cougar Way, Rotonda West 33947 Jeff Harvey	6-8	T	603 45	53%	941/697-5800 Fax 941/697-5470
Lemon Bay High Sch 2201 Placida Rd, Englewood 34224 Robert Bedford	9-12	TV	1,085 50	44%	941/474-7702 Fax 941/475-5260
Liberty Elem Sch 370 Atwater St, Pt Charlotte 33954 Sheila Brown	PK-5	T	563 32	56%	941/255-7515 Fax 941/255-7519
Meadow Park Elem Sch 750 Essex Ave, Pt Charlotte 33948 Matthew Loge	PK-5	T	729 32	57%	941/255-7470 Fax 941/255-7477
Murdock Middle Sch 17325 Mariner Way, Pt Charlotte 33948 Lyman Welton	6-8	T	683 50	46%	941/255-7525 Fax 941/255-7533
Myakka River Elem Sch 12650 Willmington Blvd, Pt Charlotte 33981 Debbie Carney	PK-5	T	537 33	46%	941/697-7111 Fax 941/697-6326
Neil A Armstrong Elem Sch 22100 Breezeswept Ave, Pt Charlotte 33952 Angela Taillon	PK-5	T	813 32	51%	941/255-7450 Fax 941/255-7456
Ⓨ Peace River Elem Sch 4070 Beaver Ln, Pt Charlotte 33952 Heidi Keegan	PK-5	MT	615 25	68%	941/255-7622 Fax 941/255-7626 Ⓕ
Port Charlotte High Sch 18200 Cochran Blvd, Pt Charlotte 33948 Louis Long	9-12	TV	1,680 80	61%	941/255-7485 Fax 941/255-7493
Port Charlotte Middle Sch 23000 Midway Blvd, Pt Charlotte 33952 John LeClair	6-8	TV	826	48%	941/255-7460 Fax 941/255-7469
Punta Gorda Middle Sch 1001 Education Ave, Punta Gorda 33950 Justina Dionisio	6-8	TV	1,169 52	58%	941/575-5485 Fax 941/575-5491
Ⓨ Sallie Jones Elem Sch 1230 Narranja St, Punta Gorda 33950 Jennie Hoke	K-5	MT	668 45	52%	941/575-5440 Fax 941/575-5444
Ⓐ The Academy High Sch 18300 Cochran Blvd, Pt Charlotte 33948 Jack Ham	9-12	V	381 15	28%	941/255-7545 Fax 941/255-7548
Vineland Elem Sch 467 Boundary Blvd, Rotonda West 33947 Laura Blunier	PK-5	T	595 32	42%	941/697-6600 Fax 941/697-5902

CHARLOTTE CATHOLIC SCHOOLS

- **Diocese of Venice Ed Office** PID: 02231695
  Listing includes only schools located in this county. See District Index for location of Diocesan Offices.

Catholic Schs..Principal	Grd	Prgm	Enr/#Cls	SN	
St Charles Borromeo Sch 21505 Augusta Ave, Pt Charlotte 33952 Tonya Peters	PK-8		250 10		941/625-5533 Fax 941/625-7359 Ⓕ

CHARLOTTE PRIVATE SCHOOLS

Private Schs..Principal	Grd	Prgm	Enr/#Cls	SN	
Charlotte Preparatory Sch 365 Orlando Blvd, Pt Charlotte 33954 Peggy Fear	PK-8		200 10		941/764-7673 Ⓕ
Community Christian Sch 20035 Quesada Ave, Pt Charlotte 33952 Dr Sarah Mielke	K-12		275 18		941/625-8977 Fax 941/625-1735
Genesis Christian Sch 19150 Helena Ave, Pt Charlotte 33948 Dr Scott Porter	PK-8		62 9		941/627-4849 Fax 941/627-5890
Good Shepard Day Sch 1800 Shreve St, Punta Gorda 33950 Roy Tuff	K-8		86		941/575-2139 Fax 941/639-2785
Grace Community Sch 4334 Laura St, Pt Charlotte 33980 Jamile Guzman	PK-K		99 6		941/625-7011

79 Student Personnel
80 Driver Ed/Safety
81 Gifted/Talented
82 Video Services
83 Substance Abuse Prev
84 Erate
85 AIDS Education
88 Alternative/At Risk
89 Multi-Cultural Curriculum
90 Social Work

91 Safety/Security
92 Magnet School
93 Parental Involvement
95 Tech Prep Program
97 Chief Information Officer
98 Chief Technology Officer
270 Character Education
271 Migrant Education
273 Teacher Mentor
274 Before/After Sch

275 Response To Intervention
277 Remedial Math K-12
280 Literacy Coach
285 STEM
286 Digital Learning
288 Common Core Standards
294 Accountability
295 Network System
296 Title II Programs
297 Webmaster

298 Grant Writer/Ptnrships
750 Chief Innovation Officer
751 Chief of Staff
752 Social Emotional Learning

Other School Types
Ⓐ = Alternative School
Ⓒ = Charter School
Ⓜ = Magnet School
Ⓨ = Year-Round School

School Programs
A = Alternative Program
G = Adult Classes
M = Magnet Program
T = Title I Schoolwide
V = Career & Tech Ed Programs

New Schools are shaded
New Superintendents and Principals are bold
Personnel with email addresses are underscored

Social Media
Ⓕ = Facebook
Ⓣ = Twitter

Port Charlotte Adventist Sch	K-10		74		941/625-5237
2100 Loveland Blvd, Pt Charlotte 33980			11		Fax 941/625-8460
Almibar Cruz					

CITRUS COUNTY

CITRUS PUBLIC SCHOOLS

- **Citrus Co School Dist** PID: 00184527 — 352/726-1931
  1007 W Main St, Inverness 34450 — Fax 352/249-2152

Schools: 23 \ **Teachers:** 1,031 \ **Students:** 15,000 \
Special Ed Students: 1,914 \ **LEP Students:** 144 \ **College-Bound:** 75%
\ **Ethnic:** Asian 2%, African American 5%, Hispanic 8%, Caucasian
85% \ **Exp:** $159 (Low) \ **Poverty:** 24% \ **Title I:** $5,103,382 \
Special Education: $11,317,000 \ **Bilingual Education:** $192,000 \
Open-Close: 08/12 - 05/29 \ **DTBP:** $195 (High) \ 🇫 🇹

Sandra Himmel 1	Jonny Bishop 2,15
Tammy Wilson 2,19	Chuck Dixon 3
Eric Stokes 3	Michael Mullen 3,5,15*
Roy Pistone 4	Cherise Cernich 7,68,91
Scott Hebert 9,18,72,296*	David Roland 10,285
Ian Bishop 11*	Patricia Douglas 12
Kathy Androski 16,73,82,286,295	Gloria Bishop 27,30*
Lynne Kirby 34,58,77	Jennifer Greco 58
Thomas Kennedy 67	Brendan Bonomo 68
Steven Baumer 68	Suzanne Swain 68
Amy Crowell 69,70,294	Belinda Woythaler 74,273,288
John Mullen 76	Stephanie Gardner 76
Kit Humbaugh 79	Karen Lisa 298*

Public Schs..Principal	Grd	Prgm	Enr/#Cls	SN	
© Acad of Environmental Science	9-12	T	81	38%	352/795-8793
12695 W Fort Island Trl, Crystal River 34429			5		Fax 352/249-2100
Ben Stofcheck					
Central Ridge Elem Sch	PK-5	T	785	68%	352/344-3833
185 W Citrus Springs Blvd, Citrus Spgs 34434					Fax 352/249-2103
Nancy Simon					
Ⓐ Citrus Co Renaissance Center	6-12	T	120	79%	352/527-4567
3630 W Educational Path, Lecanto 34461			16		Fax 352/249-2144
Katherine Vernon					
Citrus High Sch	9-12	TV	1,437	57%	352/726-2241
600 W Highland Blvd, Inverness 34452			80		Fax 352/249-2102
Laura Mason					
Citrus Springs Elem Sch	PK-5	T	710	73%	352/344-4079
3570 W Century Blvd, Dunnellon 34433			38		Fax 352/249-2110
Sharen Lowe					
Citrus Springs Middle Sch	6-8	T	804	64%	352/344-2244
150 W Citrus Springs Blvd, Citrus Spgs 34434			34		Fax 352/249-2111
John Weed					
Crest Sch	Spec	GT	108	81%	352/527-0303
2600 S Panther Pride Dr, Lecanto 34461			14		Fax 352/249-2104
Barth Mulder					
Crystal River High Sch	9-12	ATV	1,350	59%	352/795-4641
3195 Crystal River High Dr, Crystal River 34428			65		Fax 352/249-2106
Linda Connors					
Crystal River Middle Sch	6-8	T	855	69%	352/795-2116
344 NE Crystal St, Crystal River 34428			65		Fax 352/249-2107
David Roland					

Crystal River Primary Sch	PK-5	T	637	77%	352/795-2211
8624 W Crystal St, Crystal River 34428			43		Fax 352/249-2109
Donnie Brown					
Ⓐ Cypress Creek Academy	6-12		143		352/527-3091
2855 W Woodland Ridge Dr, Lecanto 34461			6		Fax 352/527-3092
Robert Cummings					
Floral City Elem Sch	PK-5	T	389	80%	352/726-1554
8457 E Marvin St, Floral City 34436			30		Fax 352/249-2127
Tara Wells					
Forest Ridge Elem Sch	PK-5	T	694	75%	352/527-1808
2927 N Forest Ridge Blvd, Hernando 34442			35		Fax 352/249-2129
Michelle McHugh					
Hernando Elem Sch	PK-5	T	756	74%	352/726-1833
2975 E Trailblazer Ln, Hernando 34442			42		Fax 352/249-2130
Chris Bosse					
Homosassa Elem Sch	PK-5	T	403	84%	352/628-2953
10935 W Yulee Dr, Homosassa 34448			21		Fax 352/249-2131
Alice Harrell					
Inverness Middle Sch	6-8	ATV	1,064	65%	352/726-1471
1950 Highway 41 N, Inverness 34450			60		Fax 352/249-2133
Robert Hermann					
Inverness Primary Sch	PK-5	T	652	68%	352/726-2632
206 S Line Ave, Inverness 34452			50		Fax 352/249-2134
Ladonna Harper					
Lecanto High Sch	9-12	ATV	1,633	53%	352/746-2334
3810 W Educational Path, Lecanto 34461			87		Fax 352/249-2136
Jason Koon					
Lecanto Middle Sch	6-8	ATV	773	65%	352/746-2050
3800 W Educational Path, Lecanto 34461			48		Fax 352/249-2137
Inge Frederick					
Lecanto Primary Sch	PK-5	T	806	71%	352/746-2220
3790 W Educational Path, Lecanto 34461			43		Fax 352/249-2139
Victoria Lofton					
Pleasant Grove Elem Sch	PK-5	T	673	72%	352/637-4400
630 Pleasant Grove Rd, Inverness 34452			38		Fax 352/249-2141
Janet Tuggle					🇫 🇹
Rock Crusher Elem Sch	PK-5	T	655	73%	352/795-2010
814 S Rock Crusher Rd, Homosassa 34448			50		Fax 352/249-2143
Sean Furniss					
Withlacoochee Tech Inst	Voc	AG	350		352/726-2430
1201 W Main St, Inverness 34450			38		Fax 352/249-2157
Gloria Bishop					

CITRUS CATHOLIC SCHOOLS

- **Diocese St Petersburg Ed Off** PID: 00200729
  Listing includes only schools located in this county. See District Index for
  location of Diocesan Offices.

Catholic Schs..Principal	Grd	Prgm	Enr/#Cls	SN	
St John Paul II Catholic Sch	PK-8		210		352/746-2020
4341 W Homosassa Trl, Lecanto 34461			17		Fax 352/746-3448
Lee Sayago					

CITRUS PRIVATE SCHOOLS

Private Schs..Principal	Grd	Prgm	Enr/#Cls	SN	
Inverness Christian Academy	PK-12		150		352/726-3759
4222 S Florida Ave, Inverness 34450					Fax 352/726-0782
Carla Beebe \ Stephen Lambert					

1 Superintendent	8 Curric/Instruct K-12	19 Chief Financial Officer	29 Family/Consumer Science	39 Social Studies K-12	49 English/Lang Arts Elem	59 Special Education Elem	69 Academic Assessment
2 Bus/Finance/Purchasing	9 Curric/Instruct Elem	20 Art K-12	30 Adult Education	40 Social Studies Elem	50 English/Lang Arts Sec	60 Special Education Sec	70 Research/Development
3 Buildings And Grounds	10 Curric/Instruct Sec	21 Art Elem	31 Career/Sch-to-Work K-12	41 Social Studies Sec	51 Reading K-12	61 Foreign/World Lang K-12	71 Public Information
4 Food Service	11 Federal Program	22 Art Sec	32 Career/Sch-to-Work Elem	42 Science K-12	52 Reading Elem	62 Foreign/World Lang Elem	72 Summer School
5 Transportation	12 Title I	23 Music K-12	33 Career/Sch-to-Work Sec	43 Science Elem	53 Reading Sec	63 Foreign/World Lang Sec	73 Instructional Tech
6 Athletic	13 Title V	24 Music Elem	34 Early Childhood Ed	44 Science Sec	54 Remedial Reading K-12	64 Religious Education K-12	74 Inservice Training
7 Health Services	14 Asst Superintendent	25 Music Sec	35 Health/Phys Education	45 Math K-12	55 Remedial Reading Elem	65 Religious Education Elem	75 Marketing/Distributive
	15 Asst Superintendent	26 Business Education	36 Guidance Services K-12	46 Math Elem	56 Remedial Reading Sec	66 Religious Education Sec	76 Info Systems
	16 Instructional Media Svcs	27 Career & Tech Ed	37 Guidance Services Elem	47 Math Sec	57 Bilingual/ELL	67 School Board President	77 Psychological Assess
	17 Chief Operations Officer	28 Technology Education	38 Guidance Services Sec	48 English/Lang Arts K-12	58 Special Education K-12	68 Teacher Personnel	78 Affirmative Action
	18 Chief Academic Officer						

Seven Rivers Christian Sch 4221 W Gulf to Lake Hwy, Lecanto 34461 Jennifer Jeffes \ Scott Jackson	PK-12	498 30	352/746-5696 Fax 352/746-5520	
Solid Rock Christian Academy 972 N Christy Way, Inverness 34453 Sheila Chau	PK-8	62 8	352/726-9788 Fax 352/726-0746	
St Pauls Lutheran Sch 6150 N Lecanto Hwy, Beverly Hills 34465 Kyle Bender	PK-8	80 5	352/489-3027 Fax 352/489-1062	
West Coast Christian Sch 718 NW 1st Ave, Crystal River 34428 Ruth Pringle	K-12	51 4	352/795-2079	

CLAY COUNTY

CLAY PUBLIC SCHOOLS

● **Clay Co School Dist** PID: 00184656
900 Walnut St, Green Cv Spgs 32043

904/336-6500
Fax 904/284-6525

Schools: 48 \ **Teachers:** 2,483 \ **Students:** 35,609 \
Special Ed Students: 7,389 \ **LEP Students:** 823 \ **College-Bound:** 65%
\ **Ethnic:** Asian 3%, African American 16%, Hispanic 12%, Caucasian
69% \ **Exp:** $205 (Med) \ **Poverty:** 12% \ **Title I:** $5,803,778 \
Special Education: $44,370,000 \ **Bilingual Education:** $1,981,000 \
Open-Close: 08/13 - 06/03 \ **DTBP:** $189 (High)

Addison Davis	1	Bertie Staefe	2
Chris Deeley-Isais	2	Janna Thornton	2
Jim Messer	2,19	Kathy McKay	2
Michelle Larson	2	Robert Johnson	2
Scott Schultz	2	Dr Susan Legutko	2,15
Toni Padgett	2	Bryce Ellis	3
Donald Bell	3	James Fossa	3
Jim Connell	3	Michael Kemp	3,15
Phil Hans	3	Tod Sweatland	3
Susie Glover	4	Derald Sweatt	5
Tommy Fitzpatrick	5	Airen Payne	7
Mike Wingate	8	Terri Stahlaman	8,11,15,34,81,89
Terry Connor	8,18	Evelyn Chastain	9,12
Ryan Widdowson	11	David Broskie	15,68,78
Michael McAuley	15	Terri Dennis	15,751
Alice Paulk	27	Kelly Mosley	27
Shannah Kosek	30*	Chereese Stewart	31,285
Terry Roth	36,77,79,81,83	Jamie Iannone	57,74,273
Katie Moeller	57,74	Chris Ryan	58
Kathryn Lawrence	58	Teresa Carlson	58
Janice Kerekes	67	Brenda Troutman	68
Cathy Richardson	68	Jackie Cory	68
Jennifer Roach	68	Samantha Wright	68
Sheila Gann	68	Sabrina Thomas	69
Rob Wilson	70,750	Michael Kerekes	71
Nicole Snyder	71	Nicole Young	71
Tom Moore	71,97	Mike Griffis	73
Candy Garcia	76,294	Chris Baker	76
Jeremy Bunkley	76	Jon Skipper	76
Steve Amburgey	76,294	Leslee Bryan	285
Lana Racine-Haffner	286*	Ethan Caren	295
Jamey Vinson	295	Nathan Wagner	295
Rich Perkins	295	Robert Leslie	295

Public Schs..Principal	Grd	Prgm	Enr/#Cls	SN
Argyle Elem Sch 2625 Spencers Plantation Blvd, Orange Park 32073 Angela Ward	PK-5	T	729	47% 904/336-0375 Fax 904/573-2368
Charles E Bennett Elem Sch 1 S Oakridge Ave, Green Cv Spgs 32043 **Sheree Cagle**	PK-6	T	690 70	69% 904/336-0475 904/336-0477
© Clay Charter Academy [133] 1417 Red Apple Rd, Middleburg 32068 Tayla Taylor	K-8		578	13% 904/406-1607 Fax 904/406-1608
Clay Co Center Adult & Cmty Ed 2306 Kingsley Ave, Orange Park 32073 Shannah Kosek	Adult		400 9	904/336-4450 Fax 904/336-4465
Clay High Sch 2025 State Road 16 W, Green Cv Spgs 32043 Wesley Dicks	9-12	V	1,471	40% 904/336-7175 Fax 904/529-3214
Clay Hill Elem Sch 6345 County Road 218, Jacksonville 32234 Adele Reed	K-6	T	414 29	66% 904/336-0775 Fax 904/336-0777
Clay Virtual Academy 2306 Kingsley Ave, Orange Park 32073 **Steve Amburgey**	K-12		212	904/336-9875 Fax 904/336-9881
Coppergate Elem Sch 3460 Copper Colts Ct, Middleburg 32068 Amy Dyal	K-6	T	540	59% 904/336-0675 Fax 904/336-0677
Discovery Oaks Elem Sch 950 Oakleaf Plantation Pkwy, Orange Park 32065 Tracy McLaughlin	K-6		500	904/336-4275
Doctors Inlet Elem Sch 2634 County Road 220, Middleburg 32068 Carolyn Ayers	PK-6	T	628 47	56% 904/336-0975 Fax 904/213-3011
© Flcca Clay Co 9143 Philips Hwy Ste 590, Jacksonville 32256 Samantha Sheffield \ **Lindsay Roache** \ Ryan Malo	K-12		83	904/247-3268
Fleming Island Elem Sch 4425 Lakeshore Dr, Orange Park 32003 Jennifer Collins	PK-6		688 50	19% 904/336-1075 Fax 904/278-2026
Fleming Island High Sch 2233 Village Square Pkwy, Orange Park 32003 Thomas Pittman	9-12	V	2,223	17% 904/336-7500 Fax 904/541-2085
ⒶFlorida Youth Challenge Acad 5629 State Road 16 W Bldg 3800, Starke 32091 James Ransom	9-12		100	866/276-9304 Fax 904/559-1778
Green Cove Springs Jr High Sch 1220 Bonaventure Ave, Green Cv Spgs 32043 Jen Halter	7-8		771 56	36% 904/336-5175 Fax 904/529-2144 🅕🅣
Grove Park Elem Sch 1643 Miller St, Orange Park 32073 **Stephanie Jackson**	K-6	T	498 40	66% 904/336-1275 Fax 904/336-1277
Keystone Heights Elem Sch 335 SW Pecan St, Keystone HGTS 32656 Melanie Sanders	PK-6	T	826 45	64% 904/336-1377 Fax 352/473-4110
Keystone Heights Jr Sr HS 900 Orchid Ave, Keystone HGTS 32656 Aaron McWilliams	7-12		1,203 75	47% 904/336-7775 Fax 352/473-5920
Lake Asbury Elem Sch 2901 Sandridge Rd, Green Cv Spgs 32043 Tiffany Outman	PK-6		827 45	40% 904/336-1525 Fax 904/291-5444
Lake Asbury Junior High Sch 2851 Sandridge Rd, Green Cv Spgs 32043 **Mallory McConnell**	7-8	T	1,109	42% 904/336-5375 Fax 904/336-5377
Lakeside Elem Sch 2752 Moody Ave, Orange Park 32073 Dawn Wolfe	K-6	T	725	57% 904/336-1675 Fax 904/213-2965
Lakeside Junior High Sch 2750 Moody Ave, Orange Park 32073 **Ivin Gunder**	7-8		834 75	37% 904/336-5575 Fax 904/336-5578

79	Student Personnel	91	Safety/Security	275	Response To Intervention	298	Grant Writer/Ptnrships
80	Driver Ed/Safety	92	Magnet School	277	Remedial Math K-12	750	Chief Innovation Officer
81	Gifted/Talented	93	Parental Involvement	280	Literacy Coach	751	Chief of Staff
82	Video Services	95	Tech Prep Program	285	STEM	752	Social Emotional Learning
83	Substance Abuse Prev	97	Chief Infomation Officer	286	Digital Learning		
84	Erate	98	Chief Technology Officer	288	Common Core Standards		
85	AIDS Education	270	Character Education	294	Accountability		
88	Alternative/At Risk	271	Migrant Education	295	Network System		
89	Multi-Cultural Curriculum	273	Teacher Mentor	296	Title II Programs		
90	Social Work	274	Before/After Sch	297	Webmaster		

School Programs
A = Alternative Program
G = Adult Classes
M = Magnet Program
T = Title I Schoolwide
V = Career & Tech Ed Programs

Other School Types
Ⓐ = Alternative School
© = Charter School
Ⓜ = Magnet School
Ⓨ = Year-Round School

Social Media
🅕 = Facebook
🅣 = Twitter

New Schools are shaded
New Superintendents and Principals are bold
Personnel with email addresses are underscored

FL—23

School	Grd	Prgm	Enr/#Cls	%	Phone
McRae Elem Sch 6770 County Road 315, Keystone HGTS 32656 Tamera Winkler	PK-6	T .	563 34	71%	904/336-2125 Fax 352/473-5148
Middleburg Elem Sch 3958 Main St, Middleburg 32068 Becky Wilkerson	K-6	T	577 35	70%	904/336-1875 Fax 904/291-5491
Middleburg High Sch 3750 County Road 220, Middleburg 32068 Roger Dailey	9-12	TV	1,742 100	51%	904/336-8075 Fax 904/291-5462
Montclair Elem Sch 2398 Moody Ave, Orange Park 32073 William Miller	K-6	T	510 32	65%	904/336-1975 Fax 904/278-2090
Oakleaf High Sch 4035 Plantation Oaks Blvd, Orange Park 32065 Treasure Pickett	9-12		2,375	33%	904/336-8375 Fax 904/272-8599
Oakleaf Junior High Sch 4085 Plantation Oaks Blvd, Orange Park 32065 Kristin Rousseau	6-8		1,544	34%	904/336-5775 Fax 904/336-5777
Oakleaf Village Elem Sch 410 Oakleaf Village Pkwy, Orange Park 32065 Tracey Kendrick	PK-5		906	37%	904/336-2425 Fax 904/336-2527
Orange Park Elem Sch 1401 Plainfield Ave, Orange Park 32073 Carolyn McCullough	K-6		484 40	24%	904/336-2275 Fax 904/336-2277
Orange Park High Sch 2300 Kingsley Ave, Orange Park 32073 Clayton Anderson	9-12	TV	1,553 180	52%	904/336-8675 Fax 904/272-8181
Orange Park Junior High Sch 1500 Gano Ave, Orange Park 32073 Justin Faulkner	7-8	T	765 75	64%	904/336-5975 Fax 904/336-5978
Ⓐ Pace Center for Girls-Clay 1241 Blanding Blvd Ste 5, Orange Park 32065 Desanti Shadrick	6-12		47	13%	904/458-0840 Fax 904/276-4295
Plantation Oaks Elem Sch 4150 Plantation Oaks Blvd, Orange Park 32065 Chastity Lee	PK-5		1,378	35%	904/336-2775 Fax 904/214-7477
Ⓐ R C Bannerman Learning Center 608 Mill St, Green Cv Spgs 32043 **Martin Aftuck**	6-12	T	175 15	74%	904/336-4975 Fax 904/529-1025
R M Paterson Elem Sch 5400 Pine Ave, Fleming Isle 32003 John O'Brain	PK-6		1,071 60	32%	904/336-2575 Fax 904/336-2576
Rideout Elem Sch 3065 Apalachicola Blvd, Middleburg 32068 Kimberly Marks	PK-6	T	528	54%	904/336-2875 Fax 904/291-5434
Ridgeview Elem Sch 421 Jefferson Ave, Orange Park 32065 Heather Roche	PK-6	T	565 40	65%	904/336-3075 Fax 904/213-2960
Ridgeview High Sch 466 Madison Ave, Orange Park 32065 **Becky Murphy**	9-12	TV	1,575	43%	904/336-8975 Fax 904/213-3033
S Bryan Jennings Elem Sch 215 Corona Dr, Orange Park 32073 **Elise Love**	PK-6	T	529	65%	904/336-3175 Fax 904/336-3177
Shadowlawn Elem Sch 2945 County Road 218, Green Cv Spgs 32043 Nancy Crowder	PK-6	T	716	47%	904/336-3375 Fax 904/529-1032
© St Johns Classical Academy 114 Canova Rd, Fleming Isle 32003 Melanie Williams	K-9		592		904/458-8240
Swimming Pen Creek Elem Sch 1630 Woodpecker Ln, Middleburg 32068 Rodney Ivey	PK-6	T	493	57%	904/336-3475 Fax 904/336-3600
Thunderbolt Elem Sch 2020 Thunderbolt Rd, Fleming Isle 32003 Lacy Healy	K-6		933 75	27%	904/336-3675 Fax 904/336-3677
Tynes Elem Sch 1550 Tynes Blvd, Middleburg 32068 Laura Fogarty	PK-6	T	964 67	48%	904/336-3850 Fax 904/336-3873
W E Cherry Elem Sch 420 Edson Dr, Orange Park 32073 Angie Whiddon	PK-6	T	740 45	64%	904/336-3975 Fax 904/278-2056
Wilkinson Elem Sch 4965 County Road 218, Middleburg 32068 **Rachael Terrell**	PK-6	T	802 63	66%	904/336-4075 Fax 904/336-4077
Wilkinson Junior High Sch 5025 County Road 218, Middleburg 32068 Christina Cornwell	7-8	T	731 65	61%	904/336-6175 Fax 904/336-6177

CLAY CATHOLIC SCHOOLS

- **Diocese St Augustine Ed Office** PID: 00202533
  Listing includes only schools located in this county. See District Index for location of Diocesan Offices.

Catholic Schs..Principal	Grd	Prgm	Enr/#Cls	SN
Annunciation Catholic Sch 1610 Blanding Blvd, Middleburg 32068 Victoria Farrington	PK-8		415 18	904/282-0504 Fax 904/282-6808

CLAY PRIVATE SCHOOLS

Private Schs..Principal	Grd	Prgm	Enr/#Cls	SN
Broach School-Orange Park 1909 Debarry Ave, Orange Park 32073 Whitney Millson	Spec		111	904/637-0300
Centerpoint Christian Academy 1650 Blanding Blvd, Middleburg 32068 Lee Fulenwider	PK-8		35	904/291-1875 Fax 904/291-1884
Congregational Holiness Sch 2079 State Road 16 W, Green Cv Spgs 32043 Brenda Surrency	K-12		12 2	904/529-1798
Grace Episcopal Day Sch 156 Kingsley Ave, Orange Park 32073 Angela Bast	PK-8		210	904/269-3718 Fax 904/269-9183 f
Heritage Christian Academy 4325 US Highway 17, Fleming Isle 32003 Melisse Kager	K-12		30 4	904/269-2405
Highpoint Christian Academy 84 Knight Boxx Rd, Orange Park 32065 Renee Pleasant	5-12		65	904/272-7949 Fax 904/272-7950
Keystone Christian Academy 5165 County Road 214, Keystone HGTS 32656 Melissa Pellerito	PK-PK		3	352/494-1829
Lighthouse Christian Sch 3925 Main St, Middleburg 32068 Ron Green	1-12		52	904/406-4866 Fax 904/406-2205
Lighthouse Christian Sch 2156 Loch Rane Blvd, Orange Park 32073 Mrs Cartner	1-12		400	904/272-2524 Fax 904/637-0638
Morningstar Christian Sch 5989 Villanueva Dr, Keystone HGTS 32656 Sylvia Croft	K-12		80	352/473-3159 Fax 352/473-0433
Pinewood Christian Academy 198 Knight Boxx Rd, Middleburg 32068 Jason Borko	PK-8		200 16	904/272-6408 Fax 904/644-0566

1 Superintendent	19 Chief Financial Officer	29 Family/Consumer Science	39 Social Studies K-12	49 English/Lang Arts Elem	59 Special Education Elem	69 Academic Assessment
2 Bus/Finance/Purchasing	8 Curric/Instruct K-12	20 Art K-12	30 Adult Education	40 Social Studies Elem	50 English/Lang Arts Sec	60 Special Education Sec	70 Research/Development
3 Buildings And Grounds	9 Curric/Instruct Elem	21 Art Elem	31 Career/Sch-to-Work K-12	41 Social Studies Sec	51 Reading K-12	61 Foreign/World Lang K-12	71 Public Information
4 Food Service	10 Curric/Instruct Sec	22 Art Sec	32 Career/Sch-to-Work Elem	42 Science K-12	52 Reading Elem	62 Foreign/World Lang Elem	72 Summer School
5 Transportation	11 Federal Program	23 Music K-12	33 Career/Sch-to-Work Sec	43 Science Elem	53 Reading Sec	63 Foreign/World Lang Sec	73 Instructional Tech
6 Athletic	12 Title I	24 Music Elem	34 Early Childhood Ed	44 Science Sec	54 Remedial Reading K-12	64 Religious Education K-12	74 Inservice Training
7 Health Services	13 Title V	25 Music Sec	35 Health/Phys Education	45 Math K-12	55 Remedial Reading Elem	65 Religious Education Elem	75 Marketing/Distributive
	14 Asst Superintendent	26 Business Education	36 Guidance Services K-12	46 Math Elem	56 Remedial Reading Sec	66 Religious Education Sec	76 Info Systems
	15 Instructional Media Svcs	27 Career & Tech Ed	37 Guidance Services Elem	47 Math Sec	57 Bilingual/ELL	67 School Board President	77 Psychological Assess
	16 Chief Operations Officer	28 Technology Education	38 Guidance Services Sec	48 English/Lang Arts K-12	58 Special Education K-12	68 Teacher Personnel	78 Affirmative Action
	17 Chief Academic Officer						
	18 Chief Academic Officer						

Seamark Ranch Sch	K-12	26	904/529-1951	
3631 Seamark Ranch Rd, Green Cv Spgs 32043			Fax 904/529-1953	
Larry Davis				
Seven Bridges Sch	K-12	40	904/269-7377	
402 Loring Ave, Orange Park 32073			Fax 904/269-0615	
Nancy Alberts				
St John's Country Day Sch	PK-12	600	904/264-9572	
3100 Doctors Lake Dr, Orange Park 32073		55	Fax 904/264-0375	
Otis Wirth \ Jacqueline Lentini				

COLLIER COUNTY

COLLIER PUBLIC SCHOOLS

● **Collier Co Public School Dist** PID: 00184814   239/377-0001
5775 Osceola Trl, Naples 34109   Fax 239/377-0181

Schools: 62 \ *Teachers:* 2,984 \ *Students:* 47,816 \
Special Ed Students: 6,006 \ *LEP Students:* 6,774 \ *College-Bound:* 71%
\ *Ethnic:* Asian 1%, African American 12%, Hispanic 51%, Native American:
1%, Caucasian 35% \ *Exp:* $258 (Med) \ *Poverty:* 19% \ *Title I:* $13,279,132
\ *Special Education:* $13,980,000 \ *Bilingual Education:* $2,538,000 \
Open-Close: 08/13 - 06/03 \ *DTBP:* $183 (High) \ 🅣

Public Schs..Principal	Grd	Prgm	Enr/#Cls	SN
Avalon Elem Sch 3300 Thomasson Dr, Naples 34112 Jessica Campbell	PK-5	T	479	88% 239/377-6200 Fax 239/377-6201
Barron G Collier High Sch 5600 Cougar Dr, Naples 34109 **Jon Bremseth**	9-12	AGV	1,727	29% 239/377-1200 Fax 239/377-1201
Ⓐ Beacon High School-Naples 3710 Estey Ave, Naples 34104 Dr Cynthia Janssen	9-12	T	284	79% 239/377-1059 Fax 239/377-1089
Big Cypress Elem Sch 3250 Golden Gate Blvd W, Naples 34120 Diana Little	PK-5	T	902 65	53% 239/377-6300 Fax 239/377-6387
Ⓒ Bridgeprep Academy of Collier 3161 Santa Barbara Blvd, Naples 34116 Dr Dayana Philippi	K-6		109	239/747-1016
Calusa Park Elem Sch 4600 Santa Barbara Blvd, Naples 34104 Lynda Walcott	PK-5	T	667	61% 239/377-6400 Fax 239/377-6401
Ⓒ Collier Charter Academy [133] 12101 Immokalee Rd, Naples 34120 Kimberly Zambito	K-7		605	239/330-3810 Fax 239/330-3811
Collier Virtual Sch 3710 Estey Ave, Naples 34104 Cynthia Janssen	K-12		47	47% 239/377-1050 Fax 239/377-1051
Corkscrew Elem Sch 1065 County Road 858, Naples 34120 Dr Rebecca Merhar	PK-5	T	647 64	36% 239/377-6500 Fax 239/377-6501
Corkscrew Middle Sch 1165 County Road 858, Naples 34120 Ronna Smith	6-8	T	822 58	51% 239/377-3400 Fax 239/377-3401
Cypress Palm Middle Sch 4255 18th Ave NE, Naples 34120 **Dr D Cox**	6-8	T	715	63% 239/377-5200 Fax 239/377-5201
East Naples Middle Sch 4100 Estey Ave, Naples 34104 Kevin Huelsman	6-8	ATV	1,003 70	77% 239/377-3600 Fax 239/377-3601 🅣
Eden Park Elem Sch 3650 Westclox St, Immokalee 34142 Mark Frehe	K-6	T	746	95% 239/377-9200 Fax 239/377-9201
Estates Elem Sch 5945 Everglades Blvd N, Naples 34120 Jill Rexford	K-5	T	586 48	66% 239/377-6600 Fax 239/377-6601
Everglade City Sch 415 School Dr, Everglades 34139 **Dr Cheri Allison**	PK-12	T	159 13	65% 239/377-9800 Fax 239/377-9801 🅣
Golden Gate Elem Sch 4911 20th Pl SW, Naples 34116 Kelly Bergey	PK-5	T	891 49	89% 239/377-6900 Fax 239/377-6901
Golden Gate High Sch 2925 Titan Way, Naples 34116 Tobin Walcott	9-12	GTV	1,830	74% 239/377-1600 Fax 239/377-1601
Golden Gate Middle Sch 2701 48th Ter SW, Naples 34116 **Kelly Bergey**	6-8	AT	1,096 40	87% 239/377-3800 Fax 239/377-3827
Golden Terrace Elem Sch 2711 44th Ter SW, Naples 34116 Terri Lonneman	PK-5	T	903 50	86% 239/377-7000 Fax 239/377-7001
Ⓒ Gulf Coast Charter Acad South [136] 215 Airport-Pulling Rd, Naples 34104 William Staros	K-8	T	637	61% 239/784-1539 Fax 239/263-4443
Gulf Coast High Sch 7878 Shark Way, Naples 34119 Joseph Mikulski	9-12	GV	2,362 80	22% 239/377-1400 Fax 239/377-1401
Gulfview Middle Sch 255 6th St S, Naples 34102 Kristina Lee	6-8	V	645 45	42% 239/377-4000 Fax 239/377-4001

79	Student Personnel	91	Safety/Security	275	Response To Intervention	298	Grant Writer/Ptnrships	
80	Driver Ed/Safety	92	Magnet School	277	Remedial Math K-12	750	Chief Innovation Officer	
81	Gifted/Talented	93	Parental Involvement	280	Literacy Coach	751	Chief of Staff	
82	Video Services	95	Tech Prep Program	285	STEM	752	Social Emotional Learning	
83	Substance Abuse Prev	97	Chief Infomation Officer	286	Digital Learning			
84	Erate	98	Chief Technology Officer	288	Common Core Standards			
85	AIDS Education	270	Character Education	294	Accountability			
88	Alternative/At Risk	271	Migrant Education	295	Network System			
89	Multi-Cultural Curriculum	273	Teacher Mentor	296	Title II Programs			
90	Social Work	274	Before/After Sch	297	Webmaster			

School Programs
A = Alternative Program
G = Adult Classes
M = Magnet Program
T = Title I Schoolwide
V = Career & Tech Ed Programs

Other School Types
Ⓐ = Alternative School
Ⓒ = Charter School
Ⓜ = Magnet School
Ⓨ = Year-Round School

Social Media
f = Facebook
🅣 = Twitter

New Schools are shaded
New Superintendents and Principals are bold
Personnel with email addresses are underscored

FL—25

School	Grades	Code	Enroll	%	Phone
Highlands Elem Sch 1101 Lake Trafford Rd, Immokalee 34142 **Margaux Horne**	PK-5	T	624 35	92%	239/377-7100 Fax 239/377-7101
© Immokalee Cmty Sch 124 N 4th St, Immokalee 34142 Zulaika Quintero	K-6	T	241 12	87%	239/867-3223 Fax 239/867-3224
Immokalee High Sch 701 Immokalee Dr, Immokalee 34142 Clara Calderon	9-12	ATV	1,756 160	92%	239/377-1800 Fax 239/377-1801
Immokalee Middle Sch 401 N 9th St, Immokalee 34142 Ryan Nemeth	7-8	ATV	1,450 56	94%	239/377-4200 Fax 239/377-4201 t
Immokalee Technical Center 508 N 9th St, Immokalee 34142 Dorin Oxender	Adult	AV	350 4		239/377-9900 Fax 239/377-7101
Lake Park Elem Sch 1295 14th Ave N, Naples 34102 Christopher Marker	PK-5	T	545 29	43%	239/377-7200 Fax 239/377-7201 t
Lake Trafford Elem Sch 3500 Lake Trafford Rd, Immokalee 34142 Elizabeth Alvarez	PK-5	T	754 54	92%	239/377-7300 Fax 239/377-7301
Laurel Oak Elem Sch 7800 Immokalee Rd, Naples 34119 Marilou Andrews	K-5		961 48	20%	239/377-7400 Fax 239/377-7401
Lely Elem Sch 8125 Lely Cultural Pkwy, Naples 34113 **Christa Crehan**	PK-5	T	611 43	70%	239/377-7500 Fax 239/377-7501
Lely High Sch 1 Lely High School Blvd, Naples 34113 Ellen Keegan	9-12	ATV	1,752 80	66%	239/377-2000 Fax 239/377-2001
Lorenzo Walker Tech High Sch 3702 Estey Ave, Naples 34104 Jeffrey Rexford	Voc	AGT	597 50	77%	239/377-3300 Fax 239/377-3301
Manatee Elem Sch 1880 Manatee Rd, Naples 34114 Dr Laurie Mearsheimer	PK-5	T	628 50	85%	239/377-7600 Fax 239/377-7601
Manatee Middle Sch 1920 Manatee Rd, Naples 34114 Jennifer Bledsoe	6-8	TV	913 50	88%	239/377-4400 Fax 239/377-4401
© Marco Island Academy 2255 San Marco Rd, Marco Island 34145 Melissa Scott	9-12		224	12%	239/393-5133 Fax 239/393-5143
© Marco Island Charter Mid Sch 1401 Trinidad Ave, Marco Island 34145 George Abounader	6-8		377 23	32%	239/377-3200 Fax 239/377-3201
© Mason Classical Academy Ⓜ 3073 Horseshoe Dr S Ste 104, Naples 34104 David Hull	K-12		898	14%	239/227-2838 Fax 239/201-2056
Mike Davis Elem Sch 3215 Magnolia Pond Dr, Naples 34116 **Tamie Stewart**	K-5	T	645	89%	239/377-9000 Fax 239/377-9001
Naples High Sch 1100 Golden Eagle Cir, Naples 34102 Darren Burkett	9-12	AGTV	1,797	42%	239/377-2200 Fax 239/377-2201
Naples Park Elem Sch 685 111th Ave N, Naples 34108 **Michelle Auger**	PK-5	T	418 46	56%	239/377-7700 Fax 239/377-7701
Ⓐ New Beginnings-Immokalee 620 S 5th St, Immokalee 34142 Dr Cynthia Janssen	3-12	T	24	88%	239/377-1130 Fax 239/377-1156
Ⓐ New Beginnings-Naples 3710 Estey Ave, Naples 34104 Dr Cynthia Janssen	6-12	T	62	90%	239/377-1070 Fax 239/377-1071
North Naples Middle Sch 16165 Learning Ln, Naples 34110 **Kimberly Lonergan**	6-8		902	34%	239/377-4600 Fax 239/377-4601
Oakridge Middle Sch 14975 Collier Blvd, Naples 34119 **Joseph Duda**	6-8	AV	1,201 55	30%	239/377-4800 Fax 239/377-4801
Osceola Elem Sch 5770 Osceola Trl, Naples 34109 Dr Brian Castellani	PK-5	T	724	34%	239/377-7800 Fax 239/377-7801
Ⓐ Pace Center for Girls-Collier 160 N 1st St, Immokalee 34142 Marianne Kearns	9-11		33	91%	239/842-5406 Fax 239/657-2002
Palmetto Elem Sch 3000 10th Ave SE, Naples 34117 Christen Krembs	K-5	T	447	66%	239/377-9100 Fax 239/377-9101
Palmetto Ridge High Sch 1655 Victory Ln, Naples 34120 **James Ragusa**	9-12	TV	1,971	48%	239/377-2400 Fax 239/377-2401
Parkside Elem Sch 5322 Texas Ave, Naples 34113 **Melanie Fike**	PK-5	T	741	90%	239/377-8900 Fax 239/377-8901
Pelican Marsh Elem Sch 9480 Airport Pulling Rd N, Naples 34109 Susan Barcellino	PK-5		742 60	31%	239/377-7900 Fax 239/377-7901
Ⓐ Phoenix-Immokalee 620 S 5th St, Immokalee 34142 Dr Cynthia Janssen	4-12		38		239/377-1130 Fax 239/377-1156
Pine Ridge Middle Sch 1515 Pine Ridge Rd, Naples 34109 Sean Kinsley	6-8	AGV	1,040 80	39%	239/377-5000 Fax 239/377-5001
Pinecrest Elem Sch 313 S 9th St, Immokalee 34142 Dr Susan Jordan	K-5	T	732 47	94%	239/377-8000 Fax 239/377-8001
Poinciana Elem Sch 2825 Airport Rd S, Naples 34105 Jessica Davis	PK-5	T	647 41	69%	239/377-8100 Fax 239/377-8101
Sabal Palm Elem Sch 4095 18th Ave NE, Naples 34120 Stephanie Jonas	PK-5	T	596	60%	239/377-8200 Fax 239/377-8201
Sea Gate Elem Sch 650 Seagate Dr, Naples 34103 Beverly Budzynski	K-5		734 34	32%	239/377-8300 Fax 239/377-8301 t
Shadowlawn Elem Sch 2161 Shadowlawn Dr, Naples 34112 Oliver Phipps	PK-5	T	473 30	82%	239/377-8400 Fax 239/377-8401
Tommie Barfield Elem Sch 101 Kirkwood St, Marco Island 34145 Kathryn Maya	K-5		543 36	35%	239/377-8500 Fax 239/377-8501
Veterans Memorial Elem Sch 15960 Veterans Memorial Blvd, Naples 34110 Jessica Vieira	K-5		811	33%	239/377-8800 Fax 239/377-8801
Village Oaks Elem Sch 1601 State Road 29 S, Immokalee 34142 **Beverly Budzynski**	PK-6	T	600 36	89%	239/377-8600 Fax 239/377-8601
Vineyards Elem Sch 6225 Arbor Blvd W, Naples 34119 Georgie Elgin	PK-5		880	34%	239/377-8700 Fax 239/377-8701

COLLIER CATHOLIC SCHOOLS

• **Diocese of Venice Ed Office** PID: 02231695
Listing includes only schools located in this county. See District Index for location of Diocesan Offices.

1	Superintendent	8	Curric/Instruct K-12	19	Chief Financial Officer	29	Family/Consumer Science	39	Social Studies K-12	49	English/Lang Arts Elem	59	Special Education Elem	69	Academic Assessment
2	Bus/Finance/Purchasing	9	Curric/Instruct Elem	20	Art K-12	30	Adult Education	40	Social Studies Elem	50	English/Lang Arts Sec	60	Special Education Sec	70	Research/Development
3	Buildings And Grounds	10	Curric/Instruct Sec	21	Art Elem	31	Career/Sch-to-Work K-12	41	Social Studies Sec	51	Reading K-12	61	Foreign/World Lang K-12	71	Public Information
4	Food Service	11	Federal Program	22	Art Sec	32	Career/Sch-to-Work Elem	42	Science K-12	52	Reading Elem	62	Foreign/World Lang Elem	72	Summer School
5	Transportation	12	Title I	23	Music K-12	33	Career/Sch-to-Work Sec	43	Science Elem	53	Reading Sec	63	Foreign/World Lang Sec	73	Instructional Tech
6	Athletic	13	Title V	24	Music Elem	34	Early Childhood Ed	44	Science Sec	54	Remedial Reading K-12	64	Religious Education K-12	74	Inservice Training
7	Health Services	15	Asst Superintendent	25	Music Sec	35	Health/Phys Education	45	Math K-12	55	Remedial Reading Elem	65	Religious Education Elem	75	Marketing/Distributive
		16	Instructional Media Svcs	26	Business Education	36	Guidance Services K-12	46	Math Elem	56	Remedial Reading Sec	66	Religious Education Sec	76	Info Systems
		17	Chief Operations Officer	27	Career & Tech Ed	37	Guidance Services Elem	47	Math Sec	57	Bilingual/ELL	67	School Board President	77	Psychological Assess
		18	Chief Academic Officer	28	Technology Education	38	Guidance Services Sec	48	English/Lang Arts K-12	58	Special Education K-12	68	Teacher Personnel	78	Affirmative Action

Catholic Schs..Principal

Catholic Schs..Principal	Grd	Prgm	Enr/#Cls	SN
Rhodora J Donahue Academy 4955 Seton Way, Ave Maria 34142 Dr Dan Guernsey	K-12		265	239/280-2450
St Ann Sch 542 8th Ave S, Naples 34102 Michael Buskirk	PK-8		330 18	239/262-4110 Fax 239/262-3991
St Elizabeth Seton Sch 2730 53rd Ter SW, Naples 34116 Maria Neibuhr	PK-8		220 10	239/455-2262 Fax 239/455-0549 f
St John Neumann High Sch 3000 53rd St SW, Naples 34116 Sr Patricia Roche	9-12		264 20	239/455-3044 Fax 239/455-2966 f

COLLIER PRIVATE SCHOOLS

Private Schs..Principal	Grd	Prgm	Enr/#Cls	SN
Community School-Naples 13275 Livingston Rd, Naples 34109 Dr Amy Moviel \ Colleen Potocki \ Dr Eric Johnson	PK-12		800 136	239/597-7575 Fax 239/598-2973
Corkscrew Baptist Sch 22022 Immokalee Rd, Naples 34120 Robert Kline	PK-12		10 4	239/348-8855
First Baptist Academy 3000 Orange Blossom Dr, Naples 34109 Linda Shaw \ Leigh Anne Bates	PK-12		560	239/597-2233
Grace Community Sch 5524 19th Ct SW, Naples 34116 Samuel Harrison	PK-K		75 15	239/455-4520 Fax 239/353-9682
Montessori Academy-Naples 2659 Professional Cir Ste 1102, Naples 34119 Kimberly Hunt	PK-12		93	239/597-2255
Naples Adventist Chrn Sch 2629 Horseshoe Dr S, Naples 34104 Audrey Wainwright	K-8		62 2	239/261-6227
Naples Christian Academy 2655 Northbrooke Dr Unit 2, Naples 34119 Dr Phillip Tingle	PK-8		150 22	239/455-1087 Fax 239/455-5225 f t
Nicaea Academy 14785 Collier Blvd, Naples 34119 Barton McIntyre	PK-12		132	239/353-9099 Fax 239/353-2645
Royal Palm Academy 16100 Livingston Rd, Naples 34110 Scott Baier	PK-8	G	250 20	239/594-9888 Fax 239/594-9893 f t
Seacrest Country Day Sch 7100 Davis Blvd, Naples 34104 Steven Caruso \ Howard Schott	PK-12		600 36	239/793-1986 Fax 239/732-5478
Seagate Christian Sch 1010 Whippoorwill Ln, Naples 34105 Glenn Wiggins	K-12		32 6	239/261-0122 Fax 239/261-0112
Village Sch 6000 Goodlette Frnk Rd N, Naples 34109 Kathy Sweet \ Jason St Amand	PK-12		525	239/593-7686 Fax 239/593-6599

COLUMBIA COUNTY

COLUMBIA PUBLIC SCHOOLS

- **Columbia Co School Dist** PID: 00185040   386/755-8000
  372 W Duval St, Lake City 32055   Fax 386/755-8008

Schools: 16 \ *Teachers:* 675 \ *Students:* 10,000 \
Special Ed Students: 1,673 \ *LEP Students:* 128 \ *College-Bound:* 70%
\ *Ethnic:* Asian 1%, African American 23%, Hispanic 7%, Caucasian
69% \ *Exp:* $226 (Med) \ *Poverty:* 22% \ *Title I:* $3,051,535 \
Special Education: $10,965,000 \ *Bilingual Education:* $311,000 \
Open-Close: 08/12 - 05/28 \ *DTBP:* $31 (Low)

Lex Carswell	1	Keith Hatcher	2
Fred Gaylord	3	Madonna Coughlin	4
Daniel Taylor	5	Kim Allison	7
Sonya Judkins	8	Cherry Hill	9,15,296
Hope Jernigan	9	Kimberlee Dekle	10,74*
Todd Widergren	10,15	Joe Adkins	11
Mona Simmons	15,751	Cindy Forsythe	16,28,73,286
Tabatha McMahon	27	Angela Coppock	30,31
Lynn Jamison	58,79	Sean Adams	58
Dana Brady-Giddens	67	Frank Moore	68,74,273
Patrick Mitchell	73	Sherry Williams	76
Meg Haley	81	Judy Tatem	83,85,88

Public Schs..Principal	Grd	Prgm	Enr/#Cls	SN
© Belmont Academy 1476 SW Walter Ave, Lake City 32024 Ron Barker	PK-11		450	2% 386/487-0487 Fax 386/755-7989
Columbia City Elem Sch 7438 SW State Road 47, Lake City 32024 Jonathan Jordan	PK-5	T	609 44	60% 386/758-4850 Fax 386/758-4857
Columbia Co Adult Ed Sch 409 SW Saint Johns St, Lake City 32025 Sherri Keen	Adult	V	1,000 70	386/755-8190 Fax 386/755-8191
Columbia High Sch 469 SE Fighting Tiger Dr, Lake City 32025 Thomas Hosford	9-12	TV	1,955 100	54% 386/755-8080 Fax 386/755-8082
Eastside Elem Sch 256 SE Beech St, Lake City 32025 Roger Little	PK-5	T	626 40	56% 386/755-8220 Fax 386/758-4885
Five Points Elem Sch 303 NW Johnson St, Lake City 32055 **Thomas Lashley**	PK-5	T	465 39	78% 386/755-8230 Fax 386/755-8240
Fort White Elem Sch 18119 SW State Road 47, Fort White 32038 **Michael Christie**	PK-5	T	650 35	67% 386/344-6301 Fax 386/497-4684
Ft White High Sch 17828 SW State Road 47, Fort White 32038 Keith Couey	6-12	TV	1,164 65	52% 386/319-7272 Fax 386/497-5951
Lake City Middle Sch 843 SW Arlington Blvd, Lake City 32025 Robert Cooper	6-8	TV	1,014 66	57% 386/758-4800 Fax 386/758-4839
Melrose Park Elem Sch 820 SE Putnam St, Lake City 32025 Syreeta Jackson-Lee	PK-5	T	489 38	77% 386/755-8260 Fax 386/755-8276
Niblack Elem Sch 837 NE Broadway Ave, Lake City 32055 Nakitha Ivery	PK-5	T	298 24	85% 386/755-8200 Fax 386/755-8218

79 Student Personnel	**91** Safety/Security	**275** Response To Intervention	**298** Grant Writer/Ptnrships	**School Programs**	**Social Media**
80 Driver Ed/Safety	**92** Magnet School	**277** Remedial Math K-12	**750** Chief Innovation Officer	A = Alternative Program	
81 Gifted/Talented	**93** Parental Involvement	**280** Literacy Coach	**751** Chief of Staff	G = Adult Classes	f = Facebook
82 Video Services	**95** Tech Prep Program	**285** STEM	**752** Social Emotional Learning	M = Magnet Program	
83 Substance Abuse Prev	**97** Chief Infomation Officer	**286** Digital Learning		T = Title I Schoolwide	t = Twitter
84 Erate	**98** Chief Technology Officer	**288** Common Core Standards	**Other School Types**	V = Career & Tech Ed Programs	
85 AIDS Education	**270** Character Education	**294** Accountability	Ⓐ = Alternative School		
88 Alternative/At Risk	**271** Migrant Education	**295** Network System	Ⓒ = Charter School	**New Schools are shaded**	
89 Multi-Cultural Curriculum	**273** Teacher Mentor	**296** Title II Programs	Ⓜ = Magnet School	**New Superintendents and Principals are bold**	
90 Social Work	**274** Before/After Sch	**297** Webmaster	Ⓨ = Year-Round School	**Personnel with email addresses are underscored**	**FL—27**

	Grd	Prgm	Enr/#Cls	SN	
Ⓐ Pathways Academy 1301 NW Labonte Ln, Lake City 32055 Alex Carswell	K-12	T	85 15	81%	386/755-8296 Fax 386/755-8291
Pinemount Elem Sch 324 SW Gabriel Pl, Lake City 32024 Donna Darby	PK-5	T	475	58%	386/755-8179 Fax 386/755-8172
Richardson 6th Grade Academy 646 SE Pennsylvania St, Lake City 32025 Sonya Judkins	6-6	V	527 46		386/755-8130 Fax 386/755-8154
Summers Elem Sch 1388 SW McFarlane Ave, Lake City 32025 Jennifer Saucer	PK-5	T	544 44	66%	386/755-8250 Fax 386/758-4916
Westside Elem Sch 1956 SW County Road 252B, Lake City 32024 Dennis Dotson	PK-5	T	767 46	47%	386/755-8280 Fax 386/755-8285

COLUMBIA CATHOLIC SCHOOLS

- **Diocese St Augustine Ed Office** PID: 00202533
  Listing includes only schools located in this county. See District Index for location of Diocesan Offices.

Catholic Schs..Principal	Grd	Prgm	Enr/#Cls	SN	
Epiphany Sch 1937 SW Epiphany Ct, Lake City 32025 Rita Klenk	K-8		135 9		386-752-2320 Fax 386-752-2364

COLUMBIA PRIVATE SCHOOLS

Private Schs..Principal	Grd	Prgm	Enr/#Cls	SN	
First Academy 162 SW Ridge St, Lake City 32024 Camilla Donnelly	PK-12		8		386/466-7034
Hart 2 Hart Academy 388 SW Birley Ave, Lake City 32024 Dallas Hart	PK-8		175		386/466-1114
Joy Explosion Christian Acad 3134 SW Pinemount Rd, Lake City 32024 Alberta Coleman	K-8		11		386/867-0749
Lake City Christian Academy 3035 SW Pinemount Rd, Lake City 32024 Tana Norris	PK-12		200		386/758-0055
Springville Preparatory Acad 950 N Marion Ave, Lake City 32055 Barbara Edwards	K-12		16		386/288-2537
Tabernacle Baptist Academy 144 SE Montrose Ave, Lake City 32025 Mike Norman	K-12		17 2		386/752-4274

DE SOTO PUBLIC SCHOOLS

- **DeSoto Co School Dist** PID: 00188664
  530 Lasolona Ave, Arcadia 34266

  863/494-4222
  Fax 863/494-0389

Schools: 5 \ **Teachers:** 295 \ **Students:** 5,238 \ **Special Ed Students:** 667 \ **LEP Students:** 453 \ **Ethnic:** African American 12%, Hispanic 47%, Caucasian 41% \ **Exp:** $262 (Med) \ **Poverty:** 34% \ **Title I:** $2,448,167 \ **Special Education:** $5,183,000 \ **Bilingual Education:** $1,529,000 \ **Open-Close:** 08/12 - 05/28 \ **DTBP:** $149 (High) \ 🅴

Public Schs..Principal	Grd	Prgm	Enr/#Cls	SN	
DeSoto Co High Sch 1710 E Gibson St, Arcadia 34266 David Bremer	9-12	TV	1,292 65	54%	863/494-3434 Fax 863/494-7867 🅴
DeSoto Middle Sch 420 E Gibson St, Arcadia 34266 **Michelle Derpich**	6-8	TV	1,031 55	64%	863/494-4133 Fax 863/494-5894
Memorial Elem Sch 851 E Hickory St, Arcadia 34266 Amanda Irby	PK-5	T	989 48	71%	863/494-2736 Fax 863/993-2202
Nocatee Elem Sch 4846 SW Shores Ave, Arcadia 34266 Jermaine Andrews	PK-5	T	641 25	74%	863/494-0755 Fax 863/494-3264
West Elem Sch 304 W Imogene St, Arcadia 34266 **Ryan Bruck**	PK-5	T	854 50	66%	863/494-3155 Fax 863/494-3689

DIXIE PUBLIC SCHOOLS

- **Dixie Co School Dist** PID: 00188731
  16077 NE Highway 19, Cross City 32628

  352/541-6250
  Fax 352/498-1308

Schools: 5 \ **Teachers:** 121 \ **Students:** 2,149 \ **Special Ed Students:** 460 \ **LEP Students:** 5 \ **College-Bound:** 54% \ **Ethnic:** African American 8%, Hispanic 4%, Caucasian 88% \ **Exp:** $182 (Low) \ **Poverty:** 32% \ **Title I:** $958,015 \ **Special Education:** $3,107,000 \ **Open-Close:** 08/12 - 06/02 \ **DTBP:** $350 (High)

1	Superintendent	8	Curric/Instruct K-12	19	Chief Financial Officer
2	Bus/Finance/Purchasing	9	Curric/Instruct Elem	20	Art K-12
3	Buildings And Grounds	10	Curric/Instruct Sec	21	Art Elem
4	Food Service	11	Federal Program	22	Art Sec
5	Transportation	12	Title I	23	Music K-12
6	Athletic	13	Title V	24	Music Elem
7	Health Services	15	Asst Superintendent	25	Music Sec
		16	Instructional Media Svcs	26	Business Education
		17	Chief Operations Officer	27	Career & Tech Ed
		18	Chief Academic Officer	28	Technology Education

29	Family/Consumer Science	39	Social Studies K-12	49	English/Lang Arts Elem
30	Adult Education	40	Social Studies Elem	50	English/Lang Arts Sec
31	Career/Sch-to-Work K-12	41	Social Studies Sec	51	Reading K-12
32	Career/Sch-to-Work Elem	42	Science K-12	52	Reading Elem
33	Career/Sch-to-Work Sec	43	Science Elem	53	Reading Sec
34	Early Childhood Ed	44	Science Sec	54	Remedial Reading K-12
35	Health/Phys Education	45	Math K-12	55	Remedial Reading Elem
36	Guidance Services K-12	46	Math Elem	56	Remedial Reading Sec
37	Guidance Services Elem	47	Math Sec	57	Bilingual/ELL
38	Guidance Services Sec	48	English/Lang Arts K-12	58	Special Education K-12

59	Special Education Elem	69	Academic Assessment
60	Special Education Sec	70	Research/Development
61	Foreign/World Lang K-12	71	Public Information
62	Foreign/World Lang Elem	72	Summer School
63	Foreign/World Lang Sec	73	Instructional Tech
64	Religious Education K-12	74	Inservice Training
65	Religious Education Elem	75	Marketing/Distributive
66	Religious Education Sec	76	Info Systems
67	School Board President	77	Psychological Assess
68	Teacher Personnel	78	Affirmative Action

Public Schs..Principal	Grd	Prgm	Enr/#Cls	SN	
Dixie Co High Sch 17924 SE Highway 19, Cross City 32628 Paul Bennett	9-12	AGV	531 45		352/541-6252
James M Anderson Elem Sch 815 SW Highway 351, Cross City 32628 Kristen McCaskill	PK-5	T	542 50	65%	352/541-6251
©Kinder Cub Sch 149 NE 221st Ave, Cross City 32628 Rita Harris	PK-2	T	92	36%	352/498-0002 Fax 352/498-0033
Old Town Elem Sch 221 SE 136th Ave, Old Town 32680 Karen Tillis	PK-5	T	596 30	69%	352/541-6253
Ruth Rains Middle Sch 981 SE Highway 351, Cross City 32628 Christie McElroy	6-8	TV	465 30	58%	352/541-6254

DIXIE PRIVATE SCHOOLS

Private Schs..Principal	Grd	Prgm	Enr/#Cls	SN	
Character Private Sch 16277 SE Highway 19, Cross City 32628 Johnnie Grimes	3-12		10		352/440-1420 Fax 352/498-3044

DUVAL COUNTY

DUVAL PUBLIC SCHOOLS

- **Duval Co Public School Dist** PID: 00188779   904/390-2000
  1701 Prudential Dr, Jacksonville 32207   Fax 904/390-2659

Schools: 193 \ **Teachers:** 7,293 \ **Students:** 129,000 \
Special Ed Students: 18,036 \ **LEP Students:** 6,534 \ **College-Bound:** 80%
\ **Ethnic:** Asian 5%, African American 46%, Hispanic 12%, Caucasian
37% \ **Exp:** $159 (Low) \ **Poverty:** 21% \ **Title I:** $49,081,692 \
Special Education: $108,134,000 \ **Bilingual Education:** $10,280,000 \
Open-Close: 08/12 - 05/29 \ **DTBP:** $193 (High) \ 🇫 🇹

Public Schs..Principal	Grd	Prgm	Enr/#Cls	SN	
Ⓐ Biscayne High Sch © 1680 Dunn Ave Ste 8, Jacksonville 32218 Erica Williams	9-12	T	204	23%	904/252-6311
© Bridgeprep Academy Duval 6400 Atlantic Blvd, Jacksonville 32211 Kharmayne Kannada	K-7		459		904/694-2660
© Duval Charter HS-Baymeadows [133] 7510 Baymeadows Way, Jacksonville 32256 Kimberly Stidham	9-12		531	32%	904/271-4127 Fax 904/446-4101
© Duval Charter Sch at Westside [133] 9238 103rd St, Jacksonville 32210 Tania Woods	K-8	T	988	75%	904/421-0250 Fax 904/423-2601
© Duval Charter Sch Baymeadows [133] 7510 Baymeadows Way, Jacksonville 32256 Kimberly Stidham	K-8		1,356	30%	904/638-7947 Fax 904/446-4101
© Duval Charter Sch Flagler Ctr [133] 12755 Flagler Center Blvd, Jacksonville 32258 Christina Hamlin	K-8		880	6%	904/899-1010 Fax 904/899-1011
© Duval Charter Sch Mandarin [133] 5209 Shad Rd, Jacksonville 32257 Gerald Hulshult	K-8	T	904	35%	904/440-2901 Fax 904/440-2146
© Duval Charter Scholars Academy [133] 100 Scholars Way Ste 100, Jacksonville 32216 **Adam Cross**	K-8	T	583	84%	904/724-1536 Fax 904/721-5381
© Duval Charter School Coastal [133] 12800 Beach Blvd, Jacksonville 32246 Greg Stickel	K-7		887		904/512-6757
© Duval Charter School-Southside [133] 8680 A C Skinner Pkwy, Jacksonville 32256 Ashley Doty	K-8		921	40%	904/423-5348 Fax 904/423-5349
Florida Virtual Academy-Duval 2370-1 3rd St S, Jacksonville 32250 Farica King	K-11		359		904/476-5526
© Global Outreach Charter Acad 9570 Regency Square Blvd, Jacksonville 32225 Liliya Soroka	K-8	T	820	68%	904/551-7104 Fax 904/551-7120
© KIPP Impact Middle Sch [139] 1440 McDuff Ave N, Jacksonville 32254 Brittany Black	5-8	T	280	71%	904/683-6643 Fax 904/683-9895
© KIPP Jacksonville Elem Sch [139] 2525 W 1st St, Jacksonville 32254 Lynneshia Coffee	K-3		380	81%	904/683-0355 Fax 904/634-7856
© KIPP Voice Elem Sch [139] 1440 McDuff Ave N, Jacksonville 32254 Melissa Lane	K-4	T	497	74%	904/683-6643 Fax 904/683-9895 🇫
Ⓐ Lone Star High Sch © 8050 Lone Star Rd Ste 1, Jacksonville 32211 Lashanda Roberts	9-12		266	38%	904/725-5998
Ⓐ Mycroschool Jacksonville CS © 1584 Normandy Village Pkwy, Jacksonville 32221 Rachel Maldonado	9-12		243	17%	904/783-3611 Fax 904/783-3703
Oak Hill Academy 6910 Daughtry Blvd S, Jacksonville 32210 Stephanie Smith	Spec		122	61%	904/573-1030 Fax 904/573-3214
© Rcsa Elem Sch 7450 Beach Blvd, Jacksonville 32216 Michael Steinhardt	K-5	T	506	52%	904/855-8010 Fax 904/727-9245
© Rcsa Middle High Sch 7565 Beach Blvd, Jacksonville 32216 Zafer Sipahioglu	6-12		920		904/855-8010 Fax 904/855-8014
© Rcsa-Innovation Sch 8313 Baycenter Rd, Jacksonville 32256 Mesut Erdogan	K-6		359	46%	904/855-8010 Fax 904/551-0821
© Rcsa-Mandarin 10911 Old Saint Augustine Rd, Jacksonville 32257 Alaaddin Akgul	K-8		846	38%	904/855-8010 Fax 904/800-1475

					School Programs	Social Media
79 Student Personnel	**91** Safety/Security	**275** Response To Intervention	**298** Grant Writer/Ptnrships		**A** = Alternative Program	
80 Driver Ed/Safety	**92** Magnet School	**277** Remedial Math K-12	**750** Chief Innovation Officer		**G** = Adult Classes	🇫 = Facebook
81 Gifted/Talented	**93** Parental Involvement	**280** Literacy Coach	**751** Chief of Staff		**M** = Magnet Program	
82 Video Services	**95** Tech Prep Program	**285** STEM	**752** Social Emotional Learning		**T** = Title I Schoolwide	🇹 = Twitter
83 Substance Abuse Prev	**97** Chief Infomation Officer	**286** Digital Learning			**V** = Career & Tech Ed Programs	
84 Erate	**98** Chief Technology Officer	**288** Common Core Standards	**Other School Types**			
85 AIDS Education	**270** Character Education	**294** Accountability	Ⓐ = Alternative School			
88 Alternative/At Risk	**271** Migrant Education	**295** Network System	© = Charter School		**New Schools are shaded**	
89 Multi-Cultural Curriculum	**273** Teacher Mentor	**296** Title II Programs	Ⓜ = Magnet School		**New Superintendents and Principals are bold**	
90 Social Work	**274** Before/After Sch	**297** Webmaster	Ⓨ = Year-Round School		**Personnel with email addresses are underscored**	

School	Grd	Prgm	Enr/#Cls	SN	Phone
© Sal Tech Charter High Sch 4751 Walgreen Rd, Jacksonville 32209 Michael LaRoche	Voc		246		904/328-5001 Fax 904/768-8618
© San Jose Academy 4072 Sunbeam Rd, Jacksonville 32257 **Michelle Knapp**	6-8		111	57%	904/425-1725
© San Jose Prep High Sch 4072 Sunbeam Rd, Jacksonville 32257 Alan Hall	9-12		223	49%	904/425-1725 Fax 904/683-9101
© School of Success Academy 6974 Wilson Blvd, Jacksonville 32210 Genell Mills	6-8	T	165	80%	904/573-0880 Fax 904/573-0889
© Seacoast Charter Academy 9100 Regency Square Blvd N, Jacksonville 32211 Marla Stremmel	K-5	T	451	8%	904/562-4780 Fax 904/726-0249
© Seaside Charter Sch San Jose 8727 San Jose Blvd, Jacksonville 32217 Rick Pinchot	K-5		168		904/619-3933 Fax 904/683-1362
© Seaside Charter School Beaches 2865 Mayport Rd Lot 1, Atlantic Bch 32233 Barbara Gerdes	K-8		188	2%	904/853-6287 Fax 904/485-8448
© Somerset Acad Eagle ES Campus [130] 8711 Lone Star Rd, Jacksonville 32211 Latatia Ray	K-9	T	115	88%	904/551-3292
© Somerset Acad Eagle MS Campus [130] 1429 Broward Rd, Jacksonville 32218 Olatunji Williams	6-8	T	127		904/503-0661
© Somerset Preparatory Academy 1429 Broward Rd, Jacksonville 32218 Tunji Williams	K-5	T	188	59%	904/503-0661 Fax 904/379-5936
© Tiger Academy 6079 Bagley Rd, Jacksonville 32209 Charles McWhite	K-5	T	239	76%	904/309-6840 Fax 904/309-6867
© Waverly Academy 5710 Wesconnett Blvd, Jacksonville 32244 **Dr Virgina Jewell**	6-8	T	100	77%	904/647-8552 Fax 904/515-5353
© Wayman Academy of the Arts 1176 Labelle St, Jacksonville 32205 Simaran Bakshi	K-5	T	281 13	99%	904/695-9995 Fax 904/693-1127

- **Duval Co PSD-Elementary Region** PID: 12036475 904/348-7866
  4037 Boulevard Center Dr, Jacksonville 32207 Fax 904/348-7889

Sheree Cagle 1

Public Schs..Principal	Grd	Prgm	Enr/#Cls	SN	Phone
Abess Park Elem Sch 12731 Abess Blvd, Jacksonville 32225 Kristin Shore	PK-5	T	650 50	41%	904/220-1260 Fax 904/220-1264
Alimacani Elem Sch 2051 San Pablo Rd S, Jacksonville 32224 Kathy Stalls	PK-5		908	33%	904/221-7101 Fax 904/221-8823
Andrew A Robinson Elem Sch 101 W 12th St, Jacksonville 32206 Latrese Fann	PK-5	T	785 45	82%	904/630-6550 Fax 904/630-6555
Annie R Morgan Elem Sch 964 Saint Clair St, Jacksonville 32254 **Laquitrice Johnson**	K-5	T	360 21	88%	904/381-3970 Fax 904/381-3998
Arlington Elem Sch 1201 University Blvd N, Jacksonville 32211 **Jasmin Gomez**	K-5	T	236 18	79%	904/745-4900 Fax 904/745-4946
Atlantic Beach Elem Sch 298 Sherry Dr, Atlantic Bch 32233 Kimberly Gallagher	PK-5		489 30	31%	904/247-5924 Fax 904/270-1894
Bartram Springs Elem Sch 14799 Bartram Springs Pkwy, Jacksonville 32258 Kim Wright	K-5		974 35	24%	904/260-5860 Fax 904/260-5868

School	Grd	Prgm	Enr/#Cls	SN	Phone
Bayview Elem Sch 3257 Lake Shore Blvd, Jacksonville 32210 **Melissa Metz**	K-5	T	369 30	71%	904/381-3920 Fax 904/381-3919
Beauclerc Elem Sch 4555 Craven Rd W, Jacksonville 32257 **A Matt Walker**	K-5	GT	774 56	49%	904/739-5226 Fax 904/739-5317
Biscayne Elem Sch 12230 Biscayne Blvd, Jacksonville 32218 Sanaa McBride	PK-5	T	694 32	64%	904/714-4650 Fax 904/714-4655
Brookview Elem Sch 10450 Theresa Dr, Jacksonville 32246 Katie O'Connell	K-5	T	534 42	62%	904/565-2720 Fax 904/565-2734
Central Riverside Elem Sch 2555 Gilmore St, Jacksonville 32204 Dinah Stewart	K-5	T	342 18	54%	904/381-7495 Fax 904/381-7423
Chaffee Trail Elem Sch 11400 Sam Caruso Way, Jacksonville 32221 Casie Doyle	K-5	T	736	48%	904/693-7510 Fax 904/693-7932
Chets Creek Elem Sch 13200 Chets Creek Blvd, Jacksonville 32224 Susan Phillips	K-5		1,280 40	35%	904/992-6390 Fax 904/992-6398
Chimney Lakes Elem Sch 9353 Staples Mill Dr, Jacksonville 32244 **Bill Gilley**	K-5	T	1,038 67	49%	904/573-1100 Fax 904/573-1109
Crown Point Elem Sch 3800 Crown Point Rd, Jacksonville 32257 Brett Hartley	PK-5	GT	842 48	48%	904/260-5808 Fax 904/260-5839
Crystal Springs Elem Sch 1200 Hammond Blvd, Jacksonville 32221 **Todd Simpson**	PK-5	T	1,044 55	61%	904/693-7645 Fax 904/693-7658
Dinsmore Elem Sch 7126 Civic Club Dr, Jacksonville 32219 Wanda Reese	PK-5	T	542 25	52%	904/924-3126 Fax 904/924-3142
Don Brewer Elem Sch 3385 Hartsfield Rd, Jacksonville 32277 Jennifer Gray	3-5	T	504 40	47%	904/745-4990 Fax 904/745-4986
Englewood Elem Sch 4359 Spring Park Rd, Jacksonville 32207 Dino Mullin	K-5	T	480 29	68%	904/739-5280 Fax 904/739-5316
Enterprise Learning Academy 8085 Old Middleburg Rd S, Jacksonville 32222 **Jeffrey Collins**	PK-5	T	823	53%	904/573-3260 Fax 904/573-3270
Fishweir Elem Sch 3977 Herschel St, Jacksonville 32205 Kimberey Dennis	K-5	T	438 20	43%	904/381-3910 Fax 904/381-3916
Ft Caroline Elem Sch 3925 Athore Dr, Jacksonville 32277 Violet Stovall	PK-5	T	547 36	79%	904/745-4904 Fax 904/745-4945
Garden City Elem Sch 2814 Dunn Ave, Jacksonville 32218 Mychelle Grover	PK-5	T	430 25	63%	904/924-3130 Fax 904/924-3178
Grasp Academy 3101 Justina Rd, Jacksonville 32277 **Annessia Powell**	2-7		250 26	42%	904/745-4909 Fax 904/745-4947
Greenfield Elem Sch 6343 Knights Ln N, Jacksonville 32216 **Tangia Anderson**	PK-5	T	613 30	59%	904/739-5249 Fax 904/739-5299
Greenland Pines Elem Sch 5050 Greenland Rd, Jacksonville 32258 **Beverly Walker**	PK-5		765 35	33%	904/260-5450 Fax 904/260-5455
Hendricks Avenue Elem Sch 3400 Hendricks Ave, Jacksonville 32207 Mindy McLendon	K-5		649 29	33%	904/346-5610 Fax 904/346-5616
Henry F Kite Elem Sch 9430 Lem Turner Rd, Jacksonville 32208 Biannca Hill	K-5	T	228 18	70%	904/924-3031 Fax 904/924-3473

1	Superintendent	8	Curric/Instruct K-12	19	Chief Financial Officer	29	Family/Consumer Science	39	Social Studies K-12	49	English/Lang Arts Elem	59	Special Education Elem	69	Academic Assessment
2	Bus/Finance/Purchasing	9	Curric/Instruct Elem	20	Art K-12	30	Adult Education	40	Social Studies Elem	50	English/Lang Arts Sec	60	Special Education Sec	70	Research/Development
3	Buildings And Grounds	10	Curric/Instruct Sec	21	Art Elem	31	Career/Sch-to-Work K-12	41	Social Studies Sec	51	Reading K-12	61	Foreign/World Lang K-12	71	Public Information
4	Food Service	11	Federal Program	22	Art Sec	32	Career/Sch-to-Work Elem	42	Science K-12	52	Reading Elem	62	Foreign/World Lang Elem	72	Summer School
5	Transportation	12	Title I	23	Music K-12	33	Career/Sch-to-Work Sec	43	Science Elem	53	Reading Sec	63	Foreign/World Lang Sec	73	Instructional Tech
6	Athletic	13	Title V	24	Music Elem	34	Early Childhood Ed	44	Science Sec	54	Remedial Reading K-12	64	Religious Education K-12	74	Inservice Training
7	Health Services	15	Asst Superintendent	25	Music Sec	35	Health/Phys Education	45	Math K-12	55	Remedial Reading Elem	65	Religious Education Elem	75	Marketing/Distributive
		16	Instructional Media Svcs	26	Business Education	36	Guidance Services K-12	46	Math Elem	56	Remedial Reading Sec	66	Religious Education Sec	76	Info Systems
		17	Chief Operations Officer	27	Career & Tech Ed	37	Guidance Services Elem	47	Math Sec	57	Bilingual/ELL	67	School Board President	77	Psychological Assess
		18	Chief Academic Officer	28	Technology Education	38	Guidance Services Sec	48	English/Lang Arts K-12	58	Special Education K-12	68	Teacher Personnel	78	Affirmative Action

School	Address	Principal (email underscored)	Grades	Prog	Enroll	Staff	%	Phone	Fax	Social
Hogan-Spring Glen Elem Sch	6736 Beach Blvd, Jacksonville 32216	Charlene James	PK-5	T	363	21	67%	904/720-1640	904/720-1706	FB, Twitter
Holiday Hill Elem Sch	6900 Altama Rd, Jacksonville 32216	Matthew Peterson	K-5	T	565	30	46%	904/720-1676	904/720-1731	
J Allen Axson Elem Sch	4763 Sutton Park Ct, Jacksonville 32224	Vanhoy Robinson	PK-5		590	27	14%	904/992-3600	904/992-3605	
Jacksonville Beach Elem Sch	315 10th St S, Jax Bch 32250	Cameron Mattingly	K-5		591	29	7%	904/247-5942	904/270-1825	
Jacksonville Hts Elem Sch	7750 Tempest St S, Jacksonville 32244	Andrea Williams-Scott	K-5	GT	718	35	79%	904/573-1120	904/573-1043	
John E Ford Elem Sch	1137 Cleveland St, Jacksonville 32209	Tina Bennett	PK-8	T	674	45	61%	904/630-6540	904/630-6548	
John NC Stockton ES	4827 Carlisle Rd, Jacksonville 32210	Stephanie Brannan	K-5		463	24	24%	904/381-3955	904/381-7408	
Joseph Finegan Elem Sch	555 Wonderwood Dr, Atlantic Bch 32233	**Lindsey Connor**	PK-5	T	392	30	39%	904/247-5996	904/270-1858	
Kernan Trail Elem Sch	2281 Kernan Blvd S, Jacksonville 32246	Suzanne Shall	K-5	T	713	29	45%	904/220-1310	904/220-1315	FB
Kings Trail Elem Sch	7401 Old Kings Rd S, Jacksonville 32217	Sanethette Shubert	K-5	T	412	28	69%	904/739-5254	904/739-5326	
Lake Lucina Elem Sch	6527 Merrill Rd, Jacksonville 32277	Michelle Walsh	PK-5	T	348	24	68%	904/745-4916	904/745-4917	
Lone Star Elem Sch	10400 Lone Star Rd, Jacksonville 32225	Gaston Quarles	K-5	T	489	39	55%	904/565-2711	904/565-2733	FB, Twitter
Loretto Elem Sch	3900 Loretto Rd, Jacksonville 32223	Kristie Kemp	K-5	G	998	52	30%	904/260-5800	904/260-5835	
Louis Sheffield Elem Sch	13333 Lanier Rd, Jacksonville 32226	Cassandra Delay	K-5	T	752	26	43%	904/696-8758	904/696-8791	
Love Grove Elem Sch	2446 University Blvd S, Jacksonville 32216	Wright Emanuel	PK-5	T	381	50	72%	904/720-1645	904/720-1742	
Mamie Agnes Jones Elem Sch	700 Orange Ave, Baldwin 32234	Marianne Lee	PK-5	T	348	22	58%	904/266-1214	904/266-1222	
Mandarin Oaks Elem Sch	10600 Hornets Nest Rd, Jacksonville 32257	Leigh Butterfield	K-5	GT	1,006	53	42%	904/260-5820	904/260-5846	
Mayport Elem Sch	2753 Shangri La Dr, Atlantic Bch 32233	Amy Novak	PK-5	T	547	42	52%	904/247-5988	904/247-5990	
Merrill Road Elem Sch	8239 Merrill Rd, Jacksonville 32277	Peggy Heybruch	PK-2	T	643	28	55%	904/745-4919	904/745-4943	
Neptune Beach Elem Sch	1515 Florida Blvd, Neptune Beach 32266	Elizabeth Kavanagh	PK-5	GT	830	40	43%	904/247-5954	904/247-5969	FB, Twitter
New Berlin Elem Sch	3613 New Berlin Rd, Jacksonville 32226	Crystal Lewis	K-5		1,178		37%	904/714-4601	904/714-4610	
North Shore Elem Sch	5701 Silver Plz, Jacksonville 32208	Felicia Hardaway	PK-5	T	656	26	87%	904/924-3081	904/924-3191	
Oceanway Elem Sch	12555 Gillespie Ave, Jacksonville 32218	Michelle Hinkley	PK-5	T	627	34	60%	904/696-8762	904/696-8788	
Ortega Elem Sch	4010 Baltic St, Jacksonville 32210	Shannon Rose	K-5	T	315	18	57%	904/381-7460	904/381-7484	
Parkwood Heights Elem Sch	1709 Lansdowne Dr, Jacksonville 32211	Ashton Price	K-5	T	348	35	70%	904/720-1670	904/720-1674	
Pickett Elem Sch	6305 Old Kings Rd, Jacksonville 32254	Carlene Smith	PK-6	T	227	17	81%	904/693-7555	904/693-7558	
Pine Estates Elem Sch	10741 Pine Estates Rd E, Jacksonville 32218	Michelle Quarles	PK-5	T	299	20	76%	904/696-8767	904/696-8745	
Pine Forest School of the Arts	3929 Grant Rd, Jacksonville 32207	Michelle Matthews	K-5	GT	449	23	43%	904/346-5600	904/346-5632	
Pinedale Elem Sch	4228 Dignan St, Jacksonville 32254	Alicia Hinson	PK-5	T	493		81%	904/381-7490	904/381-7466	
R V Daniels Elem Sch	1951 W 15th St, Jacksonville 32209	Lashawn Caldwell	K-5	T	330	18	48%	904/630-6872	904/630-6875	
Reynolds Lane Elem Sch	840 Reynolds Ln, Jacksonville 32254	Kenya Griffin	PK-5	T	327	22	76%	904/381-3960	904/381-3964	
Richard Brown Gifted Talented	1535 Milnor St, Jacksonville 32206	**Kristi Kincaid**	K-5		324	36	77%	904/630-6570	904/630-6576	
Ruth N Upson Elem Sch	1090 Dancy St, Jacksonville 32205	Yvonne Spinner	PK-5	T	433	20	67%	904/381-7485	904/381-3976	FB
Sabal Palm Elem Sch	1201 Kernan Blvd N, Jacksonville 32225	Linda Graham	PK-5		962	60	40%	904/221-7169	904/221-8811	FB, Twitter
Sadie Tillis Elem Sch	6084 Morse Ave, Jacksonville 32244	**Helen Dunbar**	K-5	T	486	28	72%	904/573-1090	904/573-1169	
Samuel A Hull Elem Sch	7528 Hull St, Jacksonville 32219	Rashard Willis	PK-5	T	283	20	74%	904/924-3136	904/924-3139	
San Jose Elem Sch	5805 Saint Augustine Rd, Jacksonville 32207	Paula Smith	PK-5	T	786	48	76%	904/739-5260	904/739-5327	
San Mateo Elem Sch	600 Baisden Rd, Jacksonville 32218	Caroline Wells	K-5	GT	617	26	44%	904/696-8750	904/696-8748	
San Pablo Elem Sch	801 18th Ave N, Jax Bch 32250	Stephanie Manabat	K-5		471	24	36%	904/247-5947	904/270-1860	
Seabreeze Elem Sch	1400 Seabreeze Ave, Jax Bch 32250	Aimee Kimball	K-5		568	30	38%	904/247-5900	904/270-1850	
Southside Estates Elem Sch	9775 Ivey Rd, Jacksonville 32246	Brown Dowdell	PK-5	T	514	42	63%	904/565-2706	904/565-2737	
Spring Park Elem Sch	2250 Spring Park Rd, Jacksonville 32207	Davina Parker	PK-5	T	449	30	74%	904/346-5640	904/346-5646	
Thomas Jefferson Elem Sch	8233 Nevada St, Jacksonville 32220	Lori Turner	K-5	T	498	27	48%	904/693-7500	904/693-7507	FB, Twitter
Timucuan Elem Sch	5429 110th St, Jacksonville 32244	**Kimberly Brown**	PK-5	T	591	32	76%	904/573-1130	904/573-1136	

79 Student Personnel	91 Safety/Security	275 Response To Intervention	298 Grant Writer/Ptnrships	**School Programs**	**Social Media**
80 Driver Ed/Safety	92 Magnet School	277 Remedial Math K-12	750 Chief Innovation Officer	A = Alternative Program	
81 Gifted/Talented	93 Parental Involvement	280 Literacy Coach	751 Chief of Staff	G = Adult Classes	= Facebook
82 Video Services	95 Tech Prep Program	285 STEM	752 Social Emotional Learning	M = Magnet Program	= Twitter
83 Substance Abuse Prev	97 Chief Information Officer	286 Digital Learning		T = Title I Schoolwide	
84 Erate	98 Chief Technology Officer	288 Common Core Standards	**Other School Types**	V = Career & Tech Ed Programs	
85 AIDS Education	270 Character Education	294 Accountability	Ⓐ = Alternative School		
88 Alternative/At Risk	271 Migrant Education	295 Network System	Ⓒ = Charter School	**New Schools are shaded**	
89 Multi-Cultural Curriculum	273 Teacher Mentor	296 Title II Programs	Ⓜ = Magnet School	**New Superintendents and Principals are bold**	
90 Social Work	274 Before/After Sch	297 Webmaster	Ⓨ = Year-Round School	Personnel with email addresses are underscored	

Ⓜ Twin Lakes Academy Elem Sch | PK-5 | T | 880 | 44% 904/538-0238
8000 Point Meadows Dr, Jacksonville 32256 | | | | Fax 904/538-0241
Deneisetres Robertson

Venetia Elem Sch | K-5 | T | 440 | 50% 904/381-3990
4300 Timuquana Rd, Jacksonville 32210 | | | 23 | Fax 904/381-7451
Monique Chatman

Waterleaf Elem Sch | PK-5 | T | 747 | 43% 904/565-8000
450 Kernan Blvd N, Jacksonville 32225 | | | | Fax 904/565-8027
Hewitt Brady

West Riverside Elem Sch | PK-5 | T | 312 | 54% 904/381-3900
2801 Herschel St, Jacksonville 32205 | | | 25 | Fax 904/381-3905
Shawna White

Whitehouse Elem Sch | PK-5 | T | 491 | 57% 904/693-7542
11160 General Ave, Jacksonville 32220 | | | 28 | Fax 904/693-7544
Angela Jordan-Long

Woodland Acres Elem Sch | PK-5 | T | 633 | 83% 904/720-1663
328 Bowlan St N, Jacksonville 32211 | | | 48 | Fax 904/720-1730
Tiffany Green

• Duval Co PSD-HS Alt Region PID: 12036516   904/348-7866
4037 Boulevard Center Dr, Jacksonville 32207

Corey Wright 1

Public Schs..Principal	Grd	Prgm	Enr/#Cls	SN

A Philip Randolph Career Acad | Voc | T | 366 | 73% 904/924-3011
1157 Golfair Blvd, Jacksonville 32209 | | | | Fax 904/924-3125
Cathy Barnes

Alden Road Excptnl Student Ctr | Spec | TV | 174 | 48% 904/565-2722
11780 Alden Rd, Jacksonville 32246 | | | 30 | Fax 904/565-2725
Joseph Blitch

Andrew Jackson High Sch | 9-12 | GTV | 659 | 78% 904/630-6950
3816 N Main St, Jacksonville 32206 | | | 60 | Fax 904/630-6955
Tracolya Clinch

© Atlantic Coast High Sch | 9-12 | | 2,269 | 29% 904/538-5120
9735 R G Skinner Pkwy, Jacksonville 32256 | | | | Fax 904/538-5159
Zeina Spaulding

Baldwin Middle Senior High Sch | 6-12 | TV | 1,241 | 45% 904/266-1200
291 Mill St W, Baldwin 32234 | | | 40 | Fax 904/266-1220
Denise Hall

Ⓐ Bridge to Success Acad HS | 9-12 | | 50 | 904/924-3470
1157 Golfair Blvd, Jacksonville 32209
Vincent Foster

Ⓜ Darnell-Cookman Middle Sch | 6-12 | T | 1,117 | 42% 904/630-6805
1701 N Davis St, Jacksonville 32209 | | | 50 | Fax 904/630-6811
Tyrus Lyles

Ⓜ Douglas Anderson Sch of Arts | 9-12 | | 1,192 | 21% 904/346-5620
2445 San Diego Rd, Jacksonville 32207 | | | 64 | Fax 904/346-5636
Melanie Hammer

Duncan U Fletcher High Sch | 9-12 | GV | 2,146 | 27% 904/247-5905
700 Seagate Ave, Neptune Beach 32266 | | | 88 | Fax 904/247-5920
James Ledford

Duval Virtual Instruction Acad | K-12 | | 260 | 32% 904/390-2037
1701 Prudential Dr, Jacksonville 32207 | | | | Fax 904/390-2075
Mark Ertel

Edward H White High Sch | 9-12 | GTV | 1,463 | 56% 904/693-7620
1700 Old Middleburg Rd N, Jacksonville 32210 | | | 110 | Fax 904/693-7639
Traci Battest

Englewood High Sch | 9-12 | GTV | 1,851 | 51% 904/739-5212
4412 Barnes Rd, Jacksonville 32207 | | | | Fax 904/739-5324
Sara Bravo

First Coast High Sch | 9-12 | GTV | 2,077 | 49% 904/757-0080
590 Duval Station Rd, Jacksonville 32218 | | | 100 | Fax 904/696-8721
Justin Fluent

Frank Peterson Academy of Tech | Voc | AT | 1,219 | 42% 904/573-1150
7450 Wilson Blvd, Jacksonville 32210 | | | | Fax 904/573-3206
Jessica Mastromatto

Ⓐ Grand Park Career Center | 6-12 | T | 94 | 80% 904/630-6894
2335 W 18th St, Jacksonville 32209 | | | 13 | Fax 904/630-6898
Tyrone Blue

Jean Ribault High Sch | 9-12 | GTV | 1,383 | 65% 904/924-3092
3701 Winton Dr, Jacksonville 32208 | | | 85 | Fax 904/924-3154
Gregory Bostic

Mandarin High Sch | 9-12 | GV | 2,522 | 27% 904/260-3911
4831 Greenland Rd, Jacksonville 32258 | | | 100 | Fax 904/260-5439
John Kniseley

Marine Science Education Ctr | 12-12 | AV | 38 | 16% 904/247-5973
1347 Palmer St, Mayport 32233 | | | 12 | Fax 904/247-5976
Dean Ledford

Ⓐ Mattie Rutherford Alt Ed Ctr | 6-8 | T | 63 | 84% 904/630-6782
1514 Hubbard St, Jacksonville 32206 | | | 15 | Fax 904/630-6789
Maurice Nesmith

Mt Herman Excptnl Student Ctr | Spec | T | 150 | 45% 904/630-6740
1741 Francis St, Jacksonville 32209 | | | 24 | Fax 904/630-6738
Tina Wilson

Ⓐ Pace Ctr for Girls-Jacksonvlle | 6-12 | | 61 | 25% 904/448-8002
2933 University Blvd N, Jacksonville 32211 | | | | Fax 904/448-2808
Kimberly Reed

Palm Ave Excptnl Student Ctr | Spec | T | 145 | 41% 904/693-7516
1301 W Palm Ave, Jacksonville 32254 | | | 14 | Fax 904/693-7521
Michael Alexander

Ⓜ Paxon School-Advanced Studies | 9-12 | G | 1,474 | 26% 904/693-7583
3239 Norman E Thagard Blvd, Jacksonville 32254 | | | 48 | Fax 904/693-7597
Royce Turner

Robert E Lee High Sch | 9-12 | GTV | 1,723 | 53% 904/381-3930
1200 McDuff Ave S, Jacksonville 32205 | | | 76 | Fax 904/381-3945
Timothy Feagins

Samuel W Wolfson High Sch | 9-12 | GTV | 721 | 56% 904/739-5265
7000 Powers Ave, Jacksonville 32217 | | | | Fax 904/739-5272
Christopher Begley

Sandalwood High Sch | 9-12 | GV | 2,910 | 40% 904/646-5100
2750 John Prom Blvd, Jacksonville 32246 | | | | Fax 904/646-5126
Saryn Hatcher

Ⓜ Stanton College Prep Sch | 9-12 | GV | 1,598 | 15% 904/630-6760
1149 W 13th St, Jacksonville 32209 | | | 66 | Fax 904/630-6758
Nongongoma Majova-Seane

Terry Parker High Sch | 9-12 | GTV | 1,610 | 55% 904/720-1650
7301 Parker School Rd, Jacksonville 32211 | | | 70 | Fax 904/720-1700
Megan Pardue

Westside High Sch | 9-12 | GTV | 1,579 | 60% 904/573-1170
5530 Firestone Rd, Jacksonville 32244 | | | 70 | Fax 904/573-1177
J Rebecca Raulerson

William M Raines High Sch | 9-12 | GTV | 1,329 | 71% 904/924-3049
3663 Raines Ave, Jacksonville 32209 | | | 60 | Fax 904/924-3058
Vincent Hall

• Duval Co PSD-Middle Schools PID: 12036504
4037 Boulevard Center Dr, Jacksonville 32207   Fax 904/348-7773

Michael Henry 1

Public Schs..Principal	Grd	Prgm	Enr/#Cls	SN

Alfred I DuPont Middle Sch | 6-8 | GTV | 880 | 64% 904/739-5200
2710 Dupont Ave, Jacksonville 32217 | | | 60 | Fax 904/739-5321
Marilyn Barnwell

Duncan U Fletcher Middle Sch | 6-8 | V | 1,324 | 34% 904/247-5929
2000 3rd St N, Jax Bch 32250 | | | 80 | Fax 904/247-5940
Chelsea Matthews

Ft Caroline Middle Sch | 6-8 | GTV | 754 | 61% 904/745-4927
3787 University Club Blvd, Jacksonville 32277 | | | 65 | Fax 904/745-4937
Chelvert Wellington

J E B Stuart Middle Sch | 6-8 | GTV | 692 | 70% 904/573-1000
4815 Wesconnett Blvd, Jacksonville 32210 | | | 55 | Fax 904/573-3213
Smith Milliner

1	Superintendent	8	Curric/Instruct K-12	19	Chief Financial Officer	29	Family/Consumer Science	39	Social Studies K-12	49	English/Lang Arts Elem	59	Special Education Elem	69	Academic Assessment
2	Bus/Finance/Purchasing	9	Curric/Instruct Elem	20	Art K-12	30	Adult Education	40	Social Studies Elem	50	English/Lang Arts Sec	60	Special Education Sec	70	Research/Development
3	Buildings And Grounds	10	Curric/Instruct Sec	21	Art Elem	31	Career/Sch-to-Work K-12	41	Social Studies Sec	51	Reading K-12	61	Foreign/World Lang K-12	71	Public Information
4	Food Service	11	Federal Program	22	Art Sec	32	Career/Sch-to-Work Elem	42	Science K-12	52	Reading Elem	62	Foreign/World Lang Elem	72	Summer School
5	Transportation	12	Title I	23	Music K-12	33	Career/Sch-to-Work Sec	43	Science Elem	53	Reading Sec	63	Foreign/World Lang Sec	73	Instructional Tech
6	Athletic	13	Title V	24	Music Elem	34	Early Childhood Ed	44	Science Sec	54	Remedial Reading K-12	64	Religious Education K-12	74	Inservice Training
7	Health Services	14	Asst Superintendent	25	Music Sec	35	Health/Phys Education	45	Math K-12	55	Remedial Reading Elem	65	Religious Education Elem	75	Marketing/Distributive
		15	Asst Superintendent	26	Business Education	36	Guidance Services K-12	46	Math Elem	56	Remedial Reading Sec	66	Religious Education Sec	76	Info Systems
		16	Instructional Media Svcs	27	Career & Tech Ed	37	Guidance Services Elem	47	Math Sec	57	Bilingual/ELL	67	School Board President	77	Psychological Assess
		18	Chief Academic Officer	28	Technology Education	38	Guidance Services Sec	48	English/Lang Arts K-12	58	Special Education K-12	68	Teacher Personnel	78	Affirmative Action

School / Address / Principal	Grd	Prgm	Enr/#Cls	SN	Phone / Fax
Ⓜ James W Johnson Prep Mid Sch 3276 Norman E Thagard Blvd, Jacksonville 32254 Tamara Feagins	6-8	V	969 70	24%	904/693-7600 Fax 904/693-7661
Jefferson Davis Middle Sch 7050 Melvin Rd, Jacksonville 32210 Andrea Talley	6-8	TV	1,000 90	73%	904/573-1060 Fax 904/573-1066
Joseph Stilwell Middle Sch 7840 Burma Rd, Jacksonville 32221 Tamara Tuschhoff	6-8	GTV	801 60	61%	904/693-7523 Fax 904/693-7539
Julia Landon College Prep 1819 Thacker Ave, Jacksonville 32207 Timothy Feagins	6-8	GV	762 40	20%	904/346-5650 Fax 904/346-5657
Kernan Middle Sch 2271 Kernan Blvd S, Jacksonville 32246 Julie Hemphill	6-8	T	1,164	45%	904/220-1350 Fax 904/220-1355
Ⓜ Kirby-Smith Middle Sch 2034 Hubbard St, Jacksonville 32206 Deshune Bush	6-8	TV	833 44	47%	904/630-6600 Fax 904/630-6605
Lake Shore Middle Sch 2519 Bayview Rd, Jacksonville 32210 Jennifer Bridwell	6-8	TV	981 75	69%	904/381-7440 Fax 904/381-7437
Landmark Middle Sch 101 Kernan Blvd N, Jacksonville 32225 Cicely Tyson-White	6-8	GTV	1,430	46%	904/221-7125 Fax 904/221-8847
Ⓜ Lavilla School of Arts 501 N Davis St, Jacksonville 32202 Lianna Knight	6-8		1,028 44	34%	904/633-6069 Fax 904/633-8089
Mandarin Middle Sch 5100 Hood Rd, Jacksonville 32257 Moses Williams	6-8	GTV	1,418 90	42%	904/292-0555 Fax 904/260-5415
Mayport Middle Sch 2600 Mayport Rd, Atlantic Bch 32233 Chris Koek	6-8	GTV	814 55	49%	904/247-5977 Fax 904/247-5987
Oceanway Middle Sch 143 Oceanway Ave, Jacksonville 32218 Emily Kristansen	6-8	T	958	50%	904/714-4680 Fax 904/714-4685
Southside Middle Sch 2948 Knights Ln E, Jacksonville 32216 Jennifer Crady	6-8	GTV	871 80	68%	904/739-5238 Fax 904/739-5244
Ⓜ Twin Lakes Academy Middle Sch 8050 Point Meadows Dr, Jacksonville 32256 Aurelia Williams	6-8	T	1,152	49%	904/538-0825 Fax 904/538-0840
Westview Sch 5270 Connie Jean Rd, Jacksonville 32210 Amand St	PK-8	T	1,274	58%	904/573-1082 Fax 904/573-1087
Young Mens Womens Ldrshp Acad 900 Acorn St, Jacksonville 32209 Truitte Moreland	6-8	T	510	80%	904/630-6900 Fax 904/630-6913

● **Duval Co PSD-Turnaround School**   PID: 12232679   904/924-3722
4037 Boulevard Center Dr, Jacksonville 32207

Public Schs..Principal	Grd	Prgm	Enr/#Cls	SN	
Arlington Heights Elem Sch 1520 Sprinkle Dr, Jacksonville 32211 Vondeira Scott	PK-5	T	328 23	77%	904/745-4923 Fax 904/745-4944
Arlington Middle Sch 8141 Lone Star Rd, Jacksonville 32211 Evan Daniels	6-8	GTV	740 52	73%	904/720-1680 Fax 904/720-1702
Biltmore Elem Sch 2101 W Palm Ave, Jacksonville 32254 Sabrina Session-Jones	PK-5	T	300 27	78%	904/693-7969 Fax 904/693-7574
Brentwood Elem Sch 3750 Springfield Blvd, Jacksonville 32206 Jacqueline Jones	PK-5	T	329 21	87%	904/630-6630 Fax 904/630-6638
Ⓐ Bridge to Success Acad MS 2115 Commonwealth Ave, Jacksonville 32209 Aleya Prier	4-8		80		904/630-6592
Carter G Woodson Elem Sch 2334 Butler Ave, Jacksonville 32209 Brandon Clayton	PK-5	T	453 35	88%	904/924-3004 Fax 904/924-3442
Cedar Hills Elem Sch 6534 Ish Brant Rd, Jacksonville 32210 Marva McKinney	K-5	T	543 19	78%	904/573-1050 Fax 904/573-1051
George W Carver Elem Sch 2854 W 45th St, Jacksonville 32209 La'Tatia Ray	PK-5	T	352 21	91%	904/924-3122 Fax 904/924-3280
Gregory Drive Elem Sch 7800 Gregory Dr, Jacksonville 32210 Augena Sapp	K-5	T	557 35	73%	904/573-1190 Fax 904/573-3218
Highlands Elem Sch 1000 DePaul Dr, Jacksonville 32218 **Tavianna Sanders**	PK-5	T	453 26	73%	904/696-8754 Fax 904/696-8787 f t
Highlands Middle Sch 10913 Pine Estates Rd E, Jacksonville 32218 **Kenyannya Wilcox**	6-8	AGTV	906 76	70%	904/696-8771 Fax 904/696-8782 f t
Hyde Grove Elem Sch 2056 Lane Ave S, Jacksonville 32210 **Erica Little**	PK-2	T	594 32	81%	904/693-7562 Fax 904/693-7565 f
Hyde Park Elem Sch 5300 Park St, Jacksonville 32205 Shirley Winfrey	3-5	T	283 24	77%	904/381-3950 Fax 904/381-3954
Jean Ribault Middle Sch 3610 Ribault Scenic Dr, Jacksonville 32208 Ronnie Williams	6-8	TV	777 52	75%	904/924-3062 Fax 904/924-3167
John Love Elem Sch 1531 Winthrop St, Jacksonville 32206 Sylvia Embry	PK-2	T	198 15	87%	904/630-6790 Fax 904/630-6793
Long Branch Elem Sch 3723 Franklin St, Jacksonville 32206 Dr Wayman Graham	3-5	GT	166 18	90%	904/630-6620 Fax 904/630-6639
Martin Luther King Fame Acad 8801 Lake Placid Dr E, Jacksonville 32208 Cindy Gentry	PK-5	T	434 30	79%	904/924-3027 Fax 904/766-9031
Matthew Gilbert Middle Sch 1424 Franklin St, Jacksonville 32206 Jamelle Goodwin	6-8	GTV	402 48	84%	904/630-6700 Fax 904/630-6713
Normandy Village Elem Sch 8257 Herlong Rd, Jacksonville 32210 **Jessica Guthrie**	PK-5	T	526 31	77%	904/693-7548 Fax 904/693-7553 f t
Northwestern Middle Sch 2100 W 45th St, Jacksonville 32209 Anna Dewese	6-8	TV	596 56	88%	904/924-3100 Fax 904/924-3284
Ramona Boulevard Elem Sch 5540 Ramona Blvd, Jacksonville 32205 **Devonne Lampkin**	K-5	T	379 30	85%	904/693-7576 Fax 904/693-7582 f t
Rufus E Payne Elem Sch 6725 Hema Rd, Jacksonville 32209 Weisha Day-Killette	PK-5	T	283 34	87%	904/924-3020 Fax 904/924-3181
Rutledge H Pearson Elem Sch 4346 Roanoke Blvd, Jacksonville 32208 Carolyn Davis	PK-5	T	276 27	83%	904/924-3077 Fax 904/924-3160
S P Livingston Elem Sch 1128 Barber St, Jacksonville 32209 Robert Gresham	K-5	T	445 40	83%	904/630-6580 Fax 904/630-6587
Sallye B Mathis Elem Sch 3501 Winton Dr, Jacksonville 32208 Kathleen Adkins	PK-5	T	416 22	82%	904/924-3086 Fax 904/924-3193
St Clair Evans Academy 5443 Moncrief Rd, Jacksonville 32209 Lawanda Polydore	PK-5	T	398 30	88%	904/924-3035 Fax 904/924-3037

79	Student Personnel	91	Safety/Security	275	Response To Intervention	298	Grant Writer/Ptnrships
80	Driver Ed/Safety	92	Magnet School	277	Remedial Math K-12	750	Chief Innovation Officer
81	Gifted/Talented	93	Parental Involvement	280	Literacy Coach	751	Chief of Staff
82	Video Services	95	Tech Prep Program	285	STEM	752	Social Emotional Learning
83	Substance Abuse Prev	97	Chief Infomation Officer	286	Digital Learning		
84	Erate	98	Chief Technology Officer	288	Common Core Standards		**Other School Types**
85	AIDS Education	270	Character Education	294	Accountability		Ⓐ = Alternative School
88	Alternative/At Risk	271	Migrant Education	295	Network System		Ⓒ = Charter School
89	Multi-Cultural Curriculum	273	Teacher Mentor	296	Title II Programs		Ⓜ = Magnet School
90	Social Work	274	Before/After Sch	297	Webmaster		Ⓨ = Year-Round School

School Programs
A = Alternative Program
G = Adult Classes
M = Magnet Program
T = Title I Schoolwide
V = Career & Tech Ed Programs

Social Media
f = Facebook
t = Twitter

New Schools are shaded
New Superintendents and Principals are bold
Personnel with email addresses are underscored

FL—33

Stonewall Jackson Elem Sch 6127 Cedar Hills Blvd, Jacksonville 32210 Shawn Platts	K-5	T	301 14	80%	904/573-1020 Fax 904/573-1059 f t
Susie E Tolbert Elem Sch 1925 W 13th St, Jacksonville 32209 Shana Adams	3-5	T	375 29	86%	904/630-6860 Fax 904/630-6868 f t
Windy Hill Elem Sch 3831 Forest Blvd, Jacksonville 32246 Calvin Reddick	PK-5	T	527 35	74%	904/565-2700 Fax 904/565-2702

DUVAL CATHOLIC SCHOOLS

- **Diocese St Augustine Ed Office** PID: 00202533   904/262-3200
  11625 Old Saint Augustine Rd, Jacksonville 32258   Fax 904/596-1042

Schools: 29 \ **Students:** 10,603 \ **Open-Close:** 08/10 - 06/01

Listing includes only schools located in this county. See District Index for location of Diocesan Offices.

Deacon Scott Conway 1   Rhonda Rose 8,15
Erin McGeever 30,64

Catholic Schs..Principal	Grd	Prgm	Enr/#Cls	SN
Assumption Catholic Sch 2431 Atlantic Blvd, Jacksonville 32207 Maryann Jimenez	K-8		526 24	904/398-1774 Fax 904/398-6712
Bishop John J Snyder High Sch 5001 Samaritan Way, Jacksonville 32210 David Yazdiya	9-12		490 30	904/771-1029 Fax 904/908-8988
Bishop Kenny High Sch 1055 Kingman Ave, Jacksonville 32207 Todd Orlando	9-12		1,200 69	904/398-7545 Fax 904/398-5728 f t
Blessed Trinity Catholic Sch 10472 Beach Blvd, Jacksonville 32246 Marie Davis	PK-8		70	904/641-6458 Fax 904/645-3762
Christ the King Catholic Sch 6822 Larkin Rd, Jacksonville 32211 Stephanie Engelhardt	PK-8		270 22	904/724-2954 Fax 904/724-8004
Guardian Catholic Sch 4920 Brentwood Ave, Jacksonville 32206 Sr Cynthia Shaffer	PK-8		414 11	904/765-6522 Fax 904/765-9486
Holy Family Catholic Sch 9800-3 Baymeadows Rd, Jacksonville 32256 Matt Moloney	PK-8		250 20	904/645-9875 Fax 904/899-6060
Holy Spirit Catholic Sch 11665 Fort Caroline Rd, Jacksonville 32225 Dr John Luciano	PK-8		255 11	904/642-9165 Fax 904/642-1047
Morning Star Sch 725 Mickler Rd, Jacksonville 32211 Jean Barnes	Spec		137 14	904/721-2144 Fax 904/721-1040
Resurrection Sch 3406 Justina Rd, Jacksonville 32277 Tim Connor	PK-8		190 9	904/744-1266 Fax 904/744-5800
Sacred Heart Catholic Sch 5752 Blanding Blvd, Jacksonville 32244 Sr Rosario Vega	PK-8		350 19	904/771-5800 Fax 904/771-5323
San Jose Catholic Sch 3619 Toledo Rd, Jacksonville 32217 Jennifer Studer	PK-8		470 20	904/733-2313 Fax 904/731-7169
St Joseph's Catholic Sch 11600 Old Saint Augustine Rd, Jacksonville 32258 Robin Fecitt	PK-8		510 20	904/268-6688 Fax 904/268-8989

St Matthew's Catholic Sch 1773 Blanding Blvd, Jacksonville 32210 Kathy Tuerk	PK-8		273 12	904/387-4401 Fax 904/388-4404
St Patrick Catholic Sch 601 Airport Center Dr E, Jacksonville 32218 Jeffery Kent	PK-8	G	325 7	904/768-6323 Fax 904/768-2144
St Paul's Catholic Sch 2609 Park St, Jacksonville 32204 Kim Repper	PK-8		225 11	904/387-2841 Fax 904/388-1781 f
St Paul's Sch 428 2nd Ave N, Jax Bch 32250 Krissy Thompson	PK-8		608 21	904/249-5934 Fax 904/595-5971

DUVAL PRIVATE SCHOOLS

Private Schs..Principal	Grd	Prgm	Enr/#Cls	SN
Al-Furqan Academy 2333 Saint Johns Bluff Rd S, Jacksonville 32246 Omar Chatila	PK-5		90 7	904/645-0810 Fax 904/646-3214
American Global Sch 841 Prudential Dr Ste 1200, Jacksonville 32207 Michelle Knapp	6-12		50	888/242-4262
Ⓐ AMI Kids School-Jacksonville 13375 Beach Blvd, Jacksonville 32246 David Cobb	6-12	V	40 4	904/223-1121 Fax 904/374-3625
Arlington Community Academy 5900 Fort Caroline Rd, Jacksonville 32277 Lauren May	PK-4		120	904/717-1590
Baymeadows Christian Academy 4826 Baymeadows Rd, Jacksonville 32217 Gary Braward	PK-8		100	904/733-3400
Beaches Chapel Sch 610 Florida Blvd, Neptune Beach 32266 Kathy McWilliams	PK-12		240 9	904/241-4211 Fax 904/249-2046
Beaches Episcopal Sch 450 11th Ave N, Jax Bch 32250 Jennifer Ketchum	PK-6		160 18	904/246-2466 Fax 904/246-1626
Beaches Sch 2049 Florida Blvd, Neptune Beach 32266 Susie Weber	PK-8		68 8	904/249-0905 Fax 904/249-5241 f
Berean Christian Academy 7268 Exline Rd, Jacksonville 32222 Wesley Roach	K-12		111 15	904/264-5333 Fax 904/264-9185
Bethel Holiness Academy 5032 Woodcrest Rd, Jacksonville 32205 Florance Anna Ferris	K-12		25 2	904/781-5400 Fax 904/781-3872
Bolles School- San Jose 7400 San Jose Blvd, Jacksonville 32217 Moya Marks	K-12		1,800 100	904/733-9292 Fax 904/739-9363 f t
Bolles School-Bartram 2264 Bartram Rd, Jacksonville 32207 Jack Milne	6-8		430	904/732-5700 Fax 904/724-8862
Broach School-South 11915 Beach Blvd Ste 101, Jacksonville 32246 Brett Walden	Spec		200	904/674-0900
Broach School-West Campus 929 McDuff Ave S Ste 101, Jacksonville 32205 Patricia Parrish	K-12	G	142 10	904/389-5106
Cedar Creek Christian Sch 1372 Lane Ave S, Jacksonville 32205 Lynn Perkins \ Randy Howell	PK-12		251	904/781-9151 Fax 904/781-9182
Cedar Hills Bapt Chrn Sch 4200 Jammes Rd, Jacksonville 32210 Judy Pugh \ Kavella Grant	PK-8		223	904/772-0812 Fax 904/771-1699

1 Superintendent	8 Curric/Instruct K-12	19 Chief Financial Officer	29 Family/Consumer Science
2 Bus/Finance/Purchasing	9 Curric/Instruct Elem	20 Art K-12	30 Adult Education
3 Buildings And Grounds	10 Curric/Instruct Sec	21 Art Elem	31 Career/Sch-to-Work K-12
4 Food Service	11 Federal Program	22 Art Sec	32 Career/Sch-to-Work Elem
5 Transportation	12 Title I	23 Music K-12	33 Career/Sch-to-Work Sec
6 Athletic	13 Title V	24 Music Elem	34 Early Childhood Ed
7 Health Services	14 Asst Superintendent	25 Music Sec	35 Health/Phys Education
	15 Asst Superintendent	26 Business Education	36 Guidance Services K-12
	16 Instructional Media Svcs	27 Career & Tech Ed	37 Guidance Services Elem
	17 Chief Operations Officer	28 Technology Education	38 Guidance Services Sec
	18 Chief Academic Officer		

39 Social Studies K-12	49 English/Lang Arts Elem	59 Special Education Elem
40 Social Studies Elem	50 English/Lang Arts Sec	60 Special Education Sec
41 Social Studies Sec	51 Reading K-12	61 Foreign/World Lang K-12
42 Science K-12	52 Reading Elem	62 Foreign/World Lang Elem
43 Science Elem	53 Reading Sec	63 Foreign/World Lang Sec
44 Science Sec	54 Remedial Reading K-12	64 Religious Education K-12
45 Math K-12	55 Remedial Reading Elem	65 Religious Education Elem
46 Math Elem	56 Remedial Reading Sec	66 Religious Education Sec
47 Math Sec	57 Bilingual/ELL	67 School Board President
48 English/Lang Arts K-12	58 Special Education K-12	68 Teacher Personnel

69 Academic Assessment
70 Research/Development
71 Public Information
72 Summer School
73 Instructional Tech
74 Inservice Training
75 Marketing/Distributive
76 Info Systems
77 Psychological Assess
78 Affirmative Action

School	Grades	Enrollment	Phone/Fax
Center Academy 10679 Old Saint Augustine Rd, Jacksonville 32257 Tanya Land	4-12	55 3	904/448-1956 Fax 904/448-0044
Center Academy 2804 St Johns Bluff Rd Ste 103, Jacksonville 32246 Ron Booker	Spec	70 3	904/645-5366 Fax 904/645-5186
Christ Church Academy 10850 Old Saint Augustine Rd, Jacksonville 32257 Shellie Hartford	K-12	610	904/268-8667 Fax 904/880-3251
Christian Heritage Academy 3930 University Blvd S, Jacksonville 32216 Jim Stephens	PK-8	120 20	904/733-4722 Fax 904/338-9977 **f**
Clarke School-Jacksonvile 9803 Old St Augustine Rd Ste 7, Jacksonville 32257 Cynthia Robinson	Spec	40	904/880-9001 Fax 904/880-9007
Conservative Christian Academy 12021 Old Saint Augustine Rd, Jacksonville 32258 Dr Gene Youngblood	K-12	129	904/268-7778 Fax 904/262-7593
Cornerstone Christian Sch 9039 Beach Blvd, Jacksonville 32216 Donna Stables	PK-12	250	904/730-5500 Fax 904/730-5502
DePaul School of NE Florida 3044 San Pablo Rd S, Jacksonville 32224 Amber Oliveira	Spec	60 5	904/223-3391 Fax 904/726-9630 **f**
Dimensions 3 Academy 440 Lenox Sq, Jacksonville 32254 Darrell Lewis	K-12	70	904/389-6166 Fax 904/395-5911
Eagle's View Academy 7788 Ramona Blvd W, Jacksonville 32221 Josh Sheetz	K-12	416 22	904/786-1411 Fax 904/786-1445 **f t**
Ephesus Junior Academy 2760 Edgewood Ave W, Jacksonville 32209 Joyceline Dudley	K-8	87 9	904/765-3225 Fax 904/924-2045
Episcopal School-Jacksonville 4455 Atlantic Blvd, Jacksonville 32207 Paige McGee \ Keesy Goebertus	6-12	900	904/396-5751 Fax 904/396-7209
Father's Harbor Academy 4519 Beach Blvd, Jacksonville 32207 Dubel Agosto	K-12	50	904/306-9579 Fax 904/306-9580
First Baptist Academy 600 N Main St, Jacksonville 32202 Debbie Moenning \ Chuck Rockholt	K-8	138	904/265-7474 Fax 904/265-7470 **f t**
First Coast Academy 2725 College St, Jacksonville 32205 Barbara Cornelius	9-12	415	904/381-1935 Fax 904/381-0135
First Coast Christian Sch 7587 Blanding Blvd, Jacksonville 32244 Larry Smith \ Karen Wilson	PK-12	525 40	904/777-3040 Fax 904/777-3045
Foundation Academy 3675 San Pablo Rd S, Jacksonville 32224 Nadia Hionides	PK-12	280 26	904/493-7300 Fax 904/821-1247 **f**
Grace Lutheran Sch 12200 McCormick Rd, Jacksonville 32225 Jennifer Tanner	PK-8	230 11	904/928-9136 Fax 904/208-5924
Great Strides Sch 12276 San Jose Blvd Ste 212, Jacksonville 32223 Lauren Albert	Spec	15	904/886-3228 Fax 904/886-3297
Greenwood Sch 9920 Regency Square Blvd, Jacksonville 32225 Anthony Mortimer	6-12	200 22	904/726-5000 Fax 904/726-5056
Harvest Christian Academy 1051 Arlington Rd N, Jacksonville 32211 Brian Samms	K-12	14 2	904/724-8223 Fax 904/724-1301
Harvest Community Sch 2360 Saint Johns Bluff Rd S, Jacksonville 32246 Patty Wilcox	PK-12	200	904/997-1882 Fax 904/997-1862
Heart to Heart Christian Acad 8247 Ramona Blvd W, Jacksonville 32221 Monique Smith	K-12	125	904/783-8631 Fax 904/224-1183
Jacksonville Adventist Academy 4298 Livingston Rd, Jacksonville 32257 Daniel Williams	PK-8	70 5	904/268-2433 Fax 904/268-7770
Jacksonville Assem Chrn Acad 6350 Old Kings Rd, Jacksonville 32254 Darrin Dyal	K-12	16	904/786-1198
Jacksonville Christian Academy 11697 Normandy Blvd, Jacksonville 32221 Eva Green	K-12	50 6	904/783-2818 Fax 904/783-9999
Jacksonville Country Day Sch 10063 Baymeadows Rd, Jacksonville 32256 Pat Walker	PK-6	500 25	904/641-6644 Fax 904/641-1494
Jacksonville School for Autism 9000 Cypress Green Dr, Jacksonville 32256 Michelle Dunham	Spec	25	904/732-4343 Fax 904/732-4344 **f t**
Joshua Christian Academy 924 Saint Clair St, Jacksonville 32254 Terrence Brandon	PK-12	300 16	904/388-2227 Fax 904/388-2262
Lighthouse Christian Sch West 6800 W 5th St, Jacksonville 32254 David Samson	4-12	50	904/854-4599 Fax 904/854-0531
Lighthouse Chrn Sch-Arlington 6801 Merrill Rd, Jacksonville 32277 Robin Schroedel	1-12	110	904/642-4043 Fax 904/642-4093
Little Country Sch 862 Baisden Rd, Jacksonville 32218 Dr Lola Jay	PK-12	65 6	904/757-8200 Fax 904/757-8209
Mainspring Academy 6700 Southpoint Pkwy Ste 400, Jacksonville 32216 Dina Parisi	Spec	401 14	904/503-0344 Fax 904/503-0469
Martin J Gottlieb Day Sch 3662 Crown Point Rd, Jacksonville 32257 Raquel Anderson	K-8	107 26	904/268-4200 Fax 904/268-5292
Monument Christian Academy 1509 Mayport Rd, Atlantic Bch 32233 Arlethia Jackson	K-12	15	904/247-0929 Fax 904/247-0950
N Florida School of Special Ed 223 Mill Creek Rd, Jacksonville 32211 Sally Hazelip	Spec	100	904/724-8323 Fax 904/724-8325
New Beginings Christian Acad 7020 Ramona Blvd, Jacksonville 32205 J Deetz	1-12	56 5	904/786-3178 Fax 904/786-3328
New Leaf Sch 407 3rd St, Neptune Beach 32266 Ronda McDonald	1-12	30 3	904/246-9100 Fax 904/372-9974
North Florida Educ Inst 580 Lawton Ave, Jacksonville 32208 David Wilson	1-12	250 20	904/764-0084 Fax 904/764-6561
Old Plank Christian Academy 8964 Old Plank Rd, Jacksonville 32220 Gary Griffis	K-12	278	904/783-4888 Fax 904/786-9809
Parkwood Preparatory Academy 7900 Lone Star Rd, Jacksonville 32211 Margaret Walker	PK-5	120	904/721-2719
Parsons Christian Academy 5705 Fort Caroline Rd, Jacksonville 32277 Grace Williams	PK-12	222	904/745-4588 Fax 904/745-6366
Potters House Christian Acad 5732 Normandy Blvd Ste 7, Jacksonville 32205 B Slater	PK-12	400	904/786-0028 Fax 904/693-6426
Providence Sch 2701 Hodges Blvd, Jacksonville 32224 Deshuan Mills \ Michael Gray	PK-12	1,487 60	904/223-5270 Fax 904/223-3028 **f t**

79 Student Personnel	91 Safety/Security	275 Response To Intervention	298 Grant Writer/Ptnrships
80 Driver Ed/Safety	92 Magnet School	277 Remedial Math K-12	750 Chief Innovation Officer
81 Gifted/Talented	93 Parental Involvement	280 Literacy Coach	751 Chief of Staff
82 Video Services	95 Tech Prep Program	285 STEM	752 Social Emotional Learning
83 Substance Abuse Prev	97 Chief Infomation Officer	286 Digital Learning	
84 Erate	98 Chief Technology Officer	288 Common Core Standards	**Other School Types**
85 AIDS Education	270 Character Education	294 Accountability	Ⓐ = Alternative School
88 Alternative/At Risk	271 Migrant Education	295 Network System	Ⓒ = Charter School
89 Multi-Cultural Curriculum	273 Teacher Mentor	296 Title II Programs	Ⓜ = Magnet School
90 Social Work	274 Before/After Sch	297 Webmaster	Ⓨ = Year-Round School

School Programs
A = Alternative Program
G = Adult Classes
M = Magnet Program
T = Title I Schoolwide
V = Career & Tech Ed Programs

Social Media
f = Facebook
t = Twitter

New Schools are shaded
New Superintendents and Principals are bold
Personnel with email addresses are underscored

Reach Academy 9857 Old St Augustine Rd Ste 6, Jacksonville 32257 Stephanie Kaloupek	Spec	20	904/268-9111
Riverside Presbyterian Day Sch 830 Oak St, Jacksonville 32204 Ben Ketchum	PK-6	500 36	904/353-5511 Fax 904/634-1739
San Jose Episcopal Day Sch 7423 San Jose Blvd, Jacksonville 32217 Lori Menger	PK-6	285 23	904/733-0352 Fax 904/733-2582
Seacoast Christian Academy 8057 Arlington Expy, Jacksonville 32211 Elton Brooke	6-12	257 12	904/722-1738 Fax 904/725-5085
Shekinah Christian Academy 10551 Beach Blvd, Jacksonville 32246 Saundra Armour	9-12	225	904/421-1015 Fax 904/421-1022
Shepherd of the Woods Luth Sch 7860 Southside Blvd, Jacksonville 32256 Madelyn Speagle	PK-PK	80	904/641-3393
Shepherd of Woods Lutheran Sch 6595 Columbia Park Ct, Jacksonville 32258 Dr Madelyn Speagle	K-8	100	904/268-6701
St Mark's Episcopal Day Sch 4114 Oxford Ave, Jacksonville 32210 Kevin Conklin	PK-6	420 34	904/388-2632 Fax 904/387-5647 **f**
St Stephen Child Care Lrng Ctr 1525 N Davis St, Jacksonville 32209 Cheryl Parker	PK-K	191 6	904/358-2799 Fax 904/359-0055
Tempette Learning Academy 1766 W 17th St, Jacksonville 32209 Dr Elmer Gregory	PK-12	62	904/598-0078 Fax 904/598-0079
Torah Academy of Jacksonville 10167 San Jose Blvd, Jacksonville 32257 Shaya Hauptman	PK-7	44 5	904/268-7719 Fax 904/268-4321
Trinity Christian Academy 800 Hammond Blvd, Jacksonville 32221 Robert Futrell \ Dan Worley	PK-12 V	1,496	904/786-5320 Fax 904/596-2531 **f t**
University Christian Sch 5520 University Blvd W, Jacksonville 32216 Hassan Champion \ Beverly Bandy	PK-12	600 70	904/737-6330 Fax 904/737-3359 **f t**
Victory Christian Academy 10613 Lem Turner Rd, Jacksonville 32218 Sandra Effler	PK-12	250	904/764-7781 Fax 904/764-7297
West Meadows Baptist Academy 11711 Normandy Blvd, Jacksonville 32221 Dr Bruce Armstrong	K-12	70 4	904/786-9308 Fax 904/786-2712
Zarephath Academy 1028 E 10th St, Jacksonville 32206 Dr Jerry Brant	K-12	401	904/374-2739

DUVAL REGIONAL CENTERS

● **FDLRS-Crown** PID: 04496243　　　　904/346-4601
4124 Boulevard Center Dr, Jacksonville 32207　　Fax 904/346-4611

Henry Schmitges ....1,11　Bruce Glendenning 73

ESCAMBIA COUNTY

ESCAMBIA PUBLIC SCHOOLS

● **Escambia Co School Dist** PID: 00190265　　　850/432-6121
75 N Pace Blvd, Pensacola 32505　　　　　　　　Fax 850/469-6379

> **Schools:** 62 \ **Teachers:** 2,732 \ **Students:** 42,211 \
> **Special Ed Students:** 5,996 \ **LEP Students:** 572 \ **College-Bound:** 81% \
> **Ethnic:** Asian 3%, African American 37%, Hispanic 7%, Native American: 1%,
> Caucasian 53% \ **Exp:** $251 (Med) \ **Poverty:** 25% \ **Title I:** $17,118,749
> \ **Special Education:** $37,915,000 \ **Bilingual Education:** $1,296,000 \
> **Open-Close:** 08/12 - 05/22 \ **DTBP:** $193 (High)

Malcom Thomas 1	Debbie Fussell 2
John Dombroskie 2	Melissa Weekley 2
Terry St Cyr 2,15	Theresa McCants 2
Anthony Noles 3	Derrick Pires 3,5
Dewey Barker 3	Gregory Gibbs 3
James Beagle 3	James Higgins 3
Mitch Mosley 3	Scott Stillman 3
Scott Joseph 3	Tommy Silvers 3
Vince Childers 3	Jaleena Davis 4
Leslie Scott 4	Robert Doss 5
Steven Harrell 5	Theresa Dimmick 5
Roger Mayo 6	Martha Hanna 7,85
Steve Marcanio 8,15	Dr Patti Thomas 9
Lesa Morgan 10	Vicki Gibowski 10
Dan Bryan 11	Dr Laura Colo 12
Dr Alan Scott 15,68	Norman Ross 15
Shawn Dennis 15	Dr Sheila Brandt 16
Angela Barberi 20,23	Dynita Bufford 34
Casandra Waller 35,80,83	Dr Lisa Joyner 36,79
Cherie Arnette 39	Carol Myers 42
Tammy Barton 45	Tammy Danielson 45,277
Jessica Rowell 48	Melissa Marsh 51,54
Dennis Wilson 57,61,70,294,298	Ramona Wright 57,271*
Sondra Hill 58	Terri Szafran 58,81
Patty Hightower 67	Beth Thompson 68
Carrie Hollan 68	Courtney Combs 68
Dawn Ramirez 68	Elizabeth Oakes 68
Keith Leonard 68	Kelly Krostag 68
Nate Hazewinkel 69	Katherine Stefansson 71
Tom Ingram 73,76,82,295	Brian Alaback 74
Dr Michelle Taylor 74	Jeff Elliott 76
Jim Branton 76	Penny Harris 76,295
Dr Marian Torrence 78	Vickie Mathis 88
Kate Lewis 91	Chris Everette 92,286
Chris McFarland 92*	Jo McArthur 93*
Dr Michael Samala 270	

Public Schs..Principal	Grd	Prgm	Enr/#Cls	SN
A K Suter Elem Sch 501 Pickens Ave, Pensacola 32503 Russell Queen	K-5	T	562 13	44% 850/595-6810 Fax 850/595-6819
Bellview Elem Sch 4425 Bellview Ave, Pensacola 32526 Melissa Groff	K-5	T	628 42	68% 850/941-6060 Fax 850/941-6062
Bellview Middle Sch 6201 Mobile Hwy, Pensacola 32526 Melia Adams	6-8	T	992 64	70% 850/941-6080 Fax 850/941-6073
© Beulah Academy of Science 8633 Beulah Rd, Pensacola 32526 Sherry Bailey	6-8	T	288 12	17% 850/944-2822 Fax 850/944-2848

---

1 Superintendent	**8** Curric/Instruct K-12	**19** Chief Financial Officer	**29** Family/Consumer Science	**39** Social Studies K-12	**49** English/Lang Arts Elem	**59** Special Education Elem	**69** Academic Assessment
2 Bus/Finance/Purchasing	**9** Curric/Instruct Elem	**20** Art K-12	**30** Adult Education	**40** Social Studies Elem	**50** English/Lang Arts Sec	**60** Special Education Sec	**70** Research/Development
3 Buildings And Grounds	**10** Curric/Instruct Sec	**21** Art Elem	**31** Career/Sch-to-Work K-12	**41** Social Studies Sec	**51** Reading K-12	**61** Foreign/World Lang K-12	**71** Public Information
4 Food Service	**11** Federal Program	**22** Art Sec	**32** Career/Sch-to-Work Elem	**42** Science K-12	**52** Reading Elem	**62** Foreign/World Lang Elem	**72** Summer School
5 Transportation	**12** Title I	**23** Music K-12	**33** Career/Sch-to-Work Sec	**43** Science Elem	**53** Reading Sec	**63** Foreign/World Lang Sec	**73** Instructional Tech
6 Athletic	**13** Title V	**24** Music Elem	**34** Early Childhood Ed	**44** Science Sec	**54** Remedial Reading K-12	**64** Religious Education K-12	**74** Inservice Training
7 Health Services	**15** Asst Superintendent	**25** Music Sec	**35** Health/Phys Education	**45** Math K-12	**55** Remedial Reading Elem	**65** Religious Education Elem	**75** Marketing/Distributive
	16 Instructional Media Svcs	**26** Business Education	**36** Guidance Services K-12	**46** Math Elem	**56** Remedial Reading Sec	**66** Religious Education Sec	**76** Info Systems
FL—36	**17** Chief Operations Officer	**27** Career & Tech Ed	**37** Guidance Services Elem	**47** Math Sec	**57** Bilingual/ELL	**67** School Board President	**77** Psychological Assess
	18 Chief Academic Officer	**28** Technology Education	**38** Guidance Services Sec	**48** English/Lang Arts K-12	**58** Special Education K-12	**68** Teacher Personnel	**78** Affirmative Action

School	Grades	Programs	Enrollment	%	Phone
Beulah Elem Sch 6201 Helms Rd, Pensacola 32526 Monica Silvers	K-5	T	914 24	52%	850/941-6180 Fax 850/941-6183
Beulah Middle Sch 6001 W Nine Mile Rd, Pensacola 32526 Wilson Taylor	6-8		830 50		850/316-3800 Fax 850/941-6008
Blue Angels Elem Sch 1551 Dog Track Rd, Pensacola 32506 Jayne Murphy	K-5	T	813 51	49%	850/457-6356 Fax 850/457-6954
Bratt Elem Sch 5721 Highway 99, Century 32535 Karen Hall	PK-5	T	513	62%	850/761-6200 Fax 850/327-4849
Ⓜ Brentwood Elem Sch 4820 N Palafox St, Pensacola 32505 Jennifer Sewell	K-5	T	473 31	78%	850/595-6800 Fax 850/595-6802
Ⓜ Brown-Barge Middle Sch 201 Hancock Ln, Pensacola 32503 Joe Snyder	6-8	T	563 22	37%	850/494-5640 Fax 850/494-5699
Ⓒ Byrneville Elem Sch 1600 Byrneville Rd, Century 32535 Dee Wolfe-Sullivan	K-5	T	195 11	71%	850/256-6350 Fax 850/256-6357
C A Weis Elem Sch 2701 N Q St, Pensacola 32505 Holly MaGee	PK-5	AT	546 21	91%	850/595-6888 Fax 850/595-6893
Ⓐ Camelot Academy Ⓒ 401 Brigadier St, Pensacola 32507 Drew Stem	6-12	GTV	157	74%	850/497-6692 Fax 850/497-6673
Ⓒ Capstone Academy 4901 W Fairfield Dr, Pensacola 32506 Aileen Ilano	Spec		32	47%	850/458-7735 Fax 850/455-7322
Cordova Park Elem Sch 2250 Semur Rd, Pensacola 32503 Aggie Bauer	K-5	T	625 23	35%	850/595-6830 Fax 850/595-6835
Ensley Elem Sch 501 E Johnson Ave, Pensacola 32514 Rhonda Shuford	PK-5	T	409 25	76%	850/494-5600 Fax 850/494-5603
Ernest Ward Middle Sch 7650 Highway 97, Walnut Hill 32568 Nancy Ginol-Perry	6-8	GTV	489 25	56%	850/761-6300 Fax 850/327-4991
Escambia High Sch 1310 N 65th Ave, Pensacola 32506 Frank Murphy	9-12	GTV	1,746	63%	850/453-3221 Fax 850/453-7502
Escambia Virtual Academy 30 E Texar Dr, Pensacola 32503 Chris McFarland	6-12		148	19%	850/469-5443 Fax 850/430-7463
Escambia Westgate Sch 10050 Ashton Brosnaham Rd, Pensacola 32534 Jobenna Lawson-Sellers	Spec	T	211 23	45%	850/494-5700 Fax 850/494-5702
Ferry Pass ES Math & Science 8310 N Davis Hwy, Pensacola 32514 Catrena Fieg	K-5	T	612 36	69%	850/494-5605 Fax 850/494-7480
Ferry Pass Middle Sch 8355 Yancey Ave, Pensacola 32514 Juanda White	6-8	T	1,203 65	67%	850/494-5650 Fax 850/494-5653
George Stone Technical Ctr 2400 Longleaf Dr, Pensacola 32526 Thomas Rollins	Voc	AG	600 50		850/941-6200 Fax 850/941-6215
Global Learning Academy 100 N P St, Pensacola 32505 Judy Labounty	PK-5	T	602	89%	850/430-7560 Fax 850/595-0421
Hellen Caro Elem Sch 12551 Meadson Rd, Pensacola 32506 Sandra Moore	K-5	T	804 37	34%	850/492-0531 Fax 850/492-3592
J M Tate Senior High Sch 1771 Tate Rd, Cantonment 32533 Richard Shackle	9-12	AGTV	2,175 85	39%	850/937-2300 Fax 850/937-2328
Ⓒ Jacqueline Harris Prep Academy 1408 E Blount St, Pensacola 32503 Celestine Lewis	K-5	T	232 12	85%	850/432-2273 Fax 850/432-4624 Ⓔ
James C Bailey Middle Sch 4110 Bauer Rd, Pensacola 32506 Janet Penrose	6-8	TV	1,389 80	57%	850/492-6136 Fax 850/492-9860
Jim Allen Elem Sch 1051 N Highway 95A, Cantonment 32533 Rachel Watts	PK-5	T	670 26	55%	850/937-2260 Fax 850/937-2269
Kingsfield Elem Sch 900 W Kingsfield Rd, Cantonment 32533 Sabrena Cunningham	PK-5		617		850/937-5200
Lakeview Center Sch 1201 W Lakeview Ave, Pensacola 32501 Tammie Kirkland	Spec	T	37 5	88%	850/469-3535
Lincoln Park Elem Sch 7600 Kershaw St, Pensacola 32534 Cassandra Smith	PK-3	T	199 20	74%	850/494-5620 Fax 850/494-7481
Longleaf Elem Sch 2600 Longleaf Dr, Pensacola 32526 Troy Brown	K-5	T	559 33	66%	850/941-6110 Fax 850/941-6112
McArthur Elem Sch 330 E Ten Mile Rd, Pensacola 32534 Dr Tama Vaughn	PK-5	T	713 28	68%	850/494-5625 Fax 850/494-5707
McMillan Learning Ctr 1403 W Saint Joseph Ave, Pensacola 32501 Dr Patrice Moody	PK-PK		121 17	61%	850/595-6910 Fax 850/595-6944
Molino Park Elem Sch 899 Highway 97, Molino 32577 Lisa Arnold	PK-5	T	495 13	60%	850/754-5000 Fax 850/587-2340
Montclair Elem Sch 820 Massachusetts Ave, Pensacola 32505 Hollie Wilkins	PK-5	T	398 26	91%	850/595-6969 Fax 850/595-6968
Myrtle Grove Elem Sch 6115 Lillian Hwy, Pensacola 32506 Robin Maloy	K-5	T	566 37	74%	850/453-7410 Fax 850/453-7740
Ⓜ N B Cook Elem Sch of the Arts 1310 N 12th Ave, Pensacola 32503 Larry Knight	K-5	T	570 30	34%	850/595-6826
Navy Point Elem Sch 1321 Patton Dr, Pensacola 32507 Dr Monica Ford-Harris	PK-5	T	537 23	71%	850/453-7415 Fax 850/453-7419
Northview High Sch 4100 W Highway 4, Century 32535 **Aaron Munoz**	9-12	GTV	499 22	50%	850/327-6681 Fax 850/327-6106
O J Semmes Elem Sch 1250 E Texar Dr, Pensacola 32503 Connie Farish	PK-5	T	445 23	88%	850/595-6975 Fax 850/595-6977
Oakcrest Elem Sch 1820 Hollywood Ave, Pensacola 32505 Linda Bonifay	PK-5	T	533 31	85%	850/595-6980 Fax 850/595-6988
Ⓐ Pace Center for Girls-Escambia 1028 Underwood Ave, Pensacola 32504 Brandi Gentry	7-12		59	34%	850/478-7060 Fax 850/494-0840
Ⓒ Pensacola Beach Charter Sch 900 Via De Luna Dr, Pensacola Bch 32561 Jeff Castleberry	K-5	T	147 6	2%	850/934-4020 Fax 850/934-4040
Ⓐ Pensacola Boys Base Sch Bldg 3780 Nttc Corry Fld Sta, Pensacola 32511 Dean McLaughlin	6-12	V	28 2		850/453-7521
Pensacola High Sch 500 W Maxwell St, Pensacola 32501 David Williams	9-12	GTV	1,424	61%	850/595-1500 Fax 850/595-1519
Pine Forest High Sch 2500 Longleaf Dr, Pensacola 32526 Laura Touchstone	9-12	GTV	1,630 70	58%	850/941-6150 Fax 850/941-6163

79	Student Personnel	91	Safety/Security	275	Response To Intervention	298	Grant Writer/Ptnrships
80	Driver Ed/Safety	92	Magnet School	277	Remedial Math K-12	750	Chief Innovation Officer
81	Gifted/Talented	93	Parental Involvement	280	Literacy Coach	751	Chief of Staff
82	Video Services	95	Tech Prep Program	285	STEM	752	Social Emotional Learning
83	Substance Abuse Prev	97	Chief Information Officer	286	Digital Learning	
84	Erate	98	Chief Technology Officer	288	Common Core Standards	**Other School Types**
85	AIDS Education	270	Character Education	294	Accountability	Ⓐ = Alternative Program
88	Alternative/At Risk	271	Migrant Education	295	Network System	Ⓒ = Charter School
89	Multi-Cultural Curriculum	273	Teacher Mentor	296	Title II Programs	Ⓜ = Magnet School
90	Social Work	274	Before/After Sch	297	Webmaster	Ⓨ = Year-Round School

School Programs
A = Alternative Program
G = Adult Classes
M = Magnet Program
T = Title I Schoolwide
V = Career & Tech Ed Programs

Social Media
f = Facebook
t = Twitter

New Schools are shaded
New Superintendents and Principals are bold
Personnel with email addresses are underscored

School	Grd	Prgm	Enr/#Cls	SN	Phone
Pine Meadow Elem Sch 10001 Omar Ave, Pensacola 32534 **Elizabeth Greenberg**	K-5	T	615 35	52%	850/494-5630 Fax 850/494-7318
Pleasant Grove Elem Sch 3000 Owen Bell Ln, Pensacola 32507 **Rs Mullen**	K-5	T	599 33	56%	850/492-0233 Fax 850/492-6991
R C Lipscomb Elem Sch 10200 Ashton Brosnaham Rd, Pensacola 32534 Susan Sanders	K-5	T	838 30	51%	850/494-5760 Fax 850/494-5722
Ransom Middle Sch 1000 W Kingsfield Rd, Cantonment 32533 Regina Lipnick	6-8	T	1,274 72	48%	850/937-2220 Fax 850/937-2232
Reinhart Holm Elem Sch 6101 Lanier Dr, Pensacola 32504 **Teri Fina**	PK-5	T	440 32	74%	850/494-5610 Fax 850/494-7290
Scenic Heights Elem Sch 3801 Cherry Laurel Dr, Pensacola 32504 **Ms Cox**	K-5	T	823 30	66%	850/494-5635 Fax 850/494-5624
Sherwood Elem Sch 501 Cherokee Trl, Pensacola 32506 Kristen Danley	PK-5	T	540 26	71%	850/453-7420 Fax 850/453-7466
Ⓐ Success Academy 129 N Merritt St, Pensacola 32507 Dawn Gibbs	6-12		300		850/941-6100 Fax 850/453-7560
Warrington Elem Sch 220 N Navy Blvd, Pensacola 32507 Tim Rose	PK-5	AT	358 34	88%	850/453-7425 Fax 850/453-7519
Warrington Middle Sch 450 S Old Corry Field Rd, Pensacola 32507 Brent Brummet	6-8	T	819 38	84%	850/453-7440 Fax 850/453-7572
Washington High Sch 6000 College Pkwy, Pensacola 32504 Michael Roberts	9-12	GTV	1,778	53%	850/475-5257 Fax 850/494-7297
Ⓜ West Florida HS Advanced Tech 150 E Burgess Rd, Pensacola 32503 Shenna Payne	9-12	T	1,338 75	39%	850/876-7300 Fax 850/471-6019
West Pensacola Elem Sch 801 N 49th Ave, Pensacola 32506 Christine Baker	PK-5	T	562 33	82%	850/453-7470 Fax 850/453-7717
Workman Middle Sch 6299 Lanier Dr, Pensacola 32504 Traci Ursrey	6-8	T	978 50	56%	850/494-5665 Fax 850/494-5697

ESCAMBIA CATHOLIC SCHOOLS

- **Diocese Pensacola-Tallahassee** PID: 01483467   850/435-3500
11 N B St, Pensacola 32502   Fax 850/436-6424

Schools: 9 \ **Students:** 2,400

Listing includes only schools located in this county. See District Index for location of Diocesan Offices.

Michael Juhas 1   Donna Bass 68,74

Catholic Schs..Principal	Grd	Prgm	Enr/#Cls	SN	Phone
Little Flower Catholic Sch 6495 Lillian Hwy, Pensacola 32506 Stephen Sanchez	PK-8		200 9		850/455-4851 Fax 850/457-8982
Pensacola Catholic High Sch 3043 W Scott St, Pensacola 32505 Sr Kierstin Martin	9-12	V	650 30		850/436-6400 Fax 850/436-6405

School	Grd		Enr/#Cls	Phone
Sacred Heart Cathedral Sch 1603 N 12th Ave, Pensacola 32503 Elizabeth Snow	PK-8		320 10	850/436-6440 Fax 850/436-6444
St John the Evangelist Sch 325 S Navy Blvd, Pensacola 32507 Dana Donahoo	PK-8		460 10	850/456-5218 Fax 850/456-5956
St Paul Catholic Sch 3121 Hyde Park Rd, Pensacola 32503 Blair Hodge	PK-8		360 13	850/436-6435 Fax 850/436-6437

ESCAMBIA PRIVATE SCHOOLS

Private Schs..Principal	Grd	Prgm	Enr/#Cls	SN	Phone
Alethia Christian Academy 1700 Woodchuck Ave, Pensacola 32504 Jeff James	PK-12	V	230 14		850/969-0088 Fax 850/969-0906
Bauers Triple D's Chrn Acad 3290 Bauer Rd, Pensacola 32506	PK-8		401		850/492-4873
Blessed Star Montessori Sch 9151 N Davis Hwy, Pensacola 32514 Olivia Chen	PK-8		30		850/476-9208 Fax 850/361-1055
Creative Learning Academy 3151 Hyde Park Rd, Pensacola 32503 Kim Stafford	PK-8		200 24		850/432-1768 Fax 850/432-1896
Deliverance Tabernacle Center 1780 W Detroit Blvd, Pensacola 32534 Christopher Robinson	K-8		49		850/479-1500
East Hill Christian Sch 1301 E Gonzalez St, Pensacola 32501 Nathan Witter	PK-12		200 22		850/438-7746 Fax 850/434-7384
Episcopal Day Sch-Christ Chrh 223 N Palafox St, Pensacola 32502 Robert Stephens	PK-8		350 18		850/434-3685 Fax 850/434-6560
Escambia Christian Sch 3311 W Moreno St, Pensacola 32505 Stephanie Davis-Keeton	PK-8		85 13		850/433-8476 Fax 850/433-8333
Jubilee Christian Academy 5910 N W St, Pensacola 32505 Jadean Stricker \ Dr Cathy Potter	PK-8		220 13		850/474-9484 Fax 850/494-2900
Marcus Pointe Christian Sch 6205 N W St, Pensacola 32505 June Godfrey	K-5		180		850/479-1605
Montessori Sch of Pensacola 4100 Montessori Dr 4101, Pensacola 32504 Maria Mitkevicius	PK-8		250		850/433-4155 Fax 850/433-5613
Montessori School of Pensacola 1010 N 12th Ave Ste 138, Pensacola 32501 Mary Gaudet	PK-K		120 8		850/469-8138 Fax 850/433-5613
Pensacola Christian Academy 10 Brent Ln, Pensacola 32503 Ryan Bucy	PK-12		150		850/478-8496 Fax 850/479-6572
Pensacola Sch of Liberal Arts 1010 N 12th Ave Ste 338, Pensacola 32501 Jacqui Tarver	7-12		33 3		850/434-2294 Fax 850/436-8890
Pensacola SDA Junior Academy 8751 University Pkwy, Pensacola 32514 April Copley	K-8		25 3		850/478-8838 Fax 850/477-9513
Redeemer Lutheran Sch 333 Commerce St, Pensacola 32507 John Price	PK-8		180 10		850/455-0330 Fax 850/455-3083
Sl Jones Christian Academy 100 Boeing St, Pensacola 32507 Millicent Hatcher Demps	K-12		218		850/456-2249 Fax 850/458-8150

1 Superintendent	8 Curric/Instruct K-12	19 Chief Financial Officer	29 Family/Consumer Science
2 Bus/Finance/Purchasing	9 Curric/Instruct Elem	20 Art K-12	30 Adult Education
3 Buildings And Grounds	10 Curric/Instruct Sec	21 Art Elem	31 Career/Sch-to-Work K-12
4 Food Service	11 Federal Program	22 Art Sec	32 Career/Sch-to-Work Elem
5 Transportation	12 Title I	23 Music K-12	33 Career/Sch-to-Work Sec
6 Athletic	13 Title V	24 Music Elem	34 Early Childhood Ed
7 Health Services	14 Asst Superintendent	25 Music Sec	35 Health/Phys Education
	15 Asst Superintendent	26 Business Education	36 Guidance Services K-12
	16 Instructional Media Svcs	27 Career & Tech Ed	37 Guidance Services Elem
	17 Chief Operations Officer	28 Technology Education	38 Guidance Services Sec
	18 Chief Academic Officer		

39 Social Studies K-12	49 English/Lang Arts Elem	59 Special Education Elem	69 Academic Assessment
40 Social Studies Elem	50 English/Lang Arts Sec	60 Special Education Sec	70 Research/Development
41 Social Studies Sec	51 Reading K-12	61 Foreign/World Lang K-12	71 Public Information
42 Science K-12	52 Reading Elem	62 Foreign/World Lang Elem	72 Summer School
43 Science Elem	53 Reading Sec	63 Foreign/World Lang Sec	73 Instructional Tech
44 Science Sec	54 Remedial Reading K-12	64 Religious Education K-12	74 Inservice Training
45 Math K-12	55 Remedial Reading Elem	65 Religious Education Elem	75 Marketing/Distributive
46 Math Elem	56 Remedial Reading Sec	66 Religious Education Sec	76 Info Systems
47 Math Sec	57 Bilingual/ELL	67 School Board President	77 Psychological Assess
48 English/Lang Arts K-12	58 Special Education K-12	68 Teacher Personnel	78 Affirmative Action

Trinitas Christian Sch	K-12		200		850/484-3515
3301 E Johnson Ave, Pensacola 32514			14		
Ron Gilley					
Walnut Hill Christian Sch	1-9		34		850/327-4994
6990 Highway 97, Mc David 32568			4		
Wesley Wenger					

ESCAMBIA REGIONAL CENTERS

● **FDLRS-Westgate** PID: 04496061　　　　　　　　850/469-5423
　30 E Texar Dr, Pensacola 32503　　　　　　　　　Fax 850/469-5574

FLAGLER COUNTY

FLAGLER PUBLIC SCHOOLS

● **Flagler Co School Dist** PID: 00191001　　　　　386/437-7526
　1769 E Moody Blvd Bldg 2, Bunnell 32110　　　　Fax 386/437-7577

> **Schools:** 12 \ **Teachers:** 766 \ **Students:** 12,904 \
> **Special Ed Students:** 1,811 \ **LEP Students:** 379 \ **College-Bound:** 73%
> \ **Ethnic:** Asian 2%, African American 16%, Hispanic 15%, Native American:
> 1%, Caucasian 67% \ **Exp:** $101 (Low) \ **Poverty:** 20% \ **Title I:** $3,694,673
> \ **Special Education:** $7,701,000 \ **Bilingual Education:** $534,000 \
> **Open-Close:** 08/12 - 05/28 \ **DTBP:** $175 (High) \

Public Schs..Principal	Grd	Prgm	Enr/#Cls	SN	
Belle Terre Elem Sch	PK-6	T	1,436	53%	386/447-1500
5545 Belle Terre Pkwy, Palm Coast 32137					Fax 386/447-1516
Terrance Culver					
Buddy Taylor Middle Sch	7-8	T	907	69%	386/446-6700
4500 Belle Terre Pkwy, Palm Coast 32164			64		Fax 386/446-6711
Robert Bossardet					
Bunnell Elem Sch	PK-6	T	1,167	73%	386/437-7533
305 N Palmetto St, Bunnell 32110			30		Fax 386/437-7591
Marcus Sanfilippo					
Flagler Co Tech & Adult Ed	Voc	G	150		386/447-4345
5400 E Highway 100, Palm Coast 32164			30		Fax 386/446-7620
Kevin McCarthy					

Flagler Palm Coast High Sch	9-12	ATV	2,601	58%	386/437-7540
5500 E Highway 100, Palm Coast 32164			134		Fax 386/437-8284
Robert Wallace					
Iflagler Virtual Sch	7-11		38		386/447-1520
3535 Pirate Nation Way, Palm Coast 32137					Fax 386/447-1583
Diane Dyer					
© Imagine Schools Town Ctr [138]	K-8	T	887	1%	386/586-0100
775 Town Center Blvd, Palm Coast 32164					Fax 386/586-2784
Lisa O'Grady					
Indian Trails Middle Sch	7-8	T	927	52%	386/446-6732
5505 Belle Terre Pkwy, Palm Coast 32137			66		Fax 386/446-7662
Jon Peacock					
Matanzas High Sch	9-12	TV	1,705	46%	386/447-1575
3535 Pirate Nation Way, Palm Coast 32137					Fax 386/447-1525
Jeffrey Reaves					
Old Kings Elem Sch	PK-6	T	1,238	50%	386/517-2060
301 Old Kings Rd S, Flagler Beach 32136			45		Fax 386/517-2074
Katherine Crooke					
Rymfire Elem Sch	K-6	T	1,060	74%	386/206-4600
1425 Rymfire Dr, Palm Coast 32164			96		Fax 386/586-2305
Lashakia Moore					
Wadsworth Elem Sch	K-6	T	954	67%	386/446-6720
4550 Belle Terre Pkwy, Palm Coast 32164			33		Fax 386/446-6728
Anna Crawford					

FLAGLER CATHOLIC SCHOOLS

● **Diocese St Augustine Ed Office** PID: 00202533
　Listing includes only schools located in this county. See District Index for
　location of Diocesan Offices.

Catholic Schs..Principal	Grd	Prgm	Enr/#Cls	SN	
St Elizabeth Ann Seton Cat Sch	PK-8		220		386/445-2411
4600 Belle Terre Pkwy, Palm Coast 32164			10		Fax 386/445-1687
Brian Wheeler					

FLAGLER PRIVATE SCHOOLS

Private Schs..Principal	Grd	Prgm	Enr/#Cls	SN	
Christ the King Luthrn CH Sch	PK-8		220		386/447-7979
5625 N US Highway 1, Palm Coast 32164					Fax 386/447-4121
Eric Brown					
First Baptist Christian Acad	PK-12		50		386/446-0094
201 E Moody Blvd, Bunnell 32110					Fax 386/445-0360
Jessica Kendra \ Mary Allman					
Flagler Christian Academy	PK-8		41		386/437-5242
3601 E Moody Blvd, Bunnell 32110			4		Fax 386/437-2751
Joyce Jolley					

79	Student Personnel	91	Safety/Security	275	Response To Intervention	298 Grant Writer/Ptnrships
80	Driver Ed/Safety	92	Magnet School	277	Remedial Math K-12	750 Chief Innovation Officer
81	Gifted/Talented	93	Parental Involvement	280	Literacy Coach	751 Chief of Staff
82	Video Services	95	Tech Prep Program	285	STEM	752 Social Emotional Learning
83	Substance Abuse Prev	97	Chief Infomation Officer	286	Digital Learning	
84	Erate	98	Chief Technology Officer	288	Common Core Standards	Other School Types
85	AIDS Education	270	Character Education	294	Accountability	Ⓐ = Alternative School
88	Alternative/At Risk	271	Migrant Education	295	Network System	Ⓒ = Charter School
89	Multi-Cultural Curriculum	273	Teacher Mentor	296	Title II Programs	Ⓜ = Magnet School
90	Social Work	274	Before/After Sch	297	Webmaster	Ⓨ = Year-Round School

School Programs
A = **Alternative Program**
G = **Adult Classes**
M = **Magnet Program**
T = **Title I Schoolwide**
V = **Career & Tech Ed Programs**

Social Media
 = **Facebook**
 = **Twitter**

New Schools are shaded
New Superintendents and Principals are bold
Personnel with email addresses are underscored

FL—39

FRANKLIN COUNTY

FRANKLIN PUBLIC SCHOOLS

- **Franklin Co School Dist** PID: 00191037　　　850/670-2810
  85 School Rd Ste 1, Eastpoint 32328　　　　　Fax 850/670-8579

Schools: 2 \ *Teachers:* 87 \ *Students:* 1,000 \ *Special Ed Students:* 244
\ *LEP Students:* 33 \ *College-Bound:* 70% \ *Ethnic:* African
American 12%, Hispanic 7%, Caucasian 81% \ *Exp:* $237 (Med) \
Poverty: 32% \ *Title I:* $567,343 \ *Special Education:* $515,000 \
Bilingual Education: $3,000 \ *Open-Close:* 08/12 - 05/22 \ *DTBP:* $350
(High)

Traci Moses	1	Shannon Venable	2
Mann Roberts	3,5	Terry Hilton	4
Jill Rudd	28,29,34,57,58,73,77,296	Stacy Kirvin	67
Karen Peddie	68	Robert Wheetley	91*
Rhonda Griffin	288		

Public Schs..Principal	Grd	Prgm	Enr/#Cls	SN
© Apalachicola Bay Charter Sch 98 12th St, Apalachicola 32320 Chimene Johnson	K-8	T	348 19	57% 850/653-1222
Franklin Co Sch 1250 US Highway 98, Eastpoint 32328 Chip Clatto	K-12	GTV	865 40	71% 850/670-2800 Fax 850/670-2801

FRANKLIN PRIVATE SCHOOLS

Private Schs..Principal	Grd	Prgm	Enr/#Cls	SN
First Baptist Christian Sch 46 9th St, Apalachicola 32320 Carline Kembro	PK-12		50 6	850/653-9540 Fax 850/653-3310

GADSDEN COUNTY

GADSDEN PUBLIC SCHOOLS

- **Gadsden Co School Dist** PID: 00191087　　　850/627-9651
  35 Martin Luther King Jr Blvd, Quincy 32351　　Fax 850/627-2760

Schools: 14 \ *Teachers:* 421 \ *Students:* 5,000 \ *Special Ed Students:* 771
\ *LEP Students:* 437 \ *College-Bound:* 33% \ *Ethnic:* African American
77%, Hispanic 19%, Native American: 1%, Caucasian 3% \ *Exp:* $187 (Low)
\ *Poverty:* 38% \ *Title I:* $4,037,886 \ *Special Education:* $6,062,000 \
Bilingual Education: $578,000 \ *Open-Close:* 08/12 - 05/29 \ *DTBP:* $276
(High)

Roger Milton	1	Bonnie Wood	2
Laclarence Mays	2	Stephanie Brown-Byrd	2
William Hunter	3	Paula Milton	4
Gerald Gay	5	Tammy McGriff	9

Dr Sylvia Jackson	10,27,30,42,45*	Rose Raynak	11,298
Joanette Thomas	12	Darlean Youmans	16,76,286
Dr Sheantika Wiggins	16,73	Carolyn Harden	34
Lakysha Perkins	34	Abria Harris	42,45
Sarah Knight	51	Maria Pouncey	57,271
Steve Scott	67	Pauline West	68
Sandra Robinson	68	Caroline McKinnon	69
Jane Butler	71	Dr Ida Walker	74,273
Sharon Thomas	81	Bruce James	91
Vicki Johnson	93*	John Thomas	295

Public Schs..Principal	Grd	Prgm	Enr/#Cls	SN
Ⓐ Carter-Parramore Academy 631 S Stewart St, Quincy 32351 Willie Jackson	4-12	T	239 10	86% 850/627-6030 Fax 850/875-3197
Ⓜ Chattahoochee Elem Sch 335 Maple St, Chattahoochee 32324 Valencia Denson	PK-5	T	193 17	77% 850/662-2080 Fax 850/663-2236
© Crossroad Academy [134] 470 Strong Rd, Quincy 32351 Kevin Forehand	PK-12	T	527 13	62% 850/875-9626 Fax 850/875-1403
Ⓐ Gadsden Central Academy 655 S Stewart St, Quincy 32351 **Carla Galvin-Wells**	3-12	T	19 7	79% 850/875-7249 Fax 850/627-1802
Gadsden Co High Sch 27001 Blue Star Hwy, Havana 32333 Pamela Jones	9-12	GTV	977 55	71% 850/662-2300 Fax 850/539-2863
Ⓜ Gadsden Elem Magnet Sch 500 W King St, Quincy 32351 Allysun Davis	PK-8	T	163 5	54% 850/627-7557 Fax 850/627-6695
Gadsden Technical Institute 201 Martin Luther King Jr Blvd, Quincy 32351 Dr Sylvia Jackson	Voc	G	100 10	850/875-8324 Fax 850/875-7297
Gadsden Virtual Sch 35 Martin Luther King Jr Blvd, Quincy 32351 Dr Silvia Jackson	K-12		6	866/339-8784 Fax 866/254-9747
George Munroe Elem Sch 1830 W King St, Quincy 32351 Ronald Peterson	PK-5	T	531 55	75% 850/875-8800 Fax 850/875-8805
Greensboro Elem Sch 559 Greensboro Hwy, Quincy 32351 Stephen Pitts	PK-5	T	321 23	75% 850/442-6327 Fax 850/442-9524
Ⓜ Havana Magnet Sch 1210 Kemp Rd, Havana 32333 Delshauna Jackson	PK-8	T	610 25	77% 850/662-2750 Fax 850/539-2866
James A Shanks Middle Sch 1400 W King St, Quincy 32351 Maurice Stokes	6-8	TV	443 45	77% 850/875-8737 Fax 850/875-8775
Stewart Street Elem Sch 749 S Stewart St, Quincy 32351 Lisa Robinson	PK-5	T	633 50	78% 850/627-3145 Fax 850/875-8750
West Gadsden Middle Sch 200 Providence Rd, Quincy 32351 Sonya Jackson	4-8	V	387 20	850/442-9500 Fax 850/442-6126

GADSDEN PRIVATE SCHOOLS

Private Schs..Principal	Grd	Prgm	Enr/#Cls	SN
Robert F Munroe Day Sch 91 Old Mt Pleasant Rd, Quincy 32352 Adam Gaffey	PK-12		200 24	850/856-5500 Fax 850/856-5856
Tallavana Christian Sch 5840 Havana Hwy, Havana 32333 Diane Townson	PK-12		200 18	850/539-5300 Fax 850/539-8785

1	Superintendent	8	Curric/Instruct K-12	19	Chief Financial Officer	29	Family/Consumer Science
2	Bus/Finance/Purchasing	9	Curric/Instruct Elem	20	Art K-12	30	Adult Education
3	Buildings And Grounds	10	Curric/Instruct Sec	21	Art Elem	31	Career/Sch-to-Work K-12
4	Food Service	11	Federal Program	22	Art Sec	32	Career/Sch-to-Work Elem
5	Transportation	12	Title I	23	Music K-12	33	Career/Sch-to-Work Sec
6	Athletic	13	Title V	24	Music Elem	34	Early Childhood Ed
7	Health Services	15	Asst Superintendent	25	Music Sec	35	Health/Phys Education
		16	Instructional Media Svcs	26	Business Education	36	Guidance Services K-12
		17	Chief Operations Officer	27	Career & Tech Ed	37	Guidance Services Elem
		18	Chief Academic Officer	28	Technology Education	38	Guidance Services Sec

39	Social Studies K-12	49	English/Lang Arts Elem	59	Special Education Elem	69	Academic Assessment
40	Social Studies Elem	50	English/Lang Arts Sec	60	Special Education Sec	70	Research/Development
41	Social Studies Sec	51	Reading K-12	61	Foreign/World Lang K-12	71	Public Information
42	Science K-12	52	Reading Elem	62	Foreign/World Lang Elem	72	Summer School
43	Science Elem	53	Reading Sec	63	Foreign/World Lang Sec	73	Instructional Tech
44	Science Sec	54	Remedial Reading K-12	64	Religious Education K-12	74	Inservice Training
45	Math K-12	55	Remedial Reading Elem	65	Religious Education Elem	75	Marketing/Distributive
46	Math Elem	56	Remedial Reading Sec	66	Religious Education Sec	76	Info Systems
47	Math Sec	57	Bilingual/ELL	67	School Board President	77	Psychological Assess
48	English/Lang Arts K-12	58	Special Education K-12	68	Teacher Personnel	78	Affirmative Action

GILCHRIST COUNTY

GILCHRIST PUBLIC SCHOOLS

- **Gilchrist Co School Dist** PID: 00191269   352/463-3200
  310 NW 11th Ave, Trenton 32693   Fax 352/463-3276

Schools: 4 \ *Teachers:* 156 \ *Students:* 2,741 \
Special Ed Students: 501 \ *LEP Students:* 58 \ *College-Bound:* 65% \
Ethnic: African American 5%, Hispanic 8%, Caucasian 87% \ *Exp:* $293
(Med) \ *Poverty:* 24% \ *Title I:* $738,676 \ *Special Education:* $3,843,000 \
Bilingual Education: $174,000 \ *Open-Close:* 08/12 - 05/22 \ *DTBP:* $161
(High)

Robert Rankin	1	David Dose 2
David Spencer	3,5,91	Linda Perry 4
Joey Whittington	6*	Ronda Parrish 7,8,15,51,69,83,288,294
Darby Allen	9,280	Linda Gartin 10,13,56,285*
Patricia Powers	11,27,274,296,298	Wendy O'Steen 57
James Surrency	58,88*	Deen Lancaster 67
Billiejo Bible	68	Aaron Wiley 73,84,295
Evelyn Barratt	76	Terri Crawford 77
Robyn Cason	82*	

Public Schs..Principal	Grd	Prgm	Enr/#Cls	SN
Bell Elem Sch 2771 E Bell Ave, Bell 32619 Suzanne Mathe	PK-5	T	624 25	59% 352/463-3275 Fax 352/463-3456
ⓨ Bell Middle High Sch 930 S Main St, Bell 32619 Sherry Lindsey	6-12	MT	629 50	50% 352/463-3232 Fax 352/463-3294
ⓨ Trenton Elem Sch 1350 SW State Road 26, Trenton 32693 Ronda Adkins	PK-5	MT	807 40	63% 352/463-3224 Fax 352/463-3299
ⓨ Trenton High Sch 1013 N Main St, Trenton 32693 Cheri Langford	6-12	MT	681 50	49% 352/463-3210 Fax 352/463-3264

GLADES COUNTY

GLADES PUBLIC SCHOOLS

- **Glades Co School Dist** PID: 00191300   863/946-2083
  400 10th St SW, Moore Haven 33471   Fax 863/946-1529

Schools: 4 \ *Teachers:* 144 \ *Students:* 1,650 \ *Special Ed Students:* 324
\ *LEP Students:* 79 \ *College-Bound:* 40% \ *Ethnic:* Asian 1%,
African American 10%, Hispanic 40%, Native American 12%, Caucasian
38% \ *Exp:* $226 (Med) \ *Poverty:* 24% \ *Title I:* $502,293 \
Special Education: $1,663,000 \ *Bilingual Education:* $216,000 \
Open-Close: 09/10 - 05/28 \ *DTBP:* $358 (High)

Scott Bass	1	Sue Woodward 2
Doug Manke	5	Max Manin 6*
Janet Harris	8,11,76,83,88,296,298	Janice Foster 36*

Vivian Bennett	58,79,270,275	Mike Pressley 67
Frank Maznicki	73	Jim Brickel 73

Public Schs..Principal	Grd	Prgm	Enr/#Cls	SN
Moore Haven Elem Sch 401 Terrier Pride Dr SW, Moore Haven 33471 Felinda Langdale	K-6	T	400 24	64% 863/946-0737 Fax 863/946-1670
Moore Haven Jr Sr High Sch 700 Terrier Pride Dr SW, Moore Haven 33471 Janice Foster	7-12	T	441 35	46% 863/946-0811 Fax 863/946-1532
© Pemayetv Emahakv Charter Sch [132] 100 E Harney Pond Rd NE, Okeechobee 34974 Brian Greseth	K-8		186	863/467-2501 Fax 863/467-8510
West Glades Sch 2586 County Road 731, Labelle 33935 Doreen Sabella	K-8	T	592 32	55% 863/675-3490 Fax 863/675-3890

GULF COUNTY

GULF PUBLIC SCHOOLS

- **Gulf Co School Dist** PID: 00191336   850/229-8256
  150 Middle School Dr, Port St Joe 32456   Fax 850/229-6089

Schools: 5 \ *Teachers:* 131 \ *Students:* 1,924 \ *Special Ed Students:* 348
\ *LEP Students:* 12 \ *College-Bound:* 75% \ *Ethnic:* African
American 13%, Hispanic 4%, Caucasian 82% \ *Exp:* $201 (Med) \
Poverty: 25% \ *Title I:* $555,917 \ *Special Education:* $1,105,000 \
Bilingual Education: $17,000 \ *Open-Close:* 08/12 - 05/22 \ *DTBP:* $370
(High) \

Jim Norton	1	Bill Carr 2,4,15,68,71
Sissy Worley	2	Woody Borders 3
Diana Dykes	5	Gregory Jordan 6*
Martha Weimorts	7,15,16,54,57,58,280,285	Duane McFarland 8,30,88
Lori Price	11,42,74,79,83,288,296,298	Brooke Wooten 67
Tracy Bowers	69	Terry Thompson 73,295*

Public Schs..Principal	Grd	Prgm	Enr/#Cls	SN
Gulf Co Adult Sch 2853 Long Ave, Port St Joe 32456 Duane McFarland	Adult		30 1	850/227-1744 Fax 850/229-2724
Port St Joe Elem Sch 2201 Long Ave, Port St Joe 32456 Jonilyn Mock	PK-6	T	605 27	63% 850/227-1221 Fax 850/227-3422
Port St Joe Jr Sr High Sch 100 Shark Dr, Port St Joe 32456 Josh Dailey	7-12	T	499 30	45% 850/229-8251 Fax 850/227-1803
Wewahitchka Elem Sch 514 E River Rd, Wewahitchka 32465 Billy Hoover	PK-6	T	483 25	70% 850/639-2476 Fax 850/639-3298
Wewahitchka Jr Sr High Sch 1 Gator Cir, Wewahitchka 32465 Jay Bidwell	7-12	T	355 20	62% 850/639-2228 Fax 850/639-5394

79 Student Personnel	**91** Safety/Security	**275** Response To Intervention	**298** Grant Writer/Ptnrships	**School Programs**	**Social Media**
80 Driver Ed/Safety	**92** Magnet School	**277** Remedial Math K-12	**750** Chief Innovation Officer	A = Alternative Program	
81 Gifted/Talented	**93** Parental Involvement	**280** Literacy Coach	**751** Chief of Staff	G = Adult Classes	🖪 = Facebook
82 Video Services	**95** Tech Prep Program	**285** STEM	**752** Social Emotional Learning	M = Magnet Program	
83 Substance Abuse Prev	**97** Chief Infomation Officer	**286** Digital Learning		T = Title I Schoolwide	🖪 = Twitter
84 Erate	**98** Chief Technology Officer	**288** Common Core Standards	**Other School Types**	V = Career & Tech Ed Programs	
85 AIDS Education	**270** Character Education	**294** Accountability	Ⓐ = Alternative School		
88 Alternative/At Risk	**271** Migrant Education	**295** Network System	© = Charter School	New Schools are shaded	
89 Multi-Cultural Curriculum	**273** Teacher Mentor	**296** Title II Programs	Ⓜ = Magnet School	New Superintendents and Principals are bold	
90 Social Work	**274** Before/After Sch	**297** Webmaster	Ⓨ = Year-Round School	Personnel with email addresses are underscored	

GULF PRIVATE SCHOOLS

Private Schs..Principal	Grd	Prgm	Enr/#Cls	SN
Faith Christian Sch 801 20th St, Port St Joe 32456 Carla McGhee	K-9		90 10	850/229-6707 Fax 850/227-1307

HAMILTON COUNTY

HAMILTON PUBLIC SCHOOLS

• **Hamilton Co School Dist** PID: 00191403   386/792-7800
    5683 US Highway 129 S Ste 1, Jasper 32052   Fax 386/792-3681

Schools: 2 \ **Teachers:** 107 \ **Students:** 1,650 \ **Special Ed Students:** 196 \ **LEP Students:** 177 \ **College-Bound:** 40% \ **Ethnic:** African American 40%, Hispanic 14%, Caucasian 46% \ **Exp:** $299 (Med) \ **Poverty:** 35% \ **Title I:** $977,624 \ **Special Education:** $2,361,000 \ **Bilingual Education:** $438,000 \ **Open-Close:** 08/12 - 05/22 \ **DTBP:** $366 (High) \ 🇫

Rex Mitchell 1	Craig Newsome 3
Ida Daniels 4	Ward Daniels 5
Richard Vester 6	Phyllis Porter 11,57,271
Philip Pinello 15,68	Michael Vinson 19
Betty Linton 27,58,81,275	Johnny Bullard 67
Micha Cassidy 73,76,295	Chris Conbass 91
Carol Milton 296,298	

Public Schs..Principal	Grd	Prgm	Enr/#Cls	SN
Hamilton Co Elem Sch 5686 US Highway 1295, Jasper 32052 Peggy Hasty	PK-6		946	386/792-8000
Hamilton Co High Sch 5683 US Highway 129 S Ste 1, Jasper 32052 Donald Harrison	7-12	AGTV	633 43	49% 386/792-8100 Fax 386/792-6594

HAMILTON PRIVATE SCHOOLS

Private Schs..Principal	Grd	Prgm	Enr/#Cls	SN
Corinth Christian Academy 7042 SW 41st Ave, Jasper 32052 Karen Godwin	K-12		125 8	386/938-2270 Fax 386/938-2342
Jennings First Christian Sch 1286 Georgia St, Jennings 32053 Ralph Blackman	K-12		20 4	386/938-1179

HAMILTON REGIONAL CENTERS

• **FDLRS-Gateway** PID: 04496229   386/792-2877
    5683 US Highway 129 S Ste 1, Jasper 32052   Fax 386/792-3273

Rex Mitchell 1   Betty Linton 58

HARDEE COUNTY

HARDEE PUBLIC SCHOOLS

• **Hardee Co School Dist** PID: 00191477   863/773-9058
    1009 N 6th Ave, Wauchula 33873   Fax 863/773-0069

Schools: 8 \ **Teachers:** 321 \ **Students:** 5,276 \ **Special Ed Students:** 684 \ **LEP Students:** 499 \ **College-Bound:** 76% \ **Ethnic:** Asian 1%, African American 6%, Hispanic 64%, Caucasian 29% \ **Exp:** $265 (Med) \ **Poverty:** 30% \ **Title I:** $1,995,740 \ **Special Education:** $5,142,000 \ **Bilingual Education:** $1,057,000 \ **Open-Close:** 08/12 - 05/27 \ **DTBP:** $150 (High)

Robert Shayman 1	Greg Harrelson 2
Martha Garza 3	Rob Krahl 3,91
La Cheron Conway 4	Ron Herron 5
Travis Tubbs 6*	Kristen Rivas 7,9,16,34,83,93,288
Theresa Hall 8,11,57,69,89,271,294,296	Todd Durden 15
Todd Markel 16,73,84,295	Meredith Durastanti 30
Kerry Terrell 58	Kim Lowe 58
Paul Samuels 67	George Kelly 68
Sheena Benbow 68	Daniel Miller 73
David Green 73	Justin Swafford 73
R DeCoteau 73	Kim Williams 76
Maria Figueroa 76	Neda Cobb 76

Public Schs..Principal	Grd	Prgm	Enr/#Cls	SN
Bowling Green Elem Sch 4530 Church Ave, Bowling Green 33834 Stuart Durastanti	K-5	T	348 39	76% 863/375-2288 Fax 863/375-3501
Hardee Junior High Sch 2401 US Highway 17 N, Wauchula 33873 Sheryl Mosley	6-8	T	1,178 80	62% 863/773-3147 Fax 863/773-3167
Hardee Senior High Sch 830 Altman Rd, Wauchula 33873 Michele Polk	9-12	T	1,395 80	56% 863/773-3181 Fax 863/773-0487
Hilltop Elem Sch 2401 US Highway 17 N, Wauchula 33873 Beverly Cornelius	K-5	T	331	69% 863/773-2750 Fax 863/773-2751
North Wauchula Elem Sch 1120 N Florida Ave, Wauchula 33873 Jessica Gray	K-5	T	533 33	55% 863/773-2183 Fax 863/773-3514
Ⓐ Pioneer Career Academy 2630 Academy Dr, Zolfo Springs 33890 Karen Gustinger	6-12	T	24 4	64% 863/735-2300 Fax 863/735-2155
Wauchula Elem Sch 400 S Florida Ave, Wauchula 33873 Sonia Bennett	PK-5	T	673 45	27% 863/773-3141 Fax 863/773-0416
Zolfo Springs Elem Sch 3215 School House Rd, Zolfo Springs 33890 Tammy Pohl	K-5	T	556 34	68% 863/735-1221 Fax 863/735-1788

HARDEE PRIVATE SCHOOLS

Private Schs..Principal	Grd	Prgm	Enr/#Cls	SN
Florida Inst for Neuro Rehab 1962 Vandolah Rd, Wauchula 33873 Dr Kevin Okeefe	Spec	G	10 2	863/773-2857 Fax 863/773-2041

1	Superintendent	8	Curric/Instruct K-12	19	Chief Financial Officer	29	Family/Consumer Science	39	Social Studies K-12	49 English/Lang Arts Elem	59 Special Education Elem	69 Academic Assessment
2	Bus/Finance/Purchasing	9	Curric/Instruct Elem	20	Art K-12	30	Adult Education	40	Social Studies Elem	50 English/Lang Arts Sec	60 Special Education Sec	70 Research/Development
3	Buildings And Grounds	10	Curric/Instruct Sec	21	Art Elem	31	Career/Sch-to-Work K-12	41	Social Studies Sec	51 Reading K-12	61 Foreign/World Lang K-12	71 Public Information
4	Food Service	11	Federal Program	22	Art Sec	32	Career/Sch-to-Work Elem	42	Science K-12	52 Reading Elem	62 Foreign/World Lang Elem	72 Summer School
5	Transportation	12	Title I	23	Music K-12	33	Career/Sch-to-Work Sec	43	Science Elem	53 Reading Sec	63 Foreign/World Lang Sec	73 Instructional Tech
6	Athletic	13	Title V	24	Music Elem	34	Early Childhood Ed	44	Science Sec	54 Remedial Reading K-12	64 Religious Education K-12	74 Inservice Training
7	Health Services	14	Asst Superintendent	25	Music Sec	35	Health/Phys Education	45	Math K-12	55 Remedial Reading Elem	65 Religious Education Elem	75 Marketing/Distributive
		15	Instructional Media Svcs	26	Business Education	36	Guidance Services K-12	46	Math Elem	56 Remedial Reading Sec	66 Religious Education Sec	76 Info Systems
		16	Chief Operations Officer	27	Career & Tech Ed	37	Guidance Services Elem	47	Math Sec	57 Bilingual/ELL	67 School Board President	77 Psychological Assess
		17	Chief Academic Officer	28	Technology Education	38	Guidance Services Sec	48	English/Lang Arts K-12	58 Special Education K-12	68 Teacher Personnel	78 Affirmative Action

HENDRY COUNTY

HENDRY PUBLIC SCHOOLS

- **Hendry Co School Dist** PID: 00191544   863/674-4642
  25 E Hickpochee Ave, Labelle 33935   Fax 863/674-4090

Schools: 15 \ **Teachers:** 431 \ **Students:** 7,500 \
Special Ed Students: 1,104 \ **LEP Students:** 1,135 \ **College-Bound:** 55%
\ **Ethnic:** Asian 1%, African American 15%, Hispanic 64%, Caucasian
20% \ **Exp:** $291 (Med) \ **Poverty:** 33% \ **Title I:** $3,516,481 \
Special Education: $7,709,000 \ **Bilingual Education:** $2,992,000 \
Open-Close: 08/12 - 05/28 \ **DTBP:** $158 (High)

Paul Puletti 1
Kevin McCarthy 3,5
Angela Stayley 7,36,58,77,79,83,88,275
Lucinda Kelley 15,69
Barbara Mundy 57,271,296
Dwayne Brown 67
James Sealy 68
Kevin Rennolds 76
Michael Yanosik 2,19
San Janita Perez 4
Robert Egley 8,13,15,16,45,51,286,288
Michael Swindle 27,30,31*
Kristi Durance 59,294*
James Fealey 68
Leslie Mathis 73,74,76,295

Public Schs..Principal	Grd	Prgm	Enr/#Cls	SN
Central Elem Sch 1000 S Deane Duff Ave, Clewiston 33440 Melissa Carter	PK-5	T	595 36	73% 863/983-1550 Fax 863/983-1558
Clewiston Adult Sch 475 E Osceola Ave, Clewiston 33440 Michael Swindle	Adult	V	25 5	863/983-1511 Fax 863/983-1517
Clewiston High Sch 1501 S Francisco St, Clewiston 33440 Roberto Sanchez	9-12	TV	956 40	57% 863/983-1520 Fax 863/983-2168
Clewiston Middle Sch 601 W Pasadena Ave, Clewiston 33440 Kristi Durance	6-8	GTV	758 50	69% 863/983-1530 Fax 863/983-1541
Ⓐ Clewiston Youth Dev Academy 475 E Osceola Ave, Clewiston 33440 Martin Espinoza	6-12	T	18 5	863/902-4216 Fax 863/983-1509
Country Oaks Elem Sch 2052 NW Eucalyptus Blvd, Labelle 33935 Robin Jones	PK-5	T	741 45	74% 863/674-4140 Fax 863/674-4129
Eastside Elem Sch 201 Arroyo Ave, Clewiston 33440 Sarah Sanchez	PK-5	T	604 60	72% 863/983-1560 Fax 863/983-1564
Edward A Upthegrove Elem Sch 280 N Main St, Labelle 33935 Richard Talada	PK-5	T	492 25	70% 863/612-0750 Fax 863/612-0753
LaBelle Adult Sch 300 W Cowboy Way, Labelle 33935 Gary Breakfield	Adult	V	75 6	863/674-4118 Fax 863/674-4117
LaBelle Elem Sch 150 W Cowboy Way, Labelle 33935 Jane Hatfield	PK-5	T	490 45	77% 863/674-4150 Fax 863/674-4155
LaBelle High Sch 4050 E Cowboy Way, Labelle 33935 Dave Kelley	9-12	TV	1,222 43	58% 863/674-4120 Fax 863/674-4571
LaBelle Middle Sch 8000 E Cowboy Way, Labelle 33935 Iris Borghese	6-8	TV	823 40	65% 863/674-4646 Fax 863/674-4645
Ⓐ LaBelle Youth Dev Academy 1100 Forestry Division Rd, Labelle 33935 Shaunna Prope	6-12	T	30 5	76% 863/674-4590 Fax 863/674-4591
Montura Early Learning Center 225 N Hacienda St, Clewiston 33440 Barbara Mundy	PK-PK		24	863/983-1417
Westside Elem Sch 205 Arroyo Ave, Clewiston 33440 Anthony Busin	K-5	T	486 38	73% 863/983-1570 Fax 863/902-4232

HENDRY PRIVATE SCHOOLS

Private Schs..Principal	Grd	Prgm	Enr/#Cls	SN
Clewiston Christian Sch 601 Caribbean Ave, Clewiston 33440 George Duckstein	PK-6		122	863/983-5388

HERNANDO COUNTY

HERNANDO PUBLIC SCHOOLS

- **Hernando Co School Dist** PID: 00191611   352/797-7000
  919 N Broad St, Brooksville 34601   Fax 352/797-7104

Schools: 27 \ **Teachers:** 1,436 \ **Students:** 21,790 \
Special Ed Students: 2,961 \ **LEP Students:** 627 \ **College-Bound:** 50%
\ **Ethnic:** Asian 2%, African American 8%, Hispanic 20%, Caucasian
70% \ **Exp:** $151 (Low) \ **Poverty:** 17% \ **Title I:** $5,973,095 \
Special Education: $20,432,000 \ **Bilingual Education:** $1,401,000 \
Open-Close: 08/12 - 05/29 \ **DTBP:** $178 (High)

John Stratton 1
Joyce McEntyre 2
Argely Cespedes 3
John Martin 3
Lori Drenth 4
Gina Michalicka 8,31,285
Angela Kennedy 11,57
Heather Martin 15
Cathy Doska 58
Susan Duval 67
Donna Reilly 69
Karen Jordan 71
Joseph Amato 73,76
Karen Klingensmith 84
Ivette Mendoza 93
Janet Alfano 2
Kendra Sittig 2
Genele Firlik 3
Sean Arnold 3
Ralph Leath 5
Lisa Cropli 10
Paula Clark 11,74,296
Sophia Watson 27,30,280
Cathy Dofka 58,79,88,90
Ray Pinder 68
Linda Peirce 69,294
Patrick Keough 71
Sandra Hurst 77,752
Jill Renanhan 91
Walter Paschke 295

Public Schs..Principal	Grd	Prgm	Enr/#Cls	SN
Ⓒ Best Academy 835 School St, Brooksville 34601 Henry Buford	6-8	T	113	67% 352/544-2373 Fax 352/544-2375
Brooksville Elem Sch 885 N Broad St, Brooksville 34601 Glenn Lastra	PK-5	T	639 52	78% 352/797-7014 Fax 352/797-7114
Central High Sch 14075 Ken Austin Pkwy, Brooksville 34613 Kelly Slusser	9-12	GTV	1,269 111	65% 352/797-7020 Fax 352/797-7120
Ⓜ Challenger Sch of Sci & Math 13400 Elgin Blvd, Spring Hill 34609 Lisa Piesik	K-8	T	1,433	38% 352/797-7024 Fax 352/797-7124

79	Student Personnel	91	Safety/Security	275	Response To Intervention	298	Grant Writer/Ptnrships	School Programs		Social Media	

79 Student Personnel
80 Driver Ed/Safety
81 Gifted/Talented
82 Video Services
83 Substance Abuse Prev
84 Erate
85 AIDS Education
88 Alternative/At Risk
89 Multi-Cultural Curriculum
90 Social Work

91 Safety/Security
92 Magnet School
93 Parental Involvement
95 Tech Prep Program
97 Chief Information Officer
98 Chief Technology Officer
270 Character Education
271 Migrant Education
273 Teacher Mentor
274 Before/After Sch

275 Response To Intervention
277 Remedial Math K-12
280 Literacy Coach
285 STEM
286 Digital Learning
288 Common Core Standards
294 Accountability
295 Network System
296 Title II Programs
297 Webmaster

298 Grant Writer/Ptnrships
750 Chief Innovation Officer
751 Chief of Staff
752 Social Emotional Learning

Other School Types
Ⓐ = Alternative School
Ⓒ = Charter School
Ⓜ = Magnet School
Ⓨ = Year-Round School

School Programs
A = Alternative Program
G = Adult Classes
M = Magnet Program
T = Title I Schoolwide
V = Career & Tech Ed Programs

New Schools are shaded
New Superintendents and Principals are bold
Personnel with email addresses are underscored

Social Media
 = Facebook
 = Twitter

Ⓜ Chocachatti Elem Sch | K-5 | T | 741 | 45% 352/797-7067
4135 California St, Brooksville 34604 | | | 30 | Fax 352/797-7167
Lara Silva

D S Parrott Middle Sch | 6-8 | TV | 670 | 80% 352/797-7075
19220 Youth Dr, Brooksville 34601 | | | 50 | Fax 352/797-7175
Edward LaRose

Deltona Elem Sch | PK-5 | T | 833 | 85% 352/797-7040
2055 Deltona Blvd, Spring Hill 34606 | | | 52 | Fax 352/797-7140
Debi Shellabarger

Eastside Elem Sch | PK-5 | T | 673 | 86% 352/797-7045
27151 Roper Rd, Brooksville 34602 | | | 34 | Fax 352/797-7145
Mary LeDoux

Ⓐ Endeavor Academy | 6-12 | T | 127 | 83% 352/797-7013
14063 Ken Austin Pkwy, Brooksville 34613 | | | 6 | Fax 352/797-7113
Stephen Crognale

Explorer K-8 Sch | PK-8 | T | 1,695 | 81% 352/797-7094
10252 Northcliffe Blvd, Spring Hill 34608 | | | | Fax 352/797-7194
Barbara Kidder

Fox Chapel Middle Sch | 6-8 | T | 768 | 84% 352/797-7025
9412 Fox Chapel Ln, Spring Hill 34606 | | | 50 | Fax 352/797-7125
Ray Pinder

Frank W Springstead High Sch | 9-12 | AGTV | 1,721 | 54% 352/797-7010
3300 Mariner Blvd, Spring Hill 34609 | | | 75 | Fax 352/797-7110
Carmine Rufa

Ⓒ Gulf Coast Acad Science Tech | 6-8 | | 236 | 41% 352/688-5092
10444 Tillery Rd, Spring Hill 34608 | | | 6 | Fax 352/688-5095
Nevian Fieserg

Ⓒ Gulf Coast Middle Sch | 6-8 | T | 110 | 48% 352/666-5790
2139 Deborah Dr, Spring Hill 34609 | | | | Fax 352/666-5792
Joe Gatti

Hernando Eschool | 6-12 | | 53 | 352/797-7072
1070 Varsity Dr, Brooksville 34601 | | | | Fax 352/797-7156
Zana Brooks

Hernando High Sch | 9-12 | GTV | 1,161 | 61% 352/797-7015
111 Ernie Chatman Run, Brooksville 34601 | | | 60 | Fax 352/797-7115
Leechele Booker

John D Floyd Elem Sch | PK-5 | T | 964 | 71% 352/797-7055
3139 Dumont Ave, Spring Hill 34609 | | | 44 | Fax 352/797-7155
Joyce Lewis

Moton Elem Sch | PK-5 | T | 569 | 83% 352/797-7065
7175 Emerson Rd, Brooksville 34601 | | | 50 | Fax 352/797-7165
Brent Gaustad

Nature Coast Technical HS | Voc | GT | 1,432 | 51% 352/797-7088
4057 California St, Brooksville 34604 | | | | Fax 352/797-7188
Toni-Ann Noyes

Pine Grove Elem Sch | PK-5 | T | 916 | 79% 352/797-7090
14411 Ken Austin Pkwy, Brooksville 34613 | | | 44 | Fax 352/797-7190
Thomas Kalament

Powell Middle Sch | 6-8 | TV | 1,014 | 65% 352/797-7095
4100 Barclay Ave, Brooksville 34609 | | | 50 | Fax 352/797-7195
Tom Dye

Spring Hill Elem Sch | PK-5 | T | 896 | 78% 352/797-7030
6001 Mariner Blvd, Spring Hill 34609 | | | 35 | Fax 352/797-7130
Michael Maine

Suncoast Elem Sch | PK-5 | T | 930 | 69% 352/797-7085
11135 Quality Dr, Spring Hill 34609 | | | 60 | Fax 352/797-7185
Scott Piesik

Weeki Wachee High Sch | 9-12 | T | 1,277 | 60% 352/797-7029
12150 Vespa Way, Weeki Wachee 34614 | | | | Fax 352/797-7129
Troy Labarbara

West Hernando Middle Sch | 6-8 | TV | 686 | 80% 352/797-7035
14325 Ken Austin Pkwy, Brooksville 34613 | | | 45 | Fax 352/797-7135
Christopher Healy

Westside Elem Sch | PK-5 | T | 564 | 88% 352/797-7080
5400 Applegate Dr, Spring Hill 34606 | | | 44 | Fax 352/797-7180
Kristina Stratton

Winding Waters Sch | PK-8 | T | 1,381 | 66% 352/797-7092
12240 Vespa Way, Weeki Wachee 34614 | | | | Fax 352/797-7192
Janet Cerro

HERNANDO CATHOLIC SCHOOLS

• **Diocese St Petersburg Ed Off** PID: 00200729
Listing includes only schools located in this county. See District Index for location of Diocesan Offices.

Catholic Schs..Principal	Grd	Prgm	Enr/#Cls	SN
Notre Dame Catholic Sch	PK-8		245	352/683-0755
1095 Commercial Way, Spring Hill 34606			16	Fax 352/683-3924
Florence Buono				

HERNANDO PRIVATE SCHOOLS

Private Schs..Principal	Grd	Prgm	Enr/#Cls	SN
Eden Christian Sch	PK-PK		22	352/796-1619
22308 Lake Lindsey Rd, Brooksville 34601			5	Fax 352/796-3889
Brenda King				
First United Methodist Sch	PK-8		176	352/796-3496
109 S Broad St, Brooksville 34601			15	Fax 352/796-3432
Erin Sullivan				
Hernando Christian Academy	PK-12		360	352/796-0616
7200 Emerson Rd, Brooksville 34601			30	Fax 352/799-3400
Tammy Vandemark				
Queen of All Saints	K-12		35	352/428-4847
20120 Barnett Rd, Brooksville 34601				
Joseph Selway				
Spring Hill Christian Academy	PK-12		300	352/683-8485
3140 Mariner Blvd, Spring Hill 34609			20	Fax 352/683-5807
Michael Willis				🅵🅴
West Hernando Christian Sch	PK-12		275	352/688-9918
2250 Osowaw Blvd, Spring Hill 34607			14	Fax 352/683-1184
David Hand				
Wider Horizons Sch	PK-12		160	352/686-1934
4060 Castle Ave, Spring Hill 34609			8	Fax 352/688-4371
Dr Dominick Maglio				

HIGHLANDS COUNTY

HIGHLANDS PUBLIC SCHOOLS

• **Highlands Co School Dist** PID: 00191702 | 863/471-5555
426 School St, Sebring 33870 | Fax 863/471-5600

Schools: 19 \ **Teachers:** 765 \ **Students:** 12,300 \
Special Ed Students: 1,844 \ **LEP Students:** 665 \ **College-Bound:** 40%
\ **Ethnic:** Asian 2%, African American 18%, Hispanic 36%, Caucasian
45% \ **Exp:** $147 (Low) \ **Poverty:** 32% \ **Title I:** $5,650,890 \
Special Education: $12,035,000 \ **Bilingual Education:** $1,740,000 \
Open-Close: 08/12 - 05/22 \ **DTBP:** $171 (High)

Dr Brenda Longshore ....1 Anjelica Tinajero 2

1	Superintendent	8	Curric/Instruct K-12	19	Chief Financial Officer	29	Family/Consumer Science	39	Social Studies K-12	49	English/Lang Arts Elem	59	Special Education Elem	69	Academic Assessment
2	Bus/Finance/Purchasing	9	Curric/Instruct Elem	20	Art K-12	30	Adult Education	40	Social Studies Elem	50	English/Lang Arts Sec	60	Special Education Sec	70	Research/Development
3	Buildings And Grounds	10	Curric/Instruct Sec	21	Art Elem	31	Career/Sch-to-Work K-12	41	Social Studies Sec	51	Reading K-12	61	Foreign/World Lang K-12	71	Public Information
4	Food Service	11	Federal Program	22	Art Sec	32	Career/Sch-to-Work Elem	42	Science K-12	52	Reading Elem	62	Foreign/World Lang Elem	72	Summer School
5	Transportation	12	Title I	23	Music K-12	33	Career/Sch-to-Work Sec	43	Science Elem	53	Reading Sec	63	Foreign/World Lang Sec	73	Instructional Tech
6	Athletic	13	Title V	24	Music Elem	34	Early Childhood Ed	44	Science Sec	54	Remedial Reading K-12	64	Religious Education K-12	74	Inservice Training
7	Health Services	14	Asst Superintendent	25	Music Sec	35	Health/Phys Education	45	Math K-12	55	Remedial Reading Elem	65	Religious Education Elem	75	Marketing/Distributive
		15	Asst Superintendent	26	Business Education	36	Guidance Services K-12	46	Math Elem	56	Remedial Reading Sec	66	Religious Education Sec	76	Info Systems
		16	Instructional Media Svcs	27	Career & Tech Ed	37	Guidance Services Elem	47	Math Sec	57	Bilingual/ELL	67	School Board President	77	Psychological Assess
		17	Chief Operations Officer	28	Technology Education	38	Guidance Services Sec	48	English/Lang Arts K-12	58	Special Education K-12	68	Teacher Personnel	78	Affirmative Action
		18	Chief Academic Officer												

Public Schs..Principal	Grd	Prgm	Enr/#Cls	SN	
Ⓐ Academy at Youth Care Lane 4121 Youth Care Ln, Sebring 33870 Darrell Heckman	6-12	T	25 2	79%	863/471-5457 Fax 863/471-5460
Avon Elem Sch 705 Winthrop St, Avon Park 33825 Carla Ball	K-5	T	603 40	87%	863/452-4355 Fax 863/452-4372
Avon Park High Sch 700 E Main St, Avon Park 33825 Danielle Erwin	9-12	TV	1,084 50	75%	863/452-4311 Fax 863/452-4324
Avon Park Middle Sch 401 S Lake Ave, Avon Park 33825 Page Green	6-8	TV	632 30	87%	863/452-4333 Fax 863/452-4341
Cracker Trail Elem Sch 8200 Sparta Rd, Sebring 33875 Richard Kogelschatz	PK-5	T	630 38	61%	863/471-5777 Fax 863/471-5785
Fred Wild Elem Sch 3550 Youth Care Ln, Sebring 33870 Jeannie Inagawa	PK-5	T	530 54	92%	863/471-5400 Fax 863/471-5426
Highlands Virtual Sch 426 School St, Sebring 33870 Lorie Layfield	6-12		25		863/471-5679 Fax 863/471-5568
Hill-Gustat Middle Sch 4700 Schumacher Rd, Sebring 33872 Christopher Doty	6-8	TV	714 48	74%	863/471-5437 Fax 863/314-5245
Kindergarten Learning Center 3560 US Highway 27 S, Sebring 33870 Karin Doty	K-K	T	355	76%	863/314-5281 Fax 863/314-5287
Lake Country Elem Sch 516 County Road 29, Lake Placid 33852 Shane Ward	PK-5	T	584 39	85%	863/699-5050 Fax 863/699-5058
Lake Placid Elem Sch 101 Green Dragon Dr, Lake Placid 33852 Candis Dean	PK-5	T	723	81%	863/699-5070 Fax 863/699-5079
Lake Placid High Sch 202 Green Dragon Dr, Lake Placid 33852 Kevin Tunning	9-12	TV	807 40	68%	863/699-5010 Fax 863/699-5094
Lake Placid Middle Sch 201 S Tangerine Ave, Lake Placid 33852 Jennifer Sanchez	6-8	TV	667 40	75%	863/699-5030 Fax 863/699-5029
Memorial Elem Sch 867 Memorial Dr, Avon Park 33825 Courtney Floyd	K-5	T	656	88%	863/784-0200 Fax 863/784-0211
Park Elem Sch 327 E Palmetto St, Avon Park 33825 **Carey Conner**	PK-5	T	533 33	85%	863/452-4373 Fax 863/452-4382
Sebring High Sch 3514 Kenilworth Blvd, Sebring 33870 Kim Ervin	9-12	TV	1,597	65%	863/471-5500 Fax 863/471-5507
Sebring Middle Sch 500 E Center Ave, Sebring 33870 Seth Lambert	6-8	TV	779	69%	863/471-5700 Fax 863/471-5710
Sun'N Lake Elem Sch 4515 Ponce De Leon Blvd, Sebring 33872 Dr Linda Laye	PK-5	T	642 38	77%	863/471-5464 Fax 863/471-5466 🔲

Woodlawn Elem Sch 817 Woodlawn Dr, Sebring 33870 Jonathon Spencer	PK-5	T	651 34	80%	863/471-5444 Fax 863/471-5446

HIGHLANDS CATHOLIC SCHOOLS

- **Diocese of Venice Ed Office** PID: 02231695
  Listing includes only schools located in this county. See District Index for location of Diocesan Offices.

Catholic Schs..Principal	Grd	Prgm	Enr/#Cls	SN	
St Catherine Catholic Sch 747 S Franklin St, Sebring 33870 Jorge Rivera	PK-8		215 2		863/873-2558 Fax 863/385-7310

HIGHLANDS PRIVATE SCHOOLS

Private Schs..Principal	Grd	Prgm	Enr/#Cls	SN	
Cornerstone Christian Academy 2600 N Highlands Blvd, Avon Park 33825 Mark Langner	K-5		90		863/453-0894
Heartland Christian Academy 1160 Persimmon Ave, Sebring 33870 Rebekah Kogelschatz	PK-12		169 15		863/385-3850 Fax 863/385-5752
Lakeview Christian Sch 496 Kent Ave, Lake Placid 33852 Christena Villarreal	PK-5		99 7		863/465-0313 Fax 863/465-0126
Walker Memorial Academy 1525 W Avon Blvd, Avon Park 33825 Jacqueline Colon Diaz	PK-12		240 15		863/453-3131 Fax 863/453-4925

HIGHLANDS REGIONAL CENTERS

- **FDLRS-Heartland** PID: 04496114   863/531-0444
  1076 US 27 N, Lake Placid 33852   Fax 863/531-0425

Kathy Mathis 1

HILLSBOROUGH COUNTY

HILLSBOROUGH PUBLIC SCHOOLS

- **Hillsborough Co Pub Sch Dist** PID: 00191805   813/272-4000
  901 E Kennedy Blvd, Tampa 33602   Fax 813/272-4510

Schools: 292 \ *Teachers:* 18,267 \
Students: 220,287 \ *Special Ed Students:* 30,299 \ *LEP Students:* 26,453
\ *College-Bound:* 75% \ *Ethnic:* Asian 4%, African American 22%, Hispanic 38%, Caucasian 36% \ *Exp:* $164 (Low) \ *Poverty:* 19% \ *Title I:* $73,743,812
\ *Special Education:* $173,300,000 \ *Bilingual Education:* $56,988,000 \
Open-Close: 08/12 - 05/29 \ *DTBP:* $198 (High) \ 🔲

Jeff Eakins 1   Gretchen Saunders 2

79	Student Personnel	91	Safety/Security	275	Response To Intervention	298	Grant Writer/Ptnrships	School Programs	Social Media
80	Driver Ed/Safety	92	Magnet School	277	Remedial Math K-12	750	Chief Innovation Officer	A = Alternative Program	
81	Gifted/Talented	93	Parental Involvement	280	Literacy Coach	751	Chief of Staff	G = Adult Classes	🔲 = Facebook
82	Video Services	95	Tech Prep Program	285	STEM	752	Social Emotional Learning	M = Magnet Program	
83	Substance Abuse Prev	97	Chief Information Officer	286	Digital Learning			T = Title I Schoolwide	🔲 = Twitter
84	Erate	98	Chief Technology Officer	288	Common Core Standards	Other School Types	V = Career & Tech Ed Programs	
85	AIDS Education	270	Character Education	294	Accountability	Ⓐ = Alternative School		
68	Alternative/At Risk	271	Migrant Education	295	Network System	Ⓒ = Charter School	New Schools are shaded	
89	Multi-Cultural Curriculum	273	Teacher Mentor	296	Title II Programs	Ⓜ = Magnet School	New Superintendents and Principals are bold	
90	Social Work	274	Before/After Sch	297	Webmaster	Ⓨ = Year-Round School	Personnel with email addresses are underscored	

Chris Farkas 3,5,17	Robert Wegmann 3
James Beekman 5	Lanness Robinson 6
Deborah Cook 8,18,288	Van Ayres 8,15
Ted Hope 10,25	Trayce Brown 11,15
Tricia McManus 15,750	Anne Townsend 17,36,77
Dana Warner 20	Melanie Faulkner 21,24
Warren Brooks 27,31	Ansberto Vallejo 33
Lisa Black 34	Steve Vanoer 35,85
Philip Francis 37	Angelique Xenick 38
Shanshera Quinn 38	Dr Dennis Holt 41
Michael Smith 47	Elizabeth Brown 50
Melissa Alonso 52	Sandra Rosario 57
Kim Workman 58	Deborah Davis 60
Melissa Morgado 61	Tamara Shamburger 67
Myra Hogue 69,90	Nicole Binder 69,294
Lisa Placko 70,298	Grayson Kamm 71
Christina Russell 73,286	Richard Laneau 73
Minerva Spanner-Morrow 78	Dr Lauri Kirsch 81
John Newman 91	Jenna Hodgens 92
Marylou Whaley 93	Lynn Underwood 280
Shana Tirado 285	Dr Marie Whelan 751
Elizabeth Tanner 752	

Public Schs..Principal

Public Schs..Principal	Grd	Prgm	Enr/#Cls	SN	
© Advantage Academy-Hillsborough [132] 304 W Prosser Dr, Plant City 33563 **Keith Miller**	K-8	T	461 18	16%	813/567-0801 Fax 813/441-0272
Aparicio-Levy Technical Center 10119 E Ellicott St, Tampa 33610 Paul Gansomer	Voc	G	200		813/740-4884 Fax 813/740-4885
© Avant Garde Academy Westchase 13901 Sheldon Rd, Tampa 33626 Virginia Maxwell	K-7		389		813/551-2144 Fax 888/799-3166
© Bell Creek Academy [132] 13221 Boyette Rd, Riverview 33569 **Chris Hammill**	6-12		643	8%	813/793-6075 Fax 813/548-2165
© Bell Creek High School Academy 13221 Boyette Rd, Riverview 33569 Dr Margaret Fahringer	9-12		451	4%	813/793-6075 Fax 813/548-2165
Brewster Tech & Adult Center 2222 N Tampa St, Tampa 33602 **Shirley Robbins**	Adult	V	400		813/276-5448 Fax 813/276-5756
© Bridgeprep Acad of Riverview 6309 US Highway 301 S, Riverview 33578 Marvin Pitts	K-7		883		813/370-1910
© Bridgeprep Academy-Tampa 2418 W Swann Ave, Tampa 33609 Christine Harris	K-6		227	16%	813/258-5652
© Brooks Debartolo Collegiate HS 10948 N Central Ave, Tampa 33612 Kristine Bennett	9-12		609	21%	813/971-5600 Fax 813/971-5656
© Channelside Acad of Math & Sci [132] 1029 E Twiggs St, Tampa 33602 Cristina Fuentes	K-5	T	378	8%	813/579-9649 Fax 813/330-3149
Channelside Academy Middle Sch 1029 E Twiggs St, Tampa 33602 **Cristina Fuentes**	6-8	T	138	9%	813/579-9649 Fax 813/330-3149
© Cmty Charter Sch of Excellence 1251 E Fowler Ave Ste A, Tampa 33612 Ebony Potts	K-8	T	302	100%	813/971-5500 Fax 813/971-5232
© Collaboratory Prep Academy 6406 E Chelsea St, Tampa 33610 Heather Jenkins	K-4		80		813/586-3172
© Creekside Charter Academy [133] 14020 US Highway 301 S, Riverview 33578 Dianne Stahl	K-6		617		813/419-5340 Fax 813/419-5341
© Dr Kiran C Patel High Sch Fowler Ave, Tampa 33614 **Dr Marlee Strawn**	9-9		300		

	Grd	Prgm	Enr/#Cls	SN	
© East Tampa Academy 4309 N 34th St, Tampa 33610 **Frankie Jones**	K-1		37		813/816-2100
Erwin Technical Center 2010 E Hillsborough Ave, Tampa 33610 **Dr James Goode**	Adult	V	1,000 35		813/769-5180 Fax 813/769-5181
© Excelsior Prep Charter Sch 2156 University Square Mall, Tampa 33612 **Stephanie Mullings**	K-3		109		813/644-9060 Fax 813/200-1113
© Florida Autism Ctr Excellence 6310 E Sligh Ave, Tampa 33617 **Sherry Maklary**	Spec	T	104	59%	813/985-3223 Fax 813/985-3199
© Florida Connections Academy 5805 Breckenridge Pkwy Ste E, Tampa 33610 **Marcie Trombino**	K-10		1,300		855/741-5127
© Florida Cyber Charter Academy 9143 Philips Hwy Ste 590, Jacksonville 32256 Sharon Williams \ Bridget White	K-12		246	18%	904/247-3268 Fax 877/719-1645
© Focus Academy 304 Druid Hills Rd, Temple Terr 33617 **Elisabeth Kraft**	Spec		75	13%	813/443-5558
Gary Adult Education Center 5101 N 40th St, Tampa 33610 Edward Cristiano	Adult		200		813/740-7660 Fax 813/740-7674
© Henderson Hammock Charter Sch [133] 10322 Henderson Rd, Tampa 33625 **James Griffin**	K-8	T	1,147	19%	813/739-6633 Fax 813/498-4304
© Hillsborough Acad Math & Sci [132] 9659 W Waters Ave, Tampa 33635 Brittany Deen	K-8		801	11%	813/793-6085 Fax 813/413-2984
Hillsborough Virtual Sch 2704 N Highland Ave, Tampa 33602 **Christina Russell**	K-12		369	20%	813/983-7278 Fax 813/983-7920
© Horizon Charter School Tampa [142] 7235 W Hillsborough Ave, Tampa 33634 Sheila Thomley	K-8		303 5	14%	813/887-3800 Fax 813/885-9626
© Ican Charter Academy 4901 E 10th Ave, Tampa 33605 **Dr Zenobia Cann**	K-8		401		813/563-3809
© Independence Academy [132] 12902 W Highway 92, Dover 33527 Jack Burkett	K-8	T	937	6%	813/473-8600 Fax 813/441-7160
© Kid's Cmty Clg Riverview South 10030 Mathog Rd, Riverview 33578 Karen Seder	K-8		565 15	31%	813/671-1440 Fax 813/671-1245
© Kids Cmty Clg SE Chtr Sch 11519 McMullen Rd, Riverview 33569 **Brandy Tackett**	K-5		353	32%	813/699-4600 Fax 813/601-9566
© Kids Cmty Clg SE Mid CS 11513 McMullen Rd, Riverview 33569 Brandy Tackett	6-8		193		813/672-0144
© Kids Cmty College Charter HS 10550 Johanna Ave, Riverview 33578 Lakeshia Cook	9-12		175		813/699-5751
Learey Technical College 5410 N 20th St, Tampa 33610 Dr James Goode	Adult	AV	300		813/231-1840
© Learning Gate Cmty Sch 16215 Hanna Rd, Lutz 33549 Michelle Mason	K-8		794 9	4%	813/948-4190 Fax 813/948-7587
© Legacy Preparatory Academy 302 E Linebaugh Ave, Tampa 33612 Yolanda Capers	K-8	T	261 12	99%	813/253-0053 Fax 813/253-0182
© Literacy Leadership Tech Acad 6771 Madison Ave, Tampa 33619 Sharla Austin \ Joanie Rutherford	K-8		632 13	7%	813/234-0940 Fax 813/234-0946

1	Superintendent	8	Curric/Instruct K-12	19	Chief Financial Officer	29	Family/Consumer Science	
2	Bus/Finance/Purchasing	9	Curric/Instruct Elem	20	Art K-12	30	Adult Education	
3	Buildings And Grounds	10	Curric/Instruct Sec	21	Art Elem	31	Career/Sch-to-Work K-12	
4	Food Service	11	Federal Program	22	Art Sec	32	Career/Sch-to-Work Elem	
5	Transportation	12	Title I	23	Music K-12	33	Career/Sch-to-Work Sec	
6	Athletic	13	Title V	24	Music Elem	34	Early Childhood Ed	
7	Health Services	15	Asst Superintendent	25	Music Sec	35	Health/Phys Education	
		16	Instructional Media Svcs	26	Business Education	36	Guidance Services K-12	
		17	Chief Operations Officer	27	Career & Tech Ed	37	Guidance Services Elem	
		18	Chief Academic Officer	28	Technology Education	38	Guidance Services Sec	

39	Social Studies K-12	49	English/Lang Arts Elem	59	Special Education Elem	69	Academic Assessment
40	Social Studies Elem	50	English/Lang Arts Sec	60	Special Education Sec	70	Research/Development
41	Social Studies Sec	51	Reading K-12	61	Foreign/World Lang K-12	71	Public Information
42	Science K-12	52	Reading Elem	62	Foreign/World Lang Elem	72	Summer School
43	Science Elem	53	Reading Sec	63	Foreign/World Lang Sec	73	Instructional Tech
44	Science Sec	54	Remedial Reading K-12	64	Religious Education K-12	74	Inservice Training
45	Math K-12	55	Remedial Reading Elem	65	Religious Education Elem	75	Marketing/Distributive
46	Math Elem	56	Remedial Reading Sec	66	Religious Education Sec	76	Info Systems
47	Math Sec	57	Bilingual/ELL	67	School Board President	77	Psychological Assess
48	English/Lang Arts K-12	58	Special Education K-12	68	Teacher Personnel	78	Affirmative Action

School	Grd	Prgm	Enr/#Cls	SN	Phone
© Lutz Preparatory Sch 17951 N US Highway 41, Lutz 33549 <u>Bonnie Guertin</u>	K-8		783	1%	813/428-7100 Fax 813/426-7061
© Mosi Partnership Sch 4801 E Fowler Ave Ste 100, Tampa 33617 <u>Renel Mathurin</u>	K-5	T	273	94%	813/983-3989 Fax 813/983-3998
ⓜ Navigator Acad of Leadership 1101 Bloomingdale Ave, Valrico 33596 **Shane Clark**	K-8		401		863/866-7566
© New Springs Elem Sch 2410 E Busch Blvd, Tampa 33612 <u>Oguz Tekin</u>	K-5	T	333	80%	813/933-5025 Fax 813/527-9982
© New Springs Middle Sch 2410 E Busch Blvd, Tampa 33612 <u>Oguz Tekin</u>	6-8		130		813/933-5025 Fax 813/527-9982
Ⓐ Pace Ctr for Girls-Hillsboro 1933 E Hillsboro Ave Ste 300, Tampa 33610 <u>Tanya Hollins</u>	6-12		60 6	13%	813/739-0410 Fax 813/739-0416
© Pepin Academies-Tampa 3916 E Hillsborough Ave, Tampa 33610 <u>Monika Perez</u>	3-12	T	789 50	11%	813/236-1755 Fax 813/236-1195
© Pepin Academy-Riverview 9304 Camden Field Pkwy, Riverview 33578 <u>Geri Henry</u>	3-12		260		813/533-2999 Fax 813/533-2966
© Pivot Charter Sch 3020 S Falkenburg Rd, Riverview 33578 <u>Elizabeth Bretz</u>	6-12		259	26%	813/626-6724
© Plato Academy Tampa CS [144] 4903 Ehrlich Rd, Tampa 33624 <u>Matthew Gunderson</u>	K-3		118		727/205-6360
© RCMA Leadership Academy 18236 S US Highway 310, Wimauma 33598 <u>Mark Haggett</u>	6-8	T	112	86%	813/672-5159 Fax 813/633-6119
© RCMA Wimauma Academy 18236 S US Highway 301, Wimauma 33598 <u>Mark Haggett</u>	K-5	T	222 10	95%	813/672-5159 Fax 813/633-6119
© Riverview Acad Math & Science 9906 Symmes Rd, Riverview 33578 **Marcy Ringdahl**	K-8		401		813/412-6111 Fax 954/755-6066
© Seminole Heights Charter HS [131] 4006 N Florida Ave, Tampa 33603 **Franca Washington**	9-12	T	254	39%	813/234-0809 Fax 813/236-2406
© Slam Apollo 5150 N US Highway 41, Apollo Beach 33572 **M Williamson**	K-8		401		813/773-4560
© Southshore Charter Academy [133] 11667 Big Bend Rd, Riverview 33579 **Dr Cecilia Garcia**	K-8		1,160	37%	813/769-1209 Fax 813/769-2161
© Sports Ldrshp Management Acad [130] 7116 Gunn Hwy, Tampa 33625 **Aimee Mielke**	6-12		532		813/920-8802
© Sunlake Academy of Math & Sci [132] 18681 N Dale Mabry Hwy, Lutz 33548 Marisa Martinez	K-8		877		813/616-5099 Fax 813/343-6099
© Terrace Community Middle Sch 11734 Jefferson Rd, Thonotosassa 33592 <u>Tahvia Shaw</u>	6-8		660 20	3%	813/987-6555 Fax 813/987-6565
© Trinity School for Children 2402 W Osborne Ave, Tampa 33603 Dr Madeline O'Dea	K-8		855 17	2%	813/874-2402 Fax 813/874-2412
© Valrico Lake Advantage Academy 13306 Boyette Rd, Riverview 33569 <u>Lauren Herbert</u>	K-5		956	4%	813/699-5049 Fax 813/413-2898
© Village of Excellence Acad MS 4602 E Busch Blvd, Tampa 33617 <u>Cametra Edwards</u>	6-8	T	110	95%	813/374-9422 Fax 813/306-2202
© Village of Excellence Academy 8718 N 46th St, Temple Terr 33617 <u>Romaine Edwards</u>	K-5	T	247 6	94%	813/988-8632 Fax 813/983-0683
© Walton Academy-Performing Arts 4817 N Florida Ave, Tampa 33603 Tanika Walton	K-5	T	212 12	91%	813/231-9272 Fax 813/231-9271
© Waterset Charter Sch [133] 6540 Knowledge Ln, Apollo Beach 33572 <u>Sara Capwell</u>	K-7		966		813/602-0622
© West University Charter HS [131] 11602 N 15th St, Tampa 33612 **Bobby Smith**	9-12	T	287	20%	813/774-4396
© Winthrop Charter Sch [133] 6204 Scholars Hill Ln, Riverview 33578 <u>Terry Johnson</u>	K-8		1,336	32%	813/235-4811 Fax 813/315-4403
© Woodmont Charter Sch [133] 10402 N 56th St, Temple Terr 33617 **Rasheema Caldwell**	K-8	T	739	21%	813/708-1596 Fax 813/739-7301

● **Hillsborough Co SD-Achievement** PID: 12309832   813/272-4000
901 E Kennedy Blvd, Tampa 33602

<u>Michelle Fitzgerald</u> 1	<u>Larry Sykes</u> 15
<u>Odalys Pritchard</u> 15	<u>Shaylia McRea</u> 15
<u>Yinka Alege</u> 15	

Public Schs..Principal	Grd	Prgm	Enr/#Cls	SN
Armwood Senior High Sch 12000 E US Highway 92, Seffner 33584 <u>Joseph Castelli</u>	9-12	ATV	2,205 100	74% 813/744-8040 Fax 813/744-8048
B C Graham Elem Sch 2915 N Massachusetts Ave, Tampa 33602 <u>Sharron Doyle</u>	PK-5	T	394 35	97% 813/276-5408 Fax 813/276-5534
Beth Shields Middle Sch 15732 Beth Shields Way, Ruskin 33573 **Colleen Carr**	6-8	T	1,579	86% 813/672-5338 Fax 813/672-5342
Booker T Washington Elem Sch 1407 Estelle St, Tampa 33605 <u>Jaime Gerding</u>	PK-5	T	462 90	99% 813/233-3720 Fax 813/233-3724
Broward Elem Sch 400 W Osborne Ave, Tampa 33603 <u>Angela Livingston</u>	PK-5	T	391 50	96% 813/276-5592 Fax 813/276-5887
Bryan Plant City Elem Sch 2006 W Oak Ave, Plant City 33563 <u>Tamethea Simmons</u>	PK-5	T	710 45	93% 813/757-9300 Fax 813/707-7075
Chamberlain Senior High Sch 9401 N Boulevard, Tampa 33612 Jake Russell	9-12	AGTV	1,597	80% 813/975-7677 Fax 813/975-7687
Clair Mel Elem Sch 1025 S 78th St, Tampa 33619 <u>Gloria Waite</u>	PK-5	T	568 40	97% 813/744-8080 Fax 813/744-8083 f
Cleveland Elem Sch 723 E Hamilton Ave, Tampa 33604 <u>Lynn Roberts</u>	PK-5	T	352 21	97% 813/276-5583 Fax 813/276-5586
Dover Elem Sch 3035 Nelson Ave, Dover 33527 <u>Gina Becker</u>	PK-5	T	631 45	96% 813/757-9457 Fax 813/707-7161
ⓜ Dunbar Magnet Sch 1730 W Union St, Tampa 33607 <u>Dawn Stites</u>	K-5	T	273 17	91% 813/276-5677 Fax 813/272-2254
E L Bing Elem Sch 6409 36th Ave S, Tampa 33619 **Melanie Hill-Anderson**	PK-5	T	504 26	94% 813/744-8088 Fax 813/740-3620
Edison Elem Sch 1607 E Curtis St, Tampa 33610 **Candice Dodd**	PK-5	T	399 30	97% 813/276-5579 Fax 813/276-5582

79 Student Personnel	91 Safety/Security	275 Response To Intervention	298 Grant Writer/Ptnrships	**School Programs**	**Social Media**
80 Driver Ed/Safety	92 Magnet School	277 Remedial Math K-12	750 Chief Innovation Officer	A = Alternative Program	
81 Gifted/Talented	93 Parental Involvement	280 Literacy Coach	751 Chief of Staff	G = Adult Classes	f = Facebook
82 Video Services	95 Tech Prep Program	285 STEM	752 Social Emotional Learning	M = Magnet Program	
83 Substance Abuse Prev	97 Chief Information Officer	286 Digital Learning		T = Title I Schoolwide	t = Twitter
84 Erate	98 Chief Technology Officer	288 Common Core Standards	**Other School Types**	V = Career & Tech Ed Programs	
85 AIDS Education	270 Character Education	294 Accountability	Ⓐ = Alternative School		
88 Alternative/At Risk	271 Migrant Education	295 Network System	© = **Charter School**	New Schools are shaded	
89 Multi-Cultural Curriculum	273 Teacher Mentor	296 Title II Programs	ⓜ = **Magnet School**	New Superintendents and Principals are bold	
90 Social Work	274 Before/After Sch	297 Webmaster	Ⓨ = **Year-Round School**	Personnel with email addresses are underscored	

Esther Burney Elem Sch 901 S Evers St, Plant City 33563 Alan Black	PK-5	T	359 10	95%	813/707-7334 Fax 813/707-7339	
Folsom Elem Sch 9855 Harney Rd, Thonotosassa 33592 Krystal Lofton	PK-5	T	493 30	88%	813/987-6755 Fax 813/987-6970	
Forest Hills Elem Sch 10112 N Ola Ave, Tampa 33612 Rachael O'Dea	PK-5	T	709 45	92%	813/975-7633 Fax 813/975-4812	🆃
Foster Elem Sch 2014 E Diana St, Tampa 33610 Francine Lazarus	PK-5	T	482 60	94%	813/276-5573 Fax 813/276-5731	
Frost Elem Sch 3950 S Falkenburg Rd, Riverview 33578 Tiffaney Mikell	PK-5	T	605	77%	813/740-4900 Fax 813/740-4904	
Gibsonton Elem Sch 7723 Gibsonton Dr, Gibsonton 33534 Cindy Guy	PK-5	T	593 45	95%	813/671-5100 Fax 813/672-5003	
Greco Middle Sch 6925 E Fowler Ave, Temple Terr 33617 Andrew Olson	6-8	TV	621 70	88%	813/987-6926 Fax 813/987-6863	🆃
Ippolito Elem Sch 6874 S Falkenburg Rd, Riverview 33578 Nicole Bennett	PK-5	T	570 38	84%	813/672-5180 Fax 813/672-5184	
Jackson Elem Sch 502 E Gilchrist St, Plant City 33563 Jarrod Haneline	PK-5	T	523 21	92%	813/757-9341 Fax 813/757-9343	
James Elem Sch 4302 E Ellicott St, Tampa 33610 Robin Hewitt	PK-5	T	650	98%	813/740-4800 Fax 813/740-4804	
Jennings Middle Sch 9325 Governors Run Dr, Seffner 33584 Latonya Anderson	6-8	T	823	91%	813/740-4575 Fax 813/740-4579	
Just Elem Sch 1315 W Spruce St, Tampa 33607 Kevin McDonald	PK-5	T	267	96%	813/276-5708 Fax 813/272-2379	
Kenly Elem Sch 2909 N 66th St, Tampa 33619 Russell Wallace	PK-5	T	509 30	94%	813/744-8074 Fax 813/744-8077	
Kimbell Elem Sch 8406 N 46th St, Tampa 33617 Daphne Fourqurean	PK-5	T	500	96%	813/983-3900 Fax 813/983-3974	
Ⓜ Lee Elem Mag Sch World & Tech 3719 N 17th St, Tampa 33610 Beverly Smith	K-5		275 20		813/276-5405 Fax 813/233-3565	
Mango Elem Sch 4220 County Road 579, Seffner 33584 Felicia Davis	PK-5	T	780 35	91%	813/744-8208 Fax 813/744-8211	
McDonald Elem Sch 501 Pruett Rd, Seffner 33584 Melanie Cochrane	PK-5	T	538 30	90%	813/744-8154 Fax 813/744-8012	
McLane Middle Sch 306 N Knights Ave, Brandon 33510 Dina Langston	6-8	TV	645	85%	813/744-8100 Fax 813/744-8135	
Memorial Middle Sch 4702 N Central Ave, Tampa 33603 April Gillyard	6-8	TV	634	92%	813/872-5230 Fax 813/872-5238	
Miles Elem Sch 317 E 124th Ave, Tampa 33612 Greg Cannella	PK-5	T	880 45	96%	813/975-7337 Fax 813/975-7099	
Mort Elem Sch 1806 E Bearss Ave, Tampa 33613 Latiecea Hailey-Brown	PK-5	T	889 40	95%	813/975-7373 Fax 813/558-5489	
Ⓥ Oak Park Elem Sch 2716 N 46th St, Tampa 33605 Ryan Moody	PK-5	MT	572 35	96%	813/740-7733 Fax 813/740-7744	

P J Sullivan Partnership Sch 2202 N Florida Ave, Tampa 33602 Dave McMeen	K-5	T	94 3	97%	813/347-4160 Fax 813/347-4167	
Palm River Elem Sch 805 Maydell Dr, Tampa 33619 Frankye Bulmer	PK-5	T	477 33	95%	813/744-8066 Fax 813/744-8069	
Pizzo K-8 Patel Lower Campus 11701 Usf Bull Run St, Tampa 33617 Amber Cronin	PK-8	T	745	89%	813/987-6500 Fax 813/987-6516	
Potter Elem Sch 3224 E Cayuga St, Tampa 33610 Sharon Waite	PK-5	T	565 40	98%	813/276-5564 Fax 813/233-3693	
Reddick Elem Sch 325 W Lake Dr, Wimauma 33598 J Thomas Roth	PK-5	T	859	91%	813/634-0809 Fax 813/634-0814	
Robles Elem Sch 4405 E Sligh Ave, Tampa 33610 Delilah Rabeiro	PK-5	T	757 30	92%	813/744-8033 Fax 813/744-8350	
Ruskin Elem Sch 101 E College Ave, Ruskin 33570 Rebecca Salgado	PK-5	T	795 40	90%	813/671-5177 Fax 813/671-5182	
Shaw Elem Sch 11311 N 15th St, Tampa 33612 Renel Mathurin	PK-5	T	702 41	95%	813/975-7366 Fax 813/558-5025	
Sheehy Elem Sch 6402 N 40th St, Tampa 33610 Delia Gadson	PK-5	T	346 31	95%	813/233-3800 Fax 813/233-3804	
Sligh Middle Sch 2011 E Sligh Ave, Tampa 33610 Anthony Jones	6-8	TV	576 60	91%	813/276-5596 Fax 813/276-5606	
Spoto High Sch 8538 Eagle Palm Dr, Riverview 33578 Jazrick Haggins	9-12	T	1,679	73%	813/672-5405 Fax 813/672-5423	
Sulphur Springs K-8 Cmty Sch 8412 N 13th St, Tampa 33604 Marc Gaillard	PK-5	T	778 34	97%	813/975-7305 Fax 813/975-7398	
Thompson Elem Sch 2020 E Shell Point Rd, Ruskin 33570 Milady Astacio	PK-5	T	820	83%	813/938-1203 Fax 813/938-1204	
Thonotosassa Elem Sch 10050 Skewlee Rd, Thonotosassa 33592 Anthony Montoto	PK-5	T	430 23	90%	813/987-6987 Fax 813/987-6865	
Woodson PK-8 Leadership Acad 8715 N 22nd St, Tampa 33604 Ovett Wilson	PK-8	V	984 72		813/975-7652 Fax 813/631-4312	🅕🆃

● **Hillsborough Co SD-Area 1** PID: 03395581   813/272-3800
    2802 W Paxton Ave, Tampa 33611   Fax 813/272-3813

Public Schs..Principal	Grd	Prgm	Enr/#Cls	SN	
Anderson Elem Sch 3910 W Fair Oaks Ave, Tampa 33611 Lydia Sierra	K-5	T	382 25	56%	813/272-3075 Fax 813/276-5919
Ballast Point Elem Sch 2802 W Ballast Point Blvd, Tampa 33611 Beth Hastings	K-5		511 21	37%	813/272-3070 Fax 813/276-5923
Blake High Sch 1701 N Boulevard, Tampa 33607 Jesse Salters	9-12	GTV	1,712 100	64%	813/272-3422 Fax 813/272-3715
Caminiti Exceptional Center 2600 W Humphrey St, Tampa 33614 Roberta Jakubowski	Spec	T	93 26	78%	813/975-7611 Fax 813/975-7617
Chiaramonte Elem Sch 6001 S Himes Ave, Tampa 33611 Daniel Opila	K-5	T	402 25	73%	813/272-3066 Fax 813/272-3284

1 Superintendent	8 Curric/Instruct K-12	19 Chief Financial Officer	29 Family/Consumer Science	39 Social Studies K-12	49 English/Lang Arts Elem	59 Special Education Elem	69 Academic Assessment
2 Bus/Finance/Purchasing	9 Curric/Instruct Elem	20 Art K-12	30 Adult Education	40 Social Studies Elem	50 English/Lang Arts Sec	60 Special Education Sec	70 Research/Development
3 Buildings And Grounds	10 Curric/Instruct Sec	21 Art Elem	31 Career/Sch-to-Work K-12	41 Social Studies Sec	51 Reading K-12	61 Foreign/World Lang K-12	71 Public Information
4 Food Service	11 Federal Program	22 Art Sec	32 Career/Sch-to-Work Elem	42 Science K-12	52 Reading Elem	62 Foreign/World Lang Elem	72 Summer School
5 Transportation	12 Title I	23 Music K-12	33 Career/Sch-to-Work Sec	43 Science Elem	53 Reading Sec	63 Foreign/World Lang Sec	73 Instructional Tech
6 Athletic	13 Title V	24 Music Elem	34 Early Childhood Ed	44 Science Sec	54 Remedial Reading K-12	64 Religious Education K-12	74 Inservice Training
7 Health Services	14 Asst Superintendent	25 Music Sec	35 Health/Phys Education	45 Math K-12	55 Remedial Reading Elem	65 Religious Education Elem	75 Marketing/Distributive
	15 Asst Superintendent	26 Business Education	36 Guidance Services K-12	46 Math Elem	56 Remedial Reading Sec	66 Religious Education Sec	76 Info Systems
	16 Instructional Media Svcs	27 Career & Tech Ed	37 Guidance Services Elem	47 Math Sec	57 Bilingual/ELL	67 School Board President	77 Psychological Assess
	17 Chief Operations Officer	28 Technology Education	38 Guidance Services Sec	48 English/Lang Arts K-12	58 Special Education K-12	68 Teacher Personnel	78 Affirmative Action

FL—48

School / Address / Principal	Grd	Prgm	Enr/#Cls	SN	Phone / Fax
Coleman Middle Sch 1724 S Manhattan Ave, Tampa 33629 Michael Hoskinson	6-8	V	1,037 48	18%	813/872-5335 Fax 813/872-5338 🅕 🅣
DeSoto Elem Sch 2618 Corrine St, Tampa 33605 Kimberly Thompson	PK-5	T	251 10	95%	813/276-5779 Fax 813/233-2475
Gorrie Elem Sch 705 W De Leon St, Tampa 33606 Marjorie Sandler	K-5		574 24	17%	813/276-5673 Fax 813/276-5880
Grady Elem Sch 3910 W Morrison Ave, Tampa 33629 Kristine Dosal	PK-5	T	544 34	36%	813/872-5325 Fax 813/356-1476
Jefferson Senior High Sch 4401 W Cypress St, Tampa 33607 Robert Quinn	9-12	AGTV	1,752 95	76%	813/872-5241 Fax 813/872-5250
Lanier Elem Sch 4704 W Montgomery Ave, Tampa 33616 Sarah Garcia	K-5	T	353	77%	813/272-3060 Fax 813/272-3065
Lavoy Exceptional Center 4410 W Main St, Tampa 33607 Amber Statham	Spec	T	80 16	76%	813/872-5285 Fax 813/872-5291
Mabry Elem Sch 4201 W Estrella St, Tampa 33629 Sherri Frick	PK-5		857 35	12%	813/872-5364 Fax 813/554-2252
ⓜ **MacFarlane Park Magnet Sch** 1721 N MacDill Ave, Tampa 33607 M Riveiro	K-5		366 16	37%	813/356-1760 Fax 813/356-1764
Madison Middle Sch 4444 W Bay Vista Ave, Tampa 33611 Joseph Brown	6-8	TV	588 60	78%	813/272-3050 Fax 813/233-2796
Mitchell Elem Sch 205 S Bungalow Park Ave, Tampa 33609 **Renee Best**	K-5		771 32	25%	813/872-5216 Fax 813/356-1662
Monroe Middle Sch 4716 W Montgomery Ave, Tampa 33616 Barbara Fillhart	6-8	TV	417 43	77%	813/272-3020 Fax 813/272-3027
ⓜ **Philip Shore Elem Sch** 1908 E 2nd Ave, Tampa 33605 Cheri Bollinger	PK-5	T	446 21	79%	813/276-5712 Fax 813/272-0426 🅕 🅣
Plant Senior High Sch 2415 S Himes Ave, Tampa 33629 Johnny Bush	9-12	AV	2,487 60	20%	813/272-3033 Fax 813/272-0624 🅣
Rampello K-8 Sch 802 E Washington St, Tampa 33602 Liz Uppercue	K-8	T	771 9	40%	813/233-2333 Fax 813/233-2337
Robinson Senior High Sch 6311 S Lois Ave, Tampa 33616 Robert Bhoolai	9-12	AGTV	1,551 85	44%	813/272-3006 Fax 813/272-3014
ⓜ **Roland Park Magnet Sch** 1510 N Manhattan Ave, Tampa 33607 Scott Weaver	K-8	T	776 42	35%	813/872-5212 Fax 813/673-4388 🅕 🅣
Roosevelt Elem Sch 3205 S Ferdinand Ave, Tampa 33629 Christina Dickens	K-5		736 28	10%	813/272-3090 Fax 813/233-3577
ⓜ **Stewart Middle Magnet Sch** 1125 W Spruce St, Tampa 33607 Baretta Wilson	6-8	GTV	1,019 65	73%	813/276-5691 Fax 813/276-5698
Tampa Bay Blvd Elem Sch 3111 W Tampa Bay Blvd, Tampa 33607 **Glenda Vinueza**	PK-5	T	687 47	92%	813/872-5208 Fax 813/871-7586
Tinker K-8 Sch 8207 Tinker St, Tampa 33621 Rachel Walters	K-8		640 40	27%	813/840-2043 Fax 813/233-3664 🅕 🅣
West Shore Elem Sch 7110 S West Shore Blvd, Tampa 33616 Linda Drawdy	PK-5	T	400 20	76%	813/272-3080 Fax 813/233-2443
West Tampa Elem Sch 2700 W Cherry St, Tampa 33607 **Kevin Kastner**	PK-5	T	424 27	96%	813/872-5200 Fax 813/356-1452
Wilson Middle Sch 1005 W Swann Ave, Tampa 33606 Colleen Faucett	6-8	V	666 37	23%	813/276-5682 Fax 813/233-2540

● **Hillsborough Co SD-Area 2**   PID: 03395610   813/631-4050
7958 Gunn Hwy, Tampa 33626   Fax 813/631-4058

Marco Murillo 1

Public Schs..Principal	Grd	Prgm	Enr/#Cls	SN	Phone / Fax
Alexander Elem Sch 5602 N Lois Ave, Tampa 33614 Kristina Alvarez	PK-5	T	603 35	90%	813/872-5395 Fax 813/356-1121
Alonso High Sch 8302 Montague St, Tampa 33635 Kenneth Hart	9-12	TV	2,564	59%	813/356-1525 Fax 813/356-1529
Bay Crest Elem Sch 4925 Webb Rd, Tampa 33615 Lisa Maltezos	PK-5	T	658 38	75%	813/872-5382 Fax 813/356-1153
Bellamy Elem Sch 9720 Wilsky Blvd, Tampa 33615 Jessica Hessler	PK-5	T	634 42	85%	813/872-5387 Fax 813/873-4877 🅕 🅣
Cannella Elem Sch 10707 Nixon Rd, Tampa 33624 Matthew Hoff	PK-5	T	696 35	74%	813/975-6941 Fax 813/631-5328
Citrus Park Elem Sch 7700 Gunn Hwy, Tampa 33625 Christopher Fonteyn	PK-5	T	583 40	57%	813/558-5356 Fax 813/558-5111
Crestwood Elem Sch 7824 N Manhattan Ave, Tampa 33614 Diane Sanchez	K-5	T	884 55	89%	813/872-5374 Fax 813/871-7788
Davidsen Middle Sch 10501 Montague St, Tampa 33626 **Stacy Arena**	6-8	TV	1,079	62%	813/558-5300 Fax 813/558-5299
Deer Park Elem Sch 11605 Citrus Park Dr, Tampa 33626 **Edith Lefler**	K-5		913	25%	813/854-6031 Fax 813/854-6041
Dickenson Elem Sch 4720 Kelly Rd, Tampa 33615 Marisa Brody	PK-5	T	597 35	87%	813/873-4732 Fax 813/356-1156
Egypt Lake Elem Sch 6707 N Glen Ave, Tampa 33614 Julie Scardino	PK-5	T	528 33	92%	813/872-5225 Fax 813/554-2358
Farnell Middle Sch 13912 Nine Eagles Dr, Tampa 33626 **Tim Binder**	6-8		1,229	21%	813/356-1640 Fax 813/356-1644
Hammond Elem Sch 8008 North Mobley Rd, Odessa 33556 Sheri Norkas	K-5		733	25%	813/792-5120 Fax 813/792-5124
Helen A Davis Elem Sch 10907 Memorial Hwy, Tampa 33615 Patrick Lalone	K-5	T	762	88%	813/854-6010 Fax 813/854-6014
Leto High Sch 4409 W Sligh Ave, Tampa 33614 **Larissa McCoy**	9-12	GTV	2,115	81%	813/872-5300 Fax 813/872-5314
Lowry Elem Sch 11505 Country Hollow Dr, Tampa 33635 Michelle Spagnuolo	K-5		986 52	39%	813/855-8178 Fax 813/356-1597
Martinez Middle Sch 5601 W Lutz Lake Fern Rd, Lutz 33558 Brent McBrien	6-8		1,198	20%	813/558-1190 Fax 813/558-1226
Mary Bryant Elem Sch 13910 Nine Eagles Dr, Tampa 33626 Ellen Oberschall	K-5		976	12%	813/356-1645 Fax 813/356-1649

79 Student Personnel	**91** Safety/Security	**275** Response To Intervention
80 Driver Ed/Safety	**92** Magnet School	**277** Remedial Math K-12
81 Gifted/Talented	**93** Parental Involvement	**280** Literacy Coach
82 Video Services	**95** Tech Prep Program	**285** STEM
83 Substance Abuse Prev	**97** Chief Infomation Officer	**286** Digital Learning
84 Erate	**98** Chief Technology Officer	**288** Common Core Standards
85 AIDS Education	**270** Character Education	**294** Accountability
88 Alternative/At Risk	**271** Migrant Education	**295** Network System
89 Multi-Cultural Curriculum	**273** Teacher Mentor	**296** Title II Programs
90 Social Work	**274** Before/After Sch	**297** Webmaster

298 Grant Writer/Ptnrships	**School Programs**	**Social Media**
750 Chief Innovation Officer	**A** = Alternative Program	
751 Chief of Staff	**G** = Adult Classes	🅕 = Facebook
752 Social Emotional Learning	**M** = Magnet Program	
	T = Title I Schoolwide	🅣 = Twitter
Other School Types	**V** = Career & Tech Ed Programs	
Ⓐ = Alternative School		
Ⓒ = Charter School	New Schools are shaded	
Ⓜ = Magnet School	New Superintendents and Principals are bold	
Ⓨ = Year-Round School	Personnel with email addresses are underscored	

School	Grd	Prgm	Enr/#Cls	SN	Phone
McKitrick Elem Sch 5503 W Lutz Lake Fern Rd, Lutz 33558 Allison Cline	K-5		934 37	14%	813/558-5427 Fax 813/558-5431
Morgan Woods Elem Sch 7001 Armand Dr, Tampa 33634 **Jessica Kepa**	PK-5	T	453 35	84%	813/872-5369 Fax 813/873-4869
Northwest Elem Sch 16438 Hutchison Rd, Tampa 33625 Bryan Quigley	PK-5	T	666 37	41%	813/975-7315 Fax 813/975-7322
Pierce Middle Sch 5511 N Hesperides St, Tampa 33614 Pablo Alvarez	6-8	TV	929 65	90%	813/872-5344 Fax 813/871-7978
Schwarzkopf Elem Sch 18333 Calusa Trace Blvd, Lutz 33558 Cheryl Holley	K-5	T	636 35	41%	813/975-6945 Fax 813/975-6948
Sgt Paul R Smith Middle Sch 14303 Citrus Pointe Dr, Tampa 33625 **Robert Kleesattel**	6-8	T	745	69%	813/792-5125 Fax 813/792-5129
Steinbrenner High Sch 5575 W Lutz Lake Fern Rd, Lutz 33558 Kelly King	9-12		2,468	21%	813/792-5131 Fax 813/792-5135
Town & Country Elem Sch 6025 Hanley Rd, Tampa 33634 **Melissa Babanats**	PK-5	T	427 37	92%	813/871-7500 Fax 813/554-2378
Twin Lakes Elem Sch 8507 N Habana Ave, Tampa 33614 **Kilsys Batista**	K-5	T	724 45	87%	813/975-7380 Fax 813/631-4153
Walker Middle Sch 8282 North Mobley Rd, Odessa 33556 Heather Holloway	6-8		955 60	33%	813/631-4726 Fax 813/631-4738
Walter Sickles High Sch 7950 Gunn Hwy, Tampa 33626 Mary Freitas	9-12		2,375	37%	813/631-4742 Fax 813/631-4754
Webb Middle Sch 6035 Hanley Rd, Tampa 33634 Frank Diaz	6-8	TV	750	85%	813/872-5351 Fax 813/872-5359
Westchase Elem Sch 9517 W Linebaugh Ave, Tampa 33626 Elise Suarez	K-5		932 35	19%	813/631-4600 Fax 813/631-4617
Woodbridge Elem Sch 8301 Woodbridge Blvd, Tampa 33615 Sarah Capps	K-5	T	681 48	89%	813/871-7460 Fax 813/871-7063

● **Hillsborough Co SD-Area 3** PID: 04869688   813/558-1406
    129 E 124th Ave, Tampa 33612   Fax 813/558-1417

Dr Anna Brown 1

Public Schs..Principal	Grd	Prgm	Enr/#Cls	SN	Phone
Adams Middle Sch 10201 N Boulevard, Tampa 33612 **Nishira Mitchell**	6-8	TV	829 75	87%	813/975-7665 Fax 813/632-6889
Buchanan Middle Sch 1001 W Bearss Ave, Tampa 33613 Scott Hilgenberg	6-8	TV	722 60	80%	813/975-7600 Fax 813/975-7610
Carrollwood Elem Sch 3516 McFarland Rd, Tampa 33618 **Maryjo Stover**	PK-5	T	748 34	44%	813/975-7640 Fax 813/631-5364
Claywell Elem Sch 4500 Northdale Blvd, Tampa 33624 Robert Jones	PK-5	T	712	55%	813/975-7300 Fax 813/631-4536
Dorothy Thomas Sch 3215 Nundy Rd, Tampa 33618 Kimberly Jahn	Spec	T	62 18	7%	813/975-7355 Fax 813/975-7361
Essrig Elem Sch 13131 Lynn Rd, Tampa 33624 Joshua Hodges	PK-5	T	633	62%	813/975-7307 Fax 813/558-5104

School	Grd	Prgm	Enr/#Cls	SN	Phone
Freedom High Sch 17410 Commerce Park Blvd, Tampa 33647 Kevin Stephenson	9-12	TV	1,924	62%	813/558-1185 Fax 813/558-1189
Gaither Senior High Sch 16200 N Dale Mabry Hwy, Tampa 33618 Thomas Morrill	9-12	AGTV	1,997 100	52%	813/975-7340 Fax 813/975-7349
Harrold Clark Elem Sch 19002 Wood Sage Dr, Tampa 33647 Paulette English	PK-5	T	836 55	44%	813/631-4333 Fax 813/631-4349
Heritage Elem Sch 18201 E Meadow Rd, Tampa 33647 **Mary Booth**	PK-5	T	556	47%	813/740-4580 Fax 813/740-4584
Hill Middle Sch 5200 Ehrlich Rd, Tampa 33624 Ronald Mason	6-8	TV	1,006	56%	813/975-7325 Fax 813/975-4819
Hunter's Green Elem Sch 9202 Highland Oak Dr, Tampa 33647 Gaye Holt	PK-5	T	739 65	63%	813/973-7394 Fax 813/631-4525
King Senior High Sch 6815 N 56th St, Tampa 33610 Arlene Castelli	9-12	AGTV	1,826	60%	813/744-8333 Fax 813/744-8343
Lake Magdalene Elem Sch 2002 Pine Lake Dr, Tampa 33612 Crystal Brown	PK-5	T	804 45	60%	813/975-7625 Fax 813/558-1209
Lawton Chiles Elem Sch 16541 Tampa Palms Blvd W, Tampa 33647 Dr Teresa Evans	K-5	T	885	40%	813/558-5422 Fax 813/558-5426
Lewis Elem Sch 6700 Whiteway Dr, Temple Terr 33617 Debra Fitzpatrick	PK-5	T	799 35	68%	813/987-6947 Fax 813/987-6920
Liberty Middle Sch 17400 Commerce Park Blvd, Tampa 33647 James Ammirati	6-8	TV	1,160 65	59%	813/558-1180 Fax 813/558-1184
Louis Benito Middle Sch 10101 Cross Creek Blvd, Tampa 33647 John Sanders	6-8	T	1,087	46%	813/631-4694 Fax 813/631-4706
Lutz K-8 Sch 202 5th Ave SE, Lutz 33549 Lori Branham	PK-8	T	652 36	44%	813/949-1452 Fax 813/909-9908
Maniscalco Elem Sch 939 Debuel Rd, Lutz 33549 Tammy Reale	PK-5	T	637 40	59%	813/949-0337 Fax 813/948-3270
Ⓜ Muller Elem Sch 13615 N 22nd St, Tampa 33613 **Melanie Bottini**	PK-5	T	407	84%	813/558-1355 Fax 813/558-1359
Paul Wharton High Sch 20150 Bruce B Downs Blvd, Tampa 33647 Michael Rowan	9-12	T	2,366 91	50%	813/631-4710 Fax 813/631-4722
Pride Elem Sch 10310 Lions Den Dr, Tampa 33647 Amy Zilbar	PK-5		738 35	23%	813/558-5400 Fax 813/558-5404
Ⓜ Riverhills Elem Magnet Sch 405 S Riverhills Dr, Temple Terr 33617 Todd Connolly	PK-5	T	506 30	60%	813/987-6911 Fax 813/987-6962
Tampa Palms Elem Sch 6100 Tampa Palms Blvd, Tampa 33647 Maryann Lippek	PK-5	T	915 70	41%	813/975-7390 Fax 813/975-6654
Temple Terrace Elem Sch 124 Flotto Ave, Temple Terr 33617 Ann Marie Perez	PK-5	T	630 40	86%	813/987-6903 Fax 813/987-6406
Turner-Bartels K-8 STEM 9190 Imperial Oak Blvd, Tampa 33647 **Robert Buggs**	PK-8		1,861	35%	813/907-6801 Fax 813/907-9066
Witter Elem Sch 10801 N 22nd St, Tampa 33612 Susan Persbacker	PK-5	T	602	96%	813/975-7383 Fax 813/631-4447

1 Superintendent	8 Curric/Instruct K-12	19 Chief Financial Officer	29 Family/Consumer Science	39 Social Studies K-12	49 English/Lang Arts Elem	59 Special Education Elem	69 Academic Assessment
2 Bus/Finance/Purchasing	9 Curric/Instruct Elem	20 Art K-12	30 Adult Education	40 Social Studies Elem	50 English/Lang Arts Sec	60 Special Education Sec	70 Research/Development
3 Buildings And Grounds	10 Curric/Instruct Sec	21 Art Elem	31 Career/Sch-to-Work K-12	41 Social Studies Sec	51 Reading K-12	61 Foreign/World Lang K-12	71 Public Information
4 Food Service	11 Federal Program	22 Art Sec	32 Career/Sch-to-Work Elem	42 Science K-12	52 Reading Elem	62 Foreign/World Lang Elem	72 Summer School
5 Transportation	12 Title I	23 Music K-12	33 Career/Sch-to-Work Sec	43 Science Elem	53 Reading Sec	63 Foreign/World Lang Sec	73 Instructional Tech
6 Athletic	13 Title V	24 Music Elem	34 Early Childhood Ed	44 Science Sec	54 Remedial Reading K-12	64 Religious Education K-12	74 Inservice Training
7 Health Services	15 Asst Superintendent	25 Music Sec	35 Health/Phys Education	45 Math K-12	55 Remedial Reading Elem	65 Religious Education Elem	75 Marketing/Distributive
	16 Instructional Media Svcs	26 Business Education	36 Guidance Services K-12	46 Math Elem	56 Remedial Reading Sec	66 Religious Education Sec	76 Info Systems
	17 Chief Operations Officer	27 Career & Tech Ed	37 Guidance Services Elem	47 Math Sec	57 Bilingual/ELL	67 School Board President	77 Psychological Assess
	18 Chief Academic Officer	28 Technology Education	38 Guidance Services Sec	48 English/Lang Arts K-12	58 Special Education K-12	68 Teacher Personnel	78 Affirmative Action

Hillsborough Co SD-Area 4 PID: 03395634 813/740-3710
1015 N Parsons Ave, Seffner 33584 Fax 813/740-3721

Owen Young ....1 Denice Stanforth 34*

Public Schs..Principal	Grd	Prgm	Enr/#Cls	SN	
Ⓜ Brandon Epic3 1015 N Parsons Ave, Seffner 33584 Cornelius Bobo	6-11	GT	98	88%	813/651-2165 Fax 813/740-4599
Brandon Senior High Sch 1101 Victoria St, Brandon 33510 Jennifer Sparano	9-12	AGTV	1,875 113	64%	813/744-8120 Fax 813/744-8129
Carver Exceptional Center 2934 E Hillsborough Ave, Tampa 33610 Earnest Wood	Spec	T	50 12	87%	813/236-3500 Fax 813/236-3513
Colson Elem Sch 1520 Lakeview Ave, Seffner 33584 Orestes Mendez	PK-5	T	713	71%	813/744-8031 Fax 813/744-8439
Ⓜ Dowdell Middle Sch 1208 Wishing Well Way, Tampa 33619 **James Boyd**	6-8	TV	637 85	92%	813/744-8322 Fax 813/740-3616
Ⓜ Ferrell Girls Prep Academy 4302 N 24th St, Tampa 33610 Karen French	6-8	GT	596 40	76%	813/276-5608 Fax 813/276-5615
Ⓜ Franklin Boys Prep Academy 3915 E 21st Ave, Tampa 33605 John Haley	6-8	V	564 45		813/744-8108 Fax 813/744-8579
Gordon Burnett Middle Sch 1010 N Kingsway Rd, Seffner 33584 **Valerie Newton**	6-8	T	795	84%	813/744-6745 Fax 813/744-8973
Hillsborough High Sch 5000 N Central Ave, Tampa 33603 Gary Brady	9-12	ATV	1,885	68%	813/276-5620 Fax 813/276-5629
Hugo Schmidt Elem Sch 1250 Williams Rd, Brandon 33510 Janet Kelly	PK-5	T	596 45	81%	813/651-2110 Fax 813/651-2114
Limona Elem Sch 1115 Telfair Rd, Brandon 33510 Marlou Bates	K-5	T	637 40	53%	813/744-8200 Fax 813/744-8147
Ⓜ Lockhart Elem Sch 3719 N 17th St, Tampa 33610 Gilda Garcia	PK-5	T	438 32	91%	813/276-5727 Fax 813/233-3565
Ⓜ Lomax Magnet Elem Sch 4207 N 26th St, Tampa 33610 Connie Chisholm	K-5	T	412 22	73%	813/276-5569 Fax 813/272-2803
Lopez Elem Sch 200 N Kingsway Rd, Seffner 33584 Michael Engle	PK-5	T	571 25	81%	813/744-8000 Fax 813/744-8005 🔳
Lopez Exceptional Student Ctr 315 W Old Hillsborough Ave, Seffner 33584 Joseph Hilbush	Spec	T	52	65%	813/744-8008 Fax 813/744-6229
Mann Middle Sch 409 E Jersey Ave, Brandon 33510 **Dante Jones**	6-8	TV	957 66	73%	813/744-8400 Fax 813/744-6707
Mendenhall Elem Sch 5202 N Mendenhall Dr, Tampa 33603 Cristina Fernandez	PK-5	T	556 40	89%	813/872-5221 Fax 813/872-5224
Mendez Exceptional Center 5707 N 22nd St, Tampa 33610 **Marvin Bell**	Spec	T	21 9	87%	813/276-5630 Fax 813/233-2314
Middleton High Sch 4801 N 22nd St, Tampa 33610 **Tiatasha Brown**	9-12	GTV	1,595	68%	813/233-3360 Fax 813/233-3364
Ⓐ North Tampa Alt Sch 8602 N Armenia Ave, Tampa 33604 Mickey Boddie	7-12	T	84 21	90%	813/631-4426 Fax 813/631-4429

Public Schs..Principal	Grd	Prgm	Enr/#Cls	SN	
Oak Grove Elem Sch 6315 N Armenia Ave, Tampa 33604 Pamela Wilkins	PK-5	T	809	92%	813/356-1532 Fax 813/356-1536
Ⓜ Orange Grove Mag Sch the Arts 3415 N 16th St, Tampa 33605 Michael Miranda	6-8	T	552 35	62%	813/276-5717 Fax 813/276-5857
Seffner Elem Sch 109 Cactus Rd, Seffner 33584 Shelly Hermann	PK-5	T	526 40	66%	813/744-8171 Fax 813/740-3984
Seminole Elem Sch 6201 N Central Ave, Tampa 33604 Elizabeth Giles	PK-5	T	441 50	76%	813/276-5556 Fax 813/272-2279
Tampa Bay Tech High Sch 6410 Orient Rd, Tampa 33610 Michael Ippolito	Voc	AGT	2,051	75%	813/744-8360 Fax 813/744-8368
Ⓜ Williams Magnet Middle Sch 5020 N 47th St, Tampa 33610 Shellie Green	6-8	V	831 40	42%	813/744-8600 Fax 813/744-8665
Yates Elem Sch 301 Kingsway Rd, Brandon 33510 Lisa Varnum	PK-5	T	696 50	81%	813/744-8177 Fax 813/744-8179
Ⓜ Young Middle Magnet Sch 1807 E Dr M L King Jr Blvd, Tampa 33610 Nadine Johnson	6-8	T	664 42	88%	813/276-5739 Fax 813/276-5893

Hillsborough Co SD-Area 5 PID: 04750221 813/707-7050
703 N Thomas St, Plant City 33563

Sharon Morris 1

Public Schs..Principal	Grd	Prgm	Enr/#Cls	SN	
Alafia Elem Sch 3535 Culbreath Rd, Valrico 33596 Lisa Jackson	PK-5		655	30%	813/744-8190 Fax 813/744-8207
Apollo Beach Elem Sch 501 Apollo Beach Blvd, Apollo Beach 33572 Kelly McMillan	K-5		644 36	33%	813/671-5172 Fax 813/671-5075
Bailey Elem Sch 4630 Gallagher Rd, Dover 33527 Scott Valdez	PK-5	T	765	71%	813/707-7531 Fax 813/707-7535
Barrington Middle Sch 5925 Village Center Dr, Lithia 33547 Amy Rappleyea	6-8	V	1,519	38%	813/657-7266 Fax 813/657-7369
Bloomingdale High Sch 1700 Bloomingdale Ave, Valrico 33596 Susan Burkett	9-12	AGV	2,334 110	41%	813/744-8018 Fax 813/744-8026
Bowers-Whitley Career Center 13609 N 22nd St, Tampa 33613 Derrick Gaines	Voc	GT	121	88%	813/558-1750 Fax 813/558-1761
Boyette Springs Elem Sch 10141 Sedgebrook Dr, Riverview 33569 Jennifer McCrystal	PK-5	T	861 35	48%	813/671-5060 Fax 813/672-5077
Brooker Elem Sch 812 Dewolf Rd, Brandon 33511 Julie Kelly	PK-5	T	957 40	48%	813/744-8184 Fax 813/740-3621
Buckhorn Elem Sch 2420 Buckhorn School Ct, Valrico 33594 Tamara Brooks	PK-5		760 37	40%	813/744-8240 Fax 813/740-3622
Burns Middle Sch 615 Brooker Rd, Brandon 33511 Matthew DiPrima	6-8	V	1,316 50	38%	813/744-8383 Fax 813/740-3623
Cimino Elem Sch 4329 Culbreath Rd, Valrico 33596 Joanne Griffiths	PK-5		894	29%	813/740-4450 Fax 813/740-4454
Colleen Bevis Elem Sch 5720 Osprey Ridge Dr, Lithia 33547 Rebecca Thoms	K-5		849 45	11%	813/740-4000 Fax 813/740-4004

79 Student Personnel	**91** Safety/Security	**275** Response To Intervention
80 Driver Ed/Safety	**92** Magnet School	**277** Remedial Math K-12
81 Gifted/Talented	**93** Parental Involvement	**280** Literacy Coach
82 Video Services	**95** Tech Prep Program	**285** STEM
83 Substance Abuse Prev	**97** Chief Information Officer	**286** Digital Learning
84 Erate	**98** Chief Technology Officer	**288** Common Core Standards
85 AIDS Education	**270** Character Education	**294** Accountability
88 Alternative/At Risk	**271** Migrant Education	**295** Network System
89 Multi-Cultural Curriculum	**273** Teacher Mentor	**296** Title II Programs
90 Social Work	**274** Before/After Sch	**297** Webmaster

298 Grant Writer/Ptnrships
750 Chief Innovation Officer
751 Chief of Staff
752 Social Emotional Learning

Other School Types
Ⓐ = Alternative School
Ⓒ = Charter School
Ⓜ = Magnet School
Ⓨ = Year-Round School

School Programs
A = Alternative Program
G = Adult Classes
M = Magnet Program
T = Title I Schoolwide
V = Career & Tech Ed Programs

New Schools are shaded
New Superintendents and Principals are bold
Personnel with email addresses are underscored

Social Media
🔵 = Facebook
🔳 = Twitter

School	Grades	Media	Enroll	%	Phone	Fax
Collins Elem Sch 12424 Summerfield Blvd, Riverview 33579 Rebecca Sargable	PK-5	T	1,009	39%	813/672-5400	Fax 813/672-5404
Cork Elem Sch 3501 Cork Rd, Plant City 33565 Sherri-Lyn Black	PK-5	T	694	73%	813/757-9353	Fax 813/707-7076
Corr Elem Sch 13020 Kings Lake Dr, Gibsonton 33534 Kristi-Lyn Ricketts	PK-5	T	729 45	74%	813/672-5345	Fax 813/672-5349
Cypress Creek Elem Sch 4040 19th Ave NE, Ruskin 33573 Roy Moral	PK-5	T	871 48	81%	813/671-5167	Fax 813/671-5204
D W Waters Career Center 2704 N Highland Ave, Tampa 33602 Holly Frazier	Voc	AT	160	90%	813/233-2655	Fax 813/233-2659
Dawson Elem Sch 12961 Boggy Creek Dr, Riverview 33579 Derrick McLaughlin	PK-5		654		813/442-7396	Fax 813/559-8492
Doby Elem Sch 6720 Covington Garden Dr, Apollo Beach 33572 Rosanne Rush	PK-5	T	767	43%	813/672-5388	Fax 813/672-5392
Don Giunta Middle Sch 4202 S Falkenburg Rd, Riverview 33578 **Cindy Land**	6-8	T	824	85%	813/740-4888	Fax 813/740-4892
Dr Lennard High Sch 2342 E Shell Point Rd, Ruskin 33570 Denise Savino	9-12	GTV	3,100 60	68%	813/641-5611	Fax 813/641-5610
Durant High Sch 4748 Cougar Path, Plant City 33567 **Gary Graham**	9-12	TV	2,398 130	48%	813/757-9075	Fax 813/707-7079
East Bay Senior High Sch 7710 Old Big Bend Rd, Gibsonton 33534 Amy Stevens-Cox	9-12	AGTV	2,256 100	60%	813/671-5134	Fax 813/671-5139
Eisenhower Middle Sch 7620 Old Big Bend Rd, Gibsonton 33534 **Robert Stingone**	6-8	TV	1,270 85	63%	813/671-5121	Fax 813/671-5039
Fishhawk Creek Elem Sch 16815 Dorman Rd, Lithia 33547 **Steven Sims**	K-5		1,022	12%	813/651-2150	Fax 813/651-2154
Hortense Mintz Elem Sch 1510 Heather Lakes Blvd, Brandon 33511 Deborah Moltisanti	PK-5	T	853 57	69%	813/744-8353	Fax 813/744-6755
J S Robinson Elem Sch 4801 Turkey Creek Rd, Plant City 33567 Alicia Wilkerson	PK-5	T	668 45	83%	813/757-9424	Fax 813/757-9074
Jack R Lamb Elem Sch 6274 S 78th St, Tampa 33619 **Chantel Angeletti**	PK-5	T	727	83%	813/605-4950	Fax 813/605-4963
Kingswood Elem Sch 3102 S Kings Ave, Brandon 33511 Lisa Amos	PK-5	T	461 29	77%	813/744-8234	Fax 813/744-8150
Knights Elem Sch 4815 Keene Rd, Plant City 33565 Janine Hall	PK-5	T	767 45	82%	813/757-9333	Fax 813/757-9319
Lillian Symmes Elem Sch 6280 Watson Rd, Riverview 33578 Annamarie Rothenbush	K-5	T	535	55%	813/740-4182	Fax 813/740-4186
Ⓜ Lincoln Magnet Sch 1207 E Renfro St, Plant City 33563 **Ann Rushing**	PK-5	T	488 22	59%	813/757-9329	Fax 813/757-9077
Lithia Springs Elem Sch 4332 Lynx Paw Trl, Valrico 33596 Kevin Martin	K-5		657 26	23%	813/744-8016	Fax 813/740-4462
Marshall Middle Sch 18 S Maryland Ave, Plant City 33563 Daphne Blanton	6-8	TV	884 50	87%	813/757-9360	Fax 813/707-7385
Mulrennan Middle Sch 4215 Durant Rd, Valrico 33596 Timothy Ducker	6-8	T	1,338	46%	813/651-2100	Fax 813/651-2104
Nelson Elem Sch 5413 Durant Rd, Dover 33527 **Mary Lou Hewitt**	PK-5	T	802	62%	813/651-2120	Fax 813/651-2124
Newsome High Sch 16550 Fishhawk Blvd, Lithia 33547 Carla Bruning	9-12	V	3,036	16%	813/740-4600	Fax 813/740-4604
Pinecrest Elem Sch 7950 Lithia Pinecrest Rd, Lithia 33547 Denise Mobley	PK-5	T	560 31	75%	813/744-8164	Fax 813/740-4456
Plant City Senior High Sch 1 Raider Pl, Plant City 33563 Susan Sullivan	9-12	AGTV	2,322	66%	813/757-9370	Fax 813/757-9135
Ⓜ Progress Village Magnet Sch 8113 Zinnia Dr, Tampa 33619 Peter Megara	6-8	T	938 40	53%	813/671-5110	Fax 813/671-5240
Randall Middle Sch 16510 Fishhawk Blvd, Lithia 33547 Claire Mawhinney	6-8	V	1,422	13%	813/740-3900	Fax 813/740-3910
Riverview Elem Sch 10809 Hannaway Dr, Riverview 33578 Melody Murphy	PK-5	T	550 35	66%	813/671-5105	Fax 813/671-5087
Riverview High Sch 11311 Boyette Rd, Riverview 33569 Danielle Shotwell	9-12	TV	2,576 170	44%	813/671-5011	Fax 813/671-5012
Rodgers Middle Sch 11910 Tucker Rd, Riverview 33569 **David New**	6-8	T	749	68%	813/671-5288	Fax 813/671-5245
Sessums Elem Sch 11525 Ramble Creek Dr, Riverview 33569 Allison Norgard	PK-5	T	997	56%	813/672-5230	Fax 813/672-5234
Ⓐ Simmons Career Center 1202 W Grant St, Plant City 33563 Cleto Chazares	9-12	V	144 10		813/707-7430	Fax 813/707-7435
South Co Career Center 2810 John Sherman Way, Ruskin 33570 Jennifer Davis	Voc	AT	209 18	77%	813/233-3335	Fax 813/233-3339
Springhead Elem Sch 3208 Nesmith Rd, Plant City 33566 **Michelle McClellan**	PK-5	T	882 42	82%	813/757-9321	Fax 813/757-9500
Stowers Elem Sch 13915 Barrington Stowers Dr, Lithia 33547 Catherine Lennard	PK-5		821	23%	813/657-7431	Fax 813/657-7435
Ⓜ Strawberry Crest High Sch 4691 Gallagher Rd, Dover 33527 David Brown	9-12	TV	2,268	51%	813/707-7522	Fax 813/707-7526 [f][t]
Summerfield Crossings Elem Sch 11050 Fairway Meadow Dr, Riverview 33579 Brian Harvey	PK-5	T	871	61%	813/672-5621	Fax 813/672-5625
Summerfield Elem Sch 11990 Big Bend Rd, Riverview 33579 Carmine Alfano	PK-5	T	778 50	67%	813/671-5115	Fax 813/672-5221
Tomlin Middle Sch 501 N Woodrow Wilson St, Plant City 33563 Traci Durrance	6-8	TV	1,672 73	72%	813/757-9400	Fax 813/707-7024
Trapnell Elem Sch 1605 W Trapnell Rd, Plant City 33566 Krissy Perkins	PK-5	T	551 33	90%	813/757-9313	Fax 813/757-9129
Turkey Creek Middle Sch 5005 Turkey Creek Rd, Plant City 33567 Fredda Johnson	6-8	TV	994 58	79%	813/757-9442	Fax 813/757-9451
Valrico Elem Sch 609 S Miller Rd, Valrico 33594 Tricia Simonsen	PK-5	T	812 53	57%	813/744-6777	Fax 813/740-3535

1 Superintendent
2 Bus/Finance/Purchasing
3 Buildings And Grounds
4 Food Service
5 Transportation
6 Athletic
7 Health Services

8 Curric/Instruct K-12
9 Curric/Instruct Elem
10 Curric/Instruct Sec
11 Federal Program
12 Title I
13 Title V
14 Asst Superintendent
15 Asst Superintendent
16 Instructional Media Svcs
17 Chief Operations Officer
18 Chief Academic Officer

19 Chief Financial Officer
20 Art K-12
21 Art Elem
22 Art Sec
23 Music K-12
24 Music Elem
25 Music Sec
26 Business Education
27 Career & Tech Ed
28 Technology Education

29 Family/Consumer Science
30 Adult Education
31 Career/Sch-to-Work K-12
32 Career/Sch-to-Work Elem
33 Career/Sch-to-Work Sec
34 Early Childhood Ed
35 Health/Phys Education
36 Guidance Services K-12
37 Guidance Services Elem
38 Guidance Services Sec

39 Social Studies K-12
40 Social Studies Elem
41 Social Studies Sec
42 Science K-12
43 Science Elem
44 Science Sec
45 Math K-12
46 Math Elem
47 Math Sec
48 English/Lang Arts K-12

49 English/Lang Arts Elem
50 English/Lang Arts Sec
51 Reading K-12
52 Reading Elem
53 Reading Sec
54 Remedial Reading K-12
55 Remedial Reading Elem
56 Remedial Reading Sec
57 Bilingual/ELL
58 Special Education K-12

59 Special Education Elem
60 Special Education Sec
61 Foreign/World Lang K-12
62 Foreign/World Lang Elem
63 Foreign/World Lang Sec
64 Religious Education K-12
65 Religious Education Elem
66 Religious Education Sec
67 School Board President
68 Teacher Personnel

69 Academic Assessment
70 Research/Development
71 Public Information
72 Summer School
73 Instructional Tech
74 Inservice Training
75 Marketing/Distributive
76 Info Systems
77 Psychological Assess
78 Affirmative Action

	Grd	Prgm	Enr/#Cls	SN	
W Peters Excptnl Center 2919 Nelson Ave, Dover 33527 Sue Bennett	Spec	T	84 	63%	813/757-9462 Fax 813/707-7211
Walden Lake Elem Sch 2800 Turkey Creek Rd, Plant City 33566 Dina Wyatt	PK-5	T	838 50	55%	813/757-9433 Fax 813/707-7170
Wilson Elem Sch 702 W English St, Plant City 33563 Kayla Forcucci	PK-5	T	367 23	93%	813/757-9307 Fax 813/757-9310
Wimauma Elem Sch 5709 Hickman St, Wimauma 33598 Ismael Lebron-Bravo	PK-5	T	611 30	95%	813/671-5159 Fax 813/672-5222

HILLSBOROUGH CATHOLIC SCHOOLS

- **Diocese St Petersburg Ed Off** PID: 00200729
  Listing includes only schools located in this county. See District Index for location of Diocesan Offices.

Catholic Schs..Principal	Grd	Prgm	Enr/#Cls	SN	
Christ the King Sch 3809 W Morrison Ave, Tampa 33629 Nick Tanis	PK-8		500 27		813/876-8770 Fax 813/879-0315 ▪️
Corpus Christi Catholic Sch 9715 N 56th St, Tampa 33617 Kelly Kearney	K-8		240		813/988-1722 Fax 813/989-2665
Incarnation Catholic Sch 5111 Webb Rd, Tampa 33615 Mary McLauhlin	PK-3		240 19		813/884-4502 Fax 813/885-3734
Morning Star Sch 210 E Linebaugh Ave, Tampa 33612 Eileen Odom	Spec		79 9		813/935-0232 Fax 813/932-2321
Mother Teresa of Calcutta CS 17524 Lakeshore Rd, Lutz 33558 Jaqueline St Charles	K-8		420 19		813/933-4750 Fax 813/933-3181
Nativity Catholic Sch 705 E Brandon Blvd, Brandon 33511 Maureen Ringley	PK-8		690 23		813/689-3395 Fax 813/681-5406 ▪️
Resurrection Early Chldhd Ctr 6819 Krycul Ave, Riverview 33578 Ivonne Roldan Cortes	PK-PK		20 3		813/672-0077 Fax 813/671-7844
St Clement Early Childhood Ctr 1104 N Alexander St, Plant City 33563 Candice Tripi	PK-PK		58		813/754-1237
St Joseph Catholic Sch 2200 N Gomez Ave, Tampa 33607 Brenda Budd	PK-8		290 13		813/879-7720
St Lawrence Sch 5223 N Himes Ave, Tampa 33614 Patricia Freund	PK-8		550		813/879-5090 Fax 813/879-6886
St Paul Child Enrichment Ctr 12708 N Dale Mabry Hwy, Tampa 33618 Abbie Johnson	PK-PK		124 6		813/264-3314 Fax 813/962-8780
St Peter Claver Sch 1401 N Governor St, Tampa 33602 Sr Maria Babatunde	PK-8		220 10		813/224-0865 Fax 813/223-6726 ▪️
St Stephen Catholic Sch 10424 Saint Stephen Cir, Riverview 33569 Linda Umoh	PK-8		325 9		813/741-9203 Fax 813/741-9622
St Timothy Early Childhood Ctr 17512 Lakeshore Rd, Lutz 33558 Daisy Cintron	PK-PK		81 4		813/960-4857 Fax 813/961-9429

	Grd	Prgm	Enr/#Cls	SN	
Tampa Catholic High Sch 4630 N Rome Ave, Tampa 33603 Robert Lees	9-12		750 39		813/870-0860 Fax 813/877-9136

HILLSBOROUGH PRIVATE SCHOOLS

Private Schs..Principal	Grd	Prgm	Enr/#Cls	SN	
Academic Achievement Center 313 Pruett Rd, Seffner 33584 Dr Arnold Stark	Spec		7 1		813/654-4198
Academy of the Holy Names 3319 Bayshore Blvd, Tampa 33629 Bridgid Fishman \ Stephanie Nitchals	PK-12		868 50		813/839-5371 Fax 813/839-7930
Academy Prep Center of Tampa 1407 E Columbus Dr, Tampa 33605 L'Tanya Evans	5-8		105		813/248-5600 Fax 813/248-5620
American Youth Academy 5905 E 130th Ave, Tampa 33617 Feras Abuzayda	PK-12		540 20		813/987-9282 Fax 813/987-9262
Ⓐ AMI Kids Tampa 1730 Maritime Blvd, Tampa 33605 Carlos Valdes	6-12	G	44 5		813/248-5091 Fax 813/247-3998
Bayshore Christian Sch 3909 S MacDill Ave, Tampa 33611 Angie Bailey	PK-12		250 25		813/839-4297 Fax 813/835-1404
Beach Park Sch 4200 W North A St, Tampa 33609 Richard Winkler	PK-8		90 5		813/289-3747
Bell Shoals Baptist Academy 2102 Bell Shoals Rd, Brandon 33511 Sandra Carnley	PK-8		400 34		813/689-9183 Fax 813/643-1649
Berkeley Preparatory Sch 4811 Kelly Rd, Tampa 33615 Joseph Seivold	PK-12		1,300 70		813/885-1673 Fax 813/886-6933
Bible Truth Ministry Academy 4902 N 22nd St, Tampa 33610 Suzette Dean	PK-12		86 5		813/231-9177 Fax 813/237-0221
Brandon Academy 801 Limona Rd, Brandon 33510 Dominick Giombetti	K-12		230 16		813/689-1952 Fax 813/651-4278
Cambridge Christian Sch 6101 N Habana Ave, Tampa 33614 Jonathan Valdez \ Cari Gibson	PK-12		650 41		813/872-6744 Fax 813/872-6013
Carrollwood Day Sch 1515 W Bearss Ave, Tampa 33613 Trudi Buscemi \ Allison Agliata \ Sara Rubinstein	PK-12		681 65		813/920-2288 Fax 813/920-8237
Center Academy 1520 Land O Lakes Blvd Ste D, Lutz 33549 Andrew Guido	4-12		100 4		813/909-9442 Fax 813/909-4483
Center Academy 10518 Riverview Dr, Riverview 33578 Dave Stone	Spec		100		813/677-7777 Fax 813/677-1940
Central Baptist Christian Sch 402 E Windhorst Rd, Brandon 33510 Dan Martin	PK-12		50		813/689-6133
Christian Crossings Academy 1840 Crossings Blvd Unit 100, Odessa 33556 Salim Karnaby	K-8		90		813/792-9070 ▪️
Citrus Park Christian Sch 7705 Gunn Hwy, Tampa 33625 Gina Betz	PK-12		350 40		813/920-3960 Fax 813/926-1240
Corbett Preparatory Sch 12015 Orange Grove Dr, Tampa 33618 Dr Joyce Swarzman	PK-8		550 30		813/961-3087 Fax 813/963-0846 ▪️

79 Student Personnel	**91** Safety/Security	**275** Response To Intervention	**298** Grant Writer/Ptnrships
80 Driver Ed/Safety	**92** Magnet School	**277** Remedial Math K-12	**750** Chief Innovation Officer
81 Gifted/Talented	**93** Parental Involvement	**280** Literacy Coach	**751** Chief of Staff
82 Video Services	**95** Tech Prep Program	**285** STEM	**752** Social Emotional Learning
83 Substance Abuse Prev	**97** Chief Information Officer	**286** Digital Learning	
84 Erate	**98** Chief Technology Officer	**288** Common Core Standards	**Other School Types**
85 AIDS Education	**270** Character Education	**294** Accountability	Ⓐ = Alternative School
88 Alternative/At Risk	**271** Migrant Education	**295** Network System	Ⓒ = Charter School
89 Multi-Cultural Curriculum	**273** Teacher Mentor	**296** Title II Programs	Ⓜ = Magnet School
90 Social Work	**274** Before/After Sch	**297** Webmaster	Ⓨ = Year-Round School

School Programs
A = Alternative Program
G = Adult Classes
M = Magnet Program
T = Title I Schoolwide
V = Career & Tech Ed Programs

Social Media
▪️ = Facebook
▪️ = Twitter

New Schools are shaded
New Superintendents and Principals are bold
Personnel with email addresses are underscored

Cristo Rey Tampa High Sch 6400 E Chelsea St, Tampa 33610 Jim Madden	9-9	82	813/621-8300
Ethline R Williams Prep Sch 4411B Kelly Rd, Tampa 33615 Dr Ethline Williams	1-12	76	813/374-9139 Fax 813/901-0424
Faith Outreach Academy 7607 Sheldon Rd, Tampa 33615 Julie Sierra	PK-12	168 12	813/887-5546 Fax 813/249-6896
Family of Christ Christian Sch 16190 Bruce B Downs Blvd # 3, Tampa 33647 Jennifer Snow	K-8	170 8	813/558-9343 Fax 813/977-0549
Florida College Academy 7032 Temple Terrace Hwy, Tampa 33637 Lynn Wade	PK-8	152 16	813/899-6800 Fax 813/984-8301
Foundation Christian Academy 3955 Lithia Pinecrest Rd, Valrico 33596 Jonathan Smith \ Sherri Smith	PK-12	350	813/654-2969 Fax 813/655-4780
Freedom Academy 1118 N Parsons Ave, Brandon 33510 Brad Bailey	K-12	55	813/654-0836 Fax 813/548-0565
Friendship Christian Academy 6522 N 43rd St, Tampa 33610 Christina Frey \ Bernard DeLaRosa	K-12	120 4	813/932-8767 Fax 813/932-8743
Gateway Christian Academy 14205 N Florida Ave, Tampa 33613 Martiza Maldonado	PK-12	50	813/964-9800 Fax 813/964-9808
Grace Christian Sch 1425 N Valrico Rd, Valrico 33594 Barry McKeen	K-12 V	200 25	813/689-8815 Fax 813/681-7396
Hebrew Academy of Tampa Bay 14908 Pennington Rd, Tampa 33624 Sulha Dubrowski	PK-8	50 11	813/963-0706 Fax 813/265-8543
Hillel Academy 2020 W Fletcher Ave, Tampa 33612 Allison Oakes	PK-8	190 32	813/963-2242 Fax 813/264-0544
Hillsborough Baptist Sch 6021 Williams Rd, Seffner 33584 Jessica Draper	PK-12	110 12	813/620-0683
Holy Trinity Lutheran Sch 3712 W El Prado Blvd, Tampa 33629 Kelly Reilly	PK-5	60 7	813/839-0665 Fax 813/839-2706
Immanuel Lutheran Sch 2913 John Moore Rd, Brandon 33511 Bonne Faherty	PK-8	185 14	813/685-1978 Fax 813/681-6852
Interactive Educ Academy 1474 Bloomingdale Ave, Valrico 33596 Maria Sharma	6-12	55 4	813/689-2087 Fax 813/689-3007
Jesuit High Sch 4701 N Himes Ave, Tampa 33614 Barry Neuburger	9-12	850 45	813/877-5344 Fax 813/872-1853
Keystone Prep High Sch 18105 Gunn Hwy, Odessa 33556 Ben Tomales	9-12	70	813/264-4500 Fax 813/963-0675
Kings Kids Christian Academy 3000 N 34th St, Tampa 33605 Angela Small	K-2	120 12	813/248-6548 Fax 813/247-4337
Lee Academy for Gifted Ed 3001 Lee Academy Ct, Tampa 33614 Jennifer Deitz	PK-12	80 14	813/931-3316 f t
Libertas Academy 15102 Amberly Dr, Tampa 33647 Hannah Vickery	K-8	30	813/964-1779
Lighthouse Ctr-Creative Lrng 516 Corner Dr, Brandon 33511 Butch Bedwell	Spec	105	813/655-6505 Fax 813/655-6506 f
Livingstone Academy 1204 Lenna Ave, Seffner 33584 Bruce Gifford	Spec	150	813/661-4200
Missionary Christian Academy 1106 E 109th Ave, Tampa 33612 Raymond Arroyo	PK-12	10 4	813/977-6513 Fax 813/977-9583
Mont Chldrn's House-Hyde Park 2416 W Cleveland St, Tampa 33609 Amanda Linton	PK-6	70	813/354-9511 Fax 813/354-1902
Monte's Montessori Sch 13227 Boyette Rd, Riverview 33569 Juliette Johnson	PK-1	100 5	813/651-0653 Fax 813/685-2010
Montessori House 5117 Ehrlich Rd, Tampa 33624 Sally Parker	PK-6	130 5	813/884-7220 Fax 813/961-8639
Montessori Preparatory Sch 11302 N 56th St, Tampa 33617 Sonia Johnson	K-5	200 10	813/899-2345 Fax 813/989-9870
Mt Calvary Junior Academy 3111 E Wilder Ave, Tampa 33610 Edson Jarvis	PK-8	155 12	813/238-0433 Fax 813/231-0804
Northdale Lutheran Sch 15709 Mapledale Dr, Tampa 33624 Mark Thiesfeldt	K-8	50 3	813/961-9195 Fax 813/961-2435 f
Odessa Christian Sch 19521 Michigan Ave, Odessa 33556 Erin Ciulla	K-12	90	813/792-1825 Fax 813/749-6690
Paideia School of Tampa Bay 7834 N 56th St, Tampa 33617 Dr Timothy Bridges	K-12	100	813/988-7700 Fax 813/988-7740
Providence Christian Sch 5416 Providence Rd, Riverview 33578 David Hubbart	PK-12	125 18	813/661-0588 Fax 813/681-3852
Resurrection Christian Sch 3215 Bell Shoals Rd, Brandon 33511 Wayne Radd	PK-8	30 4	813/685-6377
Ruskin Christian Sch 820 W College Ave, Ruskin 33570 Kent Alexander	PK-12	250 20	813/645-6441 Fax 813/641-2073 f
Seffner Christian Academy 11605 E US Highway 92, Seffner 33584 Stephanie Newland \ Amy Kretzer \ Maggie Pope	PK-12 V	675 32	813/626-0001 Fax 813/627-0330 f t
St John's Parish Lower Sch 906 S Orleans Ave, Tampa 33606 Araina Jewell	1-4	228 22	813/849-5200 Fax 813/258-2548 f
St John's Parish Middle Sch 240 S Plant Ave, Tampa 33606 Justin Smith	5-8	230	813/849-4200 Fax 813/849-1026
St Mary's Episcopal Day Sch 2101 S Hubert Ave, Tampa 33629 Scott Laird	PK-8	430 25	813/258-5508 Fax 813/258-5603
Tampa Bay Christian Academy 6815 N Rome Ave, Tampa 33604 Sharon Phillips	PK-12	365 30	813/343-0600 Fax 813/343-0601
Tampa Christian Cmty Sch 960 W Lutz Lake Fern Rd, Lutz 33548 Melissa Walker	K-12	125	813/949-2144
Tampa Day Sch 12606 Henderson Rd, Tampa 33625 Lois DeLaney	Spec	127 13	813/269-2100 Fax 813/963-7843 f
Tampa Preparatory Sch 727 W Cass St, Tampa 33606 Kevin Plummer \ Carl Carlson	6-12	680 60	813/251-8481 Fax 813/254-2106
Town & Country Christian Acad 9910 Wilsky Blvd, Tampa 33615 Dr Janis Perry	K-12	42 6	813/884-0971 Fax 813/884-5303

1	Superintendent	8	Curric/Instruct K-12	19	Chief Financial Officer
2	Bus/Finance/Purchasing	9	Curric/Instruct Elem	20	Art K-12
3	Buildings And Grounds	10	Curric/Instruct Sec	21	Art Elem
4	Food Service	11	Federal Program	22	Art Sec
5	Transportation	12	Title I	23	Music K-12
6	Athletic	13	Title V	24	Music Elem
7	Health Services	15	Asst Superintendent	25	Music Sec
		16	Instructional Media Svcs	26	Business Education
		17	Chief Operations Officer	27	Career & Tech Ed
		18	Chief Academic Officer	28	Technology Education

29	Family/Consumer Science	39	Social Studies K-12	49	English/Lang Arts Elem
30	Adult Education	40	Social Studies Elem	50	English/Lang Arts Sec
31	Career/Sch-to-Work K-12	41	Social Studies Sec	51	Reading K-12
32	Career/Sch-to-Work Elem	42	Science K-12	52	Reading Elem
33	Career/Sch-to-Work Sec	43	Science Elem	53	Reading Sec
34	Early Childhood Ed	44	Science Sec	54	Remedial Reading K-12
35	Health/Phys Education	45	Math K-12	55	Remedial Reading Elem
36	Guidance Services K-12	46	Math Elem	56	Remedial Reading Sec
37	Guidance Services Elem	47	Math Sec	57	Bilingual/ELL
38	Guidance Services Sec	48	English/Lang Arts K-12	58	Special Education K-12

59	Special Education Elem	69	Academic Assessment
60	Special Education Sec	70	Research/Development
61	Foreign/World Lang K-12	71	Public Information
62	Foreign/World Lang Elem	72	Summer School
63	Foreign/World Lang Sec	73	Instructional Tech
64	Religious Education K-12	74	Inservice Training
65	Religious Education Elem	75	Marketing/Distributive
66	Religious Education Sec	76	Info Systems
67	School Board President	77	Psychological Assess
68	Teacher Personnel	78	Affirmative Action

Tropical Acres Christian Acad	PK-K		18		813/677-8036
12107 Rhodine Rd, Riverview 33579			2		
Lois Saxe					
Universal Academy-Florida	PK-12		700		813/664-0695
6801 Orient Rd, Tampa 33610			20		Fax 813/664-4506
Rubina Taria					
Villa Madonna Sch	PK-8		350		813/229-1322
315 W Columbus Dr, Tampa 33602			23		Fax 813/223-4812
Mary Jackson					
West Gate Christian Sch	PK-12		135		813/884-5147
5121 Kelly Rd, Tampa 33615			13		Fax 813/888-5368
Justin Raymond					
Windsor Learning Acad-Presch	PK-PK		68		813/885-3424
6920 Hanley Rd, Tampa 33634					Fax 813/425-9512
Windsor Learning Academy	K-12		75		813/885-3424
6337 Memorial Hwy, Tampa 33615					Fax 813/425-9512
Cynthia Cornilous					

HILLSBOROUGH REGIONAL CENTERS

- **FDLRS-Hillsborough** PID: 04498239 — 813/837-7777
  4210 W Bay Villa Ave, Tampa 33611 — Fax 813/837-7702

Michael Levine ....1,11 Sherie Campbell 73

HOLMES COUNTY

HOLMES PUBLIC SCHOOLS

- **Holmes Co School Dist** PID: 00193255 — 850/547-6674
  701 E Pennsylvania Ave, Bonifay 32425 — Fax 850/547-0381

Schools: 7 \ *Teachers:* 231 \ *Students:* 3,500 \ *Special Ed Students:* 505 \ *LEP Students:* 5 \ *Ethnic:* African American 4%, Hispanic 4%, Caucasian 92% \ *Exp:* $152 (Low) \ *Poverty:* 27% \ *Title I:* $1,011,569 \ *Special Education:* $4,165,000 \ *Open-Close:* 08/12 - 05/22 \ *DTBP:* $153 (High)

Terry Mears 1		Kelly Leavins 2	
Mickey Hudson 3,6,78,92*		Carmen Bush 4,11,36,83,93,285,298	
Jalisa Brannon 5		Pamela Price 8,275,280,288,294,296	
Donnita Butorac 9,57,58,69,81		Melissa Baxley 16,71,73,82,84,286,295	
Shirley Owens 67		Phillip Byrd 76*	
Ron Dixon 88		Greg Sallas 91,752	
Dale Thomas 295			

Public Schs..Principal	Grd	Prgm	Enr/#Cls	SN
Bethlehem Sch	PK-12	AT	449	49% 850/547-3621
2767 Highway 160, Bonifay 32425			30	Fax 850/547-4856
Rosanne Mitchell				
Bonifay K-8 Sch	PK-8	AT	1,279	60% 850/547-3631
140 Blue Devil Dr, Bonifay 32425			53	Fax 850/547-3685
Rodd Jones				
Holmes Co High Sch	9-12	AT	474	43% 850/547-9000
105 Blue Devil Dr, Bonifay 32425			30	Fax 850/547-6694
Matt Tate				
Ponce De Leon Elem Sch	PK-5	AT	315	64% 850/836-4296
1473 Ammons Rd, Ponce De Leon 32455			21	Fax 850/836-5325
Rodd Jones				

Public Schs..Principal	Grd	Prgm	Enr/#Cls	SN
Ponce De Leon High Sch	6-12	AT	301	56% 850/836-4242
1477 Ammons Rd, Ponce De Leon 32455			34	Fax 850/836-5388
Anissa Locke				
Poplar Springs Sch	PK-12	AT	386	41% 850/263-6260
3726 Atomic Dr, Graceville 32440			30	Fax 850/263-1252
Brian Morgan				
Ⓐ The Gap	6-12	T	30	60% 850/547-0470
401 McLaughlin Ave, Bonifay 32425				Fax 850/547-0472
Ron Dixon				

HOLMES PRIVATE SCHOOLS

Private Schs..Principal	Grd	Prgm	Enr/#Cls	SN
Gateway Academy	6-12		65	850/547-9011
1213 Hope Cir, Bonifay 32425			4	Fax 850/547-2566
Susan McCall				

INDIAN RIVER COUNTY

INDIAN RIVER PUBLIC SCHOOLS

- **School Dist of Indian River Co** PID: 00193334 — 772/564-3000
  6500 57th St, Vero Beach 32967 — Fax 772/564-3054

Schools: 29 \ *Teachers:* 1,112 \ *Students:* 17,500 \ *Special Ed Students:* 2,584 \ *LEP Students:* 959 \ *College-Bound:* 60% \ *Ethnic:* Asian 2%, African American 18%, Hispanic 23%, Caucasian 57% \ *Exp:* $179 (Low) \ *Poverty:* 16% \ *Title I:* $4,062,179 \ *Special Education:* $7,224,000 \ *Bilingual Education:* $700,000 \ *Open-Close:* 08/12 - 05/28 \ *DTBP:* $194 (High)

Dr Susan Moxley 1		Jeffrey Carver 2	
Kim Copeman 2		Meri-De Mercado 2	
Ann Rieben 3		Chad Lane 3	
Jim Sanders 3		John Teske 3,15	
Michael Sturgis 3		Nicholas Westenberger 3	
Richard Huff 3		Traci Simonton 4	
Angela McCutchen 5		Jennifer Idlette 5	
Richard Trammel 5		Tony Sears 5,91	
Jessica Upchurch 6		Leonard Jankowski 6	
Caroline Maschhoff 7		Georgann Gergora 7	
Pam Dampier 8,15,72,285,288		Kelly Baysura 9	
Dr Kathrine Pierandozzi 10		Karen Malits 11,57,296	
Christi Shields 30*		Brooke Flood 34*	
Heather Clark 58		Dr Lillian Martinez 58,79,83,88,90,275	
Laura Zorc 67		Adalia Medina-Graham 68	
Danielle Howard 68		Dr Edwina Suit 68	
Dr Jayne Purcell 68		Chris Taylor 69,294	
Dr Deborah Long 78		Brian Bender 91	
Barbara Musselwhite 274*		Tiffany McKenzie 286	
Joanne Balsamo 298			

Public Schs..Principal	Grd	Prgm	Enr/#Cls	SN
Ⓐ Alternative Ctr for Education	6-12	T	46	82% 772/564-6240
1426 18th St, Vero Beach 32960			11	Fax 772/564-6265
Denny Hart				
Beachland Elem Sch	K-5	T	473	53% 772/564-3300
3350 Indian River Dr E, Vero Beach 32963			32	Fax 772/564-3350
Dr Colleen Lord				

79 Student Personnel	91 Safety/Security	275 Response To Intervention	298 Grant Writer/Ptnrships	**School Programs**	**Social Media**
80 Driver Ed/Safety	92 Magnet School	277 Remedial Math K-12	750 Chief Innovation Officer	A = Alternative Program	
81 Gifted/Talented	93 Parental Involvement	280 Literacy Coach	751 Chief of Staff	G = Adult Classes	ⓕ = Facebook
82 Video Services	95 Tech Prep Program	285 STEM	752 Social Emotional Learning	M = Magnet Program	
83 Substance Abuse Prev	97 Chief Infomation Officer	286 Digital Learning		T = Title I Schoolwide	ⓣ = Twitter
84 Erate	98 Chief Technology Officer	288 Common Core Standards	**Other School Types**	V = Career & Tech Ed Programs	
85 AIDS Education	270 Character Education	294 Accountability	Ⓐ = Alternative School		
88 Alternative/At Risk	271 Migrant Education	295 Network System	Ⓒ = Charter School	New Schools are shaded	
89 Multi-Cultural Curriculum	273 Teacher Mentor	296 Title II Programs	Ⓜ = Magnet School	New Superintendents and Principals are bold	
90 Social Work	274 Before/After Sch	297 Webmaster	Ⓨ = Year-Round School	Personnel with email addresses are underscored	

FL—55

School..Principal	Grd	Prgm	Enr/#Cls	SN	Phone
Citrus Elem Sch 2771 4th St, Vero Beach 32968 Kimberly Garcia	K-5	T	701 40	70%	772/978-8350 Fax 772/978-8351
Dodgertown Elem Sch 4350 43rd Ave, Vero Beach 32967 Aretha Vernette	PK-5	T	403 28	87%	772/564-4100 Fax 772/564-4093
Fellsmere Elem Sch 50 N Cypress St, Fellsmere 32948 Ramon Echeverria	PK-5	T	598 31	82%	772/564-5970 Fax 772/564-6020
Gifford Middle Sch 4530 28th Ct, Vero Beach 32967 Tosha Jones	6-8	TV	675 59	52%	772/564-3550 Fax 772/564-3561
Glendale Elem Sch 4940 8th St, Vero Beach 32968 Adam Faust	PK-5	T	593 30	75%	772/978-8050 Fax 772/978-8098
© Imagine Schools S Vero [138] 6000 4th St, Vero Beach 32968 Chris Rock	K-8	T	891	25%	772/567-2728 Fax 772/410-0329
Indian River Academy 500 20th St SW, Vero Beach 32962 Diane Fannin	PK-5	T	432 20	79%	772/564-3390 Fax 772/564-3443
© Indian River Charter High Sch 6055 College Ln, Vero Beach 32966 Cynthia Trevino-Aversa	9-12	T	687	7%	772/567-6600 Fax 772/567-2288
Indian River Virtual Sch 6500 57th St, Vero Beach 32967 Jody Bennett	K-12		150		772/564-3067
Ⓜ Liberty Magnet Elem Sch 6850 81st St, Vero Beach 32967 Takeisha Harris	K-5	T	542 30	40%	772/564-5300 Fax 772/564-5303
© North Co Charter Sch 6640 Old Dixie Hwy, Vero Beach 32967 Jessica Keaton	1-5	T	366	35%	772/794-1941 Fax 772/794-1945
Ⓜ Osceola Magnet Sch 1110 18th Ave SW, Vero Beach 32962 Scott Simpson	K-5	T	534 28	42%	772/564-5821 Fax 772/564-5827
Oslo Middle Sch 480 20th Ave SW, Vero Beach 32962 Beth Hofer	6-8	TV	897 52	74%	772/564-3980 Fax 772/564-6020
Pelican Island Elem Sch 1355 Schumann Dr, Sebastian 32958 Chris Kohlstedt	PK-5	T	416 44	83%	772/564-6500 Fax 772/564-6493
Ⓜ Rosewood Magnet Sch 3850 16th St, Vero Beach 32960 Casandra Flores	K-5	T	540 30	39%	772/564-3840 Fax 772/564-3888
© Sebastian Charter Jr High Sch 782 Wave St, Sebastian 32958 William Dodds	5-8	T	268 10	50%	772/388-8838 Fax 772/388-8815
Sebastian Elem Sch 400 Sebastian Blvd, Sebastian 32958 Letitia Whitfield-Hart	K-5	T	402 30	74%	772/978-8200 Fax 772/978-8205
Sebastian River High Sch 9001 90th Ave, Sebastian 32958 Dariyall Brown	9-12	TV	1,922 81	53%	772/564-4170 Fax 772/564-4182
Sebastian River Middle Sch 9400 Cr 512, Sebastian 32958 Todd Racine	6-8	TV	934 60	61%	772/564-5111 Fax 772/564-5225
© St Peter's Preparatory Academy 4250 38th Ave, Vero Beach 32967 Ruth Jefferson	K-6	T	137 6	98%	772/562-1963 Fax 772/567-8361
Storm Grove Middle Sch 6400 57th St, Vero Beach 32967 Anne Bieber	6-8	T	1,043	49%	772/564-6400 Fax 772/564-6321
Tech Ctr for Career & Adult Ed 1426 19th St, Vero Beach 32960 Christi Shields	Adult		50 5		772/564-4970 Fax 772/562-8357
Treasure Coast Elem Sch 8955 85th St, Sebastian 32958 Elizabeth Tetreault	K-5	T	662	70%	772/978-8500 Fax 772/978-8503
Vero Beach Elem Sch 1770 12th St, Vero Beach 32960 Cynthia Emerson	PK-5	T	622 40	87%	772/564-4560 Fax 772/564-4552
Vero Beach Freshman Lrng Ctr 1507 19th St, Vero Beach 32960 Shawn O'Keefe	9-9		736		772/564-5800 Fax 772/564-5679
Vero Beach Senior High Sch 1707 16th St, Vero Beach 32960 Shawn O'Keefe	9-12	ATV	2,926 120	48%	772/564-5600 Fax 772/564-5553
Wabasso Sch 8895 US 1, Wabasso 32970 Jack Bartman	Spec	T	54 7	68%	772/978-8000 Fax 772/978-8028

INDIAN RIVER CATHOLIC SCHOOLS

• **Diocese of Palm Beach Ed Off** PID: 02231700
Listing includes only schools located in this county. See District Index for location of Diocesan Offices.

Catholic Schs..Principal	Grd	Prgm	Enr/#Cls	SN
St Helen Catholic Sch 2050 Vero Beach Ave, Vero Beach 32960 Lisa Bell	K-8		275 12	772/567-5457 Fax 772/567-4823

INDIAN RIVER PRIVATE SCHOOLS

Private Schs..Principal	Grd	Prgm	Enr/#Cls	SN
Glendale Christian Sch 790 27th Ave, Vero Beach 32968 Denise MacDonald	PK-12		119 10	772/569-1095 Fax 772/562-4919
Master's Academy 1105 58th Ave, Vero Beach 32966 Eric Lantrip	PK-12		260	772/794-4655
Shiloh Youth Ranch 10655 Roseland Rd, Sebastian 32958 Mark Hinkle	3-12		15 1	772/589-4449
St Edward's Sch 1895 Saint Edwards Dr, Vero Beach 32963 Barbara Mohler \ Keira Murphy \ Bruce Wachter	PK-12	G	500	772/231-4136 Fax 772/231-2427
Suncoast Primary Sch 3050 43rd Ave, Vero Beach 32960 Candee Manwaring	PK-8		85 7	772/778-0892
Tabernacle Christian Sch 51 Old Dixie Hwy, Vero Beach 32962 Judy Bair	K-8		35 2	772/562-0720 Fax 772/562-2024
Willow Sch 950 43rd Ave, Vero Beach 32960 Stephanie Heady	K-8		33 3	772/770-0758 Fax 772/770-0725 🅕🅣

1 Superintendent	8 Curric/Instruct K-12	19 Chief Financial Officer	29 Family/Consumer Science	39 Social Studies K-12	49 English/Lang Arts Elem	59 Special Education Elem	69 Academic Assessment
2 Bus/Finance/Purchasing	9 Curric/Instruct Elem	20 Art K-12	30 Adult Education	40 Social Studies Elem	50 English/Lang Arts Sec	60 Special Education Sec	70 Research/Development
3 Buildings And Grounds	10 Curric/Instruct Sec	21 Art Elem	31 Career/Sch-to-Work K-12	41 Social Studies Sec	51 Reading K-12	61 Foreign/World Lang K-12	71 Public Information
4 Food Service	11 Federal Program	22 Art Sec	32 Career/Sch-to-Work Elem	42 Science K-12	52 Reading Elem	62 Foreign/World Lang Elem	72 Summer School
5 Transportation	12 Title I	23 Music K-12	33 Career/Sch-to-Work Sec	43 Science Elem	53 Reading Sec	63 Foreign/World Lang Sec	73 Instructional Tech
6 Athletic	13 Title V	24 Music Elem	34 Early Childhood Ed	44 Science Sec	54 Remedial Reading K-12	64 Religious Education K-12	74 Inservice Training
7 Health Services	15 Asst Superintendent	25 Music Sec	35 Health/Phys Education	45 Math K-12	55 Remedial Reading Elem	65 Religious Education Elem	75 Marketing/Distributive
	16 Instructional Media Svcs	26 Business Education	36 Guidance Services K-12	46 Math Elem	56 Remedial Reading Sec	66 Religious Education Sec	76 Info Systems
	17 Chief Operations Officer	27 Career & Tech Ed	37 Guidance Services Elem	47 Math Sec	57 Bilingual/ELL	67 School Board President	77 Psychological Assess
	18 Chief Academic Officer	28 Technology Education	38 Guidance Services Sec	48 English/Lang Arts K-12	58 Special Education K-12	68 Teacher Personnel	78 Affirmative Action

JACKSON COUNTY

JACKSON PUBLIC SCHOOLS

• **Jackson Co School Dist** PID: 00193499 850/482-1200
2903 Jefferson St, Marianna 32446 Fax 850/482-1299

Schools: 17 \ *Teachers:* 470 \ *Students:* 6,500 \
Special Ed Students: 1,025 \ *LEP Students:* 99 \ *Ethnic:* African American 32%, Hispanic 5%, Caucasian 62% \ *Exp:* $168 (Low) \
Poverty: 23% \ *Title I:* $1,835,671 \ *Special Education:* $8,493,000 \
Bilingual Education: $233,000 \ *Open-Close:* 08/12 - 05/27 \ *DTBP:* $177 (High)

Larry Moore 1	Beverly Jackson 2	
Kathy Sneads 2	Kristine Bragan 3	
Stuart Wiggins 3	Cheryl McDaniel 4,15,71,294	
James Sims 5,91	Jennifer See 6,10,13,16,72,76*	
Shirl Williams 7,36,69,79,90	Chris Franklin 8,285,288,296*	
Michael Kilts 11,57,286,298	Phyllis Daniels 27,30	
Carolyn Pilcher 34,74,273*	Shawn Larkin 58,81	
Charlotte Gardner 67	Hannah Pickels 68	
Mary Skipper 68	Rusty Simpson 73	
Nell Swalls 77	Phyllis Daniels 83,85*	
Elizabeth Walden 84,295,297		

Public Schs..Principal	Grd	Prgm	Enr/#Cls	SN	
Cottondale Elem Sch 2766 Levy St, Cottondale 32431 Jessica Craven	PK-5	T	402 21	76%	850/482-9820 Fax 850/482-9825
Cottondale High Sch 2680 Levy St, Cottondale 32431 Kenyonis Granger	6-12	TV	481	69%	850/482-9821 Fax 850/482-9827
Frank M Golson Elem Sch 4258 2nd Ave, Marianna 32446 Amy Allen	K-2	T	643	76%	850/482-9607 Fax 850/482-1203
Graceville Elem Sch 5331 Alabama St, Graceville 32440 Laura Kent	PK-5	T	256 24	83%	850/263-4402 Fax 850/263-3304
Graceville High Sch 5539 Brown St, Graceville 32440 Larry Moore	6-12	TV	255 35	74%	850/263-4451 Fax 850/263-3605
Grand Ridge Sch 6925 Florida St, Grand Ridge 32442 **Laurence Pender**	PK-8	T	592 50	74%	850/482-1273 Fax 850/482-9834
Hope Sch 2031 Hope School Dr, Marianna 32448 Millicent Braxton	Spec	T	146 11	82%	850/482-9616 Fax 850/482-9395
Ⓐ Jackson Alternative Sch 2701 Technology Cir, Marianna 32448 Rex Suggs	K-12	T	115 13	91%	850/482-9666 Fax 850/482-9800
Jackson Co Adult Educ Center 2971 Guyton St, Marianna 32446 John Ellerbee	Adult		90 3		850/482-9617 Fax 850/482-1201
Jackson Co Virtual Sch 2903 Jefferson St, Marianna 32446 Jennifer See	K-12		22		866/339-8784
Malone Sch 5361 9th St, Malone 32445 Doug Powell	PK-12	T	534 25	73%	850/482-9930 Fax 850/482-9981
Marianna High Sch 3546 Caverns Rd, Marianna 32446 Carlan Martin	9-12	TV	756 50	53%	850/482-9605 Fax 850/482-1247
Marianna Middle Sch 4144 South St, Marianna 32448 Eddie Ellis	6-8	T	604 40	61%	850/482-9609 Fax 850/482-9795
Riverside Elem Sch 2958 Cherokee St, Marianna 32446 Chris Franklin	3-5	I	677 39	67%	850/482-9611 Fax 850/482-9300
Sneads Elem Sch 1961 Lockey Dr, Sneads 32460 Steven DeWitt	PK-5	T	438 22	68%	850/482-9003 Fax 850/482-9590
Sneads High Sch 8066 Old Spanish Trl, Sneads 32460 Ronald Mitchell	9-12	TV	428 19	58%	850/482-9007 Fax 850/482-9058
Sunland Sch 3700 Connally Dr, Marianna 32446 Tim Baggett	Spec	G	312 15		850/482-9271 Fax 850/482-9444

JACKSON PRIVATE SCHOOLS

Private Schs..Principal	Grd	Prgm	Enr/#Cls	SN	
Dayspring Christian Academy 4685 Meadowview Rd, Marianna 32446 Lori Gregg	PK-12		175 11		850/526-4919 Fax 850/526-2114
Dove Vocational Academy 5229 Ezell Rd, Graceville 32440 Amy Barnes	Voc	A	24		850/263-7550 Fax 850/263-7865
Victory Christian Academy 2271 River Rd, Sneads 32460 Susan Toole	PK-12		50 9		850/593-6699 Fax 850/893-3341

JEFFERSON COUNTY

JEFFERSON PUBLIC SCHOOLS

• **Jefferson Co School Dist** PID: 00193619 850/342-0100
1490 W Washington St, Monticello 32344 Fax 850/342-0108

Schools: 1 \ *Teachers:* 55 \ *Students:* 769 \ *Special Ed Students:* 116
\ *LEP Students:* 24 \ *College-Bound:* 73% \ *Ethnic:* Asian 1%,
African American 72%, Hispanic 11%, Caucasian 16% \ *Exp:* $2 (Low)
\ *Poverty:* 27% \ *Title I:* $611,327 \ *Special Education:* $941,000 \
Bilingual Education: $55,000 \ *Open-Close:* 08/09 - 05/25 \ *DTBP:* $350
(High) \ 🅣

Marianne Arbulu 1	Robert Lloyd 2	
Reathea Knowles 4	Tammy McGriff 11*	
Tom Vogel Gesang ...16,69,73,76,82,286,295	Joshua Valentine 57	
Sherman Stroman 68		

Public Schs..Principal	Grd	Prgm	Enr/#Cls	SN	
Ⓒ Jefferson Somerset K-12 Sch 50 David Rd, Monticello 32344 Cory Oliver	PK-12	ATV	769 30	74%	850/997-3555 Fax 850/997-4773

79 Student Personnel	91 Safety/Security	275 Response To Intervention	298 Grant Writer/Ptnrships	**School Programs**
80 Driver Ed/Safety	92 Magnet School	277 Remedial Math K-12	750 Chief Innovation Officer	A = Alternative Program
81 Gifted/Talented	93 Parental Involvement	280 Literacy Coach	751 Chief of Staff	G = Adult Classes
82 Video Services	95 Tech Prep Program	285 STEM	752 Social Emotional Learning	M = Magnet Program
83 Substance Abuse Prev	97 Chief Information Officer	286 Digital Learning		T = Title I Schoolwide
84 Erate	98 Chief Technology Officer	288 Common Core Standards	**Other School Types**	V = Career & Tech Ed Programs
85 AIDS Education	270 Character Education	294 Accountability	Ⓐ = Alternative Program	
88 Alternative/At Risk	271 Migrant Education	295 Network System	Ⓒ = Charter School	
89 Multi-Cultural Curriculum	273 Teacher Mentor	296 Title II Programs	Ⓜ = Magnet School	
90 Social Work	274 Before/After Sch	297 Webmaster	Ⓨ = Year-Round School	

Social Media

🅕 = Facebook

🅣 = Twitter

New Schools are shaded
New Superintendents and Principals are bold
Personnel with email addresses are underscored

JEFFERSON PRIVATE SCHOOLS

Private Schs..Principal	Grd	Prgm	Enr/#Cls	SN
Aucilla Christian Academy	PK-12		330	850/997-3597
7803 Aucilla Rd, Monticello 32344			15	Fax 850/997-3598
Richard Finlayson				

LAFAYETTE COUNTY

LAFAYETTE PUBLIC SCHOOLS

● **Lafayette Co School Dist** PID: 00193683   386/294-1351
363 NE Crawford St, Mayo 32066   Fax 386/294-3072

Schools: 3 \ *Teachers:* 73 \ *Students:* 1,300 \ *Special Ed Students:* 184
\ *LEP Students:* 80 \ *Ethnic:* African American 8%, Hispanic 21%,
Caucasian 71% \ *Exp:* $209 (Med) \ *Poverty:* 25% \ *Title I:* $399,344
\ *Special Education:* $1,338,000 \ *Bilingual Education:* $251,000 \
Open-Close: 08/12 - 05/27 \ *DTBP:* $325 (High)

Robert Edwards 1	Tammi Maund 2
Joey Pearson 3,4,5,6	Melissa Pearson 7
Alissa Hingson 8,298	Channah Galbraith 16
Ray Hancock 35,83,85,88*	Melissa Hewett 36*
Amanda Hickman 67	Lisa Hancock 69
Adam Walker 73,84,286,295	Channah Calbrith 82

Public Schs..Principal	Grd	Prgm	Enr/#Cls	SN
Lafayette Elem Sch	PK-5	T	601	64% 386/294-2882
811 E Main St, Mayo 32066			32	Fax 386/294-4320
Stephen Clark				
Lafayette Franchise Sch	6-12		3	386/294-1351
160 NE Hornet Dr, Mayo 32066				
Stewart Hancock				
Lafayette High Sch	6-12	AGTV	626	51% 386/294-1701
160 NE Hornet Ln, Mayo 32066			30	Fax 386/294-4197
Ray Hancock				

LAFAYETTE PRIVATE SCHOOLS

Private Schs..Principal	Grd	Prgm	Enr/#Cls	SN
Lighthouse Christian Academy	K-12		110	386/294-2994
772 N State Road 51, Mayo 32066				Fax 386/294-3449
Lisa Walker				🄵 🅃

LAKE COUNTY

LAKE PUBLIC SCHOOLS

● **Lake Co School Dist** PID: 00193700   352/253-6500
201 W Burleigh Blvd, Tavares 32778   Fax 352/253-6503

Schools: 54 \ *Teachers:* 2,586 \ *Students:* 41,590 \
Special Ed Students: 6,375 \ *LEP Students:* 2,040 \ *College-Bound:* 50%
\ *Ethnic:* Asian 3%, African American 16%, Hispanic 25%, Native American:
1%, Caucasian 56% \ *Exp:* $112 (Low) \ *Poverty:* 18% \ *Title I:* $13,148,976
\ *Special Education:* $32,644,000 \ *Bilingual Education:* $3,256,000 \
Open-Close: 08/12 - 05/29 \ *DTBP:* $188 (High)

Diane Kornegay 1	Karen Briggs 2
Kim Repas 2,294	Maureen Slovak 2
Scott Ward 2,7,15	Thomas Mock 2
Calvin Wingo 3	John Carr 3,5,15,91
Lori Mattox 3	Steve Putnam 3
Teresa Putnam 3	Charlene Gatzke 4
Linda Milliken 4	Scott Pfender 5
Don Hogan 6	Kristine Landry 7,36,77,79,90
Amy Cockcroft 8,69,74	Emily Weiskopf 8,15
Kathlene Daniels 10	Elizabeth West 11
Letizia Haugabrook 11	Chad Farnsworth 15,68
Dr Loretta I Iarris 10	Frances Cells 27,31
Kati Rose Pearson 57,69,275	Melissa Lyford 58
Tara Hart 58,81	Stephanie Luke 67
David Meyers 68	Michele Hoppenstedt 68
Melissa Dejarlais 69,70,294	Sherri Owens 71
Dr Creed Wheeler 73,98	Duane Weeks 73,76
Monica Hite 79	Sebrina Dillon-Banks 88
Mark Palmer 91	Glen Reubelt 295

Public Schs..Principal	Grd	Prgm	Enr/#Cls	SN
ⒶAlee Academy Chtr Sch-Umatilla	9-12	GTV	257	65% 352/357-9426
©1705 E County Road 44, Eustis 32736			7	Fax 352/357-8426
Robin Valentino				
©Altoona Sch	K-5	T	294	69% 352/669-3444
42630 State Road 19, Altoona 32702			6	Fax 352/669-3407
Walter Schmidt				
Astatula Elem Sch	PK-5	T	656	65% 352/343-1334
13925 Florida Ave, Astatula 34705			30	Fax 352/343-1457
Robert Sherman				
Beverly Shores Elem Sch	PK-5	T	736	91% 352/787-4175
1108 Griffin Rd, Leesburg 34748			48	Fax 352/787-1760
Cindy Christidis				
Carver Middle Sch	6-8	TV	829	75% 352/787-7868
1200 Beecher St, Leesburg 34748			47	Fax 352/787-7622
Kinetrai Kelley-Truitt				
Cecile E Gray Middle Sch	6-8	T	985	62% 352/429-3322
205 E Magnolia St, Groveland 34736			57	Fax 352/429-0133
Pamela Chateauneuf				
Clermont Elem Sch	PK-5	T	481	78% 352/394-2706
680 E Highland Ave, Clermont 34711			50	Fax 352/394-5081
Jeffrey Williams				
Clermont Middle Sch	6-8	T	583	60% 352/243-2460
301 East Ave, Clermont 34711				Fax 352/243-1407
Robert McCue				
Cypress Ridge Elem Sch	PK-5		580	23% 352/394-6633
350 East Ave, Clermont 34711			25	Fax 352/394-1170
Scott Voytko				

1	Superintendent	8	Curric/Instruct K-12	19	Chief Financial Officer
2	Bus/Finance/Purchasing	9	Curric/Instruct Elem	20	Art K-12
3	Buildings And Grounds	10	Curric/Instruct Sec	21	Art Elem
4	Food Service	11	Federal Program	22	Art Sec
5	Transportation	12	Title I	23	Music K-12
6	Athletic	13	Title V	24	Music Elem
7	Health Services	15	Asst Superintendent	25	Music Sec
		16	Instructional Media Svcs	26	Business Education
		17	Chief Operations Officer	27	Career & Tech Ed
		18	Chief Academic Officer	28	Technology Education

29	Family/Consumer Science	39	Social Studies K-12
30	Adult Education	40	Social Studies Elem
31	Career/Sch-to-Work K-12	41	Social Studies Sec
32	Career/Sch-to-Work Elem	42	Science K-12
33	Career/Sch-to-Work Sec	43	Science Elem
34	Early Childhood Ed	44	Science Sec
35	Health/Phys Education	45	Math K-12
36	Guidance Services K-12	46	Math Elem
37	Guidance Services Elem	47	Math Sec
38	Guidance Services Sec	48	English/Lang Arts K-12

49	English/Lang Arts Elem	59	Special Education Elem
50	English/Lang Arts Sec	60	Special Education Sec
51	Reading K-12	61	Foreign/World Lang K-12
52	Reading Elem	62	Foreign/World Lang Elem
53	Reading Sec	63	Foreign/World Lang Sec
54	Remedial Reading K-12	64	Religious Education K-12
55	Remedial Reading Elem	65	Religious Education Elem
56	Remedial Reading Sec	66	Religious Education Sec
57	Bilingual/ELL	67	School Board President
58	Special Education K-12	68	Teacher Personnel

69	Academic Assessment
70	Research/Development
71	Public Information
72	Summer School
73	Instructional Tech
74	Inservice Training
75	Marketing/Distributive
76	Info Systems
77	Psychological Assess
78	Affirmative Action

School	Grades		Enroll	%	Phone
East Ridge High Sch 13322 Excalibur Rd, Clermont 34711 <u>Julie Lueallen</u>	9-12	GTV	2,502	50%	352/242-2080 Fax 352/242-2090
East Ridge Middle Sch 13201 Excalibur Rd, Clermont 34711 <u>Jamie Sidoruk</u>	6-8	T	1,144	44%	352/536-8020 Fax 352/536-8039
Eustis Elem Sch 714 E Citrus Ave, Eustis 32726 <u>Corrie Voytko</u>	K-5	T	458 28	73%	352/357-2779 Fax 352/357-4179
Eustis Heights Elem Sch 250 W Atwater Ave, Eustis 32726 **Chad Frazier**	PK-5	T	749 52	86%	352/357-2447 Fax 352/357-3602
Eustis High Sch 1300 Washington Ave, Eustis 32726 <u>Tracy Clark</u>	10-12	TV	1,205 55	52%	352/357-4147 Fax 352/357-7449
Eustis High School-Curtright 1801 Bates Ave, Eustis 32726 <u>Tracy Clark</u>	9-9		300		352/589-1510 Fax 352/589-1605
Eustis Middle Sch 18725 Bates Ave, Eustis 32736 <u>Abby Crosby</u>	6-8	TV	959 50	66%	352/357-3366 Fax 352/357-5963
Fruitland Park Elem Sch 304 W Fountain St, Fruitland Pk 34731 <u>Tammy Langley</u>	K-5	T	740 30	80%	352/787-2693 Fax 352/787-9402
Grassy Lake Elem Sch 1100 Fosgate Rd, Minneola 34715 <u>Julie Williams</u>	PK-5	T	1,068	49%	352/242-0313 Fax 352/242-1504
Groveland Elem Sch 930 Parkwood Ave, Groveland 34736 <u>Kimberly Sneed-Jarvis</u>	PK-5	T	739 25	77%	352/429-2472 Fax 352/429-2516
Ⓐ **Hope Forest Academy** 46821 Jane Ln, Paisley 32767 **Mike Cantrell**	3-12		20		352/742-6920
Ⓒ **Imagine Schools South Lake [138]** 2750 Hartwood Marsh Rd, Clermont 34711 <u>Kathleen Dial</u>	K-8		1,043	23%	352/243-2960 Fax 352/243-2967
Lake Co Virtual Sch 200 W Golf Links Ave, Eustis 32726 **Donald Miller**	6-12	T	90	18%	352/483-4260 Fax 352/483-4261
Lake Hills Sch 909 S Lakeshore Blvd, Howey In Hls 34737 <u>Robin Meyers</u>	Spec	T	207 20	65%	352/324-3175 Fax 352/324-3654
Lake Minneola High Sch 101 N Hancock Rd, Minneola 34715 <u>Linda Miller</u>	9-12	T	1,728	42%	352/394-9600 Fax 352/394-3601
Ⓐ **Lake Success Academy** 525 N Georgia Ave, Howey In Hls 34737 **Dr Porsha Byfield**	9-12		80		352/253-4185
Ⓒ **Lake Technical Center** 2001 Kurt St, Eustis 32726 <u>Melissa Stephan</u>	Adult	TV	1,000		352/589-2250 Fax 352/357-4776
Leesburg Elem Sch 2229 South St, Leesburg 34748 **Susan Jordan**	K-5	T	771	89%	352/365-6308 Fax 352/365-9018
Leesburg High Sch 1401 Yellow Jacket Way, Leesburg 34748 <u>Michael Randolph</u>	9-12	GTV	1,506 70	69%	352/787-5047 Fax 352/787-5091
Lost Lake Elem Sch 1901 Johns Lake Rd, Clermont 34711 <u>Kelly Cousineau</u>	PK-5	T	1,025 55	43%	352/243-2433 Fax 352/243-3541
Ⓒ **Mascotte Elem Charter Sch** 460 Midway Ave, Mascotte 34753 <u>Tiffany Mayhugh-Rego</u>	PK-5	T	783 40	84%	352/429-2294 Fax 352/429-4836
Ⓒ **Minneola Elem Sch** 320 E Pearl St, Minneola 34715 <u>Sherry Watts</u>	PK-5	T	1,102	55%	352/394-2600 Fax 352/394-2079
Mt Dora High Sch 700 N Highland St, Mount Dora 32757 <u>Dr Rhonda Boone</u>	9-12	TV	1,121 47	50%	352/383-2177 Fax 352/383-6466
Mt Dora Middle Sch 1405 Lincoln Ave, Mount Dora 32757 **Chad Frazier**	6-8	TV	851	56%	352/383-6101 Fax 352/383-4949 🅵🆃
Oak Park Middle Sch 2101 South St, Leesburg 34748 <u>Barbara Longo</u>	6-8	TV	525 38	85%	352/787-3232 Fax 352/326-2177
Pine Ridge Elem Sch 10245 County Road 561, Clermont 34711 <u>Laine Obando</u>	PK-5	T	804	46%	352/242-2223 Fax 352/242-2818
Ⓒ **Pinecrest Academy Four Corners** 1100 US Highway 27, Clermont 34714 **Jorge Rivas**	K-8		245		352/978-3397
Ⓒ **Pinecrest Lakes Academy** 14012 Old Highway 50, Clermont 34711 <u>Christina Alcalde</u>	K-7		583		352/223-4482 Fax 352/708-4240
Rimes Early Learning Center 3101 Schoolview St, Leesburg 34748 **Greggory Dudley**	PK-2	T	280 12	89%	352/787-5757 Fax 352/787-5615
Ⓒ **Round Lake Charter Sch** 31333 Round Lake Rd, Mount Dora 32757 <u>Linda Bartberger</u>	PK-5	T	956	48%	352/385-4399 Fax 352/735-1860
Sawgrass Bay Elem Sch 16325 Superior Blvd, Clermont 34714 <u>Andrea Steenken</u>	PK-5	T	1,344	76%	352/243-1845 Fax 352/394-5732
Seminole Springs Elem Sch 26200 W Huff Rd, Eustis 32736 **Michelle Work**	PK-5	T	531 34	65%	352/589-1117 Fax 352/589-1749
Sorrento Elem Sch 24605 Wallick Rd, Sorrento 32776 <u>Brenna Burkhead</u>	PK-5	T	877	56%	352/385-1140 Fax 352/385-1159
South Lake High Sch 15600 Silver Eagle Rd, Groveland 34736 <u>Steven Benson</u>	9-12	GTV	2,055 50	52%	352/394-2100 Fax 352/394-1972
Ⓒ **Spring Creek Charter Sch** 44440 Spring Creek Rd, Paisley 32767 <u>Wesley Locke</u>	PK-8	T	608 39	83%	352/669-3275 Fax 352/669-3762
Tavares Elem Sch 720 E Clifford St, Tavares 32778 <u>Durenda McKinney</u>	PK-5	T	1,002 42	70%	352/343-2861 Fax 352/343-6618
Tavares High Sch 603 N New Hampshire Ave, Tavares 32778 **Jacob Stein**	9-12	TV	1,423	50%	352/343-3007 Fax 352/343-8614
Tavares Middle Sch 1335 Lane Park Cutoff, Tavares 32778 <u>Trella Mott</u>	6-8	TV	1,104 50	62%	352/343-4545 Fax 352/343-7212
Treadway Elem Sch 10619 Treadway School Rd, Leesburg 34788 <u>Cindy Christidis</u>	PK-5	T	895 75	73%	352/742-2291 Fax 352/742-8343
Triangle Elem Sch 1707 Eudora Rd, Mount Dora 32757 **Marlene Straughan**	PK-5	T	768 38	85%	352/383-6176 Fax 352/383-6674
Umatilla Elem Sch 401 Lake St, Umatilla 32784 <u>Kimberley Dwyer</u>	PK-5	T	625 48	71%	352/669-3181 Fax 352/669-8740
Umatilla High Sch 320 N Trowell Ave, Umatilla 32784 <u>Thomas Gerds</u>	9-12	TV	794 40	65%	352/669-3131 Fax 352/669-5481
Umatilla Middle Sch 305 E Lake St, Umatilla 32784 <u>Brent Frazier</u>	6-8	TV	605 32	70%	352/669-3171 Fax 352/669-5424
Villages Elem Sch 695 Rolling Acres Rd, Lady Lake 32159 <u>Dave Bordenkircher</u>	K-5	T	861 40	78%	352/751-0111 Fax 352/751-0117

79 Student Personnel	91 Safety/Security	275 Response To Intervention	298 Grant Writer/Ptnrships
80 Driver Ed/Safety	92 Magnet School	277 Remedial Math K-12	750 Chief Innovation Officer
81 Gifted/Talented	93 Parental Involvement	280 Literacy Coach	751 Chief of Staff
82 Video Services	95 Tech Prep Program	285 STEM	752 Social Emotional Learning
83 Substance Abuse Prev	97 Chief Information Officer	286 Digital Learning	
84 Erate	98 Chief Technology Officer	288 Common Core Standards	**Other School Types**
85 AIDS Education	270 Character Education	294 Accountability	Ⓐ = Alternative Program
88 Alternative/At Risk	271 Migrant Education	295 Network System	Ⓒ = Charter School
89 Multi-Cultural Curriculum	273 Teacher Mentor	296 Title II Programs	Ⓜ = Magnet School
90 Social Work	274 Before/After Sch	297 Webmaster	Ⓨ = Year-Round School

School Programs
A = Alternative Program
G = Adult Classes
M = Magnet Program
T = Title I Schoolwide
V = Career & Tech Ed Programs

Social Media
🅵 = Facebook
🆃 = Twitter

New Schools are shaded
New Superintendents and Principals are bold
Personnel with email addresses are underscored

Windy Hill Middle Sch 3575 Hancock Rd, Clermont 34711 William Roberts	6-8	TV	1,391 54	53%	352/394-2123 Fax 352/394-7901	

LAKE CATHOLIC SCHOOLS

• **Diocese of Orlando Ed Office** PID: 00197639
Listing includes only schools located in this county. See District Index for location of Diocesan Offices.

Catholic Schs..Principal	Grd	Prgm	Enr/#Cls	SN
St Paul Catholic Sch 1320 Sunshine Ave, Leesburg 34748 Jacquelyn Gehrsitz	PK-8		220 14	352/787-4657 Fax 352/787-0324 t

LAKE PRIVATE SCHOOLS

Private Schs..Principal	Grd	Prgm	Enr/#Cls	SN
Abels Academy 355 Citrus Tower Blvd Ste 116, Clermont 34711 Terri Howard	Spec		401	352/223-1999
Adventure Christian Academy 3800 State Road 19, Tavares 32778 Dora Getsiorb	K-12		189	352/742-4543 Fax 352/343-3820
Advoserv-Carlton Palms Sch 28308 Churchill Smith Ln, Mount Dora 32757 Wilton Beemer	Spec		200 6	352/735-0588 Fax 352/735-2786
Believers Christian Academy 796 Hooks St, Clermont 34711 Amanda Davis	PK-12		40	352/404-7717
Faith Lutheran Sch 2727 S Grove St, Eustis 32726 Steven Hoffschneider	PK-8		205 14	352/589-5683 Fax 352/589-1328 f
First Academy 219 N 13th St, Leesburg 34748 Gregory Frescoln	K-12		300 30	352/787-7762 Fax 352/323-1773
His Royal Christian Academy 32630 Whitney Rd, Leesburg 34748 Betty Lewis	K-12		15 3	352/267-9525
Holy Trinity Episcopal Sch 2201 Spring Lake Rd, Fruitland Pk 34731 Ronald Bloch	6-12		25 5	352/787-8855 Fax 352/787-8063
Hope Preparatory Academy 13806 State Road 33, Groveland 34736 Eucretia Waite	6-12		65	352/557-4959
Lake Academy 2020 Talley Rd, Leesburg 34748 Chad Chiessallo	Spec		200 9	352/315-7890 Fax 352/326-3256
Lake Montessori 415 Lee St, Leesburg 34748 Hugal Hormazabal	PK-8		140 7	352/787-5333 Fax 352/787-6517
Land of Lakes Montessori Sch 1650 Oakley Seaver Dr, Clermont 34711 Rebecca Quintana	PK-5		100 3	352/242-1805 Fax 352/242-5025
Liberty Christian Prep 2451 Dora Ave, Tavares 32778 Jeremy Thomas	PK-12		260 15	352/343-0061 Fax 352/343-2424
Montverde Academy 17235 7th St, Montverde 34756 Dr Kasey Kesselring	PK-12	V	1,249 55	407/469-2561 Fax 407/469-3711

Mount Dora Christian Academy 301 W 13th Ave, Mount Dora 32757 Lori Hadley	PK-12		600 36	352/383-2155 Fax 352/383-3112 f
New Hope Chrn Academy 105 E Baker St, Minneola 34715 Janet Burmeister	1-12		65 1	352/242-9750 Fax 352/404-8943
Praise Temple Christian Acad 5910 Bible Camp Rd, Groveland 34736 Clayton Langley	PK-12		100	352/429-8813
Real Life Christian Academy 1501 Steves Rd, Clermont 34711 Michael Fernandes	PK-12		500 18	352/394-5575 Fax 352/394-7860
Solid Rock Christian Sch 21951 US Highway 441, Mount Dora 32757 Rachel Jones	PK-12		123 5	352/735-5777 Fax 352/735-1084
South Lake Montessori Sch 983 W Desoto St, Clermont 34711 Jan Sheldon	PK-6		50 2	352/243-0993
The Key to Learning 10726 Libby Number 3 Rd, Clermont 34715 Dr Mercy Nyman	K-12		150	352/432-1422
Wesley Christian Academy 950 7th St, Clermont 34711 Beth Reed	PK-2		200	352/394-0191 f

LEE COUNTY

LEE PUBLIC SCHOOLS

• **Lee Co School Dist** PID: 00194089   239/334-1102
2855 Colonial Blvd, Fort Myers 33966   Fax 239/337-8378

> **Schools:** 113 \ **Teachers:** 5,750 \ **Students:** 94,405 \
> **Special Ed Students:** 11,683 \ **LEP Students:** 8,159 \ **College-Bound:** 71%
> \ **Ethnic:** Asian 2%, African American 15%, Hispanic 41%, Caucasian
> 42% \ **Exp:** $146 (Low) \ **Poverty:** 17% \ **Title I:** $26,115,420 \
> **Special Education:** $43,253,000 \ **Bilingual Education:** $7,894,000 \
> **Open-Close:** 08/12 - 06/03 \ **DTBP:** $205 (High) \ t

Dr Gregory Adkins	1	Kelly Letcher	2
Kimberly Hutchins	2	Marc Mora	2
Mark Santiago	2	Sherry Pearsall	2
Susan Malay	2,4	Barbara Cedeno	3
James Flock	3	Roger Lloyd	3,5
Scott Reichenbacher	3	James Buchanon	5
Robert Codie	5	Dr Pete Bohatch	6,79
Lori Houchin	7,10,35	Jess Spiro	8,18,27,30,31,35,79
Dr Bethany Quisenberry	9*	Teri Cannady	11
Jeanne La Fountain	12,271,275	Ami Desamours	19
Rita Davis	28,30,31*	Lori Brooks	36
Mary Rodriguez	36	Carlos Negron	57
Evelyn Rivera	57	Theresa Bowen	58
Jessica Duncan	59,81*	Gwynetta Gittens	67
Dr Angela Pruitt	68	Lynn Herrell	68
Suzette Rivera	68	Will Rothenberg	68
Dr Richard Itzen	69,70,294	Dr Denise Carlin	71
Lauren Stillwell	71	Trey Davis	71,97
Padraic Way	73	Helen Martin	74
Shanna Flecha	74,79	Dr Sherri Freeman	74,79
Soretta Ralph	76,81	Dr Douglas Santini	79
Chuck Bradley	83	Darryl Eldon	84
Ricahrd Parfitt	91	Carol Woelke	93
Oscar Olguin	275	Dr James Short	295

1	Superintendent	8	Curric/Instruct K-12	19	Chief Financial Officer	29	Family/Consumer Science	39	Social Studies K-12	49	English/Lang Arts Elem	59	Special Education Elem	69	Academic Assessment
2	Bus/Finance/Purchasing	9	Curric/Instruct Elem	20	Art K-12	30	Adult Education	40	Social Studies Elem	50	English/Lang Arts Sec	60	Special Education Sec	70	Research/Development
3	Buildings And Grounds	10	Curric/Instruct Sec	21	Art Elem	31	Career/Sch-to-Work K-12	41	Social Studies Sec	51	Reading K-12	61	Foreign/World Lang K-12	71	Public Information
4	Food Service	11	Federal Program	22	Art Sec	32	Career/Sch-to-Work Elem	42	Science K-12	52	Reading Elem	62	Foreign/World Lang Elem	72	Summer School
5	Transportation	12	Title V	23	Music K-12	33	Career/Sch-to-Work Sec	43	Science Elem	53	Reading Sec	63	Foreign/World Lang Sec	73	Instructional Tech
6	Athletic	13	Title V	24	Music Elem	34	Early Childhood Ed	44	Science Sec	54	Remedial Reading K-12	64	Religious Education K-12	74	Inservice Training
7	Health Services	15	Asst Superintendent	25	Music Sec	35	Health/Phys Education	45	Math K-12	55	Remedial Reading Elem	65	Religious Education Elem	75	Marketing/Distributive
		16	Instructional Media Svcs	26	Business Education	36	Guidance Services K-12	46	Math Elem	56	Remedial Reading Sec	66	Religious Education Sec	76	Info Systems
		17	Chief Operations Officer	27	Career & Tech Ed	37	Guidance Services Elem	47	Math Sec	57	Bilingual/ELL	67	School Board President	77	Psychological Assess
		18	Chief Academic Officer	28	Technology Education	38	Guidance Services Sec	48	English/Lang Arts K-12	58	Special Education K-12	68	Teacher Personnel	78	Affirmative Action

Public Schs..Principal	Grd	Prgm	Enr/#Cls	SN	
Adult and Career Center 2855 Colonial Blvd, Fort Myers 33966 Rita Effing	Adult		500		239/939-6310 Fax 239/334-4568
Allen Park Elem Sch 3345 Canelo Dr, Fort Myers 33901 Lisa Eastridge	PK-5	T	998 52	48%	239/936-1459 Fax 239/936-3470
Alva Sch 17500 Church Ave, Alva 33920 Dale Houchin	K-8	T	1,033 20	46%	239/728-2494 Fax 239/728-3259
Bayshore Elem Sch 17050 Williams Rd, N Ft Myers 33917 Benjamin Ausman	K-5	T	624 30	53%	239/543-3663 Fax 239/543-4040
Bonita Spring High Sch 25592 Imperial Pkwy, Bonita Spgs 34135 Jeff Estes	9-10	V	676		239/495-3022 Fax 239/495-3042
© Bonita Springs Charter Sch [133] 25380 Bernwood Dr, Bonita Spgs 34135 Carissa Carroll	K-8	T	1,299	35%	239/992-6932 Fax 239/992-7359
Bonita Springs Elem Sch 10701 Dean St, Bonita Spgs 34135 Robert Cooper	PK-5	T	514 24	77%	239/992-0801 Fax 239/992-9118
Bonita Springs MS for the Arts 10141 W Terry St, Bonita Spgs 34135 Melissa Layner	6-8	GTV	894 48	47%	239/992-4422 Fax 239/992-9157
Buckingham Exceptional Center 3291 Buckingham Rd, Fort Myers 33905 Ruth Lohmeyer	Spec	T	87 12	46%	239/693-1233 Fax 239/693-1690
Caloosa Elem Sch 620 Del Prado Blvd S, Cape Coral 33990 **Ashley Lamar**	PK-5	T	964 50	52%	239/574-3113 Fax 239/574-1449
Caloosa Middle Sch 610 Del Prado Blvd S, Cape Coral 33990 Dr Ann Cole	6-8	TV	870 49	55%	239/574-3232 Fax 239/574-2660
© Cape Coral Charter Sch [133] 76 Mid Cape Ter, Cape Coral 33991 **Jamie Trotter**	PK-8	T	636	70%	239/995-0904 Fax 239/995-0369
Cape Coral High Sch 2300 Santa Barbara Blvd, Cape Coral 33991 **Christian Engelhart**	9-12	GTV	1,608 95	37%	239/574-6766 Fax 239/574-7799
Cape Coral Technical College 360 Santa Barbara Blvd N, Cape Coral 33993 Judy Johnson	Voc	AG	100 45		239/574-4440 Fax 239/458-3721
Cape Elem Sch 4519 Vincennes Blvd, Cape Coral 33904 Nicole Osterholm	K-5	T	672 37	43%	239/542-3551 Fax 239/542-3264
Challenger Middle Sch 624 SW Trafalgar Pkwy, Cape Coral 33991 Teri Cannady	6-8	T	1,092	42%	239/242-4341 Fax 239/242-7217
© Christa McAuliffe Charter ES 2817 SW 3rd Ln, Cape Coral 33991 Kevin Brown	PK-5	T	786	38%	239/283-4511 Fax 239/282-0376
Ⓐ City of Palms Charter HS © 2830 Winkler Ave Ste 201, Fort Myers 33916 Sarah White	9-12	T	176 7	98%	239/561-6611 Fax 239/561-6230
Colonial Elem Sch 3800 Schoolhouse Rd E, Fort Myers 33916 Dr Marsha Bur	PK-5	T	864 44	81%	239/939-2242 Fax 239/939-5143
© Coronado High Sch [131] 3057 Cleveland Ave, Fort Myers 33901 **Janet Morris**	9-12	T	178	10%	239/337-9140 Fax 239/337-9141
Cypress Lake HS for the Arts 6750 Panther Ln, Fort Myers 33919 Angela Roles	9-12	GTV	1,611 65	40%	239/481-2233 Fax 239/481-9838
Cypress Lake Middle Sch 8901 Cypress Lake Dr, Fort Myers 33919 Kelly Maniscalco	6-8	TV	900 70	33%	239/481-1533 Fax 239/481-3121
Diplomat Elem Sch 1115 NE 16th Ter, Cape Coral 33909 Mara Vertrees	K-5	T	984 38	47%	239/458-0033 Fax 239/458-1697
Diplomat Middle Sch 1039 NE 16th Ter, Cape Coral 33909 Maura Bennington	6-8	T	864 60	48%	239/574-5257 Fax 239/574-4008
© Donna J Beasley Technical Acad 60 Bell Blvd N, Lehigh Acres 33936 Dr Joseph Torregras	9-12	TV	111	97%	239/491-6822 Fax 239/561-9864
Dr C D Robinson Littleton ES 700 Hutto Rd, N Ft Myers 33903 Monica Broughton	PK-5	T	550 35	67%	239/995-3800 Fax 239/995-6551
Dunbar Cmty Sch 1857 High St, Fort Myers 33916 **Dr Samone Mitchell**	Adult		300 10		239/334-2941 Fax 239/334-3519
Ⓜ Dunbar High Sch 3800 Edison Ave, Fort Myers 33916 Carl Burnside	9-12	T	1,979 30	53%	239/461-5322 Fax 239/461-5110
Early Childhood Learning Ctr 3650 Michigan Ave Ste 4, Fort Myers 33916 Maggie Stevens	PK-PK		336	98%	239/332-2512 Fax 239/334-2629
East Lee Co High Sch 715 Thomas Sherwin Ave S, Lehigh Acres 33974 Melissa Robery	9-12	T	1,962	61%	239/369-2932 Fax 239/369-3213
Ⓜ Edgewood Academy Sch 3464 Edgewood Ave, Fort Myers 33916 **Carol Frink**	PK-5	T	583 42	81%	239/334-6205 Fax 239/334-6776
Ⓜ Edison Park Arts Sch 2401 Euclid Ave, Fort Myers 33901 Cherise Trent	K-5	T	346 20	53%	239/334-6232 Fax 239/332-3474
Estero High Sch 21900 River Ranch Rd, Estero 33928 Clayton Simmons	9-12	GTV	1,644 50	43%	239/947-9400 Fax 239/947-5017
© Florida Southwest Clg HS 8099 College Pkwy, Fort Myers 33919 Dr Brian Botts	9-12		392	30%	239/432-6767 Fax 239/433-6912
Ⓜ Franklin Park Elem Sch 2323 Ford St, Fort Myers 33916 **Michelle Freeman**	PK-5	T	467 24	85%	239/332-1969 Fax 239/337-1127
Ft Myers Beach Elem Sch 2751 Oak St, Ft Myers Bch 33931 Karen Manzi	K-5	T	108 15	51%	239/463-6356 Fax 239/463-3592
Ft Myers High Sch 2635 Cortez Blvd, Fort Myers 33901 Robert Butz	9-12	GV	1,944 85	39%	239/334-2167 Fax 239/334-3095
Ft Myers Middle Academy 3050 Central Ave, Fort Myers 33901 Lynn Edward	6-8	TV	618 60	75%	239/936-1759 Fax 239/936-4350
Ft Myers Technical College 3800 Michigan Ave, Fort Myers 33916 **Judy Johnson**	Voc	AG	125 35		239/334-4544 Fax 239/332-4839
G Weaver Hipps Elem Sch 1200 Homestead Rd N, Lehigh Acres 33936 **Dr Deborah Nauss**	PK-5	T	817	67%	239/368-7042 Fax 239/369-0469
© Gateway Charter Elem Sch [133] 12850 Commonwealth Dr, Fort Myers 33913 Angela Carter	K-5	T	1,113	66%	239/768-5048 Fax 239/768-5710
© Gateway Charter High Sch [133] 12770 Gateway Blvd, Fort Myers 33913 Amber Jensen	9-12	T	529	51%	239/768-3350 Fax 239/768-3874
© Gateway Charter Interm Sch [133] 12850 Commonwealth Dr, Fort Myers 33913 Angela Carter	6-8	T	956	58%	239/768-2491 Fax 239/768-5710

						School Programs	Social Media
279	Student Personnel	91	Safety/Security	275	Response To Intervention	298 Grant Writer/Ptnrships	
280	Driver Ed/Safety	92	Magnet School	277	Remedial Math K-12	750 Chief Innovation Officer	**A** = Alternative Program
281	Gifted/Talented	93	Parental Involvement	280	Literacy Coach	751 Chief of Staff	**G** = Adult Classes
282	Video Services	95	Tech Prep Program	285	STEM	752 Social Emotional Learning	**M** = Magnet Program
283	Substance Abuse Prev	97	Chief Infomation Officer	286	Digital Learning		**T** = Title I Schoolwide
284	Erate	98	Chief Technology Officer	288	Common Core Standards	**Other School Types**	**V** = Career & Tech Ed Programs
285	AIDS Education	270	Character Education	294	Accountability	Ⓐ = Alternative School	
288	Alternative/At Risk	271	Migrant Education	295	Network System	© = **Charter School**	**New Schools are shaded**
289	Multi-Cultural Curriculum	273	Teacher Mentor	296	Title II Programs	Ⓜ = **Magnet School**	**New Superintendents and Principals are bold**
290	Social Work	274	Before/After Sch	297	Webmaster	Ⓨ = **Year-Round School**	**Personnel with email addresses are underscored**

 = Facebook

 = Twitter

School	Grades		Enroll	%	Phone
Gateway Elem Sch 13280 Griffin Dr, Fort Myers 33913 Christine Siebenaler	PK-5	T	725 38	48%	239/768-3737 Fax 239/768-2967
Gulf Elem Sch 3400 SW 17th Pl, Cape Coral 33914 Kim Verblaauw	PK-5	T	1,100 38	38%	239/549-2726 Fax 239/549-2117
Gulf Middle Sch 1809 SW 36th Ter, Cape Coral 33914 James Moreland	6-8	T	806 48	37%	239/549-0606 Fax 239/549-2806
Hancock Creek Elem Sch 1601 Skyline Dr, N Ft Myers 33903 Cynthia Luster	PK-5	T	863 38	58%	239/995-3600 Fax 239/995-7674
© Harlem Heights Cmty CS 15570 Hagie Dr, Fort Myers 33908 Kristin Vollmer	K-3		79	89%	239/482-7706 Fax 239/204-3009
Harns Marsh Elem Sch 1800 Unice Ave N, Lehigh Acres 33971 Tracey Zenoniani	PK-5	T	982 55	72%	239/690-1249 Fax 239/694-1325
Harns Marsh Middle Sch 1820 Unice Ave N, Lehigh Acres 33971 Linda Maere	6-8	T	1,337	63%	239/690-2025 Fax 239/690-2028
Hector A Cafferata Jr Elem Sch 250 Santa Barbara Blvd N, Cape Coral 33993 Shelley Markgraf	K-5	T	673	62%	239/458-7391 Fax 239/772-0749
Heights Elem Sch 15200 Alexandria Ct, Fort Myers 33908 Douglas Palow	PK-5	T	1,164 33	40%	239/481-1761 Fax 239/481-3154
Ida S Baker High Sch 3500 Agualinda Blvd, Cape Coral 33914 Jami Covert	9-12	T	1,809	34%	239/458-6690 Fax 239/458-6691
Island Coast High Sch 2125 De Navarra Pkwy, Cape Coral 33909 Dr Michelle Cort-Mora	9-12	I	1,693	49%	239/458-0362 Fax 239/772-8405
© Island Park High Sch [131] 16520 S Tamiami Trl Ste 190, Fort Myers 33908 Arthur Nauss	9-12	T	304	13%	239/204-5965 Fax 239/243-0043
J Colin English Elem Sch 120 Pine Island Rd, N Ft Myers 33903 Joe Williams	PK-5	T	442 33	80%	239/995-2258 Fax 239/995-5681
James Stephens Int'l Academy 1333 Marsh Ave, Fort Myers 33905 Kelly Stedman	K-8	TV	360 35	82%	239/337-1333 Fax 239/334-4144
Ⓐ Lamp Sch 3650 Michigan Ave Ste 2, Fort Myers 33916 Jeanne LaFountain	6-12	TV	150 10	73%	239/332-2526 Fax 239/334-3695
Lee Virtual Sch 2855 Colonial Blvd, Fort Myers 33966 Al Shilling	K-12		250		239/337-8178 Fax 239/461-8451
Lehigh Acres Middle Sch 104 Arthur Ave, Lehigh Acres 33936 Brian Gibson	6-8	TV	1,356 50	65%	239/369-6108 Fax 239/369-8808
Lehigh Elem Sch 200 Schoolside Ct, Lehigh Acres 33936 Sherri Wipf	PK-5	T	1,202 44	72%	239/369-2477 Fax 239/369-4506
Lehigh Senior High Sch 901 Gunnery Rd N, Lehigh Acres 33971 Jackie Corey	9-12	AGTV	2,291 50	52%	239/693-5353 Fax 239/693-6702
Lexington Middle Sch 16351 Summerlin Rd, Fort Myers 33908 Kristin Bueno	6-8	T	1,118	38%	239/454-6130 Fax 239/489-3419
Manatee Elem Sch 5301 Tice St, Fort Myers 33905 Scott Lemaster	K-5	T	903	75%	239/694-2097 Fax 239/694-4282
Mariner High Sch 701 Chiquita Blvd N, Cape Coral 33993 Thomas Michel	9-12	AGTV	1,557 85	41%	239/772-3324 Fax 239/772-4880
Mariner Middle Sch 425 Chiquita Blvd N, Cape Coral 33993 Rachel Gould	6-8	T	1,011	49%	239/772-1848 Fax 239/242-1256
Mirror Lakes Elem Sch 525 Charwood Ave S, Lehigh Acres 33974 Jody Poulakis	PK-5	T	1,101 50	72%	239/369-2200 Fax 239/369-0542
N Ft Myers Academy for Arts 1856 Arts Way, N Ft Myers 33917 Thomas Millins	K-8	T	1,119 102	51%	239/997-2131 Fax 239/997-6762
North Ft Myers High Sch 5000 Orange Grove Blvd, N Ft Myers 33903 Deborah Diggs	9-12	GTV	1,878 80	46%	239/995-2117 Fax 239/995-1243
© North Nicholas High Sch [131] 428 SW Pine Island Rd Ste 1, Cape Coral 33991 Janet Morris	9-12	T	319 4	7%	239/242-4230 Fax 239/242-4231
© Northern Palms Charter HS 13251 N Cleveland Ave, N Ft Myers 33903 Bernadette Graham	9-12		141	58%	239/997-9987 Fax 239/997-9981
© Oak Creek CS of Bonita Springs [136] 28011 Performance Ln, Bonita Spgs 34135 Jose Rubio	K-8	T	488	75%	239/498-6864 Fax 239/495-7178
Oak Hammock Middle Sch 5321 Tice St, Fort Myers 33905 Jennifer Sneddon	6-8	T	1,505	66%	239/693-0469 Fax 239/694-4089
© Oasis Charter Elem Sch 3415 Oasis Blvd, Cape Coral 33914 Marybeth Grecsek	PK-5		895	29%	239/542-1577 Fax 239/549-7662
© Oasis Charter High Sch 3519 Oasis Blvd, Cape Coral 33914 Dr Christina Britton	9-12		701 40	33%	239/541-1167 Fax 239/541-1590
© Oasis Charter Middle Sch 3507 Oasis Blvd, Cape Coral 33914 Donnie Hopper	6-8		838		239/945-1999 Fax 239/540-7677 f
Orange River Elem Sch 4501 Underwood Dr, Fort Myers 33905 Cayce Staruk	PK-5	T	842	83%	239/694-1258 Fax 239/694-8680
Orangewood Elem Sch 4001 Deleon St, Fort Myers 33901 Angela Nader	PK-5	T	574 45	64%	239/936-2950 Fax 239/936-2134
Ⓐ Pace Center for Girls-Lee 3800 Evans Ave Ste 4, Fort Myers 33901 Meg Geltner	6-12		56	100%	239/425-2366 Fax 239/425-2365
Ⓐ Palm Acres Charter High Sch © 507 Sunshine Blvd, Lehigh Acres 33971 Y Sarah White	9-12	GMTV	319	30%	239/333-3300 Fax 239/368-1330
Patriot Elem Sch 711 SW 18th St, Cape Coral 33991 Jami Browder	PK-5	T	730	52%	239/242-1023 Fax 239/242-1238
Paul Laurence Dunbar Mid Sch 4750 Winkler Avenue Ext, Fort Myers 33966 Nathan Shaker	6-8	TV	1,018 80	58%	239/334-1357 Fax 239/334-7633
Pelican Elem Sch 3525 SW 3rd Ave, Cape Coral 33914 Edwin Carter	PK-5	T	966 42	49%	239/549-4966 Fax 239/549-4973
Pine Island Elem Sch 5360 Ridgewood Dr, Bokeelia 33922 Steven Hook	K-5	T	235 17	53%	239/283-0505 Fax 239/283-1748
Pinewoods Elem Sch 11900 Stoneybrook Golf Dr, Estero 33928 Leslie Gunderson	PK-5	T	1,135 40	34%	239/947-7500 Fax 239/947-0834
Ray V Pottorf Elem Sch 4600 Challenger Blvd, Fort Myers 33966 Brandy MacChia	PK-5	T	742	79%	239/274-3932 Fax 239/275-3381
Rayma C Page Elem Sch 17000 S Tamiami Trl, Fort Myers 33908 Valerie Sheckler	PK-5	T	851	40%	239/432-2737 Fax 239/432-2749 t

1 Superintendent	8 Curric/Instruct K-12	19 Chief Financial Officer	29 Family/Consumer Science	39 Social Studies K-12	49 English/Lang Arts Elem	59 Special Education Elem	69 Academic Assessment
2 Bus/Finance/Purchasing	9 Curric/Instruct Elem	20 Art K-12	30 Adult Education	40 Social Studies Elem	50 English/Lang Arts Sec	60 Special Education Sec	70 Research/Development
3 Buildings And Grounds	10 Curric/Instruct Sec	21 Art Elem	31 Career/Sch-to-Work K-12	41 Social Studies Sec	51 Reading K-12	61 Foreign/World Lang K-12	71 Public Information
4 Food Service	11 Federal Program	22 Art Sec	32 Career/Sch-to-Work Elem	42 Science K-12	52 Reading Elem	62 Foreign/World Lang Elem	72 Summer School
5 Transportation	12 Title I	23 Music K-12	33 Career/Sch-to-Work Sec	43 Science Elem	53 Reading Sec	63 Foreign/World Lang Sec	73 Instructional Tech
6 Athletic	13 Title V	24 Music Elem	34 Early Childhood Ed	44 Science Sec	54 Remedial Reading K-12	64 Religious Education K-12	74 Inservice Training
7 Health Services	14 Asst Superintendent	25 Music Sec	35 Health/Phys Education	45 Math K-12	55 Remedial Reading Elem	65 Religious Education Elem	75 Marketing/Distributive
	15 Instructional Media Svcs	26 Business Education	36 Guidance Services K-12	46 Math Elem	56 Remedial Reading Sec	66 Religious Education Sec	76 Info Systems
	16 Chief Operations Officer	27 Career & Tech Ed	37 Guidance Services Elem	47 Math Sec	57 Bilingual/ELL	67 School Board President	77 Psychological Assess
	17 Chief Operations Officer	28 Technology Education	38 Guidance Services Sec	48 English/Lang Arts K-12	58 Special Education K-12	68 Teacher Personnel	78 Affirmative Action
	18 Chief Academic Officer						

School	Grd	Prgm	Enr/#Cls	SN	Phone
River Hall Elem Sch 2800 River Hall Pkwy, Alva 33920 Alice Barfield	PK-5	T	1,029	54%	239/693-0349 Fax 239/693-5307
Riverdale High Sch 2600 Buckingham Rd, Fort Myers 33905 Scott Cook	9-12	GTV	2,316 68	39%	239/694-4141 Fax 239/694-3527 t
Royal Palm Exceptional Center 3050 Indian St, Fort Myers 33916 Robert Moretti	Spec	T	145 25	76%	239/337-3511 Fax 239/337-3694
S W Florida Pub Service Acad 4312 Michigan Ave, Fort Myers 33905	Adult		250		239/334-3897 Fax 239/334-8794
San Carlos Park Elem Sch 17282 Lee Rd, Fort Myers 33967 Christy Kutz	PK-5	T	916 40	58%	239/267-7177 Fax 239/267-0057
Sanibel Sch 3840 Sanibel Captiva Rd, Sanibel 33957 Chuck Vilardi	K-8		264 20	22%	239/472-1617 Fax 239/472-6544
© Six Mile Charter Academy [133] 6851 Lancer Ave, Fort Myers 33912 **Michelle Thompson**	PK-8	T	951	57%	239/768-9375 Fax 239/225-2477
Skyline Elem Sch 620 SW 19th St, Cape Coral 33991 Laura Trombetti	PK-5	T	1,024 42	59%	239/772-3223 Fax 239/772-8934 t
South Ft Myers High Sch 14020 Plantation Rd, Fort Myers 33912 Ed Mathews	9-12	T	1,901	45%	239/561-0060 Fax 239/561-3612
Spring Creek Elem Sch 25571 Elementary Way, Bonita Spgs 34135 Diane Sherman	PK-5	T	768 52	65%	239/947-0001 Fax 239/947-4690
Ⓐ Success Academy 3650 Michigan Ave, Fort Myers 33916 Tommy Bowens	6-12	TV	129 20	65%	239/334-3416 Fax 239/332-5028
Sunshine Elem Sch 601 Sara Ave N, Lehigh Acres 33971 Cherry Gibson	PK-5	T	1,153 53	74%	239/369-5836 Fax 239/369-1455
Tanglewood Elem Sch 1620 Manchester Blvd, Fort Myers 33919 Linda Buckley	PK-5	T	728 37	42%	239/936-0891 Fax 239/939-0411
© The Island Sch 135 1st St W, Boca Grande 33921 Jean Thompson	K-5		57 4		941/964-8016 Fax 941/964-8017
Three Oaks Elem Sch 19600 Cypress View Dr, Fort Myers 33967 Janet Moorhead	PK-5		924 38	39%	239/267-8020 Fax 239/267-9559
Three Oaks Middle Sch 18500 3 Oaks Pkwy, Fort Myers 33967 Michael Carson	6-8	T	1,055 52	48%	239/267-5757 Fax 239/267-4007
Tice Elem Sch 4524 Tice St, Fort Myers 33905 Rhonda Amaya	PK-5	T	577 50	80%	239/694-1257 Fax 239/694-8745
Tortuga Preserve Elem Sch 1711 Gunnery Rd N, Lehigh Acres 33971 Jennifer Shonak	PK-5	T	985	66%	239/693-5023 Fax 239/693-5033
Trafalgar Elem Sch 1850 SW 20th Ave, Cape Coral 33991 Lisa Murphy	PK-5	T	793	33%	239/283-3043 Fax 239/282-5595
Trafalgar Middle Sch 2120 SW Trafalgar Pkwy, Cape Coral 33991 Dr Michael Galbreath	6-8	TV	916 48	35%	239/283-2001 Fax 239/283-5620
Treeline Elem Sch 10900 Treeline Ave, Fort Myers 33913 **Jennifer Wilcken**	PK-5	T	1,056	53%	239/768-5208 Fax 239/768-5415
Tropic Isles Elem Sch 5145 Orange Grove Blvd, N Ft Myers 33903 **Rob Mazzoli**	PK-5	T	907 43	64%	239/995-4704 Fax 239/997-2422

School	Grd	Prgm	Enr/#Cls	SN	Phone
© Unity Chtr Sch of Cape Coral 2107 Santa Barbara Blvd, Cape Coral 33991 Joy Moore	K-8	T	188	99%	239/829-5134 Fax 239/242-0477
Varsity Lakes Middle Sch 801 Gunnery Rd N, Lehigh Acres 33971 Matthew Mederios	6-8	T	1,345 50	55%	239/694-3464 Fax 239/694-7093
Veterans Park Academy for Arts 49 Homestead Rd S, Lehigh Acres 33936 Mary Blackmon	PK-8	T	1,714	57%	239/303-3003 Fax 239/303-3075
Villas Elem Sch 8385 Beacon Blvd, Fort Myers 33907 Shane Musich	PK-5	T	873 37	73%	239/936-3776 Fax 239/936-6884

LEE CATHOLIC SCHOOLS

- **Diocese of Venice Ed Office** PID: 02231695
  Listing includes only schools located in this county. See District Index for location of Diocesan Offices.

Catholic Schs..Principal	Grd	Prgm	Enr/#Cls	SN	Phone
Bishop Verot High Sch 5598 Sunrise Dr, Fort Myers 33919 Dr Denny Denison	9-12		700 45		239/274-6700 Fax 239/274-6798
St Andrew Catholic Sch 1509 SE 27th St, Cape Coral 33904 David Nelson	PK-8		306 10		239/772-3922 Fax 239/772-7182 f t
St Francis Xavier Sch 2055 Heitman St, Fort Myers 33901 John Gulley	PK-8		609 30		239/334-7707 Fax 239/334-8605

LEE PRIVATE SCHOOLS

Private Schs..Principal	Grd	Prgm	Enr/#Cls	SN	Phone
Canterbury Sch 8141 College Pkwy, Fort Myers 33919 Rick Kirschner	PK-12		635		239/481-4323 Fax 239/481-8339
Cape Academy 231 Del Prado Blvd S Ste 6, Cape Coral 33990 Kristen Williamson	4-12		46		239/573-8668 Fax 239/549-3273
Cape Coral Christian Sch 811 Santa Barbara Blvd, Cape Coral 33991 Amy Marcoux	K-12		130		239/574-3707 Fax 239/574-0947
Classical Christian Academy 7101 Bayshore Rd, N Ft Myers 33917 Amy Davis	PK-12		50		239/543-1532 Fax 888/886-3144 f
Crosspointe Academy 13241 Griffin Dr, Fort Myers 33913 Debbi Coe	PK-12		61		239/225-1502
Discovery Day Academy-Bonita 23601 Commons Dr, Bonita Spgs 34134 Elizabeth Garcia	PK-8		225		239/201-4678 Fax 239/947-2565
Evangelical Christian Sch 8237 Beacon Blvd, Fort Myers 33907 Michelle Shuford \ James Stedcke	PK-12		900		239/936-3319 Fax 239/939-1445
Ft Myers Christian Sch 1550 Colonial Blvd, Fort Myers 33907 Melvern Mitchell	PK-8		212 25		239/939-4642 Fax 239/936-5016
Good Shepherd Lutheran Sch 4770 Orange Grove Blvd, N Ft Myers 33903 William Jewel	PK-12		250 13		239/995-7711

79 Student Personnel	**91** Safety/Security	**275** Response To Intervention	**298** Grant Writer/Ptnrships	**School Programs**
80 Driver Ed/Safety	**92** Magnet School	**277** Remedial Math K-12	**750** Chief Innovation Officer	**A** = Alternative Program
81 Gifted/Talented	**93** Parental Involvement	**280** Literacy Coach	**751** Chief of Staff	**G** = Adult Classes
82 Video Services	**95** Tech Prep Program	**285** STEM	**752** Social Emotional Learning	**M** = Magnet Program
83 Substance Abuse Prev	**97** Chief Information Officer	**286** Digital Learning		**T** = Title I Schoolwide
84 Erate	**98** Chief Technology Officer	**288** Common Core Standards	**Other School Types**	**V** = Career & Tech Ed Programs
85 AIDS Education	**270** Character Education	**294** Accountability	Ⓐ = Alternative School	
88 Alternative/At Risk	**271** Migrant Education	**295** Network System	© = **Charter School**	New Schools are shaded
89 Multi-Cultural Curriculum	**273** Teacher Mentor	**296** Title II Programs	Ⓜ = **Magnet School**	New Superintendents and Principals are bold
90 Social Work	**274** Before/After Sch	**297** Webmaster	Ⓨ = **Year-Round School**	Personnel with email addresses are underscored

Social Media

f = Facebook
t = Twitter

FL—63

Gospel Baptist Christian Sch 24861 Old Forty-One Rd, Bonita Spgs 34135 Marty Moon	PK-12	93 7	239/947-1285 Fax 239/947-2132
Grace Community Sch 871 Miramar St, Cape Coral 33904 Jahaira Hernandez	PK-2	100	239/549-7411 Fax 239/549-4425
Living Word Christian Sch 2900 N Tamiami Trl, N Ft Myers 33903 Jessica Horne	K-12	61	239/997-7702 Fax 239/997-7719
New Testament Baptist Sch 2805 NE Pine Island Rd, Cape Coral 33909 Bill Roan	K-12	50	239/997-1020 Fax 239/997-0769
Providence Christian Sch 701 Mohawk Pkwy, Cape Coral 33914 Jami Hommerbocker	PK-8	85 9	239/549-8024 Fax 239/549-4465
Renaissance Montessori Sch 37 Barkley Cir, Fort Myers 33907 M Kathleen Leitch	PK-6	30	239/275-2022 Fax 239/275-8638
Sonshine Christian Academy 12925 Palm Beach Blvd, Fort Myers 33905 Bob Calvert	PK-12	225 11	239/694-8882 Fax 239/694-8885
Southwest Florida Chrn Academy 3750 Colonial Blvd, Fort Myers 33966 Randy Down \ Susan Kackley	K-12	517 20	239/936-8865 Fax 239/936-7095 f
St Michael Lutheran Sch 3595 Broadway, Fort Myers 33901 Kati Miser	PK-8	360 22	239/939-1218 Fax 239/939-1839
Summit Christian Sch 9065 Ligon Ct, Fort Myers 33908 Kyle Mast	PK-8	102 11	239/482-7007 Fax 239/454-7042
Temple Christian Sch 18841 State Road 31, N Ft Myers 33917 Dawn Baker	PK-12	100 8	239/543-3222 Fax 239/543-6112

LEE REGIONAL CENTERS

- **FDLRS-Island Coast** PID: 10915370   239/337-8363
  2855 Colonial Blvd, Fort Myers 33966

Dr Deidre Philipps 1

LEON COUNTY

LEON PUBLIC SCHOOLS

- **Leon Co School Dist** PID: 00194479   850/487-7363
  2757 W Pensacola St, Tallahassee 32304   Fax 850/414-5151

Schools: 51 \ **Teachers:** 2,027 \ **Students:** 34,500 \
Special Ed Students: 5,239 \ **LEP Students:** 720 \ **College-Bound:** 70% \
\ **Ethnic:** Asian 4%, African American 45%, Hispanic 6%, Caucasian
45% \ **Exp:** $171 (Low) \ **Poverty:** 17% \ **Title I:** $9,249,296 \
Special Education: $31,621,000 \ **Bilingual Education:** $941,000 \
Open-Close: 08/12 - 05/29 \ **DTBP:** $190 (High) \ f t

Rocky Hanna 1	Kathy Sanders 2
Butch Watkins 3	Danny Allbritton 3
James Howcroft 4	James Cole 5

Manny Joanos 5	Dr Alan Cox 7,15
Terri Anderson 7	Dr Elizabeth Glenn 11
Ashley Scott 12,298	Gillian Gregory 15,16,74,271*
Kathleen Rodgers 15,78,83,275	Dr Michelle Gayle 15,70
Justin Williamson 16	Kim Banks 19
Brooke Brunner 34	Lisa Urban 57
Cathy Shields 58	Rosanne Wood 67
Mary Nicholson 68	Kris Kolp 69
Chris Petley 71	William Nimmons 73,76
Shane Syfrett 74,273	Dexter Martin 78
Ken Scott 79	John Hunkiar 91
Giselle Marsh 294	

Public Schs..Principal	Grd	Prgm	Enr/#Cls	SN
Adult & Cmty Education 526 Appleyard Dr, Tallahassee 32304 Regina Browning	Adult	AV	400 25	850/717-2020 Fax 850/717-2060
Amos P Godby High Sch 1717 W Tharpe St, Tallahassee 32303 Desmond Cole	9-12	TV	1,385 85	58% 850/617-4700 Fax 850/922-4162 f t
⊛ Apalachee Tapestry Sch of Arts 650 Trojan Trl, Tallahassee 32311 Jennifer Ricardo	PK-5	T	615 31	70% 850/488-7110 Fax 850/922-0202
Astoria Park Elem Sch 2465 Atlas Rd, Tallahassee 32303 **David Solz**	PK-5	T	591 30	74% 850/488-4673 Fax 850/922-4174 f t
Augusta Raa Middle Sch 401 W Tharpe St, Tallahassee 32303 Christopher Small	6-8	TV	875 85	44% 850/488-6287 Fax 850/922-5835
Bond Elem Sch 2204 Saxon St, Tallahassee 32310 **Delshuana Jackson**	PK-5	T	687 18	86% 850/488-7676 Fax 850/922-5206
Buck Lake Elem Sch 1600 Pedrick Rd, Tallahassee 32317 William Millard	K-5		710 40	14% 850/488-6133 Fax 850/922-4161 t
Canopy Oaks Elem Sch 3250 Point View Dr, Tallahassee 32303 Paul Lambert	PK-5	T	695 40	37% 850/488-3301 Fax 850/414-7356
Chaires Elem Sch 4774 Chaires Cross Rd, Tallahassee 32317 Michele Prescott	PK-5	T	518 40	44% 850/488-5977 Fax 850/922-6462
Conley Elem Sch 2400 Orange Ave E, Tallahassee 32311 **Jason Koerner**	PK-5	T	765 	42% 850/414-5610 Fax 850/414-8163
Deerlake Middle Sch 9902 Deer Lk W, Tallahassee 32312 Steve Mills	6-8	V	1,012 60	11% 850/922-6545 Fax 850/488-3275
DeSoto Trail Elem Sch 5200 Tredington Park Dr, Tallahassee 32309 Michele Keltner	PK-5		674 40	19% 850/488-4511 Fax 850/487-1623 f t
Elizabeth Cobb Middle Sch 915 Hillcrest Ave, Tallahassee 32308 Sarah Hembree	6-8	TV	801 45	39% 850/488-3364 Fax 850/922-2452
Fairview Middle Sch 3415 Zillah St, Tallahassee 32305 **Rusty Edwards**	6-8	TV	837 85	54% 850/488-6880 Fax 850/922-6326
Frank Hartsfield Elem Sch 1414 Chowkeebin Nene, Tallahassee 32301 Rhonda Flanagan	PK-5	T	443 34	68% 850/488-7322 Fax 850/922-2372
Ft Braden Sch 15100 Blountstown Hwy, Tallahassee 32310 Jim Jackson	PK-8	T	774 45	67% 850/488-9374 Fax 850/488-5948
Gilchrist Elem Sch 1301 Timberlane Rd, Tallahassee 32312 **Scotty Crowe**	PK-5		981 37	28% 850/487-4310 Fax 850/487-0959 f t
© Governor's Charter Academy [133] 4351 Mahan Dr, Tallahassee 32308 Amy Reynolds	K-8	T	479 	12% 850/391-5259 Fax 850/391-5260

1	Superintendent	8	Curric/Instruct K-12	19	Chief Financial Officer	29	Family/Consumer Science
2	Bus/Finance/Purchasing	9	Curric/Instruct Elem	20	Art K-12	30	Adult Education
3	Buildings And Grounds	10	Curric/Instruct Sec	21	Art Elem	31	Career/Sch-to-Work K-12
4	Food Service	11	Federal Program	22	Art Sec	32	Career/Sch-to-Work Elem
5	Transportation	12	Title I	23	Music K-12	33	Career/Sch-to-Work Sec
6	Athletic	13	Title V	24	Music Elem	34	Early Childhood Ed
7	Health Services	14	Instructional Media Svcs	25	Music Sec	35	Health/Phys Education
		15	Asst Superintendent	26	Business Education	36	Guidance Services K-12
		16	Instructional Media Svcs	27	Career & Tech Ed	37	Guidance Services Elem
		17	Chief Operations Officer	28	Technology Education	38	Guidance Services Sec
		18	Chief Academic Officer				

39	Social Studies K-12	49	English/Lang Arts Elem	59	Special Education Elem	69	Academic Assessment
40	Social Studies Elem	50	English/Lang Arts Sec	60	Special Education Sec	70	Research/Development
41	Social Studies Sec	51	Reading K-12	61	Foreign/World Lang K-12	71	Public Information
42	Science K-12	52	Reading Elem	62	Foreign/World Lang Elem	72	Summer School
43	Science Elem	53	Reading Sec	63	Foreign/World Lang Sec	73	Instructional Tech
44	Science Sec	54	Remedial Reading K-12	64	Religious Education K-12	74	Inservice Training
45	Math K-12	55	Remedial Reading Elem	65	Religious Education Elem	75	Marketing/Distributive
46	Math Elem	56	Remedial Reading Sec	66	Religious Education Sec	76	Info Systems
47	Math Sec	57	Bilingual/ELL	67	School Board President	77	Psychological Assess
48	English/Lang Arts K-12	58	Special Education K-12	68	Teacher Personnel	78	Affirmative Action

School	Grd	Prgm	Enr	%	Phone
Gretchen Everhart Sch 2750 Mission Rd, Tallahassee 32304 Jane Bullen	Spec	T	183 30	46%	850/488-5785 Fax 850/922-6487
Griffin Middle Sch 800 Alabama St, Tallahassee 32304 Zelena O'Banner	6-8	TV	636 35	76%	850/617-5353 Fax 850/617-5354
Hawks Rise Elem Sch 205 Meadow Ridge Dr, Tallahassee 32312 Evy Friend	PK-5		847 38	16%	850/487-4733 Fax 850/488-6971
Ⓐ Heritage Trails Cmty Sch 283 Trojan Trl, Tallahassee 32311 Amy Alvis	6-12		66		850/488-8927 Fax 850/922-7065
James Rickards High Sch 3013 Jim Lee Rd, Tallahassee 32301 Doug Cook	9-12	TV	1,495	54%	850/488-1783 Fax 850/922-7104
John G Riley Elem Sch 1400 Indiana St, Tallahassee 32304 **April Knight**	PK-5	T	615 35	86%	850/488-5840 Fax 850/922-4227
Kate Sullivan Elem Sch 927 Miccosukee Rd, Tallahassee 32308 Michael Bryan	PK-5	T	705 46	39%	850/487-1216 Fax 850/487-0005
Killearn Lakes Elem Sch 8037 Deer Lk E, Tallahassee 32312 Brenda Wagner	PK-5		870 35	14%	850/921-1265 Fax 850/922-2566
Lawton Chiles High Sch 7200 Lawton Chiles Ln, Tallahassee 32312 Joe Burgess	9-12	V	2,095	9%	850/488-1756 Fax 850/488-1218
Leon Co Virtual Sch 500 Appleyard Dr Bldg 9, Tallahassee 32304 Jessica Lowe	K-12		63		850/561-8366 Fax 850/487-0447
Leon High Sch 550 E Tennessee St, Tallahassee 32308 Billy Epting	9-12	V	2,047 90	27%	850/617-5700 Fax 850/922-5311
Lillian Ruediger Elem Sch 526 W 10th Ave, Tallahassee 32303 Sally Stephens	PK-5	T	497 25	76%	850/488-1074 Fax 850/487-0007
Lincoln High Sch 3838 Trojan Trl, Tallahassee 32311 Allen Burch	9-12	V	2,026	27%	850/487-2110 Fax 850/922-4173
Lively Technical Center 500 Appleyard Dr, Tallahassee 32304 **Shelly Bell**	Voc	AG	50		850/487-7555 Fax 850/922-3880
Montford Middle Sch 5789 Pimlico Dr, Tallahassee 32309 Lewis Blessing	6-8		1,067	20%	850/412-8900 Fax 850/922-4848
Oak Ridge Elem Sch 4530 Shelfer Rd, Tallahassee 32305 Jasmine Smith	PK-5	T	516 40	79%	850/488-3124 Fax 850/922-7145
Ⓐ Pace Center for Girls-Leon 311 E Jennings St, Tallahassee 32301 Kelly Otte	6-12		117	25%	850/241-0241 Fax 850/241-0242
Pineview Elem Sch 2230 Lake Bradford Rd, Tallahassee 32310 Carmen Conner	PK-5	T	330 45	81%	850/488-2819 Fax 850/487-4559
R Frank Nims Middle Sch 723 W Orange Ave, Tallahassee 32310 **Dr Benny Bolden**	6-8	TV	503 48	78%	850/617-6161 Fax 850/922-0203
Roberts Elem Sch 5777 Pimlico Dr, Tallahassee 32309 Kim McFarland	PK-5		862 38	24%	850/488-0923 Fax 850/487-2416
Sabal Palm Elem Sch 2813 Ridgeway St, Tallahassee 32310 Anicia Robinson	PK-5	T	552 37	82%	850/488-0167 Fax 850/922-8481
Sail High Sch 2006 Jackson Bluff Rd, Tallahassee 32304 Tiffany Williams	9-12	T	377 30	35%	850/488-2468 Fax 850/922-8483
© SAS at the Center 2415 N Monroe St Ste 2700, Tallahassee 32303 Lindsey Merrick	K-4		258	3%	850-999-8267
© SAS on Thomasville 3208 Thomasville Rd, Tallahassee 32308 **Eirin Lombardo**	K-8		446	2%	850-386-6566 Fax 850/386-8183
Ⓜ Sealey Elem Math Sci Mag Sch 2815 Allen Rd, Tallahassee 32312 Demetria Clemons	PK-5	T	494 28	52%	850/488-5640 Fax 850/488-1239
Ⓐ Second Chance 860 Blountstown St, Tallahassee 32304 Richard Richardson	6-12	T	91	83%	850/488-2087 Fax 850/410-1531
Springwood Elem Sch 3801 Fred George Rd, Tallahassee 32303 **Sylvia Myers**	PK-5	T	592 32	61%	850/488-6225 Fax 850/922-8932
Ⓐ Success Acad-Ghazvini Lrng Ctr 854 Blountstown St, Tallahassee 32304 **Jessica Lowe**	6-8		283 12		850/488-2087 Fax 850/410-3353
Swift Creek Middle Sch 2100 Pedrick Rd, Tallahassee 32317 Susan Rishell	6-8		834 57	29%	850/414-2670 Fax 850/414-2650
© Tallahassee Classical Sch PO Box 745, Tallahassee 32302 **Stephen Wright**	K-8		401		
© Tallahassee Sch Math & Science 3434 N Monroe St, Tallahassee 32303 Ahmet Temel	K-8	T	422	58%	850/681-7827 Fax 850/325-6706
Walter T Moore Elem Sch 1706 Dempsey Mayo Rd, Tallahassee 32308 Kerri Anderson	PK-5	T	635 35	36%	850/488-2858 Fax 850/922-6658
Ⓜ Woodville K-8 Sch 9373 Woodville Hwy, Tallahassee 32305 Lisa Mehr	PK-5	T	603 38	65%	850/487-7043 Fax 850/921-4281

LEON CATHOLIC SCHOOLS

- **Diocese Pensacola-Tallahassee** PID: 01483467
  Listing includes only schools located in this county. See District Index for location of Diocesan Offices.

Catholic Schs..Principal	Grd	Prgm	Enr/#Cls	SN	
John Paul II Catholic High Sch 5100 Terrebonne Dr, Tallahassee 32311 Joanna Copenhaver	9-12		142 12		850/201-5744 Fax 850/205-3299 f
Trinity Catholic Sch 706 E Brevard St, Tallahassee 32308 Tommy Bridges	PK-8		430 20		850/222-0444 Fax 850/224-5067 f

LEON PRIVATE SCHOOLS

Private Schs..Principal	Grd	Prgm	Enr/#Cls	SN	
Adventist Christian Academy 616 Capital Cir NE, Tallahassee 32301 Darcel Castaneda	PK-8		43 2		850/597-7825
AMI Kids Tallahassee 2514 W Tharpe St, Tallahassee 32303 Shannon Baker	6-12		43 7		850/921-1250 Fax 850/386-1352
Bethel Christian Academy 406 N Bronough St, Tallahassee 32301 Cheryl Bouyer	PK-6		83 6		850/222-6605 Fax 850/521-0216

79 Student Personnel	91 Safety/Security	275 Response To Intervention	298 Grant Writer/Ptnrships	School Programs	Social Media
80 Driver Ed/Safety	92 Magnet School	277 Remedial Math K-12	750 Chief Innovation Officer	A = Alternative Program	
81 Gifted/Talented	93 Parental Involvement	280 Literacy Coach	751 Chief of Staff	G = Adult Classes	f = Facebook
82 Video Services	95 Tech Prep Program	285 STEM	752 Social Emotional Learning	M = Magnet Program	
83 Substance Abuse Prev	97 Chief Infomation Officer	286 Digital Learning		T = Title I Schoolwide	t = Twitter
84 Erate	98 Chief Technology Officer	288 Common Core Standards	Other School Types	V = Career & Tech Ed Programs	
85 AIDS Education	270 Character Education	294 Accountability	Ⓐ = Alternative Program		
88 Alternative/At Risk	271 Migrant Education	295 Network System	© = Charter School	New Schools are shaded	
89 Multi-Cultural Curriculum	273 Teacher Mentor	296 Title II Programs	Ⓜ = Magnet School	New Superintendents and Principals are bold	
90 Social Work	274 Before/After Sch	297 Webmaster	Ⓨ = Year-Round School	Personnel with email addresses are underscored	

FL—65

Betton Hills Preparatory Sch 1815 N Meridian Rd, Tallahassee 32303 Linda Willenbrink	PK-1		90 12	850/422-2464
Betton Hills Sch 2205 Thomasville Rd, Tallahassee 32308 Ilona Faust	2-12		91	850/656-9211 Fax 850/656-9602
Capital Preparatory 2811 Industrial Plaza Dr, Tallahassee 32301 Krystal Franklin	PK-12		60	850/402-9711
Christ Classical Academy 1983 Mahan Dr, Tallahassee 32308 Hope Carrasquilla	PK-12		68	850/656-2373 Fax 850/656-6373
Community Christian Sch 4859 Kerry Forest Pkwy, Tallahassee 32309 Pam Hollingsworth \ David Pinson	K-12		345 20	850/893-6628 Fax 850/668-3966
Community Leadership Academy 3611 Austin Davis Ave, Tallahassee 32308 Trisha McKenzie	PK-11		300	850/597-9124
Cornerstone Learning Community 2524 Hartsfield Rd, Tallahassee 32303 Bev Wells	PK-8		148	850/386-5550 Fax 850/386-5421
Franklin Academy 615 Tuskegee St, Tallahassee 32305 Margaret Franklin	3-12		60 3	850/575-4826 Fax 850/576-5323
Grassroots Free Sch 2458 Grass Roots Way, Tallahassee 32311 Kimberly Weinrich	1-12	V	25 5	850/656-3629
Holy Comforter Episcopal Sch 2001 Fleischmann Rd, Tallahassee 32308 Brenda Hagen \ Amy Vernon	PK-8		665 38	850/383-1007 Fax 850/383-1021
Innovation Sch of Excellence 1410 E Indianhead Dr, Tallahassee 32301 Jack Leland	PK-8		282 5	850/575-5580 Fax 850/575-0833
MacLay Sch 3737 N Meridian Rd, Tallahassee 32312 James Milford	PK-12		950	850/893-2138 Fax 850/893-7434
Magnolia Sch 2705 W Tharpe St, Tallahassee 32303 Sophie Wacongne-Speer	K-8		60 3	850/385-3834 Fax 850/386-2923
North Florida Christian Sch 3000 N Meridian Rd, Tallahassee 32312 Nicolette Phillips	PK-12		1,000	850/386-6327 Fax 850/386-8409
Rose Academy 1268 Timberlane Rd Ste B, Tallahassee 32312 Keri Dibuono \ Rebecca Folsom	K-12		50	850/893-8743 Fax 850/893-8490
Woodland Hall Academy 5246 Centerville Rd, Tallahassee 32309 Amber Mitchell	Spec	AG	12 9	850/893-2216 Fax 850/893-2440

LEON REGIONAL CENTERS

- **FDLRS-Miccosukee** PID: 04498253 — 850/487-2630
  725 S Calhoun St, Tallahassee 32301 — Fax 850/561-6555

Eydie Tricquet ....1 Allyn Howard 73

LEVY COUNTY

LEVY PUBLIC SCHOOLS

- **Levy Co School Dist** PID: 00194807 — 352/486-5231
  480 Marshburn Dr, Bronson 32621 — Fax 352/486-5237

Schools: 12 \ ***Teachers:*** 343 \ ***Students:*** 6,100 \ ***Special Ed Students:*** 983 \ ***LEP Students:*** 249 \ ***Ethnic:*** African American 13%, Hispanic 12%, Caucasian 74% \ ***Exp:*** $173 (Low) \ ***Poverty:*** 28% \ ***Title I:*** $2,062,935 \ ***Special Education:*** $6,879,000 \ ***Bilingual Education:*** $605,000 \ ***Open-Close:*** 08/12 - 05/29 \ ***DTBP:*** $160 (High)

Jeff Edison 1
Kimberly Lake 2
Julie Oberst 4
Joseph Wain 5
Chloe Hunt 8,11,16,271,274,296
Carol Dobois 26,31,35
Laura Klock 34,79
Marcy Young 58,77
Brad Etheridge 67
Barb Rivers 71,73,76,275,294,295
Ronald Perez 76,84
Gerie Forde 285,298
Brandon Eastmon 2
William Stockman 2,3
Gary Masters 5
Rosalind Hall 7,58,83,85,88,90
John Lott 8,36,54,277,286,288,294
Carol Jones 27,280
Valerie Boughanem 57,69*
Natalie Warren 58
Marla Hiers 68,74,273
Morgan Bennett 76
Dennis Webber 91

Public Schs..Principal	Grd	Prgm	Enr/#Cls	SN	
Bronson Elem Sch 400 Ishie Ave, Bronson 32621 Cheryl Beauchamp	PK-5	T	599 38	67%	352/486-5281 Fax 352/486-5285
Bronson Middle High Sch 351 Ishie Ave, Bronson 32621 Timothy McCarthy	6-12	TV	550 39	59%	352/486-5261 Fax 352/486-5263
Cedar Key Sch 951 Whiddon Ave, Cedar Key 32625 Kathryn Lawrence	PK-12	TV	250 17	60%	352/543-5223 Fax 352/543-5988
Chiefland Elem Sch 1205 NW 4th Ave, Chiefland 32626 Michael Homan	PK-5	T	766 48	72%	352/493-6040 Fax 352/493-6042
Chiefland Middle High Sch 808 N Main St, Chiefland 32626 **Matt McLelland**	6-12	TV	815 38	52%	352/493-6000 Fax 352/493-6018
Joyce Bullock Elem Sch 130 SW 3rd St, Williston 32696 Melissa Lewis	PK-2	T	561 31	68%	352/528-3341 Fax 352/528-5541
Levy My District Virtual Sch 480 Marshburn Dr, Bronson 32621 Jeff Edison	6-12		4		352/486-5231
© Nature Coast Middle Sch 6830 NW 140th St, Chiefland 32626 Charles Bowe	6-8	T	85 6	81%	352/490-0700 Fax 352/490-0702
© Whispering Winds Charter Sch 2480 NW Old Fannin Rd, Chiefland 32626 Kimberly Bartley	K-5	T	107 7	4%	352/490-5799 Fax 352/490-7242
Williston Elem Sch 801 S Main St, Williston 32696 Jaime Handlin	3-5	T	512 35	65%	352/528-6030 Fax 352/528-5458
Williston Middle High Sch 350 Robert Philpot Way, Williston 32696 Joshua Slemp	6-12	TV	1,019 42	49%	352/528-3542 Fax 352/528-2723

1 Superintendent	8 Curric/Instruct K-12	19 Chief Financial Officer	29 Family/Consumer Science	39 Social Studies K-12	49 English/Lang Arts Elem	59 Special Education Elem	69 Academic Assessment
2 Bus/Finance/Purchasing	9 Curric/Instruct Elem	20 Art K-12	30 Adult Education	40 Social Studies Elem	50 English/Lang Arts Sec	60 Special Education Sec	70 Research/Development
3 Buildings And Grounds	10 Curric/Instruct Sec	21 Art Elem	31 Career/Sch-to-Work K-12	41 Social Studies Sec	51 Reading K-12	61 Foreign/World Lang K-12	71 Public Information
4 Food Service	11 Federal Program	22 Art Sec	32 Career/Sch-to-Work Elem	42 Science K-12	52 Reading Elem	62 Foreign/World Lang Elem	72 Summer School
5 Transportation	12 Title I	23 Music K-12	33 Career/Sch-to-Work Sec	43 Science Elem	53 Reading Sec	63 Foreign/World Lang Sec	73 Instructional Tech
6 Athletic	13 Title V	24 Music Elem	34 Early Childhood Ed	44 Science Sec	54 Remedial Reading K-12	64 Religious Education K-12	74 Inservice Training
7 Health Services	15 Asst Superintendent	25 Music Sec	35 Health/Phys Education	45 Math K-12	55 Remedial Reading Elem	65 Religious Education Elem	75 Marketing/Distributive
	16 Instructional Media Svcs	26 Business Education	36 Guidance Services K-12	46 Math Elem	56 Remedial Reading Sec	66 Religious Education Sec	76 Info Systems
	17 Chief Operations Officer	27 Career & Tech Ed	37 Guidance Services Elem	47 Math Sec	57 Bilingual/ELL	67 School Board President	77 Psychological Assess
	18 Chief Academic Officer	28 Technology Education	38 Guidance Services Sec	48 English/Lang Arts K-12	58 Special Education K-12	68 Teacher Personnel	78 Affirmative Action

	Grd	Prgm	Enr/#Cls	SN	
Yankeetown Sch 4500 Highway 40 W, Yankeetown 34498 Teiko Hurst	PK-8	T	234 18	67%	352/447-2372 Fax 352/447-3961

LEVY PRIVATE SCHOOLS

Private Schs..Principal	Grd	Prgm	Enr/#Cls	SN	
Creekside Christian Sch 171 SW 3rd St, Otter Creek 32683 Ginny Keith	PK-12		75 5		352/486-2112 Fax 352/486-2171
Williston Central Christ Acad 225 SE 4th St, Williston 32696 Julie Alexander	K-11		100		352/529-0900 Fax 352/529-0901 f

LIBERTY COUNTY

LIBERTY PUBLIC SCHOOLS

- **Liberty Co School Dist** PID: 00194895
  12926 NW County Road 12, Bristol 32321

  850/643-2275
  Fax 850/643-2533

Schools: 5 \ **Teachers:** 117 \ **Students:** 1,373 \
Special Ed Students: 286 \ **LEP Students:** 30 \ **College-Bound:** 41% \
Ethnic: African American 7%, Hispanic 6%, Caucasian 86% \ **Exp:** $170
(Low) \ **Poverty:** 25% \ **Title I:** $357,667 \ **Special Education:** $3,087,000 \
Bilingual Education: $47,000 \ **Open-Close:** 08/13 - 05/28 \ **DTBP:** $362
(High)

David Summers 1		Sheila Hall 2	
Kevin Williams 3,5		Amy Combs 4,69,286	
Derek Causseaux 6*		Gay Lewis 8,11,57,275,285,288,294,296	
Aaron Day 15,68,79		Lara Deason 58	
Daryl Hayes 67		Lynn Guthrie 73,84,295	
Jenna Chason 76			

Public Schs..Principal	Grd	Prgm	Enr/#Cls	SN	
Hosford Elem Jr High Sch 16864 NE State Road 65, Hosford 32334 Jessica Bennett	K-8	T	359 20	47%	850/379-8480 Fax 850/379-8703
Liberty Co High Sch 12592 NW Myers Ann St, Bristol 32321 Aaron Day	9-12	TV	340 28	44%	850/643-2241 Fax 850/643-4153
Ⓐ Liberty Learning Center 12926 NW County Road 12, Bristol 32321 Craig Shuler	7-12	GT	10		850/643-2275
Ⓐ Liberty Wilderness Crossroads Ⓨ Highway 65, Sumatra 32335 Carly Green	6-12	MV	38 2		850/379-8344 Fax 850/379-3351
W R Tolar Elem Middle Sch Highway 12 S, Bristol 32321 Steve Benton	K-8		495 28		850/643-2426 Fax 850/643-4168

LIBERTY PRIVATE SCHOOLS

Private Schs..Principal	Grd	Prgm	Enr/#Cls	SN	
Twin Oaks Juvenile Development 11939 NW State Road 20, Bristol 32321 Jack McClellan	Spec	V	150 14		850/643-1090

MADISON COUNTY

MADISON PUBLIC SCHOOLS

- **Madison Co School Dist** PID: 00194948
  210 NE Duval Ave, Madison 32340

  850/973-5022
  Fax 850/973-5027

Schools: 7 \ **Teachers:** 175 \ **Students:** 2,500 \ **Special Ed Students:** 495
\ **LEP Students:** 35 \ **College-Bound:** 68% \ **Ethnic:** African
American 49%, Hispanic 7%, Caucasian 43% \ **Exp:** $268 (Med) \
Poverty: 42% \ **Title I:** $1,571,226 \ **Special Education:** $3,602,000 \
Bilingual Education: $16,000 \ **Open-Close:** 08/12 - 05/22 \ **DTBP:** $153
(High)

Shirley Joseph 1		Sandra Fletcher 2	
Iris Wynn 4		Ivan Johnson 5	
Robin Hill 8,11,83,93,288,296,298*		Lisa Roderick 11	
Carol Gibson 67		Linda Irvine 68	
Sam Stalnaker 68,88*		Barbara Peddiferd 69,294	
Shane Roland 73,76,295		Melissa Cherry 90	
Ben Cremens 295		Isaac Goyette 295	

Public Schs..Principal	Grd	Prgm	Enr/#Cls	SN	
Greenville Elem Sch 729 SW Overstreet Ave, Greenville 32331 Shirley Joseph	PK-5	T	124 8	71%	850/973-5033 Fax 850/973-5040
Ⓒ James Madison Prep Chtr HS 176 NW Crane Ave, Madison 32340 **Mark Akerman**	9-10		197		850/253-2173 Fax 800/584-2003
Lee Elem Sch 7731 E US Highway 90, Lee 32059 Amanda Brown	K-5	T	211 13	57%	850/973-5030 Fax 850/973-5032
Madison Co Central Sch 2093 W US Highway 90, Madison 32340 Kim Dixon	PK-8	T	996 36	69%	850/973-5192 Fax 850/973-5194
Madison Co High Sch 2649 W US Highway 90, Madison 32340 Geraldine Wildgoose	9-12	ATV	510 50	52%	850/973-5755 Fax 850/973-5066
Ⓒ Madison Creative Arts Academy 2812 W US 90, Madison 32340 Janna Barrs \ Andrea Krell	K-8		308		850/973-2529 Fax 850/973-8974
Pinetta Elem Sch 135 NE Empress Tree Ave, Pinetta 32350 Amy Kendrick	K-5	T	192 11	65%	850/973-5028 Fax 850/973-5147

79 Student Personnel	91 Safety/Security	275 Response To Intervention	298 Grant Writer/Ptnrships	**School Programs**	**Social Media**
80 Driver Ed/Safety	92 Magnet School	277 Remedial Math K-12	750 Chief Innovation Officer	A = Alternative Program	
81 Gifted/Talented	93 Parental Involvement	280 Literacy Coach	751 Chief of Staff	G = Adult Classes	f = Facebook
82 Video Services	95 Tech Prep Program	285 STEM	752 Social Emotional Learning	M = Magnet Program	
83 Substance Abuse Prev	97 Chief Infomation Officer	286 Digital Learning		T = Title I Schoolwide	t = Twitter
84 Erate	98 Chief Technology Officer	288 Common Core Standards	**Other School Types**	V = Career & Tech Ed Programs	
85 AIDS Education	270 Character Education	294 Accountability	Ⓐ = Alternative School		
88 Alternative/At Risk	271 Migrant Education	295 Network System	Ⓒ = Charter School	**New Schools are shaded**	
89 Multi-Cultural Curriculum	273 Teacher Mentor	296 Title II Programs	Ⓜ = Magnet School	**New Superintendents and Principals are bold**	
90 Social Work	274 Before/After Sch	297 Webmaster	Ⓨ = Year-Round School	**Personnel with email addresses are underscored**	

MANATEE COUNTY

MANATEE PUBLIC SCHOOLS

- **Manatee Co School Dist** PID: 00195033   **941/708-8770**
  215 Manatee Ave W, Bradenton 34205   Fax 941/708-8686

Schools: 68 \ **Teachers:** 4,288 \ **Students:** 49,200 \
Special Ed Students: 7,827 \ **LEP Students:** 6,460 \ **College-Bound:** 50%
\ **Ethnic:** Asian 2%, African American 14%, Hispanic 34%, Caucasian
49% \ **Exp:** $140 (Low) \ **Poverty:** 16% \ **Title I:** $12,030,804 \
Special Education: $30,329,000 \ **Bilingual Education:** $7,134,000 \
Open-Close: 08/12 - 05/28 \ **DTBP:** $186 (High) \ 🇹

Cynthia Saunders	1	Doug Wagner	2,15
Gina Maliniak	2	Ruth Gruett	2
Stephanie Riviello	2	Tammy Taylor	2
Amy Anderson	3	Bill Kelley	3,68
Bill Schwanemann	3	Bill Farmer	3
Brian Mabee	3	Dan Lisenko	3
Jane Dreger	3	John Williams	3
Kyle Vickery	3	Mike Vincent	3
Mike Lowe	3	Mike Horsley	3
Pam Miller	3	Reginald Goff	3
Roberto Longoria	3	Todd Henson	3
Amy Benson	4	Matthew Brooks	4
Regina Thoma	4	Shelley Deutschle	4
Stephanie McDonald	4	Gina Miller	5
Jason Harris	5	Jerilynn Boling	5
Joshua Wanbaugh	5	Mabel Santiago	5
Orenthia Walker	5	Sandra Marines	5
Stawania Heaven	5	Won Oh	5
Willie Clark	7,77*	Dr Shirin Gibson	8,70
Annette Codelia	9	Mike Rio	9
Dr Vickie Williams	9	Lissette Fernandez	11
Megan Johnson	12	Heather Jenkins	19
Dr Robin Thompson	34	Shirley Hurley	36*
Debra Estes	57	Cheryl Mathis	58
Joe Roberts	58	Mike Muldoon	58
Nicole Cox	58	Shari Chapman	58
Dave Miner	67	Greta O'Hara-Morris	68
Wendy Mungillo	68	Mike Barber	71
Jean Miller	73	Lisa Berg	73
Dr Pamela Craig	74,270,285	Sherman Stroman	78
Michele Messina	79	Mike McCann	83,88
George Schrier	88	Suzanne Ardila	88
Tia Wilcox	88	Patrick Bartholomew	91
Sally Hull	91	Dawn Sauer	92,93*
Carol Lewis	95	Scott Hansen	98
Harold Medina	271	Cari Whiddon	274
Don Sauer	286	Jessica Norris	294
Joe Coupe	295	Vince Hoaglin	295
Elena Garcia	296,298*		

Public Schs..Principal	Grd	Prgm	Enr/#Cls	SN	
Anna Maria Elem Sch 4700 Gulf Dr, Holmes Beach 34217 Jackie Featherston	K-5		250 15	32%	**941/708-5525** Fax 941/708-5529 🇫
Annie Lucy Williams Elem Sch 3404 Fort Hamer Rd, Parrish 34219 Connie Dixon	PK-5		846	35%	**941/776-4040** Fax 941/776-4080
B D Gullett Elem Sch 12125 44th Ave E, Bradenton 34211 Todd Richardson	PK-5	T	1,080	36%	**941/727-2067** Fax 941/727-2094

School	Grd	Prgm	Enr/#Cls	SN	Phone
Ⓜ **Ballard Elem Sch** 912 18th St W, Bradenton 34205 Michael Masiello	PK-5	T	438 29	83%	**941/708-8400** Fax 941/708-8408
Barbara Harvey Elem Sch 8610 115th Ave E, Parrish 34219 **Hayley Rio**	K-5		401		**941/803-9340** Fax 941/803-9341
Bayshore Elem Sch 6120 26th St W, Bradenton 34207 **Bernadette Pletcher**	PK-5	T	733 32	72%	**941/751-7000** Fax 941/753-0802
Bayshore High Sch 5401 34th St W, Bradenton 34210 Wendell Butler	9-12	TV	1,495	60%	**941/751-7004** Fax 941/753-0953 🇫 🇹
Blackburn Elem Sch 3904 17th St E, Palmetto 34221 Latrina Singleton	PK-5	T	516 45	64%	**941/723-4800** Fax 941/721-6647
Braden River Elem Sch 6125 River Club Blvd, Bradenton 34202 **Joshua Bennett**	PK-5		621 70	35%	**941/751-7012** Fax 941/753-0911
Braden River High Sch 6545 State Road 70 E, Bradenton 34203 Sharon Scarbrough	9-12	V	2,036	34%	**941/751-8230** Fax 941/751-8250
Braden River Middle Sch 6215 River Club Blvd, Bradenton 34202 Hayley Rio	6-8	TV	1,075 60	51%	**941/751-7080** Fax 941/751-7085
Buffalo Creek Middle Sch 7320 69th St E, Palmetto 34221 **Bradley Scarbrough**	6-8	TV	1,221	55%	**941/721-2260** Fax 941/721-2275
Carlos E Haile Middle Sch 9501 E State Road 64, Bradenton 34212 Katherine Barlaug	6-8		1,231 50	38%	**941/714-7240** Fax 941/714-7245
Ⓜ **Daughtrey Prep Sch Arts & Sci** 515 63rd Ave E, Bradenton 34203 **Shelby Bench**	PK-5	T	737 32	84%	**941/751-7023** Fax 941/753-0849
Dr Mona Jain Middle Sch 12205 44th Ave E, Bradenton 34211 **Angela Hodges-Lindsay**	6-8		600		**941/727-4747** Fax 941/757-0052
Ⓜ **Electa Arcott Lee Magnet MS** 4000 53rd Ave W, Bradenton 34210 Scott Cooper	6-8	TV	1,057 53	62%	**941/727-6500** Fax 941/727-6513 🇫 🇹
Florine J Abel Elem Sch 7100 Madonna Pl, Sarasota 34243 James Horner	PK-5	T	526 30	68%	**941/751-7040** Fax 941/753-0919
Freedom Elem Sch 9515 E State Road 64, Bradenton 34212 Guy Grimes	PK-5	T	769 40	49%	**941/708-4990** Fax 941/708-4919
Gene Witt Elem Sch 200 Rye Rd E, Bradenton 34212 David Marshall	PK-5		778 36	28%	**941/741-3628** Fax 941/741-3630
H S Moody Elem Sch 5425 38th Ave W, Bradenton 34209 Tina Stancil	PK-5	T	618 34	71%	**941/741-3170** Fax 941/741-3555
Ⓐ **Horizons Academy** 1910 27th St E, Bradenton 34208 James Hird	4-12		417	76%	**941/714-7470** Fax 941/708-6417
Ida M Stewart Elem Sch 7905 15th Ave NW, Bradenton 34209 Joseph Hougland	PK-5		428 24	38%	**941/741-3176** Fax 941/741-3467
© **Imagine Schools Lakewood Ranch [137]** 10535 Portal Xing, Bradenton 34211 Selenia Quinones	PK-8	T	541	47%	**941/750-0900** Fax 941/750-0966
© **Imagine Schools North Manatee [137]** 9275 49th Ave E, Palmetto 34221 **Erin Kelly**	PK-8		607	54%	**941/981-5345** Fax 941/981-5349
Ⓜ **James Tillman Elem Sch** 1415 29th St E, Palmetto 34221 Marla Blackmore	PK-5	T	616 41	85%	**941/723-4833** Fax 941/723-4530

1	Superintendent	8	Curric/Instruct K-12	19	Chief Financial Officer	29	Family/Consumer Science
2	Bus/Finance/Purchasing	9	Curric/Instruct Elem	20	Art K-12	30	Adult Education
3	Buildings And Grounds	10	Curric/Instruct Sec	21	Art Elem	31	Career/Sch-to-Work K-12
4	Food Service	11	Federal Program	22	Art Sec	32	Career/Sch-to-Work Elem
5	Transportation	12	Title I	23	Music K-12	33	Career/Sch-to-Work Sec
6	Athletic	13	Title V	24	Music Elem	34	Early Childhood Ed
7	Health Services	15	Asst Superintendent	25	Music Sec	35	Health/Phys Education
		16	Instructional Media Svcs	26	Business Education	36	Guidance Services K-12
		17	Chief Operations Officer	27	Career & Tech Ed	37	Guidance Services Elem
		18	Chief Academic Officer	28	Technology Education	38	Guidance Services Sec

39	Social Studies K-12	49	English/Lang Arts Elem	59	Special Education Elem	69	Academic Assessment
40	Social Studies Elem	50	English/Lang Arts Sec	60	Special Education Sec	70	Research/Development
41	Social Studies Sec	51	Reading K-12	61	Foreign/World Lang K-12	71	Public Information
42	Science K-12	52	Reading Elem	62	Foreign/World Lang Elem	72	Summer School
43	Science Elem	53	Reading Sec	63	Foreign/World Lang Sec	73	Instructional Tech
44	Science Sec	54	Remedial Reading K-12	64	Religious Education K-12	74	Inservice Training
45	Math K-12	55	Remedial Reading Elem	65	Religious Education Elem	75	Marketing/Distributive
46	Math Elem	56	Remedial Reading Sec	66	Religious Education Sec	76	Info Systems
47	Math Sec	57	Bilingual/ELL	67	School Board President	77	Psychological Assess
48	English/Lang Arts K-12	58	Special Education K-12	68	Teacher Personnel	78	Affirmative Action

School	Grades		Enroll	%	Phone
Jessie P Miller Elem Sch 601 43rd St W, Bradenton 34209 Scott Boyes	PK-5	T	737 45	66%	941/741-3300 Fax 941/741-3415
© Just for Girls Academy 1011 12th St E, Bradenton 34208 Deanna Smith	K-5		82	78%	941/747-5757 Fax 941/251-4913
Kinnan Elem Sch 3415 Tallevast Rd, Sarasota 34243 Paul Hockenbury	PK-5	T	643	65%	941/358-2888 Fax 941/358-2956
Lakewood Ranch High Sch 5500 Lakewood Ranch Blvd, Bradenton 34211 **Dustin Dahlquist**	9-12		2,340 90	25%	941/727-6100 Fax 941/727-6099
Lincoln Memorial Middle Sch 305 17th St E, Palmetto 34221 **Ronnie King**	6-8	TV	468 68	68%	941/721-6840 Fax 941/721-6853
Louise R Johnson K-8 Sch Int'l 2121 26th Ave E, Bradenton 34208 **Anthony Losada \ Anthony Losada**	K-8	V	975 50		941/741-3344 Fax 941/741-3345
© Manatee Charter Sch [133] 4550 30th St E, Bradenton 34203 Bonnie Brett	K-8	T	403	100%	941/465-4296 Fax 941/465-4297
Manatee Elem Sch 1609 6th Ave E, Bradenton 34208 Tamera Vanoverbeke	PK-5	T	414 23	84%	941/741-3319 Fax 941/741-3507
Manatee High Sch 902 33rd Street Ct W, Bradenton 34205 David Underhill	9-12	TV	2,249 100	54%	941/714-7300 Fax 941/741-3443
© Manatee Sch of Arts & Science 3700 32nd St W, Bradenton 34205 Richard Ramsay	K-6		173 6	75%	941/755-5012 Fax 941/755-7934
© Manatee School for the Arts 700 Haben Blvd, Palmetto 34221 **Dr Bill Jones**	6-12		2,135 50	55%	941/721-6800 Fax 941/721-6805
Manatee Technical College 6305 State Road 70 E, Bradenton 34203 Valerie Viands	Voc	AG	900 70		941/751-7900 Fax 941/751-7927
Manatee Virtual Sch 1400 1st Ave E Bldg 6, Palmetto 34221 Frank Pistella	K-12		66	15%	941/708-4971 Fax 941/845-3312
Martha B King Middle Sch 600 75th St NW, Bradenton 34209 **Kristin Kreiling**	6-8	TV	1,111 50	64%	941/798-6820 Fax 941/741-6835
McNeal Elem Sch 6325 Lorraine Rd, Bradenton 34202 Cheryl McGrew	PK-5		778 42	25%	941/751-8165 Fax 941/751-8155
Myakka Elem Sch 37205 Manatee Ave, Myakka City 34251 **Carol Ricks**	PK-5	T	266 18	73%	941/708-5515 Fax 941/708-5517
© Oasis Middle Sch 4304 32nd St W, Bradenton 34205 Edna Bailey	6-8	T	119	82%	941/749-1979
Oneco Elem Sch 5214 22nd Street Ct E, Bradenton 34203 **Kimberly Organek**	PK-5	T	615	81%	941/751-7018 Fax 941/753-0926
Pace Center for Girls-Manatee 3508 26th St W, Bradenton 34205 **Amy Wick Mavis**	5-12		52	100%	941/751-4566 Fax 941/756-7101
Palm View Elem Sch 6025 Bayshore Rd, Palmetto 34221 Kaththea Johnson	PK-5	T	389 33	74%	941/723-4812 Fax 941/723-4532
Palma Sola Elem Sch 6806 5th Ave NW, Bradenton 34209 Jennifer Grimes	PK-5	T	623 28	58%	941/741-3179 Fax 941/741-3181 🅕🅣
© Palmetto Charter Sch 1601 17th St W, Palmetto 34221 Brian Buslte	K-8		364	27%	941/723-3711 Fax 941/729-5805
Palmetto Elem Sch 1540 10th St W, Palmetto 34221 **Dr Michelle Mealor**	PK-5	T	732 37	78%	941/723-4822 Fax 941/723-4607
Palmetto High Sch 1200 17th St W, Palmetto 34221 Carl Auckerman	9-12	TV	2,231 85	58%	941/723-4848 Fax 941/723-4952
© Parrish Charter Academy [136] 8605 Erie Rd, Parrish 34219 **Dawn Patterson**	K-3		360		941/545-6380
Parrish Cmty High Sch 7505 Ft Hamer Rd, Parrish 34219 **Craig Little**	9-12		560		941/803-9330
R Dan Nolan Middle Sch 6615 Greenbrook Blvd, Bradenton 34202 Scot Boice	6-8		1,167 45	24%	941/751-8200 Fax 941/751-8210
Robert E Willis Elem Sch 14705 the Masters Ave, Bradenton 34202 **Kathy Price**	K-5		774	19%	941/316-8245 Fax 941/316-8259
Robert H Prine Elem Sch 3801 Southern Pkwy W, Bradenton 34205 Lynne Menard	PK-5	T	762 43	74%	941/751-7006 Fax 941/753-0924
Rogers Garden-Bullock Elem Sch 515 13th Ave W, Bradenton 34205 Patricia Stream	PK-5	T	514	74%	941/209-7540 Fax 941/209-7550
© Rowlett Acad for Arts & Comm 3500 9th St E, Bradenton 34208 Charles Fradley	K-5	T	918	15%	941/708-6100 Fax 941/708-6109
© Rowlett Middle Academy 400 30th Ave W, Bradenton 34205 Jamara Clark	6-8		502		941/462-4001 Fax 941/896-3006
Samoset Elem Sch 3300 19th St E, Bradenton 34208 Maribeth Mason	PK-5	T	587 28	84%	941/708-6400 Fax 941/708-6408
Ⓐ Sara Scott Harllee Ctr-Sable © 6423 9th St E, Bradenton 34203 Karen Mills	6-12		401		941/209-6579
Sea Breeze Elem Sch 3601 71st St W, Bradenton 34209 Greg Sander	PK-5	T	626 23	65%	941/741-3190 Fax 941/741-3614
Southeast High Sch 1200 37th Ave E, Bradenton 34208 Rosa Faison	9-12	GTV	1,701 80	71%	941/741-3366 Fax 941/741-3372
© State Clg of FL Collegiate Sch 5840 26th St W, Bradenton 34207 Kelly Monod	6-12		521	32%	941/752-5494
Tara Elem Sch 6950 Linger Lodge Rd E, Bradenton 34203 Laura Campbell	PK-6	T	651 35	53%	941/751-7660 Fax 941/753-0975
© Team Success Sch of Excellence 202 13th Ave E, Bradenton 34208 Armando Viota	K-12	T	559 10	88%	941/714-7260 Fax 941/714-7333
Virgil Mills Elem Sch 7200 69th St E, Palmetto 34221 James Mennes	K-5	T	1,229 35	42%	941/721-2140 Fax 941/721-2152
© Visible Men Academy 921 63rd Ave E, Bradenton 34203 Mary Berges	K-5	T	102	72%	941/758-7588 Fax 941/761-5375
W D Sugg Middle Sch 3801 59th St W, Bradenton 34209 Ann McDonald	6-8	TV	819 56	70%	941/741-3157 Fax 941/741-3514
William H Bashaw Elem Sch 3515 57th St E, Bradenton 34208 **Mario Mendoza**	PK-5	T	624 40	72%	941/741-3307 Fax 941/741-3559

79 Student Personnel	91 Safety/Security	275 Response To Intervention	298 Grant Writer/Ptnrships	**School Programs**
80 Driver Ed/Safety	92 Magnet School	277 Remedial Math K-12	750 Chief Innovation Officer	A = Alternative Program
31 Gifted/Talented	93 Parental Involvement	280 Literacy Coach	751 Chief of Staff	G = Adult Classes
32 Video Services	95 Tech Prep Program	285 STEM	752 Social Emotional Learning	M = Magnet Program
33 Substance Abuse Prev	97 Chief Infomation Officer	286 Digital Learning		T = Title I Schoolwide
84 Erate	98 Chief Technology Officer	288 Common Core Standards	**Other School Types**	V = Career & Tech Ed Programs
85 AIDS Education	270 Character Education	294 Accountability	Ⓐ = Alternative School	
88 Alternative/At Risk	271 Migrant Education	295 Network System	© = Charter School	**Social Media**
89 Multi-Cultural Curriculum	273 Teacher Mentor	296 Title II Programs	Ⓜ = Magnet School	🅕 = Facebook
90 Social Work	274 Before/After Sch	297 Webmaster	Ⓨ = Year-Round School	🅣 = Twitter

New Schools are shaded
New Superintendents and Principals are bold
Personnel with email addresses are underscored

MANATEE CATHOLIC SCHOOLS

- **Diocese of Venice Ed Office** PID: 02231695
  Listing includes only schools located in this county. See District Index for location of Diocesan Offices.

Catholic Schs..Principal	Grd	Prgm	Enr/#Cls	SN
St Joseph Catholic Sch	PK-8		350	941/755-2611
2990 26th St W, Bradenton 34205			20	Fax 941/753-6339
Deborah Suddarth				🇫

MANATEE PRIVATE SCHOOLS

Private Schs..Principal	Grd	Prgm	Enr/#Cls	SN
Bradenton Christian Sch	PK-12		715	941/792-5454
3304 43rd St W, Bradenton 34209				Fax 941/795-7190
Jeff Myers \ Andy Bobitz \ Chad McBane				
Bradenton Early Learning Acad	PK-PK		51	941/216-3305
7700 Cortez Rd W, Bradenton 34210				
Tiffany Franco				
Center Montessori Sch	PK-8		192	941/753-4987
6024 26th St W, Bradenton 34207			10	Fax 941/756-4985
Mara Fulk				
Community Christian Sch	PK-12		250	941/756-8748
5500 18th St E, Bradenton 34203			26	Fax 941/753-7057
Terry Hale				
Edison Academics	6-12		100	941/792-7500
7710 Cortez Rd W, Bradenton 34210			16	Fax 941/792-7559
Paula Jackson				
Ellen Meade Sch Creative Lrng	PK-PK		90	941/755-1757
1323 63rd Ave E, Bradenton 34203			9	Fax 941/753-7277
Craig Thomas				
Family Life Community Sch	PK-8		130	941/792-7911
3301 Moccasin Wallow Rd, Palmetto 34221				Fax 941/479-7804
Mary Ellis Bonds				
Gulfcoast Christian Academy	K-12		29	941/755-0332
1700 51st Ave E, Bradenton 34203			7	Fax 941/981-1564
Carol Pope				
Img Academy	6-12		700	941/739-3964
5500 34th St W, Bradenton 34210				Fax 941/752-2433
Chris Locke				
Peace Lutheran Sch	K-8		36	941/747-6753
1611 30th Ave W, Bradenton 34205			3	
David Zuberbier				
St Stephen's Episcopal Sch	PK-12		660	941/746-2121
315 41st St W, Bradenton 34209				Fax 941/746-5699
Joel Erby \ Andrew Forrester				🇫🇪
Sun Academy	PK-5		40	941/752-1715
2425 38th Ave W, Bradenton 34205				Fax 941/752-3025
Heather Reardon				
Sunshine Christian Acad-Braden	PK-8		40	941/794-3143
2520 43rd St W, Bradenton 34209			7	Fax 941/794-1819
Dr Deborah Marcum				
The McKay Academy	1-12		51	941/840-5331
400 30th Ave W, Bradenton 34205				Fax 941/714-0400
Paul Lipinski				
West Coast Christian Academy	PK-8		60	941/755-9667
1112 49th Ave E, Bradenton 34203			7	Fax 941/755-4530
Cathy Langsdale				

MARION PUBLIC SCHOOLS

- **Marion Co Public Schools** PID: 00195344   352/671-7700
  512 SE 3rd St, Ocala 34471   Fax 352/671-7735

Schools: 57 \ *Teachers:* 2,720 \ *Students:* 42,624 \
Special Ed Students: 6,572 \ *LEP Students:* 2,753 \ *College-Bound:* 75%
\ *Ethnic:* Asian 2%, African American 21%, Hispanic 23%, Native American:
1%, Caucasian 54% \ *Exp:* $119 (Low) \ *Poverty:* 25% \ *Title I:* $17,833,022
\ *Special Education:* $39,100,000 \ *Bilingual Education:* $5,305,000 \
Open-Close: 08/12 - 05/28 \ *DTBP:* $196 (High)

Dr Heidi Maier	1	Theresa Boston-Ellis	2,19
Kerry Cook	3	Mike Robey	3
Robert Knight	3	Tammy Alvarez	4
Rebecca Rora	5	Jody Phillips	6
Andrea Simmons	7	Cassandra Roston	11,298
Dr Shannon Butler	12	Dr Jonathan Grantham	15,286,288
Mark Vianello	27,30,31,75	Kendra Hamby	34
Jonathan McGowan	36,77	Janice Ray	37*
Mark Ingram	57	Dwan Thomas	58
Kelly King	67	Barbara Dobbins	68
Kevin Christian	71	Anthony Clark	73*
Shana I Iornc	74	Melissa Ocasio	76
David Ellers	77,79,81,90	Dawana Gary	78
Jessica Larroque	81	Lori Lively	83,88
Dennis McFatten	91	Pamela Eubanks	274
Holly Gerlach	280,285	Alexandria Banks	294
Ed Beers	295		

Public Schs..Principal	Grd	Prgm	Enr/#Cls	SN
Anthony Elem Sch	PK-5	T	391	71% 352/671-6000
9501 NE Jacksonville Rd, Anthony 32617			22	Fax 352/671-6001
James Johnson				
Belleview Elem Sch	PK-5	T	701	74% 352/671-6100
5556 SE County Highway 484, Belleview 34420			35	Fax 352/671-6105
Dr Stacey Reece				
Belleview High Sch	9-12	TV	1,600	62% 352/671-6210
10400 SE 36th Ave, Belleview 34420				Fax 352/671-6212
Heather Guest				
Belleview Middle Sch	6-8	TV	1,324	68% 352/671-6235
10500 SE 36th Ave, Belleview 34420			70	Fax 352/671-6239
Dion Gary				
Belleview-Santos Elem Sch	PK-5	T	509	70% 352/671-6260
9600 SE US Highway 441, Belleview 34420			40	Fax 352/671-6261
Kimberly White				
College Park Elem Sch	PK-5	T	820	79% 352/291-4040
1330 SW 33rd Ave, Ocala 34474			30	Fax 352/291-4042
Teresa Forsyth				
Ⓜ Dr N H Jones Elem Sch	K-5		683	17% 352/671-7260
1900 SW 5th St, Ocala 34471			35	Fax 352/671-7266
Jennifer Houle				
Dunnellon Elem Sch	PK-5	T	554	62% 352/465-6710
10235 SW 180th Avenue Rd, Dunnellon 34432			30	Fax 352/465-6711
Karen English				
Dunnellon High Sch	9-12	TV	1,179	70% 352/465-6745
10055 SW 180th Avenue Rd, Dunnellon 34432			58	Fax 352/465-6746
Wade Martin				
Dunnellon Middle Sch	6-8	TV	665	79% 352/465-6720
21005 Chestnut St, Dunnellon 34431			55	Fax 352/465-6721
Delbert Smallridge				

1	Superintendent	8	Curric/Instruct K-12	19	Chief Financial Officer	29	Family/Consumer Science
2	Bus/Finance/Purchasing	9	Curric/Instruct Elem	20	Art K-12	30	Adult Education
3	Buildings And Grounds	10	Curric/Instruct Sec	21	Art Elem	31	Career/Sch-to-Work K-12
4	Food Service	11	Federal Program	22	Art Sec	32	Career/Sch-to-Work Elem
5	Transportation	12	Title I	23	Music K-12	33	Career/Sch-to-Work Sec
6	Athletic	13	Title V	24	Music Elem	34	Early Childhood Ed
7	Health Services	14	Asst Superintendent	25	Music Sec	35	Health/Phys Education
		15	Asst Superintendent	26	Business Education	36	Guidance Services K-12
		16	Instructional Media Svcs	27	Career & Tech Ed	37	Guidance Services Elem
		17	Chief Operations Officer	28	Technology Education	38	Guidance Services Sec
		18	Chief Academic Officer				

39	Social Studies K-12	49	English/Lang Arts Elem
40	Social Studies Elem	50	English/Lang Arts Sec
41	Social Studies Sec	51	Reading K-12
42	Science K-12	52	Reading Elem
43	Science Elem	53	Reading Sec
44	Science Sec	54	Remedial Reading K-12
45	Math K-12	55	Remedial Reading Elem
46	Math Elem	56	Remedial Reading Sec
47	Math Sec	57	Bilingual/ELL
48	English/Lang Arts K-12	58	Special Education K-12

59	Special Education Elem	69	Academic Assessment
60	Special Education Sec	70	Research/Development
61	Foreign/World Lang K-12	71	Public Information
62	Foreign/World Lang Elem	72	Summer School
63	Foreign/World Lang Sec	73	Instructional Tech
64	Religious Education K-12	74	Inservice Training
65	Religious Education Elem	75	Marketing/Distributive
66	Religious Education Sec	76	Info Systems
67	School Board President	77	Psychological Assess
68	Teacher Personnel	78	Affirmative Action

East Marion Elem Sch — PK-5 T 669 80% 352/671-4810
14550 NE 14th Street Rd, Silver Spgs 34488 — 40 — Fax 352/671-4811
Kendra Hamby

Eighth Street Elem Sch — K-5 T 402 36% 352/671-7125
513 SE 8th St, Ocala 34471 — Fax 352/671-7126
Dawn Prestipino

Emerald Shores Elem Sch — PK-5 T 644 79% 352/671-4800
404 Emerald Rd, Ocala 34472 — 35 — Fax 352/671-4805
Stacy Houston

Evergreen Elem Sch — K-5 T 458 83% 352/671-4925
4000 W Anthony Rd, Ocala 34475 — 36 — Fax 352/671-4931
Ashley Kemp

Fessenden Elem Sch — PK-5 T 436 78% 352/671-4935
4200 NW 89th Pl, Ocala 34482 — 23 — Fax 352/671-4936
Lacy Redd

Forest High Sch — 9-12 TV 2,195 46% 352/671-4700
5000 SE Maricamp Rd, Ocala 34480 — Fax 352/671-4714
Elizabeth Brown

© Frances Marion Military Acad — 9-12 170 352/245-6600
5895 SE 83rd St, Ocala 34472 — Fax 352/245-6602
James McCollum

Ft King Middle Sch — 6-8 ATV 1,078 75% 352/671-4725
545 NE 17th Ave, Ocala 34470 — 55 — Fax 352/671-4726
Gary Smallridge

Ft McCoy Sch — PK-8 T 1,004 70% 352/671-6325
16160 NE Highway 315, Fort Mc Coy 32134 — 60 — Fax 352/671-6326
Jennifer Fisher

Greenway Elem Sch — PK-5 T 682 63% 352/671-4845
207 Midway Rd, Ocala 34472 — 34 — Fax 352/671-4853
Jamie North

Hammett Bowen Jr Elem Sch — K-5 T 810 51% 352/291-7900
4397 SW 95th St, Ocala 34476 — Fax 352/291-7901
Traci Crawford

Harbour View Elem Sch — PK-5 T 850 68% 352/671-6110
8445 SE 147th Pl, Summerfield 34491 — 41 — Fax 352/671-6111
Robert Hensel

Hillcrest Sch — Spec T 193 46% 352/671-6800
3143 SE 17th St, Ocala 34471 — 23 — Fax 352/671-6806
Lori Manresa

Horizon Academy at Marion Oaks — 5-8 T 833 86% 352/671-6290
365 Marion Oaks Dr, Ocala 34473 — Fax 352/671-6293
Donald Maier

Ⓜ Howard Middle Sch — 6-8 TV 1,060 61% 352/671-7225
1655 NW 10th St, Ocala 34475 — 80 — Fax 352/671-7237
Lamar Rembert

Lake Weir High Sch — 9-12 TV 1,475 75% 352/671-4820
10351 SE Maricamp Rd, Ocala 34472 — 91 — Fax 352/671-4829
Colleen Wade

Lake Weir Middle Sch — 6-8 TV 1,128 81% 352/671-6120
10220 SE Sunset Harbor Rd, Summerfield 34491 — 74 — Fax 352/671-6121
Brian Greene

Legacy Elem Sch — PK-5 T 809 63% 352/671-0800
8496 Juniper Rd, Ocala 34480 — Fax 352/671-0801
Shameka Murphy

Liberty Middle Sch — 6-8 T 1,277 66% 352/291-7930
4773 SW 95th St, Ocala 34476 — 44 — Fax 352/291-7931
Melissa Forsyth

Ⓜ Madison St Acad Performing Art — K-5 T 449 26% 352/671-7250
401 NW Mlk Jr Ave, Ocala 34475 — 35 — Fax 352/671-7210
Ryan Bennett

Maplewood Elem Sch — PK-5 T 739 53% 352/671-6820
4751 SE 24th St, Ocala 34471 — 50 — Fax 352/671-6821
Christine Disanza

© Marion Charter Sch — K-5 T 220 67% 352/687-2100
39 Cedar Rd, Ocala 34472 — 12 — Fax 352/687-2700
Michelle Axson

Marion Co Technical College — Adult V 1,000 75% 352/671-7270
1014 SW 7th Rd, Ocala 34471 — 14 — Fax 352/629-1117
Mike Kelly

Marion Oaks Elem Sch — PK-5 T 892 65% 352/291-7975
280 Marion Oaks Trl, Ocala 34473 — Fax 352/291-7976
Lisa Dreher

Ⓜ Marion Technical Institute — 9-12 T 231 52% 352/671-4765
1614 E Fort King St, Ocala 34471 — Fax 352/671-4766
Jennifer Beasley

© McIntosh Area Sch — K-5 T 75 69% 352/591-9797
20400 10th St, Mc Intosh 32664 — 6 — Fax 352/591-9747
Cindy Roach

Mcps Virtual Sch — 6-12 32 352/867-2137
1614 E Fort King St, Ocala 34471 — Fax 352/671-6837
Paul Bowinkel

North Marion High Sch — 9-12 TV 1,314 69% 352/671-6010
151 W Cr 329, Citra 32113 — 100 — Fax 352/671-6011
Danielle Livengood

North Marion Middle Sch — 6-8 TV 811 82% 352/671-6035
2085 W Cr 329, Citra 32113 — 60 — Fax 352/671-6044
Dawn Mobley

Oakcrest Elem Sch — PK-5 T 592 80% 352/671-6350
1112 NE 28th St, Ocala 34470 — 40 — Fax 352/671-6357
Catherine Balius

Ocala Springs Elem Sch — PK-5 T 648 69% 352/671-6360
5757 NE 40th Avenue Rd, Ocala 34479 — 37 — Fax 352/671-6368
Michelle Cino

© Ocali Charter Middle Sch — 6-8 116 352/264-9940
3233 SE Maricamp Rd Ste 106, Ocala 34471
Elias Posth

Osceola Middle Sch — 6-8 TV 968 44% 352/671-7100
526 SE Tuscawilla Ave, Ocala 34471 — Fax 352/671-7101
Matthew Koff

Ⓐ Pace Center for Girls-Marion — 6-12 61 84% 352/369-0571
328 NE 1st Ave Ste 500, Ocala 34470 — Fax 352/369-0572
Carole Savage

Ⓜ Reddick-Collier Elem Sch — PK-5 T 413 75% 352/671-6070
4595 W Highway 316, Reddick 32686 — 28 — Fax 352/671-6075
Christine Sandy

Romeo Elem Sch — PK-5 T 752 73% 352/465-6700
19550 SW 36th St, Dunnellon 34431 — 44 — Fax 352/465-6701
Suzette Parker

Saddlewood Elem Sch — PK-5 T 872 52% 352/291-4075
3700 SW 43rd Ct, Ocala 34474 — 42 — Fax 352/291-4079
Heather Lipira

Shady Hill Elem Sch — K-5 T 639 54% 352/291-4085
5959 S Magnolia Ave, Ocala 34471 — 29 — Fax 352/291-4087
Debra Riedl

Ⓐ Silver River Mentor/Instr Sch — 6-12 V 160 89% 352/694-0191
2500 SE 44th Ct, Ocala 34471 — 7 — Fax 352/694-0195
Allan Nieb

South Ocala Elem Sch — PK-5 T 713 60% 352/671-4750
1430 SE 24th Rd, Ocala 34471 — 35 — Fax 352/671-4759
Stephanie Callaway

Sparr Elem Sch — PK-5 T 386 71% 352/671-6060
2525 E Hwy 329, Anthony 32617 — 35 — Fax 352/671-6061
Gay Street

Stanton-Weirsdale Elem Sch — PK-5 T 532 78% 352/671-6150
16705 SE 134th Ter, Weirsdale 32195 — 24 — Fax 352/671-6151
Cynthia Brodie

Sunrise Elem Sch — PK-4 T 836 77% 352/671-6200
375 Marion Oaks Crse, Ocala 34473 — 45 — Fax 352/671-6206
Natalia Robledo

Vanguard High Sch — 9-12 TV 1,637 59% 352/671-4900
7 NW 28th St, Ocala 34475 — 100 — Fax 352/671-4903
Christopher Carlisle

---

79 Student Personnel	91 Safety/Security	275 Response To Intervention	298 Grant Writer/Ptnrships	**School Programs**	**Social Media**
80 Driver Ed/Safety	92 Magnet School	277 Remedial Math K-12	750 Chief Innovation Officer	A = Alternative Program	
81 Gifted/Talented	93 Parental Involvement	280 Literacy Coach	751 Chief of Staff	G = Adult Classes	▯ = Facebook
82 Video Services	95 Tech Prep Program	285 STEM	752 Social Emotional Learning	M = Magnet Program	
83 Substance Abuse Prev	97 Chief Information Officer	286 Digital Learning		T = Title I Schoolwide	▯ = Twitter
84 Erate	98 Chief Technology Officer	288 Common Core Standards	**Other School Types**	V = Career & Tech Ed Programs	
85 AIDS Education	270 Character Education	294 Accountability	Ⓐ = Alternative School		
88 Alternative/At Risk	271 Migrant Education	295 Network System	© = Charter School	New Schools are shaded	
89 Multi-Cultural Curriculum	273 Teacher Mentor	296 Title II Programs	Ⓜ = Magnet School	New Superintendents and Principals are bold	
90 Social Work	274 Before/After Sch	297 Webmaster	Ⓨ = Year-Round School	Personnel with email addresses are underscored	

Ward-Highlands Elem Sch 537 SE 36th Ave, Ocala 34471 Treasa Buck	K-5	T	862 40	54%	352/671-6810 Fax 352/671-6813
West Port High Sch 3733 SW 80th Ave, Ocala 34481 Ginger Cruze	9-12	TV	2,659 85	60%	352/291-4000 Fax 352/291-4001
Wyomina Park Elem Sch 511 NE 12th Ave, Ocala 34470 Joy Baxley	PK-5	T	571	82%	352/671-6370 Fax 352/671-6372

MARION CATHOLIC SCHOOLS

- **Diocese of Orlando Ed Office** PID: 00197639
  Listing includes only schools located in this county. See District Index for location of Diocesan Offices.

Catholic Schs..Principal	Grd	Prgm	Enr/#Cls	SN	
Blessed Trinity Cath Sch 5 SE 17th St, Ocala 34471 Megan Losito	K-8		681 28		352/622-5808 Fax 352/622-1660
Trinity Catholic High Sch 2600 SW 42nd St, Ocala 34471 Dr Erika Wikstrom	9-12		540 36		352/622-9025 Fax 352/861-8164

MARION PRIVATE SCHOOLS

Private Schs..Principal	Grd	Prgm	Enr/#Cls	SN	
Ambleside School of Ocala 507 SE Broadway St, Ocala 34471 Jill Romine	K-8		100		352/694-1635 Fax 352/694-4791
Belleview Christian Academy 6107 SE Agnew Rd, Belleview 34420 Mike Lacrone	PK-7		122 9		352/245-6151 Fax 352/245-3710
Cornerstone Sch 2313 SE Lake Weir Ave, Ocala 34471 Ingrid Wasserfall	PK-8		230 11		352/351-8840 Fax 352/351-4226 🇫 🇹
Dr DD Brown Academy of Hope 519 SW 10th St Ste 100&, Ocala 34471 Kay Crowell	PK-12		401		352/351-5464
Dunnellon Christian Academy 20831 Powell Rd, Dunnellon 34431 Kristy Wheat	PK-8		150 18		352/489-7716 Fax 352/489-5760
First Assembly Christian Sch 1827 NE 14th St, Ocala 34470 Earlene Carte	PK-12		430 25		352/351-1913 Fax 352/351-5170
Grace Christian Sch 4410 SE 3rd Ave, Ocala 34480 Dr Bethany Alexander	PK-8		175 14		352/629-2312 Fax 352/629-7724
Gracepointe Academy 6185 SE 140th St, Summerfield 34491 Austin Tucker	K-12		69		352/897-0822 Fax 352/693-5825
Graceway Academy & Preschool 2255 SE 38th St, Ocala 34480	PK-5		401		352/629-4523
Kingdom Christian Acad & PS 1026 SW 9th St, Ocala 34471 Clyde Graham	PK-5		75		352/369-3119
Meadowbrook Academy 4741 SW 20th St Bldg 1, Ocala 34474 Tina Stelogeannis	K-12		281 13		352/861-0700 Fax 352/861-0533
Montessori Preparatory Sch 2967 E Silver Springs Blvd, Ocala 34470	PK-5		170		352/351-3140 Fax 352/351-2595

New Horizon Academy 1100 NE 31st St, Ocala 34479 Brenda Maynard	Spec		16		352/694-7201 Fax 352/694-7581
Ocala Christian Academy 1714 SE 36th Ave, Ocala 34471 Sharon Loyd \ Ron Carpenter	PK-12	V	425 37		352/694-4178 Fax 352/694-7192
Redeemer Christian Sch 155 SW 87th Pl, Ocala 34476 Luke Butler	PK-12		179 16		352/854-2999 Fax 352/291-9196 🇫
School of the Kingdom 1425 NE 63rd St, Ocala 34479 Joel Snellgrove	PK-12		115 6		352/620-0780 Fax 352/620-8916
Shiloh SDA Sch 500 SW 17th Ave, Ocala 34471 Lywanda Bell	K-8		71 6		352/629-6857
Souls Harbor Christian Academy 12650 SE County Highway 484, Belleview 34420 Brandy Currie	K-12		117 5		352/245-6252 Fax 352/245-4532
St John Lutheran Sch 1915 SE Lake Weir Ave, Ocala 34471 Tim Schmidt	PK-12		300 30		352/622-7275 Fax 352/433-2540

MARION REGIONAL CENTERS

- **FDLRS-Springs** PID: 04496217　　　　　　352/671-6051
  3881 NW 155th St, Reddick 32686　　　　Fax 352/671-6096

  James Husted 1

MARTIN COUNTY

MARTIN PUBLIC SCHOOLS

- **Martin Co School Dist** PID: 00195710　　　　772/219-1200
  500 SE Ocean Blvd, Stuart 34994

Schools: 29 \ **Teachers:** 1,224 \ **Students:** 19,244 \
Special Ed Students: 3,039 \ **LEP Students:** 2,879 \ **College-Bound:** 90%
\ **Ethnic:** Asian 2%, African American 7%, Hispanic 29%, Caucasian
61% \ **Exp:** $198 (Low) \ **Poverty:** 15% \ **Title I:** $3,795,998 \
Special Education: $6,198,000 \ **Bilingual Education:** $674,000 \
Open-Close: 08/12 - 05/28 \ **DTBP:** $190 (High)

Laurie Gaylord 1	Audra Curts-Whann 2,19	
Huggueth Skinner 2	Julie Sessa 2	
Justin Sage 2	Mary Wulff 2	
Garrett Gabrowski 3	Garrett Grabowski 3	
Mark Sechrist 3	Rob Phillips 3	
Ronald Martin 3	Laura Holnebel 4	
P Schaaf 4	Tina Jensen 4	
Kayleen Watts 5	Mary White 8	
Dr Tracey Miller 8,13,18,288,296	Sheila Khanal 12,57,271	
Dr Ginger Featherstone 15	Elia Parsons 27	
Melissa Eversdyke 30*	Jennifer Corkin 34	
Mark Malham 41*	Steve Layson 45	
Shannon Blount 48,51	Deb Stull 57	
Vicky Jenkins 58	Christia Liroberts 67	
Carlos Perez 68	Maurice Bonner 68,78	
Greg Laws 69	Jennifer DeShazo 71	
Drew Wessel 73	Mark Capley 73,295	

1	Superintendent	8	Curric/Instruct K-12	19	Chief Financial Officer	29	Family/Consumer Science
2	Bus/Finance/Purchasing	9	Curric/Instruct Elem	20	Art K-12	30	Adult Education
3	Buildings And Grounds	10	Curric/Instruct Sec	21	Art Elem	31	Career/Sch-to-Work K-12
4	Food Service	11	Federal Program	22	Art Sec	32	Career/Sch-to-Work Elem
5	Transportation	12	Title I	23	Music K-12	33	Career/Sch-to-Work Sec
6	Athletic	13	Title V	24	Music Elem	34	Early Childhood Ed
7	Health Services	14	Asst Superintendent	25	Music Sec	35	Health/Phys Education
		15	Asst Superintendent	26	Business Education	36	Guidance Services K-12
		16	Instructional Media Svcs	27	Career & Tech Ed	37	Guidance Services Elem
		17	Chief Operations Officer	28	Technology Education	38	Guidance Services Sec

		18	Chief Academic Officer				
39	Social Studies K-12	49	English/Lang Arts Elem	59	Special Education Elem	69	Academic Assessment
40	Social Studies Elem	50	English/Lang Arts Sec	60	Special Education Sec	70	Research/Development
41	Social Studies Sec	51	Reading K-12	61	Foreign/World Lang K-12	71	Public Information
42	Science K-12	52	Reading Elem	62	Foreign/World Lang Elem	72	Summer School
43	Science Elem	53	Reading Sec	63	Foreign/World Lang Sec	73	Instructional Tech
44	Science Sec	54	Remedial Reading K-12	64	Religious Education K-12	74	Inservice Training
45	Math K-12	55	Remedial Reading Elem	65	Religious Education Elem	75	Marketing/Distributive
46	Math Elem	56	Remedial Reading Sec	66	Religious Education Sec	76	Info Systems
47	Math Sec	57	Bilingual/ELL	67	School Board President	77	Psychological Assess
48	English/Lang Arts K-12	58	Special Education K-12	68	Teacher Personnel	78	Affirmative Action

Paul McGuinness	73,76	Heather Padgett	74
Matthew Wlodarczyk	74	Michelle Villwock	79,286
Theresa Iuliucci	79	Frank Frangella	91
Patrick Murray	274	Douglas Konopelko	286
Chris Hall	295		

Public Schs..Principal	Grd	Prgm	Enr/#Cls	SN	
Bessey Creek Elem Sch 2201 SW Matheson Ave, Palm City 34990 Tyson Villwock	K-5		575 43	19%	772/219-1500 Fax 772/219-1506
Citrus Grove Elem Sch 2527 SW Citrus Blvd, Palm City 34990 Todd Morrow	K-5		672	20%	772/223-2513 Fax 772/223-2535
© Clark Advanced Learning Ctr 2400 SE Salerno Rd, Stuart 34997 Debra Kohuth	10-12		249	20%	772/419-5750 Fax 772/419-5760
Crystal Lake Elem Sch 2095 SW 96th St, Stuart 34997 Brenda Watkins	K-5		569 43	41%	772/219-1525 Fax 772/219-1529
Dr David L Anderson Middle Sch 7000 SE Atlantic Ridge Dr, Stuart 34997 Timothy Aitken	6-8	T	1,066	60%	772/221-7100 Fax 772/221-7149
Felix A Williams Elem Sch 401 NW Baker Rd, Stuart 34994 Deborah Riley	K-5	T	604 50	39%	772/219-1640 Fax 772/219-1646
Hidden Oaks Middle Sch 2801 SW Martin Hwy, Palm City 34990 Jeri Eckler	6-8	V	1,031 55	19%	772/219-1655 Fax 772/219-1663
Hobe Sound Elem Sch 11555 SE Gomez Ave, Hobe Sound 33455 Dianne Memmer-Novak	K-5	T	602 25	57%	772/219-1540 Fax 772/219-1546
© Hope Center for Autism 1695 SE Indian St, Stuart 34997 Shannon Kiess	Spec		33		772/334-3288 Fax 772/872-7229
Indiantown Adult Learning Ctr 15255 SW Jackson St, Indiantown 34956 Mellisa Eversdyke	Adult		120		772/597-3848 Fax 772/597-2865
Indiantown Middle Sch 16303 SW Farm Rd, Indiantown 34956 Jeff Raimann	5-8	TV	632 28	72%	772/597-2146 Fax 772/597-5854
J D Parker Math-Sci-Tech Sch 1010 SE 10th St, Stuart 34996 Christopher Jones	K-5	T	630 45	65%	772/219-1580 Fax 772/219-1583
Jensen Beach Elem Sch 2525 NE Savannah Rd, Jensen Beach 34957 Joan Gibbons	K-5	T	584 35	47%	772/219-1555 Fax 772/219-1558
Jensen Beach High Sch 2875 NW Goldenrod Rd, Jensen Beach 34957 Lori Vogel	9-12	V	1,484	31%	772/232-3500 Fax 772/232-3699
Ⓐ Martin Co Acceleration Academy 742 SW Federal Hwy, Stuart 34994 **Margaret Sharp**	9-12		120		772/924-0162
Martin Co High Sch 2801 S Kanner Hwy, Stuart 34994 Al Fabrizio	9-12	GV	2,178	36%	772/219-1800 Fax 772/219-1821
Murray Middle Sch 4400 SE Murray St, Stuart 34997 Amy Laws	6-8	TV	718 58	51%	772/219-1670 Fax 772/219-1677
Palm City Elem Sch 1951 SW 34th St, Palm City 34990 Robyn Monte	K-5		626 40	24%	772/219-1565 Fax 772/219-1570
Pinewood Elem Sch 5200 SE Willoughby Blvd, Stuart 34997 Jennifer Radcliff	K-5	T	788 39	58%	772/219-1595 Fax 772/219-1603
Port Salerno Elem Sch 3260 SE Lionel Ter, Stuart 34997 Lauren Gifford	K-5	T	783 30	76%	772/219-1610 Fax 772/219-1615

	Grd	Prgm	Enr/#Cls	SN	
Riverbend Academy 11301 SE Tequesta Ter, Tequesta 33469 Gary Sparks	Spec		110		561/744-0211 Fax 561/743-8503
Seawind Elem Sch 3700 SE Seabranch Blvd, Hobe Sound 33455 Birgit Ager	K-5	T	626	58%	772/219-1625 Fax 772/219-1631
South Fork High Sch 10000 SW Bulldog Way, Stuart 34997 Jay Blavatt	9-12	GTV	1,934 100	43%	772/219-1840 Fax 772/219-1860
Ⓐ Spectrum Jr Sr High Sch 800 SE Bahama Ave, Stuart 34994 Janice Mills	6-12	GTV	76 9	64%	772/219-1870 Fax 772/219-1873
Ⓐ Stuart Cmty High Sch 1150 SE St Joseph's Ave, Stuart 34996 Melissa Eversdyke	9-12	G	62		772/219-1296
Stuart Middle Sch 575 SE Georgia Ave, Stuart 34994 Ebony Jarrett	6-8	TV	871 63	42%	772/219-1685 Fax 772/219-1690
© Treasure Coast Classical Acad 3340 SE Federal Hwy # 223, Stuart 34997 **Janine Swearingin**	K-6		550		772/783-3680
Warfield Elem Sch 15260 SW 150th St, Indiantown 34956 Ivy Menken	K-4	T	739 36	77%	772/597-2551 Fax 772/597-2119
Willoughby Learning Center 5150 SE Willoughby Blvd, Stuart 34997 Laura Husnander	Spec	T	35 12	50%	772/219-1515 Fax 772/219-1519

MARTIN CATHOLIC SCHOOLS

- **Diocese of Palm Beach Ed Off** PID: 02231700
  Listing includes only schools located in this county. See District Index for location of Diocesan Offices.

Catholic Schs..Principal	Grd	Prgm	Enr/#Cls	SN	
Hope Rural Sch 15929 SW 150th St, Indiantown 34956 Sr Martha Rohde	PK-5		121 7		772/597-2203 Fax 772/597-2259
St Joseph Sch 1200 SE 10th St, Stuart 34996 Stacy McNerney	PK-8		268 25		772/287-6975 Fax 772/287-4733

MARTIN PRIVATE SCHOOLS

Private Schs..Principal	Grd	Prgm	Enr/#Cls	SN	
Bridges Montessori Sch 51 SE Central Pkwy, Stuart 34994 Sally Padgett	PK-6		130		772/221-9490 Fax 772/221-9787
Community Christian Academy 777 SE Salerno Rd, Stuart 34997 L Lawson	PK-12		264 20		772/288-7227 Fax 772/600-2728
First Baptist Christian Sch 201 SW Ocean Blvd, Stuart 34994 Alli Blackwell	K-8		164 9		772/287-5161 Fax 772/287-7735
Hobe Sound Christian Academy 11460 SE Gomez Ave, Hobe Sound 33455 Brent Jones	PK-12		240 20		772/546-5534 Fax 772/545-1454
Redeemer Lutheran Sch 2450 SE Ocean Blvd, Stuart 34996 Jim Essig	PK-8		300 15		772/286-0932 Fax 772/287-0434

79	Student Personnel	91	Safety/Security	275	Response To Intervention	298	Grant Writer/Ptnrships
80	Driver Ed/Safety	92	Magnet School	277	Remedial Math K-12	750	Chief Innovation Officer
81	Gifted/Talented	93	Parental Involvement	280	Literacy Coach	751	Chief of Staff
82	Video Services	95	Tech Prep Program	285	STEM	752	Social Emotional Learning
83	Substance Abuse Prev	97	Chief Infomation Officer	288	Digital Learning		
84	Erate	98	Chief Technology Officer	288	Common Core Standards		Other School Types
85	AIDS Education	270	Character Education	294	Accountability	Ⓐ	= Alternative School
88	Alternative/At Risk	271	Migrant Education	295	Network System	©	= Charter School
89	Multi-Cultural Curriculum	273	Teacher Mentor	296	Title II Programs	Ⓜ	= Magnet School
90	Social Work	274	Before/After Sch	297	Webmaster	Ⓨ	= Year-Round School

School Programs
A = Alternative Program
G = Adult Classes
M = Magnet Program
T = Title I Schoolwide
V = Career & Tech Ed Programs

Social Media
 = Facebook
 = Twitter

New Schools are shaded
New Superintendents and Principals are bold
Personnel with email addresses are underscored

Samaritan Center	1-8	12	772/287-4123	
1490 SE Cove Rd, Stuart 34997		1	Fax 772/283-4623	
Barbara Testa				
The Pine Sch	K-12	375	772/675-7005	
12350 SE Federal Hwy, Hobe Sound 33455		38	Fax 772/220-9149	
Binney Caffrey			🅕 🅣	

MIAMI-DADE COUNTY

MIAMI-DADE PUBLIC SCHOOLS

- **Miami-Dade Co Public Sch Dist** PID: 00185155   305/995-1000
  1450 NE 2nd Ave, Miami 33132   Fax 305/995-1488

Schools: 467 \ **Teachers:** 20,884 \
Students: 350,101 \ **Special Ed Students:** 35,329 \ **LEP Students:** 73,561
\ **College-Bound:** 79% \ **Ethnic:** Asian 1%, African American 22%, Hispanic
70%, Caucasian 7% \ **Exp:** $172 (Low) \ **Poverty:** 21% \ **Title I:** $142,632,832
\ **Special Education:** $144,862,000 \ **Bilingual Education:** $70,391,000 \
Open-Close: 08/19 - 06/03 \ **DTBP:** $191 (High) \ 🅣

Alberto Carvalho	1	Ron Steiger	2,19
Carl Nicoleau	3,15	Jaime Torrens	3
John Whitehead	3,15,91	Valtena Brown	3,15,17
Angie Kasselakis	4	Orlando Alonso	5
George Nunez	6	Brenda Wilder	7
Dr David Moore	8,15	Maria Izquierdo	8,18,69,294
Iraida Mendez-Cartaya	11,15,298	Dr Magaly Abrahante	12,15,34,72
Joyce Castro	15,68	Lissette Alves	15,288
Luis Diaz	15	Patricia Fernandez	15,68
Raul Perez	15	Robert Gornto	15,30
Steffond Cone	15	Dr Sylvia Diaz	15,16,73
Tiffanie Pauline	15	Vivian Pardo	15
Richard Benvenuti	16	Mabel Morales	20
Bryan Petorak	23	Dr Lupe Diaz	27,30,31
Marisol Diaz	34,46	Robert Brazofsky	39
Dr Ava Rosales	44	Michelle White	45
Silvia Aday	47	Vanessa De La Pena	49
Karen Spigler	50	Melba Brito	57,61
Ava Goldman	58,77	Perla Hantman	67
Jose Dotres	68	Gisela Feild	69,70
Daisy Gonzalez-Diego	71	John Schuster	71
Eugene Baker	73,76,295	Deborah Montilla	79
Dr Lisette Rodriguez	81	Edwin Lopez	91
Victor Ferrante	274	Dr Terrence Vaccaro	275
Cristian Carranza	285	Tabitha Fazzino	294

Public Schs..Principal	Grd	Prgm	Enr/#Cls SN	
© Arts Academy of Excellence	6-9		48	786/534-4528
780 Fisherman St, Opa Locka 33054				Fax 786/452-9349
Angela Kemp				
Chapman Partnership ECC North	PK-PK		44	93% 305/329-3057
1550 N Miami Ave, Miami 33136				Fax 305/995-7650
Rita Mallett				
Chapman Partnership ECC South	PK-PK		85	96% 877/994-4357
28205 SW 124th Pl, Homestead 33033				Fax 305/416-7114
Rita Mallett				
Ⓐ Cope Center North	6-12	TV	112	90% 305/836-3300
9950 NW 19th Ave, Miami 33147			40	Fax 305/835-8818
Ebony Dunn				🅣
© Don Soffer Aventura High Sch	9-9		401	786/481-3032
3151 NE 213th St, Aventura 33180				
David McKnight				

Public Schs..Principal	Grd	Prgm	Enr/#Cls SN	
Ⓐ Dorothy M Wallace Cope Center	6-12	T	80	89% 305/233-1044
10225 SW 147th Ter, Miami 33176			22	Fax 305/256-8694
Tammy Edouard				🅣
Ⓐ Dr Marvin Dunn Acad Cmty Educ	9-12	T	70	88% 305/756-2100
8950 NW 2nd Ave, Miami 33150			9	Fax 305/756-2101
Deborah Carter				
Ethel Beckford-Richmond Plc	PK-PK	T	100	305/238-5194
16929 SW 104th Ave, Miami 33157			15	Fax 305/238-0397
Crystal Coffey				🅣
George T Baker Aviation Sch	Voc	G	500	305/871-3143
3275 NW 42nd Ave, Miami 33142			25	Fax 305/871-5840
Ciro Hidalgo				
Hialeah Miami Lakes Adult Ed	Adult		500	305/823-1330
7977 W 12th Ave, Hialeah 33014				Fax 305/828-8929
Alexis Cazanas				
I Prep	PK-12		1,000	305/523-8338
1500 Biscayne Blvd Ste 101A, Miami 33132				Fax 305/523-8393
Alberto Carvalho				
Ⓐ Jan Mann Opp Sch	7-11	TV	130	92% 305/625-0855
16101 NW 44th Ct, Opa Locka 33054			20	Fax 305/625-1605
Jamarv Dunn				
Ⓐ Juvenile Justice Center Sch	6-12	MV	107	20% 305/638-5054
⊘ 3300 NW 27th Ave Ste 1144, Miami 33142			20	Fax 305/636-6615
Alberto Iber				
Miami Beach Adult Ed	Adult		210	305/531-0451
1424 Drexel Ave, Miami Beach 33139			10	Fax 305/531-2352
Chantal Osborne				
Ⓐ Miami MacArthur South Sch	6-12	TV	120	87% 305/258-7200
13990 SW 264th St, Naranja 33032			50	Fax 305/279-7201
Daryl Branton				
Miami-Dade Online Academy	K-12		292	305/995 1267
1501 NE 2nd Ave Ste 336, Miami 33132				Fax 305/523-0736
Dr Sylvia Diaz				
Ⓐ Pace Center for Girls-Miami	8-11		51	20% 786/254-2460
1400 NW 36th St, Miami 33142				
Sherry Giordano				
Ⓐ Phoenix Acad of Excellence N	6-8		401	786/865-1346
© 13301 NW 24th Ave, Miami 33167				
Latoya Robinson				
South Dade Skills Center	Adult	V	750	305/247-7839
28300 SW 152nd Ave, Homestead 33033			15	Fax 305/247-2375
Dr Susana Mauri				
South Dade Technical College	Adult	V	700	305/248-5723
109 NE 8th St, Homestead 33030			5	Fax 305/247-8072
Dr Susana Mauri				
The English Center Adult Sch	Adult	V	3,000	305/445-7731
3501 SW 28th St, Miami 33133			32	Fax 305/441-2150
Yamila Carballo				
Thena Crowder Early Chldhd	PK-PK		69	96% 305/836-0012
757 NW 66th St, Miami 33150			10	Fax 305/836-6910
Dr Ann Marie Sasseville				

- **Miami-Dade-Central Region** PID: 00186355   305/499-5050
  5005 NW 112th Ave, Doral 33178   Fax 305/499-5051

John Pace	1	Dr Jacques Bentolila	2,73
Jason Jackson	44*	Dr Janice Cruse-Sanchez	68

Public Schs..Principal	Grd	Prgm	Enr/#Cls SN	
© Academy Int'l Education CS	K-8	T	656	66% 305/883-3900
1080 La Baron Dr, Miami Springs 33166				Fax 305/883-3901
Vera Hirsh				
ADA Merritt K-8 Center	K-8		763	35% 305/326-0791
660 SW 3rd St, Miami 33130				Fax 305/326-0927
Carmen Garcia				

1	Superintendent	8	Curric/Instruct K-12	19	Chief Financial Officer
2	Bus/Finance/Purchasing	9	Curric/Instruct Elem	20	Art K-12
3	Buildings And Grounds	10	Curric/Instruct Sec	21	Art Elem
4	Food Service	11	Federal Program	22	Art Sec
5	Transportation	12	Title I	23	Music K-12
6	Athletic	13	Title V	24	Music Elem
7	Health Services	14	Asst Superintendent	25	Music Sec
		15	Asst Superintendent	26	Business Education
		16	Instructional Media Svcs	27	Career & Tech Ed
		17	Chief Operations Officer	28	Technology Education
		18	Chief Academic Officer		

29	Family/Consumer Science	39	Social Studies K-12	49	English/Lang Arts Elem
30	Adult Education	40	Social Studies Elem	50	English/Lang Arts Sec
31	Career/Sch-to-Work K-12	41	Social Studies Sec	51	Reading K-12
32	Career/Sch-to-Work Elem	42	Science K-12	52	Reading Elem
33	Career/Sch-to-Work Sec	43	Science Elem	53	Reading Sec
34	Early Childhood Ed	44	Science Sec	54	Remedial Reading K-12
35	Health/Phys Education	45	Math K-12	55	Remedial Reading Elem
36	Guidance Services K-12	46	Math Elem	56	Remedial Reading Sec
37	Guidance Services Elem	47	Math Sec	57	Bilingual/ELL
38	Guidance Services Sec	48	English/Lang Arts K-12	58	Special Education K-12

59	Special Education Elem	69	Academic Assessment
60	Special Education Sec	70	Research/Development
61	Foreign/World Lang K-12	71	Public Information
62	Foreign/World Lang Elem	72	Summer School
63	Foreign/World Lang Sec	73	Instructional Tech
64	Religious Education K-12	74	Inservice Training
65	Religious Education Elem	75	Marketing/Distributive
66	Religious Education Sec	76	Info Systems
67	School Board President	77	Psychological Assess
68	Teacher Personnel	78	Affirmative Action

School / Address / Principal	Grades	Prog	Enroll	Staff	%	Phone	Fax
Agenoria Paschal-Olinda ES 5536 NW 21st Ave, Miami 33142 Cisely Scott	PK-5	T	415	10	93%	305/633-0308	Fax 305/635-8919 [Twitter]
© Alpha Charter Sch-Excellence 1223 SW 4th St, Miami 33135 Isabel Navas	K-5	T	318		99%	305/643-2132	Fax 305/642-3717
Arcola Lake Elem Sch 1037 NW 81st St, Miami 33150 Cynthia Hannah	PK-5	T	540	21	96%	305/836-2820	Fax 305/694-2340
Auburndale Elem Sch 3255 SW 6th St, Miami 33135 Ania Marti	PK-5	T	824	50	89%	305/445-3587	Fax 305/446-4709
Banyan Elem Sch 3060 SW 85th Ave, Miami 33155 **Vanessa Faraldo**	PK-5	T	332	40	76%	305/221-4011	Fax 305/222-4602
© Beacon College Prep Sch 2750 NW 135th St, Opa Locka 33054 Patrick Evans	K-5	T	418		97%	786/353-6109	
Benjamin Franklin K-8 Ctr 13100 NW 12th Ave, North Miami 33168 **Diana Loubeau**	PK-8	T	557	32	91%	305/681-3547	Fax 305/769-2845
Booker T Washington SHS 1200 NW 6th Ave, Miami 33136 William Aristide	9-12	TV	939	30	87%	305/324-8900	Fax 305/324-4676 [Twitter]
© Bridgeprep Acad Greater Miami 137 NE 19th St, Miami 33132 Mitzie Ortiz	K-5		458		2%	786/477-4372	Fax 786/446-8714
© Bridgeprep Acad Interamerican 621 Beacom Blvd, Miami 33135 Guillermo Gonzalez	K-6	T	192		2%	305/643-4833	Fax 305/643-4832
© Bridgeprep Acad-N Miami Beach 18801 NE 22nd Ave, Miami 33180 Ana Natali	K-8		505			305/570-4048	
Broadmoor Elem Sch 3401 NW 83rd St, Miami 33147 Dr Omar Riaz	PK-5	T	478	50	97%	305/691-0861	Fax 305/696-7908
Brownsville Middle Sch 4899 NW 24th Ave, Miami 33142 Marcus Miller	6-8	TV	374	41	94%	305/633-1481	Fax 305/635-8702
Carrie P Meek-Westview K-8 Ctr 2101 NW 127th St, Miami 33167 Marchel Woods	PK-8	T	692	32	95%	305/688-9641	Fax 305/769-0166
Charles R Drew K-8 Center 1775 NW 60th St, Miami 33142 Raymond Sands	PK-6	T	442	34	96%	305/691-8021	Fax 305/691-3960
Charles R Hadley Elem Sch 8400 NW 7th St, Miami 33126 **Reandra Jordan**	PK-5	T	874	90	81%	305/261-3719	Fax 305/267-2984 [Twitter]
© Charter HS of the Americas 970 W Flagler St 984, Miami 33130 **Ms Sanchez**	9-12		90			305/643-4888	
Citrus Grove Elem Sch 2121 NW 5th St, Miami 33125 Jennifer Savigne	PK-5	T	916		93%	305/642-4141	Fax 305/649-3789 [Twitter]
Citrus Grove Middle Sch 2153 NW 3rd St, Miami 33125 Cory Rodriguez	6-8	TV	740	60	96%	305/642-5055	Fax 305/642-9349 [Twitter]
Coconut Grove Elem Sch 3351 Matilda St, Miami 33133 **J Ordana Schneider**	PK-5	T	449	21	37%	305/445-7876	Fax 305/443-6748
Comstock Elem Sch 2420 NW 18th Ave, Miami 33142 Orna Dumeus	PK-5	T	536	30	97%	305/635-7341	Fax 305/636-1740
Coral Gables Preparatory Acad 105 Minorca Ave, Coral Gables 33134 Jeanette Sierra-Funcia	PK-8	T	979	34	41%	305/448-1731	Fax 305/442-2075
Coral Gables Sr High Sch 450 Bird Rd, Coral Gables 33146 Adolfo Costa	9-12	GTV	3,231	176	70%	305/443-4871	Fax 305/447-5896 [Twitter]
Coral Park Elem Sch 1225 SW 97th Ave, Miami 33174 Aileen Vega	PK-5	T	1,056	32	73%	305/221-5632	Fax 305/227-5734
Coral Terrace Elem Sch 6801 SW 24th St, Miami 33155 Eva Ravelo	PK-5	T	441	25	94%	305/262-8300	Fax 305/267-1526 [Twitter]
Coral Way K-8 Center 1950 SW 13th Ave, Miami 33145 **Barbara Martin**	PK-8	T	1,252	51	76%	305/854-0515	Fax 305/285-9632
D A Dorsey Technical College 7100 NW 17th Ave, Miami 33147 Angela Thomas-DuPree	Adult	AV	1,000	30		305/693-2490	Fax 305/691-7492
David Fairchild Elem Sch 5757 SW 45th St, Miami 33155 Lucy Amengual	PK-5	T	592	25	34%	305/665-5483	Fax 305/669-5401
Ⓜ Design & Architecture Sr HS 4001 NE 2nd Ave, Miami 33137 Ana Alvarez-Arimon	9-12	ATV	497	29	38%	305/573-7135	Fax 305/573-8253
© Doral Academy Charter High Sch [130] 11100 NW 27th St, Doral 33172 **Francisco Jimenez**	9-12	T	1,800	43	58%	305/597-9950	Fax 305/477-6762
© Doral Academy Charter Mid Sch [130] 2601 NW 112th Ave, Doral 33172 Carlos Ferralls	6-8	T	1,465		54%	305/591-0020	Fax 305/591-9251
© Doral Academy K-8-Technology [130] 2525 NW 112th Ave, Doral 33172 Yvette Tamargo	K-8		1,200			305/591-0020	Fax 305/919-2001
© Doral Perf Arts & Ent Academy [130] 11100 NW 27th St, Doral 33172 Carlos Ferralls	9-12	T	403		49%	305/591-0020	Fax 305/591-9251
© Downtown Doral Chart Upper Sch 8390 NW 53rd St, Miami 33166 **Wilhelm Lapica**	6-10		1,200			305/569-2223	
© Downtown Doral Charter ES 8390 NW 53rd St, Miami 33166 Jeannette Isenberg	PK-3		421		24%	305/569-2223	Fax 305/569-2226
© Downtown Miami Charter Sch [133] 305 NW 3rd Ave, Miami 33128 Amanda Padierne	K-6	T	618		91%	305/579-2112	Fax 305/579-2115
Dr H W Mack-W Little River K-8 2450 NW 84th St, Miami 33147 Kimula Oce	PK-8	T	387	23	93%	305/691-6491	Fax 305/693-1960 [Twitter]
Dr Rolando Espinosa K-8 Center 11250 NW 86th St, Doral 33178 Martha Munoz	PK-8	T	1,192		41%	305/889-5757	Fax 305/889-5758
Dr Toni Bilbao Prep Academy 8905 NW 114th Ave, Doral 33178 Tracey Crews	PK-3		597			305/863-5750	Fax 305/883-5530
E W F Stirrup Elem Sch 330 NW 97th Ave, Miami 33172 Naomi Simon	PK-5	T	930	50	78%	305/226-7001	Fax 305/220-6737
Earlington Hgts Elem Sch 4750 NW 22nd Ave, Miami 33142 Jackson Nicolas	PK-5	T	446	24	99%	305/635-7505	Fax 305/634-4973 [Twitter]
© Early Beginnings Acad-Civic CT 1411 NW 14th Ave, Miami 33125 **Tiffanie Pauline**	Spec		117			305/325-1080	Fax 305/325-1044
© Early Beginnings Acad-N Shore 985 NW 91st St, Miami 33150 Makeesha Coleman	Spec		88	6	6%	305/835-9006	Fax 305/696-1688
Edison Park K-8 Center 500 NW 67th St, Miami 33150 Carla Patrick	PK-8	T	492	27	92%	305/758-3658	Fax 305/758-5732

79 Student Personnel	91 Safety/Security	275 Response To Intervention	298 Grant Writer/Ptnrships	**School Programs**	**Social Media**
80 Driver Ed/Safety	92 Magnet School	277 Remedial Math K-12	750 Chief Innovation Officer	A = Alternative Program	f = Facebook
81 Gifted/Talented	93 Parental Involvement	280 Literacy Coach	751 Chief of Staff	G = Adult Classes	t = Twitter
82 Video Services	95 Tech Prep Program	285 STEM	752 Social Emotional Learning	M = Magnet Program	
83 Substance Abuse Prev	97 Chief Infomation Officer	286 Digital Learning		T = Title I Schoolwide	
84 Erate	98 Chief Technology Officer	288 Common Core Standards	**Other School Types**	V = Career & Tech Ed Programs	
85 AIDS Education	270 Character Education	294 Accountability	Ⓐ = Alternative School		
88 Alternative/At Risk	271 Migrant Education	295 Network System	© = Charter School	New Schools are shaded	
89 Multi-Cultural Curriculum	273 Teacher Mentor	296 Title II Programs	Ⓜ = Magnet School	New Superintendents and Principals are bold	
90 Social Work	274 Before/After Sch	297 Webmaster	Ⓨ = Year-Round School	Personnel with email addresses are underscored	

Emerson Elem Sch 8001 SW 36th St, Miami 33155 **Kristin Hayes**	PK-5	T	357 26	87%	305/264-5757 Fax 305/267-2476
Eneida Massas Hartner Elem Sch 401 NW 29th St, Miami 33127 Tangela Goa	PK-5	T	416 40	98%	305/573-8181 Fax 305/571-2511
Eugenia B Thomas K-8 Center 5950 NW 114th Ave, Doral 33178 Debbie Saumell	PK-8	T	1,637	43%	305/592-7914 Fax 305/463-7241
Everglades K-8 Center 8375 SW 16th St, Miami 33155 Ramon Garrigo	PK-8	T	987 40	80%	305/264-4154 Fax 305/261-8179
Fairlawn Elem Sch 444 SW 60th Ave, Miami 33144 Heather Tyler	PK-5	GT	601 30	92%	305/261-8880 Fax 305/267-9174
Flagami Elem Sch 920 SW 76th Ave, Miami 33144 Maria Mason	PK-5	T	377 30	88%	305/261-2031 Fax 305/267-2980
Ⓜ Frances S Tucker Elem Sch 3500 S Douglas Rd, Miami 33133 Fredrelette Pickett	PK-5	T	318 24	87%	305/567-3533 Fax 305/529-0409
Frederick Douglass Elem Sch 314 NW 12th St, Miami 33136 Yolanda Ellis	K-5	T	259	94%	305/371-4687 Fax 305/350-7590
George W Carver Elem Sch 238 Grand Ave, Coral Gables 33133 Patricia Fairclough	PK-5	T	438 25	67%	305/443-5286 Fax 305/567-3531
Ⓜ George W Carver Middle Sch 4901 Lincoln Dr, Miami 33133 Shelley Stroleny	6-8		1,008 32	27%	305/444-7388 Fax 305/529-5148
Georgia Jones-Ayers Mid Sch 1331 NW 46th St, Miami 33142 **Bernard Edwards**	6-8	ATV	423 60	85%	305/634-9787 Fax 305/638-8254
© Green Springs High Sch [131] 3555 NW 7th St, Miami 33125 Enrique Palma	9-12	T	459	10%	305/720-2996 Fax 305/541-5559
Henry M Flagler Elem Sch 5222 NW 1st St, Miami 33126 Zulema Lamazares	PK-5	T	696 30	90%	305/443-2529 Fax 305/448-8508
Henry S Reeves Elem Sch 2005 NW 111th St, Miami 33167 Julian Gibbs	PK-8	T	537 42	93%	305/953-7243 Fax 305/953-7251
Henry S West Laboratory Sch 5300 Carillo St, Miami 33146 Barbara Soto Pujadas	K-5		314 22	24%	305/661-7661 Fax 305/662-2935
Hialeah Elem Sch 550 E 8th St, Hialeah 33010 Rosa Iglesias	PK-5	T	633 35	94%	305/888-6709 Fax 305/884-6503
Holmes Elem Sch 1175 NW 67th St, Miami 33150 Ottolita Thompson	PK-5	T	437	94%	305/836-3421 Fax 305/696-4517
Horace Mann Middle Sch 8950 NW 2nd Ave, El Portal 33150 Kevin Lawrence	6-8	ATV	594	92%	305/757-9537 Fax 305/754-0724
© Integrated Sci Asian Cult Acad [130] 301 Westward Dr, Miami 33166 Eleonora Cuesta	K-5	T	216	50%	305/863-8030 Fax 305/863-8031
© International Studies Chart HS [130] 807 SW 25th Ave, Miami 33135 **Vitoriano Rodriguez**	6-12	AT	413	96%	305/643-2955 Fax 305/643-2956
Intl Studies Prep Academy 1570 Madruga Ave, Coral Gables 33146 Alina Diaz-Blanco	9-12	T	362	52%	305/663-7200 Fax 305/661-0196
Ⓜ Ipreparatory Academy 1500 Biscayne Blvd Ste 129, Miami 33132 Dr Alberto Carvalho	PK-12	T	859	35%	305/995-1929 Fax 305/523-8405
Ⓜ Itech at Thomas Edison Ed Ctr 6101 NW 2nd Ave, Miami 33127 Lashinda Moore	9-12	T	202	84%	305/762-5000 Fax 305/757-2219
Jesse J McCrary Elem Sch 514 NW 77th St, Miami 33150 Trellany Parrish-Gay	PK-5	AT	503 35	88%	305/754-7531 Fax 305/756-8768
John I Smith K-8 Center 10415 NW 52nd St, Miami 33178 Genaro Navarro	PK-8	T	1,756 50	49%	305/406-0220 Fax 305/406-0225
Jose De Diego Middle Sch 3100 NW 5th Ave, Miami 33127 April Williams	6-8	ATV	878 55	91%	305/573-7229 Fax 305/573-6415
© Just Arts/Mngmnt Charter MS 2450 NW 97th Ave, Doral 33172 Eleonora Cuesta	K-7	T	1,200	47%	305/597-9999 Fax 305/591-2669
Kelsey Pharr Elem Sch 2000 NW 46th St, Miami 33142 **Reandra Jordan**	PK-5	AT	354 30	97%	305/633-0429 Fax 305/634-8487
Kensington Park Elem Sch 711 NW 30th Ave, Miami 33125 Susana Suarez	PK-5	T	1,083 57	91%	305/649-2811 Fax 305/642-9346
Key Biscayne K-8 Center 150 W McIntyre St, Key Biscayne 33149 Silvia Tarafa	PK-8		1,241 30	7%	305/361-5418 Fax 305/361-8120
Kinloch Park Elem Sch 4275 NW 1st St, Miami 33126 Kisa Humphrey	PK-5	T	608 34	89%	305/445-1351 Fax 305/567-3530
Kinloch Park Middle Sch 4340 NW 3rd St, Miami 33126 **Sylvia Coto-Gonzalez**	6-8	TV	716 45	94%	305/445-5467 Fax 305/445-3110
© KIPP Sunrise Academy 6745 NW 23rd Ave, Miami 33147 **Monica Kress**	K-5		171		305/694-4162
Lakeview Elem Sch 1290 NW 115th St, Miami 33167 Sandra Banky	PK-5	T	403 36	96%	305/757-1535 Fax 305/754-0657
© Larkin Sch for Health Sciences 5996 SW 70th St, Miami 33143	6-8		330		
Law Enforcement Offr Mem HS 300 NW 2nd Ave, Miami 33128 Tony Ullivarri	9-12	T	402	82%	305/371-0400 Fax 305/371-0401
Lenora Braynon Smith Elem Sch 4700 NW 12th Ave, Miami 33127 Shawntai Dalton	PK-5	AT	453 40	96%	305/635-0873 Fax 305/637-1124
Liberty City Elem Sch 1855 NW 71st St, Miami 33147 Adrian Rogers	PK-5	T	382 32	98%	305/691-8532 Fax 305/696-7842
Lillie C Evans K-8 Center 1895 NW 75th St, Miami 33147 Bridgette Tate-Wyche	PK-8	T	379 36	98%	305/691-4973 Fax 305/691-4867
© Lincoln-Marti CHS of Americas 970 W Flagler St, Miami 33130 Barbara Sanchez	9-10	T	111	30%	305/325-1001 Fax 305/324-9934
© Lincoln-Marti CS-Little Havana 970 W Flagler St, Miami 33130 Nataly Parra	K-8	T	757 35	77%	305/325-1001 Fax 305/324-9934
Lindsey Hopkins Tech Ed Center 750 NW 20th St, Miami 33127 Nyce Daniel	Voc	G	800 100		305/324-6070 Fax 305/545-6397
Lorah Park Elem Sch 5160 NW 31st Ave, Miami 33142 Atunya Walker	PK-5	T	319 35	95%	305/633-1424 Fax 305/636-3075
Ludlam Elem Sch 6639 SW 74th St, South Miami 33143 Dr Georgette Menocal	PK-5	T	324 28	65%	305/667-5551 Fax 305/666-3070

1 Superintendent	8 Curric/Instruct K-12	19 Chief Financial Officer	29 Family/Consumer Science	39 Social Studies K-12	49 English/Lang Arts Elem	59 Special Education Elem	69 Academic Assessment
2 Bus/Finance/Purchasing	9 Curric/Instruct Elem	20 Art K-12	30 Adult Education	40 Social Studies Elem	50 English/Lang Arts Sec	60 Special Education Sec	70 Research/Development
3 Buildings And Grounds	10 Curric/Instruct Sec	21 Art Elem	31 Career/Sch-to-Work K-12	41 Social Studies Sec	51 Reading K-12	61 Foreign/World Lang K-12	71 Public Information
4 Food Service	11 Federal Program	22 Art Sec	32 Career/Sch-to-Work Elem	42 Science K-12	52 Reading Elem	62 Foreign/World Lang Elem	72 Summer School
5 Transportation	12 Title I	23 Music K-12	33 Career/Sch-to-Work Sec	43 Science Elem	53 Reading Sec	63 Foreign/World Lang Sec	73 Instructional Tech
6 Athletic	13 Title V	24 Music Elem	34 Early Childhood Ed	44 Science Sec	54 Remedial Reading K-12	64 Religious Education K-12	74 Inservice Training
7 Health Services	15 Asst Superintendent	25 Music Sec	35 Health/Phys Education	45 Math K-12	55 Remedial Reading Elem	65 Religious Education Elem	75 Marketing/Distributive
	16 Instructional Media Svcs	26 Business Education	36 Guidance Services K-12	46 Math Elem	56 Remedial Reading Sec	66 Religious Education Sec	76 Info Systems
	17 Chief Operations Officer	27 Career & Tech Ed	37 Guidance Services Elem	47 Math Sec	57 Bilingual/ELL	67 School Board President	77 Psychological Assess
	18 Chief Academic Officer	28 Technology Education	38 Guidance Services Sec	48 English/Lang Arts K-12	58 Special Education K-12	68 Teacher Personnel	78 Affirmative Action

School	Grades	Programs	Enrollment	%	Phone / Fax
Madison Middle Sch, 3400 NW 87th St, Miami 33147, David Ladd	6-8	TV	445 / 65	94%	305/836-2610, Fax 305/696-5249
Ⓜ Maritime & Science Tech Acad, 3979 Rickenbacker Cswy, Miami 33149, Derick McKoy	9-12		1,124 / 50		305/365-6278, Fax 305/361-0996
Ⓒ Mater Acad East Charter Mid HS [130], 998 SW 1st St, Miami 33130, Jenny Aguirre	6-12		343		305/324-6963, Fax 305/324-6966
Ⓒ Mater Acad of Int'l Studies [130], 795 NW 32nd St, Miami 33127, Ileana Melian	K-5	T	537	84%	305/634-0445, Fax 305/634-0446
Ⓒ Mater Academy East Charter ES [130], 450 SW 4th St, Miami 33130, Beatriz Riera	K-5	T	487 / 17	93%	305/324-4667, Fax 305/324-6580
Ⓒ Mater Grove Academy [130], 2805 SW 32nd Ave, Miami 33133, Sheila Caleo	K-8	T	880	5%	305/442-4992, Fax 305/442-4993
Ⓒ Mater International Academy, 3405 NW 27th Ave, Miami 33142, Olga Camarena	K-5		170	96%	305/638-8016, Fax 305/638-8017
Ⓒ Mater International Prep Acad, 795 NW 32nd St, Miami 33127, **Ileana Melian**	6-9		170		305/634-0445, Fax 305/634-0446
Ⓒ Mater Preparatory Academy, 601 NW 12th Ave, Miami 33136, **Judith Marty**	K-8		401		786/648-4580
Maya Angelou Elem Sch, 1850 NW 32nd St, Miami 33142, Donna Lewis	PK-5	AT	712 / 50	95%	305/636-3480, Fax 305/636-3486
Melrose Elem Sch, 3050 NW 35th St, Miami 33142, Sergio Munoz	PK-5	T	589 / 45	95%	305/635-8676, Fax 305/635-4006
Ⓒ Miami Arts Charter Sch, 95 Nortwest 23rd St, Miami 33127, Alfredo De La Rosa	6-12		1,609	2%	305/763-6257, Fax 305/573-5622
Miami Central Sr High Sch, 1781 NW 95th St, Miami 33147, Gregory Bethune	9-12	TV	1,648	87%	305/696-4161, Fax 305/694-3904
Miami Coral Park Sr High Sch, 8865 SW 16th St, Miami 33165, **Scott Weiner**	9-12	AGTV	2,451	79%	305/226-6565, Fax 305/553-4658
Miami Edison Sr High Sch, 6161 NW 5th Ct, Miami 33127, Leon Maycock	9-12	TV	740	84%	305/751-7337, Fax 305/759-4561
Miami Jackson Sr High Sch, 1751 NW 36th St, Miami 33142, Rennina Turner	9-12	AGTV	1,517	84%	305/634-2621, Fax 305/634-7477
Miami Northwestern Sr High Sch, 1100 NW 71st St, Miami 33150, Wallace Aristide	9-12	AGTV	1,498 / 172	83%	305/836-0991, Fax 305/631-4955, f
Miami Senior High Sch, 2450 SW 1st St, Miami 33135, Benny Valdes	9-12	AGTV	2,845	83%	305/649-9800, Fax 305/649-9475
Miami Shores Elem Sch, 10351 NE 5th Ave, Miami Shores 33138, Brenda Swain	PK-5	AT	685 / 60	68%	305/758-5525, Fax 305/756-3805
Miami Springs Elem Sch, 51 Park St, Miami Springs 33166, Sally Hutchings	PK-5	T	399 / 41	77%	305/888-4558, Fax 305/882-0521
Miami Springs Middle Sch, 150 S Royal Poinciana Blvd, Miami Springs 33166, Alina Valero	6-8	ATV	832 / 100	88%	305/888-6457, Fax 305/887-5281
Miami Springs Sr High Sch, 751 Dove Ave, Miami Springs 33166, Edward Smith	9-12	GTV	1,468 / 100	81%	305/885-3585, Fax 305/884-2632
Morningside K-8 Academy, 6620 NE 5th Ave, Miami 33138, Jordana Schneider	PK-8	AT	517 / 41	84%	305/758-6741, Fax 305/751-2980, t
Ⓜ New World School of the Arts, 25 NE 2nd St, Miami 33132, Jason Allen	9-12		489 / 60	36%	305/237-3135, Fax 305/237-3794
Ⓒ North Park High Sch [131], 3400 NW 135th St, Opa Locka 33054, Michael Rivera	9-12	T	375	20%	305/720-2995, Fax 305/953-3289
Orchard Villa Elem Sch, 5720 NW 13th Ave, Miami 33142, Tanya Daly-Barnes	PK-5	T	384 / 27	95%	305/754-0607, Fax 305/754-0929
Paul L Dunbar K-8 Center, 505 NW 20th St, Miami 33127, Maria DeArmas	PK-8	T	354 / 40	96%	305/573-2344, Fax 305/573-8482
Phillis Wheatley Elem Sch, 1801 NW 1st Pl, Miami 33136, Cathy Williams	PK-5	T	236 / 35	99%	305/573-2638, Fax 305/573-2423
Phyllis R Miller Elem Sch, 840 NE 87th St, Miami 33138, Kimberley Emmanuel	PK-5	AT	660 / 36	86%	305/756-3800, Fax 305/756-3804
Ⓒ Pinecrest Academy [130], 10207 W Flagler St, Miami 33174, Victoria Larrauri	K-8	T	494	68%	305/553-9762, Fax 305/553-9763
Poinciana Park Elem Sch, 6745 NW 23rd Ave, Miami 33147, Tania Jones	PK-5	T	306 / 45	91%	305/691-5640, Fax 305/696-8624, t
Ponce De Leon Middle Sch, 5801 Augusto St, Coral Gables 33146, Hebert Penton	6-8	ATV	1,235 / 60	80%	305/661-1611, Fax 305/666-3140
Ⓒ Renaissance CS Elem-Doral [133], 10651 NW 19th St, Doral 33172, Hortensia Torres	K-5		909 / 25	1%	305/591-2225, Fax 305/591-2336
Ⓒ Renaissance CS Mid-Doral [133], 8360 NW 33rd St, Doral 33122, Maria Torres	6-8	T	450 / 5	4%	305/728-4622, Fax 786/401-1978
Riverside Elem Sch, 1190 SW 2nd St, Miami 33130, Erica Respress	PK-5	T	1,155	93%	305/547-1520, Fax 305/547-4102
Rockway Elem Sch, 2790 SW 93rd Ct, Miami 33165, Denise Vigoa	PK-5	T	443 / 24	78%	305/221-1192, Fax 305/223-5794, t
Rockway Middle Sch, 9393 SW 29th Ter, Miami 33165, Josephine Otero	6-8	TV	1,152 / 60	82%	305/221-8212, Fax 305/221-5940
Ronald Reagan-Doral Senior HS, 8600 NW 107th Ave, Doral 33178, Juan Boue	9-12	TV	2,533	45%	305/805-1900, Fax 305/805-1901
Ruben Dario Middle Sch, 350 NW 97th Ave, Miami 33172, Dr Verona McCarthy	6-8	GTV	582 / 60	88%	305/226-0179, Fax 305/559-0919
Santa Clara Elem Sch, 1051 NW 29th Ter, Miami 33127, **Ramses Ancheta**	PK-5		631	98%	305/635-1417, Fax 305/637-1705
Seminole Elem Sch, 121 SW 78th Pl, Miami 33144, Mayra DeLeon	PK-5	T	567 / 30	82%	305/261-7071, Fax 305/262-8740, t
Shadowlawn Elem Sch, 149 NW 49th St, Miami 33127, Gwendolyn Haynes	PK-5	AT	218 / 20	93%	305/758-3673, Fax 305/759-9352
Shenandoah Elem Sch, 1023 SW 21st Ave, Miami 33135, Michelle Coto-Viltre	PK-5	AT	860 / 60	92%	305/643-4433, Fax 305/643-3745
Shenandoah Middle Sch, 1950 SW 19th St, Miami 33145, Bianca Calzadilla	6-8	TV	1,303	89%	305/856-8282, Fax 305/856-7049, t

79 Student Personnel
80 Driver Ed/Safety
81 Gifted/Talented
82 Video Services
83 Substance Abuse Prev
84 Erate
85 AIDS Education
88 Alternative/At Risk
89 Multi-Cultural Curriculum
90 Social Work

91 Safety/Security
92 Magnet School
93 Parental Involvement
95 Tech Prep Program
97 Chief Infomation Officer
98 Chief Technology Officer
270 Character Education
271 Migrant Education
273 Teacher Mentor
274 Before/After Sch

275 Response To Intervention
277 Remedial Math K-12
280 Literacy Coach
285 STEM
286 Digital Learning
288 Common Core Standards
294 Accountability
295 Network System
296 Title II Programs
297 Webmaster

298 Grant Writer/Ptnrships
750 Chief Innovation Officer
751 Chief of Staff
752 Social Emotional Learning

Other School Types
Ⓐ = Alternative School
Ⓒ = Charter School
Ⓜ = Magnet School
Ⓨ = Year-Round School

School Programs
A = Alternative Program
G = Adult Classes
M = Magnet Program
T = Title I Schoolwide
V = Career & Tech Ed Programs

New Schools are shaded
New Superintendents and Principals are bold
Personnel with email addresses are underscored

Social Media
f = Facebook
t = Twitter

Silver Bluff Elem Sch 2609 SW 25th Ave, Miami 33133 **Mayra Barreira**	PK-5	T	459 24	81%	305/856-5197 Fax 305/854-9671
© Slam Charter School Miami [130] 604 NW 12th Ave, Miami 33136 Rey Breto	6-12	T	1,063	87%	305/326-0003 Fax 305/326-0004
© Somerset Academy-Gables [130] 624 Anastasia Ave, Miami 33134 Suzette Ruiz	K-5		478	19%	305/442-8626 Fax 305/442-8627
© Somerset Academy-South Miami [130] 5876 SW 68th St, South Miami 33143 K Guilarte Gil	K-8		422	17%	305/740-0509 Fax 305/740-0510
© Somerset Virtual Acad Mid HS 305 NE 2nd Rd, Homestead 33030 **Alina Lopez**	6-12		100		305/258-7497 Fax 305/258-7498
South Hialeah Elem Sch 265 E 5th St, Hialeah 33010 Linette Tellez	PK-5	T	930 35	95%	305/885-4556 Fax 305/888-7730 📵
South Miami K-8 Center 6800 SW 60th St, South Miami 33143 Lourdes Lopez	PK-8	T	771 30	61%	305/667-8847 Fax 305/665-3217
South Miami Middle Sch 6750 SW 60th St, South Miami 33143 Fabiola Izaguirre	6-8	TV	871 56	57%	305/661-3481 Fax 305/665-6728
South Miami Senior High Sch 6856 SW 53rd St, Miami 33155 Gilberto Bonce	9-12	TV	1,950	81%	305/666-5871 Fax 305/666-6359
Ⓜ Southside Elem Sch 45 SW 13th St, Miami 33130 Annette Degoti	PK-5	T	818 16	63%	305/371-3311 Fax 305/381-6237
Springview Elem Sch 1122 Bluebird Ave, Miami Springs 33166 Catalina Flor	PK-5	I	449 18	58%	305/885-6466 Fax 305/883-8391 📵
© Stellar Leadership Academy 7900 NW 27th Ave F20, Miami 33147 Angel Chaisson	9-12	T	275	11%	305/693-2273 Fax 305/693-8016
Sunset Elem Sch 5120 SW 72nd St, Miami 33143 Dr Marlene Leyte-Vidal	PK-5		1,188 40	15%	305/661-8527 Fax 305/666-2327 📵
Sweetwater Elem Sch 10655 SW 4th St, Miami 33174 Janet Olivera	PK-5	T	578 50	92%	305/559-1101 Fax 305/485-9396
Sylvania Heights Elem Sch 5901 SW 16th St, Miami 33155 Amor Reyes	PK-5	T	501 40	81%	305/266-3511 Fax 305/266-4435
© Theodore & Thelma Gibson CS [130] 1698 & 1682 NW 4th Ave, Miami 33136 Jennifer DeSousa	K-8	T	274 1	98%	305/438-0895 Fax 305/392-0144
Toussaint L'Ouverture Elem Sch 120 NE 59th St, Miami 33137 Lilia Dobao	PK-5	AT	381 35	95%	305/758-2600 Fax 305/751-6764
Van E Blanton Elem Sch 10327 NW 11th Ave, Miami 33150 Pedro Cedeno	PK-5	T	526 31	96%	305/696-9241 Fax 305/693-5375
West Miami Middle Sch 7525 Coral Way, Miami 33155 Katyna Lopez-Martin	6-8	TV	672 50	90%	305/261-8383 Fax 305/267-8204
Wm Turner Tech & Arts HS 10151 NW 19th Ave, Miami 33147 Uwezo Frazier	Voc	GT	1,374	85%	305/691-8324 Fax 305/693-9463
Ⓜ Young Men's Prep Academy 3001 NW 2nd Ave, Miami 33127 Pierre Edouard	6-12	T	216	82%	305/571-1111 Fax 305/571-1112
Ⓜ Young Women's Prep Academy 1150 SW 1st St, Miami 33130 Concepcion Martinez	6-12	T	399 20	62%	305/575-1200 Fax 305/325-8071

● Miami-Dade-North Region PID: 11449960   305/572-2800
733 E 57th St, Hialeah 33013   Fax 305/572-2801

Jose Bueno 1

Public Schs..Principal	Grd	Prgm	Enr/#Cls	SN
Alonzo & Tracy Mourning Sr HS 2601 NE 151st St, N Miami Beach 33160 Christopher Shinn	9-12	T	1,716	57% 305/919-2000 Fax 305/919-2001
Amelia Earhart Elem Sch 5987 E 7th Ave, Hialeah 33013 Lisa Wiggins	PK-5	T	447 32	91% 305/688-9619 Fax 305/769-9038
American Senior High Sch 18350 NW 67th Ave, Hialeah 33015 **Stephen Papp**	9-12	GTV	2,010 110	81% 305/557-3770 Fax 305/557-3771
Andover Middle Sch 121 NE 207th St, Miami 33179 **Rennina Turner**	6-8	T	494	90% 305/654-2727 Fax 305/654-2728 📵
Arch Creek Elem Sch 702 NE 137th St, North Miami 33161 Dr Marie Bazile	PK-5	T	553	87% 305/892-4000 Fax 305/892-4001
© Aventura City of Excellence CS [133] 3333 NE 188th St, Aventura 33180 Julie Alm	K-8		1,025	305/466-1499 Fax 305/466-1339
Aventura Waterways K-8 Center 21101 NE 26th Ave, Miami 33180 Yesenia Aponte	K-8	T	2,134	47% 305/933-5200 Fax 305/933-5201
Barbara Goleman Sr High Sch 14100 NW 89th Ave, Miami Lakes 33018 Manuel Sanchez	9-12	GTV	2,160 210	67% 305/362-0676 Fax 305/827-0249 📵
Barbara Hawkins Elem Sch 19010 NW 37th Ave, Miami Gardens 33056 Rhonda Williams	PK-5	T	285 25	95% 305/624-2615 Fax 305/621-9839 📵
Ben Sheppard Elem Sch 5700 W 24th Ave, Hialeah 33016 Dr Eduardo Tagle	PK-5	T	918 50	91% 305/556-2204 Fax 305/822-0558
Biscayne Elem Sch 800 77th St, Miami Beach 33141 Karen Belusic	PK-5	T	735 35	90% 305/868-7727 Fax 305/864-5543
Biscayne Gardens Elem Sch 560 NW 151st St, Miami 33169 Deborah Riera	PK-5	T	533	93% 305/681-5721 Fax 305/685-8036 📵
Bob Graham Education Center 15901 NW 79th Ave, Miami Lakes 33016 Yecenia Martinez-Lopez	PK-8	T	1,623	58% 305/557-3303 Fax 305/826-5434
Brentwood Elem Sch 3101 NW 191st St, Miami Gardens 33056 **Dr Sharon Jackson**	PK-5	T	552 50	92% 305/624-2657 Fax 305/625-4981
Bunche Park Elem Sch 16001 Bunche Park School Dr, Miami Gardens 33054 Jacqueline Lewis	PK-5	T	384 30	96% 305/621-1469 Fax 305/430-3120 📵
© C G Bethel High Sch 16150 NE 17th Ave, N Miami Beach 33162 Alejandro Madrigal	9-12	T	487	8% 786/629-7053 Fax 305/949-5604
Carol City Elem Sch 4375 NW 173rd Dr, Miami Gardens 33055 Dr Thayla Watkins	PK-5	T	402 40	92% 305/621-0509 Fax 305/620-5638
Carol City Middle Sch 3737 NW 188th St, Miami Gardens 33055 Derek Negron	6-8	ATV	363 200	91% 305/624-2652 Fax 305/623-2955 📵
Charles D Wyche Elem Sch 5241 NW 195th Dr, Miami Gardens 33055 Dr Barbara Johnson	PK-5	T	678 45	88% 305/628-5776 Fax 305/628-5775
© City of Hialeah Educ Academy [130] 2590 W 76th St, Hialeah 33016 Carlos Alvarez	6-12	T	933 12	84% 305/362-4006 Fax 305/362-7006

1	Superintendent	8	Curric/Instruct K-12	19	Chief Financial Officer	29	Family/Consumer Science
2	Bus/Finance/Purchasing	9	Curric/Instruct Elem	20	Art K-12	30	Adult Education
3	Buildings And Grounds	10	Curric/Instruct Sec	21	Art Elem	31	Career/Sch-to-Work K-12
4	Food Service	11	Federal Program	22	Art Sec	32	Career/Sch-to-Work Elem
5	Transportation	12	Title I	23	Music K-12	33	Career/Sch-to-Work Sec
6	Athletic	13	Title V	24	Music Elem	34	Early Childhood Ed
7	Health Services	14	Asst Superintendent	25	Music Sec	35	Health/Phys Education
		15	Asst Superintendent	26	Business Education	36	Guidance Services K-12
		16	Instructional Media Svcs	27	Career & Tech Ed	37	Guidance Services Elem
		17	Chief Operations Officer	28	Technology Education	38	Guidance Services Sec
		18	Chief Academic Officer				

39	Social Studies K-12	49	English/Lang Arts Elem	59	Special Education Elem	69	Academic Assessment
40	Social Studies Elem	50	English/Lang Arts Sec	60	Special Education Sec	70	Research/Development
41	Social Studies Sec	51	Reading K-12	61	Foreign/World Lang K-12	71	Public Information
42	Science K-12	52	Reading Elem	62	Foreign/World Lang Elem	72	Summer School
43	Science Elem	53	Reading Sec	63	Foreign/World Lang Sec	73	Instructional Tech
44	Science Sec	54	Remedial Reading K-12	64	Religious Education K-12	74	Inservice Training
45	Math K-12	55	Remedial Reading Elem	65	Religious Education Elem	75	Marketing/Distributive
46	Math Elem	56	Remedial Reading Sec	66	Religious Education Sec	76	Info Systems
47	Math Sec	57	Bilingual/ELL	67	School Board President	77	Psychological Assess
48	English/Lang Arts K-12	58	Special Education K-12	68	Teacher Personnel	78	Affirmative Action

School / Address / Principal	Grades	Programs	Enroll	%	Phone	Fax
Country Club Middle Sch 18305 NW 75th Pl, Hialeah 33015 **Rafael Crespo**	6-8	T	660	87%	305/820-8800	Fax 305/820-8801
Crestview Elem Sch 2201 NW 187th St, Miami Gardens 33056 Maria Kerr	PK-5	GT	303 30	88%	305/624-1495	Fax 305/628-3198
David Lawrence Jr K-8 Center 15000 Bay Vista Blvd, North Miami 33181 Mary Parton	PK-8	T	1,461	76%	305/354-2600	Fax 305/354-2601
© Doctors CS of Miami Shores 11301 NW 5th Ave, Miami Shores 33168 Douglas Garber \ **Dr C Edward Jackson**	6-12		585 8	1%	305/754-2381	Fax 305/751-5833
© Doral Academy Charter Elem Sch [130] 2450 NW 97th Ave, Doral 33172 Eleonora Cuesta	K-8	T	1,300 29	44%	305/597-9999	Fax 305/591-2669
© Doral Int'l Acad Math & Sci [132] 6700 NW 104th Ave, Miami 33178 Victoria Ramos	K-8	T	853	6%	786/270-2088	Fax 786/221-2238
Dr Frederica Wilson-Skyway ES 4555 NW 206th Ter, Miami Gardens 33055 Dr Linda Whye	PK-5	T	226 52	92%	305/621-5838	Fax 305/621-0919 [t]
Ⓜ Dr Michael M Krop Sr High Sch 1410 NE 215th St, Miami 33179 **Dr Adam Kosnitzky**	9-12	T	2,561	58%	305/652-6808	Fax 305/651-8043
Dr Robert B Ingram Elem Sch 600 Ahmad St, Opa Locka 33054 Cynthia Clay	PK-5	T	378 30	98%	305/688-4605	Fax 305/688-3971
Ernest R Graham K-8 Center 7330 W 32nd Ave, Hialeah 33018 Mayra Alfaro	PK-8	T	1,209	83%	305/825-2122	Fax 305/557-5739
© Excelsior Charter Academy 18200A NW 22nd Ave, Miami Gardens 33056 Janell Ferguson	K-9	T	330	64%	786/565-9188	Fax 305/621-8960
© Excelsior Lang Acad of Hialeah [130] 369 E 10th St, Hialeah 33010 Carolina Alfonso	K-8	T	210	92%	305/879-9004	Fax 305/883-5279 [t]
Fienberg-Fisher K-8 Center 1420 Washington Ave, Miami Beach 33139 Maria Costa	PK-8	T	869	83%	305/531-0419	Fax 305/534-3925
Flamingo Elem Sch 701 E 33rd St, Hialeah 33013 Ileana Sotolongo	PK-5	T	588 48	89%	305/691-5531	Fax 305/835-8525
Fulford Elem Sch 16140 NE 18th Ave, N Miami Beach 33162 Jean Gordon	PK-5	T	519 22	91%	305/949-3425	Fax 305/949-2243
G K Edelman-Sabal Palm ES 17101 NE 7th Ave, Miami 33162 Alicia Costa-DeVito	PK-5	T	611 32	96%	305/651-2411	Fax 305/654-7219
Golden Glades Elem Sch 16520 NW 28th Ave, Miami Gardens 33054 **Crystal Spence**	PK-5	T	211 18	98%	305/624-9641	Fax 305/628-5760
Gratigny Elem Sch 11905 N Miami Ave, Miami 33168 Bisleixis Tejeiro	PK-5	T	503 27	91%	305/681-6685	Fax 305/681-3321
Greynolds Park Elem Sch 1536 NE 179th St, N Miami Beach 33162 Janine Townsley	PK-5	T	725	91%	305/949-2129	Fax 305/949-0899
Henry H Filer Middle Sch 531 W 29th St, Hialeah 33012 John Donohue	6-8	TV	614 82	93%	305/822-6601	Fax 305/822-2063 [t]
Hialeah Gardens Elem Sch 9702 NW 130th St, Hialeah GDNS 33018 Rachel Autler	PK-5	T	1,015 70	83%	305/827-8830	Fax 305/818-7970
Hialeah Gardens Middle Sch 11690 NW 92nd Ave, Hialeah GDNS 33018 **Cynthia Lima**	6-8	T	1,685	82%	305/817-0017	Fax 305/817-0018
Hialeah Gardens Sr High Sch 11700 Hialeah Gardens Blvd, Hialeah 33018 Dr Louis Algaze	9-12	T	2,741	82%	305/698-5000	Fax 305/698-5001
Hialeah Middle Sch 6027 E 7th Ave, Hialeah 33013 Nelson Gonzalez	6-8	TV	910	89%	305/681-3527	Fax 305/681-6225
Hialeah Senior High Sch 251 E 47th St, Hialeah 33013 Heriberto Sanchez	9-12	AGTV	2,086 160	85%	305/822-1500	Fax 305/828-5513
Hialeah-Miami Lakes Sr HS 7977 W 12th Ave, Hialeah 33014 Lisa Garcia	9-12	GTV	1,561	83%	305/823-1330	Fax 305/362-4188 [t]
Hibiscus Elem Sch 18701 NW 1st Ave, Miami 33169 Veronica Bello	PK-5	T	524 24	84%	305/652-3018	Fax 305/654-5700
Highland Oaks Middle Sch 2375 NE 203rd St, Miami 33180 Cheryl Kushi	6-8	TV	989 70	69%	305/932-3810	Fax 305/932-0676
© Hive Preparatory Sch 5855 NW 171st St, Hialeah 33015 Carlos Moreno	K-8	T	730	77%	305/231-4888	Fax 305/231-4881
Hubert O Sibley K-8 Center 255 NW 115th St, Miami 33168 Michael Charlot	PK-8	T	752	92%	305/953-3737	Fax 305/953-5447
© Imater Academy Elem Sch [130] 600 W 20th St, Hialeah 33010 Elizabeth Poveda	K-5	T	670	93%	305/884-6320	
© Imater Academy Middle Sch [130] 651 W 20th St, Hialeah 33010 Teresa Santalo	6-8	T	840	21%	305/802-5722	Fax 305/805-5723
© Imater Prep Academy High Sch [130] 651 W 20th St, Hialeah 33010 Teresa Santalo	9-12	T	922	25%	305/805-5722	Fax 305/805-5723
James H Bright-J W Johnson ES 2530 W 10th Ave, Hialeah 33010 Claudine Winsor	PK-5	T	575 32	95%	305/885-1683	Fax 305/888-7059 [t]
Joella Good Elem Sch 6350 NW 188th Ter, Hialeah 33015 Lizette O'Halloran	PK-5	T	978 40	81%	305/625-2008	Fax 305/628-0460
John F Kennedy Middle Sch 1075 NE 167th St, Miami 33162 Bernard Osborn	6-8	TV	1,033 70	88%	305/947-1451	Fax 305/949-9046
John G DuPuis Elem Sch 1150 W 59th Pl, Hialeah 33012 Lourdes Nunez	PK-5	T	496 40	92%	305/821-6361	Fax 305/825-2433 [t]
Jose Marti Mast 6-12 Academy 5701 W 24th Ave, Hialeah 33016 Jose Enriquez	6-12	AT	931	77%	305/557-5931	Fax 305/556-6917
Lake Stevens Elem Sch 5101 NW 183rd St, Miami Gardens 33055 **Marc Schwam**	PK-5	T	275 20	90%	305/625-6536	Fax 305/624-0437
Lake Stevens Middle Sch 18484 NW 48th Pl, Opa Locka 33055 **Elizabeth Chardon**	6-8	ATV	536 81	92%	305/620-1294	Fax 305/620-1345
Lawton Chiles Middle Sch 8190 NW 197th St, Hialeah 33015 Stephanie Tudor	6-8	T	800 70	76%	305/816-9101	Fax 305/816-9248
© Lba Const & Bus Mgt Charter HS 11093 NW 138th St Unit 207, Hialeah GDNS 33018 Jennifer Jaynes	9-12	V	135		305/822-8455	
© Lincoln-Marti CS-Hialeah 3550 W 84th St, Hialeah 33018 Yaimy Fernandes	K-8	T	342	39%	305/827-8080	Fax 305/827-8004
Linda Lentin K-8 Center 14312 NE 2nd Ct, Miami 33161 Monefe Young	PK-8	T	869 52	91%	305/891-4011	Fax 305/895-0545

---

79 Student Personnel	91 Safety/Security	275 Response To Intervention	298 Grant Writer/Ptnrships	**School Programs**
80 Driver Ed/Safety	92 Magnet School	277 Remedial Math K-12	750 Chief Innovation Officer	A = Alternative Program
81 Gifted/Talented	93 Parental Involvement	280 Literacy Coach	751 Chief of Staff	G = Adult Classes
82 Video Services	95 Tech Prep Program	285 STEM	752 Social Emotional Learning	M = Magnet Program
83 Substance Abuse Prev	97 Chief Infomation Officer	286 Digital Learning		T = Title I Schoolwide
84 Erate	98 Chief Technology Officer	288 Common Core Standards	**Other School Types**	V = Career & Tech Ed Programs
85 AIDS Education	270 Character Education	294 Accountability	Ⓐ = Alternative School	
88 Alternative/At Risk	271 Migrant Education	295 Network System	© = Charter School	**New Schools are shaded**
89 Multi-Cultural Curriculum	273 Teacher Mentor	296 Title II Programs	Ⓜ = Magnet School	**New Superintendents and Principals are bold**
90 Social Work	274 Before/After Sch	297 Webmaster	Ⓨ = Year-Round School	Personnel with email addresses are underscored

Social Media
[f] = Facebook
[t] = Twitter

School	Grades	Media	Enroll	%	Phone
Madie Ives Community Elem Sch 20770 NE 14th Ave, N Miami Beach 33179 <u>Deborah Brinson</u>	PK-8	T	716 100	88%	305/651-3155 Fax 305/770-3740 🅵🅣
Mae Walters Elem Sch 650 W 33rd St, Hialeah 33012 **Mileydis Torrens**	PK-5	T	523 34	91%	305/822-4600 Fax 305/827-4465
Marcus A Milam K-8 Center 6020 W 16th Ave, Hialeah 33012 Anna Hernandez	PK-8	T	895 65	89%	305/822-0301 Fax 305/556-1388 🅣
Mast-Biscayne Bay Campus 3000 NE 151st St Rm 395, Miami 33181 <u>Dr Matthew Welker</u>	9-11		205		305/919-4450 Fax 305/919-4615
© Mater Academy [130] 7700 NW 98th St, Hialeah GDNS 33016 <u>Cecilia Guilarte</u>	K-5	T	1,171 31 .	90%	305/698-9900 Fax 305/698-3822 🅣
© Mater Academy Charter High Sch [130] 7901 NW 103rd St, Hialeah GDNS 33016 Jose Nunez	9-12	T	1,687	81%	305/828-1886 Fax 305/828-6175
© Mater Academy Charter Mid Sch [130] 7901 NW 103rd St, Hialeah GDNS 33016 **Jose Nunez**	6-8	T	1,344 37	86%	305/828-1886 Fax 305/828-6175
© Mater Academy Lakes Mid HS [130] 17300 NW 87th Ave, Hialeah 33015 Rene Rovirosa	6-12	T	1,269	74%	305/698-8000 Fax 305/698-1800
© Mater Academy-Miami Beach [130] 8625 Byron Ave, Miami Beach 33141 <u>Marisol Gomez</u>	K-9	T	547	51%	305/864-2889 Fax 305/864-2890 🅣
© Mater Academy-Mount Sinai [130] 4300 Alton Rd, Miami Beach 33140 <u>Eileen Hernandez</u>	K-5	T	152	35%	305/604-1453 Fax 305/604-1454
© Mater Gardens Elem Mid Academy [130] 9010 NW 178th Ln, Hialeah 33018 Pilar Rives	PK-8	T	205	51%	305/512-9775 Fax 305/512-3708
© Mater Perform Arts & Ent Acad [130] 7901 NW 103rd St, Hialeah GDNS 33016 **Jose Nunez \ Jose Nunez**	6-12	T	193	76%	305/828-1886 Fax 305/828-6175
© Mater Virtual Acad Chart MS HS 17300 NW 87th Ave, Hialeah 33015 **Ofelia Alvarez**	6-12		43		305/495-6846
Meadowlane Elem Sch 4280 W 8th Ave, Hialeah 33012 **Maritza Garcia**	PK-5	T	738 50	90%	305/822-0660 Fax 305/362-9904 🅣
Miami Beach Senior High Sch 2231 Prairie Ave, Miami Beach 33139 Dr Maria Rodriguez	9-12	GTV	2,340	64%	305/532-4515 Fax 305/531-9209
Miami Carol City Senior HS 3301 Miami Gardens Dr, Miami Gardens 33056 Adrena Williams	9-12	AGTV	963 75	82%	305/621-5681 Fax 305/620-8862
© Miami Children's Museum CS [130] 980 MacArthur Cswy, Miami 33132 Cristina Carmona	K-5		292 7	29%	305/373-5437 Fax 305/373-5431
Miami Gardens Elem Sch 4444 NW 195th St, Miami Gardens 33055 Kathleen Louissaint	PK-5	T	265 25	90%	305/625-5321 Fax 305/628-5764 🅣
Miami Lakes Ed Ctr & Tech Clg 5780 NW 158th St, Miami Lakes 33014 Lourdes Diaz	Voc	GT	1,224	78%	305/557-1100 Fax 305/827-9317
Miami Lakes K-8 Center 14250 NW 67th Ave, Miami Lakes 33014 Yanelys Canales	PK-8	T	1,290 36	53%	305/822-7757 Fax 305/557-6595
Miami Lakes Middle Sch 6425 Miami Lakeway N, Miami Lakes 33014 Maria Medina	6-8	TV	1,313 64	84%	305/557-3900 Fax 305/828-6753
Miami Norland Sr High Sch 1193 NW 193rd St, Miami 33169 **Ronald Redmon**	9-12	TV	1,813	81%	305/653-1416 Fax 305/651-6175
Myrtle Grove K-8 Center 3125 NW 176th St, Opa Locka 33056 <u>Apryle Kirnes</u>	PK-8	T	438 20	94%	305/624-8431 Fax 305/627-5232
N Edelcup-Sunny Isles Bch K-8 201 182nd Dr, Sunny Isl Bch 33160 **Melissa Mesa**	K-8	T	2,097	45%	305/933-6161 Fax 305/933-6162
Nathan B Young Elem Sch 14120 NW 24th Ave, Opa Locka 33054 <u>Tonya Dillard</u>	PK-5	T	347 32	94%	305/685-7204 Fax 305/688-6465 🅣
Natural Bridge Elem Sch 1650 NE 141st St, North Miami 33181 <u>Frank MacBride</u>	PK-5	T	675 60	91%	305/891-8649 Fax 305/899-9695 🅣
Nautilus Middle Sch 4301 N Michigan Ave, Miami Beach 33140 Rene Bellmas	6-8	T	1,032 52	63%	305/532-3481 Fax 305/532-8906
Norland Elem Sch 19340 NW 8th Ct, Miami Gardens 33169 Christina Ravelo	PK-5	T	678 34	91%	305/652-6074 Fax 305/651-4553
Norland Middle Sch 1235 NW 192nd Ter, Miami Gardens 33169 Ronald Redmond	6-8	TV	877 75	87%	305/653-1210 Fax 305/654-1237
North Beach Elem Sch 4100 Prairie Ave, Miami Beach 33140 Melanie Fishman	PK-5		1,072 48	30%	305/531-7666 Fax 305/674-8425
North County K-8 Center 3250 NW 207th St, Opa Locka 33056 Melissa Mesa	PK-8	T	400 28	91%	305/624-9648 Fax 305/620-2372
North Dade Ctr for Modern Lang 1840 NW 157th St, Miami Gardens 33054 Maria Castaigne	1-5	T	361 20	79%	305/625-3885 Fax 305/625-6069
North Dade Middle Sch 1840 NW 157th St, Miami Gardens 33054 Kharim Armand	6-8	ATV	489	93%	305/624-8415 Fax 305/628-2954
© North Gardens High Sch [131] 4692 NW 183rd St, Miami Gardens 33055 Porshia Jones	9-12	T	267	27%	786/528-6308 Fax 305/621-1611
North Glade Elem Sch 5000 NW 177th St, Miami Gardens 33055 Ann Lewis	PK-5	T	229 33	95%	305/624-3608 Fax 305/621-3606
North Hialeah Elem Sch 4251 E 5th Ave, Hialeah 33013 <u>Carlos Salcedo</u>	PK-5	T	517 39	87%	305/681-4611 Fax 305/688-6652 🅣
North Miami Beach Sr High Sch 1247 NE 167th St, Miami 33162 <u>Randy Milliken</u>	9-12	GTV	1,441	80%	305/949-8381 Fax 305/949-0491
ⓨ North Miami Elem Sch 655 NE 145th St, North Miami 33161 **Dr Deborah Darbonne**	PK-5	MT	502 44	93%	305/949-6156 Fax 305/949-3153
North Miami Middle Sch 700 NE 137th St, North Miami 33161 Miriame Stewart	6-8	TV	910	86%	305/891-5611 Fax 305/891-4057
North Miami Senior High Sch 13110 NE 8th Ave, North Miami 33161 <u>Patrick Lacouty</u>	9-12	GTV	2,343	84%	305/891-6590 Fax 305/895-1788
North Twin Lakes Elem Sch 625 W 74th Pl, Hialeah 33014 <u>Jose Fernandez</u>	PK-5	T	501 36	90%	305/822-0721 Fax 305/558-1697
Norwood Elem Sch 19810 NW 14th Ct, Miami 33169 <u>Dr Kevin Williams</u>	PK-5	T	462 35	86%	305/653-0068 Fax 305/654-5702
Oak Grove Elem Sch 15640 NE 8th Ave, N Miami Beach 33162 <u>Joyce Jones</u>	PK-5	T	595 40	94%	305/945-1511 Fax 305/949-4090
Ojus Elem Sch 18600 W Dixie Hwy, Miami 33180 <u>Marta Mejia</u>	PK-5	T	900	76%	305/931-4881 Fax 305/933-8592 🅣

1	Superintendent	19	Chief Financial Officer	39	Social Studies K-12	59	Special Education Elem	69	Academic Assessment
2	Bus/Finance/Purchasing	8	Curric/Instruct K-12	29	Family/Consumer Science	49	English/Lang Arts Elem	60	Special Education Sec	70	Research/Development
3	Buildings And Grounds	9	Curric/Instruct Elem	20	Art K-12	40	Social Studies Elem	50	English/Lang Arts Sec	61	Foreign/World Lang K-12	71	Public Information
4	Food Service	10	Curric/Instruct Sec	21	Art Elem	30	Adult Education	41	Social Studies Sec	51	Reading K-12	62	Foreign/World Lang Elem	72	Summer School
5	Transportation	11	Federal Program	22	Art Sec	31	Career/Sch-to-Work K-12	42	Science K-12	52	Reading Elem	63	Foreign/World Lang Sec	73	Instructional Tech
6	Athletic	12	Title I	23	Music K-12	32	Career/Sch-to-Work Elem	43	Science Elem	53	Reading Sec	64	Religious Education K-12	74	Inservice Training
7	Health Services	13	Title V	24	Music Elem	33	Career/Sch-to-Work Sec	44	Science Sec	54	Remedial Reading K-12	65	Religious Education Elem	75	Marketing/Distributive
		15	Asst Superintendent	25	Music Sec	34	Early Childhood Ed	45	Math K-12	55	Remedial Reading Elem	66	Religious Education Sec	76	Info Systems
		16	Instructional Media Svcs	26	Business Education	35	Health/Phys Education	46	Math Elem	56	Remedial Reading Sec	67	School Board President	77	Psychological Assess
		17	Chief Operations Officer	27	Career & Tech Ed	36	Guidance Services K-12	47	Math Sec	57	Bilingual/ELL	68	Teacher Personnel	78	Affirmative Action
		18	Chief Academic Officer	28	Technology Education	37	Guidance Services Elem	48	English/Lang Arts K-12	58	Special Education K-12				
						38	Guidance Services Sec							

School	Grd	Prgm	Enr/#Cls	SN	Phone
Palm Lakes Elem Sch 7450 W 16th Ave, Hialeah 33014 **Jacqueline Arias-Gonzalez**	PK-5	T	622 40	83%	305/823-6970 Fax 305/828-6136 🇹
Palm Springs Elem Sch 6304 E 1st Ave, Hialeah 33013 Roxana Herrera	PK-5	T	546 40	86%	305/822-0911 Fax 305/828-5802
Palm Springs Middle Sch 1025 W 56th St, Hialeah 33012 Leonard Torres	6-8	ATV	926 72	93%	305/821-2460 Fax 305/828-3987
Palm Springs North Elem Sch 17615 NW 82nd Ave, Hialeah 33015 Maribel Dotres	PK-5	T	1,040	73%	305/821-4631 Fax 305/825-0422
Parkview Elem Sch 17631 NW 20th Ave, Miami Gardens 33056 Crystal Spence	PK-5	T	291 22	94%	305/625-1591 Fax 305/621-5027 🇹
Parkway Elem Sch 1320 NW 188th St, Miami 33169 Maria Fernandez	PK-5	T	283 17	92%	305/653-0066 Fax 305/654-5701 🇹
Rainbow Park Elem Sch 15355 NW 19th Ave, Opa Locka 33054 Robin Armstrong	PK-5	T	303 22	95%	305/688-4631 Fax 305/685-0693
Robert J Renick Ed Center 2201 NW 207th St, Miami Gardens 33056 Emirce Guerra	Spec	T	160 27	95%	305/624-1171 Fax 305/625-5830
Ruth Broad/Bay Harbor K-8 Ctr 1155 93rd St, Bay Harbor Is 33154 Scott Saperstein	PK-8	T	1,368	37%	305/865-7912 Fax 305/864-1396 🇹
Scott Lake Elem Sch 1160 NW 175th St, Miami 33169 Lakesha Wilson-Rochell	PK-5	T	448 23	90%	305/624-1443 Fax 305/625-2567 🇹
©Slam North Campus 16551 NE 16th Ave, Miami 33162 Edward Gorriz	6-8		269		305/333-5702 Fax 305/326-0004
©South Florida Autism Chtr Sch 18305 NW 75th Pl, Hialeah 33015 Dr Tamara Moodie-Ramdeen	Spec	T	212	45%	305/823-2700 Fax 305/823-2705
South Pointe Elem Sch 1050 4th St, Miami Beach 33139 Jorge Mazon	PK-5	T	549 27	50%	305/531-5437 Fax 305/532-6096
Spanish Lake Elem Sch 7940 NW 194th St, Hialeah 33015 **Milko Brito**	PK-5	T	1,530	78%	305/816-0300 Fax 305/816-0301 🇹
©The Seed School of Miami [129] 1901 NW 127th St, Miami 33167 Kara Locke	6-8	T	221	27%	855/818-7333 Fax 305/503-7033
Thomas Jefferson Middle Sch 525 NW 147th St, Miami 33168 Alexander Santoyo	6-8	TV	320 40	92%	305/681-7481 Fax 305/688-5912
Treasure Island Elem Sch 7540 E Treasure Dr, North Bay Vlg 33141 Dalia Villar	PK-5	T	555 35	78%	305/865-3141 Fax 305/864-1729
Twin Lakes Elem Sch 6735 W 5th Pl, Hialeah 33012 Ivette Bernal-Pino	PK-5	T	419 45	87%	305/822-0770 Fax 305/824-0915 🇹
V Boone-Highland Oaks Elem Sch 20500 NE 24th Ave, Miami 33180 Julio Fong	PK-5	T	585 50	52%	305/931-1770 Fax 305/936-5722
West Hialeah Gardens Elem Sch 11990 NW 92nd Ave, Hialeah GDNS 33018 Sharon Gonzalez	PK-5	T	1,233	89%	305/818-4000 Fax 305/818-4001
West Lakes Preparatory Academy 13835 NW 97th Ave, Hialeah 33018 Richelle Thomas	PK-6		308		305/826-6104 Fax 305/826-6105
Westland Hialeah Sr High Sch 4000 W 18th Ave, Hialeah 33012 Giovanna Blanco	9-12	T	1,619	88%	305/818-3000 Fax 305/818-3002
William J Bryan Elem Sch 1201 NE 125th St, North Miami 33161 Milagros Maytin-Miret	PK-5	T	716 70	90%	305/891-0602 Fax 305/895-4708
©Youth Co-op Charter Sch 7700 W 20th Ave, Hialeah 33016 Maritza Aragon	K-12	T	1,177 29	78%	305/819-8855 Fax 305/826-9212

- **Miami-Dade-South Region** PID: 00187244   305/252-3041
  18180 SW 122nd Ave, Miami 33177   Fax 305/251-2198

Barbara Mendizabal 1

Public Schs..Principal	Grd	Prgm	Enr/#Cls	SN	Phone
©Academir Charter Sch Prep 19185 SW 127th Ave, Miami 33177 Dr M Kristina Ledo	K-5		850	73%	305/964-7542 Fax 305/964-7458
©Academir Charter School Middle 5800 SW 135th Ave, Miami 33183 Karla Rodriguez	6-8	T	361	31%	305/967-8492 Fax 305/392-1928
©Academir Charter School-West 14880 SW 26th St, Miami 33185 Olivia Bernal	K-5	T	619	52%	305/485-9911 Fax 305/485-9944
©Academir Preparatory Academy 5800 SW 135th Ave, Miami 33183 Antonio Cejas	K-5		440		305/967-8492 Fax 305/392-1928
©Advantage Acad-Math & Sci 855 Waterstone Way, Homestead 33033 Nancy Roque	K-8	T	1,029	64%	305/248-6206 Fax 305/248-6208
Air Base K-8 Ctr for Int'l Ed 12829 SW 272nd St, Homestead 33032 Raul Calzadilla	PK-8	T	1,117 43	60%	305/258-3676 Fax 305/258-7241
©Archimedean Academy 12425 SW 72nd St, Miami 33183 Jose Martinez	K-5	T	633	47%	305/279-6572 Fax 305/675-8448
©Archimedean Middle Conserv Sch 12425 SW 72nd St, Miami 33183 Afshin Mirhaj	6-8	T	327	50%	305/279-6572 Fax 305/675-8448
©Archimedean Upper Conserv Sch 12425 SW 72nd St, Miami 33183 Afshin Mirhaj	9-12	T	328	57%	305/279-6572 Fax 305/675-8448
Arvida Middle Sch 10900 SW 127th Ave, Miami 33186 Angela Holbrook	K-8	ATV	337 80	57%	305/385-7144 Fax 305/383-9472
Avocado Elem Sch 16969 SW 294th St, Homestead 33030 Jacqua Little	PK-3	T	544 40	93%	305/247-4942 Fax 305/246-9603
Bel-Aire Elem Sch 10205 SW 194th St, Cutler Bay 33157 Prudence Hill	PK-5	T	278 35	94%	305/233-5401 Fax 305/256-3101 🇹
©Ben Gamla Charter Sch [130] 11155 SW 112th Ave Bldg 1, Miami 33176 **Tina Frometa**	K-8	T	251	44%	305/596-6266 Fax 305/596-6964
Bent Tree Elem Sch 4861 SW 140th Ave, Miami 33175 Emily Falcon	PK-5	T	422 30	78%	305/221-0461 Fax 305/551-2661
ⓂBiotech-Richmond Heights HS 15020 SW 102nd Ave, Miami 33176 Daniel Mateo	9-12	T	409	64%	786/573-5353 Fax 786/573-5350
Blue Lakes Elem Sch 9250 SW 52nd Ter, Miami 33165 Aida Marrero	PK-5	T	521 48	62%	305/271-7411 Fax 305/279-5103
Bowman-Ashe-Doolin K-8 Acad 6601 SW 152nd Ave, Miami 33193 Lisset Vazquez-Rios	PK-8	T	949 56	87%	305/386-6667 Fax 305/385-6408
©Bridgeprep Academy South 10700 SW 56th St, Miami 33165 Yvette Rodriguez	K-8		637	1%	305/271-3109 Fax 305/271-5315

79	Student Personnel	91	Safety/Security	275	Response To Intervention	298 Grant Writer/Ptnrships
80	Driver Ed/Safety	92	Magnet School	277	Remedial Math K-12	750 Chief Innovation Officer
81	Gifted/Talented	93	Parental Involvement	280	Literacy Coach	751 Chief of Staff
82	Video Services	95	Tech Prep Program	285	STEM	752 Social Emotional Learning
83	Substance Abuse Prev	97	Chief Infomation Officer	286	Digital Learning	
84	Erate	98	Chief Technology Officer	288	Common Core Standards	**Other School Types**
85	AIDS Education	270	Character Education	294	Accountability	Ⓐ = Alternative School
88	Alternative/At Risk	271	Migrant Education	295	Network System	Ⓒ = Charter School
89	Multi-Cultural Curriculum	273	Teacher Mentor	296	Title II Programs	Ⓜ = Magnet School
90	Social Work	274	Before/After Sch	297	Webmaster	Ⓨ = Year-Round School

School Programs
A = Alternative Program
G = Adult Classes
M = Magnet Program
T = Title I Schoolwide
V = Career & Tech Ed Programs

Social Media
🇫 = Facebook
🇹 = Twitter

New Schools are shaded
New Superintendents and Principals are bold
Personnel with email addresses are underscored

School	Grades		Enroll	%	Phone
© Bridgeprep Academy-Vlg Green 13300 SW 120th St, Miami 33186 Patty Garcia	K-8		704	3%	305/253-8775
Ⓨ Brucie Ball Education Center 11001 SW 76th St, Miami 33173 Dr Amrita Prakash	Spec	MT	365 8	57%	305/514-5100 Fax 305/447-3761
Calusa Elem Sch 9580 W Calusa Club Dr, Miami 33186 Suzet Hernandez	PK-5	T	832 48	55%	305/385-0589 Fax 305/383-3829 🇹
Campbell Drive K-8 Center 15790 SW 307th St, Homestead 33033 Thelma Fornell	PK-8	GT	1,044 25	96%	305/245-0270 Fax 305/247-7903 🇹
Caribbean K-8 Center 11990 SW 200th St, Miami 33177 Maria Calvet-Cuba	PK-8	T	751 48	92%	305/233-7131 Fax 305/238-7082
© Chambers High Sch 698 N Homestead Blvd, Homestead 33030 Daniel Walke	9-12		513	9%	305/909-6307 Fax 305/248-2913
Christina M Eve Elem Sch 16251 SW 99th St, Miami 33196 Lidia Gonzalez	PK-5	T	746 40	59%	305/383-9392 Fax 305/380-1919
Claude Pepper Elem Sch 14550 SW 96th St, Miami 33186 Annette Diaz	PK-5	T	562 42	69%	305/386-5244 Fax 305/382-7150
Ⓜ Coconut Palm K-8 Academy 24400 SW 124th Ave, Homestead 33032 Dr Carmen Jones-Carey	K-8	T	1,410	92%	305/257-0500 Fax 305/257-0501
Colonial Drive Elem Sch 10755 SW 160th St, Miami 33157 Laura Tennant	K-5	T	295 17	94%	305/238-2392 Fax 305/232-4674 🇹
Coral Reef Elem Sch 7955 SW 152nd St, Palmetto Bay 33157 Christina Guerra	PK-5	T	881 31	37%	305/235-1464 Fax 305/254-3725
© Coral Reef Montessori Acad CS 10853 SW 216th St, Miami 33170 Lucy Golden	K-8		511 7	17%	305/255-0064 Fax 305/255-4085
Ⓜ Coral Reef Senior High Sch 10101 SW 152nd St, Miami 33157 Thomas Ennis	9-12	TV	3,413 120	45%	305/232-2044 Fax 305/252-3454 📘
Ⓜ Ctr for Int'l Educ-Cambridge 900 NE 23rd Ave, Homestead 33033 Lisa Bradshaw	9-9	T	65	79%	305/248-7911 Fax 305/248-3518
Cutler Bay Middle Sch 19400 Gulfstream Rd, Miami 33157 Ignacio Rodriguez	6-8	ATV	831	87%	305/235-4761 Fax 305/254-3746
Cutler Bay Senior High Sch 8601 SW 212th St, Cutler Bay 33189 Lucas Dela Torre	9-12	ATV	467 40	62%	305/235-1581 Fax 305/234-8071
Cutler Ridge Elem Sch 20210 Coral Sea Rd, Miami 33189 Adrienne Mullings	PK-5	T	499 36	79%	305/235-4611 Fax 305/232-6740 🇹
Cypress K-8 Center 5400 SW 112th Ct, Miami 33165 Eduardo Alonso	PK-6	T	320 35	83%	305/271-1611 Fax 305/279-3622 🇹
Dante B Fascell Elem Sch 15625 SW 80th St, Miami 33193 Margaret Ferrarone	PK-5	T	475 44	89%	305/380-1901 Fax 305/380-1912
Devon Aire K-8 Center 10501 SW 122nd Ave, Miami 33186 Brian Hamilton	PK-8	T	1,466 43	53%	305/274-7100 Fax 305/270-1826 📘
Dr Carlos J Finlay Elem Sch 851 SW 117th Ave, Miami 33184 Marie Orth-Sanchez	PK-5	T	536 40	84%	305/552-7122 Fax 305/480-7652
Dr Edward Whigham Elem Sch 21545 SW 87th Ave, Miami 33189 Kathryn Guerra	PK-5	T	758 48	82%	305/234-4840 Fax 305/234-4837
Dr Gilbert L Porter Elem Sch 15851 SW 112th St, Miami 33196 Raul Gutierrez	PK-5	T	675 68	70%	305/382-0792 Fax 305/383-2761
Dr Henry E Perrine Acad 8851 SW 168th St, Palmetto Bay 33157 Carla Rivas	K-5	T	677	70%	305/235-2442 Fax 305/253-2442 🇹
Dr Manuel Barreiro Elem Sch 5125 SW 162nd Ave, Miami 33185 Maritza Correa	PK-5	T	700	68%	305/229-4800 Fax 305/229-4801 📘🇹
Dr William A Chapman Elem Sch 27190 SW 140th Ave, Homestead 33032 Carzell Morris	PK-5	T	534 30	95%	305/245-1055 Fax 305/245-1187
Ethel K Beckham Elem Sch 4702 SW 143rd Ct, Miami 33175 Cecilia Sanchez	K-5	T	766 25	70%	305/222-8161 Fax 305/222-4900 🇹
© Everglades Preparatory Academy [132] 2251 E Mowry Dr, Homestead 33033 **Aida Marrero**	6-12	T	820	76%	786/601-1969 Fax 305/230-0254
Felix Varela Sr High Sch 15255 SW 96th St, Miami 33196 Nery Fins	9-12	T	2,413 110	68%	305/752-7900 Fax 305/386-8987
Florida City Elem Sch 364 NW 6th Ave, Florida City 33034 Rachelle Surrancy	PK-5	T	767 45	94%	305/247-4676 Fax 305/248-8317
Frank C Martin K-8 Center 14250 Boggs Dr, Miami 33176 Felicia Joseph	PK-8	T	1,068	65%	305/238-3688 Fax 305/232-4068 🇹
G Holmes Braddock Sr High Sch 3601 SW 147th Ave, Miami 33185 Allen Breeding	9-12	GTV	3,102 204	76%	305/225-9729 Fax 305/221-3312 🇹
Gateway Environmental K-8 LC 955 SE 18th Ave, Homestead 33035 Tiffany Anderson-Dorse	PK-8	T	1,669	90%	305/257-6000 Fax 305/257-6001
Glades Middle Sch 9451 SW 64th St, Miami 33173 Cynthia Valdes-Garcia	6-8	TV	825 50	69%	305/271-3342 Fax 305/271-0402
Gloria M Floyd Elem Sch 12650 SW 109th Ave, Miami 33176 Mayte Dovale	PK-5	T	484 60	66%	305/255-3934 Fax 305/234-0484
Goulds Elem Sch 23555 SW 112th Ave, Homestead 33032 Alonza Pendergrass	K-5	T	347	94%	305/257-4400 Fax 305/257-4401
Greenglade Elem Sch 3060 SW 127th Ave, Miami 33175 Dr Maria Tercilla	PK-5	T	483 34	78%	305/223-5330 Fax 305/222-8141
Gulfstream Elem Sch 20900 SW 97th Ave, Miami 33189 Marybel Baldessari	PK-5	T	699 53	84%	305/235-6811 Fax 305/254-1721
Hammocks Middle Sch 9889 Hammocks Blvd, Miami 33196 Deborah Leal	6-8	TV	690	77%	305/385-0896 Fax 305/382-0861
Herbert A Ammons Middle Sch 17990 SW 142nd Ave, Miami 33177 Maria Costa	6-8	TV	1,064 40	49%	305/971-0158 Fax 305/971-0179
Homestead Middle Sch 650 NW 2nd Ave, Homestead 33030 Contessa Bryant	6-8	TV	616 50	92%	305/247-4221 Fax 305/247-1098 🇹
Homestead Senior High Sch 2351 SE 12th Ave, Homestead 33034 **John Galardi**	9-12	TV	2,050	89%	305/245-7000 Fax 305/247-5757
Howard D McMillan Middle Sch 13100 SW 59th St, Miami 33183 Hilca Thomas	6-8	TV	1,015 80	77%	305/385-6877 Fax 305/387-9641
Howard Drive Elem Sch 7750 SW 136th St, Miami 33156 Deanna Dalby	PK-5	T	514 30	42%	305/235-1412 Fax 305/256-3105

#		#		#		#		#		#		#	
1	Superintendent	8	Curric/Instruct K-12	19	Chief Financial Officer	29	Family/Consumer Science	39	Social Studies K-12	49	English/Lang Arts Elem	59	Special Education Elem	69	Academic Assessment
2	Bus/Finance/Purchasing	9	Curric/Instruct Elem	20	Art K-12	30	Adult Education	40	Social Studies Elem	50	English/Lang Arts Sec	60	Special Education Sec	70	Research/Development
3	Buildings And Grounds	10	Curric/Instruct Sec	21	Art Elem	31	Career/Sch-to-Work K-12	41	Social Studies Sec	51	Reading K-12	61	Foreign/World Lang K-12	71	Public Information
4	Food Service	11	Federal Program	22	Art Sec	32	Career/Sch-to-Work Elem	42	Science K-12	52	Reading Elem	62	Foreign/World Lang Elem	72	Summer School
5	Transportation	12	Title I	23	Music K-12	33	Career/Sch-to-Work Sec	43	Science Elem	53	Reading Sec	63	Foreign/World Lang Sec	73	Instructional Tech
6	Athletic	13	Title V	24	Music Elem	34	Early Childhood Ed	44	Science Sec	54	Remedial Reading K-12	64	Religious Education K-12	74	Inservice Training
7	Health Services	15	Asst Superintendent	25	Music Sec	35	Health/Phys Education	45	Math K-12	55	Remedial Reading Elem	65	Religious Education Elem	75	Marketing/Distributive
		16	Instructional Media Svcs	26	Business Education	36	Guidance Services K-12	46	Math Elem	56	Remedial Reading Sec	66	Religious Education Sec	76	Info Systems
		17	Chief Operations Officer	27	Career & Tech Ed	37	Guidance Services Elem	47	Math Sec	57	Bilingual/ELL	67	School Board President	77	Psychological Assess
		18	Chief Academic Officer	28	Technology Education	38	Guidance Services Sec	48	English/Lang Arts K-12	58	Special Education K-12	68	Teacher Personnel	78	Affirmative Action

School	Grades	Prog	Enroll	%	Phone	Fax	SM
© Int'l Studies Charter Mid Sch [130] 807 SW 25th Ave, Miami 33135 Victoriano Rodriguez	6-12	T	311	96%	305/643-2955	Fax 305/643-2956	
Irving Beatrice Peskoe K-8 Ctr 29035 SW 144th Ave, Homestead 33033 Madelyn Hernandez	PK-8		900 50		305/242-8340	Fax 305/242-8351	
Jack D Gordon Elem Sch 14600 Country Walk Dr, Miami 33186 Maileen Ferrer	PK-5	T	979 73	73%	305/234-4805	Fax 305/234-4815	t
Jane Roberts K-8 Center 14850 Cottonwood Cir, Miami 33185 Milagro Arango	PK-8	T	811 40	65%	305/220-8254	Fax 305/226-8345	
Joe Hall Elem Sch 1901 SW 134th Ave, Miami 33175 Cathay Abreu	PK-5	T	450 40	74%	305/223-9823	Fax 305/220-9758	
John A Ferguson Sr High Sch 15900 SW 56th St, Miami 33185 Rafael Villalobos	9-12	TV	4,341	65%	305/408-2700	Fax 305/408-6487	
Jorge Mas Canosa Middle Sch 15735 SW 144th St, Miami 33196 Elio Falcon	6-8	T	1,718	78%	305/252-5900	Fax 305/252-5901	
Kendale Elem Sch 10693 SW 93rd St, Miami 33176 Aryam Alvarez-Garcia	PK-5	T	504 33	56%	305/274-2735	Fax 305/274-4792	t
Kendale Lakes Elem Sch 8000 SW 142nd Ave, Miami 33183 Martha Jaureguizar	PK-5	T	757	78%	305/385-2575	Fax 305/386-2718	
Kendall Square K-8 Center 9235 SW 169th Pl, Miami 33196 Carmen Fuentes	K-2		34		305/382-6830	Fax 305/383-0352	
Kenwood K-8 Center 9300 SW 79th Ave, Miami 33156 **Rudy Rodriguez**	PK-8	T	1,096	58%	305/271-5061	Fax 305/273-2132	
© Keys Gate Charter High Sch [133] 2325 SE 28th Ave, Homestead 33035 Rodney Hull	9-12	T	835	3%	786/272-9600	Fax 786/272-9602	
© Keys Gate Charter Sch [133] 2325 SE 28th Ave, Homestead 33035 Corinne Baez	7-8		450		786/272-9600	Fax 305/230-1347	
Lamar Louise Curry Middle Sch 15750 SW 47th St, Miami 33185 Jean Baril	6-8	T	1,202	75%	305/222-2775	Fax 305/229-1521	
Laura Saunders Elem Sch 505 SW 8th St, Homestead 33030 Barbara Leveille-Brown	PK-5	T	598 36	97%	305/247-3933	Fax 305/247-8522	t
Leewood K-8 Center 10343 SW 124th St, Miami 33176 Bart Christie	PK-8		772 25	30%	305/233-7430	Fax 305/256-3104	t
Leisure City K-8 Center 14950 SW 288th St, Homestead 33033 Kenneth Williams	PK-8	T	1,067 46	97%	305/247-5431	Fax 305/247-5179	t
© Lincoln-Marti CS-Intl Campus 103 E Lucy St, Florida City 33034 Barbara Sanchez	K-6	T	286	80%	305/242-3330	Fax 305/242-3331	
Mandarin Lakes K-8 Academy 12225 SW 280th St, Homestead 33032 Cadian Collman	K-8	T	910	96%	305/257-0377	Fax 305/257-0378	
Marjory Stoneman Douglas ES 11901 SW 2nd St, Miami 33184 Moraima Almeida-Perez	PK-5	T	857	78%	305/226-4356	Fax 305/553-0001	
© Mater Academy Cutler Bay [130] 22025 SW 87th Ave, Cutler Bay 33190 Brenda Cruz	PK-8		150	49%	305/969-5989	Fax 305/969-5990	
Ⓜ Mays Conservatory of Arts 11700 SW 216th St, Miami 33170 Martin Reid	6-12	TV	600 40	87%	305/233-2300	Fax 305/378-4705	
Ⓜ Medical Acad-Science Tech 1220 NW 1st Ave, Homestead 33030 Lisa Noffo	9-12	T	731	66%	305/257-4500	Fax 305/257-4501	
Ⓜ Miami Arts 6-12 Zelda Glazer 15015 SW 24th St, Miami 33185 Dr Miguel Balsera	6-12	T	1,564	65%	305/485-2323	Fax 305/485-2324	
© Miami Cmty Charter Elem Sch 101 S Redland Rd, Florida City 33034 Maria Alba	K-5	T	529	95%	305/245-2552	Fax 305/245-2527	
© Miami Cmty Charter High Sch 18720 SW 352nd St, Florida City 33034 Stephany Papili	9-12	T	206	82%	786/243-9981	Fax 786/217-6804	
© Miami Cmty Charter Middle Sch 18720 SW 352nd St, Florida City 33034 Jila Rezaie	6-8	T	287	91%	786/243-9981	Fax 786/217-6804	
Miami Heights Elem Sch 17661 SW 117th Ave, Miami 33177 Renita Lee	PK-5	T	821 80	90%	305/238-3602	Fax 305/238-0991	
Miami Killian Sr High Sch 10655 SW 97th Ave, Miami 33176 Magda Pereira	9-12	GTV	1,627	66%	305/271-3311	Fax 305/270-9142	t
Miami Palmetto Sr High Sch 7460 SW 118th St, Pinecrest 33156 Victoria Dobbs	9-12	AGTV	2,779	42%	305/235-1360	Fax 305/378-9724	
Miami Southridge Sr High Sch 19355 SW 114th Ave, Miami 33157 Humberto Miret	9-12	GTV	1,883	83%	305/238-6110	Fax 305/253-4456	
Miami Sunset Sr High Sch 13125 SW 72nd St, Miami 33183 John Lux	9-12	AGTV	1,292	79%	305/385-4255	Fax 305/385-6458	
Neva King Cooper Education Ctr 151 NW 5th St, Homestead 33030 Tracy Roos	Spec	T	99 16	83%	305/247-4307	Fax 305/248-8517	
Norma Butler Bossard Elem Sch 15950 SW 144th St, Miami 33196 Concepcion Santana	PK-5	T	1,116	69%	305/254-5200	Fax 305/254-5201	
Oliver Hoover Elem Sch 9050 Hammocks Blvd, Miami 33196 Mercy Aguilar	PK-5	T	705	73%	305/385-4382	Fax 305/380-9609	
Olympia Heights Elem Sch 9797 SW 40th St, Miami 33165 Victoria Bourland	PK-5	T	393 35	90%	305/221-3821	Fax 305/221-5195	
© Palm Glades Preparatory Acad [132] 22655 SW 112th Ave, Miami 33170 **Laura Ferreira**	6-12	T	200	74%	786/272-2269	Fax 786/446-8956	
Palmetto Elem Sch 12401 SW 74th Ave, Pinecrest 33156 Eric Torres	PK-5		612 30	25%	305/238-4306	Fax 305/254-7774	t
Palmetto Middle Sch 7351 SW 128th St, Pinecrest 33156 Jesus Gonzalez	6-8	TV	1,031 68	38%	305/238-3911	Fax 305/233-4849	
Paul W Bell Middle Sch 11800 NW 2nd St, Miami 33182 Ingrid Soto	6-8	T	431 72	86%	305/220-2075	Fax 305/229-0798	
Pine Lake Elem Sch 16700 SW 109th Ave, Miami 33157 Crystal Coffey	PK-5	T	409 37	95%	305/233-7018	Fax 305/233-4042	
Pine Villa Elem Sch 21799 SW 117th Ct, Miami 33170 Elianeys Basulto	PK-5	T	394	98%	305/258-5366	Fax 305/258-5848	
© Pinecrest Acad ES-South Campus [130] 15130 SW 80th St, Miami 33193 Elaine Clemente	K-5	T	751	59%	305/386-0800	Fax 305/386-6298	
© Pinecrest Cove Academy [130] 4301 SW 107th Ave, Miami 33165 Susie Dopico	K-8	T	947	58%	305/480-2097	Fax 305/480-2098	

Legend:

79 Student Personnel	91 Safety/Security	275 Response To Intervention
80 Driver Ed/Safety	92 Magnet School	277 Remedial Math K-12
81 Gifted/Talented	93 Parental Involvement	280 Literacy Coach
82 Video Services	95 Tech Prep Program	285 STEM
83 Substance Abuse Prev	97 Chief Information Officer	286 Digital Learning
84 Erate	98 Chief Technology Officer	288 Common Core Standards
85 AIDS Education	270 Character Education	294 Accountability
88 Alternative/At Risk	271 Migrant Education	295 Network System
89 Multi-Cultural Curriculum	273 Teacher Mentor	296 Title II Programs
90 Social Work	274 Before/After Sch	297 Webmaster

298 Grant Writer/Ptnrships
750 Chief Innovation Officer
751 Chief of Staff
752 Social Emotional Learning

Other School Types
Ⓐ = Alternative School
© = Charter School
Ⓜ = Magnet School
Ⓨ = Year-Round School

School Programs
A = Alternative Program
G = Adult Classes
M = Magnet Program
T = Title I Schoolwide
V = Career & Tech Ed Programs

Social Media
f = Facebook
t = Twitter

New Schools are shaded
New Superintendents and Principals are bold
Personnel with email addresses are underscored

School	Grades		Enroll	%	Phone
Pinecrest Elem Sch 10250 SW 57th Ave, Pinecrest 33156 Lynn Zaldua	PK-5		1,000 40	18%	305/667-5579 Fax 305/662-7163
© Pinecrest Glades Academy 15250 SW 8th Way, Miami 33194 Carrie Montano	K-5		619	55%	305/299-6949
© Pinecrest Prep Middle/High Sch [130] 14901 SW 42nd St, Miami 33185 Betty Nunez	6-12		525		305/559-8583 Fax 305/559-8584
© Pinecrest Preparatory Academy [130] 14301 SW 42nd St, Miami 33175 Ana Diaz	K-5	T	585	61%	305/207-1027 Fax 305/207-1897
Redland Elem Sch 24501 SW 162nd Ave, Homestead 33031 Adrian Montes	PK-5	T	747 50	89%	305/247-8141 Fax 305/242-4698
Redland Middle Sch 16001 SW 248th St, Homestead 33031 Gregory Beckford	6-8	ATV	497 52	90%	305/247-6112 Fax 305/248-0628
Redondo Elem Sch 18480 SW 304th St, Homestead 33030 Keith Anderson	PK-3	T	600 28	98%	305/247-5943 Fax 305/242-0318
Richmond Heights Middle Sch 15015 SW 103rd Ave, Miami 33176 Larhonda Donaldson	6-8	TV	448 85	87%	305/238-2316 Fax 305/251-3712
Riviera Middle Sch 10301 SW 48th St, Miami 33165 Jorge Bulnes	6-8	ATV	501 45	82%	305/226-4286 Fax 305/226-1025
Robert Morgan Ed Ctr/Tech Clg 18180 SW 122nd Ave, Miami 33177 Reginald Fox	Voc	GT	2,088 25	73%	305/253-9920 Fax 305/259-1495
Robert Russa Moton Elem Sch 18050 Homestead Ave, Miami 33157 Eric Wright	K-5	T	317 30	98%	305/235-3612 Fax 305/256-3128
Royal Green Elem Sch 13047 SW 47th St, Miami 33175 Alba Misas	PK-5	T	461	88%	305/221-4452 Fax 305/220-6238
Royal Palm Elem Sch 4200 SW 112th Ct, Miami 33165 Marta Garcia	PK-5	T	535	89%	305/221-7961 Fax 305/222-8145
Ruth Owens Kruse Center 11001 SW 76th St, Miami 33173 Cathay Abreu	Spec	TV	180 40	90%	305/270-8699 Fax 305/598-8147
Ⓐ School Adv Studies-Homestead 500 College Ter, Homestead 33030 Dr Omar Monteagudo	11-12	T	123 3	62%	305/237-5062 Fax 305/237-5232
Ⓐ School Adv Studies-South 11011 SW 104th St T 706, Miami 33176 Dr Omar Monteagudo	11-12	T	247 6	40%	305/237-0510 Fax 305/237-0511
Ⓐ School Adv Studies-Wolfson 25 NE 2nd St Rm 5515, Miami 33132 Dr Omar Monteagudo	11-12	T	126 3	54%	305/237-7270 Fax 305/237-7271
Ⓐ School Advanced Studies-North 11380 NW 27th Ave Rm 1111, Miami 33167 Dr Omar Monteagudo	11-12	T	124 4	61%	305/237-1089 Fax 305/237-1610
School for Advanced Studies-W 3800 NW 115th Ave, Doral 33178 Dr Omar Monteagudo	11-12		117	44%	305/237-0510 Fax 305/237-0511
Snapper Creek Elem Sch 10151 SW 64th St, Miami 33173 Mirta Segredo	PK-5	T	438 31	67%	305/271-2111 Fax 305/596-2475
© Somerset Acad HS Soho [130] 713 W Palm Dr, Homestead 33034 Dr Cristina Cruz	9-12		28		305/245-6108 Fax 305/245-6109
© Somerset Academy Bay Mid Sch [130] 9500 SW 97th Ave, Miami 33176 Saili Hernandez	6-8		91	21%	305/274-0682 Fax 305/274-0683
© Somerset Academy CS-Dade [130] 18491 SW 134th Ave, Miami 33177 Suzette Ruiz	K-8	T	615	65%	305/969-6074 Fax 305/969-6077
© Somerset Academy ES-Bay [130] 9500 SW 97th Ave, Miami 33176 Saili Hernandez	K-5		276	15%	305/274-0682
© Somerset Academy Palms 12001 SW 72nd St, Miami 33183 Suzette Ruiz	K-8		120		786/574-5287 Fax 786/574-5288
© Somerset Academy Soho [130] 300 SE 1st Dr, Homestead 33030 Layda Morales	K-5	T	536	75%	305/245-6107 Fax 305/245-6109
© Somerset Academy Soho MS [130] 300 SE 1st Dr, Homestead 33030 Layda Morales	6-8	T	590 4	81%	305/245-6108 Fax 305/245-6109
© Somerset Academy-Silver Palms [130] 12425 SW 248th St, Homestead 33032 Kerri Rodriguez	K-6	T	775	76%	305/257-3737 Fax 305/257-3751
© Somerset City Arts Academy [130] 47 NW 16th St, Homestead 33030 Idalia Suarez	K-6	T	472 11	71%	305/246-4949 Fax 305/249-4919
© Somerset Oaks Academy [130] 1000 Old Dixie Hwy, Homestead 33030 Idalia Suarez	K-6	T	570	86%	305/247-3993 Fax 305/247-3994
© Somerset Prep Acad Sunset 11155 SW 112th Ave, Miami 33176 Angela Nunez	K-5		330	41%	305/274-5696
South Dade Middle Sch 29100 SW 194th Ave, Homestead 33030 Guillermo Munoz	4-8	T	1,286	94%	305/224-5200 Fax 305/224-5201
South Dade Senior High Sch 28401 SW 167th Ave, Homestead 33030 Juan DeArmas	9-12	AGTV	2,964	83%	305/247-4244 Fax 305/248-3867
South Miami Heights Elem Sch 12231 SW 190th Ter, Miami 33177 Yolanda Green-Samuel	PK-5	T	504	91%	305/238-6610 Fax 305/233-7632
Southwest Miami Sr High Sch 8855 SW 50th Ter, Miami 33165 Carlos Rios	9-12	GTV	2,460 105	77%	305/274-0181 Fax 305/596-7370
Southwood Middle Sch 16301 SW 80th Ave, Palmetto Bay 33157 Raul Garcia	6-8	ATV	1,324	52%	305/251-5361 Fax 305/251-7464
© Summerville Advantage Academy [132] 11575 SW 243rd St, Homestead 33032 Archalena Coats	K-5	T	552	79%	305/253-2123 Fax 305/907-5909
Sunset Park Elem Sch 10235 SW 84th St, Miami 33173 Wendy Hernandez	PK-5	T	577 34	75%	305/279-3222 Fax 305/273-2130
Ⓜ Terra Environ Research Inst 11005 SW 84th St, Miami 33173 Jose Sirven	9-12	T	1,847	44%	305/412-5800 Fax 305/412-5801
© The Charter School-Waterstone [132] 855 Waterstone Way, Homestead 33033 Melissa Aguilar	K-5	T	1,002	75%	305/248-6206 Fax 786/349-3726
Tropical Elem Sch 4545 SW 104th Ave, Miami 33165 Viviana Bouza Debs	PK-5	T	429 45	83%	305/221-0284 Fax 305/220-4902
© True North Classical Academy 9393 SW 72nd St, Miami 33173 Dr Marc Snyder	1-9		336	14%	305/749-5725 Fax 305/271-0952
Village Green Elem Sch 12265 SW 34th St, Miami 33175 Henry Fernandez	PK-5	T	272 30	78%	305/226-0441 Fax 305/222-8140
Vineland K-8 Center 8455 SW 119th St, Miami 33156 Catherine Krtausch	PK-8	T	869 40	39%	305/238-7931 Fax 305/378-0776

1	Superintendent	8	Curric/Instruct K-12	19	Chief Financial Officer	29	Family/Consumer Science	39	Social Studies K-12
2	Bus/Finance/Purchasing	9	Curric/Instruct Elem	20	Art K-12	30	Adult Education	40	Social Studies Elem
3	Buildings And Grounds	10	Curric/Instruct Sec	21	Art Elem	31	Career/Sch-to-Work K-12	41	Social Studies Sec
4	Food Service	11	Federal Program	22	Art Sec	32	Career/Sch-to-Work Elem	42	Science K-12
5	Transportation	12	Title I	23	Music K-12	33	Career/Sch-to-Work Sec	43	Science Elem
6	Athletic	13	Title V	24	Music Elem	34	Early Childhood Ed	44	Science Sec
7	Health Services	14	Asst Superintendent	25	Music Sec	35	Health/Phys Education	45	Math K-12
		15	Asst Superintendent	26	Business Education	36	Guidance Services K-12	46	Math Elem
		16	Instructional Media Svcs	27	Career & Tech Ed	37	Guidance Services Elem	47	Math Sec
		17	Chief Operations Officer	28	Technology Education	38	Guidance Services Sec	48	English/Lang Arts K-12
		18	Chief Academic Officer						

49	English/Lang Arts Elem	59	Special Education Elem	69	Academic Assessment
50	English/Lang Arts Sec	60	Special Education Sec	70	Research/Development
51	Reading K-12	61	Foreign/World Lang K-12	71	Public Information
52	Reading Elem	62	Foreign/World Lang Elem	72	Summer School
53	Reading Sec	63	Foreign/World Lang Sec	73	Instructional Tech
54	Remedial Reading K-12	64	Religious Education K-12	74	Inservice Training
55	Remedial Reading Elem	65	Religious Education Elem	75	Marketing/Distributive
56	Remedial Reading Sec	66	Religious Education Sec	76	Info Systems
57	Bilingual/ELL	67	School Board President	77	Psychological Assess
58	Special Education K-12	68	Teacher Personnel	78	Affirmative Action

W R Thomas Middle Sch 13001 SW 26th St, Miami 33175 Wendy Barnett	6-8	TV	1,076 70	79%	305/995-3800 Fax 305/995-3537
Wesley Matthews Elem Sch 12345 SW 18th Ter, Miami 33175 Armandina Acosta-Leon	PK-5	T	464	79%	305/222-8150 Fax 305/222-8168
West Homestead K-8 Center 1550 SW 6th St, Homestead 33030 Dr Earl Burth	PK-8	T	826 75	99%	305/248-0812 Fax 305/247-3205
Whispering Pines Elem Sch 18929 SW 89th Rd, Cutler Bay 33157 Tamela Brown	PK-5	T	541 25	64%	305/238-7382 Fax 305/251-3615 🅣
William Lehman Elem Sch 10990 SW 113th Pl, Miami 33176 Ada Montero	PK-5	T	637 45	57%	305/273-2140 Fax 305/273-2228
Winston Park K-8 Center 13200 SW 79th St, Miami 33183 Raquel Pelletier	PK-8	T	1,433	73%	305/386-7622 Fax 305/386-5684 🅣
Zora N Hurston Elem Sch 13137 SW 26th St, Miami 33175 Isabel Valenzano	PK-5	T	560 40	81%	305/222-8152 Fax 305/222-4923

MIAMI-DADE CATHOLIC SCHOOLS

● **Archdiocese of Miami Ed Office** PID: 00187854   305/757-6241
9401 Biscayne Blvd, Miami Shores 33138   Fax 305/762-1115

Schools: 60 \ **Students:** 35,000

Listing includes only schools located in this county. See District Index for location of Diocesan Offices.

Catholic Schs..Principal	Grd	Prgm	Enr/#Cls	SN	
Adom Virtual Sch 12566 NW 32nd Ave, Miami Gardens 33054 Rebecca Bautista	6-12		100		305/508-5556 Fax 305/521-0185
Archbishop Carroll Catholic HS 10300 SW 167th Ave, Miami 33196 Sr Margaret Ann	9-12	GV	500		305/388-6700 Fax 305/388-4371 🅕
Belen Jesuit Preparatory Sch 500 SW 127th Ave, Miami 33184 Jose Roca	6-12		1,124 60		305/223-8600 Fax 305/227-2565 🅕🅣
Blessed Trinity Sch 4020 Curtiss Pkwy, Miami 33166 Maria Perez	PK-8		275 13		305/871-5766 Fax 305/876-1755
Christopher Columbus High Sch 3000 SW 87th Ave, Miami 33165 Dave Pugh	9-12		1,269 60		305/223-5650 Fax 305/480-4057
Epiphany Sch 5557 SW 84th St, Miami 33143 Ana Oliva	PK-8		900 40		305/667-5251 Fax 305/667-6828
Good Shepherd Catholic Sch 14187 SW 72nd Ave, Miami 33183 Clara Cabrera	PK-8		211 17		305/385-7002 Fax 305/385-7026
Holy Family Sch 14650 NE 12th Ave, Miami 33161 Doreen Roberts	PK-8		190 11		305/947-6535 Fax 305/947-1826
Immaculata-La Salle High Sch 3601 S Miami Ave, Coconut Grove 33133 Sr Kim Keraitis	9-12		866 37		305/854-2334 Fax 305/858-5971
Immaculate Conception Sch 125 W 45th St, Hialeah 33012 Victoria Leon	PK-8		800 30		305/822-6461 Fax 305/822-0289
Marian Center Sch 15701 NW 37th Ave, Miami Gardens 33054 Sr Lidia Valli	Spec		40 4		305/625-8354 Fax 305/625-0744
Mother of Christ Elem Sch 14141 SW 26th St, Miami 33175 Rita Marti	PK-8		200		786/497-6111 Fax 786/497-6113
Mother of Our Redeemer 8445 NW 186th St, Hialeah 33015 Ana Casariego	PK-8		220		305/829-3988 Fax 305/829-3019 🅕
Msgr Edward Pace High Sch 15600 NW 32nd Ave, Opa Locka 33054 Ana Garcia	9-12		1,271 60		305/623-7223 Fax 305/521-0185
Our Lady of Holy Rosary Sch 18455 SW 97th Ave, Miami 33157 lima Lozano	PK-8		487 15		305/235-5442 Fax 305/235-5670
Our Lady of Lourdes Academy 5525 SW 84th St, Miami 33143 Sr Kathryn Donze	9-12		800 30		305/667-1623 Fax 305/663-3121
Our Lady of Lourdes Sch 14000 SW 112th St, Miami 33186 Thomas Halfaker	PK-8		637 22		305/386-8446 Fax 305/386-6694
Our Lady of the Lakes ES 6600 Miami Lakeway N, Hialeah 33014 Barbra Picazo	PK-8		500 20		305/362-5315 Fax 305/362-4573
St Agatha Catholic Sch 1125 SW 107th Ave, Miami 33174 Caridad Hernandez	PK-8		500 21		305/222-8751 Fax 305/222-1517
St Agnes Academy 122 Harbor Dr, Key Biscayne 33149 Susana Rivera	PK-8		500 14		305/361-3245 Fax 305/361-6329
St Brendan Elem Sch 8755 SW 32nd St, Miami 33165 Cristina Capote-Alonso	PK-8		700 20		305/221-2722 Fax 305/554-6726 🅕
St Brendan High Sch 2950 SW 87th Ave, Miami 33165 Jose Rodelgo-Bueno	9-12		1,194 45		305/223-5181 Fax 305/220-7434
St Hugh Catholic Sch 3460 Royal Rd, Miami 33133 Mary Fernandez	PK-8		300 11		305/448-5602 Fax 305/444-4299
St James Sch 601 NW 131st St, North Miami 33168 Sr Stephanie Flynn	PK-8		465 11		305/681-3822 Fax 305/681-6435
St John Neumann Prep Cath Sch 12115 SW 107th Ave, Miami 33176 Maria Vilas	PK-8		330 10		305/255-7315 Fax 305/255-7316
St John the Apostle Sch 479 E 4th St, Hialeah 33010 Robert Hernandez	K-8		240 32		305/888-6819 Fax 305/887-1256
St Kevin Catholic Sch 4001 SW 127th Ave, Miami 33175 Dr Mayra Constantino	PK-8		639 17		305/227-7571 Fax 305/227-7574
St Lawrence Sch 2200 NE 191st St, Miami 33180 Diane Hyatt	K-8		158 9		305/932-4912 Fax 305/932-7898
St Louis Covenant Sch 7270 SW 120th St, Pinecrest 33156 Edward Garcia	PK-8		527 16		305/238-7562 Fax 305/238-4296
St Mary Cathedral Sch 7485 NW 2nd Ave, Miami 33150 Sr Michell Fernandez	PK-8		410 16		305/795-2000 Fax 305/795-2013
St Michael the Archangel Sch 300 NW 28th Ave, Miami 33125 Carman Alfonso	PK-8		325 15		305/642-6732 Fax 305/649-5867

79 Student Personnel	91 Safety/Security	275 Response To Intervention	298 Grant Writer/Ptnrships	**School Programs**	**Social Media**
80 Driver Ed/Safety	92 Magnet School	277 Remedial Math K-12	750 Chief Innovation Officer	A = Alternative Program	
81 Gifted/Talented	93 Parental Involvement	280 Literacy Coach	751 Chief of Staff	G = Adult Classes	🅕 = Facebook
82 Video Services	95 Tech Prep Program	285 STEM	752 Social Emotional Learning	M = Magnet Program	
83 Substance Abuse Prev	97 Chief Infomation Officer	286 Digital Learning		T = Title I Schoolwide	🅣 = Twitter
84 Erate	98 Chief Technology Officer	288 Common Core Standards	**Other School Types**	V = Career & Tech Ed Programs	
85 AIDS Education	270 Character Education	294 Accountability	Ⓐ = Alternative School		
88 Alternative/At Risk	271 Migrant Education	295 Network System	Ⓒ = Charter School	New Schools are shaded	
89 Multi-Cultural Curriculum	273 Teacher Mentor	296 Title II Programs	Ⓜ = Magnet School	New Superintendents and Principals are bold	
90 Social Work	274 Before/After Sch	297 Webmaster	Ⓨ = Year-Round School	Personnel with email addresses are underscored	**FL—85**

School	Grd	Enr/#Cls	Phone
St Patrick Grade Sch 3700 Garden Ave, Miami Beach 33140 Bertha Moro	K-8	250 20	305/534-4616 Fax 305/538-5463
St Rose of Lima Sch 425 NE 105th St, Miami Shores 33138 Dr Stephen Brown	PK-8	541 22	305/751-4257
St Theresa Catholic Sch 2701 Indian Mound Trl, Coral Gables 33134 Sr Rosalie	PK-8	883 30	305/446-1738 Fax 305/446-2877
St Thomas the Apostle Sch 7303 SW 64th St, Miami 33143 Lisa Figueredo	PK-8	521	305/661-8591 Fax 305/661-2181
St Timothy Parish Sch 5400 SW 102nd Ave, Miami 33165 Annie Seiglie	PK-8	625 21	305/274-8229 Fax 305/598-7107
Sts Peter & Paul Sch 1435 SW 12th Ave, Miami 33129 Dr Carlota Morales	PK-8	450 23	305/858-3722 Fax 305/856-4322

MIAMI-DADE PRIVATE SCHOOLS

Private Schs..Principal	Grd	Prgm	Enr/#Cls	SN
Alexander Montessori Sch 6050 SW 57th Ave, Miami 33143 Joyce McGhee	PK-5		580 20	305/665-6274 Fax 305/665-7726
Alexander Sch 14850 SW 67th Ave, Miami 33158 James McGhee	1-5		280 16	305/235-3995 Fax 305/252-9778
Alhambra Height Challenger Sch 12128 NW 2nd Ave, Miami 33168 Beverly Hilton	PK-12		50	786/553-8555
All Angels Academy 1801 Ludlam Dr, Miami Springs 33166 Terry Alexander	PK-8		72	305/888-9483 Fax 305/675-8572
Allison Academy 1881 NE 164th St, N Miami Beach 33162 Dr Sarah Allison	6-12	G	116 18	305/940-3922 Fax 305/940-1820
American Christian Sch 5888 W 20th Ave, Hialeah 33016 Marcela Chavarri	PK-12		148	305/827-6544 Fax 305/827-6620
American High School Academy 10300 SW 72nd St Ste 427, Miami 33173 R Valentino	6-12		913	305/270-1440
Asbury Christian Sch 5559 Palm Ave, Hialeah 33012 DeMaris Nodal	PK-8		200 18	305/823-5313 Fax 305/823-5329
Atala Montessori Sch 240 N Krome Ave, Homestead 33030 Dr Kristine Burns	PK-8		150	786/738-1210
Atlantis Academy 9600 SW 107th Ave, Miami 33176 Carlos Aballi	Spec		135 24	305/271-9771 Fax 305/271-7078
Beacon Hill Preparatory Sch 18001 NW 22nd Ave, Miami Gardens 33056 Aliza Kadesh	PK-8		217	305/624-1600
Betesda Christian Sch 3300 NW 135th St, Opa Locka 33054 Miriam Armas	K-12		100	305/685-7566 Fax 305/685-5338
Beth Jacob High Sch 1110 NE 163rd St, Miami 33162 Ephraim Liiyerson	6-12		350 13	305/957-1670 Fax 305/957-1677
Bethel SDA Elem Sch 32900 SW 187th Ave, Florida City 33034 Tiffany McNealy	K-8		45	305/248-4973
Biltmore Sch 1600 S Red Rd, Miami 33155 Dr Gina Duante-Romeno	PK-8		150	305/266-4666 Fax 305/266-0299
Brito Miami Private Sch 2732 SW 32nd Ave Stop 1, Miami 33133 Beatriz Brito	PK-12		247 8	305/448-1463 Fax 305/448-0181
Calusa Prep Sch 12515 SW 72nd St, Miami 33183 Tim Fowler	PK-12		157 15	305/596-3787 Fax 305/596-7589
Care Elem Sch 2025 NW 1st Ave, Miami 33127 Christopher Simmonds	K-5		100	305/572-2072
Carrollton Sch of Sacred Heart 3747 Main Hwy, Miami 33133 Paola Consuegra \ Lourdes Wood \ Dr Susan Dempf	PK-12		700 59	305/446-5673 Fax 305/446-4160
Casa Dei Bambini Mont Sch 4025 Pine Tree Dr, Miami Beach 33140 Rachel Reddington	PK-5		150 7	305/534-8152 Fax 305/531-6667
Champagnat Catholic Sch 1851 Palm Ave, Hialeah 33010 Nuria Sanchez	6-12		250 17	305/888-3760 Fax 305/883-1174
Children's Academy 13801 Memorial Hwy, Miami 33161 Patrick Adeleke	PK-PK		40 3	305/947-1731
Christ Fellowship Academy 8900 SW 168th St, Palmetto Bay 33157 Christina Blanco	PK-6		253 45	305/238-1833 Fax 786/430-1061
Christ-Mar Sch 7031 W 14th Ct, Hialeah 33014 Nerida Valdes	PK-8		201 9	305/823-6515 Fax 305/823-9758
Citygate University Sch 16400 NW 15th Ave, Miami 33169 Carmen Bell	PK-8		25	786/802-3240
Colonial Christian Sch 17105 SW 296th St, Homestead 33030 Nadine Vargas \ Michael Stewart	PK-12		185 20	305/246-8608 Fax 305/246-1542
Conchita Espinoza Academy 12975 SW 6th St, Miami 33184 Cassandra Jolliff \ Carol Diaz-Zubieta	PK-8		620	305/227-1149 Fax 305/227-0184
Coral Park Christian Academy 8755 SW 16th St, Miami 33165 Jesus Perez	PK-7		112	305/559-9409
Cutler Ridge Christian Academy 10301 Caribbean Blvd, Miami 33189 Linda Jones	PK-8		130 20	305/251-1534 Fax 305/255-6978
Dade Christian Sch 6601 NW 167th St, Hialeah 33015 Paul Humphreys	PK-12		620 78	305/822-7690 Fax 305/826-4072
Divine Savior Academy 10311 NW 58th St, Doral 33178 Ben Troge	PK-12		900	305/597-4545 Fax 305/597-4077
Dr John A McKinney Chrn Acad 2300 NW 135th St, Miami 33167 Dr Victor Curry	K-6		105	786/318-3818 Fax 786/685-6886
Early Years Academy 17790 NW 78th Ave, Hialeah 33015 Christina Woodson	PK-1		120	305/824-3500 Fax 305/824-3505
Easter Seal Academy 1475 NW 14th Ave, Miami 33125 Camilla Rocha	Spec		140 18	305/325-0470 Fax 305/325-0578
Ebenezer Christian Academy 3925 NW 2nd Ave, Miami 33127 Nerline Etienne	K-12		401	305/573-2867 Fax 305/573-2865
Edison Private Sch 3720 E 4th Ave, Hialeah 33013 Margarita Jimenez	PK-12		300 18	305/824-0303 Fax 305/822-4205

1	Superintendent	8	Curric/Instruct K-12	19	Chief Financial Officer	29	Family/Consumer Science
2	Bus/Finance/Purchasing	9	Curric/Instruct Elem	20	Art K-12	30	Adult Education
3	Buildings And Grounds	10	Curric/Instruct Sec	21	Art Elem	31	Career/Sch-to-Work K-12
4	Food Service	11	Federal Program	22	Art Sec	32	Career/Sch-to-Work Elem
5	Transportation	12	Title I	23	Music K-12	33	Career/Sch-to-Work Sec
6	Athletic	13	Title V	24	Music Elem	34	Early Childhood Ed
7	Health Services	15	Asst Superintendent	25	Music Sec	35	Health/Phys Education
		16	Instructional Media Svcs	26	Business Education	36	Guidance Services K-12
		17	Chief Operations Officer	27	Career & Tech Ed	37	Guidance Services Elem
		18	Chief Academic Officer	28	Technology Education	38	Guidance Services Sec

39	Social Studies K-12	49	English/Lang Arts Elem	59	Special Education Elem
40	Social Studies Elem	50	English/Lang Arts Sec	60	Special Education Sec
41	Social Studies Sec	51	Reading K-12	61	Foreign/World Lang K-12
42	Science K-12	52	Reading Elem	62	Foreign/World Lang Elem
43	Science Elem	53	Reading Sec	63	Foreign/World Lang Sec
44	Science Sec	54	Remedial Reading K-12	64	Religious Education K-12
45	Math K-12	55	Remedial Reading Elem	65	Religious Education Elem
46	Math Elem	56	Remedial Reading Sec	66	Religious Education Sec
47	Math Sec	57	Bilingual/ELL	67	School Board President
48	English/Lang Arts K-12	58	Special Education K-12	68	Teacher Personnel

69	Academic Assessment
70	Research/Development
71	Public Information
72	Summer School
73	Instructional Tech
74	Inservice Training
75	Marketing/Distributive
76	Info Systems
77	Psychological Assess
78	Affirmative Action

Emmanuel Christian Sch 3001 NW 167th Ter, Opa Locka 33056 Iris Maldonado	1-6	130 11	305/474-0658 Fax 305/625-2136
Faith Lutheran Sch 293 Hialeah Dr, Hialeah 33010 Ruth Wessling	PK-8	111 9	305/885-2845
First Um Christian Sch 622A N Krome Ave, Homestead 33030 Windy Parker	PK-8	300	305/248-7992
Florida Christian Sch 4200 SW 89th Ave, Miami 33165 Sherril Nealey \ Kerry Wicks \ Jim Arnold	PK-12	1,385 65	305/226-8152 Fax 305/226-8166
French American Sch of Miami 7701 SW 76th Ave, Miami 33143 Lena Salvant	PK-5	150	786/268-1914 Fax 786/268-1941
Fulford Christian Day Care Ctr 1900 NE 164th St, Uleta 33162	PK-2	45	786/916-2135
Fusion Academy-Miami 9130 S Dadeland Blvd Ste 102, Miami 33156 Maria Cardenas	6-12	401	305/831-0041
Gladeview Christian Sch 12201 SW 26th St, Miami 33175 Maljamy Duncan	PK-8	285 15	305/226-1414 Fax 305/225-1632
Glory of God Sch 440 E 13th St, Hialeah 33010 Ana Perez	K-12	61 3	305/884-4000 Fax 305/885-5553
Gordon Day Sch 2625 SW 3rd Ave, Miami 33129 Miriam Rube	K-5	150 7	305/854-3282 Fax 305/285-5841
Grace Baptist Academy 19301 SW 127th Ave, Miami 33177 Paul Provost	K-12	70 3	305/238-7332 Fax 305/238-3538
Grace Christian Prep Sch 11000 SW 216th St, Miami 33170 Mark Coats	K-12	100	305/259-1929
Great Heights Academy 9280 Hammocks Blvd Ste 103, Miami 33196 Khia Lopez	Spec	38	786/773-2285
Greater Miami Adventist Acad 500 NW 122nd Ave, Miami 33182 Mr Cortes	PK-12	380 13	305/220-5955 Fax 305/220-5970
Gulliver Acad-Montgomery 7500 SW 120th St, Pinecrest 33156 Donna Fong-Yee	5-8	97 9	305/238-3424
Gulliver Academy 12595 SW 57th Ave, Coral Gables 33156 Rachel Griffin \ Elizabeth Scott	PK-12	900	305/665-3593 Fax 305/669-1569
Gulliver Preparatory Sch 6575 SW 88th St, Miami 33156 Frank Steel	9-12	850	305/666-7937 Fax 305/665-3791
Gulliver School-Miller Drive 8000 Miller Dr, Miami 33155 Melissa Sullivan	9-12	220 23	305/274-9535 Fax 786/294-6184
Hebrew Academy-Greater Miami 2400 Pine Tree Dr, Miami Beach 33140 Debra Hamburg \ Andrea Lucero \ Dr Dara Lieber	PK-12 G	560 40	305/532-6421 Fax 305/672-6191
Highpoint Academy 12101 SW 34th St, Miami 33175 Alicia Casanova	PK-8	370 16	305/552-0202 Fax 305/559-8253
Hochberg Preparatory Sch 20350 NE 26th Ave, Miami 33180 Dayna Wald	K-5	400 10	305/932-2829 Fax 786/279-7811
Holy Cross Lutheran Sch 650 NE 135th St, North Miami 33161 Sherri Mackey	PK-8	300 12	305/893-0851 Fax 305/893-3044

Hope Academy 1100 Old Dixie Hwy, Homestead 33030 Nirvala Autar	K-12	325	786/243-3390 Fax 786/243-3391
Horeb Christian Sch 795 W 68th St, Hialeah 33014 Kevin Macki	PK-12	215 30	305/557-6811 Fax 305/821-5048
Jitta Bug Learning Center 1530 NW 124th St, Miami 33167 Adrienne Jitta	PK-2	12	786/274-2519
Jose Marti Sch 1685 SW 32nd Ave, Miami 33145 Edith Ysada	4-8	100 8	305/441-0565 Fax 305/443-9359
Jose Marti/Little Shaver 1 2660 SW 17th St, Miami 33145 Millie Beovides	PK-3	201 20	305/856-9044 Fax 305/858-0858
Kendall Christian Sch 8485 SW 112th St, Miami 33156 Alex Gispert	PK-5	120 17	305/271-3723 Fax 305/274-0648
Keypoint Christian Academy 609 Brickell Ave, Miami 33131 Claudiane Moraes	PK-8	140	305/998-5413
Killian Oaks Academy 10545 SW 97th Ave, Miami 33176 Mercedes Rincon	Spec	150	305/274-2221 Fax 305/279-5460
Kingdom Academy 9010 SW 157th Ave, Miami 33196 Paula Margary	PK-7	262	305/385-3761 Fax 305/385-3768
Kings Christian Sch 8951 SW 44th St, Miami 33165 Katie De La Fe	PK-8	142 12	305/221-2008 Fax 305/223-3823
Kingswood Montessori Academy 20130 SW 304th St, Homestead 33030 Maday Rodriguez	PK-6	120 6	305/248-2308 Fax 305/248-4484
La Progresiva Presbyterian Sch 2480 NW 7th St, Miami 33125 Melissa Rego \ Monica Aramillo	PK-12	360 25	305/642-8600 Fax 305/642-2169
Learning Experience Sch 5651 SW 82nd Avenue Rd, Miami 33143 Kevin Grace	Spec G	100 11	305/279-9811 Fax 305/275-4440
Lehrman Community Day Sch 727 77th St, Miami Beach 33141 Jodi Bruce	PK-5 G	370 40	305/866-2771 Fax 305/865-6575
Lovely Stars Academy II 24655 SW 112th Ave Ste 115, Homestead 33032 Zamara Lopez	PK-1	83	305/257-0028 Fax 305/257-0128
Lubavitch Educational Center 17330 NW 7th Ave, Miami 33169 Daniel Jacoby \ Angela Capurso	PK-12	800	305/653-8770 Fax 305/532-9820
Mandelstam Sch 8530 SW 57th Ave, Miami 33143 Marilucy Amezquita	PK-5	41	305/662-2736
Masters Prep Sch 1395 E 4th Ave, Hialeah 33010 Enrique Miranda	PK-8	77 1	305/887-4233 Fax 305/887-4514
Miami Christian Sch 200 NW 109th Ave, Miami 33172 Dr Lorena Morrison \ James Gentry	PK-12	308 25	305/221-7754 Fax 305/221-7783
Miami Country Day Sch 601 NE 107th St, Miami 33161 John Davies	PK-12	1,075	305/779-7200 Fax 305/759-4871
Miami Dade South 1820 Arthur Lamb Jr Rd, Key Biscayne 33149 Terrence Lavell	Spec	50 6	305/361-7934 Fax 305/361-9298
Miami Shores Montessori Sch 577 NE 107th St, Miami 33161 Sylvia Laurent	PK-3	45	305/756-7733 Fax 305/756-7721

79	Student Personnel	91	Safety/Security	275	Response To Intervention
80	Driver Ed/Safety	92	Magnet School	277	Remedial Math K-12
81	Gifted/Talented	93	Parental Involvement	280	Literacy Coach
82	Video Services	95	Tech Prep Program	285	STEM
83	Substance Abuse Prev	97	Chief Information Officer	286	Digital Learning
84	Erate	98	Chief Technology Officer	288	Common Core Standards
85	AIDS Education	270	Character Education	294	Accountability
88	Alternative/At Risk	271	Migrant Education	295	Network System
89	Multi-Cultural Curriculum	273	Teacher Mentor	296	Title II Programs
90	Social Work	274	Before/After Sch	297	Webmaster

298	Grant Writer/Ptnrships		
750	Chief Innovation Officer		
751	Chief of Staff		
752	Social Emotional Learning		

Other School Types
Ⓐ = Alternative School
Ⓒ = Charter School
Ⓜ = Magnet School
Ⓨ = Year-Round School

School Programs
A = Alternative Program
G = Adult Classes
M = Magnet Program
T = Title I Schoolwide
V = Career & Tech Ed Programs

New Schools are shaded
New Superintendents and Principals are bold
Personnel with email addresses are underscored

Social Media
 = Facebook
 = Twitter

School	Grades		Enrollment	Phone
Miami Shores Presbyterian Sch 602 NE 96th St, Miami 33138 Anita Stevens	PK-5		170	305/759-2548
Miami Springs Adventist Sch 701 Curtiss Pkwy, Miami Springs 33166 Eugenia Vega	K-8		48 4	305/888-2244 Fax 305/888-5149
Miami Springs Learning Center 200 Canal St, Miami Springs 33166 Lizitte Morales	PK-PK		90 7	305/888-1715 Fax 305/885-7868
Miami Union Academy 12600 NW 4th Ave, North Miami 33168 Edwin Silie	PK-12		294 20	305/953-9907 Fax 305/953-3602
Montessori Achieve Ctr-Learnng 10832 NE 6th Ave, Miami 33161 Jane Romero	PK-8		200	305/893-5994
Montessori Children's House 6381 Miami Lakeway N, Miami Lakes 33014 Paul Thibodeau	PK-6		110 3	305/823-5632
Montessori School-N Miami 695 NE 123rd St, Miami 33161 Evelyn Lopez-Couto	PK-8		150	305/893-5994
Mothers' Care and Learning Ctr 5861 NW 17th Ave, Miami 33142 Eddie Ford	PK-PK		52 4	305/696-3802 Fax 305/696-2918
New Jerusalem Christian Acad 777 NW 85th St, Miami 33150 Mayola Connor	K-5		167	305/691-1291 Fax 305/693-2430
Northwest Christian Academy 951 NW 136th St, Miami 33168 Jerry Nelson	PK-12	V	310 22	305/685-8734 Fax 305/685-5341 🅵 🅴
Nuestra Senora De Lourdes Sch 1164 W 71st St, Hialeah 33014 Teresa Menendez	PK-3		143 14	305/822-2645 Fax 305/822-2656
Our Lady of Charity Pvt Sch 1900 W 44th Pl, Hialeah 33012 Xenia Torrs	PK-12		340 16	305/556-5409 Fax 305/819-0057
Palmer Trinity Sch 8001 SW 184th St, Cutler Bay 33157 Patrick Roberts	6-12		600	305/251-2230 Fax 305/251-2917 🅵 🅴
Palmetto Christian Sch 6790 Miller Dr, Miami 33155 Edwin Collado	K-5		80	305/666-0632
Pentab Academy 18415 NW 7th Ave, Miami 33169 Barbara Sharpe	PK-6		56	305/651-9696
Perrine SDA Sch 9750 W Datura St, Miami 33157 Sandra Fletcher	K-8		20	305/259-0059
Prestige Christian Academy 9801 NW 24th Ave, Miami 33147 Ireal Gordon	K-8		52	305/836-9747 Fax 305/836-4767
Princeton Christian Sch 13390 SW 248th St, Princeton 33032 Pam Armstrong \ Eric Spee	PK-12		550 25	305/258-3107 Fax 305/257-5799
Promised Land Academy 27500 Old Dixie Hwy, Homestead 33032 Veronica Ward	Spec		35	305/255-9561
Ransom Everglades Middle Sch 2045 S Bayshore Dr, Miami 33133 Rachel Rodriguez	6-8		465 28	305/250-6850 Fax 305/250-4205
Ransom Everglades Upper Sch 3575 Main Hwy, Coconut Grove 33133 Patricia Sasser	9-12		620	305/460-8800 Fax 305/443-0735
Reagan Educational Academy 3168 W 76th St, Hialeah 33018 Dulce Madera	PK-1		80	305/818-3044
Redland Christian Academy 17700 SW 280th St, Homestead 33031 Daniel Carrillo	PK-12		170 20	305/247-7399 Fax 305/247-1147
Riviera Day Sch 6800 Nervia St, Coral Gables 33146 Dr Ana Rodriguez	PK-5		700 26	305/666-1856 Fax 305/661-5437
Riviera Preparatory Sch 9775 SW 87th Ave, Miami 33176 Patrick Snay	6-12		270	786/300-0300 Fax 305/274-1950
Roblanca Academy 1174 W 70th Pl, Hialeah 33014 Alina Santos	PK-8		72 8	305/557-3871
Rohr Middle Sch 1051 N Miami Beach Blvd, Miami 33162 Ephraim Palgon	7-8		100	305/947-7779 Fax 305/947-7221
Royal Kids Academy 12503 W Okeechobee Rd, Hialeah 33018 Lawrence Barimo	PK-4		189	305/557-5437 Fax 305/557-5579
Scheck Hillel Community Sch 19000 NE 25th Ave, Miami 33180 Ezra Levy	PK-12		1,000	305/931-2831 Fax 305/932-7463
School of Virtue & Acad Excell 8567 Coral Way Ste 144, Miami 33155 Dr Mary Reguera	7-12		25	786/220-0037
Shelton Academy 11300 NW 41st St, Doral 33178 Paola Smith	K-8		100	305/599-9967 Fax 305/599-8565
Shepherd of God Christian Acad 824 W Palm Dr, Homestead 33034 T Gates	PK-12		150	786/339-8503 Fax 786/410-5157
Sister Clara Muhammad Sch 5245 NW 7th Ave, Miami 33127 Lillian Brown	PK-8		38 4	305/757-8741 Fax 305/757-9768
Sjb Leadership Academy 99 NW 183rd St Ste 115, Miami 33169 Patrick Burrows	9-12		75	786/529-7750
St Christopher's Mont Sch 95 Harbor Dr, Key Biscayne 33149 Leslie Lasseville	PK-6		85	305/361-5080 🅵 🅴
St John's Episcopal Sch 145 NE 10th St, Homestead 33030 Lakshmi Nair	PK-8		170 11	305/247-5445 Fax 305/245-4063
St Matthew Lutheran Sch 621 Beacom Blvd, Miami 33135 Luis Santana	PK-8		68 10	305/642-4177 Fax 305/642-3477
St Philip's Episcopal Sch 1121 Andalusia Ave, Coral Gables 33134 Dr Gregory Blackburn	PK-5		180 8	305/444-6366 Fax 305/442-0236
St Stephen's Episcopal Day Sch 3439 Main Hwy, Miami 33133 Silvia Larrauri	PK-5		307 20	305/445-2606 Fax 305/445-7320
St Thomas Episcopal Sch 5692 N Kendall Dr, Coral Gables 33156 Lillian Issa	PK-5		430	305/665-4851 Fax 305/669-9449
Sunflowers Academy 2901 SW 7th St, Miami 33135 Dr Christopher Ventura	PK-8		100	305/631-1284 Fax 305/649-0084
Sunset Preparatory Sch 11925 SW 72nd St, Miami 33183 Jack Schechter	K-9		115	305/274-5111 Fax 305/273-8486
Temple Beth Am Day Sch 5950 N Kendall Dr, Miami 33156 Dr Deborah Starr	PK-5		403 44	305/665-6228 Fax 305/668-6340
The Cushman Sch 592 NE 60th St, Miami 33137 Cheryl Rogers	PK-8		500 25	305/757-1966 Fax 305/757-1632

1 Superintendent	8 Curric/Instruct K-12	19 Chief Financial Officer	29 Family/Consumer Science	39 Social Studies K-12	49 English/Lang Arts Elem	59 Special Education Elem	69 Academic Assessment
2 Bus/Finance/Purchasing	9 Curric/Instruct Elem	20 Art K-12	30 Adult Education	40 Social Studies Elem	50 English/Lang Arts Sec	60 Special Education Sec	70 Research/Development
3 Buildings And Grounds	10 Curric/Instruct Sec	21 Art Elem	31 Career/Sch-to-Work K-12	41 Social Studies Sec	51 Reading K-12	61 Foreign/World Lang K-12	71 Public Information
4 Food Service	11 Federal Program	22 Art Sec	32 Career/Sch-to-Work Elem	42 Science K-12	52 Reading Elem	62 Foreign/World Lang Elem	72 Summer School
5 Transportation	12 Title I	23 Music K-12	33 Career/Sch-to-Work Sec	43 Science Elem	53 Reading Sec	63 Foreign/World Lang Sec	73 Instructional Tech
6 Athletic	13 Title V	24 Music Elem	34 Early Childhood Ed	44 Science Sec	54 Remedial Reading K-12	64 Religious Education K-12	74 Inservice Training
7 Health Services	15 Asst Superintendent	25 Music Sec	35 Health/Phys Education	45 Math K-12	55 Remedial Reading Elem	65 Religious Education Elem	75 Marketing/Distributive
	16 Instructional Media Svcs	26 Business Education	36 Guidance Services K-12	46 Math Elem	56 Remedial Reading Sec	66 Religious Education Sec	76 Info Systems
	17 Chief Operations Officer	27 Career & Tech Ed	37 Guidance Services Elem	47 Math Sec	57 Bilingual/ELL	67 School Board President	77 Psychological Assess
	18 Chief Academic Officer	28 Technology Education	38 Guidance Services Sec	48 English/Lang Arts K-12	58 Special Education K-12	68 Teacher Personnel	78 Affirmative Action

FL—88

Three Flags Academy 6861 W 14th Ct, Hialeah 33014 Dania Jurado	PK-3		50 5	305/821-5964 Fax 305/821-7964
Toras Emes Academy-Miami 1051 N Miami Beach Blvd, N Miami Beach 33162 Kalman Baumann	K-8		789 22	305/947-6000 Fax 305/675-3384
Tree of Knowledge Lrng Academy 4000 Alton Rd, Miami Beach 33140 Nicki Salfer	Spec		50	305/705-2211
Trinity Christian Academy 17801 NW 2nd Ave, Miami 33169 Kathleen Hardcastle	PK-3		162	786/888-5433
Ⓨ Uco Diamond Minds Academy 1160 NW 159th Dr, Miami 33169 Dr Tamika Lewis	PK-12	M	145	305/623-4438 Fax 305/623-4440
Vanguard Sch 3939 Main Hwy, Coconut Grove 33133 Beth Havrilla	Spec		51 10	305/445-7992 Fax 305/441-9255
Villa Lyan Sch 14520 SW 8th St, Miami 33184 Henny Cristobol	Spec		56	305/752-0220
Villa Preparatory Academy 14112 SW 288th St, Homestead 33033 Zoraida Villanueva	PK-12		161	305/247-5858 Fax 305/247-2414
Village Pines Sch 15000 SW 92nd Ave, Miami 33176 Lucille Frazier	PK-5		170	305/235-6621 Fax 305/253-1445
Westminster Christian Sch 6855 SW 152nd St, Miami 33157 John Manoogian \ Alejandro Gonzalez	PK-12		1,225	305/233-2030 Fax 305/232-4547 f t
Westwood Christian Sch 5801 SW 120th Ave, Miami 33183 Christie Ross \ Bill Thomson	K-12		410 45	305/274-3380 Fax 305/595-7519
William A Kirlew Jr Academy 18900 NW 32nd Ave, Miami Gardens 33056 Hermine Thompson	K-8		166	305/474-4760 Fax 305/474-4762
Winhold Montessori Sch 17555 S Dixie Hwy, Miami 33157 Eleanor Winhold	PK-K		80 5	305/253-3225 Fax 305/253-3270
Worshipers House of Prayr Acad 8350 NW 7th Ave, Miami 33150 Deborah Zizi	PK-12		100	305/490-5806 Fax 305/835-1770
Xceed Preparatory Acad Kendall 9350 S Dixie Hwy Ste 160, Miami 33156 Miriam Rube	6-12		23	305/901-2115
Yeshiva Elem Sch of Miami 7902 Carlyle Ave, Miami Beach 33141 Yisroel Janowski	PK-6		500 28	305/867-3322 Fax 305/867-3388
Yeshiva Toras Chaim High Sch 1025 NE Miami Gardens Dr, N Miami Beach 33179 Mordechai Palgon	9-12		120	305/944-5344

MIAMI-DADE REGIONAL CENTERS

- **FDLRS-South** PID: 04496085
  6521 SW 62nd Ave, Miami 33143
  305/274-3501
  Fax 305/598-7752

Ana Torres ....1,11 Carmen Molinaris 8

MONROE COUNTY

MONROE PUBLIC SCHOOLS

- **Monroe Co School Dist** PID: 00195849
  241 Trumbo Rd, Key West 33040
  305/293-1400
  Fax 305/293-1408

> *Schools:* 19 \ *Teachers:* 640 \ *Students:* 8,849 \
> *Special Ed Students:* 1,331 \ *LEP Students:* 922 \ *College-Bound:* 83%
> \ *Ethnic:* Asian 1%, African American 11%, Hispanic 39%, Caucasian
> 48% \ *Exp:* $164 (Low) \ *Poverty:* 17% \ *Title I:* $1,681,043 \
> *Special Education:* $3,089,000 \ *Bilingual Education:* $301,000 \
> *Open-Close:* 08/14 - 06/02 \ *DTBP:* $171 (High)

Mark Porter 1	Jim Drake 2
Jeff Barrow 3	Patrick Lefere 3,91
William Shoemaker 3	James Faggione 4
Randy Fabal 5	Talley Reeb 7
Beryl Morgan 11,57	Kristin Coudella 16
Trevor Tyler 27,30	Marla Russell 34
Marla Russell 34*	Theresa Axford 35,83
Dr Lesley Thompson 58,79	Robert Highsmith 67
Dr Ramon Dawkins 68	David Murphy 69,294
David Murphy 69,294*	Lynsey Saunders 71,297
Joy Nulisch 73,95	Michael Michaud 76

Public Schs..Principal	Grd	Prgm	Enr/#Cls	SN	
Ⓐ Academic Connection Excellence 241 Trumbo Rd, Key West 33040 Sunny Booker	6-12		11		305/293-1400 Fax 305/293-1407
Ⓒ Big Pine Academy 30220 Overseas Hwy, Big Pine Key 33043 **Sarah Williams**	PK-8	T	175 9	38%	305/872-1266 Fax 305/872-1265
Coral Shores High Sch 89901 Overseas Hwy, Tavernier 33070 Blake Fry	9-12	GV	721 35	38%	305/853-3222 Fax 305/853-3228
Gerald Adams Elem Sch 5855 W Junior College Rd, Key West 33040 Anne Herrin	PK-5	T	566 34	74%	305/293-1609 Fax 305/293-1608
Horace O'Bryant Sch 1105 Leon St, Key West 33040 Christina McPherson	PK-8	ATV	1,100 45	67%	305/296-5628 Fax 305/293-1644
Key Largo Sch 104801 Overseas Hwy, Key Largo 33037 Laura Lietaert	PK-8	T	856 85	66%	305/453-1255 Fax 305/453-1248
Ⓒ Key West Collegiate Sch [130] 5901 College Rd, Key West 33040 Thomas Rompella	9-12		71	18%	305/296-5927 Fax 305/809-3191
Key West High Sch 2100 Flagler Ave, Key West 33040 Amber Acevedo	9-12	AGTV	1,261 75	37%	305/293-1549 Fax 305/293-1547
Ⓐ Lower Keys Ace 2100 Flagler Ave, Key West 33040 **Michael Henriquez**	6-12		18		305/293-1549
Marathon Middle High Sch 350 Sombrero Beach Rd, Marathon 33050 Wendelynn McPherson	6-12	ATV	638 60	56%	305/289-2480 Fax 305/289-2486
Ⓒ May Sands Montessori Sch 1400 United St Ste 110, Key West 33040 Lynn Barras	K-8		141		305/293-1400

79	Student Personnel	91	Safety/Security	275	Response To Intervention	298	Grant Writer/Ptnrships
80	Driver Ed/Safety	92	Magnet School	277	Remedial Math K-12	750	Chief Innovation Officer
81	Gifted/Talented	93	Parental Involvement	280	Literacy Coach	751	Chief of Staff
82	Video Services	95	Tech Prep Program	285	STEM	752	Social Emotional Learning
83	Substance Abuse Prev	97	Chief Infomation Officer	286	Digital Learning		
34	Erate	98	Chief Technology Officer	288	Common Core Standards		**Other School Types**
85	AIDS Education	270	Character Education	294	Accountability	Ⓐ	= Alternative School
88	Alternative/At Risk	271	Migrant Education	295	Network System	Ⓒ	= Charter School
89	Multi-Cultural Curriculum	273	Teacher Mentor	296	Title II Programs	Ⓜ	= Magnet School
90	Social Work	274	Before/After Sch	297	Webmaster	Ⓨ	= Year-Round School

School Programs
A = Alternative Program
G = Adult Classes
M = Magnet Program
T = Title I Schoolwide
V = Career & Tech Ed Programs

Social Media
f = Facebook
t = Twitter

New Schools are shaded
New Superintendents and Principals are bold
Personnel with email addresses are underscored

© Ocean Studies Charter Sch 92295 Overseas Hwy, Tavernier 33070 Trisha Woods	K-5		100	3%	305/852-7700
Ⓐ Options Center 1105 Leon St, Key West 33040 Carol Eismann	9-12	T	18	73%	305/293-1400 Fax 305/293-1485
Plantation Key Elem Sch 100 Lake Rd, Tavernier 33070 Lisa Hayes-Taylor	K-8	T	516 35	44%	305/853-3281 Fax 305/853-3279
Poinciana Elem Sch 1407 Kennedy Dr, Key West 33040 Larry Schmiegel	PK-5	T	578 35	56%	305/293-1630 Fax 305/293-1667
© Sigsbee Charter Sch 939 Felton Rd, Key West 33040 Eli Jannes	K-8		545 14	2%	305/294-1861 Fax 305/292-6869 ⓕ
Stanley Switlik Elem Sch 3400 Overseas Hwy, Marathon 33050 Brett Unke	PK-5	T	580 32	71%	305/289-2490 Fax 305/289-2496
Sugarloaf Sch 255 Crane Blvd, Sugarloaf Key 33042 Harry Russell	PK-8	T	613 50	40%	305/745-3282 Fax 305/745-2019
© Treasure Village Montessori CS 86731 Old Hwy, Islamorada 33036 Kelly Mangel	PK-8		219 10	21%	305/852-3482 Fax 305/852-2432

MONROE CATHOLIC SCHOOLS

- **Archdiocese of Miami Ed Office** PID: 00187854
  Listing includes only schools located in this county. See District Index for location of Diocesan Offices.

Catholic Schs..Principal	Grd	Prgm	Enr/#Cls SN	
Basilica School St Mary 700 Truman Ave, Key West 33040 Robert Wright	PK-8		300 12	305/294-1031 Fax 305/294-2095

MONROE PRIVATE SCHOOLS

Private Schs..Principal	Grd	Prgm	Enr/#Cls SN	
Academy at Ocean Reef 395 S Harbor Dr, Key Largo 33037 Christina Simons	PK-8		40 6	305/367-2409 Fax 305/367-2055
Island Christian Sch 83400 Overseas Hwy, Islamorada 33036 Terri White	PK-12		220 18	305/664-4933 Fax 305/664-8170 ⓕ

NASSAU PUBLIC SCHOOLS

- **Nassau Co School Dist** PID: 00196013
  1201 Atlantic Ave, Fernandina 32034

904/491-9900
Fax 904/277-9042

> **Schools:** 18 \ **Teachers:** 696 \ **Students:** 12,000 \
> **Special Ed Students:** 1,638 \ **LEP Students:** 132 \ **College-Bound:** 81%
> \ **Ethnic:** Asian 1%, African American 7%, Hispanic 6%, Caucasian
> 86% \ **Exp:** $154 (Low) \ **Poverty:** 12% \ **Title I:** $1,657,733 \
> **Special Education:** $6,949,000 \ **Bilingual Education:** $179,000 \
> **Open-Close:** 08/12 - 05/22 \ **DTBP:** $187 (High)

Dr Kathy Burns 1		Shana Brannon 2	
Susan Farmer 2		David Kramer 3	
Jeffrey Bunch 3		Audra Bower 4	
Katrina Flannery 4		Dr Lauren Jones 4	
Tom Chapp 4		Trevor Kennedy 4	
Evelyn McKie 5		Nina Boyd 5	
Andreu Powell 7,83,91,275		Mark Durham 8	
Kristi Simpkins 9		Katie Cubbel 12	
Kari Burgess 16		Brent Lemond 27,30,88*	
Kathleen Hardee 58,81		Misty Mathis 58,81	
Patricia Kelly 58		Rosalina Stelma 58	
Donna Martin 6/		Suzanne Davis 68,273	
J Ray Poole 71		Julie Brown 73	
Kari Watkins 73,76*		Dr Cindy Grooms 79	
Tanya Mungin 83,91,275		Adam Henderson 84,295	
Angela McClellan 275			

Public Schs..Principal	Grd	Prgm	Enr/#Cls SN	
Bryceville Elem Sch 6504 Church Ave, Bryceville 32009 Amber Nicholas-Bovin	K-5	T	187 17	48% 904/266-9241 Fax 904/266-2155
Callahan Elem Sch 449618 US Highway 301, Callahan 32011 Sabrina Faircloth	PK-2	T	669 36	58% 904/879-2121 Fax 904/879-5560
Callahan Intermediate Sch 34586 Ball Park Rd, Callahan 32011 Ronda Devereaux	3-5	AT	596 25	56% 904/879-1114 Fax 904/879-5288
Callahan Middle Sch 450121 Old Dixie Hwy, Callahan 32011 Kimberly Harrison	6-8	TV	788 25	55% 904/879-3606 Fax 904/879-2860
Emma Love Hardee Elem Sch 2200 Susan Dr, Fernandina 32034 Dr Eric Larsen	3-5	T	614 35	50% 904/491-7936 Fax 904/321-5890
Fernandina Beach High Sch 435 Citrona Dr, Fernandina 32034 Spencer Lodree	9-12	AV	960 55	34% 904/491-7937 Fax 904/277-3754
Fernandina Beach Middle Sch 315 Citrona Dr, Fernandina 32034 Dr John Mazzella	6-8	V	688 40	39% 904/491-7938 Fax 904/261-8919
Hilliard Elem Sch 27568 Ohio St, Hilliard 32046 Leann Jackson	PK-5	T	707 42	62% 904/845-4471 Fax 904/845-7427
Hilliard Middle Sr High Sch 1 Flashes Ave, Hilliard 32046 Dr Brent Tilley	6-12	ATV	725 60	55% 904/845-2171 Fax 904/845-7662
Nassau Co Adult Sch 76346 William Burgess Rd, Yulee 32097 Brent Lemond	Adult	V	100 4	904/548-1750 Fax 904/548-4499

1 Superintendent	8 Curric/Instruct K-12	19 Chief Financial Officer	29 Family/Consumer Science	39 Social Studies K-12	49 English/Lang Arts Elem	59 Special Education Elem	69 Academic Assessment
2 Bus/Finance/Purchasing	9 Curric/Instruct Elem	20 Art K-12	30 Adult Education	40 Social Studies Elem	50 English/Lang Arts Sec	60 Special Education Sec	70 Research/Development
3 Buildings And Grounds	10 Curric/Instruct Sec	21 Art Elem	31 Career/Sch-to-Work K-12	41 Social Studies Sec	51 Reading K-12	61 Foreign/World Lang K-12	71 Public Information
4 Food Service	11 Federal Program	22 Art Sec	32 Career/Sch-to-Work Elem	42 Science K-12	52 Reading Elem	62 Foreign/World Lang Elem	72 Summer School
5 Transportation	12 Title I	23 Music K-12	33 Career/Sch-to-Work Sec	43 Science Elem	53 Reading Sec	63 Foreign/World Lang Sec	73 Instructional Tech
6 Athletic	13 Title V	24 Music Elem	34 Early Childhood Ed	44 Science Sec	54 Remedial Reading K-12	64 Religious Education K-12	74 Inservice Training
7 Health Services	15 Asst Superintendent	25 Music Sec	35 Health/Phys Education	45 Math K-12	55 Remedial Reading Elem	65 Religious Education Elem	75 Marketing/Distributive
	16 Instructional Media Svcs	26 Business Education	36 Guidance Services K-12	46 Math Elem	56 Remedial Reading Sec	66 Religious Education Sec	76 Info Systems
	17 Chief Operations Officer	27 Career & Tech Ed	37 Guidance Services Elem	47 Math Sec	57 Bilingual/ELL	67 School Board President	77 Psychological Assess
FL—90	18 Chief Academic Officer	28 Technology Education	38 Guidance Services Sec	48 English/Lang Arts K-12	58 Special Education K-12	68 Teacher Personnel	78 Affirmative Action

Ⓐ Nassau Virtual Sch	6-12		16		866/339-8784
1201 Atlantic Ave, Fernandina 32034					Fax 850/254-9747
Kari Watkins					

Southside Elem Sch	PK-2	T	636	55%	904/491-7941
1112 Jasmine St, Fernandina 32034			46		Fax 904/321-5873
Rebecca Smith					

West Nassau Co High Sch	9-12	V	1,007	40%	904/879-3461
1 Warrior Dr, Callahan 32011			52		Fax 904/879-5843
Curtis Gaus					

Wildlight Elem Sch	PK-5		712		904/225-3053
550 Curiosity Ave, Yulee 32097					Fax 904/225-3054
Scott Hodges					

Yulee Elem Sch	3-5	AT	724	50%	904/225-5192
86063 Felmor Rd, Yulee 32097			27		Fax 904/225-9993
Scott Hodges					

Yulee High Sch	9-12	TV	1,307	40%	904/225-8641
85375 Miner Rd, Yulee 32097					Fax 904/225-8658
Natasha Drake					

Yulee Middle Sch	6-8	TV	1,012	48%	904/491-7944
85439 Miner Rd, Yulee 32097			25		Fax 904/225-0104
Jeremy Boatright					

Yulee Primary Sch	PK-2	T	724	51%	904/491-7945
86426 Goodbread Rd, Yulee 32097					Fax 904/225-8269
Misty Mathis					

NASSAU CATHOLIC SCHOOLS

• **Diocese St Augustine Ed Office** PID: 00202533
Listing includes only schools located in this county. See District Index for location of Diocesan Offices.

Catholic Schs..Principal	Grd	Prgm	Enr/#Cls	SN
St Michael Academy	PK-8		220	904/321-2102
228 N 4th St, Fernandina 32034			10	Fax 904/321-2330
Dr Christopher Hampton				

NASSAU PRIVATE SCHOOLS

Private Schs..Principal	Grd	Prgm	Enr/#Cls	SN
Amelia Island Mont Sch	PK-8		140	904/261-6610
1423 Julia St, Fernandina 32034			8	Fax 904/261-6196
Diane Dodds				
Faith Christian Academy	PK-8		120	904/321-2137
96282 Brady Point Rd, Fernandina 32034			9	Fax 904/321-1707
Bryan Alvare				🇫 🇹
Fernandina Bch Christian Acad	K-6		401	904/491-5664
1600 S 8th St, Fernandina 32034				
Dr John Ackermann				
Sonshine Christian Academy	PK-12		250	904/879-1260
45082 Frank Brookins Dr, Callahan 32011			19	Fax 904/879-2640
Lorie Johnson				

OKALOOSA COUNTY

OKALOOSA PUBLIC SCHOOLS

• **Okaloosa Co School Dist** PID: 00196128
120 Lowery Pl SE, Ft Walton Bch 32548
850/833-3100
Fax 850/833-3436

Schools: 46 \ *Teachers:* 1,868 \ *Students:* 30,638 \
Special Ed Students: 4,525 \ *LEP Students:* 1,030 \ *College-Bound:* 50%
\ *Ethnic:* Asian 2%, African American 13%, Hispanic 11%, Caucasian
74% \ *Exp:* $162 (Low) \ *Poverty:* 15% \ *Title I:* $6,467,059 \
Special Education: $23,039,000 \ *Bilingual Education:* $1,967,000 \
Open-Close: 08/12 - 05/29 \ *DTBP:* $195 (High) \ 🇫 🇹

Public Schs..Principal	Grd	Prgm	Enr/#Cls	SN
Addie R Lewis Elem Sch	K-8	TV	760	50% 850/833-4130
281 Mississippi Ave, Valparaiso 32580			20	Fax 850/833-4197
Jason Driver				
Ⓒ AMI Kids Emerald Coast	6-12	A	32	37% 850/244-2711
207 4th St SE, Ft Walton Bch 32548			5	Fax 850/244-2171
Maria Przybylski				
Annette P Edwins Elem Sch	PK-5	T	465	76% 850/833-3333
7 Wright Pkwy SW, Ft Walton Bch 32548			30	Fax 850/833-3480
Phyllis Morris				
Antioch Elem Sch	K-5		946	39% 850/683-7540
4700 Whitehurst Ln, Crestview 32536			42	Fax 850/683-7561
Kelli Sanders				
Baker Sch	PK-12	TV	1,496	50% 850/689-7279
1369 14th St, Baker 32531			70	Fax 850/689-7416
Mike Martello				
Ⓐ Best Chance North	4-12		50	850/689-5535
500 Alabama St, Crestview 32536				Fax 850/689-5534
Nicole Rickmon				
Bluewater Elem Sch	K-5		949	14% 850/833-4240
4545 Range Rd, Niceville 32578			25	Fax 850/833-4232
Amy Klugh				
Bob Sikes Elem Sch	K-5	T	832	50% 850/689-7268
425 Adams Dr, Crestview 32536			37	Fax 850/689-7263
Vicky Hayden				
C W Ruckel Middle Sch	6-8	V	1,188	22% 850/833-4142
201 Partin Dr N, Niceville 32578			48	Fax 850/833-3291
Paul Whiddon				

| 79 | Student Personnel | 91 | Safety/Security | 275 | Response To Intervention | 298 | Grant Writer/Ptnrships | **School Programs** | **Social Media** |

80 Driver Ed/Safety — 92 Magnet School — 277 Remedial Math K-12 — 750 Chief Innovation Officer — A = Alternative Program
81 Gifted/Talented — 93 Parental Involvement — 280 Literacy Coach — 751 Chief of Staff — G = Adult Classes — 🇫 = Facebook
82 Video Services — 95 Tech Prep Program — 285 STEM — 752 Social Emotional Learning — M = Magnet Program
83 Substance Abuse Prev — 97 Chief Infomation Officer — 286 Digital Learning — T = Title I Schoolwide — 🇹 = Twitter
84 Erate — 98 Chief Technology Officer — 288 Common Core Standards — **Other School Types** — V = Career & Tech Ed Programs
35 AIDS Education — 270 Character Education — 294 Accountability — Ⓐ = Alternative School
88 Alternative/At Risk — 271 Migrant Education — 295 Network System — Ⓒ = Charter School — New Schools are shaded
89 Multi-Cultural Curriculum — 273 Teacher Mentor — 296 Title II Programs — Ⓜ = Magnet School — New Superintendents and Principals are bold
90 Social Work — 274 Before/After Sch — 297 Webmaster — Ⓨ = Year-Round School — Personnel with email addresses are underscored

FL—91

School	Grd	Prgm	Enr/#Cls	SN	Phone
Choctawhatchee Senior High Sch 110 Racetrack Rd NW, Ft Walton Bch 32547 **Michelle Heck**	9-12	AGTV	1,638 102	43%	850/833-3614 Fax 850/833-3410
Choice High & Tech Center 1976 Lewis Turner Blvd, Ft Walton Bch 32547 **Jerry Sansom**	Voc	AG	300 18		850/833-3500 Fax 850/833-3466
Clifford Meigs Middle Sch 150 Richbourg Ave, Shalimar 32579 <u>Tracey Lamb</u>	6-8	T	561 39	46%	850/833-4301 Fax 850/833-9392
Crestview High Sch 1250 N Ferdon Blvd, Crestview 32536 <u>Dexter Day</u>	9-12	AV	2,096 100	39%	850/689-7177 Fax 850/689-7332
Davidson Middle Sch 6261 Old Bethel Rd, Crestview 32536 <u>Jay Sanders</u>	6-8	TV	1,071	48%	850/683-7500 Fax 850/683-7523
Destin Elem Sch 630 Kelly St, Destin 32541 Joe Jannazo	PK-5	T	950 46	41%	850/833-4360 Fax 850/833-4370
Destin Middle Sch 4608 Legendary Marina Dr, Destin 32541 Grant Meyer	5-8	V	760 37	30%	850/833-7655 Fax 850/833-7677
Edge Elem Sch 300 Highway 85 N, Niceville 32578 <u>Dr Samantha Dawson</u>	K-5	T	554 28	38%	850/833-4138 Fax 850/833-3496
Eglin Elem Sch 200 Gaffney Rd, Eglin Afb 32542 Dennis Samac	K-4		518 21	24%	850/833-4320 Fax 850/833-3671
Elliott Point Elem Sch 301 Hughes St NE, Ft Walton Bch 32548 Kathleen Ard	K-5	T	578 36	72%	850/833-3355 Fax 850/833-3473
Florosa Elem Sch 1700 W Highway 98, Mary Esther 32569 Dawn Massey	PK-5	I	545 24	58%	850/833-4381 Fax 850/833-4391
Ft Walton Beach High Sch 400 Hollywood Blvd SW, Ft Walton Bch 32548 John Spolski	9-12	AV	1,720	36%	850/833-3300 Fax 850/833-3332
Kenwood Elem Sch 15 Eagle St NE, Ft Walton Bch 32547 <u>Joan Pickard</u>	K-5	T	604 34	60%	850/833-3570 Fax 850/833-3597
Laurel Hill Sch 8078 4th St, Laurel Hill 32567 <u>Lee Martello</u>	K-12	TV	380 27	68%	850/652-4111 Fax 850/652-4659
© Liza Jackson Preparatory Sch 546 Mary Esther Blvd Ste 1, Ft Walton Bch 32548 **Kaye McKinley**	K-8		848 35	24%	850/833-3321 Fax 850/833-3292
Longwood Elem Sch 50 Holly Ave, Shalimar 32579 **Yvonne Michna**	PK-5	T	584 25	74%	850/833-4329 Fax 850/833-4336
Mary Esther Elem Sch 320 E Miracle Strip Pkwy, Mary Esther 32569 <u>Jason McClelland</u>	PK-5	T	581 31	68%	850/833-3371 Fax 850/833-3474
Max Bruner Jr Middle Sch 322 Holmes Blvd NW, Ft Walton Bch 32548 **Gary Massey**	6-8	TV	801 57	61%	850/833-3266 Fax 850/833-3434
Niceville High Sch 800 John Sims Pkwy E, Niceville 32578 <u>Charlie Marello</u>	9-12	AV	2,094 125	17%	850/833-4114 Fax 850/833-4267
Northwood Elem Sch 501 4th Ave, Crestview 32536 <u>Donna Goode</u>	PK-5	T	875 32	59%	850/689-7252 Fax 850/689-7488
© NW Florida Ballet Academie 310 Perry Ave SE, Ft Walton Bch 32548 <u>Kelly Day</u>	3-8		140	28%	850/664-7787 Fax 850/664-0130
© NWFSC Collegiate High Sch 100 College Blvd E, Niceville 32578 <u>Anthony Boyer</u>	10-12	V	284 9	6%	850/729-4949 Fax 850/729-4950
Ⓐ Okaloosa Acad Charter Sch [143] © 720 Lovejoy Rd NW, Ft Walton Bch 32548 <u>Christol Jarrett</u> \ <u>Stephanie Glover</u>	4-12	T	378 8	79%	850/864-3133 Fax 850/864-4305
Ⓐ Okaloosa Regional Djj Academy 4448 Straight Line Rd, Crestview 32539 Forrest Ward	6-12		50 6	94%	850/689-7800 Fax 850/689-7970
Okaloosa Stemm Academy 379 Edge Ave, Valparaiso 32580 **Scheree Martin**	6-8		239	21%	850/833-4120 Fax 850/833-4177
Okaloosa Virtual Sch 461 School Ave, Crestview 32536 <u>Christy Corbin</u>	K-12		260	23%	850/689-2043
Okaloosa Youth Academy 4455 Straight Line Rd, Crestview 32539 Mr Ward	9-12		75		850/689-1984 Fax 850/682-5410
Plew Elem Sch 220 Pine Ave, Niceville 32578 **Tammy Matz**	K-5		793 35	30%	850/833-4100 Fax 850/833-4103
Richbourg Sch 500 Alabama St, Crestview 32536 **Amy Anderson**	Spec	T	79	54%	850/689-5089 Fax 850/689-7817
Riverside Elem Sch 3400 E Redstone Ave, Crestview 32539 <u>Tamara Matz</u>	PK-5	T	855 29	63%	850/689-7203 Fax 850/689-7401
Shalimar Elem Sch 1350 Joe Martin Cir, Shalimar 32579 Camellia McSparren	PK-5	T	639 30	64%	850/833-4339 Fax 850/833-4357
Shoal River Middle Sch 3200 E Redstone Ave, Crestview 32539 **Craig Miller**	6-8	TV	842 45	48%	850/689-7229 Fax 850/689-7245
Silver Sands Sch 349 Holmes Blvd NW, Ft Walton Bch 32548 **Stephanie Wheat**	Spec	I	148 20	57%	850/833-3364 Fax 850/833-3366
Southside Primary Sch 650 S Pearl St, Crestview 32539 <u>Debbie Haan</u>	PK-2	T	323	53%	850/689-7211 Fax 850/689-7999
W C Pryor Middle Sch 201 Racetrack Rd NW, Ft Walton Bch 32547 <u>Brooke Barron</u>	6-8	TV	691 44	71%	850/833-3613 Fax 850/833-4276
Walker Elem Sch 2988 Stillwell Blvd, Crestview 32539 <u>Lorna Carnley</u>	K-5	T	872 31	63%	850/689-7220 Fax 850/689-7654
Wright Elem Sch 305 Lang Rd, Ft Walton Bch 32547 <u>Anita Choice</u>	PK-5	T	625 47	77%	850/833-3580 Fax 850/833-3584

OKALOOSA CATHOLIC SCHOOLS

- **Diocese Pensacola-Tallahassee** PID: 01483467
  Listing includes only schools located in this county. See District Index for location of Diocesan Offices.

Catholic Schs..Principal	Grd	Prgm	Enr/#Cls	SN	
St Mary Catholic Sch 110 Robinwood Dr SW, Ft Walton Bch 32548 <u>Amy Akins</u>	PK-8		400 28		850/243-8913 Fax 850/243-7895

1	Superintendent	8	Curric/Instruct K-12	19	Chief Financial Officer	29	Family/Consumer Science
2	Bus/Finance/Purchasing	9	Curric/Instruct Elem	20	Art K-12	30	Adult Education
3	Buildings And Grounds	10	Curric/Instruct Sec	21	Art Elem	31	Career/Sch-to-Work K-12
4	Food Service	11	Federal Program	22	Art Sec	32	Career/Sch-to-Work Elem
5	Transportation	12	Title I	23	Music K-12	33	Career/Sch-to-Work Sec
6	Athletic	13	Title V	24	Music Elem	34	Early Childhood Ed
7	Health Services	14	Asst Superintendent	25	Music Sec	35	Health/Phys Education
		15	Instructional Media Svcs	26	Business Education	36	Guidance Services K-12
		16	Instructional Media Svcs	27	Career & Tech Ed	37	Guidance Services Elem
		17	Chief Operations Officer	28	Technology Education	38	Guidance Services Sec
		18	Chief Academic Officer				

39	Social Studies K-12	49	English/Lang Arts Elem
40	Social Studies Elem	50	English/Lang Arts Sec
41	Social Studies Sec	51	Reading K-12
42	Science K-12	52	Reading Elem
43	Science Elem	53	Reading Sec
44	Science Sec	54	Remedial Reading K-12
45	Math K-12	55	Remedial Reading Elem
46	Math Elem	56	Remedial Reading Sec
47	Math Sec	57	Bilingual/ELL
48	English/Lang Arts K-12	58	Special Education K-12

59	Special Education Elem	69	Academic Assessment
60	Special Education Sec	70	Research/Development
61	Foreign/World Lang K-12	71	Public Information
62	Foreign/World Lang Elem	72	Summer School
63	Foreign/World Lang Sec	73	Instructional Tech
64	Religious Education K-12	74	Inservice Training
65	Religious Education Elem	75	Marketing/Distributive
66	Religious Education Sec	76	Info Systems
67	School Board President	77	Psychological Assess
68	Teacher Personnel	78	Affirmative Action

OKALOOSA PRIVATE SCHOOLS

Private Schs..Principal	Grd	Prgm	Enr/#Cls	SN	
Calvary Christian Academy 535 Clifford St, Ft Walton Bch 32547 Soila McGill	PK-12		240 17		850/862-1414 Fax 850/862-9826 f
Rocky Bayou Christian Sch 2101 Partin Dr N, Niceville 32578 Joe Quilit	K-12		700		850/678-7358 Fax 850/729-2513

OKEECHOBEE COUNTY

OKEECHOBEE PUBLIC SCHOOLS

● **Okeechobee Co School Dist** PID: 00196506   863/462-5000
700 SW 2nd Ave, Okeechobee 34974   Fax 863/462-5151

> **Schools:** 11 \ **Teachers:** 424 \ **Students:** 6,200 \
> **Special Ed Students:** 1,299 \ **LEP Students:** 888 \ **College-Bound:** 50%
> \ **Ethnic:** Asian 1%, African American 7%, Hispanic 42%, Native American:
> 1%, Caucasian 49% \ **Exp:** $338 (High) \ **Poverty:** 28% \ **Title I:** $2,311,873
> \ **Special Education:** $8,769,000 \ **Bilingual Education:** $2,631,000 \
> **Open-Close:** 08/12 - 05/29 \ **DTBP:** $160 (High) \ f t

Ken Kenworthy 1	Corey Wheeler 2
Brian Barrett 3,91	Lisa Bell 4
Nicole Havee 5	Pat McCoy 8,11,15,16
Leslie Lundy 12,298	Lonnie Steiert 13,27,79,92,270,271,296
Renee Geeting 15	Tuuli Robinson 30,69,294*
Wendy Coker 58,77,81,85,90,275	Jill Holcomb 67
Dr Joseph Stanley 68	Britani Stanley 69,294
Shawna May 73,76	Andi Canaday 74,280
Lauren Myers 79*	Rashan Jones 295

Public Schs..Principal	Grd	Prgm	Enr/#Cls	SN	
Central Elem Sch 610 SW 5th Ave, Okeechobee 34974 Joseph Stanley	K-5	T	532 25	89%	863/462-5077 Fax 863/462-5082
Everglades Elem Sch 3725 SE 8th St, Okeechobee 34974 Tracy Downing	K-5	T	662 50	91%	863/462-5108 Fax 863/462-5113 f
North Elem Sch 3000 NW 10th Ter, Okeechobee 34972 Pat McCoy	K-5	T	623 40	78%	863/462-5100 Fax 863/462-5107
Ⓐ Okeechobee Achievement Academy 1000 NW 34th St, Okeechobee 34972 Randal Weigum	PK-12	T	158 14	87%	863/462-5125 Fax 863/462-5295
Okeechobee Freshman Campus 610 SW 2nd Ave, Okeechobee 34974 Carol Revels	9-9	V	439 29		863/462-5288 Fax 863/462-5258
Okeechobee High Sch 2800 US Highway 441 N, Okeechobee 34972 Dylan Tedders	10-12	TV	1,238 80	73%	863/462-5025 Fax 863/462-5037
Okeechobee Virtual Sch 700 SW 2nd Ave, Okeechobee 34974 **Lauren Myers**	6-12		26	54%	863/462-5000 Fax 863/462-5204
Osceola Middle Sch 825 SW 28th St, Okeechobee 34974 Sean Downing	6-8	TV	766 45	82%	863/462-5070 Fax 863/462 5076

Seminole Elem Sch 2690 NW 42nd Ave, Okeechobee 34972 Thelma Jackson	K-5	T	549 40	94%	863/462-5116 Fax 863/462-5119
South Elem Sch 2468 SW 7th Ave, Okeechobee 34974 Emily Streelman	PK-5	T	582 28	79%	863/462-5087 Fax 863/462-5094 f t
Yearling Middle Sch 925 NW 23rd Ln, Okeechobee 34972 David Krakoff	6-8	TV	720 32	86%	863/462-5056 Fax 863/462-5062

OKEECHOBEE PRIVATE SCHOOLS

Private Schs..Principal	Grd	Prgm	Enr/#Cls	SN	
Okeechobee Christian Academy 701 S Parrott Ave, Okeechobee 34974 Melissa King	PK-12		250 11		863/763-3072
Okeechobee SDA Sch 412 NW 6th St, Okeechobee 34972 John Sufficool	1-8		8 1		863/763-0763
Rock Solid Christian Academy 401 SW 4th St, Okeechobee 34974 Latishia Alderman	K-8		200		863/763-1847 Fax 863/763-0968
Washington Co Sch 7200 US Highway 441 N, Okeechobee 34972 Jan Johnson	6-12	V	80 11		863/763-9648

ORANGE COUNTY

ORANGE PUBLIC SCHOOLS

● **Florida Virtual School Dist** PID: 11830113   407/513-3627
2145 Metrocenter Blvd Ste 100, Orlando 32835

> **Schools:** 3 \ **Teachers:** 1,633 \ **Students:** 5,540 \ **Special Ed Students:** 320
> \ **LEP Students:** 64 \ **Open-Close:** 08/12 - 05/27

Dr Louis Algazi 1	John Pavelchak 2,19
Jason Schultz 8	Martin Kelly 8
Robin Weiner 8	Andy Tuck 67
Alfred Lopez 68	Cassie Nielsen 71
Jennifer Whiting 73	Serena Frank 73,76,295

Public Schs..Principal	Grd	Prgm	Enr/#Cls	SN	
Florida Virtual Elem Sch 5401 S Kirkman Rd Ste 550, Orlando 32819 Marcie Trombino	K-5		1,168		407/857-6588 Fax 407/513-3480
Florida Virtual High Sch 2145 Metrocenter Blvd Ste 100, Orlando 32835 Kenneth Henson	9-12		2,797		407/857-6588 Fax 407/513-3480
Florida Virtual Middle Sch 5401 S Kirkman Rd, Orlando 32819 **Kenneth Henson**	6-8		1,575		407/857-6588

79	Student Personnel	91	Safety/Security	275	Response To Intervention	298	Grant Writer/Ptnrships
80	Driver Ed/Safety	92	Magnet School	277	Remedial Math K-12	750	Chief Innovation Officer
81	Gifted/Talented	93	Parental Involvement	280	Literacy Coach	751	Chief of Staff
82	Video Services	95	Tech Prep Program	285	STEM	752	Social Emotional Learning
83	Substance Abuse Prev	97	Chief Infomation Officer	286	Digital Learning		
84	Erate	98	Chief Technology Officer	288	Common Core Standards		**Other School Types**
85	AIDS Education	270	Character Education	294	Accountability		Ⓐ = Alternative School
88	Alternative/At Risk	271	Migrant Education	295	Network System		Ⓒ = Charter School
89	Multi-Cultural Curriculum	273	Teacher Mentor	296	Title II Programs		Ⓜ = Magnet School
90	Social Work	274	Before/After Sch	297	Webmaster		Ⓨ = Year-Round School

School Programs	**Social Media**
A = Alternative Program	
G = Adult Classes	f = Facebook
M = Magnet Program	
T = Title I Schoolwide	t = Twitter
V = Career & Tech Ed Programs	

New Schools are shaded
New Superintendents and Principals are bold
Personnel with email addresses are underscored

• Orange Co Public School Dist PID: 00196568   407/317-3200
445 W Amelia St, Orlando 32801   Fax 407/317-3353

Schools: 251 \
Teachers: 12,480 \ **Students:** 215,703 \ **Special Ed Students:** 21,645
\ **LEP Students:** 29,063 \ **College-Bound:** 33% \ **Ethnic:** Asian 5%,
African American 26%, Hispanic 41%, Caucasian 28% \ **Exp:** $210 (Med) \
Poverty: 20% \ **Title I:** $71,373,935 \ **Special Education:** $109,087,000
\ **Bilingual Education:** $47,646,000 \ **Open-Close:** 08/12 - 05/27 \
DTBP: $188 (High) \ [f]

Dr Barbara Jenkins 1
Dale Kelly 2,19
Robert Pacheco 3,17
William Wen 5
Kathy Shuler 8,18
Meg Bowen 9
Kimberly Gilbert 11
Bridget Williams 15,751
Dr John Wright 15,71
Dr Michael Armbruster 15,27
Scott Evans 20,23
Michelle Platzer 52
Leigh Austin 58,81
James Preusser 68
Illatawie Showalter 69,294
Mary Ann White 70
Scott Howat 71
William Tovine 88
Shawn Sanchez 93
Frenchie Porter 298

Catherine Nguyen 2
John Morris 3
Lora Gilbert 4
John Zerega 7
Rob Bixler 8,15,286
Pamela Villalba 10
Linda Bowman 12
Jennifer Sasser 15,70,294,298
Maria Vasquez 15
Daniela Mitchell 16,73
Anna Williams-Jones 36
Jose Medina 57,271
Teresa Jacobs 67
Erin Vacchio 69
Mary Bridges 69,77,79,90
Robert Curran 71,97
Carol Sousa 77,752
Bryan Holmes 91
Alfredo Ortiz 298

Public Schs..Principal	Grd	Prgm	Enr/#Cls	SN	
Ⓐ Acceleration East High Sch 2274 S Semoran Blvd, Orlando 32822 Douglas Loftus	8-12	T	212	99%	407/992-0917 Fax 407/207-4961
Ⓐ Acceleration West High Sch 2751 Lake Stanley Rd, Orlando 32818 George Morse	7-12	T	174	98%	407/521-2358 Fax 407/521-2369
© Access Charter Sch 6000 E Colonial Dr, Orlando 32807 Roger Watkins	Spec		104		321/319-0640 Fax 321/319-0643
© Aloma Charter High Sch [131] 495 N Semoran Blvd Ste 8, Winter Park 32792 Jacqueline Evans	9-12		396	1%	407/657-4343 Fax 407/657-4317
Ⓐ AMI Kids-Orlando Sch 1461 S Lake Pleasant Rd, Apopka 32703 **William Tovine**	6-12		38	85%	407/886-5405 Fax 407/886-7022
© Aspire Charter Academy 928 Malone Dr, Orlando 32810 Pamela Schenkel	K-3	T	120	92%	407/297-9955 Fax 407/297-9944
Avalon Tech Center 2201 Crown Hill Blvd, Orlando 32828 Jayne Lychako	Voc	G	50		407/281-5155 Fax 407/281-5127
© Bridgeprep Academy Orange 5710 La Costa Dr, Orlando 32807 Dr Joy Fernandez	K-7		346	83%	321/775-2119
© Central Florida Ldrshp Academy 427 N Primrose Dr, Orlando 32803 Joanne Goubourn	6-9	T	233	66%	407/480-2352
© Chancery Charter High Sch [131] 7001 S Orange Blossom Trl, Orlando 32809 **Isabel Villanueva**	9-12		388	1%	407/850-9791 Fax 407/850-9856
© Cornerstone Charter Acad [130] 5903 Randolph Ave, Belle Isle 32809 Dr Renee Pancoast	K-12		449	34%	407/608-7171 Fax 407/608-7172
© Econ River High Sch [131] 14180 E Colonial Dr Ste A, Orlando 32826 Nichole Bracey	9-12		253	2%	407/641-1062

	Grd	Prgm	Enr/#Cls	SN	
Esteem Academy 12301 Warrior Rd, Winter Garden 34787 Elizabeth Theis	Spec		25		407/656-2399 Fax 407/656-0972
© Hope Charter Sch 1550 E Crown Point Rd, Ocoee 34761 Allen Quain	K-8		437 10	1%	407/656-4673 Fax 407/264-6960
© Innovation Mont High Sch 1644 N Lakewood Ave, Ocoee 34761 **Patrice Cherico**	9-10		24		407/654-2045
© Innovation Mont-Ocoee 1644 N Lakewood Ave, Winter Garden 34787 Patrice Cherico	K-8		606		407/654-2045 [f]
© Innovations Middle Charter Sch 2768 N Hiawassee Rd, Orlando 32818 Dr Patricia Lightner	6-9	T	187	47%	407/440-2846 Fax 407/440-2852
© Kids Cmty Clg-Orange Co Campus 1475 E Silver Star Rd, Ocoee 34761 Keri Hefferin	K-5		189	54%	407/982-2421
© Lake Eola Charter Sch 135 N Magnolia Ave, Orlando 32801 Luanne Schendel	K-8		212 12		407/246-0900 Fax 407/246-6334
© Legacy Charter High Sch 1550 E Crown Point Rd, Ocoee 34761 Roberta VanHouten	7-12		168		407/656-4673 Fax 407/264-6960
© Legends Academy Charter Sch 3032 Monte Carlo Trl, Orlando 32805 Dr Porter Smith	K-6		230	90%	407/985-5195 Fax 407/650-8355
© Lucious & Emma Nixon Acad 1780 Mercy Dr, Orlando 32808 Melanie Harp	K-4		112	96%	407/412-6968 Fax 407/930-5754
© Nap Ford Cmty Charter Sch 1001 S Goldwyn Ave, Orlando 32805 Dr Jennifer Porter-Smith	PK-5	T	115 7	86%	407/245-8711 Fax 407/245-8712
© Oakland Avenue Charter Sch 456 E Oakland Ave, Oakland 34760 Pamela Dwyer	K-5		537		407/877-2039 Fax 407/877-6222
© Orange Co Preparatory Academy [132] 10250 University Blvd, Orlando 32817 **Chentella Graham**	K-8		336	59%	407/440-9293 Fax 407/960-2662
Orange County Virtual Sch 1600 Silver Star Rd, Orlando 32804 Brandi Gurley	K-12		71	19%	407/317-3327 Fax 407/317-3407
Orange Tech College Mid FL 2900 W Oak Ridge Rd, Orlando 32809 Alex Heidelberg	Adult	V	400		407/251-6047 Fax 407/858-2239
Orange Tech College Orlando 301 W Amelia St, Orlando 32801 Andrew Jenkins	Adult	V	485 45		407/246-7060 Fax 407/317-3372
Ⓐ Orange Youth Academy 3150 39th St, Orlando 32839 **William Tovine**	6-12		52	91%	407/835-0111
© Orlando Science Elem Sch 2611 Technology Dr, Orlando 32804 Michael Singleton	K-5		712	33%	407/299-6595 Fax 407/299-6594
© Orlando Science Middle & HS 2427 Lynx Ln, Orlando 32804 Abdulaziz Yalcin	6-12		1,090	35%	407/253-7304 Fax 407/253-7305
Ⓐ Pace Ctr for Girls-Orange 445 N Wymore Rd, Winter Park 32789 Dee Rosado-Chan	6-12		44		407/992-0456 Fax 407/992-0455
© Passport Charter Sch 5221 Curry Ford Rd, Orlando 32812 Dr Osvaldo Garcia	K-8	T	179 9	88%	407/658-9900 Fax 407/658-9911
© Pinecrest Collegiate Acad 13993 Mailer Blvd, Orlando 32828 Mrs Khan	K-5		183		407/432-5441

School	Grd	Prgm	Enr/#Cls	%	Phone
© Pinecrest Creek Academy [130] 1100 Lee Rd, Orlando 32810 Ericka Briones	K-5	T	110	79%	407/757-2706 Fax 407/757-2710 [f]
© Pinecrest Preparatory Academy [130] 8503 Daetwyler Dr, Orlando 32827 **Desiree Lumpuy**	K-8	T	239	85%	407/856-8359 Fax 407/856-8361
Ⓐ Positive Pathways Ctr 6125 N Orange Blossom Trl, Orlando 32810 **William Tovine**	6-12	T	291	87%	407/992-0914
© Princeton House Charter ES 1166 Lee Rd, Orlando 32810 Kim Gelalia	Spec		131 11		407/523-7121 Fax 407/523-7187
Ⓐ Project Compass 7531 S Orange Blossom Trl, Orlando 32809 William Tovine	8-12	T	37	90%	407/745-5475
Ⓐ Prosperitas Leadership Academy © 4504 S Orange Blossom Trl, Orlando 32839 Nadia Pierre	9-12	T	140	94%	407/854-3945 Fax 407/854-3955
© Renaissance CS at Crown Point [133] 83 West Rd, Ocoee 34761 Brett Taylor	K-8		1,027		321/573-1080 Fax 407/573-1081
© Renaissance CS at Goldenrod [133] 6004 S Goldenrod Rd, Orlando 32822 Priscilla Mendez	K-8		1,097	80%	407/536-2952 Fax 407/536-2953
© Renaissance CS Chickasaw Trail [133] 8203 Valencia College Ln, Orlando 32825 Dr Latonia Harris	K-8	T	1,121	1%	321/206-0662 Fax 321/206-0664
© Renaissance CS-Hunters Creek [133] 4140 W Town Center Blvd, Orlando 32837 **Patrice Knowles**	K-8	T	1,238	68%	321/206-3103 Fax 321/206-3104
© Sheeler Charter High Sch [131] 871 E Semoran Blvd, Apopka 32703 Johnathan Owens	9-12		250 5	2%	407/886-1825 Fax 407/866-7482
© Sunshine Charter High Sch [131] 6600 Old Winter Garden Rd, Orlando 32835 **Don Rugraff**	9-12		301	1%	407/641-4156 Fax 407/521-2944
© Transitional Learning Acad 3305 S Orange Ave, Orlando 32806 David DeAmato	Spec		55		407/852-3300
© UCP Charter Sch-Bailes Campus 12702 Science Dr, Orlando 32826 Dr Jennifer Holbrook	Spec	T	292	1%	407/852-3300 Fax 407/270-9253
© UCP Charter Sch-West Orange 1297 Winter Garden Vineland Rd, Winter Garden 34787 Thomas Brickel	Spec		31	62%	407/852-3300 Fax 407/654-7543
© UCP Charter School-Downtown 4680 Lake Underhill Rd, Orlando 32807 **Jodi Shea**	Spec	T	284 8	73%	407/852-3300 Fax 407/381-0907
© UCP Charter School-Pine Hills 5800 Golf Club Pkwy, Orlando 32808 Karyn Hawkins-Scott	Spec	T	93 6	85%	407/852-3300 Fax 407/299-7426
Ⓐ Universal Education Center 1000 Universal Studios Plz, Orlando 32819 William Tovine	10-12		17	81%	407/224-6634 Fax 407/224-6636
Westside Tech Center 955 E Story Rd, Winter Garden 34787 Crystal Davidson	Voc	G	110 45		407/905-2018 Fax 407/656-3970
Winter Park Tech Center 901 W Webster Ave, Winter Park 32789 Capildeo Jadonath	Voc	G	13		407/622-2900 Fax 407/975-2435
© Workforce Advantage Academy 2210 S Rio Grande Ave, Orlando 32805 Belinda Jones	11-12	A	248 6	1%	407/898-7228 Fax 407/898-6448

● Orange Co PSD-Transformation PID: 12367341
445 W Amelia St, Orlando 32801   407/317-3244   Fax 407/317-3358

Tashanda Brown-Cannon 1

Public Schs..Principal	Grd	Prgm	Enr/#Cls	SN	
Carver Middle Sch 4500 Columbia St, Orlando 32811 Jackie Ramsey	6-8	T	832 30	80%	407/296-5110 Fax 407/445-5238
Ivey Lane Elem Sch 209 Silverton St, Orlando 32811 Samuel Danner	PK-5	T	383 21	90%	407/296-6420 Fax 407/521-3324
Lake Weston Elem Sch 5500 Milan Dr, Orlando 32810 James Leslie	PK-5	T	537 40	90%	407/296-6430 Fax 407/521-3341
Meadowbrook Middle Sch 6000 North Ln, Orlando 32808 **David Hardrick**	6-8	TV	994 60	97%	407/296-5130 Fax 407/296-5139 [f]
Mollie Ray Elem Sch 2000 Beecher St, Orlando 32808 Lindsey Smestad	PK-5	T	494	88%	407/296-6460 Fax 407/521-3327
Ocps Acad Ctr for Excellence 701 W Livingston St, Orlando 32805 Wendy Ivory	PK-8		959		407/866-1280
Orlo Vista Elem Sch 3 N Hastings St, Orlando 32835 Tamara Barton	PK-5	T	602	100%	407/296-6490 Fax 407/521-3315
Rock Lake Elem Sch 408 N Tampa Ave, Orlando 32805 Linton Atkinson	PK-5	T	370 25	87%	407/245-1880 Fax 407/245-1885
Rosemont Elem Sch 4650 Point Look Out Rd, Orlando 32808 Tracey Gibson	PK-5	T	651 69	78%	407/522-6050 Fax 407/522-6064
Wheatley Elem Sch 1475 Marvin C Zanders Ave, Apopka 32703 **Lukeshia Miller**	PK-5	T	472 27	88%	407/884-2250 Fax 407/884-8832

● Orange Co Public SD-Dep Supt PID: 12308072
445 W Amelia St, Orlando 32801   407/317-3313   Fax 407/317-3310

John Wright 1

Public Schs..Principal	Grd	Prgm	Enr/#Cls	SN	
Arbor Ridge Sch 2900 Logandale Dr, Orlando 32817 Vanessa DeMars	PK-8	T	789 45	53%	407/672-3110 Fax 407/672-1310
Audubon Park K-8 Sch 1500 Falcon Dr, Orlando 32803 Trevor Honohan	K-8		788		407/317-5829 Fax 407/317-5836
Avalon Elem Sch 13500 Tanja King Blvd, Orlando 32828 Jeffrey Aldridge	K-5		847	26%	407/207-3825 Fax 407/207-3828
Avalon Middle Sch 13914 Mailer Blvd, Orlando 32828 Karen Furno	6-8	T	1,023	38%	407/207-7839 Fax 407/207-7872
Blankner Sch 2500 S Mills Ave, Orlando 32806 Junella Kreil	PK-8		974 66	39%	407/245-1720 Fax 407/245-1725
Discovery Middle Sch 601 Woodbury Rd, Orlando 32828 Dr Gloria Fernandez	6-8	TV	901	42%	407/384-1555 Fax 407/384-1580
Hillcrest Elem Sch 1010 E Concord St, Orlando 32803 Ruth Ortega	PK-5		382 26	36%	407/245-1770 Fax 407/245-1779
Howard Middle Sch 800 E Robinson St, Orlando 32801 Kimberly Beckler	6-8	TV	1,014 65	57%	407/245-1780 Fax 407/245-1785 [f]

79 Student Personnel	91 Safety/Security	275 Response To Intervention	298 Grant Writer/Ptnrships	School Programs	Social Media
30 Driver Ed/Safety	92 Magnet School	277 Remedial Math K-12	750 Chief Innovation Officer	A = Alternative Program	
81 Gifted/Talented	93 Parental Involvement	280 Literacy Coach	751 Chief of Staff	G = Adult Classes	[f] = Facebook
32 Video Services	95 Tech Prep Program	285 STEM	752 Social Emotional Learning	M = Magnet Program	
33 Substance Abuse Prev	97 Chief Information Officer	286 Digital Learning		T = Title I Schoolwide	[t] = Twitter
34 Erate	98 Chief Technology Officer	288 Common Core Standards	Other School Types	V = Career & Tech Ed Programs	
35 AIDS Education	270 Character Education	294 Accountability	Ⓐ = Alternative School		
38 Alternative/At Risk	271 Migrant Education	295 Network System	© = Charter School	New Schools are shaded	
39 Multi-Cultural Curriculum	273 Teacher Mentor	296 Title II Programs	Ⓜ = Magnet School	New Superintendents and Principals are bold	
90 Social Work	274 Before/After Sch	297 Webmaster	Ⓨ = Year-Round School	Personnel with email addresses are underscored	

School / Principal	Grd	Prgm	Enr/#Cls	SN
Hungerford Elem Sch 230 S College Ave, Maitland 32751 Letecia Foster	PK-5	GT	278 22	87% 407/623-1430 Fax 407/623-1498
Hunter's Creek Middle Sch 13400 Town Loop Blvd, Orlando 32837 Joumana Moukaddam	6-8	TV	1,341	48% 407/858-4620 Fax 407/858-4621 f
John Young Elem Sch 12550 Marsfield Ave, Orlando 32837 Lino Rodriguez	PK-5	T	763 52	100% 407/858-3120 Fax 407/858-2224
Northlake Park Cmty Sch 9055 Northlake Pkwy, Orlando 32827 Lee Parker	K-5		919 27	38% 407/852-3500 Fax 407/850-5173
Orlando Gifted Academy 1121 N Fern Creek Ave, Orlando 32803 **John Wright**	2-5		172	407/897-6410
Pershing Elem Sch 1800 E Pershing Ave, Orlando 32806 Bernadette Jaster	K-8	T	438 21	99% 407/251-2363 Fax 407/251-2312
Princeton Elem Sch 311 W Princeton St, Orlando 32804 Amanda Maxwell	K-5		445 30	49% 407/245-1840 Fax 407/245-1849
Stone Lakes Elem Sch 15200 Stoneybrook Blvd, Orlando 32828 Andronidus Rollins	K-5		772	28% 407/207-7793 Fax 407/207-7805
Sunridge Middle Sch 14955 Sunridge Blvd, Winter Garden 34787 Amy McHale	6-8		1,407	28% 407/656-0794 Fax 407/656-0806
Timber Lakes Elem Sch 2149 Crown Hill Blvd, Orlando 32828 Jared Scott	K-5		919	39% 407/249-6177 Fax 407/249-6172
Windy Ridge Sch 3900 Beech Tree Dr, Orlando 32835 Charles Jackson	K-8	T	1,171 84	52% 407/296-5100 Fax 407/296-5107

• **Orange Co Public SD-East** PID: 04803610   407/737-1490
601 Woodbury Rd, Orlando 32828   Fax 407/737-1497

Leigh Ann Bradshaw 1

Public Schs..Principal	Grd	Prgm	Enr/#Cls	SN
Aloma Elem Sch 2949 Scarlet Rd, Winter Park 32792 Donald Vega	PK-5	T	557 37	74% 407/672-3100 Fax 407/672-0391 f
Azalea Park Elem Sch 1 Carol Ave, Orlando 32807 Sheila Burke	PK-5	T	585 58	99% 407/249-6280 Fax 407/249-4419
Baldwin Park Elem Sch 1750 Common Way Rd, Orlando 32814 Anna Ferratusco	PK-5		856	34% 407/897-6400 Fax 407/897-2415
Bonneville Elem Sch 14700 Sussex Dr, Orlando 32826 Kimrey Sheehan	PK-5	T	601 30	100% 407/249-6290 Fax 407/249-4420 f
Brookshire Elem Sch 2500 Cady Way, Winter Park 32792 Jason Fritz	PK-5	T	562 32	42% 407/623-1400 Fax 407/623-5739 f
Camelot Elem Sch 14501 Waterford Chase Pkwy, Orlando 32828 Yvette Irizarry	PK-5	T	727 34	57% 407/207-3875 Fax 407/207-3881
Castle Creek Elem Sch 1245 Avalon Park North Blvd, Orlando 32828 Monica Johnson	PK-5	T	829 40	100% 407/207-7428 Fax 407/207-7723
Cheney Elem Sch 2000 N Forsyth Rd, Orlando 32807 Robin Broner	PK-5	T	525 42	99% 407/672-3120 Fax 407/672-3126
Chickasaw Elem Sch 6900 Autumnvale Dr, Orlando 32822 Janet Medina-Maestre	PK-5	T	656 40	100% 407/249-6300 Fax 407/249-4407

School / Principal	Grd	Prgm	Enr/#Cls	SN
Columbia Elem Sch 18501 Cypress Lake Glen Blvd, Orlando 32820 Matthew Pritts	PK-5	T	550 43	57% 407/568-2921 Fax 407/568-7330
Corner Lake Middle Sch 1700 Chuluota Rd, Orlando 32820 **Paul Browning**	6-8	T	943	65% 407/568-0510 Fax 407/568-0920
Cypress Springs Elem Sch 10401 Cypress Springs Pkwy, Orlando 32825 Dr Ruthie Haniff	PK-5	T	793 52	48% 407/249-6950 Fax 407/249-4537
Deerwood Elem Sch 1356 S Econlockhatchee Trl, Orlando 32825 Melanie May	PK-5	T	508 40	57% 407/249-6320 Fax 407/249-4422
Dommerich Elem Sch 601 N Thistle Ln, Maitland 32751 Karen Verano	K-5		625 36	21% 407/623-1407 Fax 407/623-5738 f
East Lake Elem Sch 3971 N Tanner Rd, Orlando 32826 **Latonya Brown**	PK-5	T	602	53% 407/658-6825 Fax 407/658-6830
Engelwood Elem Sch 5985 La Costa Dr, Orlando 32807 Andrew Agudo	PK-5	T	550 45	74% 407/249-6340 Fax 407/249-6344 f
Forsyth Woods Elem Sch 6651 Curtis St, Orlando 32807 Kelly Maldonado	PK-5	T	605	80% 407/207-7495 Fax 407/250-6212
Glenridge Middle Sch 2900 Upper Park Rd, Orlando 32814 Christopher Camacho	6-8	TV	1,341	46% 407/623-1415 Fax 407/623-1427
Lakemont Elem Sch 901 N Lakemont Ave, Winter Park 32792 Karl Fox	K-5	T	665 36	57% 407/623-1453 Fax 407/623-5737 f
Lawton Chiles Elem Sch 11001 Bloomfield Dr, Orlando 32825 Dennis Gonzalez	PK-5	T	655 40	100% 407/737-1470 Fax 407/737-1471
Legacy Middle Sch 11398 Lake Underhill Rd, Orlando 32825 Hilary Buckridge	6-8	T	924	65% 407/658-5330 Fax 407/658-5334
Little River Elem Sch 100 Caswell Dr, Orlando 32825 Wilma Baez	PK-5	T	438 40	89% 407/249-6360 Fax 407/249-4409
Maitland Middle Sch 701 N Thistle Ln, Maitland 32751 Andrew Leftakis	6-8	V	795 75	41% 407/623-1462 Fax 407/623-1474
Riverdale Elem Sch 11301 Lokanotosa Trl, Orlando 32817 William Charlton	PK-5	T	621 50	100% 407/737-1400 Fax 407/437-1414
Sunrise Elem Sch 101 Lone Palm Rd, Orlando 32828 Denise Bainbridge	PK-5		533 44	31% 407/384-1585 Fax 407/381-1599
Timber Springs Middle Sch 16001 Timber Park Ln, Orlando 32828 Eric Cantrell	6-8	V	933	321/413-2201 Fax 407/250-6233
Union Park Elem Sch 1600 N Dean Rd, Orlando 32825 **Ashlynn Ramirez**	PK-5	T	493 40	99% 407/249-6390 Fax 407/249-4416 f
Union Park Middle Sch 1844 Westfall Dr, Orlando 32817 Anthony Serianni	6-8	GTV	782 70	89% 407/249-6309 Fax 407/249-4404
Waterford Elem Sch 12950 Lake Underhill Rd, Orlando 32828 Kathy Petersen	PK-5	T	730 57	49% 407/249-6410 Fax 407/249-4425
Wedgefield Sch 3835 Bancroft Blvd, Orlando 32833 Natalie Stevens	PK-8	G	941	47% 321/413-2989 Fax 321/413-2998

1 Superintendent	8 Curric/Instruct K-12	19 Chief Financial Officer	29 Family/Consumer Science	39 Social Studies K-12	49 English/Lang Arts Elem	59 Special Education Elem	69 Academic Assessment
2 Bus/Finance/Purchasing	9 Curric/Instruct Elem	20 Art K-12	30 Adult Education	40 Social Studies Elem	50 English/Lang Arts Sec	60 Special Education Sec	70 Research/Development
3 Buildings And Grounds	10 Curric/Instruct Sec	21 Art Elem	31 Career/Sch-to-Work K-12	41 Social Studies Sec	51 Reading K-12	61 Foreign/World Lang K-12	71 Public Information
4 Food Service	11 Federal Program	22 Art Sec	32 Career/Sch-to-Work Elem	42 Science K-12	52 Reading Elem	62 Foreign/World Lang Elem	72 Summer School
5 Transportation	12 Title I	23 Music K-12	33 Career/Sch-to-Work Sec	43 Science Elem	53 Reading Sec	63 Foreign/World Lang Sec	73 Instructional Tech
6 Athletic	13 Title V	24 Music Elem	34 Early Childhood Ed	44 Science Sec	54 Remedial Reading K-12	64 Religious Education K-12	74 Inservice Training
7 Health Services	15 Asst Superintendent	25 Music Sec	35 Health/Phys Education	45 Math K-12	55 Remedial Reading Elem	65 Religious Education Elem	75 Marketing/Distributive
	16 Instructional Media Svcs	26 Business Education	36 Guidance Services K-12	46 Math Elem	56 Remedial Reading Sec	66 Religious Education Sec	76 Info Systems
	17 Chief Operations Officer	27 Career & Tech Ed	37 Guidance Services Elem	47 Math Sec	57 Bilingual/ELL	67 School Board President	77 Psychological Assess
	18 Chief Academic Officer	28 Technology Education	38 Guidance Services Sec	48 English/Lang Arts K-12	58 Special Education K-12	68 Teacher Personnel	78 Affirmative Action

• Orange Co Public SD-High Sch PID: 12308060

445 W Amelia St, Orlando 32801

407/317-3382
Fax 407/317-3451

Harold Border 1

Public Schs..Principal	Grd	Prgm	Enr/#Cls	SN	
Apopka High Sch 555 Martin St, Apopka 32712 Lyle Heinz	9-12	AGTV	3,371	58%	407/905-5500 Fax 407/814-6130
Boone High Sch 1000 E Kaley St, Orlando 32806 Dusty Johns	9-12	GTV	2,874 125	49%	407/893-7200 Fax 407/897-2466
Colonial High 9th Grade Ctr 7775 Valencia College Ln, Orlando 32807 **Dr Hector Maestre**	9-9	V	1,000 40		407/249-6369 Fax 407/249-6297
Colonial High Sch 6100 Oleander Dr, Orlando 32807 **Dr Hector Maestre**	9-12	GTV	3,403	100%	407/482-6300 Fax 407/737-1450 f t
Cypress Creek High Sch 1101 Bear Crossing Dr, Orlando 32824 Walton McHale	9-12	GTV	3,369 125	100%	407/852-3400 Fax 407/850-5160
Dr Phillips High Sch 6500 Turkey Lake Rd, Orlando 32819 Suzanne Knight	9-12	GTV	3,870	53%	407/355-3200 Fax 407/355-3288
East River High Sch 650 East River Falcons Way, Orlando 32833 **Nikki Campbell**	9-12	T	2,043	60%	407/956-8550 Fax 407/956-8565 f t
Edgewater High Sch 3100 Edgewater Dr, Orlando 32804 Mark Shanoff	9-12	GTV	2,017	63%	407/835-4900 Fax 407/245-2758
Evans High Sch 4949 Silver Star Rd, Orlando 32808 Rolando Bailey	9-12	TV	2,515 45	100%	407/552-3400 Fax 407/522-3458
Freedom High Sch 2500 W Taft Vineland Rd, Orlando 32837 Cheryl Neely	9-12	GTV	3,990	58%	407/816-5600 Fax 407/816-5616
Jones High Sch 801 S Rio Grande Ave, Orlando 32805 Allison Kirby	9-12	GTV	1,577	100%	407/835-2300 Fax 407/835-2337
Lake Nona High Sch 12500 Narcoossee Rd, Orlando 32832 Martha Chang	9-12	T	3,266	41%	407/956-8300 Fax 407/956-8315 t
Oak Ridge High Sch 700 W Oak Ridge Rd, Orlando 32809 Jennifer Bellinger	9-12	GTV	2,610	89%	407/852-3200 Fax 407/852-3222
Ocoee High Sch 1925 Ocoee Crown Point Pkwy, Ocoee 34761 Laura Beusse	9-12	T	2,576	68%	407/905-3000 Fax 407/905-3099
Olympia High Sch 4301 S Apopka Vineland Rd, Orlando 32835 Guy Swenson	9-12	GTV	3,266	46%	407/905-6400 Fax 407/905-6465
Timber Creek High Sch 1001 Avalon Park South Blvd, Orlando 32828 Kelly Paduano	9-12	V	3,477	32%	321/235-7800 Fax 321/235-7821
University High Sch 2450 Cougar Way, Orlando 32817 Dr Anne Carcara	9-12	GTV	2,839 140	60%	407/482-8700 Fax 407/482-8791
Wekiva High Sch 2501 N Hiawassee Rd, Apopka 32703 Michelle Erickson	9-12	T	2,174	100%	407/297-4900 Fax 407/297-4970
West Orange High Sch 1625 Beulah Rd, Winter Garden 34787 William Floyd	9-12	GV	2,448 250	34%	407/905-2400 Fax 407/656-4970
Windermere High Sch 5523 Winter Garden Vineland Rd, Windermere 34786 Douglas Guthrie	9-12	V	1,884		407/347-0980

	Grd	Prgm	Enr	SN	
Winter Park 9th Grade Center 528 Huntington Ave, Winter Park 32789 **Dr Paul White**	9-9	V	800		407/623-1476 Fax 407/623-1485
Winter Park High Sch 2100 Summerfield Rd, Winter Park 32792 Matthew Arnold	9-12	GV	3,355	35%	407/622-3200 Fax 407/975-2434

• Orange Co Public SD-North PID: 04803608

5146 N Pine Hills Rd, Orlando 32808

407/532-7970
Fax 407/532-7980

Rahin Jones 1

Public Schs..Principal	Grd	Prgm	Enr/#Cls	SN	
Apopka Elem Sch 311 Vick Rd, Apopka 32712 **Latricia Pinder**	PK-5	T	791 34	100%	407/884-2200 Fax 407/884-2296
Apopka Middle Sch 425 N Park Ave, Apopka 32712 Kelly Pelletier	6-8	T	1,083	71%	407/884-2208 Fax 407/884-2217
Clay Springs Elem Sch 555 N Wekiwa Springs Rd, Apopka 32712 Patricia Weisbach	PK-5	T	758 35	72%	407/884-2275 Fax 407/884-2289 f
College Park Middle Sch 1201 Maury Rd, Orlando 32804 Sanjay Brown	6-8	TV	964 50	100%	407/245-1800 Fax 407/245-1809
Dream Lake Elem Sch 500 N Park Ave, Apopka 32712 Carol-Ann Clenton-Martin	PK-5	T	807 64	100%	407/884-2227 Fax 407/884-2298
Gateway Sch 4000 Silver Star Rd, Orlando 32808 Dr Elaine Scott	Spec	T	78 25	85%	407/296-6449 Fax 407/521-3309
Killarney Elem Sch 2401 Wellington Blvd, Winter Park 32789 **Debra Vereen**	PK-5	T	419 26	90%	407/623-1438 Fax 407/623-1437
Lake Gem Elem Sch 4801 Bloodhound St, Orlando 32818 Latonya Brown	PK-5	T	653 46	100%	407/532-7900 Fax 407/532-7911
Lake Silver Elem Sch 2401 N Rio Grande Ave, Orlando 32804 Alyson Muse	K-5	T	556 50	66%	407/245-1850 Fax 407/245-1865
Lake Sybelia Elem Sch 600 Sandspur Rd, Maitland 32751 John Dobbs	PK-5	T	541 35	53%	407/623-1445 Fax 407/623-1452
Lakeville Elem Sch 2015 Lakeville Rd, Apopka 32703 Cynthia Swanson	PK-5	T	663 50	100%	407/814-6110 Fax 407/814-6120
Lockhart Elem Sch 7500 Edgewater Dr, Orlando 32810 Ella Patriarch	PK-5		445 23		407/296-6440 Fax 407/521-3342
Lockhart Middle Sch 3411 Dr Love Rd, Orlando 32810 Lisa James	6-8	TV	865 60	93%	407/296-5120 Fax 407/296-6549
Lovell Elem Sch 815 Roger Williams Rd, Apopka 32703 **Melissa Sarasty**	PK-5	T	713 37	95%	407/884-2235 Fax 407/884-6302
Piedmont Lakes Middle Sch 2601 Lakeville Rd, Apopka 32703 Edward Thompson	6-8	TV	1,095	100%	407/884-2265 Fax 407/884-2287 f
Pinewood Elem Sch 3005 N Apopka Vineland Rd, Orlando 32818 **Kelly Steinke**	PK-5	T	583 48	96%	407/532-7930 Fax 407/532-7933
Prairie Lake Elem Sch 8723 Hackney Prairie Rd, Orlando 32818 Robert Strenth	PK-5	T	877 36	100%	407/884-2220 Fax 407/884-6314 f
Ridgewood Park Elem Sch 3401 Pioneer Rd, Orlando 32808 Deborah Coffie	K-5	T	574 54	81%	407/296-6510 Fax 407/521-3345

79	Student Personnel	91	Safety/Security	275	Response To Intervention	298	Grant Writer/Ptnrships
30	Driver Ed/Safety	92	Magnet School	277	Remedial Math K-12	750	Chief Innovation Officer
31	Gifted/Talented	93	Parental Involvement	280	Literacy Coach	751	Chief of Staff
32	Video Services	95	Tech Prep Program	285	STEM	752	Social Emotional Learning
33	Substance Abuse Prev	97	Chief Information Officer	286	Digital Learning		
34	Erate	98	Chief Technology Officer	288	Common Core Standards		Other School Types
35	AIDS Education	270	Character Education	294	Accountability		Ⓐ = Alternative School
38	Alternative/At Risk	271	Migrant Education	295	Network System		Ⓒ = Charter School
39	Multi-Cultural Curriculum	273	Teacher Mentor	296	Title II Programs		Ⓜ = Magnet School
90	Social Work	274	Before/After Sch	297	Webmaster		Ⓨ = Year-Round School

School Programs
A = Alternative Program
G = Adult Classes
M = Magnet Program
T = Title I Schoolwide
V = Career & Tech Ed Programs

Social Media
f = Facebook
t = Twitter

New Schools are shaded
New Superintendents and Principals are bold
Personnel with email addresses are underscored

Public Schs..Principal	Grd	Prgm	Enr/#Cls	SN	
Riverside Elem Sch 3125 Pembrook Dr, Orlando 32810 Kimberly Hankerson	PK-5	T	586 38	100%	407/296-6520 Fax 407/521-3346
Rock Springs Elem Sch 2400 Rock Springs Rd, Apopka 32712 Nathan Hay	PK-5	T	803 40	65%	407/884-2242 Fax 407/884-6225
Spring Lake Elem Sch 1105 Sarah Lee Ln, Ocoee 34761 Patty Harrelson	PK-5	T	592 28	92%	407/877-5047 Fax 407/877-5062
Wolf Lake Elem Sch 1771 W Ponkan Rd, Apopka 32712 Caroll Grimando	PK-5	T	1,215 55	43%	407/464-3342 Fax 407/464-3366
Wolf Lake Middle Sch 1725 W Ponkan Rd, Apopka 32712 Cynthia Haupt	6-8	T	1,370	59%	407/464-3317 Fax 407/464-3336
Zellwood Elem Sch 3551 N Washington St, Zellwood 32798 Frank Mattucci	PK-5	T	604 32	84%	407/884-2258 Fax 407/884-3100

• Orange Co Public SD-Southeast PID: 04803581 407/317-3740
6501 Magic Way Bldg 700, Orlando 32809 Fax 407/317-3746

William Bohn 1

Public Schs..Principal	Grd	Prgm	Enr/#Cls	SN	
Andover Elem Sch 3100 Sanctuary Point Blvd, Orlando 32825 Angela Clayton	PK-5	T	835	57%	407/658-6800 Fax 407/658-6801
Conway Elem Sch 4100 Lake Margaret Dr, Orlando 32812 Sean MaGuire	PK-5	T	569 33	99%	407/249-6310 Fax 407/249-6319
Conway Middle Sch 4600 Anderson Rd, Orlando 32812 Margaret Nampon	6-8	TV	989	69%	407/249-6420 Fax 407/249-6429
Eagle Creek Elem Sch 10025 Eagle Creek Sanctuary Rd, Orlando 32832 Robert McCloe	PK-5		1,011	25%	407/930-5592 Fax 407/930-5599
Hidden Oaks Elem Sch 9051 Suburban Dr, Orlando 32829 Kenisha Holmes	PK-5	T	431 50	66%	407/249-6350 Fax 407/249-4406
Innovation Middle Sch 13950 Storey Park Blvd, Orlando 32832 Hector Maestre	6-8		1,206		407/730-4670 Fax 407/207-7213
Jackson Middle Sch 6000 Stonewall Jackson Rd, Orlando 32807 Betzabeth Reussow	6-8	TV	1,009	100%	407/249-6430 Fax 407/249-6438
Lake George Elem Sch 4101 Gatlin Ave, Orlando 32812 **Lauren Watson**	PK-5	T	604 36	100%	407/737-1430 Fax 407/737-1440
Lake Nona Middle Sch 13700 Narcoossee Rd, Orlando 32832 Stephanie Jackson	6-8	T	1,485	41%	407/858-5522 Fax 407/858-5530
Lancaster Elem Sch 6700 Sheryl Ann Dr, Orlando 32809 Lisa Suggs	PK-5	T	815 30	97%	407/858-3130 Fax 407/858-2202
Laureate Park Elem Sch 7800 Laureate Blvd, Orlando 32827 Suzanne Workum	K-5		797		407/730-8730
Liberty Middle Sch 3405 S Chickasaw Trl, Orlando 32829 Lovely Tinsley	6-8	TV	1,147 67	100%	407/249-6440 Fax 407/249-6449
McCoy Elem Sch 5225 S Semoran Blvd, Orlando 32822 Christina Howell	PK-5	T	580 38	95%	407/249-6370 Fax 407/249-4423
Meadow Woods Elem Sch 500 Rhode Island Woods Cir, Orlando 32824 Aleli Santiago	PK-5	T	775 24	90%	407/858-3140 Fax 407/858-2200

Public Schs..Principal	Grd	Prgm	Enr/#Cls	SN	
Meadow Woods Middle Sch 1800 Rhode Island Woods Cir, Orlando 32824 Marisol Mendez	6-8	T	982	100%	407/850-5180 Fax 407/850-5190
Moss Park Elem Sch 9301 N Shore Golf Club Blvd, Orlando 32832 Stephanie Osmond	PK-5		1,055	36%	407/249-4747 Fax 407/249-4469
Oakshire Elem Sch 14501 Oakshire Blvd, Orlando 32824 Mark Charlton	PK-5	T	716 60	100%	407/251-2500 Fax 407/251-2514
Odyssey Middle Sch 9290 Lee Vista Blvd, Orlando 32829 **Beatriz Smith**	6-8	TV	876 60	65%	407/207-3850 Fax 407/207-3873
Pinar Elem Sch 3701 Anthony Ln, Orlando 32822 Joscelyn Gladden	PK-5	T	390 40	90%	407/249-6380 Fax 407/249-4424
Sally Ride Elem Sch 9601 11th Ave, Orlando 32824 Raquel Flores	PK-5	T	445 35	94%	407/858-3100 Fax 407/858-2222
Shenandoah Elem Sch 4827 Conway Rd, Orlando 32812 Pamela Crabb	PK-5	T	684 35	58%	407/858-3180 Fax 407/858-2208
South Creek Middle Sch 3801 E Wetherbee Rd, Orlando 32824 Sean Brown	6-8	T	1,096	100%	407/251-2413 Fax 407/251-2464
Southwood Elem Sch 12600 Bisted Dr, Orlando 32824 Stacey Tanenbaum	PK-5	T	496 50	99%	407/858-2230 Fax 407/858-4698
Sun Blaze Elem Sch 9101 Randal Park Blvd, Orlando 32832 **Christine Szymanski**	K-5	T	1,160	47%	407/203-5110 Fax 407/250-6228
Three Points Elem Sch 4001 S Goldenrod Rd, Orlando 32822 Tiffany Stokes	PK-5	T	466	75%	407/207-3800 Fax 407/207-3803
Ventura Elem Sch 4400 Woodgate Blvd, Orlando 32822 **Ana Gonzalez**	PK-5	T	726 60	100%	407/249-6400 Fax 407/249-4417
Vista Lakes Elem Sch 6050 Lake Champlain Dr, Orlando 32829 Kristy Key	PK-5	T	745	48%	407/207-4991 Fax 407/207-7701
Walker Middle Sch 150 Amidon Ln, Orlando 32809 Rebecca Watson	6-8	TV	1,000 50	93%	407/858-3210 Fax 407/858-3218
Wetherbee Elem Sch 701 E Wetherbee Rd, Orlando 32824 Kristy Logue	PK-5	T	1,053	100%	407/850-5130 Fax 407/850-5159
Winegard Elem Sch 7055 Winegard Rd, Orlando 32809 Meigan Rivera	PK-5	T	687 33	93%	407/858-3200 Fax 407/858-2215
Wyndham Lakes Elem Sch 14360 Wyndham Lakes Blvd, Orlando 32824 Margarita Zizza	K-5	T	995	100%	407/251-2347 Fax 407/251-2376

• Orange Co Public SD-Southwest PID: 10020444 407/318-3110
6501 Magic Way Bldg 100A, Orlando 32809 Fax 407/318-3115

James Larsen 1

Public Schs..Principal	Grd	Prgm	Enr/#Cls	SN	
Bay Lake Elem Sch 12005 Silverlake Park Dr, Windermere 34786 Myrlene Jackson-Kimble	K-5		1,161	31%	407/217-7960 Fax 407/217-7969
Bay Meadows Elem Sch 9150 S Apopka Vineland Rd, Orlando 32836 Krista Bixler	K-5		603 45	34%	407/876-7500 Fax 407/876-7509
Castleview Elem Sch 9131 Taborfield Ave, Orlando 32836 **Julie Helton**	K-5		722		407/250-6290 Fax 407/909-5419

1	Superintendent	8	Curric/Instruct K-12	19	Chief Financial Officer	29	Family/Consumer Science
2	Bus/Finance/Purchasing	9	Curric/Instruct Elem	20	Art K-12	30	Adult Education
3	Buildings And Grounds	10	Curric/Instruct Sec	21	Art Elem	31	Career/Sch-to-Work K-12
4	Food Service	11	Federal Program	22	Art Sec	32	Career/Sch-to-Work Elem
5	Transportation	12	Title I	23	Music K-12	33	Career/Sch-to-Work Sec
6	Athletic	13	Title V	24	Music Elem	34	Early Childhood Ed
7	Health Services	14	Asst Superintendent	25	Music Sec	35	Health/Phys Education
		15	Instructional Media Svcs	26	Business Education	36	Guidance Services K-12
		16	Instructional Media Svcs	27	Career & Tech Ed	37	Guidance Services Elem
		17	Chief Operations Officer	28	Technology Education	38	Guidance Services Sec
		18	Chief Academic Officer				

39	Social Studies K-12	49	English/Lang Arts Elem	59	Special Education Elem	69 Academic Assessment
40	Social Studies Elem	50	English/Lang Arts Sec	60	Special Education Sec	70 Research/Development
41	Social Studies Sec	51	Reading K-12	61	Foreign/World Lang K-12	71 Public Information
42	Science K-12	52	Reading Elem	62	Foreign/World Lang Elem	72 Summer School
43	Science Elem	53	Reading Sec	63	Foreign/World Lang Sec	73 Instructional Tech
44	Science Sec	54	Remedial Reading K-12	64	Religious Education K-12	74 Inservice Training
45	Math K-12	55	Remedial Reading Elem	65	Religious Education Elem	75 Marketing/Distributive
46	Math Elem	56	Remedial Reading Sec	66	Religious Education Sec	76 Info Systems
47	Math Sec	57	Bilingual/ELL	67	School Board President	77 Psychological Assess
48	English/Lang Arts K-12	58	Special Education K-12	68	Teacher Personnel	78 Affirmative Action

School	Grd	Prgm	Enr/#Cls	SN	Phone
Catalina Elem Sch 2448 29th St, Orlando 32805 Seth Daub	PK-5	T	733 35	82%	407/245-1735 Fax 407/245-2744
Chain of Lakes Middle Sch 8700 Conroy Windermere Rd, Orlando 32835 Cheron Anderson	6-8	T	1,302 48	68%	407/909-5400 Fax 407/909-5410
Cherokee Sch 555 S Eola Dr, Orlando 32801 Rojina Durant	Spec	T	35 25	89%	407/897-6440 Fax 407/897-2402
Dover Shores Elem Sch 1200 Gaston Foster Rd, Orlando 32812 Randall Hart	K-5	T	418 36	99%	407/249-6330 Fax 407/249-4401
Dr Phillips Elem Sch 6909 Dr Phillips Blvd, Orlando 32819 **Christine Rogers**	PK-5	T	729 37	37%	407/354-2600 Fax 407/354-2606
Eagle's Nest Elem Sch 5353 Metrowest Blvd, Orlando 32811 **Lisa Adams**	PK-5	T	710	91%	407/521-2795 Fax 407/521-2797
Eccleston Elem Sch 1500 Aaron Ave, Orlando 32811 **Janet Bittick**	K-5	T	541 36	80%	407/296-6400 Fax 407/521-3321
Endeavor Elem Sch 13501 Balcombe Rd, Orlando 32837 Dr Amanda Ellis	K-5	T	726 43	66%	407/251-2560 Fax 407/251-2561
Freedom Middle Sch 2850 W Taft Vineland Rd, Orlando 32837 **Cheri Leavitt**	6-8	T	1,255	100%	407/858-6130 Fax 407/858-6132
Horizon West Middle Sch 8200 Tattant Blvd, Windermere 34786 **Michelle Thomas**	6-8		401		407/544-1570 Fax 407/374-2627
Hunter's Creek Elem Sch 4650 W Town Center Blvd, Orlando 32837 Fresia Urdaneta	PK-5	T	905 60	47%	407/858-4610 Fax 407/858-4611
Lake Como K-8 Sch 1600 E Kaley Ave, Orlando 32806 Isolda Antonio Fisher	PK-8	T	612 26	99%	407/897-6420 Fax 407/897-2407
Memorial Middle Sch 2220 29th St, Orlando 32805 Tamara Drayton	6-8	TV	803	76%	407/245-1810 Fax 407/245-1820
Millennia Elem Sch 5301 Cypress Creek Dr, Orlando 32811 **Dyanira Pena**	PK-5	T	1,031	100%	407/355-5730 Fax 407/355-5711
Millennia Gardens Elem Sch 3515 Gardens Ridge Way, Orlando 32839 **Michelle Carralero**	PK-5		997	100%	407/845-0665 Fax 407/845-0674
Palm Lake Elem Sch 8000 Pin Oak Dr, Orlando 32819 James Weis	K-5		674 36	43%	407/354-2610 Fax 407/354-2618
Palmetto Elem Sch 2015 Duskin Ave, Orlando 32839 Faythia Carpenter	PK-5	T	914 75	100%	407/858-3150 Fax 407/858-3159
Pineloch Elem Sch 3101 Woods St, Orlando 32805 Stacey Price	PK-5	T	834 30	100%	407/245-1825 Fax 407/245-1830 [f]
Sadler Elem Sch 4000 W Oak Ridge Rd, Orlando 32809 Kahlil Ortiz	PK-5	T	827 62	100%	407/354-2620 Fax 407/354-2665
Sand Lake Elem Sch 8301 Buenavista Woods Blvd, Orlando 32836 Laura Suprenard	K-5	T	672	45%	407/903-7400 Fax 407/903-7411
Shingle Creek Elem Sch 5620 Harcourt Ave, Orlando 32839 Jennifer Schafer	PK-5	T	855 30	100%	407/354-2650 Fax 407/354-2657
Southwest Middle Sch 6450 Dr Phillips Blvd, Orlando 32819 Raymond Yockel	6-8	TV	1,446 65	52%	407/370-7200 Fax 407/370-7210
Sunset Park Elem Sch 12050 Overstreet Rd, Windermere 34786 **Jay Gangwisch**	K-5		933 61	26%	407/905-3724 Fax 407/905-3815
Tangelo Park Elem Sch 5115 Anzio St, Orlando 32819 Lakeitha Black	PK-5	T	666 24	92%	407/354-2630 Fax 407/354-2663
Waterbridge Elem Sch 11100 Galvin Dr, Orlando 32837 John Carcara	PK-5	T	1,352 63	100%	407/858-3190 Fax 407/858-2205
West Creek Elem Sch 5056 Tacon Dr, Orlando 32837 Michelle Couret	K-5		857	44%	407/858-5920 Fax 407/858-5922
Westridge Middle Sch 3800 W Oak Ridge Rd, Orlando 32809 Matthew Turner	6-8	TV	1,249 65	100%	407/354-2640 Fax 407/354-2637

- **Orange Co Public SD-West** PID: 04803579   407/905-3200
  1399 Windermere Rd, Winter Garden 34787   Fax 407/905-3213

Patricia Fritzler 1

Public Schs..Principal	Grd	Prgm	Enr/#Cls	SN	Phone
Bridgewater Middle Sch 5600 Tiny Rd, Winter Garden 34787 Andrew Jackson	6-8		2,608	28%	407/905-3710 Fax 407/905-3858
Citrus Elem Sch 87 N Clarke Rd, Ocoee 34761 Delaine Bender	K-5	T	596 63	99%	407/445-5475 Fax 407/445-5499
Dillard Street Elem Sch 311 N Dillard St, Winter Garden 34787 **Tiffany Smid**	PK-5	T	530	100%	407/877-5000 Fax 407/877-5009 [f]
Frangus Elem Sch 380 Killington Way, Orlando 32835 Decheryl Britton	K-5	T	458 50	99%	407/296-6469 Fax 407/521-3323
Gotha Middle Sch 9155 Gotha Rd, Windermere 34786 Monica Emery	6-8	T	1,217 60	58%	407/521-2360 Fax 407/203-2112
Hiawassee Elem Sch 6800 Hennepin Blvd, Orlando 32818 Sharon Jenkins	PK-5	T	655 30	91%	407/296-6410 Fax 407/521-3340
Independence Elem Sch 6255 New Independence Pkwy, Winter Garden 34787 Dr Angela Murphy-Osborne	K-5		1,307	20%	407/217-7727 Fax 407/217-7731
Keene's Crossing Elem Sch 5240 Keenes Pheasant Dr, Windermere 34786 Sherry Donaldson	PK-5		1,466	24%	407/654-1351 Fax 407/654-1829
Lake Whitney Elem Sch 1351 Windermere Rd, Winter Garden 34787 Dr Elizabeth Prince	PK-5		544 50	17%	407/877-8888 Fax 407/877-1181
Lakeview Middle Sch 1200 W Bay St, Winter Garden 34787 Gracemarie Howland	6-8	TV	908 55	66%	407/877-5010 Fax 407/877-5019
Magnolia Sch 1900 Matterhorn Dr, Orlando 32818 **Latonia Green**	Spec	T	117 33	86%	407/296-6499 Fax 407/521-3301
Maxey Elem Sch 602 E Story Rd, Winter Garden 34787 Carletta Davis-Wilson	PK-5	T	351 19	91%	407/877-5020 Fax 407/877-2580 [f]
MetroWest Elem Sch 1801 Lake Vilma Dr, Orlando 32835 **Xhuljeta Gjini**	K-5	T	649 60	70%	407/296-6450 Fax 407/445-5432
Oak Hill Elem Sch 11 S Hiawassee Rd, Orlando 32835 Dr June Jones	PK-5	T	515 27	99%	407/296-6470 Fax 407/521-3343
Ocoee Elem Sch 400 S Lakewood Ave, Ocoee 34761 **Kandace Goshe**	PK-5	T	778 25	100%	407/877-5027 Fax 407/877-8583 [f]

79	Student Personnel	91	Safety/Security	275	Response To Intervention	298	Grant Writer/Ptnrships	School Programs	Social Media
80	Driver Ed/Safety	92	Magnet School	277	Remedial Math K-12	750	Chief Innovation Officer	A = Alternative Program	
81	Gifted/Talented	93	Parental Involvement	280	Literacy Coach	751	Chief of Staff	G = Adult Classes	[f] = Facebook
82	Video Services	95	Tech Prep Program	285	STEM	752	Social Emotional Learning	M = Magnet Program	
83	Substance Abuse Prev	97	Chief Infomation Officer	286	Digital Learning			T = Title I Schoolwide	[t] = Twitter
84	Erate	98	Chief Technology Officer	288	Common Core Standards	Other School Types		V = Career & Tech Ed Programs	
85	AIDS Education	270	Character Education	294	Accountability	Ⓐ = Alternative School			
86	Alternative/At Risk	271	Migrant Education	295	Network System	Ⓒ = Charter School		New Schools are shaded	
87	Multi-Cultural Curriculum	273	Teacher Mentor	296	Title II Programs	Ⓜ = Magnet School		New Superintendents and Principals are bold	
90	Social Work	274	Before/After Sch	297	Webmaster	Ⓨ = Year-Round School		Personnel with email addresses are underscored	

School	Grd	Prgm	Enr/#Cls	SN	Phone
Ocoee Middle Sch 300 S Bluford Ave, Ocoee 34761 Sam Davis	6-8	T	1,356 63	71%	407/877-5035 Fax 407/877-5045
Orange Center Elem Sch 621 S Texas Ave, Orlando 32805 Ladonna Johnson	PK-5	T	376 45	86%	407/296-6480 Fax 407/521-3344 [f]
Pine Hills Elem Sch 1006 Ferndell Rd, Orlando 32808 Fredrick Brooks	PK-5		713 27		407/296-6500 Fax 407/296-6436
Robinswood Middle Sch 6305 Balboa Dr, Orlando 32818 Nicole Jefferson	6-8	TV	1,221	94%	407/296-5140 Fax 407/296-5148
Rolling Hills Elem Sch 4903 Donovan St, Orlando 32808 Farah Henderson	PK-5	T	494 35	82%	407/296-6530 Fax 407/521-3347
Sunridge Elem Sch 14455 Sunridge Blvd, Winter Garden 34787 Christy Gorberg	K-5	T	730	55%	407/656-0809 Fax 407/656-0830
Thornebrooke Elem Sch 601 Thornebrooke Dr, Ocoee 34761 Christopher Daniels	PK-5		752	30%	407/909-1301 Fax 407/909-1318 [f]
Tildenville Elem Sch 1221 Brick Rd, Winter Garden 34787 Agatha Alvarez	PK-5	T	541 30	65%	407/877-5054 Fax 407/877-5060 [f]
Washington Shores Elem Sch 944 W Lake Mann Dr, Orlando 32805 Nathaniel Stephens	PK-5	T	642 40	87%	407/296-6540 Fax 407/521-3348 [f]
Water Spring Elem Sch 1600 Waterspring Blvd, Winter Garden 34787 Amy Klaber	K-5		864		407/993-7310 Fax 407/250-6297
West Oaks Elem Sch 905 Dorscher Rd, Orlando 32818 Cherie Thompson	PK-5	T	598	93%	407/532-3875 Fax 407/532-3878
Westbrooke Elem Sch 500 Tomyn Blvd, Ocoee 34761 Vidal Reyes	PK-5		673 35	43%	407/656-6228 Fax 407/656-6741
Westpointe Elem Sch 7525 Westpointe Blvd, Orlando 32835 **Atresa Grubbs-Holmes**	K-5		715		407/866-1271 Fax 407/866-1278
Whispering Oak Elem Sch 15300 Stoneybrook West Pkwy, Winter Garden 34787 Lee Montgomery	PK-5		1,088	24%	407/656-7773 Fax 407/905-3566
Windermere Elem Sch 11125 Park Ave, Windermere 34786 Diana Greer	K-5		703 37	12%	407/876-7520 Fax 407/876-7523

ORANGE CATHOLIC SCHOOLS

- **Diocese of Orlando Ed Office** PID: 00197639   407/246-4900
  50 E Robinson St, Orlando 32801   Fax 407/246-4940

Schools: 37 \ **Students:** 14,673

Listing includes only schools located in this county. See District Index for location of Diocesan Offices.

Catholic Schs..Principal	Grd	Prgm	Enr/#Cls	SN
Bishop Moore High Sch 3901 Edgewater Dr, Orlando 32804 Scott Brogan	9-12		1,175 57	407/293-7561 Fax 407/296-8135
Good Shepherd Cath Sch 5902 Oleander Dr, Orlando 32807 Jayme Hartmann	PK-8		520 34	407/277-3973 Fax 407/277-2605
Holy Family Catholic Sch 5129 S Apopka Vineland Rd, Orlando 32819 Sr Dorothy Sayers	PK-8		690 20	407/876-9344 Fax 407/876-8775 [f]
Morning Star Sch 954 Leigh Ave, Orlando 32804 Sandra Cooney	Spec		75 6	407/295-3077 Fax 407/522-1700
St Andrew Sch 877 N Hastings St, Orlando 32808 Latrina Peters-Gipson	PK-8		350 20	407/295-4230 Fax 407/290-0959
St Charles Borromeo Sch 4005 Edgewater Dr, Orlando 32804 Nathan Nadeau	PK-8		462 23	407/293-7691 Fax 407/295-9839 [f][t]
St James Cathedral Sch 505 E Ridgewood St, Orlando 32803 Anthony Gutierrez	PK-8		504 20	407/841-4432 Fax 407/648-4603
St John Vianney Sch 6200 S Orange Blossom Trl, Orlando 32809 Cathy Marshall	PK-8		530 21	407/855-4660 Fax 407/857-7932
St Margaret Mary Sch 142 E Swoope Ave, Winter Park 32789 Kathleen Walsh	PK-8		532 25	407/644-7537 Fax 407/644-7357

ORANGE PRIVATE SCHOOLS

Private Schs..Principal	Grd	Prgm	Enr/#Cls	SN
Academy for Autism 11 E Lancaster Rd, Orlando 32809 Zulma Rivas-Vetell	Spec		50	407/852-9922 Fax 407/852-9944
Agape Christian Academy 2425 N Hiawassee Rd, Orlando 32818 Michelange Bertrand	PK-12		416 50	407/298-1111 Fax 407/298-0400
Alpha Learning Academy 1960 Bruton Blvd, Orlando 32805 Shakelia Henderson	K-5		145	407/422-6941 Fax 407/841-0307
Apopka Christian Academy 509 S Park Ave, Apopka 32703 Jessica Haught	K-12		138	407/889-7288 Fax 407/889-9001
Avalon Sch 5002 Andrus Ave, Orlando 32804 Dr Robert Shafer	K-12		120	407/297-4353 Fax 407/578-5418
Azalea Park Baptist Sch 5725 Dahlia Dr, Orlando 32807 Alexa Ortega	PK-12		132 20	407/277-4056 Fax 407/277-4068
Baptist Temple Sch 4400 N Powers Dr, Orlando 32818 Dr Russel Riggs	PK-12		82 10	407/293-2772 Fax 407/293-6683
Beeman Park Preparatory Sch 2300 Ridge Ave, Orlando 32803 Jeanne Smith	PK-5		75 5	407/894-5121 Fax 407/894-6579
Beryl Wisdom Adventist Sch 4955 Rose Ave, Orlando 32808 Brenda Trim	PK-8		110 8	407/291-3073 Fax 407/291-6149
Bright Learning-Cyber High Sch 7300 Aloma Ave, Winter Park 32792 Joanne Friedland	K-12		42	407/455-0622 Fax 321/295-7906
Brush Arbor Christian Sch 2304 N Goldenrod Rd, Orlando 32807 Kim Pierce	PK-9		180 12	407/671-9774 Fax 407/678-4807

1 Superintendent	8 Curric/Instruct K-12	19 Chief Financial Officer	29 Family/Consumer Science	39 Social Studies K-12	49 English/Lang Arts Elem	59 Special Education Elem	69 Academic Assessment
2 Bus/Finance/Purchasing	9 Curric/Instruct Elem	20 Art K-12	30 Adult Education	40 Social Studies Elem	50 English/Lang Arts Sec	60 Special Education Sec	70 Research/Development
3 Buildings And Grounds	10 Curric/Instruct Sec	21 Art Elem	31 Career/Sch-to-Work K-12	41 Social Studies Sec	51 Reading K-12	61 Foreign/World Lang K-12	71 Public Information
4 Food Service	11 Federal Program	22 Art Sec	32 Career/Sch-to-Work Elem	42 Science K-12	52 Reading Elem	62 Foreign/World Lang Elem	72 Summer School
5 Transportation	12 Title I	23 Music K-12	33 Career/Sch-to-Work Sec	43 Science Elem	53 Reading Sec	63 Foreign/World Lang Sec	73 Instructional Tech
6 Athletic	13 Title V	24 Music Elem	34 Early Childhood Ed	44 Science Sec	54 Remedial Reading K-12	64 Religious Education K-12	74 Inservice Training
7 Health Services	15 Asst Superintendent	25 Music Sec	35 Health/Phys Education	45 Math K-12	55 Remedial Reading Elem	65 Religious Education Elem	75 Marketing/Distributive
	16 Instructional Media Svcs	26 Business Education	36 Guidance Services K-12	46 Math Elem	56 Remedial Reading Sec	66 Religious Education Sec	76 Info Systems
	17 Chief Operations Officer	27 Career & Tech Ed	37 Guidance Services Elem	47 Math Sec	57 Bilingual/ELL	67 School Board President	77 Psychological Assess
	18 Chief Academic Officer	28 Technology Education	38 Guidance Services Sec	48 English/Lang Arts K-12	58 Special Education K-12	68 Teacher Personnel	78 Affirmative Action

FL—100

School	Grades		Enroll/Staff	Phone
Calvary City Chrn Acad & PS 2500 W Oak Ridge Rd, Orlando 32809	PK-12		401	407/581-6120
Center Academy 341 N Orlando Ave, Maitland 32751 Joann Sas	Spec		80 3	407/772-8727 Fax 407/772-8747
Central Christian Academy 6927 University Blvd, Winter Park 32792 Les Rawle	1-12		350	407/332-6988
Central Florida Chrn Academy 700 Good Homes Rd, Orlando 32818 Pam Theobald	PK-12	V	250	407/293-8062 Fax 407/290-1579
Central Florida Prep Sch 1450 Citrus Oaks Ave Bldg 300, Gotha 34734 Sandy Gomez	PK-12		240 25	407/290-8073 Fax 407/298-6443 f t
Changing Lives Academy 7215 Monetary Dr Ste 109, Orlando 32809	K-12		401	407/613-2445
Christ Sch 106 E Church St, Orlando 32801 Michael Noto \ T Ross	K-8		327 25	407/849-1665 Fax 407/481-2325 f t
Christian Learning Academy 750 Roger Williams Rd, Apopka 32703 Louis Pfleger	K-12		220	407/410-0049 Fax 407/386-3252
Circle Christian Sch 2134 Kentucky Ave, Winter Park 32789 Jim Werner	K-12		900	407/740-8877 Fax 407/740-8580
Cranium Clubhouse Sch 4068 Winter Garden Vineland Rd, Winter Garden 34787 Ester Grillo	PK-5		150	407/347-5021
Crenshaw School Florida 2342 Hempel Ave, Gotha 34734 Tanya Williams	PK-12		110	407/757-2241 Fax 407/613-5845
Downey Christian Sch 10201 E Colonial Dr, Orlando 32817 Charles Dees	K-12		87 14	407/275-0340 Fax 407/275-1481
Eastland Christian Sch 9000 Lake Underhill Rd, Orlando 32825 Tony Sales	PK-12		300 7	407/277-5858 Fax 407/658-1013
El Bethel Christian Academy 3000 Bruton Blvd, Orlando 32805 Allison Riley-Moore	K-12		58 4	407/648-1978 Fax 407/648-1979
Faith Christian Academy 9307 Curry Ford Rd, Orlando 32825 Lacey Mahoney \ Maribeliz Ramos \ Lonzo Caves	PK-12		450 29	407/275-8031 Fax 407/281-3710
Family Christian Academy 15060 Old Cheney Hwy, Orlando 32828 Tracy Kleinwort \ Taina Glemser	K-12		105	407/568-9837 Fax 407/568-1479
Family Christian Sch 671 Beulah Rd, Winter Garden 34787 Terri Schneberger	PK-8		120	407/656-7904 Fax 407/656-0274
Forest City Adventist Sch 7563 Forest City Rd, Orlando 32810 Humberto Lopez	K-8		90 7	407/299-0703 Fax 407/299-9481
Forest Lake Academy 500 Education Loop, Apopka 32703 Glen Baker	9-12		388 16	407/862-8411 Fax 407/862-7050
Foundation Academy-North 125 E Plant St, Winter Garden 34787 Angel Whitehead	PK-6		400 36	407/656-3677 Fax 407/656-0118 f
Foundation Academy-South 15304 Tilden Rd, Winter Garden 34787 Sarah Reynolds	6-12		250	407/877-2744 Fax 407/877-1985 f
Grace Christian Academy 5401 Curry Ford Rd, Orlando 32812 Steve Thomas	K-12		56 7	407/617-8833 Fax 321/247-5001
Hampden Dubose Academy 5400 Sadler Road, Zellwood 32798 Michael Jackson	K-12		100 8	407/880-4321 Fax 407/886-2297
Heritage Preparatory Sch 6000 W Colonial Dr, Orlando 32808 Dr Barbara Stewart	PK-12		250 20	407/295-3086 Fax 407/292-7246
House of Hope Academy 2036 36th St, Orlando 32839	7-12		20 2	407/843-8686
Ibn Seena Academy 12908 S Orange Blossom Trl, Orlando 32837 Rehannah Hemille	PK-12		180	407/888-1000 Fax 407/240-1603
International Community Sch 4800 Howell Branch Rd, Winter Park 32792 Robyn Terwilleger	PK-12		420 17	407/645-2343
Jewish Academy of Orlando 851 N Maitland Ave, Maitland 32751 Alan Rusonik	K-8		200 16	407/647-0713 Fax 407/647-1223 f
King of Kings Lutheran Sch 1101 N Wymore Rd, Maitland 32751 Randy Cochran	K-8		60 4	407/628-5696 Fax 407/628-5230
Kingsway Christian Academy 4161 N Powers Dr, Orlando 32818 Diane Copeland	PK-8		415 18	407/295-8901 Fax 407/295-9651
La Amistad Sch 1650 N Park Ave, Maitland 32751 Michelle Nye	Spec		60 5	407/647-0660 Fax 407/637-3067
Lake Forrest Preparatory Sch 866 Lake Howell Rd, Maitland 32751 Michele Purvis	PK-8		225	407/331-5144 Fax 407/331-1849
Lake Highland Preparatory Sch 901 Highland Ave, Orlando 32803 Debbie DeLoach \ Derrick Daly \ Mike Jakubisin	PK-12		1,890	407/206-1900 Fax 407/206-1933
Lake Rose Christian Academy 4340 N Hiawassee Rd, Orlando 32818 Keisha Long	K-12		50	407/297-6995 Fax 407/297-7887
Leaders Preparatory Sch 1021 N Goldenrod Rd, Orlando 32807 Dr Feryal Elkhaldi	PK-12		200 10	407/382-9900 Fax 407/277-4190
Living Word Academy 653 E Wetherbee Rd, Orlando 32824 Michelle Nieves	PK-7		120	407/851-6464 Fax 407/447-7638
Maitland Montessori Sch 236 N Swoope Ave, Maitland 32751 Adele Fondo	PK-8	G	170 9	407/628-0019 Fax 407/628-9796
Montessori School-Orlando 1187 Florida Mall Ave Ste 108, Orlando 32809 Marilou Esguerra	PK-6		85	407/601-4247
Montessori Way Sch 4124 W Town Center Blvd, Orlando 32837 Samantha Kaufmann	PK-6		50	407/852-1997 Fax 407/438-7881
Mt Sinai Jr Academy 2610 Orange Center Blvd, Orlando 32805 Dr Lee Buddy	K-8		74 5	407/298-7871 Fax 407/298-7874
Muslim Academy-Greater Orlando 11551 Ruby Lake Rd, Orlando 32836 Jameer Abass	K-8		295	407/238-0144 Fax 407/238-4689
Orangewood Christian Sch 1300 W Maitland Blvd, Maitland 32751 Dawn Miller \ Joe Austin	K-12	V	701 55	407/339-0223 Fax 407/339-4148
Orlando Christian Prep 500 S Semoran Blvd, Orlando 32807 Jennie Jacobson	PK-12		400 30	407/823-9744 Fax 407/380-1186
Orlando Junior Academy 30 E Evans St, Orlando 32804 Neil Hawkins	PK-8		260 17	407/898-1251 Fax 407/894-6213
Page Pvt Sch-Univ Park Campus 10250 University Blvd, Orlando 32817 Patricia Klindworth	PK-8		250 40	407/678-0333 Fax 407/657-7288

79	Student Personnel	91	Safety/Security	275	Response To Intervention	298	Grant Writer/Ptnrships	**School Programs**	**Social Media**
80	Driver Ed/Safety	92	Magnet School	277	Remedial Math K-12	750	Chief Innovation Officer	A = Alternative Program	
81	Gifted/Talented	93	Parental Involvement	280	Literacy Coach	751	Chief of Staff	G = Adult Classes	f = Facebook
82	Video Services	95	Tech Prep Program	285	STEM	752	Social Emotional Learning	M = Magnet Program	
83	Substance Abuse Prev	97	Chief Infomation Officer	286	Digital Learning			T = Title I Schoolwide	t = Twitter
84	Erate	98	Chief Technology Officer	288	Common Core Standards	**Other School Types**		V = Career & Tech Ed Programs	
85	AIDS Education	270	Character Education	294	Accountability	Ⓐ = Alternative School			
86	Alternative/At Risk	271	Migrant Education	295	Network System	Ⓒ = Charter School		**New Schools are shaded**	
88	Multi-Cultural Curriculum	273	Teacher Mentor	296	Title II Programs	Ⓜ = Magnet School		**New Superintendents and Principals are bold**	
90	Social Work	274	Before/After Sch	297	Webmaster	Ⓨ = Year-Round School		Personnel with email addresses are underscored	

Park Maitland Sch 1450 S Orlando Ave, Maitland 32751 Cindy Moon	PK-6	700 43	407/647-3038 Fax 407/645-4755	
Parke House Academy 1776 Minnesota Ave, Winter Park 32789 Danelle Restrepo	PK-5	190 13	407/647-1121 Fax 407/647-1134	
Pathways Sch 1877 W Oak Ridge Rd, Orlando 32809 Christy James	PK-12	207 20	407/816-2040 Fax 407/816-2080	
Peaceforce Christian Academy 501 Wilmer Ave, Orlando 32808 Eli Gonzalez	K-12	40	407/290-9279 Fax 407/523-6501	
Pine Castle Christian Academy 7101 Lake Ellenor Dr, Orlando 32809 Michelle Pacheco	PK-12	155	407/313-7222 Fax 407/313-7226	
Potters House Academy & DCC 7051 Pershing Ave, Orlando 32822 Emelie Alvarez	PK-12	266	407/367-0435 Fax 407/736-0762	
Providence Academy-W Campus 7605 Conroy Windermere Rd, Orlando 32835 Jennifer Foor	Spec	46	407/298-8699 Fax 407/293-2109	
Radiant Life Acad & Child Care 8151 Clarcona Ocoee Rd, Orlando 32818 Stacia Cromwell	PK-8	170 12	407/299-7460 Fax 407/299-7462	
South Orlando Christian Acad 5815 Makoma Dr, Orlando 32839 Elizabeth Campo	PK-12	200 15	407/859-9511 Fax 407/859-1510	
The First Academy 2667 Bruton Blvd, Orlando 32805 Dr Shayne Grove \ Jennifer Jackson	PK-12	1,006	407/206-8600 Fax 407/206-8700	
The Geneva Sch 2025 State Road 436, Winter Park 32792 Robert Ingram	PK-12	454	407/332-6363 Fax 407/332-1664	
The Lyman Sch 1870 State Road 436, Winter Park 32792 Linda Elchak	1-12	70	407/898-7099	
Trinity Christian Sch 1022 S Orange Blossom Trl, Apopka 32703 Raeann Johnson	PK-9	250 26	407/886-0212 Fax 407/886-3052	
Trinity Preparatory Sch 5700 Trinity Prep Ln, Winter Park 32792 Jason Dowdy \ Patrick Mulloy	6-12	860 53	407/671-4140 Fax 407/671-6935	
Victory Christian Academy 240 N Ivey Ln, Orlando 32811 Lakeisha Robinson	K-12	165 6	407/295-3332 Fax 407/295-3331	
Victory Christian Academy 1601 A D Mims Rd, Ocoee 34761 Jason Davis	PK-8	100 14	407/656-1295 Fax 407/656-6895	
West Oaks Academy 8624 A D Mims Rd, Orlando 32818 Thomas Parlier	K-12	375 13	407/292-8481 Fax 407/292-8838	
Windermere Preparatory Sch 6189 State Road 535, Windermere 34786 Thomas Marcy	PK-12	1,500 70	407/905-7737 Fax 407/905-7710	

ORANGE REGIONAL CENTERS

• **FDLRS-Action** PID: 04496205
3130 Edgewater Dr, Orlando 32804

407/317-3660
Fax 407/317-3680

Sandra Collins ....1,11 Mia Laudato 73
Andrea Dunckel 90

OSCEOLA PUBLIC SCHOOLS

• **Osceola Co School Dist** PID: 00197964
817 Bill Beck Blvd, Kissimmee 34744

407/870-4600
Fax 407/870-4010

Schools: 77 \ **Teachers:** 3,863 \ **Students:** 67,709 \
Special Ed Students: 6,837 \ **LEP Students:** 12,294 \ **College-Bound:** 75%
\ **Ethnic:** Asian 2%, African American 11%, Hispanic 62%, Caucasian
25% \ **Exp:** $134 (Low) \ **Title I:** $18,126,668 \
Special Education: $42,555,000 \ **Bilingual Education:** $23,253,000 \
Open-Close: 08/12 - 05/28 \ **DTBP:** $181 (High) \ 🅣

Dr Debra Pace 1	Amanda Kraft 2,7
Cheryl Hood 2	Cindy Stevens 2
Edward Parker 2	Lisa Lynch 2
Sarah Graber 2,19	Charlie Bishop 3
David Barkholz 3	Marc Clinch 3,17
Mark Cavinee 3	Mark Scheuer 3
Randy Shuttera 3,15	Rhonda Blake 3
Judith Gordon 4	Edward Jones 5
T Arby Creach 5	Ryan Adams 6,80
Yolanda Brinkley 8	Dr Jane Respess 9
Dr Laura Rhinehart 10	Michael Allen 10
Dlane Rivers 11	John Boyd 11
Dr Scott Fritz 15,751	Thomas Phelps 15,68
Carol Etter 16,73	Michelle Jarrett 16,73
Scott Clark 16,27,73,82,84	Brenda Berube 27,30,31
Mary Ann Perez 34,274*	Sara Schumacher 36
Belinda Reyes 57,89	Leslie Campbell 58,296
Linda Schroder-King 58	Lisa Overton 58
Ricky Booth 67	Tammy Cope-Otterson 68
Angela Barner 69	Dr Leah Torres 69,70,294
Dana Lee Schafer 71	Peter Thorne 71
Russell Holmes 73	Janice Franceschi 74
Karen Vislocky 74	MacKenzie Bertram 74
Michelle Henninger 74	Virginia Ramie 74
Ulysses Vazquez 76,97	Daryla Bungo 79
Patricia Vickers 79	Karen Combs 88*
Beverly Hughes 91	Lester Yeates 91
Dr Sonia Esposito 92	Trenisha Davis-Simmons 274
Dr Edwin Rentas 286*	

Public Schs..Principal	Grd	Prgm	Enr/#Cls	SN
Adult Lrng Center Osceola 2320 New Beginnings Rd, Kissimmee 34744 **Karen Combs**	Adult		460 12	407/518-8140 Fax 407/518-8141
© Avant Garde Academy 3540 Pleasant Hill Rd, Kissimmee 34746 Guillermo Moreno	K-8		262	71% 407/944-4464 Fax 407/386-6048
© Avant Garde Academy of Osceola 2880 N Orange Blossom Trl, Kissimmee 34744 Jason Gines	6-12	T	544	59% 321/697-3800 Fax 321/697-3850
© Bellalago Charter Academy 3651 Pleasant Hill Rd, Kissimmee 34746 Jonathan Rasmussen	PK-8	T	1,472	67% 407/933-1690 Fax 407/933-2143
Boggy Creek Elem Sch 810 Florida Pkwy, Kissimmee 34743 Rhonda McMahon	PK-5	T	715 36	72% 407/344-5060 Fax 407/344-5070
© Bridgeprep Academy Osceola 4851 K O A St, Kissimmee 34758 Dr Linton Atkinson	K-8		449	407/603-3890

1	Superintendent	8	Curric/Instruct K-12	19	Chief Financial Officer
2	Bus/Finance/Purchasing	9	Curric/Instruct Elem	20	Art K-12
3	Buildings And Grounds	10	Curric/Instruct Sec	21	Art Elem
4	Food Service	11	Federal Program	22	Art Sec
5	Transportation	12	Title I	23	Music K-12
6	Athletic	13	Title V	24	Music Elem
7	Health Services	14	Instructional Media Svcs	25	Music Sec
		15	Asst Superintendent	26	Business Education
		16	Instructional Media Svcs	27	Career & Tech Ed
		17	Chief Operations Officer	28	Technology Education
		18	Chief Academic Officer		

29	Family/Consumer Science	39	Social Studies K-12
30	Adult Education	40	Social Studies Elem
31	Career/Sch-to-Work K-12	41	Social Studies Sec
32	Career/Sch-to-Work Elem	42	Science K-12
33	Career/Sch-to-Work Sec	43	Science Elem
34	Early Childhood Ed	44	Science Sec
35	Health/Phys Education	45	Math K-12
36	Guidance Services K-12	46	Math Elem
37	Guidance Services Elem	47	Math Sec
38	Guidance Services Sec	48	English/Lang Arts K-12

49	English/Lang Arts Elem	59	Special Education Elem
50	English/Lang Arts Sec	60	Special Education Sec
51	Reading K-12	61	Foreign/World Lang K-12
52	Reading Elem	62	Foreign/World Lang Elem
53	Reading Sec	63	Foreign/World Lang Sec
54	Remedial Reading K-12	64	Religious Education K-12
55	Remedial Reading Elem	65	Religious Education Elem
56	Remedial Reading Sec	66	Religious Education Sec
57	Bilingual/ELL	67	School Board President
58	Special Education K-12	68	Teacher Personnel

69	Academic Assessment
70	Research/Development
71	Public Information
72	Summer School
73	Instructional Tech
74	Inservice Training
75	Marketing/Distributive
76	Info Systems
77	Psychological Assess
78	Affirmative Action

School	Grades	Programs	Enroll	%	Phone
© Canoe Creek Charter Academy [133] 3600 Canoe Creek Rd, Saint Cloud 34772 **Alan Ramos**	K-8	T	491	50%	407/891-7320 Fax 407/891-7330
Celebration High Sch 1809 Celebration Blvd, Celebration 34747 Conner Gilbert	9-12	T	2,663	63%	321/939-6600 Fax 321/939-6652
Celebration Sch 510 Campus St, Celebration 34747 Kimberly Manion	PK-8	V	1,531	24%	407/566-2300 Fax 321/939-6694
Central Ave Elem Sch 500 W Columbia Ave, Kissimmee 34741 Nadia Winston	PK-5	T	704 48	71%	407/343-7330 Fax 407/343-7332
Chestnut ES-Sci & Engineering 4300 Chestnut St, Kissimmee 34759 Gary Bressler	PK-5	T	716	63%	407/870-4862 Fax 407/870-4864
© Creative Inspiration Journey 2030 Old Hickory Rd, Saint Cloud 34769 **Patricia Marquis**	K-5		401		877/244-8562
Cypress Elem Sch 2251 Lakeside Dr, Kissimmee 34743 Libby Raymond	PK-5	T	623 100	67%	407/344-5000 Fax 407/344-5006
Deerwood Elem Sch 3701 Marigold Ave, Kissimmee 34758 Audie Confesor	PK-5	T	578 40	71%	407/870-2400 Fax 407/870-2648
Denn John Middle Sch 2001 Denn John Ln, Kissimmee 34744 Hank Hoyle	6-8	ATV	964 75	66%	407/935-3560 Fax 407/935-3572
Discovery Intermediate Sch 5350 San Miguel Rd, Kissimmee 34758 Henry Santiago	6-8	T	937 40	66%	407/343-7300 Fax 407/343-7310
East Lake Elem Sch 4001 Boggy Creek Rd, Kissimmee 34744 Hilary DeLuca	PK-5	T	943	49%	407/943-8450 Fax 407/943-7255
Flora Ridge Elem Sch 2900 Dyer Blvd, Kissimmee 34741 **William Dwyer**	PK-5	T	1,075	44%	407/933-3999 Fax 407/933-3998
© Florida Cyber CS Acad Osceola 9143 Philips Hwy Ste 590, Jacksonville 32256 Farica King	K-12		155		904/247-3268 Fax 877/719-1645
© Florida Virtual Acad Osceola 817 Bill Beck Blvd, Kissimmee 34744 Patty Betoni	K-9		106		407/870-1445 Fax 407/870-4600
© Four Corners Charter Sch [133] 9100 Teacher Ln, Davenport 33897 Audrelia Thompson	K-5	T	989	65%	407/787-4300 Fax 407/787-4331 �facebook 🇹
© Four Corners Upper Sch [133] 9160 Bella Citta Blvd, Davenport 33896 Denise Thompson	6-12		1,099		407/589-4600 Fax 407/589-4601 �facebook 🇹
Gateway High Sch 93 Panther Paws Trl, Kissimmee 34744 James Long	9-12	ATV	1,729 120	51%	407/935-3600 Fax 407/935-3609
Harmony Community Sch 3365 Schoolhouse Rd, Harmony 34773 Sandra Davenport	PK-8		1,104	36%	407/892-1655 Fax 407/343-8745
Harmony High Sch 3601 Arthur J Gallagher Blvd, Saint Cloud 34771 James Hickey	9-12	ATV	2,004	42%	407/933-9900 Fax 407/933-9901 🇹
Harmony Middle Sch 3725 Arthur J Gallagher Blvd, Saint Cloud 34771 **Frank Telemko**	6-8		1,050		407/593-0416 Fax 407/593-0417
Hickory Tree Elem Sch 2355 Old Hickory Tree Rd, Saint Cloud 34772 Alison Doe	PK-5	T	1,006 54	45%	407/891-3120 Fax 407/891-3129
Highlands Elem Sch 800 W Donegan Ave, Kissimmee 34741 Patricia Cummins	PK-5	T	856 40	74%	407/935-3620 Fax 407/935-3629
Horizon Middle Sch 2020 Ham Brown Rd, Kissimmee 34746 Michael Ballone	6-8	AT	1,336 55	50%	407/943-7240 Fax 407/943-7250
© Imagine Schools Kissimmee CA [138] 2850 Bill Beck Blvd, Kissimmee 34744 Lori McCarley	K-8	T	780 28	53%	407/847-1400 Fax 407/847-1401
Kissimmee Elem Sch 3700 W Donegan Ave, Kissimmee 34741 David Noyes	PK-5	T	1,023 48	67%	407/935-3640 Fax 407/935-3651
Kissimmee Middle Sch 2410 Dyer Blvd, Kissimmee 34741 **Eugenia Rolando**	6-8	ATV	1,341 80	60%	407/870-0857 Fax 407/870-5669
Koa Elem Sch 5000 K O A St, Kissimmee 34758 **Ashton Terry**	PK-5	T	653	71%	407/518-1161 Fax 407/518-2012
Lakeview Elem Sch 2900 5th St, Saint Cloud 34769 Tracy Shenuski	PK-5	T	737 30	59%	407/891-3220 Fax 407/891-3228
Liberty High Sch 4250 Pleasant Hill Rd, Kissimmee 34746 **Cruz Misty**	9-12	T	2,020	53%	407/933-3910 Fax 407/933-9990
© Lincoln-Marti CS-Osceola 2244 Fortune Rd, Kissimmee 34744 Alexandr Plaza	PK-4		65		407/530-5000 Fax 407/518-9047
© Main St High Sch Ⓨ 1100 N Main St Ste A, Kissimmee 34744 Christine Perez	9-12	MTV	488	48%	321/250-1871 Fax 407/846-0816
© Mater Acad St Cloud 1925 Nora Tyson Rd, Saint Cloud 34771 **Victoria Singh**	K-7		90		407/325-0762
© Mater Brighton Lakes Academy 3200 Pleasant Hill Rd, Kissimmee 34746 Carmen Cangemi	K-8		924	60%	407/931-0325
© Mater Palms Academy 401 S Poinciana Blvd, Kissimmee 34746 Monica Cueto	K-8		549		407/390-1106
Michigan Ave Elem Sch 2015 Michigan Ave, Saint Cloud 34769 Diane Crook-Nichols	PK-5	T	655 32	58%	407/891-3140 Fax 407/891-3149
Mill Creek Elem Sch 1700 Mill Slough Rd, Kissimmee 34744 Susan Cavinee	PK-5	T	924	70%	407/935-3660 Fax 407/935-3667
Narcoossee Elem Sch 2690 N Narcoossee Rd, Saint Cloud 34771 Scott Knoebel	PK-5	T	1,070	41%	407/892-6858 Fax 407/518-2009
Narcoossee Middle Sch 2700 N Narcoossee Rd, Saint Cloud 34771 **Gary Weeden**	6-8	T	1,295 40	51%	407/891-6600 Fax 407/891-6610
Neocity Academy 93 Panther Paws Trl, Kissimmee 34744 Michael Meechin	9-9		107		407/933-3903 Fax 407/933-9903
Neptune Elem Sch 1200 Betsy Ross Ln, Saint Cloud 34769 Linda Harwood	PK-5	T	1,002	59%	407/892-8387 Fax 407/957-2684
Neptune Middle Sch 2727 Neptune Rd, Kissimmee 34744 Thomas Rademacher	6-8	ATV	1,330 67	48%	407/935-3500 Fax 407/935-3519
Ⓐ New Beginnings Education Ctr 2599 W Vine St, Kissimmee 34741 Nina Wehmeyer	K-12	TV	230 20	70%	407/348-4466 Fax 407/348-4069
© New Dimensions High Sch 4900 Old Pleasant Hill Rd, Kissimmee 34759 Dr Christina Cafiero	9-12	T	474 14	43%	407/870-9949
Ⓜ Osceola County Sch for Arts 3151 N Orange Blossom Trl, Kissimmee 34744 Chundra Evens	6-12	T	942 25	47%	407/931-4803 Fax 407/931-3019

79	Student Personnel	91	Safety/Security	275	Response To Intervention	298	Grant Writer/Ptnrships
80	Driver Ed/Safety	92	Magnet School	277	Remedial Math K-12	750	Chief Innovation Officer
81	Gifted/Talented	93	Parental Involvement	280	Literacy Coach	751	Chief of Staff
82	Video Services	95	Tech Prep Program	285	STEM	752	Social Emotional Learning
83	Substance Abuse Prev	97	Chief Information Officer	286	Digital Learning		
84	Erate	98	Chief Technology Officer	288	Common Core Standards		**Other School Types**
85	AIDS Education	270	Character Education	294	Accountability		Ⓐ = Alternative School
88	Alternative/At Risk	271	Migrant Education	295	Network System		© = Charter School
89	Multi-Cultural Curriculum	273	Teacher Mentor	296	Title II Programs		Ⓜ = Magnet School
90	Social Work	274	Before/After Sch	297	Webmaster		Ⓨ = Year-Round School

School Programs
A = Alternative Program
G = Adult Classes
M = Magnet Program
T = Title I Schoolwide
V = Career & Tech Ed Programs

Social Media
� = Facebook
🇹 = Twitter

New Schools are shaded
New Superintendents and Principals are bold
Personnel with email addresses are underscored

School	Grd	Prgm	Enr/#Cls	SN	Phone
Osceola High Sch 420 S Thacker Ave, Kissimmee 34741 Nia Campbell	9-12	AGTV	2,467 92	56%	407/518-5400 Fax 407/943-7909
© Osceola Science Charter Sch 2880 N Orange Blossom Trl, Kissimmee 34744 Murat Cetin	K-6		462	58%	407/846-0121 Fax 407/847-0831
Osceola Virtual Sch 1200 Vermont Ave, Saint Cloud 34769 **Pete Hodges**	K-12		52	31%	407/870-1445 Fax 407/870-1441
© P M Wells Charter Academy [133] 2426 Remington Blvd, Kissimmee 34744 Alan Ramos	K-8	T	678	59%	321/697-1020 Fax 321/697-1021 🅵🅣
Parkway Middle Sch 857 Florida Pkwy, Kissimmee 34743 Megan Gould	6-8	ATV	961 60	60%	407/344-7000 Fax 407/348-2797
Partin Settlement Elem Sch 2434 Remington Blvd, Kissimmee 34744 Karen Corbett	PK-5	T	858 50	46%	407/518-2000 Fax 407/518-2019
Pleasant Hill Elem Sch 1253 Pleasant Hill Rd, Kissimmee 34741 Shelby Pagan	PK-5	T	795 50	63%	407/935-3700 Fax 407/935-3705
Poinciana Academy of Fine Arts 4201 Rhododendron Ave, Kissimmee 34758 Kimberley Dos Santos	PK-5	T	626	74%	407/343-4500 Fax 407/343-4519
Poinciana High Sch 2300 S Poinciana Blvd, Kissimmee 34758 Jeffrey Schwartz	9-12	ATV	2,080	53%	407/870-4860 Fax 407/870-0382
Professional & Tech HS 501 Simpson Rd, Kissimmee 34744 Tom Ott	Voc	T	515 35	58%	407/518-5407 Fax 407/344-2467
Reedy Creek Elem Sch 5100 Eagles Trl, Kissimmee 34758 Timi Godin	PK-5	T	1,100 60	65%	407/935-3580 Fax 407/935-3590
© Renaissance CS at Boggy Creek [133] 4480 Boggy Creek Rd, Kissimmee 34744 Julie Ramirez	K-7		450		407/785-6495 Fax 407/785-6233
© Renaissance CS at Tapestry [133] 2510 W Carroll St, Kissimmee 34741 **Sandy Owens**	K-8		1,396	59%	407/569-0163 Fax 407/569-0164
© Renaissance CS-Poinciana [133] 5125 Robert McLane Blvd, Kissimmee 34758 **Maria Gomez**	K-8	T	860	77%	407/569-0639 Fax 407/569-0640
© Slam Osceola [130] 611 Line Dr, Kissimmee 34744 Monique Machado	6-9		90		407/569-7637
St Cloud Elem Sch 2701 Budinger Ave, Saint Cloud 34769 Megan Dierickx	PK-5	T	1,006 40	56%	407/891-3160 Fax 407/891-3169
St Cloud High Sch 2000 Bulldog Ln, Saint Cloud 34769 Nathaniel Fancher	9-12	ATV	2,412	58%	407/891-3100 Fax 407/891-3114
St Cloud Middle Sch 1975 Michigan Ave, Saint Cloud 34769 Cynthia Chiavini	6-8	ATV	1,450 44	60%	407/891-3200 Fax 407/891-3206
© St Cloud Preparatory Academy 3101 Progress Ln, Saint Cloud 34769 Michele Quinn	K-11	T	527	56%	407/593-6601 Fax 407/891-0145
Sunrise Elem Sch 1925 Ham Brown Rd, Kissimmee 34746 Wendy Honeycutt	PK-5	T	895 60	55%	407/870-4866 Fax 407/870-4868
Tech Ed Center-Osceola 501 Simpson Rd, Kissimmee 34744 Thomas Ott	Adult	V	500 35		407/344-5080 Fax 407/344-5089
Thacker Avenue Elem Sch 301 N Thacker Ave, Kissimmee 34741 Yara La Fuentes	PK-5	T	837	64%	407/935-3540 Fax 407/935-3549
Tohopekaliga High Sch 3675 Boggy Creek Rd, Kissimmee 34744 David Phelps	9-12		2,327		407/483-3685
© UCP of Central FL-Osceola 1820 Armstrong Blvd, Kissimmee 34741 Beth Morris	Spec	T	63 7	60%	407/852-3300 Fax 407/932-3480
Ventura Elem Sch 275 Waters Edge Dr, Kissimmee 34743 Ashley Condo	PK-5	T	862 46	64%	407/344-5040 Fax 407/344-5046
Westside K-8 Sch 2551 Westside Blvd, Kissimmee 34747 Christina Ray	PK-8	T	1,667	59%	407/390-1748 Fax 407/518-2010
Ⓐ Zenith Accelerated Lrng Acad 2218 E Irlo Bronson Hwy, Kissimmee 34744 Robert Studly	9-12	T	552	66%	407/846-3976 Fax 407/933-9920

OSCEOLA CATHOLIC SCHOOLS

• **Diocese of Orlando Ed Office** PID: 00197639
Listing includes only schools located in this county. See District Index for location of Diocesan Offices.

Catholic Schs..Principal	Grd	Prgm	Enr/#Cls	SN
Holy Redeemer Catholic Sch 1800 W Columbia Ave, Kissimmee 34741 Gloria Del Orbe	PK-8		400 20	407/870-9055 Fax 407/870-2214
St Thomas Aquinas Catholic Sch 800 Brown Chapel Rd, Saint Cloud 34769 Nicholas Pavgouzas	PK-8		320 25	407/957-1772 Fax 407/957-8700 🅵

OSCEOLA PRIVATE SCHOOLS

Private Schs..Principal	Grd	Prgm	Enr/#Cls	SN
City of Life Christian Academy 2874 E Irlo Bronson Mem Hwy, Kissimmee 34744 Kathy Harkema	PK-12		380 21	407/847-5184 Fax 407/870-2679
Esther's School Kissimmee 522 Simpson Rd, Kissimmee 34744 Elizabeth Carter	Spec		55	407/873-2235 Fax 727/544-8700
First United Methodist Sch 122 W Sproule Ave, Kissimmee 34741 Mrs Cross	PK-8		244 20	407/847-8805 Fax 407/847-7952 🅵
Heritage Christian Sch 1500 E Vine St, Kissimmee 34744 Karla Beaver	PK-12		660 24	407/847-4087 Fax 407/932-2806
Life Christian Academy 2269 Partin Settlement Rd, Kissimmee 34744 Jessica Wilikson	K-12		250	407/847-8222 Fax 407/847-8223
North Kissimmee Christian Sch 425 W Donegan Ave, Kissimmee 34741 Rick Johnson	PK-12		170 17	407/847-2877 Fax 407/847-5372
Osceola Adventist Church Sch 2391 Fortune Rd, Kissimmee 34744 Nieves Jenkins	PK-8		84 2	407/348-2226
Peace Lutheran Sch 3249 Windmill Point Blvd, Kissimmee 34746 Adam Pavelchik	PK-8		46	407/870-5965 🅵
Southland Christian Sch 2440 Fortune Rd, Kissimmee 34744 Rob Ennis	PK-12		400 22	407/201-7999 Fax 407/348-7870

1	Superintendent	8	Curric/Instruct K-12	19	Chief Financial Officer	29	Family/Consumer Science	39	Social Studies K-12	49	English/Lang Arts Elem	59	Special Education Elem	69	Academic Assessment
2	Bus/Finance/Purchasing	9	Curric/Instruct Elem	20	Art K-12	30	Adult Education	40	Social Studies Elem	50	English/Lang Arts Sec	60	Special Education Sec	70	Research/Development
3	Buildings And Grounds	10	Curric/Instruct Sec	21	Art Elem	31	Career/Sch-to-Work K-12	41	Social Studies Sec	51	Reading K-12	61	Foreign/World Lang K-12	71	Public Information
4	Food Service	11	Federal Program	22	Art Sec	32	Career/Sch-to-Work Elem	42	Science K-12	52	Reading Elem	62	Foreign/World Lang Elem	72	Summer School
5	Transportation	12	Title I	23	Music K-12	33	Career/Sch-to-Work Sec	43	Science Elem	53	Reading Sec	63	Foreign/World Lang Sec	73	Instructional Tech
6	Athletic	13	Title V	24	Music Elem	34	Early Childhood Ed	44	Science Sec	54	Remedial Reading K-12	64	Religious Education K-12	74	Inservice Training
7	Health Services	14	Asst Superintendent	25	Music Sec	35	Health/Phys Education	45	Math K-12	55	Remedial Reading Elem	65	Religious Education Elem	75	Marketing/Distributive
		15	Asst Superintendent	26	Business Education	36	Guidance Services K-12	46	Math Elem	56	Remedial Reading Sec	66	Religious Education Sec	76	Info Systems
		16	Instructional Media Svcs	27	Career & Tech Ed	37	Guidance Services Elem	47	Math Sec	57	Bilingual/ELL	67	School Board President	77	Psychological Assess
		17	Chief Operations Officer	28	Technology Education	38	Guidance Services Sec	48	English/Lang Arts K-12	58	Special Education K-12	68	Teacher Personnel	78	Affirmative Action

Trinity Lutheran Sch	PK-12	200	407/847-5377
3016 W Vine St, Kissimmee 34741		15	Fax 407/944-0805
Sheila Miles			

PALM BEACH COUNTY

PALM BEACH PUBLIC SCHOOLS

• **Palm Beach Co School Dist** PID: 00198073   561/434-8000
   3300 Forest Hill Blvd, West Palm Bch 33406   Fax 561/434-8651

Schools: 223 \ **Teachers:** 12,698 \
Students: 195,455 \ **Special Ed Students:** 30,089 \ **LEP Students:** 24,530
\ **College-Bound:** 69% \ **Ethnic:** Asian 3%, African American 29%,
Hispanic 34%, Native American: 1%, Caucasian 32% \ **Exp:** $149 (Low) \
Poverty: 15% \ **Title I:** $48,694,397 \ **Special Education:** $77,432,000
\ **Bilingual Education:** $20,228,000 \ **Open-Close:** 08/12 - 05/29 \
DTBP: $186 (High)

Dr Donald Fennoy	1	Darci Garbacz	2,298
Heather Knust	2	Michael Burke	2,19
Thomas Hogarth	3	Wanda Paul	3,17
Allison Monbleau	4	Carl Boucard	5
Diane Fedderman	8,15	Keith Oswald	8,15,18
Dr Dana Zorovich-Godek	11	Barbara Terembes	15,294
Margarita Pinkos	15,57,89,271	Dr Peter Licata	15,27,31
Fred Barch	30	Mary Steele	34
Eric Stern	35,80	Kevin McCormick	58
Frank Barbieri	67	Dr Gonzalo La-Cava	68
Mark Mitchell	68	Dr Cheryl McKeever	69
Paul Houchens	69,70	Deepak Agarwal	71,76,97
Dr Adam Miller	73	Carlene Millen	74
Jenifer Kuras	74	Dr Laurie Riopelle	74
Dr Angela Bess	88	Kiwana Howell	274
Julia Mate	285	Jimmy Peterkin	298

Public Schs..Principal	Grd	Prgm	Enr/#Cls	SN	
© Academy for Positive Learning	K-8	T	131	87%	561/585-6104
1200 N Dixie Hwy, Lake Worth 33460					Fax 561/585-7849
Renatta Espinoza					
Ⓨ Adult Education Center	Adult	MV	600		561/616-7800
2161 N Military Trl, West Palm Bch 33409			25		Fax 561/616-7850
Stuart Mears					
Ⓐ Believers Academy	9-12	GT	120	82%	561/340-2507
© 5840 Corporate Way Ste 100, West Palm Bch 33407			6		Fax 561/340-2510
Lori Dyer					
© Ben Gamla Charter Palm Beach [130]	Spec		245	25%	561/742-8017
8600 S Jog Rd, Boynton Beach 33472					Fax 561/742-8018
Elaniit Weizman					
© Bridgeprep Academy-Palm Beach	K-7		288		561/406-0709
9085 Happy Hollow Rd, Delray Beach 33446					
Paul Sirota					
© Bright Futures Acad Riverside	K-8	T	211	66%	561/253-7504
10350 Riverside Dr, Palm Bch Gdns 33410			7		Fax 561/658-0565
Lauren Colloca \ Ashley Wheeler-Slone					
© Connections Education Center	Spec		35		561/328-6044
1310 Old Congress Ave Ste A, West Palm Bch 33409					
Debra Johnson					
Ⓐ Crossroads Academy	6-12	T	148	94%	561/993-8400
225 SW 12th St, Belle Glade 33430			20		Fax 561/993-8450
Diane Howard					

Delray Full Service Center	Adult		100		561/266-1200
301 SW 14th Ave, Delray Beach 33444					Fax 561/266-1250
Sandra Caruso					
© Ed Venture Charter Sch	Spec	T	90	17%	561/582-1454
117 East Coast Ave, Hypoluxo 33462			10		Fax 561/547-9682
Patricia Kealey-Ryan					
© Everglades Preparatory Academy	9-12	TV	102	84%	561/924-3002
360 E Main St Bldg C, Pahokee 33476			10		Fax 561/924-3013
Linda Earsley					
© Florida Futures Academy	9-12	A	122	14%	561/215-0933
1760 N Congress Ave Ste 100, West Palm Bch 33409					
Carolyn Taylor					
© Franklin Acad Palm Beach Gdns	K-8	V	867		561/348-2525
5651 Hood Rd, Palm BCH GDNS 33418					Fax 561/775-1899
Margaret Ellis					
© Franklin Academy-Boynton Beach	K-8		1,332	9%	561/767-4700
7882 S Military Trl, Lake Worth 33463					Fax 561/432-3200
Rena Tornopsky					
© G-Star School of the Arts	9-12	T	855	49%	561/967-2023
2065 Prairie Rd Bldg J, West Palm Bch 33406			8		Fax 561/963-8975
Kim Collins					
© Gardens School-Technology Arts	K-8	T	360	55%	561/290-7661
9153 Roan Ln, Palm BCH GDNS 33403					Fax 866/449-3470
Dr Kevin Kovacs					
© Glades Academy	K-8	T	279	99%	561/924-9402
7368 State Road 15 Bldg E, Pahokee 33476			5		Fax 561/924-9279
Vincynthia Jones					
© Gulfstream Goodwill Life Acad	Spec		71		561/259-1000
3800 S Congress Ave Ste 12, Boynton Beach 33426					Fax 561/259-1011
Cindy Maunder					
© Imagine Schools Chancellor [137]	K-8	T	1,035	59%	561/585-1189
3333 High Ridge Rd, Boynton Beach 33426			22		Fax 561/585-1166
Susan Onori					
© Inlet Grove Cmty High Sch	9-12	GTV	750	87%	561/881-4600
600 W 28th St, Riviera Beach 33404					Fax 561/881-4668
Francisco Lopez					
© Learning Ctr-Els Ctr Excel	Spec		100	4%	561/296-1776
18370 Limestone Creek Rd, Jupiter 33458			5		Fax 561/296-1791
Stacie Routt					
© Mont Academy Early Enrichment	K-5	T	176	88%	561/649-0004
6300 Lake Worth Rd, Greenacres 33463			10		Fax 561/649-0964
Myra Ranck					
© Olympus International Academy	K-8		199		561/900-5323
8411 W Palmetto Park Rd, Boca Raton 33433					
Nancy Swenson					
Pace Ctr for Girls-Palm Beach	5-12		42	36%	561/472-1990
1225 S Military Trl Ste D, West Palm Bch 33415					Fax 561/472-1991
Aggie Pappas					
© Palm Beach Maritime Acad HS	6-12		150		561/578-5700
600 S East Coast Ave, Lake Worth 33462					Fax 561/540-5177
Cesare Boffice					
© Palm Beach Maritime Academy	K-5	T	1,064	84%	561/547-3775
1518 W Lantana Rd, Lake Worth 33462			30		Fax 561/540-5177
Paul Copeland					
© Palm Beach Preparatory Academy	9-12	AG	399	14%	561/623-6935
3525 S Congress Ave, Palm Springs 33461					Fax 561/641-6370
Deanna Allen					
© Palm Beach School for Autism	Spec	T	255	99%	561/533-9917
8480 Lantana Rd, Lake Worth 33467			3		Fax 561/533-9918
Juliet Bliss \ Olive Balbosa \ Jonathan Coyle					
Palm Beach Virtual Sch	K-12		108		561/366-6161
9482 MacArthur Blvd, West Palm Bch 33403					
Bradley Henry					
© Potentials Charter Sch	Spec	T	29	76%	561/842-3213
1201 Australian Ave, Riviera Beach 33404			2		Fax 561/863-4352
Bairbre Flood					

				School Programs	Social Media
79 Student Personnel	91 Safety/Security	275 Response To Intervention	298 Grant Writer/Ptnrships	**A** = Alternative Program	
80 Driver Ed/Safety	92 Magnet School	277 Remedial Math K-12	750 Chief Innovation Officer	**G** = Adult Classes	ⓕ = Facebook
81 Gifted/Talented	93 Parental Involvement	280 Literacy Coach	751 Chief of Staff	**M** = Magnet Program	
82 Video Services	95 Tech Prep Program	285 STEM	752 Social Emotional Learning	**T** = Title I Schoolwide	ⓣ = Twitter
83 Substance Abuse Prev	97 Chief Infomation Officer	286 Digital Learning		**V** = Career & Tech Ed Programs	
84 Erate	98 Chief Technology Officer	288 Common Core Standards	Other School Types		
85 AIDS Education	270 Character Education	294 Accountability	Ⓐ = Alternative School		
88 Alternative/At Risk	271 Migrant Education	295 Network System	© = Charter School	New Schools are shaded	
89 Multi-Cultural Curriculum	273 Teacher Mentor	296 Title II Programs	Ⓜ = Magnet School	New Superintendents and Principals are bold	
90 Social Work	274 Before/After Sch	297 Webmaster	Ⓨ = Year-Round School	Personnel with email addresses are underscored	

FL—105

School	Grade	Prgm	Enr	SN%	Phone
Ⓐ Quantum High Sch [131] Ⓒ 1275 Gateway Blvd, Boynton Beach 33426 Dr Joy Gomez-Hicks	9-12		250	20%	561/293-2971 Fax 561/742-5716
Ⓒ Renaissance CS Central Palm [133] 6696 S Military Trl, Lake Worth 33463 Katrina Samuels	K-8	TV	889	20%	561/209-7106 Fax 561/209-7107
Ⓒ Renaissance CS-Cypress [133] 8151 Okeechobee Blvd, West Palm Bch 33411 Anthony Stewart	K-8	TV	677	15%	561/282-5860 Fax 561/282-5866
Ⓒ Renaissance CS-Palms West [133] 12031 Southern Blvd, Loxahatchee 33470 Steve Epstein	K-8	T	567	6%	561/214-6782 Fax 561/214-6783
Ⓒ Renaissance CS-Summit [133] 2001 Summit Blvd, West Palm Bch 33406 Heather Czeskleba	K-8	T	1,037	16%	561/228-5240 Fax 561/228-5241
Ⓒ Renaissance CS-W Palm Beach [133] 1889 Palm Beach Lakes Blvd, West Palm Bch 33409 Michael Lupton	K-8	T	994	15%	561/839-1994 Fax 561/839-1995
Ⓒ Renaissance CS-Wellington [133] 3200 S State Road 7, Wellington 33449 Mary Beth Greene	K-8	V	497		561/228-5242 Fax 561/228-5243
Ⓐ Riviera Beach Prep & Achv Acad 7071 Garden Rd, Riviera Beach 33404 Mark Simmonds	9-12	T	175 15	85%	561/881-4740 Fax 561/881-4731
Ⓒ Seagull Academy of Ind Living 6250 N Military Trl Ste 101, West Palm Bch 33407 Linda Moore	Spec	T	43 3	70%	561/540-8110 Fax 561/540-8331
Ⓒ Slam High School Palm Beach 2845 Summit Blvd, West Palm Bch 33406 **Clint Duvo**	9-12		401		561/434-2162
Ⓒ Slam Middle Sch 2845 Summit Blvd, West Palm Bch 33406 Clint Duvo	6-9		224		561/434-2162 Fax 561/434-2163
Ⓒ Somerset Acad Canyons Mid HS [130] 9385 Boynton Beach Blvd, Boynton Beach 33472 George Groezinger	6-12		1,286	8%	561/732-8252 Fax 561/732-8253
Ⓒ Somerset Academy Boca [130] 333 SW 4th Ave, Boca Raton 33432 Daniel Shourds	K-8		357	5%	561/393-1091 Fax 561/393-1092
Ⓒ Somerset Academy JFK Chtr Sch 4696 Davis Rd, Lake Worth 33461 Sharon Hench	K-8	T	520 18	64%	561/868-6100 Fax 561/433-4158
Ⓒ Somerset Academy Lakes 2845 Summit Blvd, West Palm Bch 33406 Clint Duvo	K-5		235	79%	561/641-4449 Fax 561/360-2452
Ⓒ Somerset Academy of the Arts 1000 Wellington Trce, Wellington 33414 **Elizabeth Sauri**	K-8		401		561/421-5510
Ⓐ South Intensive Transition Sch 1509 Barton Rd, Lake Worth 33460 Reginald Jeudy	6-12	T	58 19	87%	561/202-0600 Fax 561/202-0650
Ⓒ South Tech Academy 1300 SW 30th Ave, Boynton Beach 33426 Eileen Turenne	9-12	GTV	1,095	80%	561/369-7000 Fax 561/369-7024
Ⓒ South Tech Prep Academy 1325 Gateway Blvd, Boynton Beach 33426 Nicole Handy	6-8		544		561/318-8087
Ⓐ Southtech Siccess Center Ⓒ 1300 SW 305H Ave, Boynton Beach 33426 **Maynard Harvey**	9-10		25		561/369-7000 Fax 561/369-7024
Ⓒ Toussaint L'Ouverture High Sch 2601 S Military Trail, Delray Beach 33444 Mandy Freedman	9-12	T	101 25	50%	561/350-9487 Fax 561/763-7361 🅵🅴
Ⓐ Turning Points Academy 1950 N Benoist Farms Rd, West Palm Bch 33411 Kevin Gatlin	6-12	T	66	91%	561/681-3700 Fax 561/681-3750

School	Grade	Prgm	Enr	SN%	Phone
Ⓒ University Preparatory Academy 2101 N Australian Ave, West Palm Bch 33407 Richard Ledgister	K-3		166	90%	561/670-1138
Ⓒ Western Academy Charter Sch 650 Royal Palm Beach Blvd, West Palm Bch 33411 **Jessica Manriquez**	K-8		523 25	41%	561/792-4123 Fax 561/422-0674
Ⓒ Worthington High Sch [131] 1711 Worthington Rd, West Palm Bch 33409 Porshia Jones	9-12		239	15%	561/537-5696

● **Palm Beach Co SD-Ctl Region** PID: 12170928 **561/804-3254**
4703 10th Ave N, Greenacres 33463   **Fax 561/804-3252**

Valerie Zuloaga-Haines 1   Jennifer Sanders 9
Edward Tierney 10

Public Schs..Principal	Grd	Prgm	Enr/#Cls	SN	
Barton Elem Sch 1700 Barton Rd, Lake Worth 33460 Denise Sanon	PK-5	T	856 35	97%	561/540-9100 Fax 561/540-9128
Belvedere Elem Sch 3000 Parker Ave, West Palm Bch 33405 Ruth Mahar	PK-5	T	557 30	95%	561/838-5900 Fax 561/838-5950
Benoist Farms Elem Sch 1765 N Benoist Farms Rd, West Palm Bch 33411 Ruthann Miller	PK-5	T	497	91%	561/681-2250 Fax 561/383-9756
Berkshire Elem Sch 1060 Kirk Rd, West Palm Bch 33406 Diana Perez	PK-5	T	1,109 40	83%	561/304-2000 Fax 561/304-2051
Binks Forest Elem Sch 15101 Bent Creek Rd, Wellington 33414 Michella Levy	K-5		951 58	23%	561/904-9800 Fax 561/904-9850
C O Taylor-Kirklane Elem Sch 4200 Purdy Ln, Palm Springs 33461 Patricia Lucas	PK-5	GT	1,207 50	88%	561/804-3500 Fax 561/804-3551
Cholee Lake Elem Sch 6680 Dillman Rd, Greenacres 33413 Marline Campbell	PK-5	AT	1,088	91%	561/681-1417 Fax 561/383-9650
Conniston Cmty Middle Sch 3630 Parker Ave, West Palm Bch 33405 Oscar Otero	6-8	GT	1,172 60	82%	561/802-5400 Fax 561/802-5409
Crestwood Middle Sch 64 Sparrow Dr, West Palm Bch 33411 Stephanie Nance	6-8	TV	786 74	64%	561/753-5000 Fax 561/753-5035
Cypress Trails Elem Sch 133 Park Rd N, West Palm Bch 33411 Bruce Saulter	K-5	T	462 50	67%	561/904-9000 Fax 561/904-9050
Discovery Key Elem Sch 3550 Lyons Rd, Lake Worth 33467 Catherine Lewis	K-5	T	957 55	42%	561/491-8200 Fax 561/491-8250
Egret Lake Elem Sch 5115 47th Pl N, West Palm Bch 33417 **Dionne Napier**	K-5	T	632 40	88%	561/616-7900 Fax 561/616-7950
Elbridge Gale Elem Sch 1915 Royal Fern Dr, Wellington 33414 Gail Pasterczyk	PK-5	T	1,095	47%	561/422-9300 Fax 561/422-9310
Emerald Cove Middle Sch 9950 Stribling Way, Wellington 33414 Eugina Feaman	6-8	V	1,280	39%	561/803-8000 Fax 561/803-8050 🅵🅴
Equestrian Trails Elem Sch 9720 Stribling Way, Wellington 33414 **Michele Johnson**	PK-5		879	23%	561/904-9600 Fax 561/904-9650 🅵
Everglades Elem Sch 407 Marginal Rd, West Palm Bch 33411 Dwan Ross	K-5	T	943	42%	561/792-9500 Fax 561/792-9550

1 Superintendent	8 Curric/Instruct K-12	19 Chief Financial Officer	29 Family/Consumer Science	39 Social Studies K-12	49 English/Lang Arts Elem	59 Special Education Elem	69 Academic Assessment
2 Bus/Finance/Purchasing	9 Curric/Instruct Elem	20 Art K-12	30 Adult Education	40 Social Studies Elem	50 English/Lang Arts Sec	60 Special Education Sec	70 Research/Development
3 Buildings And Grounds	10 Curric/Instruct Sec	21 Art Elem	31 Career/Sch-to-Work K-12	41 Social Studies Sec	51 Reading K-12	61 Foreign/World Lang K-12	71 Public Information
4 Food Service	11 Federal Program	22 Art Sec	32 Career/Sch-to-Work Elem	42 Science K-12	52 Reading Elem	62 Foreign/World Lang Elem	72 Summer School
5 Transportation	12 Title I	23 Music K-12	33 Career/Sch-to-Work Sec	43 Science Elem	53 Reading Sec	63 Foreign/World Lang Sec	73 Instructional Tech
6 Athletic	13 Title V	24 Music Elem	34 Early Childhood Ed	44 Science Sec	54 Remedial Reading K-12	64 Religious Education K-12	74 Inservice Training
7 Health Services	14 Asst Superintendent	25 Music Sec	35 Health/Phys Education	45 Math K-12	55 Remedial Reading Elem	65 Religious Education Elem	75 Marketing/Distributive
	15 Instructional Media Svcs	26 Business Education	36 Guidance Services K-12	46 Math Elem	56 Remedial Reading Sec	66 Religious Education Sec	76 Info Systems
	16 Chief Operations Officer	27 Career & Tech Ed	37 Guidance Services Elem	47 Math Sec	57 Bilingual/ELL	67 School Board President	77 Psychological Assess
	17 Chief Academic Officer	28 Technology Education	38 Guidance Services Sec	48 English/Lang Arts K-12	58 Special Education K-12	68 Teacher Personnel	78 Affirmative Action

School / Address / Principal	Grd	Prgm	Enr/#Cls	SN	Phone / Fax
Forest Hill Cmty High Sch 6901 Parker Ave, West Palm Bch 33405 **Esther Rivera**	9-12	TV	2,458 150	80%	561/540-2400 Fax 561/540-2440
Forest Hill Elem Sch 5555 Purdy Ln, West Palm Bch 33415 Scott McNichols	PK-5	T	808 35	90%	561/432-2300 Fax 561/432-2350
Grassy Waters Elem Sch 3550 N Jog Rd, West Palm Bch 33411 Jennifer Galindo	PK-5	T	864	73%	561/383-9000 Fax 561/383-9050
Greenacres Elem Sch 405 Jackson Ave, Greenacres 33463 Deborah McNichols	PK-5	T	768 32	94%	561/649-7200 Fax 561/649-7250
H L Johnson Elem Sch 1000 Crestwood Blvd N, West Palm Bch 33411 Jennifer Makowski	PK-5	GT	766	46%	561/904-9300 Fax 561/904-9350
Heritage Elem Sch 5100 Melaleuca Ln, Greenacres 33463 Nina Lant	K-5	T	809	95%	561/804-3200 Fax 561/804-3250
Highland Elem Sch 500 Highland Ave, Lake Worth 33460 **Elena Villani**	PK-5	T	1,224 40	97%	561/202-0500 Fax 561/202-0550
© Hope-Centennial Elem Sch 5350 Stacy St, West Palm Bch 33417 **Lakeisha Nathan**	PK-5	T	652	96%	561/640-1200 Fax 561/640-1250
Indian Ridge Sch 1955 Golden Lakes Blvd, West Palm Bch 33411 **Eugene Ford**	Spec	T	110 25	85%	561/681-0000 Fax 561/681-0050
John I Leonard High Sch 4701 10th Ave N, Greenacres 33463 Melissa Patterson	9-12	GTV	3,416	79%	561/641-1200 Fax 561/357-1100
Lake Worth Cmty High Sch 1701 Lake Worth Rd, Lake Worth 33460 Elvis Epps	9-12	GTV	2,588 170	85%	561/533-6300 Fax 561/493-0888
Liberty Park Elem Sch 6601 Constitution Way, Greenacres 33413 Joseph Schneider	PK-5	T	970 47	91%	561/804-3400 Fax 561/804-3450
Loxahatchee Groves Elem Sch 16020 Okeechobee Blvd, Loxahatchee 33470 Richard Myerson	PK-5	T	615 34	62%	561/904-9200 Fax 561/904-9250
Meadow Park Elem Sch 956 Florida Mango Rd, West Palm Bch 33406 Valerie Zuloaga-Haines	PK-5	T	773 24	80%	561/357-2800 Fax 561/357-2828
Melaleuca Elem Sch 5759 Gun Club Rd, West Palm Bch 33415 Deborah Maupin	K-5	T	726 45	91%	561/598-7300 Fax 561/598-7350
New Horizons Elem Sch 13900 Greenbriar Blvd, Wellington 33414 **Dana Pallaria**	PK-5	T	684 30	56%	561/651-0500 Fax 561/651-0550
North Grade Elem Sch 824 N K St, Lake Worth 33460 Nicole Patterson	K-5	T	685 30	79%	561/202-9300 Fax 561/202-9350
Palm Beach Central High Sch 8499 Forest Hill Blvd, Wellington 33411 Darren Edgecomb	9-12	T	3,065	44%	561/304-1000 Fax 561/304-1017
Palm Beach Public Sch 239 Cocoanut Row, Palm Beach 33480 Christie Schwab	K-5	T	383 18	44%	561/822-0700 Fax 561/822-0750
Palm Springs Elem Sch 101 Davis Rd, Lake Worth 33461 **Bonnie Fox**	PK-5	T	846 41	93%	561/804-3000 Fax 561/804-3050
Palmetto Elem Sch 5801 Parker Ave, West Palm Bch 33405 Gladys Harris	PK-5	T	571 34	97%	561/202-0400 Fax 561/202-0450
Panther Run Elem Sch 10775 Lake Worth Rd, Lake Worth 33449 **Edilia De La Vega**	PK-5		883	21%	561/804-3900 Fax 561/804-3950
Pine Jog Elem Sch 6315 Summit Blvd, West Palm Bch 33415 Tarachell Thomas	K-5	T	897	76%	561/656-5400 Fax 561/656-5450
Polo Park Middle Sch 11901 Lake Worth Rd, Lake Worth 33449 Michael Aronson	6-8	T	1,070 70	41%	561/333-5500 Fax 561/333-5505
Rolling Green Elem Sch 550 Miner Rd, Boynton Beach 33435 Allyson Manning	PK-5	T	788	97%	561/202-9500 Fax 561/202-9550
Royal Palm Beach Cmty High Sch 10600 Okeechobee Blvd, West Palm Bch 33411 Jesus Armas	9-12	TV	2,308	71%	561/753-4000 Fax 561/753-4015
Royal Palm Beach Elem Sch 11911 Okeechobee Blvd, West Palm Bch 33411 Tracy Gaugler	K-5	T	695 40	48%	561/633-4400 Fax 561/633-4450
Seminole Trails Elem Sch 4075 Willow Pond Rd, West Palm Bch 33417 Judith Garrard	PK-5	T	794 40	80%	561/598-7000 Fax 561/598-7050
South Grade Elem Sch 716 S K St, Lake Worth 33460 Ana Arce-Gonzalez	PK-5	T	867 35	98%	561/202-9400 Fax 561/202-9450
South Olive Elem Sch 7101 S Olive Ave, West Palm Bch 33405 Melinda Springman	K-5	T	581 31	62%	561/202-0200 Fax 561/202-0250
Starlight Cove Elem Sch 6300 Seminole Dr, Lantana 33462 Kimberly Jules	PK-5	T	878 50	91%	561/804-3601 Fax 561/804-3650
U B Kinsey-Palmview Elem Sch 800 11th St, West Palm Bch 33401 Adrienne Howard	PK-5	T	615 30	88%	561/671-6500 Fax 561/671-6550
Wellington Cmty High Sch 2101 Greenview Shores Blvd, Wellington 33414 Cara Hayden	9-12	GV	2,584	36%	561/795-4900 Fax 561/795-4948
Wellington Elem Sch 13000 Paddock Dr, Wellington 33414 Maria Vaughan	PK-5	T	930 50	44%	561/651-0600 Fax 561/651-0650
Wellington Landings Middle Sch 1100 Aero Club Dr, Wellington 33414 Blake Bennett	6-8	GV	1,334 40	36%	561/792-8100 Fax 561/792-8106
West Gate Elem Sch 1545 Loxahatchee Dr, West Palm Bch 33409 Juana Feliciano	PK-5	T	811 54	97%	561/684-7100 Fax 561/684-7150
Wynnebrook Elem Sch 1167 Drexel Rd, West Palm Bch 33417 Suzanne Berry	K-5	T	856 36	92%	561/598-7400 Fax 561/598-7450

• Palm Beach Co SD-Glades Region   PID: 12170954   561/996-4900
2625 NW 16th St, Belle Glade 33430   Fax 561/996-4912

Angela Avery-Moore 1   Dr Moneek McTier 8

Public Schs..Principal	Grd	Prgm	Enr/#Cls	SN	
Belle Glade Elem Sch 500 NW Avenue L, Belle Glade 33430 Robera Thompson	PK-5	T	741 54	96%	561/829-4800 Fax 561/829-4850
Glade View Elem Sch 1100 SW Avenue G, Belle Glade 33430 **Shundra Dowers**	K-5	T	273 21	98%	561/993-8800 Fax 561/993-8851
Glades Central Cmty High Sch 1001 SW Ave, Belle Glade 33430 Melanie Bolden-Morris	9-12	GTV	1,025 75	94%	561/993-4403 Fax 561/993-4414
Ⓜ Gove Elem Sch 900 SE Avenue G, Belle Glade 33430 Kimberly Thomasson	PK-6	T	714 56	96%	561/993-8700 Fax 561/993-8750
K E Cunningham-Canal Point ES 37000 Main St, Canal Point 33438 Derrick Hibler	K-5	T	305 21	99%	561/924-9800 Fax 561/924-9850

79	Student Personnel	91	Safety/Security	275	Response To Intervention	298	Grant Writer/Ptnrships	School Programs	Social Media
80	Driver Ed/Safety	92	Magnet School	277	Remedial Math K-12	750	Chief Innovation Officer	A = Alternative Program	
81	Gifted/Talented	93	Parental Involvement	280	Literacy Coach	751	Chief of Staff	G = Adult Classes	Ⓕ = Facebook
82	Video Services	95	Tech Prep Program	285	STEM	752	Social Emotional Learning	M = Magnet Program	
83	Substance Abuse Prev	97	Chief Information Officer	286	Digital Learning			T = Title I Schoolwide	Ⓣ = Twitter
84	Erate	98	Chief Technology Officer	288	Common Core Standards	Other School Types		V = Career & Tech Ed Programs	
85	AIDS Education	270	Character Education	294	Accountability	Ⓐ = Alternative School			
86	Alternative/At Risk	271	Migrant Education	295	Network System	Ⓒ = Charter School		New Schools are shaded	
87	Multi-Cultural Curriculum	273	Teacher Mentor	296	Title II Programs	Ⓜ = Magnet School		New Superintendents and Principals are bold	
90	Social Work	274	Before/After Sch	297	Webmaster	Ⓨ = Year-Round School		Personnel with email addresses are underscored	

Lake Shore Middle Sch 425 W Canal St N, Belle Glade 33430 Carl Gibbons	6-8	TV	685 63	94%	561/829-1100 Fax 561/829-1130
Pahokee Elem Sch 560 E Main Pl, Pahokee 33476 Dr Karen Abrams	PK-5	T	458 35	96%	561/924-9700 Fax 561/924-9751
Pahokee High Sch 900 Larrimore Rd, Pahokee 33476 **Dwayne Dennard**	9-12	GTV	424 40	95%	561/924-6400 Fax 561/924-6457
Pahokee Middle Sch 850 Larrimore Rd, Pahokee 33476 Dwayne Dennard	6-8		356		561/924-6500 Fax 561/924-6561
Pioneer Park Elem Sch 39500 Pioneer Park Rd, Belle Glade 33430 Pamela Bockman	PK-5	T	389	99%	561/993-8600 Fax 561/993-8650
Rosenwald Elem Sch 1321 W Palm Beach Rd, South Bay 33493 **Bruce Hightower**	K-5	T	283 20	98%	561/993-8900 Fax 561/993-8938
West Technical Education Ctr 2625 NW 16th St, Belle Glade 33430 Dr Charlene Ford	Voc	AG	50		561/829-4620 Fax 561/829-4627

- **Palm Beach Co SD-North Region** PID: 12170942　561/494-1500
  1160 Avenue N, Riviera Beach 33404　　　　　　　Fax 561/494-1551

Dr Camille Coleman ....1　Maria Bishop 9
Dr Joseph Lee 10

Public Schs..Principal	Grd	Prgm	Enr/#Cls	SN	
Acreage Pines Elem Sch 14200 Orange Blvd, Loxahatchee 33470 **Darline Karbowski**	PK-5	T	529 35	52%	561/904-9500 Fax 561/904-9550
Alex W Dreyfoos Jr Sch of Arts 501 S Sapodilla Ave, West Palm Bch 33401 Dr Susan Atherley	9-12		1,382 65	22%	561/802-6000 Fax 561/802-6059
Allamanda Elem Sch 10300 Allamanda Dr, Palm Bch Gdns 33410 Marilu Garcia	PK-5	T	719 22	56%	561/803-7200 Fax 561/803-7250
Bak Middle School of Art 1725 Echo Lake Dr, West Palm Bch 33407 Sally Rozanski	6-8	V	1,381	23%	561/882-3870 Fax 561/882-3879
Beacon Cove Interm Sch 150 Schoolhouse Rd, Jupiter 33458 Leslie Bolte	3-5		740	20%	561/366-6400 Fax 561/366-6450
Bear Lakes Middle Sch 3505 Shenandoah Rd, West Palm Bch 33409 Dr Kirk Howell	6-8	TV	781	88%	561/615-7700 Fax 561/615-7756
Dr Mary McLeod Bethune ES 1501 Avenue U, Riviera Beach 33404 Katrina Granger	PK-5	T	624 40	94%	561/882-7600 Fax 561/882-7650
Dwight D Eisenhower Elem Sch 2926 Lone Pine Rd, Palm Bch Gdns 33410 Debbie Battles	PK-5	T	519 37	65%	561/366-6000 Fax 561/366-6050
Frontier Elem Sch 6701 180th Ave N, Loxahatchee 33470 Susan Groth	K-5	T	600 30	46%	561/904-9900 Fax 561/904-9950
Golden Grove Elem Sch 5959 140th Ave N, West Palm Bch 33411 Linda Edgecomb	K-5	T	651	57%	561/904-9700 Fax 561/904-9750
Grove Park Elem Sch 8330 N Military Trl, Palm Bch Gdns 33410 Jo Rogers	PK-5	T	548 45	93%	561/904-7700 Fax 561/904-7750
Howell L Watkins Middle Sch 9480 MacArthur Blvd, Palm BCH GDNS 33403 **Awilda Tomas-Andres**	6-8	T	912 60	89%	561/776-3600 Fax 561/776-3603

Independence Middle Sch 4001 Greenway Dr, Jupiter 33458 **E Lundman**	6-8	V	1,378	30%	561/799-7500 Fax 561/799-7505
Jeaga Middle Sch 3777 N Jog Rd, West Palm Bch 33411 Anthony Allen	6-8	T	932	90%	561/242-8000 Fax 561/242-8005
Jerry Thomas Elem Sch 800 Maplewood Dr, Jupiter 33458 Jeffrey Eassa	K-5	T	819 50	50%	561/741-9100 Fax 561/741-9150
ⓦ John F Kennedy Middle Sch 1901 Avenue S, Riviera Beach 33404 Ricky Clark	6-8	T	788 77	94%	561/845-4501 Fax 561/845-4537
Jupiter Cmty High Sch 500 Military Trl, Jupiter 33458 Dr Colleen Iannitti	9-12	GV	3,139	31%	561/744-7900 Fax 561/744-7978
Jupiter Elem Sch 200 S Loxahatchee Dr, Jupiter 33458 Nicole Daly	K-5	T	924 30	81%	561/741-5300 Fax 561/741-5350
Jupiter Farms Elem Sch 17400 Haynie Ln, Jupiter 33478 Suzanne Matuella	K-5		645 31	28%	561/741-5400 Fax 561/741-5450
Jupiter Middle Sch 15245 Military Trl, Jupiter 33458 Lisa Hastey	6-8	T	1,435 70	42%	561/745-7200 Fax 561/745-7242
Lake Park Elem Sch 410 3rd St, Lake Park 33403 Michelle Fleming	PK-5	T	376	95%	561/494-1300 Fax 561/494-1350
Lighthouse Elem Sch 4750 Dakota Dr, Jupiter 33458 Julie Hopkins	PK-2		709 53	16%	561/741-9400 Fax 561/741-9450
Limestone Creek Elem Sch 6701 Church St, Jupiter 33458 Maria Lloyd	K-5		1,030 39	26%	561/741-9200 Fax 561/741-9250
ⓦ Lincoln Elem Sch 1160 Avenue N, Riviera Beach 33404 Alicia Porter	K-5	T	438 60	95%	561/624-5175 Fax 561/840-3227
Marsh Pointe Elem Sch 12649 Ibiiza Dr, Palm BCH GDNS 33418 Maureen Werner	K-5		886	18%	561/366-6800 Fax 561/366-6850
Northboro Elem Sch 400 40th St, West Palm Bch 33407 Gayle Harper	PK-5	T	769 47	77%	561/494-1600 Fax 561/494-1650
Northmore Elem Sch 4111 N Terrace Dr, West Palm Bch 33407 Vonda Daniels	PK-5	T	570 60	97%	561/494-1700 Fax 561/494-1750
Osceola Creek Middle Sch 6775 180th Ave N, Loxahatchee 33470 Brian McClellan	6-8	TV	742	51%	561/422-2500 Fax 561/422-2510
ⓦ Palm Beach Gardens Cmty HS 4245 Holly Dr, Palm Bch Gdns 33410 **Dr Donald Hoffman**	9-12	GTV	2,736 99	70%	561/694-7300 Fax 561/691-0515
Palm Beach Gardens Elem Sch 10060 Riverside Dr, Palm Bch Gdns 33410 Marie Caracuzzo	PK-5	T	723 30	52%	561/366-6500 Fax 561/366-6550
Palm Beach Lakes Cmty HS 3505 Shiloh Dr, West Palm Bch 33407 David Alfonso	9-12	GTV	2,399	78%	561/640-5000 Fax 561/688-4350
Pierce Hammock Elem Sch 14255 Hamlin Blvd, Loxahatchee 33470 Ariel Alejo	K-5		454 34	43%	561/633-4500 Fax 561/633-4550
Pleasant City Elem Sch 2222 Spruce Ave, West Palm Bch 33407 Valarie Jones	PK-5	T	317 15	99%	561/838-5800 Fax 561/838-5850
Roosevelt Cmty Middle Sch 1900 N Australian Ave, West Palm Bch 33407 Jeremiah Stewart	6-8	T	1,074 70	87%	561/822-0200 Fax 561/822-0222

1 Superintendent	19 Chief Financial Officer	39 Social Studies K-12	59 Special Education Elem	69 Academic Assessment
2 Bus/Finance/Purchasing	20 Art K-12	40 Social Studies Elem	60 Special Education Sec	70 Research/Development
3 Buildings And Grounds	21 Art Elem	41 Social Studies Sec	61 Foreign/World Lang K-12	71 Public Information
4 Food Service	22 Art Sec	42 Science K-12	62 Foreign/World Lang Elem	72 Summer School
5 Transportation	23 Music K-12	43 Science Elem	63 Foreign/World Lang Sec	73 Instructional Tech
6 Athletic	24 Music Elem	44 Science Sec	64 Religious Education K-12	74 Inservice Training
7 Health Services	25 Music Sec	45 Math K-12	65 Religious Education Elem	75 Marketing/Distributive
8 Curric/Instruct K-12	26 Business Education	46 Math Elem	66 Religious Education Sec	76 Info Systems
9 Curric/Instruct Elem	27 Career & Tech Ed	47 Math Sec	67 School Board President	77 Psychological Assess
10 Curric/Instruct Sec	28 Technology Education	48 English/Lang Arts K-12	68 Teacher Personnel	78 Affirmative Action
11 Federal Program	29 Family/Consumer Science	49 English/Lang Arts Elem		
12 Title I	30 Adult Education	50 English/Lang Arts Sec		
13 Title V	31 Career/Sch-to-Work K-12	51 Reading K-12		
14 Instructional Media Svcs	32 Career/Sch-to-Work Elem	52 Reading Elem		
15 Asst Superintendent	33 Career/Sch-to-Work Sec	53 Reading Sec		
16 Instructional Media Svcs	34 Early Childhood Ed	54 Remedial Reading K-12		
17 Chief Operations Officer	35 Health/Phys Education	55 Remedial Reading Elem		
18 Chief Academic Officer	36 Guidance Services K-12	56 Remedial Reading Sec		
	37 Guidance Services Elem	57 Bilingual/ELL		
	38 Guidance Services Sec	58 Special Education K-12		

School	Grd	Prgm	Enr/#Cls	SN	Phone
Roosevelt Elem Sch 1220 15th St, West Palm Bch 33401 Sharonda Alleyne	K-5	T	342 53	96%	561/653-5100 Fax 561/653-5150
Seminole Ridge Cmty High Sch 4601 Seminole Pratt Whitney Rd, Loxahatchee 33470 James Campbell	9-12	V	2,192	44%	561/422-2600 Fax 561/422-2623
Ⓜ Suncoast High Sch 1717 Avenue S, Riviera Beach 33404 Karen Whetsell	9-12	GV	1,591 55	33%	561/882-3401 Fax 561/882-3443
The Conservatory Sch 401 Anchorage Dr, N Palm Beach 33408 Teresa Stoupas	PK-6	T	700 23	67%	561/494-1800 Fax 561/494-1850
Timber Trace Elem Sch 5200 117th Ct N, Palm BCH GDNS 33418 Kathy Pasquariello	K-5		1,007 42	38%	561/366-6200 Fax 561/366-6250
Ⓜ Washington Elem Sch 1709 W 30th St, Riviera Beach 33404 Carissa Battle	PK-5	T	339 27	96%	561/494-1200 Fax 561/494-1250
Watson B Duncan Middle Sch 5150 117th Ct N, Palm BCH GDNS 33418 Phillip Damico	6-8	GV	1,317 70	44%	561/776-3500 Fax 561/776-3550
Ⓜ West Riviera Elem Sch 1057 W 6th St, Riviera Beach 33404 **Dr Alisha McKnight**	PK-5	T	609 35	97%	561/494-1900 Fax 561/494-1951
Western Pines Middle Sch 5949 140th Ave N, West Palm Bch 33411 Robert Hatcher	6-8	T	1,147	47%	561/792-2500 Fax 561/792-2530
Westward Elem Sch 1101 Golf Ave, West Palm Bch 33401 Bobbie Brooks	K-5	T	581 45	95%	561/653-5200 Fax 561/653-5238
Ⓜ William T Dwyer High Sch 13601 N Military Trl, Palm Bch Gdns 33410 Corey Brooks	9-12	TV	2,310 81	45%	561/625-7800 Fax 561/625-7870

● Palm Beach Co SD-South Region   PID: 12170930   561/982-0919
1790 NW Spanish River Blvd, Boca Raton 33431   Fax 561/982-0959

Peter Licata 1   Jeffrey Pegg 9
Glenda Sheffield 10

Public Schs..Principal	Grd	Prgm	Enr/#Cls	SN	Phone
Addison Mizner Elem Sch 199 SW 12th Ave, Boca Raton 33486 Joshua Davidow	K-5		855 32	23%	561/362-3100 Fax 561/362-3150
Atlantic Cmty High Sch 2455 W Atlantic Ave, Delray Beach 33445 Tara Dellegrotti	9-12	GT	2,303 85	68%	561/243-1500 Fax 561/243-1532
Banyan Creek Elem Sch 4243 Sabal Lakes Rd, Delray Beach 33445 Gerald Riopelle	PK-5	T	994 52	54%	561/894-7100 Fax 561/894-7150
Boca Raton Cmty High Sch 1501 NW 15th Ct, Boca Raton 33486 Suzanne King	9-12	GV	3,379 102	36%	561/338-1400 Fax 561/338-1440
Boca Raton Cmty Middle Sch 1251 NW 8th St, Boca Raton 33486 Peter Slack	6-8	GTV	1,547	45%	561/416-8700 Fax 561/416-8777
Boca Raton Elem Sch 103 SW 1st Ave, Boca Raton 33432 Renee Elfe	K-5	T	355 20	73%	561/544-1700 Fax 561/544-1750
Boynton Beach Cmty High Sch 4975 Park Ridge Blvd, Boynton Beach 33426 Anthony Lockhart	9-12	GTV	1,828	76%	561/752-1200 Fax 561/752-1205
Calusa Elem Sch 2051 Clint Moore Rd, Boca Raton 33496 Dianne Schreiber	K-5		1,140 32	26%	561/989-7500 Fax 561/989-7550

School	Grd	Prgm	Enr/#Cls	SN	Phone
Carver Cmty Middle Sch 101 Barwick Rd, Delray Beach 33445 Sandra Edwards	6-8	GTV	929 44	85%	561/638-2100 Fax 561/638-2181
Christa McAuliffe Middle Sch 6500 Le Chalet Blvd, Boynton Beach 33472 Jeff Silverman	6-8	V	1,453	35%	561/374-6600 Fax 561/374-6636
Citrus Cove Elem Sch 8400 Lawrence Rd, Boynton Beach 33436 **Dr Natalie Cromwell**	PK-5	T	1,128 59	61%	561/292-7000 Fax 561/292-7050
Congress Middle Sch 101 S Congress Ave, Boynton Beach 33426 Denise Oconnor	6-8	GTV	1,264 75	86%	561/374-5600 Fax 561/374-5642
Coral Reef Elem Sch 6151 Hagen Ranch Rd, Lake Worth 33467 Bobbi Moretto	PK-5		1,011 70	37%	561/804-3700 Fax 561/804-3750
Coral Sunset Elem Sch 22400 Hammock St, Boca Raton 33428 Danielle Garcia	PK-5	T	837 60	71%	561/477-2100 Fax 561/477-2150
Crosspointe Elem Sch 3015 S Congress Ave, Boynton Beach 33426 Annmarie Dilbert	PK-5	T	708 30	89%	561/292-4100 Fax 561/292-4150
Crystal Lakes Elem Sch 6050 Gateway Blvd, Boynton Beach 33472 **Laura Green**	PK-5	GT	791 54	46%	561/292-6600 Fax 561/292-6650
Del Prado Elem Sch 7900 Del Prado Cir N, Boca Raton 33433 Kathryn Morem	K-5		920 50	27%	561/544-1800 Fax 561/544-1850
Diamond View Elem Sch 5300 S Haverhill Rd, Greenacres 33463 Carolyn Seal	PK-5	T	807 58	84%	561/304-4200 Fax 561/304-4210
Ⓜ Don Estridge High Tech Mid Sch 1798 NW Spanish River Blvd, Boca Raton 33431 Rachel Capitano	6-8		1,286	34%	561/989-7800 Fax 561/989-7810
Eagles Landing Middle Sch 19500 Coral Ridge Dr, Boca Raton 33498 Joseph Peccia	6-8	V	1,458 60	40%	561/470-7000 Fax 561/470-7030
Forest Park Elem Sch 1201 SW 3rd St, Boynton Beach 33435 Nancy Robinson	PK-5	T	521 40	93%	561/292-6900 Fax 561/292-6950
Freedom Shores Elem Sch 3400 Hypoluxo Rd, Boynton Beach 33436 Michael Sabatino	PK-5	T	813	70%	561/804-3100 Fax 561/804-3150
Galaxy Elem Sch 550 NW 4th Ave, Boynton Beach 33435 Lisa Steele	PK-5	AT	631 26	91%	561/739-5600 Fax 561/739-5650
Hagen Road Elem Sch 10565 Hagen Ranch Rd, Boynton Beach 33437 **Bernadette Standish**	PK-5	T	748 36	54%	561/292-6700 Fax 561/292-6750
Hammock Pointe Elem Sch 8400 SW 8th St, Boca Raton 33433 Stephanie Cook	PK-5	T	945 40	67%	561/477-2200 Fax 561/477-2250
Hidden Oaks Elem Sch 7685 S Military Trl, Lake Worth 33463 Shari Bremekamp	K-8	T	696	65%	561/804-3800 Fax 561/804-3850
Indian Pines Elem Sch 6000 Oak Royal Dr, Lake Worth 33463 Jill Robinson	PK-5	GT	640 60	96%	561/804-3300 Fax 561/804-3350
J C Mitchell Elem Sch 2470 NW 5th Ave, Boca Raton 33431 Joan Pierre-Jerome	PK-5	GT	951 47	60%	561/750-4900 Fax 561/750-4906
L C Swain Middle Sch 5332 Lake Worth Rd, Greenacres 33463 James Thomas	6-8	T	1,394	91%	561/649-6900 Fax 561/649-6904
Lake Worth Cmty Middle Sch 1300 Barnett Dr, Lake Worth 33461 Michael Williams	6-8	TV	1,163 125	92%	561/540-5500 Fax 561/540-5559

79 Student Personnel	91 Safety/Security	275 Response To Intervention	298 Grant Writer/Ptnrships	**School Programs**
30 Driver Ed/Safety	92 Magnet School	277 Remedial Math K-12	750 Chief Innovation Officer	A = Alternative Program
31 Gifted/Talented	93 Parental Involvement	280 Literacy Coach	751 Chief of Staff	G = Adult Classes
32 Video Services	95 Tech Prep Program	285 STEM	752 Social Emotional Learning	M = Magnet Program
33 Substance Abuse Prev	97 Chief Information Officer	286 Digital Learning		T = Title I Schoolwide
34 Erate	98 Chief Technology Officer	288 Common Core Standards	**Other School Types**	V = Career & Tech Ed Programs
35 AIDS Education	270 Character Education	294 Accountability	Ⓐ = Alternative School	
38 Alternative/At Risk	271 Migrant Education	295 Network System	Ⓒ = Charter School	**Social Media**
39 Multi-Cultural Curriculum	273 Teacher Mentor	296 Title II Programs	Ⓜ = Magnet School	Ⓕ = Facebook
90 Social Work	274 Before/After Sch	297 Webmaster	Ⓨ = Year-Round School	Ⓣ = Twitter

New Schools are shaded
New Superintendents and Principals are bold
Personnel with email addresses are underscored

School	Grade	Prgm	Enr/#Cls	%	Phone
Lantana Cmty Middle Sch 1225 W Drew St, Lantana 33462 Edward Burke	6-8	GTV	906 43	90%	561/540-3400 Fax 561/540-3435
Lantana Elem Sch 710 W Ocean Ave, Lantana 33462 Janyn Robinson	PK-5	T	511 23	92%	561/202-0300 Fax 561/202-0350
Loggers Run Cmty Middle Sch 11584 W Palmetto Park Rd, Boca Raton 33428 **Krista Hierholzer**	6-8	GT	1,206	43%	561/883-8000 Fax 561/883-8027
Manatee Elem Sch 7001 Charleston Shores Blvd, Lake Worth 33467 Mary Jones	PK-5		1,252 45	32%	561/357-1800 Fax 561/357-1850
Morikami Park Elem Sch 6201 Morikami Park Rd, Delray Beach 33484 Stacey Quinones	K-5		794 36	19%	561/894-7300 Fax 561/894-7350
Okeeheelee Middle Sch 2200 Pinehurst Dr, Greenacres 33413 Elizabeth Morales	6-8	ATV	1,471	84%	561/434-3200 Fax 561/434-3244
Olympic Heights Cmty High Sch 20101 Lyons Rd, Boca Raton 33434 Kelly Burke	9-12	GTV	2,170 120	43%	561/852-6900 Fax 561/852-6974
Omni Middle Sch 5775 Jog Rd, Boca Raton 33496 **Nikkia DeLuz**	6-8		1,473 70	35%	561/989-2800 Fax 561/989-2851
Orchard View Elem Sch 4050 Germantown Rd, Delray Beach 33445 Lisa Lee	PK-5	T	591 47	89%	561/894-7400 Fax 561/894-7450
Palm Springs Cmty Middle Sch 1560 Kirk Rd, Palm Springs 33406 Sandra Jinks	6-8	GTV	1,586	86%	561/434-3300 Fax 561/434-3303
Park Vista Cmty High Sch 7900 S Jog Rd, Lake Worth 33467 Reginald Myers	9-12	V	3,093	34%	561/491-8400 Fax 561/493-6854
Pine Grove Elem Sch 400 SW 10th St, Delray Beach 33444 Shauntay King	PK-5	T	413 31	96%	561/266-1100 Fax 561/266-1150
Plumosa School of the Arts 2501 Seacrest Blvd, Delray Beach 33444 Catherine Reynolds	K-5	T	636 24	79%	561/330-3900 Fax 561/330-3950
Poinciana Elem Sch 1203 N Seacrest Blvd, Boynton Beach 33435 Kathleen Depuma	K-5	T	546 40	67%	561/739-5700 Fax 561/739-5750
Royal Palm Sch 6650 Lawrence Rd, Lantana 33462 Bradley Henry	Spec	T	386 36	99%	561/357-1900 Fax 561/357-1950
S D Spady Elem Sch 901 NW 3rd St, Delray Beach 33444 Rona Tata	PK-5	T	588 30	50%	561/454-7800 Fax 561/454-7801
Sandpiper Shores Elem Sch 11201 Glades Rd, Boca Raton 33498 Stephanie Coletto	PK-5	T	875 30	44%	561/883-4000 Fax 561/883-4050
Santaluces Cmty High Sch 6880 Lawrence Rd, Lantana 33462 Tameka Robinson	9-12	GTV	2,400	75%	561/642-6200 Fax 561/642-6255
Spanish River Cmty High Sch 5100 Jog Rd, Boca Raton 33496 **Allison Castellano**	9-12	GV	2,343 110	27%	561/241-2200 Fax 561/241-2236
Sunrise Park Elem Sch 19400 Coral Ridge Dr, Boca Raton 33498 Alicia Steiger	PK-5		941 45	26%	561/477-4300 Fax 561/477-4350
Sunset Palms Elem Sch 8650 Boynton Beach Blvd, Boynton Beach 33472 Karen Riddle	K-5		1,001	17%	561/752-1100 Fax 561/752-1150
Tradewinds Middle Sch 5090 S Haverhill Rd, Greenacres 33463 Rebecca Subin	6-8	T	1,066	83%	561/493-6400 Fax 561/493-6410
Verde Elem Sch 6590 Verde Trl, Boca Raton 33433 Seth Moldovan	K-5	GT	1,113 49	40%	561/218-6800 Fax 561/218-6850
Village Academy 400 SW 12th Ave, Delray Beach 33444 Latoya Dixon	PK-12	T	700 20	95%	561/243-6100 Fax 561/243-6150
Waters Edge Elem Sch 21601 Shorewind Dr, Boca Raton 33428 **Juliann Walker**	K-5		819 27	20%	561/852-2400 Fax 561/852-2450
West Boca Raton Cmty High Sch 12811 Glades Rd, Boca Raton 33498 **Edmund Capitano**	9-12	V	2,217	38%	561/672-2001 Fax 561/672-2014
Whispering Pines Elem Sch 9090 Spanish Isles Blvd, Boca Raton 33496 Barbara Riemer	K-5		924 50	35%	561/672-2700 Fax 561/672-2750
Woodlands Middle Sch 5200 Lyons Rd, Lake Worth 33467 Enrique Vela	6-8	T	1,348	56%	561/357-0300 Fax 561/357-0307

PALM BEACH CATHOLIC SCHOOLS

• **Diocese of Palm Beach Ed Off** PID: 02231700 561/775-9547
9995 N Military Trl, Palm Bch Gdns 33410 Fax 561/775-9545

Schools: 19 \ *Students:* 6,300

Listing includes only schools located in this county. See District Index for location of Diocesan Offices.

Catholic Schs..Principal	Grd	Prgm	Enr/#Cls	SN	
All Saints Catholic Sch 1759 Indian Creek Pkwy, Jupiter 33458 Jill Broz	PK-8		477 37		561/748-8994 Fax 561/748-8979
Cardinal Newman High Sch 512 Spencer Dr, West Palm Bch 33409 Dr Christine Higgins	9-12		520 50		561/683-6266 Fax 561/683-7307 f
Holy Cross Pre-School & Center 930 Southern Blvd, West Palm Bch 33405 Ana Fundora	PK-PK		100		561/366-8026 Fax 561/366-8577
Pope John Paul II High Sch 4001 N Military Trl, Boca Raton 33431 Edward Bernot	9-12		504 75		561/994-8998 Fax 561/989-8582
Rosarian Academy 807 N Flagler Dr, West Palm Bch 33401 Peggy McCray	PK-8		400 30		561/832-5131 Fax 561/820-8750
Sacred Heart Sch 410 N M St, Lake Worth 33460 Tricia DuVall	PK-8		175 16		561/582-2242 Fax 561/547-9699 f t
St Ann Catholic Sch 324 N Olive Ave, West Palm Bch 33401 Susan Demes	PK-8		264 12		561/832-3676 Fax 561/832-1791
St Clare Sch 821 Prosperity Farms Rd, N Palm Beach 33408 Rita Kissel	K-8		548 18		561/622-7171 Fax 561/627-4426
St Joan of Arc Sch 501 SW 3rd Ave, Boca Raton 33432 Caroline Roberts	PK-8		525 25		561/392-7974 Fax 561/368-6671
St Jude Sch 21689 Toledo Rd, Boca Raton 33433 Debbie Armstrong	PK-8		430 19		561/392-9160 Fax 561/392-5815

1 Superintendent	8 Curric/Instruct K-12	19 Chief Financial Officer	29 Family/Consumer Science	39 Social Studies K-12	49 English/Lang Arts Elem	59 Special Education Elem	69 Academic Assessment
2 Bus/Finance/Purchasing	9 Curric/Instruct Elem	20 Art K-12	30 Adult Education	40 Social Studies Elem	50 English/Lang Arts Sec	60 Special Education Sec	70 Research/Development
3 Buildings And Grounds	10 Curric/Instruct Sec	21 Art Elem	31 Career/Sch-to-Work K-12	41 Social Studies Sec	51 Reading K-12	61 Foreign/World Lang K-12	71 Public Information
4 Food Service	11 Federal Program	22 Art Sec	32 Career/Sch-to-Work Elem	42 Science K-12	52 Reading Elem	62 Foreign/World Lang Elem	72 Summer School
5 Transportation	12 Title I	23 Music K-12	33 Career/Sch-to-Work Sec	43 Science Elem	53 Reading Sec	63 Foreign/World Lang Sec	73 Instructional Tech
6 Athletic	13 Title V	24 Music Elem	34 Early Childhood Ed	44 Science Sec	54 Remedial Reading K-12	64 Religious Education K-12	74 Inservice Training
7 Health Services	15 Asst Superintendent	25 Music Sec	35 Health/Phys Education	45 Math K-12	55 Remedial Reading Elem	65 Religious Education Elem	75 Marketing/Distributive
	16 Instructional Media Svcs	26 Business Education	36 Guidance Services K-12	46 Math Elem	56 Remedial Reading Sec	66 Religious Education Sec	76 Info Systems
	17 Chief Operations Officer	27 Career & Tech Ed	37 Guidance Services Elem	47 Math Sec	57 Bilingual/ELL	67 School Board President	77 Psychological Assess
	18 Chief Academic Officer	28 Technology Education	38 Guidance Services Sec	48 English/Lang Arts K-12	58 Special Education K-12	68 Teacher Personnel	78 Affirmative Action

School	Grd	Enr/#Cls	Phone
St Juliana Sch 4355 S Olive Ave, West Palm Bch 33405 Katie Kervi	PK-8	366 20	561/655-1922 Fax 561/655-8552
St Luke Sch 2896 S Congress Ave, Palm Springs 33461 Diann Bacchus	PK-8	265 10	561/965-8190 Fax 561/965-2404
St Thomas More Pre-School 10935 S Military Trl, Boynton Beach 33436 Anne Marie Fischer	PK-PK	100	561/737-3770 Fax 561/737-8697
St Vincent Ferrer Sch 810 George Bush Blvd, Delray Beach 33483 M Vikki DelGado	PK-8	350 10	561/278-3868 Fax 561/279-9508

PALM BEACH PRIVATE SCHOOLS

Private Schs..Principal	Grd	Prgm	Enr/#Cls	SN
Academic High Sch 23123 State Road 7 Ste 107, Boca Raton 33428 Sheldon Klasfeld	6-12		300 6	561/929-0333 Fax 561/883-2525
Advent Lutheran Sch 300 E Yamato Rd, Boca Raton 33431 Laura Bluhm	PK-8		180 15	561/395-3623 Fax 561/750-3632
American Heritage-Boca Delray 6200 Linton Blvd, Delray Beach 33484 Patricia Cobos \ Maria Benkirane \ Lisa LeFevre	PK-12		1,100	561/495-7272 Fax 561/495-1544
Arthur I Meyer Jewish Academy 5225 Hood Rd, Palm BCH GDNS 33418 Beth Spier	K-8		385	561/686-6520 Fax 561/686-8522
Atlantic Christian Academy 4900 Summit Blvd, West Palm Bch 33415 Jarid Fagin \ Michelle Beatty	PK-12		600 30	561/686-8081 Fax 561/640-7613
Atlantis Academy 1950 Prairie Rd, West Palm Bch 33406 Evan Moody	Spec		150 13	561/642-3100 Fax 561/969-1950
Baldwin Preparatory Sch 200 Castlewood Dr, N Palm Beach 33408 Jena Bauldwin	K-12		135	561/844-7700 Fax 561/844-7707
Benjamin Sch 11000 Ellison Wilson Rd, N Palm Beach 33408 Kristen Sheehan \ Charles Hagy	PK-12		1,100 70	561/626-3747 Fax 561/626-8752
Berean Christian Sch 8350 Okeechobee Blvd, West Palm Bch 33411 Melissa Allen \ Glenn Waters	PK-12		650	561/798-9300 Fax 561/792-3073
Bethel Junior Academy 2850 Avenue F, Riviera Beach 33404 James Previlus	K-8		110	561/881-0130 Fax 561/881-7098
Boca Prep International Sch 10333 Diego Dr S, Boca Raton 33428 Yamile Zeidan	PK-12		250 14	561/852-1410 Fax 561/490-6124
Boca Raton Christian Sch 470 NW 4th Ave, Boca Raton 33432 Clint Erickson \ Stephen Smith	PK-12		615 36	561/391-2727 Fax 561/226-0617
Coastal Middle Sr High Sch 730 5th St, Lake Park 33403 Lisa Collum	6-12		55 3	561/842-6349 Fax 561/842-0911
Coram Deo Academy 10334 Trailwood Cir, Jupiter 33478 Mary Katurna	K-12		125	561/401-0754
Daughter of Zion Jr Academy 250 NW 3rd Ave, Delray Beach 33444 Marliano Smith	PK-8		160 10	561/243-0715 Fax 561/243-0919
Donna Klein Jewish Academy 9701 Donna Klein Blvd, Boca Raton 33428 Marshall Lesack	K-8		800	561/852-3300 Fax 561/852-3327
Fau High Sch 777 Glades Rd, Boca Raton 33431 Sherry Bees	9-12		100	561/297-3970 Fax 561/297-3939
Forest Trail Academy 3111 Fortune Way Ste B4, Wellington 33414 Dr Gifty Chung	K-12		425	800/890-6269 Fax 866/230-0259
Fusion Academy-Boca Raton 5050 Conference Way N, Boca Raton 33431 Christina Seamster	6-12		401	561/953-9365
Garden of Sahaba Academy 3100 NW 5th Ave, Boca Raton 33431 Radwin Baytiyeh	PK-10		193 16	561/395-3011 Fax 561/395-3029
Glades Day Sch 400 Gator Blvd, Belle Glade 33430 Amie Pitts	PK-12		475 40	561/996-6769 Fax 561/992-9274
Gold Coast Junior Academy 138 SE 27th Ave, Boynton Beach 33435 Vera Hart	PK-8		20 3	561/364-7388
Good Shepherd Episcopal Sch 402 Seabrook Rd, Tequesta 33469 Dr Rosemary Marshall	PK-5		120 16	561/746-5507
Grandview Preparatory Sch 336 NW Spanish River Blvd, Boca Raton 33431 Jackie Westerfield	PK-12		300 50	561/416-9737 Fax 561/416-9739
Greenacres Christian Academy 4982 Cambridge St, Lake Worth 33463 Billy Fritsch	K-12		130 6	561/965-0363 Fax 561/439-7149
Gulf Stream Sch 3600 Gulfstream Rd, Gulf Stream 33483 Gray Smith	PK-8		250 26	561/276-5225 Fax 561/276-7115
Haverhill Baptist Day Sch 671 N Haverhill Rd, Haverhill 33415 Diana Atwell	PK-3		109 9	561/683-1780 Fax 561/683-1803
His Academy/Institute 1259 10th St, Lake Park 33403 John Green	Spec		17 4	561/881-5412 Fax 561/881-4312
Jupiter Academy 125 S Pennock Ln, Jupiter 33458 Neall Jones	PK-8		100 25	561/747-1003 Fax 561/747-8480
Jupiter Christian Sch 700 S Delaware Blvd, Jupiter 33458 Susan Rivera \ Joe Zambrano	PK-12		585 45	561/746-7800 Fax 561/746-1955
Katz Hillel Day Sch Boca Raton 21011 95th Ave S, Boca Raton 33428 Chayim Dimont \ Hadassah Smolarcik	PK-8		350	561/470-5000 Fax 561/470-5005
Katz Yeshiva HS South Florida 20900 Ruth & Baron Coleman, Boca Raton 33428 Ora Kanner	9-12		210 8	561/417-7422 Fax 561/417-7028
Kings Academy 8401 Belvedere Rd, West Palm Bch 33411 Adam Miller \ Sonya Jones	PK-12		1,150 62	561/686-4244 Fax 561/686-8017
Lake Park Baptist Sch 625 Park Ave, Lake Park 33403 Dr Anthony Bryan	PK-8		225 10	561/844-2747 Fax 561/848-8310
Lake Worth Christian Sch 7592 High Ridge Rd, Boynton Beach 33426 Lorin Shropshire \ Wes Davidson	PK-12		450 6	561/586-8216 Fax 561/586-4382
Montessori Ind Learning Ctr 3807 Park Ln, West Palm Bch 33406 Anne Lobeck	PK-K		52 4	561/968-2642
Northern Private Sch 1822 High Ridge Rd, Lake Worth 33461 Michelle Hoelzel	PK-2		40 7	561/585-4053 Fax 561/585-4553
Oxbridge Academy 3151 N Military Trl, West Palm Bch 33409 Ralph Maurer	9-12		400	561/972-9600 Fax 561/515-6791

Palm Beach Day Academy 1901 S Flagler Dr, West Palm Bch 33401 Dr Edwin Gordon	PK-3	525 14	561/832-8815 Fax 561/832-3343 🅵🆃
Palm Beach Day Academy 241 Seaview Ave, Palm Beach 33480 Dr Edwin Gordon	4-9	500	561/655-1188 Fax 561/655-5794 🅵🆃
Pine Crest School-Boca Raton 2700 Saint Andrews Blvd, Boca Raton 33434 Sharon Schmidt \ Kristi Combs	PK-8	860 50	561/852-2800 Fax 561/852-2832
Precious Promise Chrn Academy 210 N J St, Lake Worth 33460 K Washington	PK-12	19	561/540-4459 Fax 561/540-8811
R J Hendley Christian Cmty Sch 2800 R J Hendley Ave, Riviera Beach 33404 Marie Robinson \ Linda Knight	PK-8	152 25	561/842-1349 Fax 561/840-0716
Shepherd's Sch 1800 Bacom Point Rd, Pahokee 33476 Tamey Jones	PK-12	55	561/924-9578 Fax 561/924-7287
Southwide Academy 100 Cypress Lake Dr, West Palm Bch 33411 Barbara O'Malley	K-12	80 4	561/793-0657
Spanish River Christian Sch 2400 W Yamato Rd, Boca Raton 33431 Jason Zecca \ Markus Spotts	PK-8	515 25	561/994-5006 Fax 561/994-1160
St Andrew's Sch 3900 Jog Rd, Boca Raton 33434 Ethan Shapiro \ Ann Haynes \ Gregg Good	PK-12	1,300 85	561/210-2000 Fax 561/210-2007 🅵🆃
St Davids In Pine Episcopal SC 465 Forest Hill Blvd, Wellington 33414 Kathy Vandamas	PK-2	75	561/793-1272 Fax 561/793-2301
St Josephs Episcopal Sch 3300B S Seacrest Blvd, Boynton Beach 33435 Audrey MacPhee \ Kyle Aubrey	PK-8	250 18	561/732-2045 Fax 561/732-1315
St Mark's Episcopal Sch 3395 Burns Rd, Palm Bch Gdns 33410 Page Cash \ Nicole Robison	PK-8	500 27	561/622-1504 Fax 561/622-6801
St Paul Lutheran Sch 701 W Palmetto Park Rd, Boca Raton 33486 James Richards	PK-8	375 20	561/395-8548 Fax 561/395-2902
Sunshine Tree Montessori Sch 701 Ocean Dr, Juno Beach 33408 Elizabeth Hof	PK-6	40 3	561/281-0085
The Greene Sch 2001 S Dixie Hwy, West Palm Bch 33401 Dr Denise Spirou	PK-8	401	561/293-2888
The Learning Foundation of FL 507A Royal Palm Beach Blvd, West Palm Bch 33411 Debra Thornby	3-12	51	561/795-6886 Fax 561/795-6884
Torah Academy of Boca Raton 447 NW Spanish River Blvd, Boca Raton 33431 Jacy Orlinsky \ Gita Guttman \ Yosef Bondi	PK-8	250 14	561/465-2200 Fax 561/463-6484
Trinity Christ Sch-Palm Bch 9625 N Military Trl, Palm Bch Gdns 33410 Vernita Martial	PK-6	300	561/253-3950 Fax 561/253-3953
Trinity Christian Academy 7259 S Military Trl, Lake Worth 33463 Kevyn Brown	PK-12	550	561/967-1900 Fax 561/965-4347
Trinity Lutheran Sch 400 N Swinton Ave, Delray Beach 33444 Heather Lowing	PK-8	400 20	561/276-8458 Fax 561/272-3215
Turtle River Montessori 926 Maplewood Dr, Jupiter 33458 Bharati Dandiya	K-12	250	561/745-1995 Fax 561/745-1313
Unity Sch 101 NW 22nd St, Delray Beach 33444 Louis St-Laurent	PK-8	319 30	561/276-4414 Fax 561/265-0990 🅵

Weiss Sch 4176 Burns Rd, Palm Bch Gdns 33410 Dr Tammy Ferguson	PK-8	215 21	561/627-0740 Fax 561/775-7794 🅵
West Palm Beach Junior Academy 6300 Summit Blvd, West Palm Bch 33415 Glenn Timmons	PK-8	89 7	561/689-9575

PALM BEACH REGIONAL CENTERS

● **FDLRS-Alpha** PID: 04498241   561/434-8626
   3378 Forest Hill Blvd, West Palm Bch 33406   Fax 561/434-8384
Dr Donald Sennoy ....1 Jim Dunlap 73

PASCO COUNTY

PASCO PUBLIC SCHOOLS

● **Pasco Co School Dist** PID: 00199156   813/794-2000
   7227 Land O Lakes Blvd, Land O Lakes 34638   Fax 813/794-2326

> **Schools:** 97 \ **Teachers:** 6,159 \ **Students:** 75,001 \
> **Special Ed Students:** 11,415 \ **LEP Students:** 3,057 \ **College-Bound:** 60%
> \ **Ethnic:** Asian 3%, African American 7%, Hispanic 23%, Caucasian
> 66% \ **Exp:** $145 (Low) \ **Poverty:** 17% \ **Title I:** $20,626,625 \
> **Special Education:** $75,595,000 \ **Bilingual Education:** $7,093,000 \
> **Open-Close:** 08/12 - 05/27 \ **DTBP:** $192 (High) \ 🆃

Kurt Browning 1	James Class 2
Olga Swinson 2,11,19	Harry Keenan 3
Mark Fox 3	Julie Hedine 4
Thaddeus Kledzik 5	Matthew Wicks 6
Lisa Kern 7	Vanessa Hilton 8,12,15,18
Betsy Kuhn 15	David Scanga 15
Kevin Shibley 15,68,69	Marcy Nettles 15
Ray Gadd 15	Tammy Berryhill 15
Lea Mitchell 20,35,39,44,74	Keiva Wiley 27,31
Angela Porterfield 34	Melissa Musselwhite ..34,36,58,81,88
Roberta Starling 46	Alicia Montijo 57,61
Cynthia Armstrong 67	Christine Pejot 68
Chris Williams 70	Dr Peggy Jones 70,294
Linda Cobbe 71	John Simon 73,76
Andy Dunn 82,295	Danica Cockrell 90
Mary Grey 274	Richard Maclemale 297
Lori Romano 298	Vicki Papaemanuel 752

Public Schs..Principal	Grd	Prgm	Enr/#Cls	SN
© Academy at the Farm 9500 Alex Lange Way, Dade City 33525 Ray Polk	K-8		588 20	24% 352/588-9737 Fax 352/588-0508
© Athenian Acad-Tech & Arts 3118 Seven Springs Blvd, New Prt Rchy 34655 **Evan Markowitz**	K-8	T	359 12	73% 727/372-0200 Fax 727/376-1916
© Classical Preparatory Sch 16500 Lyceum Ln, Spring Hill 34610 Dr Tina Errthum	K-11		676	29% 813/803-7903 Fax 813/402-0603
© Countryside Montessori Academy 5852 Ehren Cutoff, Land O Lakes 34639 **Michael Picone**	1-8		344	12% 813/996-0991 Fax 813/996-0993

1	Superintendent	8	Curric/Instruct K-12	19	Chief Financial Officer	29	Family/Consumer Science
2	Bus/Finance/Purchasing	9	Curric/Instruct Elem	20	Art K-12	30	Adult Education
3	Buildings And Grounds	10	Curric/Instruct Sec	21	Art Elem	31	Career/Sch-to-Work K-12
4	Food Service	11	Federal Program	22	Art Sec	32	Career/Sch-to-Work Elem
5	Transportation	12	Title I	23	Music K-12	33	Career/Sch-to-Work Sec
6	Athletic	13	Title V	24	Music Elem	34	Early Childhood Ed
7	Health Services	15	Asst Superintendent	25	Music Sec	35	Health/Phys Education
		16	Instructional Media Svcs	26	Business Education	36	Guidance Services K-12
		17	Chief Operations Officer	27	Career & Tech Ed	37	Guidance Services Elem
		18	Chief Academic Officer	28	Technology Education	38	Guidance Services Sec

39	Social Studies K-12	49	English/Lang Arts Elem	59	Special Education Elem	69	Academic Assessment
40	Social Studies Elem	50	English/Lang Arts Sec	60	Special Education Sec	70	Research/Development
41	Social Studies Sec	51	Reading K-12	61	Foreign/World Lang K-12	71	Public Information
42	Science K-12	52	Reading Elem	62	Foreign/World Lang Elem	72	Summer School
43	Science Elem	53	Reading Sec	63	Foreign/World Lang Sec	73	Instructional Tech
44	Science Sec	54	Remedial Reading K-12	64	Religious Education K-12	74	Inservice Training
45	Math K-12	55	Remedial Reading Elem	65	Religious Education Elem	75	Marketing/Distributive
46	Math Elem	56	Remedial Reading Sec	66	Religious Education Sec	76	Info Systems
47	Math Sec	57	Bilingual/ELL	67	School Board President	77	Psychological Assess
48	English/Lang Arts K-12	58	Special Education K-12	68	Teacher Personnel	78	Affirmative Action

School	Grd	Prgm	Enr/#Cls	SN	Phone
© Dayspring Academy Elem Sch 8911 Timber Oaks Ave, Port Richey 34668 Wendy Finlay	K-5	T	348 15	46%	727/862-8600 Fax 727/868-5175
© Dayspring Academy Sec Sch 9509 Palm Ave, Port Richey 34668 Timothy Greenier	6-12		290		727/847-9003 Fax 727/848-8774
© Florida Virtual Academy-Pasco 9143 Philips Hwy Ste 590, Jacksonville 32256 Bridget White	K-12		373	32%	904/247-3268
© Imagine School at Land O'Lakes [137] 2940 Sunlake Blvd, Land O Lakes 34638 Aimee Williams	K-8		803	14%	813/428-7444 Fax 813/428-7445
© Learning Lodge Academy 5844 Pine Hill Rd, Port Richey 34668 Kerrie Cuffe	K-5	T	218	63%	727/389-0067 Fax 727/807-6051
Pace Center for Girls-Pasco 7545 Little Rd, New Prt Rchy 34654 Gail Armstrong	6-12		54	52%	727/849-1901 Fax 727/842-5979
Pasco E-School 15144 Shady Hills Rd, Spring Hill 34610 Joanne Glenn	K-12		200	21%	813/346-1900 Fax 813/346-1991
© Pepin Acad-Pasco Campus 9804 Little Rd, New Prt Rchy 34654 Celeste Kellar	3-12	T	323	17%	727/233-2961 Fax 727/233-2963
© Plato Academy Trinity [144] 8812 Old County Road 54, New Prt Rchy 34653 Hayley Harris	K-8		260	19%	727/877-2437 Fax 727/799-0200
© Union Park Charter Academy [133] 32775 Oldwoods Ave, Wesley Chapel 33543 Tracy Ware	K-6		610		813/358-7306 Fax 813/358-7307

● Pasco CSD-Elementary Schools PID: 12234938 813/794-2695
7227 Land O Lakes Blvd, Land O Lakes 34638

Kimberly Poe 15

Public Schs..Principal	Grd	Prgm	Enr/#Cls	SN	Phone
Achieve Center at Richey 6915 Madison St, New Prt Rchy 34652 Christopher Clayton	Spec		30		727/774-7860
Anclote Elem Sch 3610 Madison St, New Prt Rchy 34652 Ellen Thomas	PK-5	T	556 34	81%	727/774-3200 Fax 727/774-3291
Bexley Elem Sch 4380 Ballantrae Blvd, Land O Lakes 34638 Vicki Wolin	K-5		804		813/346-4300 Fax 813/346-4391
Calusa Elem Sch 7520 Orchid Lake Rd, New Prt Rchy 34653 **Trudy Hartman**	K-5	T	510 41	81%	727/774-3700 Fax 727/774-3791
Centennial Elem Sch 38501 Centennial Rd, Dade City 33525 Gretchen Fladd	PK-5	T	471 34	80%	352/524-5000 Fax 352/524-5091
Chasco Elem Sch 7906 Ridge Rd, Port Richey 34668 Michele Boylan	PK-5	T	688 32	81%	727/774-1200 Fax 727/774-1291
Chester W Taylor Elem Sch 3638 Morris Bridge Rd, Zephyrhills 33543 Julie Marks	PK-5	T	610 39	80%	813/794-6900 Fax 813/794-6991
Connerton Elem Sch 9300 Flourish Dr, Land O Lakes 34637 **Kelly Edwards**	PK-5	T	921 30	38%	813/346-1800 Fax 813/346-1891
Cotee River Elem Sch 7515 Plathe Rd, New Prt Rchy 34653 Sharon Sacco Slusser	PK-5	T	658	77%	727/774-3000 Fax 727/774-3091
Cypress Elem Sch 10055 Sweet Bay Ct, New Prt Rchy 34654 **Tammy Berryhill**	PK-5	T	722 28	60%	727/774-4500 Fax 727/774-4591
Deer Park Elem Sch 8636 Trouble Creek Rd, New Prt Rchy 34653 Jeanne Krapfl	PK-5	T	502	53%	727/774-8900 Fax 727/774-8991
Denham Oaks Elem Sch 1422 Oak Grove Blvd, Lutz 33559 Mardee Powers	PK-5	T	781 46	41%	813/794-1600 Fax 813/794-1691
Double Branch Elem Sch 31500 Chancey Rd, Wesley Chapel 33543 **Lori Wiggins**	PK-5	T	751	32%	813/346-0400 Fax 813/346-0491
Dr Mary Giella Elem Sch 14710 Shady Hills Rd, Spring Hill 34610 Tracy Bonnett	PK-5	T	670 40	78%	727/774-5800 Fax 727/774-5891
Fox Hollow Elem Sch 8309 Fox Hollow Dr, Port Richey 34668 Karyn Kinzie	PK-5	T	559	85%	727/774-7600 Fax 727/774-7691
Gulf Highlands Elem Sch 8019 Gulf Highlands Dr, Port Richey 34668 Judy Cosh	PK-5	T	681	89%	727/774-7700 Fax 727/774-7791
Gulf Trace Elem Sch 3303 Gulf Trace Blvd, Holiday 34691 **Dawn Scilex**	PK-5	T	633	83%	727/246-3600 Fax 727/246-3691
Gulfside Elem Sch 2329 Anclote Blvd, Holiday 34691 Clara Craig	K-5	T	383 35	87%	727/774-6000 Fax 727/774-6091
Hudson Elem Sch 7229 Hudson Ave, Hudson 34667 Dawn Scilex	PK-5	T	581	85%	727/774-4000 Fax 727/774-4091
James M Marlowe Elem Sch 5642 Cecelia Dr, New Prt Rchy 34652 Rayann Mitchell	PK-5	T	495 31	89%	727/774-8600 Fax 727/774-8691
Lacoochee Elem Sch 38815 Cummer Rd, Dade City 33523 Latoya Jordan	PK-5	T	319 25	97%	352/524-5600 Fax 352/524-5691
Lake Myrtle Elem Sch 22844 Weeks Blvd, Land O Lakes 34639 Megan Hermansen	PK-5	T	597 50	37%	813/794-1000 Fax 813/794-1091
Longleaf Elem Sch 3253 Town Ave, New Prt Rchy 34655 **Jennifer McCormack**	PK-5		678	32%	727/774-0800 Fax 727/774-0891
Mittye P Locke Elem Sch 4339 Evans Ave, New Prt Rchy 34652 Cynthia Bauman	PK-5	T	594 46	82%	727/774-3100 Fax 727/774-3191
Moon Lake Elem Sch 12019 Treebreeze Dr, New Prt Rchy 34654 Elise Landahl	PK-5	T	605 34	81%	727/774-4600 Fax 727/774-4691
New River Elem Sch 4710 River Glen Blvd, Wesley Chapel 33545 Sarah Bordner	PK-5	T	832	52%	813/346-0500 Fax 813/346-0591
Northwest Elem Sch 14302 Cobra Way, Hudson 34669 Nicole Reynolds	PK-5	T	612 40	90%	727/774-4700 Fax 727/774-4791
Oakstead Elem Sch 19925 Lake Patience Rd, Land O Lakes 34638 Claudia Steinacker	PK-5		825	31%	813/346-1500 Fax 813/346-1591
Odessa Elem Sch 12810 Interlaken Rd, New Prt Rchy 34655 Teresa Love	PK-5		872	26%	727/246-3700 Fax 727/246-3791
Pasco Elem Sch 37350 Florida Ave, Dade City 33525 Nena Green	PK-5		582 38	90%	352/524-5200 Fax 352/524-5291
Pine View Elem Sch 5333 Parkway Blvd, Land O Lakes 34639 Kathryn Moore	PK-5		575	43%	813/794-0600 Fax 813/794-0691
Quail Hollow Elem Sch 7050 Quail Hollow Blvd, Wesley Chapel 33544 Kara Smucker	PK-5		509	65%	813/794-1100 Fax 813/794-1191

79	Student Personnel	91	Safety/Security	275	Response To Intervention	298	Grant Writer/Ptnrships	**School Programs**		**Social Media**
80	Driver Ed/Safety	92	Magnet School	277	Remedial Math K-12	750	Chief Innovation Officer	A = Alternative Program		
81	Gifted/Talented	93	Parental Involvement	280	Literacy Coach	751	Chief of Staff	G = Adult Classes		❏ = Facebook
82	Video Services	95	Tech Prep Program	285	STEM	752	Social Emotional Learning	M = Magnet Program		
83	Substance Abuse Prev	97	Chief Infomation Officer	286	Digital Learning			T = Title I Schoolwide		❏ = Twitter
84	Erate	98	Chief Technology Officer	288	Common Core Standards	**Other School Types**		V = Career & Tech Ed Programs		
85	AIDS Education	270	Character Education	294	Accountability	Ⓐ = Alternative School				
88	Alternative/At Risk	271	Migrant Education	295	Network System	© = Charter School		New Schools are shaded		
89	Multi-Cultural Curriculum	273	Teacher Mentor	296	Title II Programs	Ⓜ = Magnet School		New Superintendents and Principals are bold		
90	Social Work	274	Before/After Sch	297	Webmaster	Ⓨ = Year-Round School		Personnel with email addresses are underscored		

School	Grd	Prgm	Enr/#Cls	SN	Phone
Richey Elem Sch 6850 Adams St, New Prt Rchy 34652 Keri Allen	PK-5	T	677 36	89%	727/774-3500 Fax 727/774-3591
Rodney B Cox Elem Sch 37615 Martin Luther King Blvd, Dade City 33523 **Kimberly Natal**	PK-5	T	510 30	96%	352/524-5100 Fax 352/524-5191
San Antonio Elem Sch 32416 Darby Rd, Dade City 33525 Kimberly Anderson	K-5	T	682 35	68%	352/524-5300 Fax 352/524-5391
Sand Pine Elem Sch 29040 County Line Rd, Wesley Chapel 33543 Christina Twardosz	K-5	T	561 42	31%	813/794-1900 Fax 813/794-1991
Ⓜ Sanders Memorial Elem Sch 5126 School Rd, Land O Lakes 34638 Jason Petry	K-5		810	20%	813/794-1500 Fax 813/794-1591
Schrader Elem Sch 11041 Little Rd, New Prt Rchy 34654 Lee-Anne Yerkey	PK-5	T	712 40	81%	727/774-5900 Fax 727/774-5991
Seven Oaks Elem Sch 27633 Mystic Oak Blvd, Wesley Chapel 33544 Shauntte Butcher	PK-5		768	26%	813/794-0700 Fax 813/794-0791
Seven Springs Elem Sch 8025 Mitchell Ranch Rd, New Prt Rchy 34655 Todd Cluff	K-5	T	458 48	71%	727/774-9600 Fax 727/774-9691
Shady Hills Elem Sch 18000 Shady Hills Rd, Spring Hill 34610 Tom Barker	K-5	T	545	76%	727/774-4100 Fax 727/774-4191
Sunray Elem Sch 4815 Sunray Dr, Holiday 34690 Debra Viggiano	K-5	T	456	87%	727/774-9100 Fax 727/774-9191
Trinity Elem Sch 2209 Duck Slough Blvd, New Prt Rchy 34655 **Adam Wolin** 🇹	K-5	T	616 32	24%	727/774-9900 Fax 727/774-9991
Trinity Oaks Elem Sch 1827 Trinity Oaks Blvd, New Prt Rchy 34655 Allison Hoskins	K-5		631	28%	727/774-0900 Fax 727/774-0991
Veterans Elem Sch 26940 Progress Pkwy, Wesley Chapel 33544 Melissa Bidgood	PK-5	T	775	37%	813/346-1400 Fax 813/346-1491
Watergrass Elem Sch 32750 Overpass Rd, Wesley Chapel 33545 Scott Mitchell	K-5	T	608	49%	813/346-0600 Fax 813/346-0691
Wesley Chapel Elem Sch 30243 Wells Rd, Wesley Chapel 33545 Stanley Mykita	K-5	T	645	41%	813/794-0100 Fax 813/794-0191
West Zephyrhills Elem Sch 37900 14th Ave, Zephyrhills 33542 Scott Atkins	PK-5	T	857	84%	813/794-6300 Fax 813/794-6391
Wiregrass Elem Sch 29732 Wiregrass School Rd, Wesley Chapel 33543 Steven Williams	K-5		641	33%	813/346-0700 Fax 813/346-0791
Woodland Elem Sch 38203 Henry Dr, Zephyrhills 33542 Shirley Ray	PK-5	T	868 50	80%	813/794-6400 Fax 813/794-6491

● **Pasco CSD-High Schools** PID: 12234952   813/794-2753
7227 Land O Lakes Blvd, Land O Lakes 34638

Dr Monica Ilse 15

Public Schs..Principal	Grd	Prgm	Enr/#Cls	SN	Phone
Anclote High Sch 1540 Sweetbriar Dr, Holiday 34691 Vanessa Moon	9-12	GTV	1,184	75%	727/246-3000 Fax 727/246-3091
Cypress Creek Middle High Sch 8701 Old Pasco Rd, Wesley Chapel 33544 Carin Nettles	6-12		2,049		813/346-4400 Fax 813/346-4491

School	Grd	Prgm	Enr/#Cls	SN	Phone
F K Marchman Tech Ed Center 7825 Campus Dr, New Prt Rchy 34653 Robert Aguis	Voc	GT	300 50	63%	727/774-1700 Fax 727/774-1791
Fivay High Sch 12115 Chicago Ave, Hudson 34669 **Jason Joens**	9-12	GTV	1,763	70%	727/246-4000 Fax 727/246-4091
Gulf High Sch 5355 School Rd, New Prt Rchy 34652 **Jeff Morgenstein**	9-12	AGTV	1,561 100	67%	727/774-3300 Fax 727/774-3391
Ⓐ Harry Schwettman Ed Center 5520 Grand Blvd, New Prt Rchy 34652 Randall Koenigsfeld	6-12	GTV	140 14	88%	727/774-0000 Fax 727/774-0091
Hudson High Sch 14410 Cobra Way, Hudson 34669 Dr David LaRoche	9-12	AGTV	1,142	69%	727/774-4200 Fax 727/774-4291
J W Mitchell High Sch 2323 Little Rd, New Prt Rchy 34655 Jessica Schultz	9-12	GV	2,068	29%	727/774-9200 Fax 727/774-9291
Ⓐ James Irvin Education Center 35830 State Road 52, Dade City 33525 Cloty Davis	6-12	GT	148 16	82%	352/524-5700 Fax 352/524-5791
Land O'Lakes High Sch 20325 Gator Ln, Land O Lakes 34638 Fredric Mellin	9-12	AGV	1,840 74	31%	813/794-9400 Fax 813/794-9491
Pasco High Sch 36850 State Road 52, Dade City 33525 Kari Kadlub	9-12	AGTV	1,768 77	60%	352/524-5500 Fax 352/524-5591
River Ridge High Sch 11646 Town Center Rd, New Prt Rchy 34654 Dr Toni Zetzsche	9-12	AGTV	1,638	45%	727/774-7200 Fax 727/774-7291
Sunlake High Sch 3023 Sunlake Blvd, Land O Lakes 34638 Michael Cloyd	9-12	G	2,010	28%	813/346-1000 Fax 813/346-1091
Wendell Krinn Technical HS 7650 Orchid Lake Rd, New Prt Rchy 34653 Dr Chris Dunning	Voc		401		727/774-3900
Wesley Chapel High Sch 30651 Wells Rd, Wesley Chapel 33545 Matt McDermott	9-12	T	1,433 60	46%	813/794-8700 Fax 813/794-8791
Wiregrass Ranch High Sch 2909 Mansfield Blvd, Wesley Chapel 33543 Robyn White	9-12	G	2,220	28%	813/346-6000 Fax 813/346-6091
Zephyrhills High Sch 6335 12th St, Zephyrhills 33542 **Dr Christina Stanley**	9-12	AGTV	1,477 75	67%	813/794-6100 Fax 813/794-6191

● **Pasco CSD-Middle Schools** PID: 12234940   813/794-2753
7227 Land O Lakes Blvd, Land O Lakes 34638

Marcy Nettles 15

Public Schs..Principal	Grd	Prgm	Enr/#Cls	SN	Phone
Achieve Center at Pasco 18950 Michigan Ln, Spring Hill 34610 Paul Lipinski	Spec		42		813/346-2000 Fax 813/346-2010
Bayonet Point Middle Sch 11125 Little Rd, New Prt Rchy 34654 Shelley Carrino	6-8	ATV	822	81%	727/774-7400 Fax 727/774-7491
Centennial Middle Sch 38505 Centennial Rd, Dade City 33525 Rick Saylor	6-8	TV	688 27	71%	352/524-9700 Fax 352/524-9791
Charles S Rushe Middle Sch 18654 Mentmore Blvd, Land O Lakes 34638 David Salerno	6-8		1,223	30%	813/346-1200 Fax 813/346-1291
Chasco Middle Sch 7702 Ridge Rd, Port Richey 34668 Brandon Bracciale	6-8	TV	693	81%	727/774-1300 Fax 727/774-1391

1 Superintendent	8 Curric/Instruct K-12	19 Chief Financial Officer	29 Family/Consumer Science	39 Social Studies K-12	49 English/Lang Arts Elem	59 Special Education Elem	69 Academic Assessment
2 Bus/Finance/Purchasing	9 Curric/Instruct Elem	20 Art K-12	30 Adult Education	40 Social Studies Elem	50 English/Lang Arts Sec	60 Special Education Sec	70 Research/Development
3 Buildings And Grounds	10 Curric/Instruct Sec	21 Art Elem	31 Career/Sch-to-Work K-12	41 Social Studies Sec	51 Reading K-12	61 Foreign/World Lang K-12	71 Public Information
4 Food Service	11 Federal Program	22 Art Sec	32 Career/Sch-to-Work Elem	42 Science K-12	52 Reading Elem	62 Foreign/World Lang Elem	72 Summer School
5 Transportation	12 Title I	23 Music K-12	33 Career/Sch-to-Work Sec	43 Science Elem	53 Reading Sec	63 Foreign/World Lang Sec	73 Instructional Tech
6 Athletic	13 Title V	24 Music Elem	34 Early Childhood Ed	44 Science Sec	54 Remedial Reading K-12	64 Religious Education K-12	74 Inservice Training
7 Health Services	15 Asst Superintendent	25 Music Sec	35 Health/Phys Education	45 Math K-12	55 Remedial Reading Elem	65 Religious Education Elem	75 Marketing/Distributive
	16 Instructional Media Svcs	26 Business Education	36 Guidance Services K-12	46 Math Elem	56 Remedial Reading Sec	66 Religious Education Sec	76 Info Systems
	17 Chief Operations Officer	27 Career & Tech Ed	37 Guidance Services Elem	47 Math Sec	57 Bilingual/ELL	67 School Board President	77 Psychological Assess
	18 Chief Academic Officer	28 Technology Education	38 Guidance Services Sec	48 English/Lang Arts K-12	58 Special Education K-12	68 Teacher Personnel	78 Affirmative Action

School	Grd	Prgm	Enr/#Cls	%	Phone
Crews Lake Middle Sch 15144 Shady Hills Rd, Spring Hill 34610 David Huyck	6-8	T	757	73%	727/246-1600 Fax 727/246-1691
Dr John Long Middle Sch 2025 Mansfield Blvd, Wesley Chapel 33543 Christine Wolff	6-8		1,544	30%	813/346-6200 Fax 813/346-6291
Gulf Middle Sch 6419 Louisiana Ave, New Prt Rchy 34653 Jason Joens	6-8	ATV	958 45	84%	727/774-8000 Fax 727/774-8091
Hudson Middle Sch 14540 Cobra Way, Hudson 34669 Joseph Musselman	6-8	AT	674 70	80%	727/774-8200 Fax 727/774-8291
Pasco Middle Sch 13925 14th St, Dade City 33525 Danielle Johnson	6-8	ATV	859 57	76%	352/524-8400 Fax 352/524-8491
Paul R Smith Middle Sch 1410 Sweetbriar Dr, Holiday 34691 Joel Divincent	6-8	T	997	82%	727/246-3200 Fax 727/246-3291
Pine View Middle Sch 5334 Parkway Blvd, Land O Lakes 34639 Jennifer Warren	6-8	A	1,050 60	33%	813/794-4800 Fax 813/794-4891
Raymond B Stewart Middle Sch 38505 10th Ave, Zephyrhills 33542 Shae Davis	6-8	ATV	989 60	76%	813/794-6500 Fax 813/794-6591
River Ridge Middle Sch 11646 Town Center Rd, New Prt Rchy 34654 Angela Murphy	6-8	T	1,181	52%	727/774-7000 Fax 727/774-7290
Seven Springs Middle Sch 2441 Little Rd, New Prt Rchy 34655 Cortney Gantt	6-8		1,574 80	33%	727/774-6700 Fax 727/774-6791
Thomas E Weightman Middle Sch 30649 Wells Rd, Wesley Chapel 33545 Rachel Fowler	6-8	AT	1,056 65	48%	813/794-0200 Fax 813/794-0291

PASCO CATHOLIC SCHOOLS

• **Diocese St Petersburg Ed Off** PID: 00200729

Listing includes only schools located in this county. See District Index for location of Diocesan Offices.

Catholic Schs..Principal	Grd	Prgm	Enr/#Cls	SN
Bishop Larkin Sch 8408 Monarch Dr, Port Richey 34668 Sr Regina Ozuzu	PK-8		300 20	727/862-6981 Fax 727/869-9893
Bishop McLaughlin Catholic HS 13651 Hays Rd, Spring Hill 34610 Camille Jowanna	9-12		300	727/857-2600 Fax 727/857-2610
Sacred Heart Early Chldhd Ctr 32245 Saint Joe Rd, Dade City 33525 Lucinda O'Quinn	PK-PK		180 9	352/588-4060 Fax 352/588-4871
St Anthony Catholic Sch 12155 Joe Herrmann Dr, San Antonio 33576 Sr Alice Ottapurackal	K-8		210 11	352/588-3041 Fax 352/588-3142
St Thomas Aquinas ECC 8320 Old County Road 54, New Prt Rchy 34653 Alicia Mumma	PK-PK		100 5	727/376-2330

PASCO PRIVATE SCHOOLS

Private Schs..Principal	Grd	Prgm	Enr/#Cls	SN
Academy at the Lakes 2331 Collier Pkwy, Land O Lakes 34639 Mark Heller	PK-12		400	813/948-2133 Fax 813/948-2943
East Pasco Adventist Academy 38434 Centennial Rd, Dade City 33525 Jesse Benton	PK-8		67 8	352/567-3646 Fax 352/567-1907
Elfers Christian Sch 5630 Olympia St, New Prt Rchy 34652 Rick Robertson	K-12		211 16	727/845-0235 Fax 727/848-5135
Fellowship Baptist Academy 5940 Massachusetts Ave, New Prt Rchy 34652 Josh Martin	K-12		52 6	727/848-4593 Fax 727/846-7347
First Christian Academy 6800 Trouble Creek Rd, New Prt Rchy 34653 Susan Kunsman	PK-8		205 16	727/943-7411 Fax 727/943-7412
Genesis Preparatory Sch 7710 Osteen Rd, New Prt Rchy 34653 Antonia Hapsis	6-12		100 16	727/846-8407 Fax 727/844-3601
Genesis Sch 8100 Mitchell Ranch Rd, New Prt Rchy 34655 Dr Missy Nurrenbrock	PK-5		100 15	727/372-9333 Fax 727/372-6520
Genesis Sch 6609 River Rd, New Prt Rchy 34652 Dr Missy Nurrenbrock	PK-5		180 9	727/845-1111 Fax 727/845-0089
Grace Christian Sch 9403 Scot St, Hudson 34669 Glen Pratt	K-12		135 11	727/863-1825 Fax 888/486-5536
Hope Ranch Learning Academy 17933 East Rd, Hudson 34667 Ampy Suarez	Spec		130	727/232-0119 Fax 727/233-0628
Land O'Lakes Christian Sch 5105 School Rd, Land O Lakes 34638 Michelle Fleeman	PK-12		250 18	813/995-9040 Fax 813/996-6106
Millenium Academy 10005 Ridge Rd, New Prt Rchy 34654 Lori Ekblad	K-12		120	727/845-8150
North Tampa Christian Academy 5585 E County Line Rd, Wesley Chapel 33544 Merili Wyatte \ Kevin Cameron	PK-12		280	813/991-0801
Raintree Christian Academy 4917 State Road 54, New Prt Rchy 34652 Marilyn Tiglao	K-8		31	727/845-8998
Saddlebrook Prep Sch 5700 Saddlebrook Way, Wesley Chapel 33543 Deanna Garrett	3-12		100 12	813/907-4300 Fax 813/991-4713
Torchbearers' Christian Acad 12747 Happy Hill Rd, Dade City 33525 Jan Yarbrough	K-12		77 6	352/567-3100
World of Knowledge Mont Sch 1935 Abacus Rd, Holiday 34690 Gail Gilmore	PK-8		100 7	727/934-3028 Fax 727/937-0642
Zephyrhills Christian Academy 34927 Eiland Blvd, Zephyrhills 33541 Michael Smith	PK-12		250	813/779-1648 Fax 813/779-9829

79 Student Personnel	91 Safety/Security	275 Response To Intervention	298 Grant Writer/Ptnrships
30 Driver Ed/Safety	92 Magnet School	277 Remedial Math K-12	750 Chief Innovation Officer
31 Gifted/Talented	93 Parental Involvement	280 Literacy Coach	751 Chief of Staff
32 Video Services	95 Tech Prep Program	285 STEM	752 Social Emotional Learning
33 Substance Abuse Prev	97 Chief Information Officer	286 Digital Learning	
34 Erate	98 Chief Technology Officer	288 Common Core Standards	Other School Types
35 AIDS Education	270 Character Education	294 Accountability	Ⓐ = Alternative School
38 Alternative/At Risk	271 Migrant Education	295 Network System	Ⓒ = Charter School
39 Multi-Cultural Curriculum	273 Teacher Mentor	296 Title II Programs	Ⓜ = Magnet School
90 Social Work	274 Before/After Sch	297 Webmaster	Ⓨ = Year-Round School

School Programs
A = Alternative Program
G = Adult Classes
M = Magnet Program
T = Title I Schoolwide
V = Career & Tech Ed Programs

Social Media
= Facebook
= Twitter

New Schools are shaded
New Superintendents and Principals are bold
Personnel with email addresses are underscored

PINELLAS COUNTY

PINELLAS PUBLIC SCHOOLS

- **Pinellas Co School Dist** PID: 00199429   727/588-6000
  301 4th St SW, Largo 33770   Fax 727/588-6437

> **Schools:** 152 \ **Teachers:** 6,823 \ **Students:** 101,427 \
> **Special Ed Students:** 13,530 \ **LEP Students:** 6,653 \ **College-Bound:** 60%
> \ **Ethnic:** Asian 5%, African American 19%, Hispanic 17%, Caucasian
> 59% \ **Exp:** $164 (Low) \ **Poverty:** 16% \ **Title I:** $28,404,269 \
> **Special Education:** $66,480,000 \ **Bilingual Education:** $7,867,000 \
> **Open-Close:** 08/14 - 05/29 \ **DTBP:** $192 (High) \ **f**

Dr Michael Grego	1	Kevin Smith	2,15
Clint Herbic	3,5,15	Doug Pollei	3
Lynnanne Geist	4	Rick McBride	5
Al Bennett	6,35,80	Sara O'Toole	7
Kevin Hendrick	8,15,288	Shana Rafalski	9,274
Rita Vasquez	10	Dr Felita Grant	12
Lori Matway	15,79	Paula Texel	15,68,78
Tom Lechner	15,76,295	Dr William Corbett	15
Connie Kolosey	16,286	Mark Hunt	27,30,31
Dr Natasa Karac	57	Renee Flowers	67
Dr Seymour Brown	68	Sherry Aemisegger	68
Dr Dan Evans	69,70,294	Octavio Salcedo	69,70,294
Donna Sicilian	79	Lisa DePaolo	83
Michelle Topping	88	Matthew Blum	89
Dennis Russo	91	Dr Valerie Brimm	93
Laura Spence	285	Mary Conage	298

Public Schs..Principal	Grd	Prgm	Enr/#Cls	SN	
© Academie Da Vinci Charter Sch 1060 Keene Rd, Dunedin 34698 Michele Morgan	K-5	A	240 6	27%	727/298-2778 Fax 727/502-6065
© Alfred Adler Elem Sch 4515 38th Ave N, St Petersburg 33713 Yuri Yamashita	K-8	T	97	42%	727/329-9545 Fax 727/522-2854
© Athenian Academy Charter Sch 2289 N Hercules Ave, Clearwater 33763 Page Tavoularis	K-8	T	511 13	39%	727/298-2718 Fax 727/298-2719
Clearview Adult Education Ctr 3815 43rd St N, St Petersburg 33714 Brenda Vlach	Adult	V	100 120		727/221-5395 Fax 727/754-8649
Clearwater Adult Ed Center 1895 Gulf to Bay Blvd, Clearwater 33765 James Joyer	Adult		100		727/469-5817 Fax 727/469-4193
© Discovery Academy of Science ⓨ 1380 Pinehurst Rd, Dunedin 34698 Emre Akbaba	K-1	M	291	41%	727/330-2424 Fax 727/499-6828
Dixie Hollins Adult Ed Ctr 4940 62nd St N, St Petersburg 33709 Brenda Vlach	Adult		100		727/547-7872 Fax 727/547-7873 f
Ⓐ Enterprise High Sch © 2461 N McMullen Booth Rd Ste B, Clearwater 33759 Donna Hulbert	9-12	TV	375	45%	727/474-1237 Fax 727/725-3470
Lakewood Community Adult Ctr 1400 54th Ave S, St Petersburg 33705 Harriet Davis	Adult		100		727/893-2955 Fax 727/893-1375
© Mycroschool Charter Sch 840 3rd Ave S, St Petersburg 33701 Steven Humphries	9-12	T	149	68%	727/825-3710 Fax 727/825-3751

Public Schs..Principal	Grd	Prgm	Enr/#Cls	SN	
Ⓐ Pace Center for Girls-Pinellas 4000 Gateway Centre Blvd, Pinellas Park 33782 Tanya Hollis	6-12		38	43%	727/456-1566 Fax 727/456-1570
Palm Harbor Cmty Adult Ctr 1900 Omaha St, Palm Harbor 34683 Anne Januario	Adult		100		727/669-1140 Fax 727/725-7936
© Pinellas Academy Math & Sci [132] 1775 S Highland Ave, Clearwater 33756 Linda Schwerer	K-8		812	3%	727/330-9449 Fax 727/581-9205
© Pinellas Prep Academy 2300 Belcher Rd S Ste 100, Largo 33771 Amanda Roberts	4-8		440	27%	727/536-3600 Fax 727/536-3661
© Pinellas Primary Academy 2300 Belcher Rd S Ste 100, Largo 33771 Nancy Walker	K-3		324	31%	727/536-3600 Fax 727/536-3661
© Plato Academy Clearwater [144] 2045 Palmetto St, Clearwater 33765 Adam Beard	K-8		479 16	24%	727/228-9517 Fax 727/793-2405
© Plato Academy Largo [144] 7100 142nd Ave, Largo 33771 Stephen Donnelly	K-8		361	34%	727/228-9952 Fax 727/228-9953
© Plato Academy Palm Harbor [144] 1601 Curlew Rd, Palm Harbor 34683 Carri Aranzabal	K-8		362	16%	727/228-6850 Fax 727/228-6851
© Plato Academy Pinellas Park [144] 9200 49th St N, Pinellas Park 33782 Tonia Cunningham	PK-5		54	39%	727/521-7260 Fax 727/521-7261
© Plato Academy Seminole [144] 10888 126th Ave, Largo 33778 Karen Staab	K-8		363	31%	727/228-9950 Fax 727/228-9951
© Plato Academy St Petersburg [144] 3901 Park St N, St Petersburg 33709 Michelle West	PK-6		279	33%	727/521-7258 Fax 727/521-7259
© Plato Academy Tarpon Springs [144] 2795 Keystone Rd, Tarpon Spgs 34688 Danielle Turro	K-7		362	19%	727/939-6413 Fax 727/939-6414
PTC-Clearwater Campus 6100 154th Ave N, Clearwater 33760 Jakub Prokop	Voc	AG	400		727/538-7167 Fax 727/507-4423
ⓨ PTC-St Petersburg Campus 901 34th St S, St Petersburg 33711 Sylester Norwood	Voc	AGM	1,500 51		727/893-2500 Fax 727/893-2776 f t
© St Petersburg Collegiate HS 6605 5th Ave N, St Petersburg 33710 Starla Metz	10-12		245 4	21%	727/341-4610 Fax 727/341-4226
Tomlinson Adult Learning Ctr 296 Mirror Lake Dr N, St Petersburg 33701 Godfrey Watson	Adult	V	500 20		727/893-2723 Fax 727/552-2449

- **Pinellas Co Schools-Area 1** PID: 11716660   727/588-5023
  301 4th St SW, Largo 33770   Fax 727/588-5035

Ward Kennedy 15

Public Schs..Principal	Grd	Prgm	Enr/#Cls	SN	
Brooker Creek Elem Sch 3130 Forelock Rd, Tarpon Spgs 34688 Jennifer Mekler	PK-5		634 34	11%	727/943-4600 Fax 727/943-4603
Carwise Middle Sch 3301 Bentley Dr, Palm Harbor 34684 Chad Eiben	6-8	T	1,273 64	38%	727/724-1442 Fax 727/724-1446
Clearwater Fundamental Mid Sch 1660 Palmetto St, Clearwater 33755 Stephanie Joyner	6-8	V	800	27%	727/298-1609 Fax 727/298-1614
Countryside High Sch 3000 State Road 580, Clearwater 33761 Mr Vicari	9-12	V	2,103	39%	727/725-7956 Fax 727/725-7990

1 Superintendent	8 Curric/Instruct K-12	19 Chief Financial Officer	29 Family/Consumer Science	39 Social Studies K-12	49 English/Lang Arts Elem	59 Special Education Elem	69 Academic Assessment
2 Bus/Finance/Purchasing	9 Curric/Instruct Elem	20 Art K-12	30 Adult Education	40 Social Studies Elem	50 English/Lang Arts Sec	60 Special Education Sec	70 Research/Development
3 Buildings And Grounds	10 Curric/Instruct Sec	21 Art Elem	31 Career/Sch-to-Work K-12	41 Social Studies Sec	51 Reading K 12	61 Foreign/World Lang K-12	71 Public Information
4 Food Service	11 Federal Program	22 Art Sec	32 Career/Sch-to-Work Elem	42 Science K-12	52 Reading Elem	62 Foreign/World Lang Elem	72 Summer School
5 Transportation	12 Title I	23 Music K-12	33 Career/Sch-to-Work Sec	43 Science Elem	53 Reading Sec	63 Foreign/World Lang Sec	73 Instructional Tech
6 Athletic	13 Title V	24 Music Elem	34 Early Childhood Ed	44 Science Sec	54 Remedial Reading K-12	64 Religious Education K-12	74 Inservice Training
7 Health Services	15 Asst Superintendent	25 Music Sec	35 Health/Phys Education	45 Math K-12	55 Remedial Reading Elem	65 Religious Education Elem	75 Marketing/Distributive
	16 Instructional Media Svcs	26 Business Education	36 Guidance Services K-12	46 Math Elem	56 Remedial Reading Sec	66 Religious Education Sec	76 Info Systems
	17 Chief Operations Officer	27 Career & Tech Ed	37 Guidance Services Elem	47 Math Sec	57 Bilingual/ELL	67 School Board President	77 Psychological Assess
	18 Chief Academic Officer	28 Technology Education	38 Guidance Services Sec	48 English/Lang Arts K-12	58 Special Education K-12	68 Teacher Personnel	78 Affirmative Action

School..Principal	Grd	Prgm	Enr/#Cls	SN	Phone/Fax
Curlew Creek Elem Sch 3030 Curlew Rd, Palm Harbor 34684 Kathy Brickley	PK-5	T	685 40	38%	727/724-1423 Fax 727/724-1426
ⓂCurtis Fundamental Elem Sch 531 Beltrees St, Dunedin 34698 Richard Knight	K-5		534 18	15%	727/738-6483 Fax 727/738-6488
Cypress Woods Elem Sch 4900 Cypress Woods Blvd, Palm Harbor 34685 Kimberly Hill	PK-5		797 41	24%	727/538-7325 Fax 727/725-7988
Dunedin Elem Sch 900 Union St, Dunedin 34698 Kerry Wyatt	PK-5	T	570 35	73%	727/738-2990 Fax 727/738-2994
Dunedin High Sch 1651 Pinehurst Rd, Dunedin 34698 Kyle Johnson	9-12	TV	1,320 80	47%	727/469-4100 Fax 727/469-4143 f t
Dunedin Highland Middle Sch 70 Patricia Ave, Dunedin 34698 **Michael Vasallo**	6-8	TV	1,024 55	61%	727/469-4112 Fax 727/469-4115
East Lake High Sch 1300 Silver Eagle Dr, Tarpon Spgs 34688 Carmela Haley	9-12	V	2,234 80	20%	727/942-5419 Fax 727/942-5441
East Lake MS-Acad Engineering 1200 Silver Eagle Dr, Tarpon Spgs 34688 Karen Huzar	6-8	V	395	13%	727/940-7624 Fax 727/754-8653
Eisenhower Elem Sch 2800 Drew St Frnt, Clearwater 33759 Antonette Wilson	PK-5	T	693 50	69%	727/725-7978 Fax 727/725-7981
Elisa Nelson Elem Sch 415 15th St, Palm Harbor 34683 **Hema Adhia**	1-5		401		727/298-2788 Fax 727/754-8396 f
Forest Lakes Elem Sch 301 Pine Ave N, Oldsmar 34677 **Michael McHugh**	PK-5		510 36	41%	813/891-0785 Fax 813/891-9178
Garrison-Jones Elem Sch 3133 Garrison Rd, Dunedin 34698 Karen Buckles	PK-5	T	618	53%	727/469-5716 Fax 727/469-5725
Highland Lakes Elem Sch 1230 Highlands Blvd, Palm Harbor 34684 **Donna Gehringer**	PK-5	T	584 42	40%	727/724-1429 Fax 727/724-1435
Lake St George Elem Sch 2855 County Road 95, Palm Harbor 34684 Monika Wolcott	PK-5	T	672 43	45%	727/669-1161 Fax 727/669-1165
Leila G Davis Elem Sch 2630 Landmark Dr, Clearwater 33761 William Durst	PK-5		757 45	35%	727/725-7972 Fax 727/725-7975
McMullen-Booth Elem Sch 3025 Union St, Clearwater 33759 Susan Manche	PK-5	T	655 35	65%	727/669-1800 Fax 727/669-1803
Oldsmar Elem Sch 302 Dartmouth Ave W, Oldsmar 34677 **Kristina Bauman**	PK-5	T	600 35	53%	813/855-7316 Fax 813/855-5136
Ozona Elem Sch 601 Tampa Rd, Palm Harbor 34683 Lisa Freeman	PK-5		809 39	31%	727/724-1589 Fax 727/724-1591
Palm Harbor Middle Sch 1800 Tampa Rd, Palm Harbor 34683 Mary Athanson	6-8	V	1,256 45	35%	727/669-1146 Fax 727/669-1244
Palm Harbor University HS 1900 Omaha St, Palm Harbor 34683 Dr Christen Gonzalez	9-12	GV	2,540 64	23%	727/669-1131 Fax 727/725-7936
Paul B Stephens Sch 2935 County Road 193, Clearwater 33759 Deborah Thornton	Spec	TV	159 26	59%	727/725-7982 Fax 727/725-7985
Safety Harbor Elem Sch 535 5th Ave N, Safety Harbor 34695 Cecilia Palmer	PK-5	T	693 42	44%	727/724-1462 Fax 727/724-1461
San Jose Elem Sch 1670 San Helen Dr, Dunedin 34698 Lisa Brown	PK-5	T	337 30	65%	727/469-5956 Fax 727/469-5960
Sunset Hills Elem Sch 1347 Gulf Rd, Tarpon Spgs 34689 Johnnie Crawford	PK-5	T	532 27	47%	727/943-5523 Fax 727/943-4939
Sutherland Elem Sch 3150 N Belcher Rd, Palm Harbor 34683 Kristy Cantu	PK-5	T	649 35	45%	727/724-1466 Fax 727/724-1469
ⓂTarpon Spgs Fundmntl Elem Sch 400 E Harrison St, Tarpon Spgs 34689 Holly Oakes	K-5		272 12	18%	727/943-5508 Fax 727/942-5443
Tarpon Springs Elem Sch 555 Pine St, Tarpon Spgs 34689 Art Steullet	PK-5	T	626	72%	727/943-5500 Fax 727/943-5580
Tarpon Springs High Sch 1411 Gulf Rd, Tarpon Spgs 34689 Leza Fatolitis	9-12	TV	1,373 83	43%	727/943-4900 Fax 727/943-4907
Tarpon Springs Middle Sch 501 N Florida Ave, Tarpon Spgs 34689 **E Phelps**	6-8	TV	809 70	49%	727/943-5511 Fax 727/943-5519

• **Pinellas Co Schools-Area 2** PID: 01220693 727/588-5024
301 4th St SW, Largo 33770   Fax 727/588-5035

Dr Barbara Hires 15

Public Schs..Principal	Grd	Prgm	Enr/#Cls	SN	Phone/Fax
Anona Elem Sch 12301 Indian Rocks Rd, Largo 33774 Ann Welsh	PK-5	T	459 19	53%	727/588-4730 Fax 727/588-4733
Bardmoor Elem Sch 8900 Greenbriar Rd, Seminole 33777 Leigh Brown	PK-5	T	496 35	62%	727/547-7824 Fax 727/545-6593
ⒶBayside High Sch 14405 49th St N, Clearwater 33762 Dawn Coffin	9-12	T	222	64%	727/507-4730 Fax 727/507-4735
Belcher Elem Sch 2215 Lancaster Dr, Clearwater 33764 **Kristy Moody**	PK-5		685 24	65%	727/538-7437 Fax 727/538-7255
Belleair Elem Sch 1156 Lakeview Rd, Clearwater 33756 **Kelly Austin**	PK-5		552 27	85%	727/469-5983 Fax 727/469-5972
Calvin Hunsinger Sch 1863 N Betty Ln, Clearwater 33755 Douglas Keimig	Spec	TV	109 18	69%	727/469-4260 Fax 727/469-4163
ⒶCHI CHI Rodriguez Academy 3030 N McMullen Booth Rd, Clearwater 33761 Cathleen Brickley	4-8	T	90	81%	727/791-3522 Fax 727/724-1426
Clearwater High Sch 540 S Hercules Ave, Clearwater 33764 Keith Mastorides	9-12	GTV	1,798 75	55%	727/298-1620 Fax 727/469-5981
ⒶClearwater Intermediate Sch 1220 Palmetto St, Clearwater 33755 Tonya Mitchell	5-9	TV	308 45	84%	727/298-1616 Fax 727/469-4189
Cross Bayou Elem Sch 6886 102nd Ave N, Pinellas Park 33782 Kathy Wickett	PK-5	T	459 36	65%	727/547-7834 Fax 727/547-7837
ⒶDisston Academy for P & E 5125 11th Ave S, Gulfport 33707 Dr Tamika Hughes-Leeks	9-12		102 28	66%	727/893-1115 Fax 727/893-2131
ⓎFrontier Elem Sch 6995 Hopedale Ln, Clearwater 33764 Heather Peters	PK-5	MT	621 41	65%	727/538-7335 Fax 727/538-7444
Fuguitt Elem Sch 13010 101st St, Largo 33773 Kathlene Bentley	PK-5	T	545 43	61%	727/588-3576 Fax 727/588-4630

79 Student Personnel	91 Safety/Security	275 Response To Intervention	298 Grant Writer/Ptnrships	**School Programs**	**Social Media**
80 Driver Ed/Safety	92 Magnet School	277 Remedial Math K-12	750 Chief Innovation Officer	A = Alternative Program	
81 Gifted/Talented	93 Parental Involvement	280 Literacy Coach	751 Chief of Staff	G = Adult Classes	f = Facebook
82 Video Services	95 Tech Prep Program	285 STEM	752 Social Emotional Learning	M = Magnet Program	
83 Substance Abuse Prev	97 Chief Information Officer	286 Digital Learning		T = Title I Schoolwide	t = Twitter
84 Erate	98 Chief Technology Officer	288 Common Core Standards	**Other School Types**	V = Career & Tech Ed Programs	
85 AIDS Education	270 Character Education	294 Accountability	Ⓐ = Alternative School		
88 Alternative/At Risk	271 Migrant Education	295 Network System	Ⓒ = **Charter School**		
89 Multi-Cultural Curriculum	273 Teacher Mentor	296 Title II Programs	Ⓜ = **Magnet School**	New Schools are shaded	
90 Social Work	274 Before/After Sch	297 Webmaster	Ⓨ = Year-Round School	New Superintendents and Principals are bold Personnel with email addresses are underscored	

School / Address / Principal	Grd	Prgm	Enr/#Cls	SN	Phone
High Point Elem Sch 5921 150th Ave N, Clearwater 33760 **Melody Mendoza**	PK-5	T	671 35	73%	727/538-7440 Fax 727/538-7442
Kings Highway Elem Sch 1715 Kings Hwy, Clearwater 33755 Garen Boyd	PK-5	T	402	68%	727/223-8949
Largo High Sch 410 Missouri Ave N, Largo 33770 Bradley Finkbiner	9-12	TV	1,705 110	54%	727/588-3758 Fax 727/588-4037
Largo Middle Sch 155 8th Ave SE, Largo 33771 Linda Burris	6-8	TV	805	61%	727/588-4600 Fax 727/588-3720
Ⓐ Lealman Innovation Academy 4900 28th St N, St Petersburg 33714 Connisheia Garcia	6-12	TV	425 25	75%	727/528-5802 Fax 727/528-5807
Mildred Helms Elem Sch 561 Clearwater Largo Rd S, Largo 33770 Shannon Brennan	PK-5	T	594 36	62%	727/588-3569 Fax 727/588-3603
Oak Grove Middle Sch 1370 S Belcher Rd, Clearwater 33764 Barry Brown	6-8	TV	1,143 56	59%	727/524-4430 Fax 727/524-4416
Osceola Fundamental High Sch 9751 98th St, Seminole 33777 Michael Bohnet	9-12	V	1,718 71	20%	727/547-7717 Fax 727/545-6412
Osceola Middle Sch 9301 98th St, Seminole 33777 **Dr Solomon Lowery**	6-8	T	1,207 62	58%	727/547-7689 Fax 727/547-7667
Pinellas Gulf Coast Academy 1197 East Bay Dr, Largo 33770 Bonnie Solinsky	9-12	TV	275	48%	727/474-8836 Fax 727/581-9557
Ⓐ Pinellas Secondary Sch 8570 66th St N, Pinellas Park 33781 Darren Hammond	6-12	T	300 35	81%	727/549-6550 Fax 727/549-6555
Pinellas Virtual Sch 14405 49th St N, Clearwater 33762 Mandy Perry	K-12		182	20%	727/588-6448 Fax 727/588-6085
Plumb Elem Sch 1920 Lakeview Rd, Clearwater 33764 **Holly Delduca**	PK-5	T	735 43	58%	727/469-5976 Fax 727/469-5728
Ponce De Leon Elem Sch 1301 Ponce De Leon Blvd, Clearwater 33756 Tracie Bergman	PK-5	T	524 33	74%	727/588-3573 Fax 727/588-3700
Ridgecrest Elem Sch 1901 119th St, Largo 33778 Vickie Graham	PK-5	T	722 40	50%	727/588-3580 Fax 727/588-4608
Ⓜ Safety Harbor Middle Sch 901 1st Ave N, Safety Harbor 34695 Danny Boulieris	6-8	TV	1,189 80	49%	727/724-1400 Fax 727/724-1407
Sandy Lane Elem Sch 1360 Sandy Ln, Clearwater 33755 **Dr Jeff Moss**	K-5	T	346 41	87%	727/469-5974 Fax 727/469-5986
Skycrest Elem Sch 10 N Corona Ave, Clearwater 33765 **Eliza Defant**	PK-5	T	618 43	79%	727/469-5987 Fax 727/469-4186
Southern Oak Elem Sch 9101 Walsingham Rd, Largo 33773 Susan Taylor	PK-5	T	550 37	57%	727/588-4654 Fax 727/588-4656
Starkey Elem Sch 9300 86th Ave, Seminole 33777 Audrey Chaffin	PK-5	T	667 31	47%	727/547-7841 Fax 727/545-7550
Walsingham Elem Sch 9099 Walsingham Rd, Largo 33773 Quinn Williams	PK-5	T	455 54	62%	727/588-3519 Fax 727/588-6990

● Pinellas Co Schools-Area 3   PID: 11716672   727/588-5020
301 4th St SW, Largo 33770

Robert Poth 15

Public Schs..Principal	Grd	Prgm	Enr/#Cls	SN	Phone
Azalea Elem Sch 1680 74th St N, St Petersburg 33710 Michael Rebman	PK-5	T	609 38	62%	727/893-2187 Fax 727/893-2190
Azalea Middle Sch 7855 22nd Ave N, St Petersburg 33710 Thomas Brittain	6-8	TV	837 80	73%	727/893-2606 Fax 727/893-2624
Bauder Elem Sch 12755 86th Ave, Seminole 33776 **Jodi Leichman**	PK-5		769 36	28%	727/547-7829 Fax 727/547-4564
Bay Point Elem Sch 5800 22nd St S, St Petersburg 33712 Sara Deperro	PK-5	T	597 34	63%	727/552-1449 Fax 727/552-1455
Bay Point Middle Sch 2151 62nd Ave S, St Petersburg 33712 Jason Shedrick	6-8	T	1,039	60%	727/893-1153 Fax 727/893-1181
Bay Vista Fundamental Sch 5900 Dr Martin L King Jr St S, St Petersburg 33705 **Ms Hall**	K-5		647 25	39%	727/893-2335 Fax 727/893-1800
Bear Creek Elem Sch 350 61st St S, St Petersburg 33707 Willette Houston	PK-5	T	347 26	80%	727/893-2332 Fax 727/893-2334
Boca Ciega High Sch 924 58th St S, Gulfport 33707 Michael Vigue	9-12	GTV	1,724	50%	727/893-2780 Fax 727/893-1382
Dixie Hollins High Sch 4940 62nd St N, St Petersburg 33709 Robert Florio	9-12	GTV	1,821 112	46%	727/547-7876 Fax 727/547-7727
Douglas L Jamerson Elem Sch 1200 37th St S, St Petersburg 33711 Brandie Williams-Macon	PK-5	T	576 30	53%	727/552-1703 Fax 727/552-1704
Ⓜ Gulf Beaches Elem Sch 8600 Boca Ciega Dr, St Petersburg 33706 Robert Kalach	K-5	T	334	37%	727/893-2630 Fax 727/754-8651
Gulfport Elem Montessori Acad 2014 52nd St S, Gulfport 33707 **Wendy Bryan**	PK-5	T	643 22	75%	727/893-2643 Fax 727/552-1574
Ⓨ Jacobson Tech HS at Seminole 12611 86th Ave, Seminole 33776 Martha Giancola	Voc	GM	80 14		727/545-6405 Fax 727/545-6408
James B Sanderlin IB World Sch 2350 22nd Ave S, St Petersburg 33712 **Ms Armstrong**	PK-8	T	573 34	37%	727/552-1700 Fax 727/552-1701
John Hopkins Middle Sch 701 16th St S, St Petersburg 33705 Dominique Clarkson	6-8	T	764	70%	727/893-2400 Fax 727/893-1600
Ⓜ Lakeview Fundamental Elem Sch 2229 25th St S, St Petersburg 33712 **Tijuana Baker**	K-5		345 12	34%	727/893-2139 Fax 727/893-1359
Lakewood Elem Sch 4151 6th St S, St Petersburg 33705 **Stephanie Woodford**	PK-5	T	379	84%	727/893-2196 Fax 727/893-9152
Lakewood High Sch 1400 54th Ave S, St Petersburg 33705 Erin Savage	9-12	GTV	1,012 73	53%	727/893-2916 Fax 727/893-1387
Madeira Beach Fund Sch 591 Tom Stuart Cswy, Madeira Beach 33708 Christopher Ateek	K-8		1,379 60	25%	727/547-7697 Fax 727/547-7528
Ⓨ Maximo Elem Sch 4850 31st St S, St Petersburg 33712 **Tekoa Moses**	PK-5	MT	517 32	82%	727/893-2191 Fax 727/893-5525

#		#		#		#		#		#	
1	Superintendent	8	Curric/Instruct K-12	19	Chief Financial Officer	29	Family/Consumer Science	39	Social Studies K-12	49	English/Lang Arts Elem	59	Special Education Elem	69	Academic Assessment
2	Bus/Finance/Purchasing	9	Curric/Instruct Elem	20	Art K-12	30	Adult Education	40	Social Studies Elem	50	English/Lang Arts Sec	60	Special Education Sec	70	Research/Development
3	Buildings And Grounds	10	Curric/Instruct Sec	21	Art Elem	31	Career/Sch-to-Work K-12	41	Social Studies Sec	51	Reading K-12	61	Foreign/World Lang K-12	71	Public Information
4	Food Service	11	Federal Program	22	Art Sec	32	Career/Sch-to-Work Elem	42	Science K-12	52	Reading Elem	62	Foreign/World Lang Elem	72	Summer School
5	Transportation	12	Title I	23	Music K-12	33	Career/Sch-to-Work Sec	43	Science Elem	53	Reading Sec	63	Foreign/World Lang Sec	73	Instructional Tech
6	Athletic	13	Title V	24	Music Elem	34	Early Childhood Ed	44	Science Sec	54	Remedial Reading K-12	64	Religious Education K-12	74	Inservice Training
7	Health Services	14	Asst Superintendent	25	Music Sec	35	Health/Phys Education	45	Math K-12	55	Remedial Reading Elem	65	Religious Education Elem	75	Marketing/Distributive
		15	Asst Superintendent	16	Instructional Media Svcs	26	Business Education	36	Guidance Services K-12	46	Math Elem	56	Remedial Reading Sec	66	Religious Education Sec	76	Info Systems
		16	Instructional Media Svcs	17	Chief Operations Officer	27	Career & Tech Ed	37	Guidance Services Elem	47	Math Sec	57	Bilingual/ELL	67	School Board President	77	Psychological Assess
		17	Chief Operations Officer	18	Chief Academic Officer	28	Technology Education	38	Guidance Services Sec	48	English/Lang Arts K-12	58	Special Education K-12	68	Teacher Personnel	78	Affirmative Action

School	Grd	Prgm	Enr/#Cls	SN	Phone
Melrose Elem Sch 1752 13th Ave S, St Petersburg 33712 Donnika Jones	PK-5	T	408 28	91%	727/893-2175 Fax 727/893-1884
Oakhurst Elem Sch 10535 Antilles Dr, Largo 33774 Kelly Kennedy	PK-5	T	703 32	36%	727/588-6801 Fax 727/588-6811
Orange Grove Elem Sch 10300 65th Ave, Seminole 33772 Christine Porter	PK-5	T	377 22	48%	727/547-7845 Fax 727/547-7505
Ⓜ Pasadena Fundamental Elem Sch 95 72nd St N, St Petersburg 33710 Donita Moody	K-5		464 24	24%	727/893-2646 Fax 727/893-2408
Seminole Elem Sch 10950 74th Ave, Seminole 33772 Nanette Grasso	PK-5	T	562 45	63%	727/547-7668 Fax 727/545-6585
Seminole High Sch 8401 131st St, Seminole 33776 Jane Lucas	9-12	V	1,892 88	33%	727/547-7536 Fax 727/547-7503
Seminole Middle Sch 8701 131st St, Seminole 33776 Michael Moss	6-8	T	1,107 65	40%	727/547-4520 Fax 727/547-7741
Seventy-Fourth St Elem Sch 3801 74th St N, St Petersburg 33709 **Jessley Hathaway**	PK-5	T	519 54	68%	727/893-2120 Fax 727/893-2143
Thurgood Marshall Fundmntl MS 3901 22nd Ave S, St Petersburg 33711 **Nicole Wilson**	6-8		940 47	38%	727/552-1737 Fax 727/552-1741

● Pinellas Co Schools-Area 4 PID: 10901501
301 4th St SW, Largo 33770

727/588-5022
Fax 727/588-5035

Patricia Wright 15

Public Schs..Principal	Grd	Prgm	Enr/#Cls	SN	Phone
Blanton Elem Sch 6400 54th Ave N, St Petersburg 33709 **Lisa Roth**	PK-5	T	523 45	70%	727/547-7820 Fax 727/545-6562
Campbell Park Elem Sch 1051 7th Ave S, St Petersburg 33705 Kathleen Young-Parker	PK-5	T	617 18	86%	727/893-2650 Fax 727/893-2652
Fairmount Park Elem Sch 575 41st St S, St Petersburg 33711 **Lakisha Lawson**	PK-5	T	565 38	88%	727/893-2132 Fax 727/893-5451
Gibbs High Sch 850 34th St S, St Petersburg 33711 Reuben Hepburn	9-12	TV	1,159 70	58%	727/893-5452 Fax 727/893-5461
John M Sexton Elem Sch 1997 54th Ave N, St Petersburg 33714 Tony Pleshe	PK-5	T	570 45	70%	727/570-3400 Fax 727/217-7236
Lealman Avenue Elem Sch 4001 58th Ave N, St Petersburg 33714 **Kim Duffy**	PK-5	T	451 26	78%	727/570-3020 Fax 727/570-3300
Lynch Elem Sch 1901 71st Ave N, St Petersburg 33702 Cynthia Kidd	PK-5	T	658 45	64%	727/570-3170 Fax 727/570-3186
Marjorie Rawlings Elem Sch 6505 68th St N, Pinellas Park 33781 Rebecca Moore	PK-5	T	610 45	62%	727/547-7828 Fax 727/547-7777
Meadowlawn Middle Sch 6050 16th St N, St Petersburg 33703 Ursula Parris	6-8	TV	1,072	73%	727/570-3097 Fax 727/570-3396
Midtown Academy 1701 10th St S, St Petersburg 33705 **Keila Victor**	K-5		306	85%	727/893-1358 Fax 727/754-8292
Morgan Fitzgerald Middle Sch 6410 118th Ave, Largo 33773 Ija Hawthorne	6-8	TV	1,111 75	61%	727/547-4526 Fax 727/547-6631
Mt Vernon Elem Sch 4629 13th Ave N, St Petersburg 33713 Robert Ovalle	PK-5	T	423 25	72%	727/893-1815 Fax 727/550-4149
New Heights Elem Sch 3901 37th St N, St Petersburg 33714 Lisa Austin	PK-5	T	734	71%	727/521-5350 Fax 727/521-5355
Nina Harris Sch 6000 70th Ave N, Pinellas Park 33781 Arlene Sullivan	Spec	T	183 31	39%	727/547-7850 Fax 727/547-7800
North Shore Elem Sch 200 35th Ave NE, St Petersburg 33704 Wilhemina Dawson	K-5	T	359 24	69%	727/893-2181 Fax 727/893-5483
Northeast High Sch 5500 16th St N, St Petersburg 33703 Michael Hernandez	9-12	GTV	1,653 84	53%	727/570-3138 Fax 727/507-3147
Northwest Elem Sch 5601 22nd Ave N, St Petersburg 33710 Marie Brainard	PK-5	T	540 33	57%	727/893-2147 Fax 727/893-1888
Perkins Elem Sch 2205 18th Ave S, St Petersburg 33712 Laura Kranzel	PK-5	T	575 24	49%	727/893-2117 Fax 727/893-1113 f t
Pinellas Central Elem Sch 10501 58th St N, Pinellas Park 33782 Daphne Miles	PK-5	T	614 43	71%	727/547-7853 Fax 727/547-7856
Pinellas Park Elem Sch 7520 52nd St N, Pinellas Park 33781 **Lori Frodine**	PK-5	T	557 41	76%	727/547-7888 Fax 727/547-7892
Pinellas Park High Sch 6305 118th Ave, Largo 33773 Brett Patterson	9-12	TV	1,982	61%	727/538-7410 Fax 727/507-4563
Pinellas Park Middle Sch 6940 70th Ave N, Pinellas Park 33781 **Dr Jason Shedrick**	6-8	T	1,183 65	61%	727/545-6400 Fax 727/547-7894
Richard L Sanders Sch 5025 76th Ave N, Pinellas Park 33781 Heidi D'Ambrosio	Spec	T	115 30	78%	727/547-7728 Fax 727/545-6413
Sawgrass Lake Elem Sch 1815 77th Ave N, St Petersburg 33702 Jessica Clements	PK-5	T	607 50	64%	727/570-3121 Fax 727/217-7251
Shore Acres Elem Sch 1800 62nd Ave NE, St Petersburg 33702 **Kris Sulte**	PK-5	T	636 28	56%	727/570-3173 Fax 727/570-3175
Skyview Elem Sch 8601 60th St N, Pinellas Park 33782 Suzanne Hester	PK-5	T	630 35	63%	727/547-7857 Fax 727/545-7521
St Petersburg High Sch 2501 5th Ave N, St Petersburg 33713 Darlene Lebo	9-12	TV	1,965 100	39%	727/893-1842 Fax 727/893-1399
Tyrone Middle Sch 6421 22nd Ave N, St Petersburg 33710 Robin Mobley	6-8	T	941 60	58%	727/893-1819 Fax 727/893-1946
Westgate Elem Sch 3560 58th St N, St Petersburg 33710 Bonita Paquette	PK-5	T	591 36	60%	727/893-2144 Fax 727/893-2146
Woodlawn Elem Sch 1600 16th St N, St Petersburg 33704 Tammy Keiper	PK-5	T	344 40	77%	727/893-1857 Fax 727/893-5482

79 Student Personnel	91 Safety/Security	275 Response To Intervention	298 Grant Writer/Ptnrships	**School Programs**	**Social Media**
80 Driver Ed/Safety	92 Magnet School	277 Remedial Math K-12	750 Chief Innovation Officer	A = Alternative Program	
81 Gifted/Talented	93 Parental Involvement	280 Literacy Coach	751 Chief of Staff	G = Adult Classes	f = Facebook
82 Video Services	95 Tech Prep Program	285 STEM	752 Social Emotional Learning	M = Magnet Program	
83 Substance Abuse Prev	97 Chief Infomation Officer	286 Digital Learning		T = Title I Schoolwide	t = Twitter
84 Erate	98 Chief Technology Officer	288 Common Core Standards	**Other School Types**	V = Career & Tech Ed Programs	
85 AIDS Education	270 Character Education	294 Accountability	Ⓐ = Alternative School		
88 Alternative/At Risk	271 Migrant Education	295 Network System	Ⓒ = Charter School	New Schools are shaded	
89 Multi-Cultural Curriculum	273 Teacher Mentor	296 Title II Programs	Ⓜ = Magnet School	New Superintendents and Principals are bold	
90 Social Work	274 Before/After Sch	297 Webmaster	Ⓨ = Year-Round School	Personnel with email addresses are underscored	

FL—119

PINELLAS CATHOLIC SCHOOLS

- **Diocese St Petersburg Ed Off** PID: 00200729   727/344-1611
  6363 9th Ave N, St Petersburg 33710   Fax 727/341-6848

Schools: 41 \ **Students:** 12,000

Listing includes only schools located in this county. See District Index for location of Diocesan Offices.

Christopher Pastura 1,11   Dr Mark Majeski 8,76
Dr Ann Davis 15

Catholic Schs..Principal	Grd	Prgm	Enr/#Cls	SN
Blessed Sacrament Cath Sch 11501 66th Ave, Seminole 33772 Becky Clark	PK-8		220 15	727/391-4060 Fax 727/391-5638
Clearwater Ctrl Cath High Sch 2750 Haines Bayshore Rd, Clearwater 33760 James Deputy	9-12		535	727/531-1449 Fax 727/535-7034
Espiritu Santo Catholic Sch 2405A Phillippe Pkwy, Safety Harbor 34695 Veronica Slain	PK-8		440 25	727/812-4650
Guardian Angels Catholic Sch 2270 Evans Rd, Clearwater 33763 Mary Stalzer	PK-8		210 24	727/799-6724 Fax 727/724-9018
Holy Family Catholic Sch 250 78th Ave NE, St Petersburg 33702 Abigail Rudderham	PK-8		263 12	727/526-8194 Fax 727/527-6567 f
Light of Christ Early Chld Ctr 2176 Marilyn St, Clearwater 33765 Becky Daschbach	PK-PK		80 5	727/442-4797 Fax 727/409-1903
Morning Star Sch 4661 80th Ave N, Pinellas Park 33781 Susan Conza	Spec		87 4	727/544-6036 Fax 727/546-9058
Our Lady of Lourdes Sch 730 San Salvador Dr, Dunedin 34698 Dr Anne Penny	PK-8		250 10	727/733-3776 Fax 727/733-4333 f t
Sacred Heart Catholic Sch 7951 46th Way N, Pinellas Park 33781 Robert Yevich	PK-8		260 10	727/544-1106 Fax 727/544-1737 f t
St Cecelia Interparochial Sch 1350 Court St, Clearwater 33756 Valerie Wostbrock	PK-8		500 23	727/461-1200 Fax 727/446-9140
St Ignatius Early Chldhd Ctr 715 E Orange St, Tarpon Spgs 34689 Sharon Stokely	PK-PK		100 6	727/937-5427 Fax 727/943-0676
St Jerome Early Childhood Ctr 10895 Hamlin Blvd, Largo 33774 Denise Roach	PK-PK		75 4	727/596-9491 Fax 727/596-8953 f
St John Vianney Sch 500 84th Ave, St Pete Beach 33706 Gina Code	PK-8		250 10	727/360-1113 Fax 727/367-8734 f t
St Jude Cathedral Sch 600 58th St N, St Petersburg 33710 Jesse Gaudette	PK-8		397 22	727/347-8622 Fax 727/343-0305 f
St Luke Early Chldhd Center 2757 Alderman Rd, Palm Harbor 34684 Kathleen Mitchell	PK-PK		85	727/787-2914
St Patrick Catholic Sch 1501 Trotter Rd, Largo 33770 Keith Galley	PK-8		200 10	727/581-4865 Fax 727/581-7842

St Paul Catholic Sch 1900 12th St N, St Petersburg 33704 Sr Joan Carberry	PK-8		331 11	727/823-6144 Fax 727/896-0609
St Petersburg Cath High Sch 6333 9th Ave N, St Petersburg 33710 Ross Bubolz	9-12		550 35	727/344-4065 Fax 727/343-9311
St Raphael Catholic Sch 1376 Snell Isle Blvd NE, St Petersburg 33704 Katharine Bogataj	PK-8		232 12	727/821-9663 Fax 727/502-9594 f t

PINELLAS PRIVATE SCHOOLS

Private Schs..Principal	Grd	Prgm	Enr/#Cls	SN
Academy for Love & Learning 2901 54th Ave S, St Petersburg 33712 Manuel Sykes	K-12		78	727/865-3962 Fax 727/865-7522
Academy Prep Center for Educ 2301 22nd Ave S, St Petersburg 33712 Gina Burkett	5-8		80	727/322-0800 Fax 727/328-8904
Admiral Farragut Academy 501 Park St N, St Petersburg 33710 Robert Fine	PK-12		400	727/384-5501 Fax 727/384-5507
AMI Kids Pinellas 6500 102nd Ave N, Pinellas Park 33782 Robert Johnson	6-9	AV	24 4	727/471-0390 Fax 727/471-0395
Argonauta Preschool 6646 1st Ave S, St Petersburg 33707 Cindy Fierros	PK-PK		28	727/347-8783
Bay Pines Lutheran Sch 7589 113th Ln, Seminole 33772 Jeff Sell	K-8		58 4	727/397-3204 Fax 727/391-6823
Blossom Montessori Sch-Deaf 14088 Icot Blvd, Clearwater 33760 Julie Rutenberg	Spec		23	727/539-7879 Fax 727/539-7627
Brighton Prep Sch 4355 Central Ave, St Petersburg 33713 Gayle Cooper	1-8		30 3	727/327-1454
Calvary Christian High Sch 110 N McMullen Booth Rd, Clearwater 33759 David Kilgore	9-12		400 17	727/449-2247 Fax 727/461-5421 f
Canterbury School of Flordia 1200 Snell Isle Blvd NE Side, St Petersburg 33704 Claudine Cieutat	PK-4		186	727/521-5925
Canterbury School of Florida 990 62nd Ave NE, St Petersburg 33702 Ashley Swanegan \ Donnamarie Hehn	5-12		249 15	727/525-1419 Fax 727/525-2545
Center Academy 6710 86th Ave N, Pinellas Park 33782 Neil Jones	Spec		96 8	727/541-5716 Fax 727/544-8186
Center Academy Sch 34054 US Highway 19 N, Palm Harbor 34684 David Kaser	Spec		83 5	727/781-2986 Fax 727/781-2936
Classical Christian Sch Arts 4981 78th Ave N, Pinellas Park 33781 Shawn Williams	K-12		105	727/547-6820 Fax 727/545-3579 f
Clearwater Academy Int'l 801 Drew St, Clearwater 33755 James Zwers	PK-12		240 8	727/446-1722 Fax 727/443-5252 f
Country Day Sch 11499 131st St, Largo 33774 Ted Gillette	PK-8		350 7	727/596-1902 Fax 727/596-5479 f t
Countryside Christian Academy 1850 N McMullen Booth Rd, Clearwater 33759 Crystal Mascaro	PK-8		150	727/799-1618 Fax 727/499-1841

1	Superintendent	8	Curric/Instruct K-12
2	Bus/Finance/Purchasing	9	Curric/Instruct Elem
3	Buildings And Grounds	10	Curric/Instruct Sec
4	Food Service	11	Federal Program
5	Transportation	12	Title I
6	Athletic	13	Title V
7	Health Services	14	Instructional Media Svcs
		15	Asst Superintendent
		16	Instructional Media Svcs
		17	Chief Operations Officer
		18	Chief Academic Officer

19	Chief Financial Officer
20	Art K-12
21	Art Elem
22	Art Sec
23	Music K-12
24	Music Elem
25	Music Sec
26	Business Education
27	Career & Tech Ed
28	Technology Education

29	Family/Consumer Science
30	Adult Education
31	Career/Sch-to-Work K-12
32	Career/Sch-to-Work Elem
33	Career/Sch-to-Work Sec
34	Early Childhood Ed
35	Health/Phys Education
36	Guidance Services K-12
37	Guidance Services Elem
38	Guidance Services Sec

39	Social Studies K-12
40	Social Studies Elem
41	Social Studies Sec
42	Science K-12
43	Science Elem
44	Science Sec
45	Math K-12
46	Math Elem
47	Math Sec
48	English/Lang Arts K-12

49	English/Lang Arts Elem
50	English/Lang Arts Sec
51	Reading K-12
52	Reading Elem
53	Reading Sec
54	Remedial Reading K-12
55	Remedial Reading Elem
56	Remedial Reading Sec
57	Bilingual/ELL
58	Special Education K-12

59	Special Education Elem
60	Special Education Sec
61	Foreign/World Lang K-12
62	Foreign/World Lang Elem
63	Foreign/World Lang Sec
64	Religious Education K-12
65	Religious Education Elem
66	Religious Education Sec
67	School Board President
68	Teacher Personnel

69	Academic Assessment
70	Research/Development
71	Public Information
72	Summer School
73	Instructional Tech
74	Inservice Training
75	Marketing/Distributive
76	Info Systems
77	Psychological Assess
78	Affirmative Action

School	Grades		Enroll/Teachers	Phone
Covenant Academy 5495 Park Blvd N, Pinellas Park 33781 Dr Kira Wilson	K-10		25	727/542-6294
Delphi Academy 1831 Drew St, Clearwater 33765 Colin Taufer	PK-12	V	135 11	727/447-6385 Fax 727/447-3679
DePaul Sch 2747 Sunset Point Rd, Clearwater 33759 Amy Gorst	Spec	G	80 7	727/796-7679
Dunedin Academy & Day Sch 1408 County Road 1, Dunedin 34698 Kathleen Porter	PK-12		245 16	727/580-2042 Fax 727/733-6696
Elim Jr Academy 4824 2nd Ave S, St Petersburg 33711 Dr Sandra Fletcher	K-8		92	727/289-7089
First Lutheran Sch 1644 Nursery Rd, Clearwater 33756 Elaine Popp	PK-8		130 11	727/461-3444 🇹
Genesis Christian Academy 2110 N Hercules Ave, Clearwater 33763 Rob Rary	K-12		38	727/738-1656
Grace Lutheran Sch 4301 16th St N, St Petersburg 33703 Nicole Clifton	PK-8		231 13	727/527-6213 Fax 727/522-4535
Gulfcoast SDA Sch 6001 7th Ave S, St Petersburg 33707 Angela Peoples	K-8		30 2	727/345-2141
Indian Rocks Christian Sch 12685 Ulmerton Rd, Largo 33774 Perry Banse \ Tim Rhine	PK-12	V	900	727/596-4321 Fax 727/593-5485
Keswick Christian Sch 10101 54th Ave N, St Petersburg 33708 Diana Dumais \ Jon Skilton	PK-12		650 45	727/393-9100 Fax 727/397-5378 🇫🇹
Lakeside Christian Sch 1897 Sunset Point Rd, Clearwater 33765 Denise Nielson \ Phil Jones	K-12		300 26	727/461-3311 Fax 727/445-1835 🇫
Liberty Christian Sch 9401 4th St N, St Petersburg 33702 Helen Wilson	PK-5		140 16	727/576-9635 Fax 727/576-4992
Luth CH of the Cross Day Sch 4400 Chancellor St NE, St Petersburg 33703 Holly Carlson	PK-8		500	727/522-8331
New Horizons Country Day Sch 2060 Nebraska Ave, Palm Harbor 34683 Jennifer Hammill	PK-5		150 16	727/785-8591 Fax 727/786-8591
Northside Christian Sch 7777 62nd Ave N, St Petersburg 33709 Katherine Rotunno \ Brandon Elam	PK-12		350	727/541-7593 Fax 727/546-5836
Oldsmar Christian Sch 650 Burbank Rd, Oldsmar 34677 Br Eddie	PK-12		200 15	813/855-5746 Fax 813/855-4476
Our Savior Lutheran Sch 5843 4th Ave S, St Petersburg 33707 Jesse Crosmer	PK-8		216 13	727/344-1026 Fax 727/381-3980 🇫
Palm Harbor Montessori Academy 2355 Nebraska Ave, Palm Harbor 34683 Carol Mercier	PK-8	G	215 13	727/786-1854 Fax 727/786-5160 🇫🇹
Shorecrest Prep Sch 5101 1st St NE, St Petersburg 33703 Dr Lisa Bianco \ Kristine Grant \ Donald Paige	PK-12		850	727/522-2111 Fax 727/527-4191
Skycrest Christian Sch 129 N Belcher Rd, Clearwater 33765 Michael Dyck	PK-8		450 19	727/797-1186 Fax 727/797-8516 🇫🇹
Solid Rock Community Sch 2801 Keystone Rd, Tarpon Spgs 34688 Mickey Maiorana	K-12		120	727/934-0909 Fax 727/934-0933
Southside Christian Sch 3624 Queensboro Ave S, St Petersburg 33711 Richard Jackson	PK-5		110 5	727/327-2691 Fax 727/321-2981
Spring Valley Sch 2109 Nebraska Ave, Palm Harbor 34683 Diane Ballou	K-12		35	727/781-1234 Fax 727/474-3736
St Paul's Sch 1600 Saint Pauls Dr, Clearwater 33764 Samantha Campbell	PK-8		300 57	727/536-2756 Fax 727/531-2276 🇫🇹
St Petersburg Christian Sch 2021 62nd Ave N, St Petersburg 33702 Kathleen Spangler	K-8		458 43	727/522-3000 Fax 727/525-0998
Suncoast Waldorf Sch 1857 Curlew Rd, Palm Harbor 34683 Amanda Tipton	PK-5		65 12	727/786-8311 Fax 727/789-8265 🇫
Sunflower Sch 5313 27th Ave S, Gulfport 33707 Marie Breslin	K-5		36 5	727/321-7657
Superior Collegiate High Sch 2045 Palmetto St Bldg B, Clearwater 33765 Nick Koularmanis	9-12		115	727/799-1200 Fax 727/799-0200
Surge Christian Academy 21810 US Hwy 19 N, Clearwater 33765	K-12		401	727/223-4524
Walden Sch 2728 53rd St S, Gulfport 33707 Judi Jemison	6-8		18 3	727/321-7441
Westlake Christian Sch 1551 Belcher Rd, Palm Harbor 34683 Jayanne Roggenbaum	K-8		300 25	727/781-3808 Fax 727/785-2608
Westside Christian Sch 11633 137th St N, Largo 33774 Robert Pitts	K-12		87 11	727/517-2153 Fax 727/593-7700
Woodlawn Community Academy 11225 US Highway 19 N, Clearwater 33764 Charlotte Tollefson	K-12		120	727/914-6916 Fax 727/914-6917

PINELLAS REGIONAL CENTERS

● **FDLRS-Gulfcoast** PID: 04496152   727/793-2723
2929 County Road 193, Clearwater 33759   Fax 727/793-2730

Shery Aemisegger 1,11   Kristen Redding 11
Susanne Moeller 58   Roberta Pawlowski 73

POLK COUNTY

POLK PUBLIC SCHOOLS

● **Polk Co School Dist** PID: 00201187   863/534-0500
1915 S Floral Ave, Bartow 33830   Fax 863/519-8231

> **Schools:** 156 \ **Teachers:** 6,740 \
> **Students:** 105,000 \ **Special Ed Students:** 11,954 \ **LEP Students:** 10,926
> \ **College-Bound:** 79% \ **Ethnic:** Asian 2%, African American 21%, Hispanic 34%, Caucasian 42% \ **Exp:** $178 (Low) \ **Poverty:** 25% \ **Title I:** $44,002,414
> \ **Special Education:** $76,109,000 \ **Bilingual Education:** $32,207,000 \
> **Open-Close:** 08/12 - 05/28 \ **DTBP:** $190 (High) \ 🇫 🇹

279 Student Personnel	91 Safety/Security	275 Response To Intervention	298 Grant Writer/Ptnrships	**School Programs**	**Social Media**
280 Driver Ed/Safety	92 Magnet School	277 Remedial Math K-12	750 Chief Innovation Officer	**A = Alternative Program**	
281 Gifted/Talented	93 Parental Involvement	280 Literacy Coach	751 Chief of Staff	**G = Adult Classes**	🇫 = Facebook
282 Video Services	95 Tech Prep Program	285 STEM	752 Social Emotional Learning	**M = Magnet Program**	
283 Substance Abuse Prev	97 Chief Infomation Officer	286 Digital Learning		**T = Title I Schoolwide**	🇹 = Twitter
284 Erate	98 Chief Technology Officer	288 Common Core Standards	**Other School Types**	**V = Career & Tech Ed Programs**	
285 AIDS Education	270 Character Education	294 Accountability	Ⓐ = Alternative School		
288 Alternative/At Risk	271 Migrant Education	295 Network System	Ⓒ = Charter School	New Schools are shaded	
289 Multi-Cultural Curriculum	273 Teacher Mentor	296 Title II Programs	Ⓜ = Magnet School	New Superintendents and Principals are bold	
290 Social Work	274 Before/After Sch	297 Webmaster	Ⓨ = Year-Round School	Personnel with email addresses are underscored	

- **Polk Co SD-Four Regions HS** PID: 12036059   863/647-4810
  5204 US Highway 98 S, Lakeland 33812

Tami Dawson 15

Public Schs..Principal	Grd	Prgm	Enr/#Cls	SN	
Auburndale High Sch 1 Bloodhound Trl, Auburndale 33823 Tye Bruno	9-12	TV	1,654	40%	863/965-6200 Fax 863/965-6245
Bartow Int'l Baccalaureat HS 1270 S Broadway Ave, Bartow 33830 **Brian Andrews**	9-12		227		863/534-0194 Fax 863/534-0077
Bartow Senior High Sch 1270 S Broadway Ave, Bartow 33830 Betty Clemons	9-12	GTV	2,273 84	37%	863/534-0194 Fax 863/534-0077
Frostproof Middle Sr High Sch 1000 N Palm Ave, Frostproof 33843 Kyle Windham	6-12	GTV	1,196 70	58%	863/635-7809 Fax 863/635-7812
Ft Meade Middle Senior HS 700 Edgewood Dr N, Fort Meade 33841 Amy Hardee	6-12	GTV	756 46	55%	863/285-1180 Fax 863/285-1186 f t
George Jenkins High Sch 6000 Lakeland Highlands Rd, Lakeland 33813 Thomas Patton	9-12	TV	2,292 100	38%	863/648-3566 Fax 863/648-3573
Haines City High Sch 2800 Hornet Dr, Haines City 33844 Adam Lane	9-12	TV	2,510 80	48%	863/421-3281 Fax 863/421-3283
Haines City High School-IB 2800 Hornet Dr, Haines City 33844 Adam Lane	9-12		237 12		863/419-3371 Fax 863/419-3373
Kathleen High Sch 1100 Red Devil Way, Lakeland 33815 Johnnie Jackson	9-12	ATV	2,230 80	48%	863/499-2655 Fax 863/499-2726 f t
Lake Gibson High Sch 7007 N Socrum Loop Rd, Lakeland 33809 Ryan Vann	9-12	AGTV	1,818 73	40%	863/853-6100 Fax 863/853-6108
Lake Region High Sch 1995 Thunder Rd, Eagle Lake 33839 Maryjo Costine	9-12	AGTV	1,510	46%	863/297-3099 Fax 863/297-3097
Lakeland High Sch 726 Hollingsworth Rd, Lakeland 33801 Arthur Martinez	9-12	GTV	2,105 120	35%	863/499-2900 Fax 863/499-2917 f t
Mulberry High Sch 4th Circle NE, Mulberry 33860 **Sharon Chipman**	9-12	TV	1,193	45%	863/701-1104 Fax 863/701-1109 f t
Ridge Cmty High Sch 500 Orchid Dr, Davenport 33837 Stephen Ely	9-12	T	2,951	42%	863/419-3315 Fax 863/419-3334
Summerlin Academy 1500 S Jackson Ave, Bartow 33830 **Cynthia Downing**	9-12		511		863/519-7504 Fax 863/519-8774

Tenoroc Senior High Sch 4905 Saddle Creek Rd, Lakeland 33801 Jason Looney	9-12	T	1,091	54%	863/614-9183 Fax 863/614-9192 f t
Truecore Highlands Youth Acad 242 South Blvd, Avon Park 33825 Jeanette Phipps	6-12		80	96%	863/452-3815 Fax 863/452-3714
Winter Haven High Sch 600 6th St SE, Winter Haven 33880 Gina Williams	9-12	GTV	2,318	42%	863/291-5330 Fax 863/297-3024

- **Polk Co SD-Four Regions MS** PID: 12036047   863/519-7562
  1915 S Floral Ave, Bartow 33830

Tracy Collins 15

Public Schs..Principal	Grd	Prgm	Enr/#Cls	SN	
Bartow Middle Sch 550 E Clower St, Bartow 33830 Christopher Roberts	6-8	TV	891 65	57%	863/534-7415 Fax 863/534-7418 f t
Citrus Ridge A Civic Academy 1775 Sand Mine Rd, Davenport 33897 Nikeshia Leatherwood	PK-8		1,895	55%	863/259-4001 Fax 863/424-2242
Ⓜ Daniel Jenkins Academy 701 Ledwith Ave, Haines City 33844 Brad Tarver	6-8	TV	494 13	48%	863/421-3267 Fax 863/421-3269
Ⓜ Davenport School of the Arts 4751 County Road 547 N, Davenport 33837 **Cynthia Braaten**	K-8	T	1,157 22	52%	863/420-2557 Fax 863/424-3611 f t
Dundee Ridge Middle Academy 5555 Lake Trask Rd, Dundee 33838 Stacy Gideons	5-8	T	758 38	53%	863/419-3088 Fax 863/419-3157
Jere L Stambaugh Middle Sch 226 N Main St, Auburndale 33823 Matthew Blankenship	6-8	TV	1,102 78	61%	863/965-5494 Fax 863/965-5496
Ⓜ Jewett Middle Academy 601 Martin Luther King Blvd NE, Winter Haven 33881 Jacquelyn Moore	6-8		601 35	40%	863/291-5320 Fax 863/297-3049 f t
Ⓜ Jewett School of the Arts 2250 8th St NE, Winter Haven 33881 Michael Sears	K-8	T	737 32	56%	863/291-5373 Fax 863/295-5963
Lake Gibson Middle Sch 6901 N Socrum Loop Rd, Lakeland 33809 Alain Douge	6-8	TV	1,294 82	49%	863/853-6151 Fax 863/853-6184
Lake Marion Creek Sch 3055 Lake Marion Creek Dr, Poinciana 34759 Johna Jozwiak	5-8	T	908	72%	863/427-1471 Fax 863/427-1502
Lakeland Highlands Middle Sch 740 Lake Miriam Dr, Lakeland 33813 **Edgar Santiago**	6-8	TV	1,278	44%	863/648-3500 Fax 863/648-3580
Ⓜ Lawton Chiles Middle Academy 400 N Florida Ave, Lakeland 33801 **Telay Kendrick**	6-8		649 40	30%	863/499-2742 Fax 863/499-2774
Mulberry Middle Sch 500 Dr Mlk Jr Ave, Mulberry 33860 Cynthia Cangelose	6-8	TV	1,151 42	56%	863/701-1066 Fax 863/701-1068
Ⓜ Rochelle School of the Arts 1501 Martin L King Jr Ave, Lakeland 33805 Julie Ward	PK-8	T	823 48	47%	863/499-2810 Fax 863/499-2797
Rosabelle Blake Academy 510 Hartsell Ave, Lakeland 33815 Ruth Reimer	PK-8	T	726 23	49%	863/499-2870 Fax 863/284-4521
Sleepy Hill Middle Sch 2215 Sleepy Hill Rd, Lakeland 33810 **Wallace Selph**	6-8	TV	1,051 50	67%	863/815-6577 Fax 863/815-6586
Ⓜ Union Academy Magnet Sch 1795 E Wabash St, Bartow 33830 Stephen Scheloske	6-8		407 25	36%	863/534-7435 Fax 863/534-7487

1 Superintendent	8 Curric/Instruct K-12	19 Chief Financial Officer	29 Family/Consumer Science	39 Social Studies K-12	49 English/Lang Arts Elem	59 Special Education Elem	69 Academic Assessment
2 Bus/Finance/Purchasing	9 Curric/Instruct Elem	20 Art K-12	30 Adult Education	40 Social Studies Elem	50 English/Lang Arts Sec	60 Special Education Sec	70 Research/Development
3 Buildings And Grounds	10 Curric/Instruct Sec	21 Art Elem	31 Career/Sch-to-Work K-12	41 Social Studies Sec	51 Reading K-12	61 Foreign/World Lang K-12	71 Public Information
4 Food Service	11 Federal Program	22 Art Sec	32 Career/Sch-to-Work Elem	42 Science K-12	52 Reading Elem	62 Foreign/World Lang Elem	72 Summer School
5 Transportation	12 Title I	23 Music K-12	33 Career/Sch-to-Work Sec	43 Science Elem	53 Reading Sec	63 Foreign/World Lang Sec	73 Instructional Tech
6 Athletic	13 Title V	24 Music Elem	34 Early Childhood Ed	44 Science Sec	54 Remedial Reading K-12	64 Religious Education K-12	74 Inservice Training
7 Health Services	15 Asst Superintendent	25 Music Sec	35 Health/Phys Education	45 Math K-12	55 Remedial Reading Elem	65 Religious Education Elem	75 Marketing/Distributive
	16 Instructional Media Svcs	26 Business Education	36 Guidance Services K-12	46 Math Elem	56 Remedial Reading Sec	66 Religious Education Sec	76 Info Systems
	17 Chief Operations Officer	27 Career & Tech Ed	37 Guidance Services Elem	47 Math Sec	57 Bilingual/ELL	67 School Board President	77 Psychological Assess
	18 Chief Academic Officer	28 Technology Education	38 Guidance Services Sec	48 English/Lang Arts K-12	58 Special Education K-12	68 Teacher Personnel	78 Affirmative Action

- **Polk Co SD-Multiple Pathways** PID: 12036073   863/519-8438
  1915 S Floral Ave, Bartow 33830

Steven Cochrane 15

Public Schs..Principal	Grd	Prgm	Enr/#Cls	SN	
© Achievement Acad-Bartow 695 E Summerlin St, Bartow 33830 Cindi Parker-Pearson	Spec	M	52 2		863/533-0690 Fax 863/534-0798 f t
© Achievement Acad-Lakeland 716 E Bella Vista St, Lakeland 33805 John Burton	Spec	M	52 10	48%	863/683-6504 Fax 863/688-9292 f t
© Achievement Acad-Winter Haven 2211 28th St NW, Winter Haven 33881 Cindi Parker-Pearson	Spec	M	52		863/683-6504 Fax 863/968-5016
© Berkley Accelerated Middle Sch 5316 Berkley Rd, Auburndale 33823 Jill Bolender	6-8		478 24	23%	863/984-2400 Fax 863/984-2411
© Berkley Charter Elem Sch 5240 Berkley Rd, Auburndale 33823 Gayle Thomas	K-5		695 35	31%	863/968-5024 Fax 863/968-5026
Ⓐ Bill Duncan Opportunity Center 3333 Winter Lake Rd, Lakeland 33803 Leigh Anne Cooley	6-12	TV	37 15	58%	863/499-2860 Fax 863/499-2863
© Chain of Lakes Collegiate HS 999 Avenue H NE, Winter Haven 33881 **Keith Bonney**	11-12	V	313	2%	863/298-6800 Fax 863/298-6801
© Compass Charter Middle Sch 550 E Clower St, Bartow 33830 Anita Fine	6-8	T	163 13	73%	863/519-8701 Fax 863/519-8704
© Cypress Junction Mont Sch 220 5th St SW, Winter Haven 33880 **Curtis Romey**	K-8		193	2%	863/259-1490
© Dale R Fair Babson Park ES [140] 815 N Scenic Hwy, Babson Park 33827 Elizabeth Tyler	K-5		469 23	5%	863/678-4664 Fax 863/678-4669
© Discovery Acad of Lake Alfred 1000 N Buena Vista Dr, Lake Alfred 33850 Kevin Warren	6-8	T	968 40	75%	863/295-5955 Fax 863/295-5978
© Discovery High Sch 640 Evenhouse Rd, Lake Alfred 33850 Darryl Jemison	9-10	V	463		863/268-7178 Fax 863/956-0059
Ⓐ Donald E Woods Opportunity Ctr 213 Lake Ave, Dundee 33838 Rodney Bellamy	6-12	T	150 14	83%	863/421-3325 Fax 863/421-3390
Ⓨ Doris A Sanders Learning Ctr 1201 Enchanted Dr, Lakeland 33801 **Polly Bruno**	Spec	MT	109 18	46%	863/499-2980 Fax 863/603-6326
East Area Adult & Cmty Sch 300 E Bridgers Ave, Auburndale 33823 Loretta Cameron	Adult		300 22		863/965-5475 Fax 863/965-5477
© Edward W Bok Academy [140] 13901 Hwy 27, Lake Wales 33859 Damien Moses	6-8		600	53%	863/638-1010 Fax 863/638-1212
© Edward W Bok Academy North 338 E Central Ave, Lake Wales 33853 **Damien Moses**	6-7		160		863/232-4665 Fax 863/929-4920
Ⓐ Gause Academy of Leadership 1395 Polk St, Bartow 33830 Daraford Jones	6-12	T	184 35	73%	863/534-7425 Fax 863/519-3716
© Hartridge Academy 1400 US Highway 92, Winter Haven 33881 Debra Richards	K-5	T	212 4	37%	863/956-4434 Fax 863/956-3267
© Hillcrest Elem Sch [140] 1051 State Road 60 E, Lake Wales 33853 Jennifer Barrow	K-5		675 30	7%	863/678-4215 Fax 863/678-4086 f

	Grd	Prgm	Enr/#Cls	SN	
© Janie Howard Wilson Elem Sch [140] 306 Florida Ave, Lake Wales 33853 **Dr Linda Ray**	K-5		409 25	10%	863/678-4211 Fax 863/678-4217
Jean O'Dell Learning Center 1310 S Floral Ave, Bartow 33830 April Sumner	Spec	T	85 12	39%	863/534-7440 Fax 863/519-3810 f t
Karen M Siegel Academy 935 Evenhouse Rd, Lake Alfred 33850 Maggie Reynolds	Spec	T	147 13	36%	863/965-5566 Fax 863/968-5151
© Lake Wales High Sch [140] 1 Highlander Way, Lake Wales 33853 Donna Dunson	9-12	GV	1,571 65	48%	863/678-4222 Fax 863/678-4064 f
© Lakeland Mont Schoolhouse 1124 N Lake Parker Ave, Lakeland 33805 Heather Manrow	PK-6		78 3	11%	863/413-0003 Fax 863/413-0006
© Lakeland Montessori Middle Sch 800 E Palmetto St, Lakeland 33801 Heather Manrow	7-8		60	18%	863/413-0003 Fax 863/812-4689
© Language & Literacy Acad Lrng 330 Avenue C SE, Winter Haven 33880 Dr Tandria Callins	Spec		305		863/268-2903
© Magnolia Montessori Academy 1540 New Jersey Rd, Lakeland 33803 Katie Harris	K-5		92		863/797-4991
© McKeel Academy of Technology 1810 W Parker St, Lakeland 33815 Joyce Powell	6-12	V	1,283 50	26%	863/499-2818 Fax 863/603-6339
© McKeel Central Academy 411 N Florida Ave, Lakeland 33801 **Angela Massung**	K-5		570 22	31%	863/499-1287 Fax 863/688-1607
© Navigator Acad of Leadership 495 Holly Hill Rd, Davenport 33837 **Shane Clark**	K-8		401		
© New Beginnings High Sch 250 Magnolia Ave SW Ste 200, Winter Haven 33880 **Terri Nelson**	6-12	T	500	49%	863/298-5666 Fax 863/298-5675
Ⓐ New Horizons 6980 State Road 37 S, Mulberry 33860 Brett Butler	7-11		10	80%	863/428-1520 Fax 863/428-2204
Ⓐ Pace Center for Girls-Polk 213 Tyler Ave, Lakeland 33801 **Ellen Katzman**	6-12		55 5	20%	863/688-5596
© Polk Avenue Elem Sch [140] 110 E Polk Ave, Lake Wales 33853 Gail Quam	PK-5		516 25	7%	863/678-4244 Fax 863/678-4680
Ⓐ Polk Grad Academy 910 Lowry Ave, Lakeland 33801 Asonja Corbett	9-12		110		863/413-2948 Fax 863/499-2706
© Polk Pre-Collegiate Academy 5316 Berkley Rd, Auburndale 33823 Cathy Carver	9-10		120	23%	863/984-2400 Fax 863/984-2411
© Polk State Gateway to Clg CHS 3425 Winter Lake Rd, Lakeland 33803 Corey Barnes	11-12		232	5%	863/669-2923 Fax 863/669-2330
© Polk State Lakeland Clgt HS 3425 Winter Lake Rd, Lakeland 33803 Rick Jeffries	11-12	GV	328	3%	863/669-2322 Fax 863/669-2944
Polk Virtual Sch 900 Lowry Ave, Lakeland 33801 Deron Williams	6-12		170		863/665-4538 Fax 863/665-5272
Ⓐ Real Academy 951 Mount Airy Ave, Lakeland 33801 John Wilson	4-10		253		863/413-2838 Fax 863/413-2530
Ridge Technical College 7700 Lucerne Park Rd, Winter Haven 33881 Wayne Dickens	Voc	AG	100 30	20%	863/419-3060 Fax 863/419-3062

79 Student Personnel	91 Safety/Security	275 Response To Intervention	296 Grant Writer/Ptnrships
80 Driver Ed/Safety	92 Magnet School	277 Remedial Math K-12	750 Chief Innovation Officer
81 Gifted/Talented	93 Parental Involvement	280 Literacy Coach	751 Chief of Staff
82 Video Services	95 Tech Prep Program	285 STEM	752 Social Emotional Learning
83 Substance Abuse Prev	97 Chief Infomation Officer	286 Digital Learning	
84 Erate	98 Chief Technology Officer	288 Common Core Standards	**Other School Types**
85 AIDS Education	270 Character Education	294 Accountability	Ⓐ = Alternative School
88 Alternative/At Risk	271 Migrant Education	295 Network System	© = **Charter School**
89 Multi-Cultural Curriculum	273 Teacher Mentor	296 Title II Programs	Ⓜ = **Magnet School**
90 Social Work	274 Before/After Sch	297 Webmaster	Ⓨ = **Year-Round School**

School Programs
A = Alternative Program
G = Adult Classes
M = Magnet Program
T = Title I Schoolwide
V = Career & Tech Ed Programs

Social Media
f = Facebook
t = Twitter

New Schools are shaded
New Superintendents and Principals are bold
Personnel with email addresses are underscored

School	Grd	Prgm	Enr/#Cls	SN	Phone
© Ridgeview Global Studies Acad 1000 Dunson Rd, Davenport 33896 Samuel Johnson	K-5	T	956	61%	863/419-3171 Fax 863/419-3172
Ⓐ Roosevelt Academy 115 E St, Lake Wales 33853 Deborah Kindel	6-12	TV	275 40	55%	863/678-4252 Fax 863/678-4250
© South McKeel Academy 2222 Edgewood Dr S, Lakeland 33803 **Mrs Powell**	K-8		1,164 30	20%	863/510-0044 Fax 863/510-0021
Traviss Technical College 3225 Winter Lake Rd, Lakeland 33803 David Wiggs	Voc	AGT	118	52%	863/499-2700 Fax 863/499-2706 🅕🅣
© Victory Ridge Academy 427 Burns Ave, Lake Wales 33853 Debra Johnson	Spec		247		863/679-3338 Fax 863/679-3944 🅕🅣
West Area Adult & Cmty Sch 604 S Central Ave, Lakeland 33815 Loretta Cameron	Adult		1,500 17		863/499-2835 Fax 863/499-2727 🅕🅣

● **Polk Co SD-NE & SE** PID: 12036023   863/291-5251
400 W Crystal Beach Rd, Eagle Lake 33839

Michelle Townley 15

Public Schs..Principal	Grd	Prgm	Enr/#Cls	SN	Phone
Alta Vista Elem Sch 801 Scenic Hwy, Haines City 33844 Celeste Stewart	PK-5	T	751 49	73%	863/421-3235 Fax 863/421-3344
Alturas Elem Sch 420 4th St, Alturas 33820 Charles Pemberton	PK-5	T	366	63%	863/519-3917 Fax 863/519-3923 🅕🅣
Ⓜ Bartow Elem Academy 590 S Wilson Ave, Bartow 33830 Tracy Nelson	K-5		480 22	33%	863/534-7410 Fax 863/534-7218
Ben Hill Griffin Jr Elem Sch 501 McLeod Rd, Frostproof 33843 Patti McGill	3-5	T	433 22	68%	863/635-7820 Fax 863/635-8500 🅕🅣
Ⓜ Bethune Academy 900 Avenue F, Haines City 33844 Sharon Knowles	K-5	T	462 24	48%	863/421-3334 Fax 863/421-3243
Chain of Lakes Elem Sch 7001 State Road 653, Winter Haven 33884 Victor Duncan	PK-5	T	1,179	47%	863/326-5388 Fax 863/326-5391
Eagle Lake Elem Sch 400 W Crystal Beach Rd, Eagle Lake 33839 Connie Loutzenhiser	PK-5	T	576 32	67%	863/291-5357 Fax 863/291-5360
Elbert Elem Sch 205 1st St NE, Winter Haven 33881 William Dawson	PK-5	T	793 32	62%	863/291-5364 Fax 863/291-5363 🅕🅣
Floral Ave Elem Sch 1530 S Floral Ave, Bartow 33830 Rebekah Eckman	PK-5	T	556 28	62%	863/534-7420 Fax 863/534-5003
Ⓜ Frank E Brigham Academy 601 Avenue C SE, Winter Haven 33880 Lynn Boland	PK-5	T	562 30	40%	863/291-5300 Fax 863/298-7913 🅕🅣
Fred G Garner Elem Sch 2500 Havendale Blvd NW, Winter Haven 33881 Qvonda Birdsong	PK-5	T	701 50	75%	863/965-5455 Fax 863/965-5459
Frostproof Elem Sch 118 W 3rd St, Frostproof 33843 **Dart Meyers**	PK-2	T	428 25	75%	863/635-7802 Fax 863/635-8501
Garden Grove Elem Sch 4599 Cypress Gardens Rd, Winter Haven 33884 **Shauna Bergwall**	PK-5	T	512 30	56%	863/291-5396 Fax 863/297-3061
Gibbons St Pre-Sch Center 1860 E Gibbons St, Bartow 33830 **Gregory Kent**	PK-PK	T	228 25	81%	863/535-6489 Fax 863/534-7472 🅕🅣

School	Grd	Prgm	Enr/#Cls	SN	Phone
Highland City Elem Sch 5355 9th Street SE, Highland City 33846 Amy Weingarth	PK-5	T	426 26	52%	863/648-3540 Fax 863/648-3542 🅕🅣
Horizons Elem Sch 1700 Forest Lake Dr, Davenport 33837 Amy Heiser-Meyers	PK-5	T	1,382	61%	863/419-3430 Fax 863/419-3432
James E Stephens Elem Sch 1350 N Maple Ave, Bartow 33830 **James Bracey**	PK-5	T	426 32	74%	863/534-7455 Fax 863/534-0438 🅕🅣
Lewis Anna Woodbury Elem Sch 115 S Oak Ave, Fort Meade 33841 Alexandra Wise	PK-5	T	710 26	73%	863/285-1150 Fax 863/285-1155 🅕🅣
Loughman Oaks Elementary 4600 US Highway 17 92 N, Davenport 33837 Wanda Aponte	PK-5	T	881 48	69%	863/421-3309 Fax 863/421-3333
Palmetto Elem Sch 315 Palmetto St, Poinciana 34759 **Jessica Short**	PK-4	T	551	74%	863/427-6012 Fax 863/427-6013
Pinewood Elem Sch 1400 Gilbert St, Eagle Lake 33839 April Campbell	PK-5	T	656 36	64%	863/298-7977 Fax 863/298-7978
Sandhill Elem Sch 1801 Tyner Rd, Haines City 33844 Kathleen Conely	PK-5	T	986 31	64%	863/419-3166 Fax 863/419-3167
Spessard L Holland Elem Sch 2342 Ef Griffin Rd, Bartow 33830 Melody Butler	PK-5	T	727	41%	863/648-3031 Fax 863/648-3033
Spook Hill Elem Sch 321 Dr J A Wiltshire Ave E, Lake Wales 33853 Chabre Timmons	PK-5	T	646 36	78%	863/678-4262 Fax 863/678-4210
Wahneta Elem Sch 205 4th Wahneta St E, Winter Haven 33880 Nildalis Caraballo	PK-5	T	465 33	84%	863/291-5392 Fax 863/295-5962 🅕🅣

● **Polk Co SD-School Improvement** PID: 12036061   863/815-6722
2285 Sleepy Hill Rd, Lakeland 33810

Patricia Barnes 15

Public Schs..Principal	Grd	Prgm	Enr/#Cls	SN	Phone
Ⓜ Combee Acad of Design & Eng Ⓨ 2805 Morgan Combee Rd, Lakeland 33801 Tammy Farrens	PK-5	MT	628 32	78%	863/499-2960 Fax 863/284-4421
Crystal Lake Elem Sch 700 Galvin Dr, Lakeland 33801 Kristan Fowler	PK-5	T	462 38	76%	863/499-2966 Fax 863/603-6329
Crystal Lake Middle Sch 2410 N Crystal Lake Dr, Lakeland 33801 Ronda Cotter	6-8	T	932 50	68%	863/499-2970 Fax 863/603-6267
Denison Middle Sch 400 Avenue A SE, Winter Haven 33880 Terri Christian	6-8	TV	727 54	59%	863/291-5353 Fax 863/291-5347
Dundee Elem Academy 415 E Frederick Ave, Dundee 33838 Lana Tatom	PK-5	T	644 30	54%	863/421-3316 Fax 863/421-3317
Ⓨ Eastside Elem Sch 1820 E Johnson Ave, Haines City 33844 Dawn Jeffords	PK-5	MT	648 34	76%	863/421-3254 Fax 863/421-3256
Griffin Elem Sch 3315 Kathleen Rd, Lakeland 33810 Dr Melissa Durrance	K-5	T	314 30	73%	863/853-6020 Fax 863/853-6189
Inwood Elem Sch 2200 Avenue G NW, Winter Haven 33880 Donna Camp	PK-5	T	410 24	75%	863/291-5369 Fax 863/291-5342 🅕🅣
Ⓨ Jesse Keen Elem Sch 815 Plateau Ave, Lakeland 33815 Joseph Griffin	PK-5	MT	654 36	81%	863/499-2880 Fax 863/413-2506

1	Superintendent	8	Curric/Instruct K-12	19	Chief Financial Officer	29	Family/Consumer Science	39	Social Studies K-12	49	English/Lang Arts Elem	59	Special Education Elem	69	Academic Assessment
2	Bus/Finance/Purchasing	9	Curric/Instruct Elem	20	Art K-12	30	Adult Education	40	Social Studies Elem	50	English/Lang Arts Sec	60	Special Education Sec	70	Research/Development
3	Buildings And Grounds	10	Curric/Instruct Sec	21	Art Elem	31	Career/Sch-to-Work K-12	41	Social Studies Sec	51	Reading K-12	61	Foreign/World Lang K-12	71	Public Information
4	Food Service	11	Federal Program	22	Art Sec	32	Career/Sch-to-Work Elem	42	Science K-12	52	Reading Elem	62	Foreign/World Lang Elem	72	Summer School
5	Transportation	12	Title I	23	Music K-12	33	Career/Sch-to-Work Sec	43	Science Elem	53	Reading Sec	63	Foreign/World Lang Sec	73	Instructional Tech
6	Athletic	13	Title V	24	Music Elem	34	Early Childhood Ed	44	Science Sec	54	Remedial Reading K-12	64	Religious Education K-12	74	Inservice Training
7	Health Services	15	Asst Superintendent	25	Music Sec	35	Health/Phys Education	45	Math K-12	55	Remedial Reading Elem	65	Religious Education Elem	75	Marketing/Distributive
		16	Instructional Media Svcs	26	Business Education	36	Guidance Services K-12	46	Math Elem	56	Remedial Reading Sec	66	Religious Education Sec	76	Info Systems
		17	Chief Operations Officer	27	Career & Tech Ed	37	Guidance Services Elem	47	Math Sec	57	Bilingual/ELL	67	School Board President	77	Psychological Assess
		18	Chief Academic Officer	28	Technology Education	38	Guidance Services Sec	48	English/Lang Arts K-12	58	Special Education K-12	68	Teacher Personnel	78	Affirmative Action

School / Address / Principal	Grd	Prgm	Enr/#Cls	SN	Phone / Fax
John Snively Elem Sch 848 Snively Ave, Eloise 33880 Diane Rosebrough	PK-5	T	461 27	78%	863/291-5325 Fax 863/297-3080 f t
Kathleen Middle Sch 3627 Kathleen Pnes, Lakeland 33810 Sheila Gregory	6-8	TV	645 53	64%	863/853-6040 Fax 863/853-6037
Ⓐ Lake Alfred Polytech Academy Ⓜ 925 N Buena Vista Dr, Lake Alfred 33850 Julie Grice	6-8	TV	549 40	64%	863/295-5988 Fax 863/295-5992 f t
Lake Shipp Elem Sch 250 Camellia Dr, Winter Haven 33880 Kathryn Raub	PK-5	T	520 32	68%	863/291-5384 Fax 863/298-7511
Laurel Elem Sch 1851 Laurel Ave, Poinciana 34759 Julia Allen	PK-4	T	785	72%	863/427-1375 Fax 863/427-1303
McLaughlin Mid Fine Art Acad 800 4th St S, Lake Wales 33853 **Debra Wright**	6-8	TV	832 53	68%	863/678-4233 Fax 863/678-4033
Oscar J Pope Elem Sch 2730 Maine Ave, Eaton Park 33840 Carol Griffin	PK-5	T	475 43	77%	863/499-2992 Fax 863/499-2996
Philip O'Brien Elem Sch 1225 E Lime St, Lakeland 33801 **Charlie Huntley**	PK-5	T	695 33	69%	863/499-2950 Fax 863/688-8774
Purcell Elem Sch 305 NE 1st Ave, Mulberry 33860 Beth Nave	PK-5	T	501 29	70%	863/701-1061 Fax 863/701-1064
Shelley S Boone Middle Sch 225 S 22nd St, Haines City 33844 **Michael Sears**	6-8	TV	1,180 60	67%	863/421-3302 Fax 863/421-3305
Southwest Middle Sch 2815 Eden Pkwy, Lakeland 33803 Sybille Oldham	6-8	TV	802	61%	863/499-2840 Fax 863/499-2762
Walter Caldwell Elem Sch 141 Dairy Rd, Auburndale 33823 Cheryl Hill	PK-5	T	649 37	62%	863/965-5470 Fax 863/965-5473
Westwood Middle Sch 3520 Avenue J NW, Winter Haven 33881 Todd Bennett	6-8	GTV	742 65	68%	863/965-5484 Fax 863/965-5585 f t
Winston Academy of Engineering 3415 Swindell Rd, Lakeland 33810 Ava Brown	PK-5	T	556 31	52%	863/499-2890 Fax 863/499-2894

● **Polk Co SD-W & N Ctrl** PID: 12036035   863/648-3060
3425 New Jersey Rd, Lakeland 33803

Deborah Henderson 15

Public Schs..Principal	Grd	Prgm	Enr/#Cls	SN	
Auburndale Central Elem Sch 320 Lemon St, Auburndale 33823 Octavia May	PK-5	T	413 19	77%	863/965-5450 Fax 863/965-6390 f t
Carlton Palmore Elem Sch 3725 Cleveland Heights Blvd, Lakeland 33803 Badonna Dardis	PK-5	T	433 30	65%	863/648-3510 Fax 863/648-3122
Clarence Boswell Elem Sch 2820 K Ville Ave, Auburndale 33823 Martin Young	PK-5	T	609 28	71%	863/499-2990 Fax 863/284-4251 f t
Cleveland Court Elem Sch 328 E Edgewood Dr, Lakeland 33803 Cheryl Rutenbar	K-5	T	381 24	47%	863/499-2929 Fax 863/499-2625
Dixieland Elem Sch 416 Ariana St, Lakeland 33803 Dawn Clark	K-5	T	433 23	68%	863/499-2930 Fax 863/499-2932
Dr N E Roberts Elem Sch 6600 Green Rd, Lakeland 33810 Timothy Warren	PK-5	T	800 46	62%	863/815-6633 Fax 863/815-6640
Edgar L Padgett Elem Sch 110 Leelon Rd, Lakeland 33809 Antoinette Kirby	PK-5	T	576 32	65%	863/853-6044 Fax 863/853-6092
Highlands Grove Elem Sch 4510 Lakeland Highlands Rd, Lakeland 33813 Dr Benjamin Henry	PK-5	T	855	40%	863/648-3002 Fax 863/648-3005
James W Sikes Elem Sch 2727 Shepherd Rd, Lakeland 33811 Kerry Chapman	K-5	T	829 37	47%	863/648-3525 Fax 863/648-3187 f t
Kathleen Elem Sch 3515 Sherertz Rd, Lakeland 33810 Nadia Lewis	PK-5	T	536 35	67%	863/853-6030 Fax 863/853-6033
Kingsford Elem Sch 1400 Dean St, Mulberry 33860 Susanne Bizerra	PK-5	T	637 25	77%	863/701-1054 Fax 863/701-1059
Lake Alfred Elem Sch 550 E Cummings St, Lake Alfred 33850 Matt Burkett	PK-5	T	667 25	62%	863/295-5985 Fax 863/295-5987
Lena Vista Elem Sch 925 Berkley Rd, Auburndale 33823 **Deneece Sharp**	PK-5	T	892 42	70%	863/965-5464 Fax 863/965-6274
Ⓜ Lincoln Avenue Academy 1330 N Lincoln Ave, Lakeland 33805 Evelyn Hollen	K-5	T	528 21	25%	863/499-2955 Fax 863/499-2959
Medulla Elem Sch 850 Schoolhouse Rd, Lakeland 33813 Myra Richardson	PK-5	T	699 46	57%	863/648-3515 Fax 863/648-3214
Ⓨ North Lakeland Elem Sch 410 W Robson St, Lakeland 33805 Kim Sealey	PK-5	MT	720 45	65%	863/499-2850 Fax 863/499-2760
Polk City Elem Sch 125 S Bougainvillea Ave, Polk City 33868 Jennifer Erb-Hancock	PK-5	T	506 29	61%	863/965-6338 Fax 863/965-6340 f t
R Bruce Wagner Elem Sch 5500 Yates Rd, Lakeland 33811 Christopher Miller	PK-5	T	800 49	60%	863/701-1450 Fax 863/701-1457
R Clem Churchwell Elem Sch 8201 Park Byrd Rd, Lakeland 33810 Jacqueline Agard	PK-5	T	733 500	55%	863/853-6011 Fax 863/815-6538
Scott Lake Elem Sch 1140 E County Road 540A, Lakeland 33813 Tangela Durham	PK-5	T	854 36	44%	863/648-3520 Fax 863/701-1076
Sleepy Hill Elem Sch 2285 Sleepy Hill Rd, Lakeland 33810 Gregory Deal	PK-5	T	753	67%	863/815-6768 Fax 863/815-6775
Socrum Elem Sch 9400 Old Dade City Rd, Lakeland 33810 Kenyetta Feacher	PK-5	T	536 35	68%	863/853-6050 Fax 863/853-6059
Southwest Elem Sch 2650 Southwest Ave, Lakeland 33803 Julie Sloan	PK-5	T	414 24	62%	863/499-2830 Fax 863/499-2943
Ⓨ Valleyview Elem Sch 2900 E County Road 540A, Lakeland 33813 Katherine Riley	PK-5	MT	773 53	43%	863/648-3535 Fax 863/648-3598
Wendell Watson Elem Sch 6800 Walt Williams Rd, Lakeland 33809 Kelly Burgess	K-5	T	793 36	44%	863/853-6060 Fax 863/853-6056

POLK CATHOLIC SCHOOLS

● **Diocese of Orlando Ed Office** PID: 00197639
Listing includes only schools located in this county. See District Index for location of Diocesan Offices.

279 Student Personnel	91 Safety/Security	275 Response To Intervention	298 Grant Writer/Ptnrships
280 Driver Ed/Safety	92 Magnet School	277 Remedial Math K-12	750 Chief Innovation Officer
281 Gifted/Talented	93 Parental Involvement	280 Literacy Coach	751 Chief of Staff
282 Video Services	95 Tech Prep Program	285 STEM	752 Social Emotional Learning
283 Substance Abuse Prev	97 Chief Infomation Officer	286 Digital Learning	
284 Erate	98 Chief Technology Officer	288 Common Core Standards	
285 AIDS Education	270 Character Education	294 Accountability	
288 Alternative/At Risk	271 Migrant Education	295 Network System	
289 Multi-Cultural Curriculum	273 Teacher Mentor	296 Title II Programs	
290 Social Work	274 Before/After Sch	297 Webmaster	

Other School Types
Ⓐ = Alternative Program
Ⓒ = Charter School
Ⓜ = Magnet School
Ⓨ = Year-Round School

School Programs
A = Alternative Program
G = Adult Classes
M = Magnet Program
T = Title I Schoolwide
V = Career & Tech Ed Programs

Social Media
f = Facebook
t = Twitter

New Schools are shaded
New Superintendents and Principals are bold
Personnel with email addresses are underscored

Catholic Schs..Principal	Grd	Prgm	Enr/#Cls	SN
Resurrection Catholic Sch 3720 Old Road 37, Lakeland 33813 Deborah Schwope	PK-8		500 29	863/644-3931 Fax 863/648-0625
Santa Fe Catholic High Sch 3110 US Highway 92 E, Lakeland 33801 Matt Franzino	9-12		350 18	863/665-4188 Fax 863/665-4151
St Anthony Sch 924 Marcum Rd, Lakeland 33809 Janet Peddecord	PK-8		186 10	863/858-0671 Fax 863/858-0876
St Joseph Academy 310 Frank Lloyd Wright Way, Lakeland 33803 Jessica Bruchey	PK-8		240 17	863/686-6415 Fax 863/687-8074
St Joseph Catholic Sch 535 Avenue M NW, Winter Haven 33881 Tammy Haas	PK-8		460 30	863/293-3311 Fax 863/299-7894

POLK PRIVATE SCHOOLS

Private Schs..Principal	Grd	Prgm	Enr/#Cls	SN
All Saints Acad-Bostick Campus 5001 State Road 540 W, Winter Haven 33880 Ryan Walsh \ Gwen Kessell	PK-12		330 20	863/293-5980 Fax 863/595-1157 f
All Saints Acad-Hampton Campus 5001 State Road 540 W, Winter Haven 33880 Ryan Walsh	6-12		330	863/293-5980 Fax 863/298-8489
Ⓐ Calvary Academy 5400 Bethlehem Rd, Mulberry 33860 Roger Schultz	6-12		13	863/428-2071 Fax 863/428-2584
Candlelight Christian Academy 209 E Sessoms Ave, Lake Wales 33853 Dr Taccara Grubbs	K-12		110	863/676-0049 Fax 863/676-0040
Crossroads Lakeland Sch 615 Old Polk City Rd, Lakeland 33809 Dr Bryan Williams	K-3		35	863/859-0848 Fax 863/858-0963
Excel Christian Academy 6505 Odom Rd, Lakeland 33809 Dr Jennifer Clark	PK-12		230	863/853-9235 Fax 863/853-1835
First Methodist Sch 455 S Broadway Ave, Bartow 33830 Jackie Stoltz	PK-8		123 13	863/533-0905 Fax 863/533-9023
Geneva Classical Academy 4204 Lakeland Highlands Rd, Lakeland 33813 Laura McGinnis \ Michael Strawbridge	K-12		159 15	863/644-1408 Fax 863/619-5841
Grace Lutheran Sch 320 Bates Ave SE, Winter Haven 33880 Michael Rottmann	PK-8		141 22	863/293-9744 Fax 863/595-0106 f
Grant Career & Tech Ed Ctr 820 Spring Lake Sq, Winter Haven 33881 Larry Grant	Voc	G	25	863/875-2785
Heritage Christian Academy 244 Avenue D SW, Winter Haven 33880 Mark Montgomery	K-8		86 13	863/293-0012 Fax 863/299-4146
Ⓨ Husky Prep Academy 204 Jocelyn Dr, Davenport 33897 Denise Clark	PK-12	M	55	863/866-2017
Immanuel Lutheran Sch 1449 34th St NW, Winter Haven 33881 Sam Rodebaugh	PK-8		15 2	863/967-5145
Lakeland Christian Sch 1111 Forest Park St, Lakeland 33803 Luci O'Byrne \ Keith Overholt	PK-12		1,000 50	863/688-2771 Fax 863/682-5637 f t
Landmark Christian Elem Sch 2020 E Hinson Ave, Haines City 33844 Scott Birt	PK-6		160	863/422-2037 Fax 863/421-7729

	Grd	Enr/#Cls	SN
Landmark Christian High Sch 2100 E Hinson Ave, Haines City 33844 Scott Birt	7-12	135 22	863/419-1401 Fax 863/419-1256
Mulberry Christian Academy 200 Dean St, Mulberry 33860 Deron Daniel	K-12	75 4	863/425-1822 Fax 863/425-1241
New Direction Academy 218 S Dixie Dr, Haines City 33844 Anthony Grant	4-12	401	863/438-7493
Oasis Christian Academy 151 King Rd, Winter Haven 33880 Jenny Addison	PK-12	217 17	863/293-0930 Fax 863/293-0429
Parkway Christian Academy 4210 Lakeland Highlands Rd, Lakeland 33813 Terry Odum	K-12	75 15	863/646-5031 Fax 863/646-2267
St Paul Lutheran Sch 4450 Harden Blvd, Lakeland 33813 Robert Boyd	PK-8	489 20	863/644-7710 Fax 863/644-7491
Vanguard School of Lake Wales 22000 Hwy 27, Lake Wales 33859 Marya Marcum-Jones	Spec	120 20	863/676-6091 Fax 863/676-8297
Victory Christian Academy 1401 Griffin Rd, Lakeland 33810 Mark Thomas	PK-12	500 16	863/859-6000 Fax 863/853-9538
Whitestone Academy 3151 Hardin Combee Rd, Lakeland 33801 Susan Burton	PK-12	112	863/665-4187 Fax 863/665-6065
Winter Haven Christian Sch 1700 Buckeye Loop Rd, Winter Haven 33881 Jeannette Williams \ Jeanette Venable	PK-12	372 14	863/294-4135 Fax 863/508-6354
Word of Life Christian Sch 1555 W Main St, Bartow 33830 Pam Moore	K-12	42	863/519-5747 Fax 863/533-8257

POLK REGIONAL CENTERS

● **FDLRS-Sunrise** PID: 04496140   863/647-4258
  698 Cessna St, Bartow 33830   Fax 863/647-4257

Poinsetta Tillman 1,11   Krista Elder 73
Christina Williamson 74

PUTNAM COUNTY

PUTNAM PUBLIC SCHOOLS

● **Putnam Co School Dist** PID: 00202193   386/329-0538
  200 Reid St Ste 1, Palatka 32177   Fax 386/312-4918

Schools: 21 \ **Teachers:** 704 \ **Students:** 11,000 \
Special Ed Students: 1,936 \ **LEP Students:** 658 \ **College-Bound:** 53%
\ **Ethnic:** Asian 1%, African American 26%, Hispanic 18%, Caucasian
55% \ **Exp:** $186 (Low) \ **Poverty:** 40% \ **Title I:** $6,707,273 \
Special Education: $11,726,000 \ **Bilingual Education:** $1,627,000 \
Open-Close: 08/12 - 05/29 \ **DTBP:** $172 (High)

Dr Richard Surrency 1   Deborah Crowley 2
Rhonda Odom 2,15,19   Shannon Wilson 2

1 Superintendent	8 Curric/Instruct K-12	19 Chief Financial Officer	29 Family/Consumer Science	39 Social Studies K-12	49 English/Lang Arts Elem	59 Special Education Elem	69 Academic Assessment
2 Bus/Finance/Purchasing	9 Curric/Instruct Elem	20 Art K-12	30 Adult Education	40 Social Studies Elem	50 English/Lang Arts Sec	60 Special Education Sec	70 Research/Development
3 Buildings And Grounds	10 Curric/Instruct Sec	21 Art Elem	31 Career/Sch-to-Work K-12	41 Social Studies Sec	51 Reading K-12	61 Foreign/World Lang K-12	71 Public Information
4 Food Service	11 Federal Program	22 Art Sec	32 Career/Sch-to-Work Elem	42 Science K-12	52 Reading Elem	62 Foreign/World Lang Elem	72 Summer School
5 Transportation	12 Title I	23 Music K-12	33 Career/Sch-to-Work Sec	43 Science Elem	53 Reading Sec	63 Foreign/World Lang Sec	73 Instructional Tech
6 Athletic	13 Title V	24 Music Elem	34 Early Childhood Ed	44 Science Sec	54 Remedial Reading K-12	64 Religious Education K-12	74 Inservice Training
7 Health Services	15 Asst Superintendent	25 Music Sec	35 Health/Phys Education	45 Math K-12	55 Remedial Reading Elem	65 Religious Education Elem	75 Marketing/Distributive
	16 Instructional Media Svcs	26 Business Education	36 Guidance Services K-12	46 Math Elem	56 Remedial Reading Sec	66 Religious Education Sec	76 Info Systems
	17 Chief Operations Officer	27 Career & Tech Ed	37 Guidance Services Elem	47 Math Sec	57 Bilingual/ELL	67 School Board President	77 Psychological Assess
	18 Chief Academic Officer	28 Technology Education	38 Guidance Services Sec	48 English/Lang Arts K-12	58 Special Education K-12	68 Teacher Personnel	78 Affirmative Action

Public Schs..Principal	Grd	Prgm	Enr/#Cls	SN	
Browning Pearce Elem Sch 100 Bear Blvd, San Mateo 32187 Ashley McCool	PK-5	AT	647 50	74%	386/329-0557 Fax 386/329-0623
C H Price Middle Sch 140 N County Road 315, Interlachen 32148 Edith Higginbotham	6-8	ATV	644 45	76%	386/684-2113 Fax 386/684-3908
C L Overturf Jr 6th Grade Ctr 1100 S 18th St, Palatka 32177 Tammie Driggers	6-6	ATV	402 33	66%	386/329-0569 Fax 386/329-0670
© Childrens Reading Center CS 7901 Saint Johns Ave, Palatka 32177 Dr Geri Melosh	K-5	AT	246 11	48%	386/328-9990 Fax 386/328-2747
Crescent City High Sch 2201 S US Highway 17, Crescent City 32112 John Shelby	9-12	ATV	582 57	75%	386/698-1629 Fax 386/698-3073
Eleanor H Miller Sch 156 Horseman Club Rd, Palatka 32177 **Rodney Symonds**	Spec	T	133 11	73%	386/329-0595 Fax 386/329-0601
George C Miller Middle Sch 101 S Prospect St, Crescent City 32112 Tim Adams	6-8	ATV	548 25	79%	386/698-1360 Fax 386/698-1973
Interlachen Elem Sch 251 S County Road 315, Interlachen 32148 Melanie Nelson	PK-6	AT	904 45	77%	386/684-2130 Fax 386/684-3909
Interlachen High Sch 126 N County Road 315, Interlachen 32148 Bryan Helms	9-12	ATV	711 61	61%	386/684-2116 Fax 386/684-3915
James A Long Elem Sch 1400 Old Jacksonville Rd, Palatka 32177 Mary Hedstrom	PK-5	AT	671 29	61%	386/329-0575 Fax 386/329-0675
Kelley Smith Elem Sch 141 Kelley Smith School Rd, Palatka 32177 **Tracy Taylor**	PK-5	AT	474 37	71%	386/329-0568 Fax 386/329-0629
Mellon Elem Sch 301 Mellon Rd, Palatka 32177 Sandra Weaver	PK-5	AT	314 22	87%	386/329-0593 Fax 386/329-0594
Melrose Elem Sch 401 State Road 26, Melrose 32666 Leah Lundy	PK-6	AT	410 20	59%	352/475-2060 Fax 352/475-1049
Middleton-Burney Elem Sch 1020 Huntington Rd, Crescent City 32112 Joseph Theobold	PK-5	AT	987 49	82%	386/698-1238 Fax 386/698-4364
Ochwilla Elem Sch 299 N State Road 21, Hawthorne 32640 Evelyn Langston	PK-5	AT	372 23	74%	352/481-0204 Fax 352/481-5541
Palatka High Sch 302 Mellon Rd, Palatka 32177 Thomas Bolling	9-12	ATV	1,106 57%	57%	386/329-0577 Fax 386/329-0624
Putman My District Virtual Sch 200 Reid St, Palatka 32177 Renee Hough	K-12		34 	41%	386/329-0635
© Putnam Acad of Arts & Sciences 310 S Palm Ave Ste 10, Palatka 32177 Curtis Ellis	6-8	T	198 	58%	386/326-4212 Fax 386/326-6235
Q I Roberts Jr Sr High Sch 901 State Road 100, Florahome 32140 Mary Wood-Piazza	7-9	T	526 22	36%	386/659-1737 Fax 386/659-1986

	Grd	Prgm	Enr/#Cls	SN	
Robert H Jenkins Middle Sch 1100 N 19th St, Palatka 32177 Randall Hedstrom	7-8	ATV	529 32	72%	386/329-0588 Fax 386/329-0636
William D Moseley Elem Sch 1100 Husson Ave, Palatka 32177 Sarajean McDaniel	PK-5	AT	537 29	91%	386/329-0562 Fax 386/329-0563

PUTNAM PRIVATE SCHOOLS

Private Schs..Principal	Grd	Prgm	Enr/#Cls	SN	
Deseret Academy 304 5th St, Satsuma 32189 Cinthia Trunk	1-12	G	150 8		386/649-4978 Fax 386/649-4479
Peniel Baptist Academy 110 Peniel Church Rd, Palatka 32177 Merri Treadway	PK-12	V	350 27		386/328-1707 Fax 386/328-0950

PUTNAM REGIONAL CENTERS

- **FDLRS-Nefec** PID: 04433148
  3841 Reid St, Palatka 32177
  386/329-3800
  Fax 386/329-3684

SANTA ROSA COUNTY

SANTA ROSA PUBLIC SCHOOLS

- **Santa Rosa Co School Dist** PID: 00203006
  5086 Canal St, Milton 32570
  850/983-5010
  Fax 850/983-5013

Schools: 37 \ **Teachers:** 1,785 \ **Students:** 29,089 \
Special Ed Students: 3,606 \ **LEP Students:** 209 \ **College-Bound:** 76%
\ **Ethnic:** Asian 1%, African American 6%, Hispanic 7%, Caucasian
85% \ **Exp:** $152 (Low) \ **Poverty:** 12% \ **Title I:** $4,606,632 \
Special Education: $24,064,000 \ **Bilingual Education:** $504,000 \
Open-Close: 08/12 - 05/29 \ **DTBP:** $192 (High)

							School Programs	Social Media
79	Student Personnel	91	Safety/Security	275	Response To Intervention	298	Grant Writer/Ptnrships	A = Alternative Program	
80	Driver Ed/Safety	92	Magnet School	277	Remedial Math K-12	750	Chief Innovation Officer	G = Adult Classes	�f = Facebook
81	Gifted/Talented	93	Parental Involvement	280	Literacy Coach	751	Chief of Staff	M = Magnet Program	
82	Video Services	95	Tech Prep Program	285	STEM	752	Social Emotional Learning	T = Title I Schoolwide	�t = Twitter
83	Substance Abuse Prev	97	Chief Infomation Officer	286	Digital Learning			V = Career & Tech Ed Programs	
84	Erate	98	Chief Technology Officer	288	Common Core Standards	Other School Types			
85	AIDS Education	270	Character Education	294	Accountability	Ⓐ = Alternative School			
86	Alternative/At Risk	271	Migrant Education	295	Network System	Ⓒ = Charter School	New Schools are shaded		
87	Multi-Cultural Curriculum	273	Teacher Mentor	296	Title II Programs	Ⓜ = Magnet School	New Superintendents and Principals are bold		
88	Social Work	274	Before/After Sch	297	Webmaster	Ⓨ = Year-Round School	Personnel with email addresses are underscored		

Public Schs..Principal	Grd	Prgm	Enr/#Cls	SN
Avalon Middle Sch 5445 King Arthurs Way, Milton 32583 Tonya Shepherd	6-8	ATV	786 35	51% 850/983-5540 Fax 850/983-5545
Bagdad Elem Sch 4512 Forsyth St, Milton 32583 Daniel Baxley	PK-5	AT	444 32	73% 850/983-5680 Fax 850/983-5687
Bennett C Russell Elem Sch 3740 Excalibur Way, Milton 32583 Suzette Godwin	PK-5	T	866	60% 850/983-7000 Fax 850/983-7007
Berryhill Elem Sch 4900 Berryhill Rd, Milton 32570 Roger Golden	PK-5	AT	848 35	53% 850/983-5690 Fax 850/983-5694
© Capstone Acad Milton Campus 5038 Stewart St, Milton 32570 Claire Errington	Spec		26	83% 850/626-3091 Fax 850/455-7322
Central Sch 6180 Central School Rd, Milton 32570 Sean Twitty	PK-12	TV	591 17	65% 850/983-5640 Fax 850/983-5645
Chumuckla Elem Sch 2312 Highway 182, Jay 32565 James Carnley	K-6	T	345 17	51% 850/995-3690 Fax 850/995-3695
East Milton Elem Sch 5156 Ward Basin Rd, Milton 32583 Terry Paschall	PK-5	AT	707 40	84% 850/983-5620 Fax 850/983-5625
Gulf Breeze Elem Sch 549 Gulf Breeze Pkwy, Gulf Breeze 32561 Warren Stevens	PK-5		747 37	19% 850/934-5185 Fax 850/934-5189
Gulf Breeze High Sch 675 Gulf Breeze Pkwy, Gulf Breeze 32561 Daniel Brothers	9-12	AV	1,811	21% 850/916-4100 Fax 850/916-4109
Gulf Breeze Middle Sch 649 Gulf Breeze Pkwy, Gulf Breeze 32561 Michael Brandon	6-8	AV	991 40	23% 850/934-4080 Fax 850/934-4085
Holley-Navarre Interm Sch 1936 Navarre School Rd, Navarre 32566 Vesta Mosley	3-5	AT	911 38	47% 850/936-6020 Fax 850/936-6026
Holley-Navarre Middle Sch 1976 Williams Creek Dr, Navarre 32566 Joann DeStefano	6-8		991	41% 850/936-6040 Fax 850/936-6049
Holley-Navarre Primary Sch 8019 Escola St, Navarre 32566 Barbara Scott	PK-2	T	886 34	44% 850/936-6130 Fax 850/936-6132
Jay Elem Sch 13833 Alabama St, Jay 32565 Kelly Short	PK-6	T	513 25	55% 850/359-8230 Fax 850/359-8669
Jay High Sch 3741 School St, Jay 32565 Stephen Knowlton	7-12	V	448 35	36% 850/675-4507 Fax 850/675-8573
Ⓐ Learning Academy of Santa Rosa [143] © 5880 Stewart St, Milton 32570 Kara Whitney	6-12	T	167 5	86% 850/983-3495 Fax 850/983-8098
Locklin Tech Center 5330 Berryhill Rd, Milton 32570 Maria Ladouceur	Voc	AG	380 13	850/983-5700 Fax 850/983-5715
Martin L King Middle Sch 5928 Stewart St, Milton 32570 Darren Brock	6-8	ATV	654 28	78% 850/983-5660 Fax 850/983-5665
Milton High Sch 5445 Stewart St, Milton 32570 Tim Short	9-12	TV	1,871 80	53% 850/983-5600 Fax 850/983-5610
Navarre High Sch 8600 High School Blvd, Navarre 32566 Brian Noack	9-12	A	2,306	28% 850/936-6080 Fax 850/936-6088
Oriole Beach Elem Sch 1260 Oriole Beach Rd, Gulf Breeze 32563 Joshua McGrew	PK-5	T	901 40	36% 850/934-5160 Fax 850/934-5166
Pace High Sch 4065 Norris Rd, Pace 32571 Stephen Shell	9-12	ATV	1,971 90	33% 850/995-3600 Fax 850/995-3620
Pea Ridge Elem Sch 4775 School Ln, Pace 32571 Dana Fleming	PK-5	AT	803 35	50% 850/995-3680 Fax 850/995-3688
R Hobbs Middle Sch 5317 Glover Ln, Milton 32570 Brandon Koger	6-8	ATV	740 40	56% 850/983-5630 Fax 850/983-5635
S S Dixon Intermediate Sch 5540 Education Dr, Pace 32571 Linda Gooch	3-5	AT	885 50	43% 850/995-3650 Fax 850/995-3655
S S Dixon Primary Sch 4560 Pace Patriot Blvd, Milton 32571 Nancy Haupt	K-2	T	825 31	43% 850/995-3660 Fax 850/995-3675
Ⓐ Sail 6556 Firehouse Rd, Milton 32570 Alexis Cash	6-12		120	850/983-5150
Santa Rosa Adult Sch 5332 Berryhill Rd, Milton 32570 Lawrence Heringer	Adult	AV	150	850/983-5710 Fax 850/983-5345
Ⓐ Santa Rosa High Sch 5332 Berryhill Rd, Milton 32570 Larry Heringer	9-12		200	850/983-5710 Fax 850/983-5345
Santa Rosa Online Academy 5330 Berryhill Rd, Milton 32570 Laura Austin	K-12	T	92	72% 850/981-7860 Fax 850/983-5715
T R Jackson Pre-K Center 4950 Susan St, Milton 32570 Dawn Alt	PK-PK		203 25	95% 850/983-5720 Fax 850/983-5722
Thomas Sims Middle Sch 5500 Education Dr, Pace 32571 Emily Donalson	6-8		1,062 42	32% 850/995-3676 Fax 850/995-3696
W H Rhodes Elem Sch 5563 Byrom St, Milton 32570 Michele Barlow	PK-5	AT	876 35	80% 850/983-5670 Fax 850/983-5672
West Navarre Interm Sch 1970 Cotton Bay Ln, Navarre 32566 Shana Dorsey	3-5		983 44	37% 850/936-6060 Fax 850/936-6067
West Navarre Primary Sch 1955 Lowe Rd, Navarre 32566 William Price	PK-2	T	956	39% 850/936-6000 Fax 850/936-6010
Woodlawn Beach Middle Sch 1500 Woodlawn Way, Gulf Breeze 32563 Victor Lowrimore	6-8	V	1,075 35	29% 850/934-4010 Fax 850/934-4015

SANTA ROSA PRIVATE SCHOOLS

Private Schs..Principal	Grd	Prgm	Enr/#Cls	SN
Good Shepherd Lutheran Sch 4237 Gulf Breeze Pkwy, Gulf Breeze 32563 Sue Mathews	PK-1		55 7	850/932-9127 Fax 850/344-9684
Gulf Breeze Elementary 5613 Gulf Breeze Pkwy, Gulf Breeze 32563 Michelle Hamilton	K-5		115 11	850/934-0180 Fax 850/950-0851
Lead Academy 4106 Berryhill Rd, Pace 32571 H Frank Lay	PK-12		100	850/995-1900
Santa Rosa Christian Sch 6331 Chestnut St, Milton 32570 Doris Peppard \ Adam Watt	K-12		250 15	850/623-4671 Fax 850/623-9559
St Pauls Methodist Sch 4901 Gulf Breeze Pkwy, Gulf Breeze 32563 Libbra Barker	PK-PK		114	850/932-0692 Fax 850/932-2953

1 Superintendent	19 Chief Financial Officer	39 Social Studies K-12	59 Special Education Elem	69 Academic Assessment
2 Bus/Finance/Purchasing	8 Curric/Instruct K-12	20 Art K-12	29 Family/Consumer Science	40 Social Studies Elem	50 English/Lang Arts Sec	60 Special Education Sec	70 Research/Development
3 Buildings And Grounds	9 Curric/Instruct Elem	21 Art Elem	30 Adult Education	41 Social Studies Sec	51 Reading K-12	61 Foreign/World Lang K-12	71 Public Information
4 Food Service	10 Curric/Instruct Sec	22 Art Sec	31 Career/Sch-to-Work K-12	42 Science K-12	52 Reading Elem	62 Foreign/World Lang Elem	72 Summer School
5 Transportation	11 Federal Program	23 Music K-12	32 Career/Sch-to-Work Elem	43 Science Elem	53 Reading Sec	63 Foreign/World Lang Sec	73 Instructional Tech
6 Athletic	12 Title I	24 Music Elem	33 Career/Sch-to-Work Sec	44 Science Sec	54 Remedial Reading K-12	64 Religious Education K-12	74 Inservice Training
7 Health Services	13 Title V	25 Music Sec	34 Early Childhood Ed	45 Math K-12	55 Remedial Reading Elem	65 Religious Education Elem	75 Marketing/Distributive
	15 Asst Superintendent	26 Business Education	35 Health/Phys Education	46 Math Elem	56 Remedial Reading Sec	66 Religious Education Sec	76 Info Systems
	16 Instructional Media Svcs	27 Career & Tech Ed	36 Guidance Services K-12	47 Math Sec	57 Bilingual/ELL	67 School Board President	77 Psychological Assess
	17 Chief Operations Officer	28 Technology Education	37 Guidance Services Elem	48 English/Lang Arts K-12	58 Special Education K-12	68 Teacher Personnel	78 Affirmative Action
	18 Chief Academic Officer		38 Guidance Services Sec	49 English/Lang Arts Elem			

West Florida Baptist Academy	PK-12	400	850/623-8984
5621 Highway 90, Milton 32583		18	Fax 850/623-8383
Linda Bacon			

SARASOTA COUNTY

SARASOTA PUBLIC SCHOOLS

● **Sarasota Co School Dist** PID: 00203238   **941/927-9000**
1960 Landings Blvd, Sarasota 34231   **Fax 941/927-2539**

Schools: 59 \ **Teachers:** 3,091 \ **Students:** 43,150 \
Special Ed Students: 6,737 \ **LEP Students:** 2,892 \ **College-Bound:** 70%
\ **Ethnic:** Asian 3%, African American 9%, Hispanic 21%, Caucasian
67% \ **Exp:** $154 (Low) \ **Poverty:** 13% \ **Title I:** $7,873,213 \
Special Education: $13,685,000 \ **Bilingual Education:** $671,000 \
Open-Close: 08/12 - 05/29 \ **DTBP:** $192 (High) \ 🇹

Dr Todd Bowden	1	Christa Curtner	2
Joan Saari	2	Leslie Gillis	2
Manuel Martin Ventura	2	Mary Carr	2
Mitsi Corcoran	2,15,19	Renee Hayes	2
Sandy Gannon	2	Sheina Runions	2
Valerie Maggi	2	Don Hampton	3
James Woodson	3	James Deunger	3
Jeff Maultsby	3,15,17	Jody Dumas	3
Louis Stoecklin	3	Mark Smith	3
Melanie Gombos	3	Melissa Yavalar	3
Michael Siciliano	3	Russell Brock	3
Stephen Clark	3	Teresa Clarke	3,5
Wayne Starr	3	William Grant	3
Dr Beverly Girard	4	Don Mankie	4
Judith Coomer	4	Karla Ellison	4
Laura Love	4	Nancy Gooch	4
Natalie Von Suskil	4	Richard Wittstruck	4
Sara Dan	4	Tracy Marchese	4
Charlotte Price	5	Diane Preston	5
Donald Stucke	5	Edward Vargas	5
James Basilotto	5	Lisa Wallace	5
Michael Tellone	5	Robert Kopp	5
Sandie Kovalsky	5	Senita Robinson	5
Simon Nelson	5	Susan Schlabach	5
Thomas Higgins	5	Wendy York	5
James Slaton	6	Janice Merritt	7
Karen McCormack	7	Suzanne Dubose	7,83,85,270
Kati Burns	8	Dr Laura Kingsley	8,15,18
Chris Renouf	9	Karen Rose	10,72*
Stephen Cantees	10,80	Tara Konraidy	11
Robert Manoogian	16	Angela Hartvigsen	20,23
Tripp Jennings	27	Ronald Dipillo	30,31*
Sonia Alberts	34,79,81	James Clark	35*
Jamie Rodriguez	57,271	Tammy Cassels	58
Jane Goodwin	67	Danielle Schwied	68
Lynn Peterson-Quinn	68	Roy Sprinkle	68
Dr Denise Cantalupo	69,70,294,298	Carly Gordon	70
Kristi Alexander	70	Mina Ajrab	71,297
Tracey Beeker	71	Colin Enos	73
Dawn Stoudt	73	Eric Showalter	73
James Nalefski	73	Michael Wheeler	73
Todd Alexander	73	Kelly Ellington	74,296
Diana Messina	76	Donna Fernandez	76
Joe Binswanger	76,295	Kay Adams	76
Linda Seibel	76	Rodney Davidson	76
Debra Giacolone	79	Sid Friedman	79
Tracey Cardenas	79	Bethany King	88,93*
Michael Sobrower	91	Paul Grohowski	91

Simonetta Pascarella	91	Victor Stevens	91
Wayne Johnson	95,295	Julie Vreuis	275
Katrina Ward	286*	Amanda Coker	295
Anthony Dolciotto	295	Brandon Miller	295
Cary Gillit	295	David Lawson	295
Ertac Gurcan	295	George Guck	295
James Ferrara	295	John Solum	295
Mark Sprague	295	Raymond Ebersole	295
Richard Freck	295	Sean O'Keefe	295
Tracey Craft	295		

Public Schs..Principal	Grd	Prgm	Enr/#Cls	SN
Alta Vista Elem Sch 1050 S Euclid Ave, Sarasota 34237 Dr Barbara Shirley	K-5	T	542 53	92% 941/361-6400 Fax 941/361-6956
Ashton Elem Sch 5110 Ashton Rd, Sarasota 34233 Kristi Jarvis	K-5		1,051 63	26% 941/361-6440 Fax 941/361-6444
Atwater Elem Sch 4701 Huntsville Ave, North Port 34288 Cynthia Thro	K-5	T	665	65% 941/257-2317 Fax 941/257-2319
Ⓜ Bay Haven School Basics Plus 2901 W Tamiami Cir, Sarasota 34234 Chad Erickson	K-5	T	612	43% 941/359-5800 Fax 941/359-5694
Booker High Sch 3201 N Orange Ave, Sarasota 34234 Dr Rachel Shelley	9-12	TV	1,285 80	62% 941/355-2967 Fax 941/359-5757 🇹
Booker Middle Sch 2250 Myrtle St, Sarasota 34234 Lashawn Frost	6-8	T	805 70	76% 941/359-5824 Fax 941/359-5898
Brentwood Elem Sch 2500 Vinson Ave, Sarasota 34232 John Weida	PK-5	T	655 48	68% 941/361-6230 Fax 941/361-6381
Brookside Middle Sch 3636 S Shade Ave, Sarasota 34239 Matthew Gruhl	6-8	T	755 48	60% 941/361-6472 Fax 941/361-6508
Cranberry Elem Sch 2775 Shalimar Ter, North Port 34286 **Brad Porinchak**	PK-5	T	681	62% 941/480-3400 Fax 941/480-3401
Emma E Booker Elem Sch 2350 Dr M L King Jr Way, Sarasota 34234 Edwina Oliver	PK-5	T	560 36	93% 941/361-6480 Fax 941/361-6484 🇹
Englewood Elem Sch 150 N McCall Rd, Englewood 34223 Mark Grossenbacher	K-5	T	585 26	52% 941/474-3247 Fax 941/474-0872
Fruitville Elem Sch 601 Honore Ave, Sarasota 34232 Steven French	PK-5	T	753 100	58% 941/361-6200 Fax 941/361-6203
Garden Elem Sch 700 Center Rd, Venice 34285 Amy Archer	K-5	T	571 46	55% 941/486-2110 Fax 941/486-2610
Glenallen Elem Sch 7050 Glenallen Blvd, North Port 34287 Rebecca Drum	PK-5	T	700 30	75% 941/426-9517 Fax 941/423-8131
Gocio Elem Sch 3450 Gocio Rd, Sarasota 34235 Steven Royce	PK-5	T	624 41	85% 941/361-6405 Fax 941/361-6793
Gulf Gate Elem Sch 6500 S Lockwood Ridge Rd, Sarasota 34231 Robin Magac	PK-5	T	711 46	54% 941/361-6499 Fax 941/361-6799
Heron Creek Middle Sch 6501 W Price Blvd, North Port 34291 Kristine Lawrence	6-8	T	863	71% 941/480-3371 Fax 941/480-3398
© Imagine Schools North Port ES [137] 1000 Innovation Ave, North Port 34289 Aleischa Coover	K-5	T	1,127	53% 941/426-2050 Fax 941/423-8659

79	Student Personnel	91	Safety/Security	275	Response To Intervention	298 Grant Writer/Ptnrships
80	Driver Ed/Safety	92	Magnet School	277	Remedial Math K-12	750 Chief Innovation Officer
81	Gifted/Talented	93	Parental Involvement	280	Literacy Coach	751 Chief of Staff
82	Video Services	95	Tech Prep Program	285	STEM	752 Social Emotional Learning
83	Substance Abuse Prev	97	Chief Infomation Officer	286	Digital Learning	
84	Erate	98	Chief Technology Officer	288	Common Core Standards	**Other School Types**
85	AIDS Education	270	Character Education	294	Accountability	Ⓐ = Alternative School
88	Alternative/At Risk	271	Migrant Education	295	Network System	© = Charter School
89	Multi-Cultural Curriculum	273	Teacher Mentor	296	Title II Programs	Ⓜ = Magnet School
90	Social Work	274	Before/After Sch	297	Webmaster	Ⓨ = Year-Round School

School Programs
A = Alternative Program
G = Adult Classes
M = Magnet Program
T = Title I Schoolwide
V = Career & Tech Ed Programs

Social Media
🇫 = Facebook
🇹 = Twitter

New Schools are shaded
New Superintendents and Principals are bold
Personnel with email addresses are underscored

FL—129

School	Grades		Enroll	%	Phone
© Imagine Schools North Port Up [137] 2757 Sycamore St, North Port 34289 John Halcomb	6-12		400		941/426-2050 Fax 941/426-1326
© Imagine Schools Palmer Rnch [137] 6220 McIntosh Rd, Sarasota 34238 Alisa Wright	K-8		502	9%	941/923-1125 Fax 941/923-1124
© Island Village Mont Sch-Saraso 11011 Clark Rd, Sarasota 34241 Cindy Hoffman	K-6		75 18		941/954-4999 Fax 941/925-0267
© Island Village Mont-Venice 2001 Pinebrook Rd, Venice 34292 Jason Hunter	K-8	T	662	36%	941/484-4999 Fax 941/484-2150
Lakeview Elem Sch 7299 Proctor Rd, Sarasota 34241 Lisa Wheatley	K-5		594 44	37%	941/361-6571 Fax 941/361-6573
LaMarque Elem Sch 3415 Lamarque Ave, North Port 34286 Troy Thompson	PK-5	T	856	68%	941/426-6371 Fax 941/426-6392
Laurel-Nokomis Sch 1900 Laurel Rd E, Nokomis 34275 Ray Wilson	PK-8	T	1,181 84	41%	941/486-2171 Fax 941/486-2013
McIntosh Middle Sch 701 McIntosh Rd, Sarasota 34232 Dr Harriet Moore	6-8	T	714 60	58%	941/361-6520 Fax 941/361-6340
North Port High Sch 6400 W Price Blvd, North Port 34291 Brandon Johnson	9-12	T	2,344	57%	941/423-8558 Fax 941/480-3199
Oak Park Sch 7285 Proctor Rd, Sarasota 34241 Jamie Lowicz	Spec	T	325 40	64%	941/361-6428 Fax 941/378-2743
Phillippi Shores Elem Sch 4747 S Tamiami Trl, Sarasota 34231 Allison Foster	K-5	T	785 45	46%	941/361-6424 Fax 941/361-6814
Ⓜ Pine View Sch 1 Python Path, Osprey 34229 Stephen Covert	2-12		1,925 80	13%	941/486-2001 Fax 941/486-2042
Riverview High Sch 1 Ram Way, Sarasota 34231 Erin Del Castillo	9-12	V	2,490 130	35%	941/923-1484 Fax 941/361-6175
© Sarasota Academy of the Arts 4466 Fruitville Rd, Sarasota 34232 Cheryl Korwin	K-8	T	229	49%	941/377-2278 Fax 941/404-4492
Sarasota Co Technical Inst 4748 Beneva Rd, Sarasota 34233 **Ronald Dipillo**	Voc	G	702 60	33%	941/924-1365 Fax 941/921-7902
Sarasota High Sch 2155 Bahia Vista St, Sarasota 34239 David Jones	9-12	AGTV	2,142	42%	941/955-0181 Fax 941/361-6380
Sarasota Middle Sch 4826 Ashton Rd, Sarasota 34233 Laurie Breslin	6-8		1,244 80	25%	941/361-6464 Fax 941/361-6798
© Sarasota Military Academy 801 N Orange Ave, Sarasota 34236 Christina Bowman	9-12		939	33%	941/926-1700 Fax 941/926-1701
© Sarasota Military Academy Prep 3101 Bethel Ln, Sarasota 34240 Thomas Vara	6-8	TV	572	50%	941/877-7737 Fax 941/877-7738
© Sarasota School-Arts & Science 717 Central Ave, Sarasota 34236 Tara Tahmosh	6-8	T	750 15	41%	941/330-1855 Fax 941/330-1835
© Sarasota Suncoast Academy 8084 Hawkins Rd, Sarasota 34241 Steve Crump	K-5		507 23	30%	941/924-4242 Fax 941/924-8282
Ⓐ Sarasota Virtual Sch 4748 Beneva Rd, Sarasota 34233 Katrina Ward	K-12		32		941/924-1365
© Sky Academy-Englewood 881 S River Rd, Englewood 34223 John Bailey	6-8		280	4%	941/999-4775
© Sky Academy-Venice 705 Center Rd, Venice 34285 Steve Smith	6-8		166	11%	941/244-2626 Fax 941/244-2319
Southside Elem Sch 1901 Webber St, Sarasota 34239 Jennifer Nzeza	K-5		729 34	27%	941/361-6420 Fax 941/361-6866
© State Clg of FL Collegiate Sch 8000 Tamiami Trl S Bldg 800, Venice 34293 **Kelly Monod**	6-12		401		941/408-1430
© Student Leadership Academy 200 Field Ave E, Venice 34285 Jonathan Cooley	6-8	T	253	35%	941/485-5551 Fax 941/485-2694
© Suncoast Innovative Studies ES 845 S School Ave, Sarasota 34237 Stephen Evans	PK-5	T	280	83%	941/953-4433 Fax 941/953-4435
© Suncoast Innovative Studies MS 4311 Wilkinson Rd, Sarasota 34233 Stephen Evans	6-8		160 13		941/342-0963 Fax 941/342-0967
Suncoast Polytechnical HS 4650 Beneva Rd, Sarasota 34233 **John Turgeon**	Voc	T	565	37%	941/921-3981 Fax 941/921-9900
Tatum Ridge Elem Sch 4100 Tatum Rd, Sarasota 34240 Barry Dunn	K-5		666	23%	941/316-8188 Fax 941/316-8189
Taylor Ranch Elem Sch 2500 Taylor Ranch Trl, Venice 34293 William Bolander	PK-5	T	749 39	39%	941/486-2000 Fax 941/486-2129
Toledo Blade Elem Sch 1201 Geranium Ave, North Port 34288 Jennifer Dolciotto	PK-5		758 65	50%	941/426-6100 Fax 941/426-9340
Tuttle Elem Sch 2863 8th St, Sarasota 34237 Patricia Folino	K-5	T	702 35	84%	941/361-6433 Fax 941/361-6530
Venice Elem Sch 150 Miami Ave E, Venice 34285 Kirk Hutchinson	K-5	T	565 30	40%	941/486-2111 Fax 941/486-2117
Venice High Sch 1 Indian Ave, Venice 34285 Eric Jackson	9-12	V	2,238 120	32%	941/488-6726 Fax 941/486-2034
Venice Middle Sch 1900 Center Rd, Venice 34292 Tomas Dinverno	6-8	T	784 42	47%	941/486-2100 Fax 941/486-2108
Wilkinson Elem Sch 3400 Wilkinson Rd, Sarasota 34231 Susan Nations	PK-5	T	511 40	75%	941/361-6477 Fax 941/361-1877
Woodland Middle Sch 2700 Panacea Blvd, North Port 34289 Dr Cindy Hall	6-8	T	942	60%	941/240-8590 Fax 941/240-8595
Ⓐ YMCA Triad Alt Sch-North 4430 Beneva Rd, Sarasota 34233 **Melanie Ritter**	6-12	T	61 5	87%	941/925-6693 Fax 941/925-6696
Ⓐ YMCA Triad-South Campus 1130 Indian Hills Blvd, Venice 34293 Margaret King	6-12		35		941/493-9660 Fax 941/493-9657

1	Superintendent	8	Curric/Instruct K-12	19	Chief Financial Officer	29	Family/Consumer Science	39	Social Studies K-12	49	English/Lang Arts Elem	59	Special Education Elem	69	Academic Assessment
2	Bus/Finance/Purchasing	9	Curric/Instruct Elem	20	Art K-12	30	Adult Education	40	Social Studies Elem	50	English/Lang Arts Sec	60	Special Education Sec	70	Research/Development
3	Buildings And Grounds	10	Curric/Instruct Sec	21	Art Elem	31	Career/Sch-to-Work K-12	41	Social Studies Sec	51	Reading K-12	61	Foreign/World Lang K-12	71	Public Information
4	Food Service	11	Federal Program	22	Art Sec	32	Career/Sch-to-Work Elem	42	Science K-12	52	Reading Elem	62	Foreign/World Lang Elem	72	Summer School
5	Transportation	12	Title I	23	Music K-12	33	Career/Sch-to-Work Sec	43	Science Elem	53	Reading Sec	63	Foreign/World Lang Sec	73	Instructional Tech
6	Athletic	13	Title V	24	Music Elem	34	Early Childhood Ed	44	Science Sec	54	Remedial Reading K-12	64	Religious Education K-12	74	Inservice Training
7	Health Services	14	Asst Superintendent	25	Music Sec	35	Health/Phys Education	45	Math K-12	55	Remedial Reading Elem	65	Religious Education Elem	75	Marketing/Distributive
		15	Instructional Media Svcs	26	Business Education	36	Guidance Services K-12	46	Math Elem	56	Remedial Reading Sec	66	Religious Education Sec	76	Info Systems
		16	Chief Operations Officer	27	Career & Tech Ed	37	Guidance Services Elem	47	Math Sec	57	Bilingual/ELL	67	School Board President	77	Psychological Assess
		18	Chief Academic Officer	28	Technology Education	38	Guidance Services Sec	48	English/Lang Arts K-12	58	Special Education K-12	68	Teacher Personnel	78	Affirmative Action

SARASOTA CATHOLIC SCHOOLS

● **Diocese of Venice Ed Office** PID: 02231695   941/484-9543
1000 Pinebrook Rd, Venice 34285   Fax 941/484-1121

Schools: 15 \ **Students:** 4,350

Listing includes only schools located in this county. See District Index for location of Diocesan Offices.

Dr Benjamin H Moore 1   Peter McPartland 2

Catholic Schs..Principal	Grd	Prgm	Enr/#Cls SN	
Cardinal Mooney High Sch 4171 Fruitville Rd, Sarasota 34232 Ben Hopper	9-12		570 31	941/371-4917 Fax 941/371-6924 f t
Dreams Are Free-Nevins Acad 4380 Fruitville Rd, Sarasota 34232 Rebecca Reynolds	Spec		50 5	941/366-4010 Fax 941/366-3819
Epiphany Cathedral Sch 316 Sarasota St, Venice 34285 Mary Heffner	PK-8		172 18	941/488-2215 Fax 941/480-1565
Incarnation Catholic Sch 2911 Bee Ridge Rd, Sarasota 34239 Coleen Curlett	PK-8		147 14	941/924-8588 Fax 941/925-1248
St Martha Catholic Sch 4380 Fruitville Rd, Sarasota 34232 Siobhan Young	PK-8		433 15	941/953-4181 Fax 941/366-5580

SARASOTA PRIVATE SCHOOLS

Private Schs..Principal	Grd	Prgm	Enr/#Cls SN	
Achievement Center 1201 N Beneva Rd, Sarasota 34232 Nicole Trapani	6-12	G	21 8	941/504-7547
Brickhouse Academy 3552 Webber St, Sarasota 34239 Allison Detra	1-12		45 7	941/924-7681
Calvary Chapel Sch 3800 27th Pkwy, Sarasota 34235 Nicholas Sommer	K-8		120 10	941/366-6522
Classical Academy of Sarasota 8751 Fruitville Rd, Sarasota 34240 Josh Longenecker	PK-12		270	941/925-2153
Community Haven Center 4405 Desoto Rd, Sarasota 34235 Ellicia Parker	Spec		30 5	941/355-8808 Fax 941/359-8520
El-Bethel Apos Tab & Bible Sch 4814 S Chamberlain Blvd, North Port 34286 Andrew Urshan	K-12		150	941/429-2127
Elevation Academy High Sch 582 McIntosh Rd, Sarasota 34232 John Cobb	6-12		40	941/371-0462 Fax 941/371-1750
Good Shepard Lutheran Sch 5651 Honore Ave, Sarasota 34233 Patricia Wiengard	PK-PK		100 9	941/922-8164 Fax 941/927-0926
Hershorin Schiff Comm Day Sch 1050 S Tuttle Ave, Sarasota 34237 Dan Ceaser	PK-8		240 9	941/552-2770 Fax 941/552-2771
Out-of-Door Academy 444 Reid St, Sarasota 34242 Tanna Horner \ Julie Bianchi \ Christopher Chesley	PK-12	G	630 50	941/349-3223 Fax 941/349-8133

School..Principal	Grd	Prgm	Enr/#Cls SN	
Palm Grove Mennonite Sch 1087 Beneva Rd, Sarasota 34232 Randy Miller	K-12		33 3	941/373-0089 Fax 941/957-1710
Prew Academy 5020 Fielding Ln, Sarasota 34233 Mary Eisenbise	6-12		56 7	941/921-7739 Fax 941/922-4799
Providence Community Sch 5600 Deer Dr, Lakewood Rch 34240 Barry Batson \ Cathy Sharek	PK-12		130 10	941/727-6860 Fax 877/766-7269
Sarasota Christian Sch 5415 Bahia Vista St, Sarasota 34232 Christine Bradford \ Mark Martell	PK-12		408 39	941/371-6481 Fax 941/371-0898
Sea of Strengths Academy 7313 International Pl Ste 90, Sarasota 34240 John Hettler	Spec		28	941/538-6822
Shepherd's Hill Christian Sch 3333 12th St, Sarasota 34237 Tom Wilhoit	K-12		30	941/957-3333 Fax 941/957-3300
Venice Christian Sch 1200 Center Rd, Venice 34292 Jerry Frimmel	PK-12		258 16	941/496-4411 Fax 941/408-8362
Westcoast Sch-Human Dev 403 N Washington Blvd, Sarasota 34236 Dr Marvin Hendon	K-12		35 6	941/366-4539

SARASOTA REGIONAL CENTERS

● **FDLRS-Suncoast** PID: 04496126   941/927-9000
1960 Landings Blvd, Sarasota 34231   Fax 941/927-4018

Tracey Cardenas 1   Joe Binswanger 73
Kim Seth 74

SEMINOLE COUNTY

SEMINOLE PUBLIC SCHOOLS

● **Seminole Co Public School Dist** PID: 00203575   407/320-0000
400 E Lake Mary Blvd, Sanford 32773   Fax 407/320-0285

Schools: 68 \ **Teachers:** 5,004 \ **Students:** 68,000 \
Special Ed Students: 9,177 \ **LEP Students:** 3,350 \ **College-Bound:** 85%
\ **Ethnic:** Asian 5%, African American 15%, Hispanic 26%, Caucasian
53% \ **Exp:** $110 (Low) \ **Poverty:** 13% \ **Title I:** $13,953,724 \
Special Education: $45,552,000 \ **Bilingual Education:** $6,556,000 \
Open-Close: 08/12 - 05/27 \ **DTBP:** $182 (High)

Dr Walt Griffin 1	Cheryl Olson 2
Elayne Nichols 2	Mike Gravier 2
Ralph Caravello 2	Todd Seis 2
Trudi Murdock 2	William Kelly 2,19
David Hawk 3	George Criner 3
Jerry Henkins 3	Joe Ranaldi 3
Joy Ford 3	Kevin Wright 3
Kim Dove 3	Richard LeBlanc 3
Robert Little 3	Stacey Strader 3
Auden Joseph 4	Chad Chesley 4
Chad Wilsky 4	Jim McGonagle 4
Julia Tolentino 4	Michael Lombardo 4
Richard Miles 4	Salah Ismail 4

79 Student Personnel	91 Safety/Security	275 Response To Intervention	298 Grant Writer/Ptnrships	**School Programs**	**Social Media**
80 Driver Ed/Safety	92 Magnet School	277 Remedial Math K-12	750 Chief Innovation Officer	A = Alternative Program	
81 Gifted/Talented	93 Parental Involvement	280 Literacy Coach	751 Chief of Staff	G = Adult Classes	f = Facebook
82 Video Services	95 Tech Prep Program	285 STEM	752 Social Emotional Learning	M = Magnet Program	
83 Substance Abuse Prev	97 Chief Infomation Officer	286 Digital Learning		T = Title I Schoolwide	t = Twitter
84 Erate	98 Chief Technology Officer	288 Common Core Standards	**Other School Types**	V = Career & Tech Ed Programs	
85 AIDS Education	270 Character Education	294 Accountability	Ⓐ = Alternative School		
88 Alternative/At Risk	271 Migrant Education	295 Network System	Ⓒ = Charter School	New Schools are shaded	
89 Multi-Cultural Curriculum	273 Teacher Mentor	296 Title II Programs	Ⓜ = Magnet School	New Superintendents and Principals are bold	
90 Social Work	274 Before/After Sch	297 Webmaster	Ⓨ = Year-Round School	Personnel with email addresses are underscored	

FL—131

Public Schs..Principal	Grd	Prgm	Enr/#Cls	SN	
Altamonte Elem Sch 525 Pineview St, Altamonte SPG 32701 Pam Gamble	PK-5	T	712 35	73%	407/746-2950 Fax 407/746-2999
Bear Lake Elem Sch 3399 Gleaves Ct, Apopka 32703 **Kristen Ramkissoon**	PK-5	T	1,080 80	50%	407/746-5550 Fax 407/746-5599
Bentley Elem Sch 2190 S Oregon Ave, Sanford 32771 Martha Garcia	PK-5	T	1,019	60%	407/871-9950 Fax 407/871-9996
Carillon Elem Sch 3200 Lockwood Blvd, Oviedo 32765 Daniel Windish	PK-5		1,000 60	30%	407/320-4650 Fax 407/320-4699
Casselberry Elem Sch 1075 Crystal Bowl Cir, Casselberry 32707 Mallory Holliday	PK-5	T	726 40	67%	407/746-2550 Fax 407/746-2599
© Choices In Learning Chtr Sch 1100 E State Road 434, Winter Spgs 32708 Janet Kearney	K-5		696 13	20%	407/302-1005 Fax 407/542-5553
Ⓜ Crooms Academy of Info Tech 2200 Historic Goldsboro Blvd, Sanford 32771 Brandon Hanshaw	9-12	T	685 9	41%	407/320-5750 Fax 407/320-5798
Crystal Lake Elem Sch 231 Rinehart Rd, Lake Mary 32746 **Rick Carver**	PK-5	T	768	44%	407/871-8150 Fax 407/871-8199
Eastbrook Elem Sch 5525 Tangerine Ave, Winter Park 32792 **Rod Dunaye**	PK-5	T	787	56%	407/746-7950 Fax 407/746-7999
Endeavor Sch 3010 Old Lake Mary Rd, Lake Mary 32746 Paul Harshman	Spec	T	65 25	71%	407/320-3350 Fax 407/320-3379
English Estates Elem Sch 299 Oxford Rd, Fern Park 32730 Shannon Burgessakerson	PK-5	T	791 35	77%	407/746-2850 Fax 407/746-2858
Ⓐ Eugene Gregory Mem Youth Acad 1151 E 28th St, Sanford 32773 Dr Erica Pooler	6-12		29		407/708-7673 Fax 407/708-7674
Evans Elem Sch 100 E Chapman Rd, Oviedo 32765 Carolann Darnell	PK-5		972 50	37%	407/320-9850 Fax 407/320-9899
Forest City Elem Sch 1010 Sand Lake Rd, Altamonte SPG 32714 Paul Senko	PK-5		872 36	67%	407/746-1050 Fax 407/746-1099
© Galileo CS for Gifted Learning 3900 E State Road 46, Sanford 32771 Michelle Nunez	K-6		275	26%	321/249-9221 Fax 407/878-0791
Geneva Elem Sch 275 1st St, Geneva 32732 Rod Dunaye	PK-5	T	590 35	48%	407/320-4950 Fax 407/320-4981
Ⓜ Goldsboro Elem Magnet Sch 1300 W 20th St, Sanford 32771 **Chris Mulholland**	PK-5	T	886	58%	407/320-5850 Fax 407/320-5896
Greenwood Lakes Middle Sch 601 Lake Park Dr, Lake Mary 32746 Breezi Erickson	6-8	T	965 94	58%	407/320-7650 Fax 407/320-7699
Hagerty High Sch 3225 Lockwood Blvd, Oviedo 32765 **Rob Frasca**	9-12		2,417	21%	407/871-0750 Fax 407/871-0749
Hamilton Elem Sch 1501 E 8th St, Sanford 32771 **Michael Pfeiffer**	PK-5	T	717 50	90%	407/320-6050 Fax 407/320-6005
Heathrow Elem Sch 5715 Markham Woods Rd, Lake Mary 32746 **Brett White**	PK-5		847 25	20%	407/320-6850 Fax 407/320-6890
Highlands Elem Sch 1600 Shepard Rd, Winter Spgs 32708 Robert Navarro	PK-5	T	585 52	60%	407/746-6650 Fax 407/746-6700
Hopper Center 612 Newport Ave, Altamonte SPG 32701 Donna Weaver	Spec	T	16 8	83%	407/746-2650 Fax 407/746-2699
Idyllwilde Elem Sch 430 Vihlen Rd, Sanford 32771 Lenore Logsdon	PK-5	T	786 49	82%	407/320-3750 Fax 407/320-3799
Indian Trails Middle Sch 415 Tuskawilla Rd, Winter Spgs 32708 Craig Johnson	6-8	T	1,248 60	39%	407/320-4350 Fax 407/320-4399
Jackson Heights Middle Sch 41 Academy Ave, Oviedo 32765 Sarah Mansur-Blythe	6-8		1,406 65	31%	407/320-4550 Fax 407/320-4599
Ⓐ Journeys Academy 1722 W Airport Blvd, Sanford 32771 Kenneth Bevan	G-12	T	187	71%	407/320 7820 Fax 407/320-7849
Keeth Elem Sch 425 Tuskawilla Rd, Winter Spgs 32708 **Joanne Kramperth**	PK-5		643 50	27%	407/320-5350 Fax 407/320-5399
Lake Brantley High Sch 991 Sand Lake Rd, Altamonte SPG 32714 Trent Daniel	9-12	TV	2,686 110	41%	407/746-3450 Fax 407/746-3600 f
Lake Howell High Sch 4200 Dike Rd, Winter Park 32792 Michael Kotkin	9-12	TV	2,227 100	49%	407/746-9050 Fax 407/746-9025 f
Lake Mary Elem Sch 132 S Country Club Rd, Lake Mary 32746 Christine Peacock	PK-5	T	912 40	51%	407/320-5650 Fax 407/320-5699
Lake Mary High Sch 655 Longwood Lake Mary Rd, Lake Mary 32746 **Mickey Reynolds**	9-12	V	2,914	38%	407/320-9550 Fax 407/320-9512
Lake Orienta Elem Sch 612 Newport Ave, Altamonte SPG 32701 Donna Weaver	PK-5	T	717	72%	407/746-2650 Fax 407/746-2699
Lawton Chiles Middle Sch 1240 Sanctuary Dr, Oviedo 32766 John Antmann	6-8		1,321 57	24%	407/871-7050 Fax 407/871-7099
Lawton Elem Sch 151 Graham Ave, Oviedo 32765 Leslie Durias	PK-5		838 45	25%	407/320-6350 Fax 407/320-6399
Layer Elem Sch 4201 State Road 419, Winter Spgs 32708 Cheryl Nicholas	PK-5	T	522	63%	407/871-8050 Fax 407/871-8099
Longwood Elem Sch 840 Orange Ave, Longwood 32750 Brian Emmans	PK-5		593		407/746-5250
Lyman High Sch 865 S Ronald Reagan Blvd, Longwood 32750 Mike Rice	9-12	TV	2,341	49%	407/746-2050 Fax 407/746-2024

1	Superintendent	8	Curric/Instruct K-12	19	Chief Financial Officer	29	Family/Consumer Science
2	Bus/Finance/Purchasing	9	Curric/Instruct Elem	20	Art K-12	30	Adult Education
3	Buildings And Grounds	10	Curric/Instruct Sec	21	Art Elem	31	Career/Sch-to-Work K-12
4	Food Service	11	Federal Program	22	Art Sec	32	Career/Sch-to-Work Elem
5	Transportation	12	Title I	23	Music K-12	33	Career/Sch-to-Work Sec
6	Athletic	13	Title V	24	Music Elem	34	Early Childhood Ed
7	Health Services	14	Asst Superintendent	25	Music Sec	35	Health/Phys Education
		15	Instructional Media Svcs	26	Business Education	36	Guidance Services K-12
		16	Chief Operations Officer	27	Career & Tech Ed	37	Guidance Services Elem
		17	Chief Academic Officer	28	Technology Education	38	Guidance Services Sec

39	Social Studies K-12	49	English/Lang Arts Elem	59	Special Education Elem	69	Academic Assessment
40	Social Studies Elem	50	English/Lang Arts Sec	60	Special Education Sec	70	Research/Development
41	Social Studies Sec	51	Reading K-12	61	Foreign/World Lang K-12	71	Public Information
42	Science K-12	52	Reading Elem	62	Foreign/World Lang Elem	72	Summer School
43	Science Elem	53	Reading Sec	63	Foreign/World Lang Sec	73	Instructional Tech
44	Science Sec	54	Remedial Reading K-12	64	Religious Education K-12	74	Inservice Training
45	Math K-12	55	Remedial Reading Elem	65	Religious Education Elem	75	Marketing/Distributive
46	Math Elem	56	Remedial Reading Sec	66	Religious Education Sec	76	Info Systems
47	Math Sec	57	Bilingual/ELL	67	School Board President	77	Psychological Assess
48	English/Lang Arts K-12	58	Special Education K-12	68	Teacher Personnel	78	Affirmative Action

School..Principal	Grd	Prgm	Enr/#Cls	SN	Phone/Fax
Markham Woods Middle Sch 6003 Markham Woods Rd, Lake Mary 32746 Linda Mumey	6-8	T	1,120	43%	407/871-1750 Fax 407/871-1799
Midway Elem Sch of Arts 2368 Brisson Ave, Sanford 32771 Cathy Lambert	PK-5	T	906 24	84%	407/320-5950 Fax 407/320-5961
Millennium Middle Sch 2330 E Sr 46, Sanford 32773 Dr Maggie Gunderson	6-8	T	1,544 50	64%	407/320-6550 Fax 407/320-6599
Milwee Middle Sch 1341 S Ronald Reagan Blvd, Longwood 32750 James Kubis	6-8	T	1,465	59%	407/746-3850 Fax 407/746-3899
Oviedo High Sch 601 King St, Oviedo 32765 Joe Trybus	9-12	V	2,468 124	34%	407/320-4050 Fax 407/320-4000
Partin Elem Sch 1500 Twin Rivers Blvd, Oviedo 32766 Nancy Urban	PK-5		714 47	21%	407/320-4850 Fax 407/320-4899
Pinecrest Elem Sch 405 W 27th St, Sanford 32773 Alexis Agosto	PK-5	T	722 40	91%	407/320-5450 Fax 407/320-5499
Rainbow Elem Sch 1412 Rainbow Trl, Winter Spgs 32708 Mrs Marshall	PK-5		778 47	35%	407/320-8450 Fax 407/320-8499
Red Bug Elem Sch 4000 Red Bug Lake Rd, Casselberry 32707 Christine Sharpe	PK-5	T	853 33	46%	407/746-8350 Fax 407/746-8399
Rock Lake Middle Sch 250 Slade Dr, Longwood 32750 Martin Dunlop	6-8		943 60	36%	407/746-9350 Fax 407/746-9399
Sabal Point Elem Sch 960 Wekiva Springs Rd, Longwood 32779 Christina Langdon	PK-5		917	33%	407/746-3050 Fax 407/746-3098
Sanford Middle Magnet Sch 1700 S French Ave, Sanford 32771 Byron Durias	6-8	T	1,526 75	45%	407/320-6150 Fax 407/320-6265
Scps Early Learning Center 1101 S Bay Ave, Sanford 32771 Carla Bettts	PK-PK		78	92%	407/320-3940
Seminole Co Virtual Sch 450 Technology Park, Lake Mary 32746 Dr Deborah Camillieri	6-12		82		407/871-7287 Fax 407/871-7299
Seminole High Sch 2701 Ridgewood Ave, Sanford 32773 Jordan Rodriguez	9-12	TV	3,189 115	49%	407/320-5050 Fax 407/320-5024
Seminole Science Charter Sch 3580 N US Highway 17/92, Lake Mary 32746 Yunus Aksu	K-5		381	28%	407/268-3727 Fax 407/268-3729
South Seminole Middle Sch 101 S Winter Park Dr, Casselberry 32707 Dr Mia Coleman-Baker	6-8	T	1,155 70	65%	407/746-1350 Fax 407/746-1420
Spring Lake Elem Sch 695 Orange Ave, Altamonte SPG 32714 Kelly Mitchell	PK-5	T	705	79%	407/746-1650 Fax 407/746-1695
Stenstrom Elem Sch 1800 Alafaya Woods Blvd, Oviedo 32765 Janet Garzia	PK-5	T	690 55	41%	407/320-2450 Fax 407/320-2488
Sterling Park Elem Sch 905 Eagle Cir S, Casselberry 32707 Dumarie Dillard	PK-5	T	827 54	53%	407/746-8250 Fax 407/746-8299
Teague Middle Sch 1350 McNeil Rd, Altamonte SPG 32714 Debra Abbott	6-8	T	1,387 80	54%	407/320-1550 Fax 407/320-1545
Tuskawilla Middle Sch 1801 Tuskawilla Rd, Oviedo 32765 Randy Shuler	6-8	T	1,091 60	52%	407/746-8550 Fax 407/746-8599
© UCP Seminole Child Dev Ctr 756 N Sun Dr, Lake Mary 32746 Marife Gomez	Spec	T	69 6	51%	407/852-3300 Fax 407/322-5596
Walker Elem Sch 3101 Snow Hill Rd, Chuluota 32766 Debbie Jose	PK-5		764	20%	407/871-7350 Fax 407/871-7399
Wekiva Elem Sch 1450 E Wekiva Trl, Longwood 32779 Keaton Schreiner	PK-5		830	32%	407/746-3150 Fax 407/746-3163
Wicklow Elem Sch 100 Placid Lake Dr, Sanford 32773 Martina Herndon	PK-5	T	754 55	82%	407/320-1250 Fax 407/320-1215
Wilson Elem Sch 985 Orange Blvd, Sanford 32771 Ryan Gard-Harrold	PK-5		985	26%	407/320-6950 Fax 407/320-6999
Winter Springs Elem Sch 701 W State Road 434, Winter Spgs 32708 Amy Barone	PK-5	T	628	73%	407/320-0650 Fax 407/320-0600
Winter Springs High Sch 130 Tuskawilla Rd, Winter Spgs 32708 Peter Gaffney	9-12	TV	2,037 160	50%	407/320-8750 Fax 407/320-8700
Woodlands Elem Sch 1420 EE Williamson Rd, Longwood 32750 Patricia May	PK-5		762 47	31%	407/746-2750 Fax 407/746-2799

SEMINOLE CATHOLIC SCHOOLS

• **Diocese of Orlando Ed Office** PID: 00197639
Listing includes only schools located in this county. See District Index for location of Diocesan Offices.

Catholic Schs..Principal	Grd	Prgm	Enr/#Cls	SN	Phone/Fax
All Souls Catholic Sch 810 S Oak Ave, Sanford 32771 Barbara Schirard	PK-8		237 13		407/322-7090 Fax 407/321-7255
Annunciation Catholic Academy 593 Jamestown Blvd, Altamonte SPG 32714 Patty Kahle	K-8		500 22		407/774-2801 Fax 407/774-2826
St Mary Magdalen Sch 869 Maitland Ave, Altamonte SPG 32701 Lorianne Rotz	PK-8		600		407/339-7301 Fax 407/339-9556

SEMINOLE PRIVATE SCHOOLS

Private Schs..Principal	Grd	Prgm	Enr/#Cls	SN	Phone/Fax
Altamonte Christian Sch 601 Palm Springs Dr, Altamonte SPG 32701 Dr Sharon Nix	K-12		270 18		407/831-0950 Fax 407/831-6840
Alternative Choices Edu Acad 215 Ridgewood St, Altamonte SPG 32701 Lloyd Reynolds	K-12		80		407/339-6632
Double R Private Sch 725 Country School Rd, Chuluota 32766 Trudie Fluharty	K-8		160 9		407/365-6856 Fax 407/365-0543
Forest Lake Education Center 1275 Learning Loop, Longwood 32779 Chris Juhl	PK-8		627 28		407/862-7688 Fax 407/774-7723
Holy Cross Lutheran Academy 5450 Holy Cross Ct, Sanford 32771 Rob Sinninger \ Shirley Geiss	PK-12		480		407/936-3636 Fax 407/936-0041

79	Student Personnel	91	Safety/Security	275	Response To Intervention	298	Grant Writer/Ptnrships	**School Programs**		**Social Media**
30	Driver Ed/Safety	92	Magnet School	277	Remedial Math K-12	750	Chief Innovation Officer	A = Alternative Program		
31	Gifted/Talented	93	Parental Involvement	280	Literacy Coach	751	Chief of Staff	G = Adult Classes	= Facebook
32	Video Services	95	Tech Prep Program	285	STEM	752	Social Emotional Learning	M = Magnet Program	
35	Substance Abuse Prev	97	Chief Information Officer	286	Digital Learning			T = Title I Schoolwide	= Twitter
34	Erate	98	Chief Technology Officer	288	Common Core Standards	**Other School Types**		V = Career & Tech Ed Programs	
35	AIDS Education	270	Character Education	294	Accountability	Ⓐ = Alternative School			
38	Alternative/At Risk	271	Migrant Education	295	Network System	Ⓒ = Charter School		New Schools are shaded	
39	Multi-Cultural Curriculum	273	Teacher Mentor	296	Title II Programs	Ⓜ = Magnet School		New Superintendents and Principals are bold	
30	Social Work	274	Before/After Sch	297	Webmaster	Ⓨ = Year-Round School		Personnel with email addresses are underscored	

Lake Mary Preparatory Sch 650 Rantoul Ln, Lake Mary 32746 Lynna Varitek \ Amy Petrousky \ Preston Emerton	PK-12	650	407/805-0095 Fax 407/322-3872 🅵🅣
Liberty Christian Sch 2626 S Palmetto Ave, Sanford 32773 Bill Simpson	PK-12	180 12	407/323-1583 Fax 407/323-1588
Lifeskills Academy of Orlando 1010 Spring Villas Pt, Winter Spgs 32708 Wendy Cox-Blair	Spec	82	407/388-1808 Fax 407/636-6915
Master's Academy 1530 Lukas Ln, Oviedo 32765 Brian Urichko \ Dr Dana Dionne	PK-12	746	407/706-2221 Fax 407/706-1373
One School of the Arts 1675 Dixon Rd, Longwood 32779 William Seidel	PK-12	400 18	407/774-0168 Fax 407/774-9778 🅵
Pace-Brantley Sch 3221 Sand Lake Rd, Longwood 32779 Jennifer Foor	Spec	160 22	407/869-8882 Fax 407/869-8717
Riverwalk Christian Academy 801 W 22nd St, Sanford 32771 Darlene Clark	PK-1	112 8	407/321-2723 Fax 407/322-7627
St Luke's Lutheran Sch 2025 W State Road 426, Oviedo 32765 Greg Register	PK-8	775 28	407/365-3228 Fax 407/366-9346
Sweetwater Episcopal Academy 251 E Lake Brantley Dr, Longwood 32779 Cynthia Lane	PK-8	200 15	407/862-1882 Fax 407/788-1714 🅵
Tuskawilla Montessori Academy 1625 Montessori Pt, Oviedo 32765 Dr Thomas Phillips	PK-8	200 11	407/678-3879 Fax 407/678-3987

ST JOHNS COUNTY

ST JOHNS PUBLIC SCHOOLS

● **St Johns Co School Dist** PID: 00202363　　904/547-7500
40 Orange St, St Augustine 32084　　Fax 904/547-7523

Schools: 44 \ *Teachers:* 2,744 \ *Students:* 42,222 \
Special Ed Students: 5,903 \ *LEP Students:* 268 \ *College-Bound:* 62%
\ *Ethnic:* Asian 4%, African American 7%, Hispanic 9%, Caucasian
80% \ *Exp:* $174 (Low) \ *Poverty:* 7% \ *Title I:* $3,571,180 \
Special Education: $20,503,000 \ *Bilingual Education:* $386,000 \
Open-Close: 08/12 - 05/27 \ *DTBP:* $175 (High)

Public Schs..Principal	Grd	Prgm	Enr/#Cls	SN
Alice B Landrum Middle Sch 230 Landrum Ln, Ponte Vedra 32082 Ryan Player	6-8	V	1,230 50	10% 904/547-8410 Fax 904/547-8415
Allen D Nease High Sch 10550 Ray Rd, Ponte Vedra 32081 Felessia Kunze	9-12	V	2,628 50	15% 904/547-8300 Fax 904/547-8305
Bartram Trail High Sch 7399 Longleaf Pine Pkwy, Saint Johns 32259 Christopher Phelps	9-12	V	2,666 80	9% 904/547-8340 Fax 904/547-8359
Creekside High Sch 100 Knights Ln, Saint Johns 32259 Stephen McCormick	9-12		2,269	9% 904/547-7300
Cunningham Creek Elem Sch 1205 Roberts Rd, Saint Johns 32259 Edie Jarrell	PK-5		585 65	12% 904/547-7860 Fax 904/547-7854
Durbin Creek Elem Sch 4100 Race Track Rd, Saint Johns 32259 Angie Fuller	PK-5		808	12% 904/547-3880 Fax 904/547-3885
Freedom Crossing Academy 1365 Shetland Dr, Saint Johns 32259 Allen Anderson	K-8		1,016	904/547-4230
Fruit Cove Middle Sch 3180 Race Track Rd, Saint Johns 32259 Kelly Jacobson	6-8		1,276 40	13% 904/547-7880 Fax 904/547-7885
Ⓐ Gaines Alt Ctr-Hamblen 1 Christopher St, St Augustine 32084 Patricia McMahon	6-12	T	38 9	37% 904/547-8560 Fax 904/547-7145
Gamble Rogers Middle Sch 6250 US Highway 1 S, St Augustine 32086 Greg Bergamasco	6-8	T	915 38	43% 904/547-8700 Fax 904/547-8705
Hickory Creek Elem Sch 235 Hickory Creek Trl, Saint Johns 32259 Dr Joy Reichenberg	K-5		713	13% 904/547-7450 Fax 904/547-7455
John A Crookshank Elem Sch 1455 N Whitney St, St Augustine 32084 Mr Jackson	PK-5	T	812 37	65% 904/547-7840 Fax 904/547-7845
Julington Creek Elem Sch 2316 Race Track Rd, Saint Johns 32259 Jeanette Murphy	K-5		965 31	15% 904/547-7980 Fax 904/547-7985
Ketterlinus Elem Sch 67 Orange St, St Augustine 32084 Kathlene Tucker	PK-5	T	427 24	42% 904/547-8540 Fax 904/547-8554
Liberty Pines Academy 10901 Russell Sampson Rd, Saint Johns 32259 Traci Hemingway	K-8		1,592	13% 904/547-7900 Fax 904/547-7905
Mill Creek Academy 3750 International Golf Pkwy, St Augustine 32092 Amanda Riedl	K-8		788 37	22% 904/547-3720 Fax 904/547-3730
Ocean Palms Elem Sch 355 Landrum Ln, Ponte Vedra 32082 Tiffany Cantwell	PK-5		531 27	8% 904/547-3760 Fax 904/819-3775
Osceola Elem Sch 1605 Osceola Elementary Rd, St Augustine 32084 Tina Waldrop	PK-5	T	759 35	69% 904/547-3780 Fax 904/547-3795

1	Superintendent	8	Curric/Instruct K-12	19	Chief Financial Officer	29	Family/Consumer Science	39	Social Studies K-12
2	Bus/Finance/Purchasing	9	Curric/Instruct Elem	20	Art K-12	30	Adult Education	40	Social Studies Elem
3	Buildings And Grounds	10	Curric/Instruct Sec	21	Art Elem	31	Career/Sch-to-Work K-12	41	Social Studies Sec
4	Food Service	11	Federal Program	22	Art Sec	32	Career/Sch-to-Work Elem	42	Science K-12
5	Transportation	12	Title I	23	Music K-12	33	Career/Sch-to-Work Sec	43	Science Elem
6	Athletic	13	Title V	24	Music Elem	34	Early Childhood Ed	44	Science Sec
7	Health Services	15	Asst Superintendent	25	Music Sec	35	Health/Phys Education	45	Math K-12
		16	Instructional Media Svcs	26	Business Education	36	Guidance Services K-12	46	Math Elem
		17	Chief Operations Officer	27	Career & Tech Ed	37	Guidance Services Elem	47	Math Sec
		18	Chief Academic Officer	28	Technology Education	38	Guidance Services Sec	48	English/Lang Arts K-12

49	English/Lang Arts Elem	59	Special Education Elem	69	Academic Assessment
50	English/Lang Arts Sec	60	Special Education Sec	70	Research/Development
51	Reading K-12	61	Foreign/World Lang K-12	71	Public Information
52	Reading Elem	62	Foreign/World Lang Elem	72	Summer School
53	Reading Sec	63	Foreign/World Lang Sec	73	Instructional Tech
54	Remedial Reading K-12	64	Religious Education K-12	74	Inservice Training
55	Remedial Reading Elem	65	Religious Education Elem	75	Marketing/Distributive
56	Remedial Reading Sec	66	Religious Education Sec	76	Info Systems
57	Bilingual/ELL	67	School Board President	77	Psychological Assess
58	Special Education K-12	68	Teacher Personnel	78	Affirmative Action

School	Grd	Prgm	Enr/#Cls	SN	Phone
Otis A Mason Elem Sch 207 Mason Manatee Way, St Augustine 32086 Nigel Pillay	PK-5	T	666 42	47%	904/547-8440 Fax 904/547-8445
Pacetti Bay Middle Sch 245 Meadowlark Ln, St Augustine 32092 Jay Willets	6-8		1,472	18%	904/547-8760 Fax 904/547-8775
Palencia Elem Sch 355 Palencia Village Dr, St Augustine 32095 **Catherine Goodrich**	K-5		841	20%	904/547-4010 Fax 904/547-4015
Palm Valley Academy 700 Bobcat Ln, Ponte Vedra 32081 Jessica Richardson	K-8		1,292		904/547-4201
Patriot Oaks Academy 475 Longleaf Pine Pkwy, Saint Johns 32259 Allison Olson	K-8		1,443	5%	904/547-4050 Fax 904/547-4055
Pedro Menendez High Sch 600 State Road 206 W, St Augustine 32086 Patrick Carmichael	9-12	TV	1,326 65	39%	904/547-8660 Fax 904/547-8675
Picolata Crossing Elem Sch 2675 Pacetti Rd, St Augustine 32092 Kenneth Goodwin	PK-5		691		904/547-4160
Ponte Vedra High Sch 460 Davis Park Rd, Ponte Vedra 32081 Fredrik Oberkehr	9-12		1,816	8%	904/547-7350 Fax 904/547-7355
Pvpv/Rawlings Elem Sch 610 A1A N, Ponte Vedra 32082 **Dr Gates**	K-5		1,020 59		904/547-3820 Fax 904/547-3825
R B Hunt Elem Sch 125 Magnolia Dr, St Augustine 32080 Amanda Garman	K-5		638 34	29%	904/547-7960 Fax 904/547-7955
R J Murray Middle Sch 150 N Holmes Blvd, St Augustine 32084 **Paula Steele**	6-8	T	765 35	51%	904/547-8470 Fax 904/547-8475
Sebastian Middle Sch 2955 Lewis Speedway, St Augustine 32084 **Kirstie Gabaldon**	6-8	TV	727 48	46%	904/547-3840 Fax 904/547-3845
South Woods Elem Sch 4750 State Road 206 W, Elkton 32033 Randy Kelley	PK-5	T	675 17	77%	904/547-8610 Fax 904/547-8615
St Augustine High Sch 3205 Varella Ave, St Augustine 32084 DeArmas Graham	9-12	TV	1,767	42%	904/547-8530 Fax 904/547-8535
Ⓒ St Augustine Pub Mont ES 7 Williams St, St Augustine 32084 Judi Dunlap	1-6		121		904/342-5350 Fax 904/342-5354
St John's Virtual Sch 2980 Collins Ave Bldg 1, St Augustine 32084 Cynthia Williams	K-12		1,238	3%	904/547-8080 Fax 904/547-8085
Ⓒ St Johns Cmty Campus 62 Cuna St, St Augustine 32084 Lynne Funcheon	Spec		33	10%	904/209-6842
Ⓒ St Johns Technical High Sch 2970 Collins Ave, St Augustine 32084 **Ms Force**	Voc	G	1,250 70		904/547-8500 Fax 904/547-8505
Switzerland Point Middle Sch 777 Greenbriar Rd, Saint Johns 32259 **Ms Brunet**	6-8	V	1,313 48	11%	904/547-8650 Fax 904/547-8635
Ⓒ Therapeutic Learning Center 2109 Arc Dr, St Augustine 32084 Paulette Hudson	Spec		20 2	21%	904/824-8932 **f**
Timberlin Creek Elem Sch 555 Pine Tree Ln, St Augustine 32092 Linda Edel	PK-5		995 49	10%	904/547-7400 Fax 904/547-7405
Ⓐ Transition School at Hamblen 1 Christopher St, St Augustine 32084 Patricia McMahon	PK-12		32		904/547-8560
Valley Ridge Academy 105 Greenleaf Dr, Ponte Vedra 32081 **Sandra McMandon**	K-8		1,406	10%	904/547-4090 Fax 904/547-4095
W Douglas Hartley Elem Sch 260 Cacique Dr, St Augustine 32086 Paul Goricki	K-5	T	628 34	40%	904/547-8400 Fax 904/547-8385
Wards Creek Elem Sch 6555 State Road 16, St Augustine 32092 Bethany Mitidieri	PK-5		718	23%	904/547-8730 Fax 904/547-8735
Webster Sch 420 N Orange St, St Augustine 32084 Bethany Groves	PK-5	T	542 65	72%	904/547-3860 Fax 904/547-3865

ST JOHNS CATHOLIC SCHOOLS

- **Diocese St Augustine Ed Office** PID: 00202533
  Listing includes only schools located in this county. See District Index for location of Diocesan Offices.

Catholic Schs..Principal	Grd	Prgm	Enr/#Cls	SN	Phone
Cathedral Parish Early Ed Ctr 10 Sebastian Ave, St Augustine 32084 Jill Valley	PK-PK		85 5		904/829-2933 Fax 904/829-9339
Cathedral Parish Sch 259 Saint George St, St Augustine 32084 Kathy Boice	PK-8		270 18		904/824-2861 Fax 904/829-2059
Palmer Catholic Academy 4889 Palm Valley Rd, Ponte Vedra 32082 Linda Earp	PK-8		450 18		904/543-8515 Fax 904/543-8750
San Juan Del Rio Catholic Sch 1714 State Road 13, Saint Johns 32259 Michael Masi	PK-8		460 10		904/287-8081 Fax 904/287-4574
St Joseph Academy 155 State Road 207, St Augustine 32084 Todd Declemente	9-12		325 23		904/824-0431 Fax 904/826-4477

ST JOHNS PRIVATE SCHOOLS

Private Schs..Principal	Grd	Prgm	Enr/#Cls	SN	Phone
Beacon of Hope Chrn Sch 1230 Kings Estate Rd, St Augustine 32086 Lavoy Newton	K-12		65		904/797-6996 Fax 904/797-6997
Bolles School-Ponte Vedra 200 Atp Tour Blvd, Ponte Vedra 32082 Tyler Hodges	PK-5		216 13		904/285-4658 Fax 904/285-1423
Island Prep Primary Sch 4171 A1A S Ste 2, St Augustine 32080 K Batzel	PK-2		92		904/547-2996
Memorial Lutheran Chapel Sch 3375 US Highway 1 S, St Augustine 32086	PK-PK		40		904/797-8777
Pioneer Sch 105 Masters Dr, St Augustine 32084 Cristina Pope	6-9		15		904/209-5891
St John's Academy 1533 Wildwood Dr, St Augustine 32086 Wallis Brooks	PK-8		118 11		904/824-9224 Fax 904/823-1145
Turning Point Christian Acad 3500 State Road 16, St Augustine 32092 Lynne Gregory	PK-8		425		904/824-0744 Fax 904/829-3555

79 Student Personnel	91 Safety/Security	275 Response To Intervention	298 Grant Writer/Ptnrships	**School Programs**
30 Driver Ed/Safety	92 Magnet School	277 Remedial Math K-12	750 Chief Innovation Officer	A = Alternative Program
31 Gifted/Talented	93 Parental Involvement	280 Literacy Coach	751 Chief of Staff	G = Adult Classes
32 Video Services	95 Tech Prep Program	285 STEM	752 Social Emotional Learning	M = Magnet Program
33 Substance Abuse Prev	97 Chief Infomation Officer	286 Digital Learning		T = Title I Schoolwide
34 Erate	98 Chief Technology Officer	288 Common Core Standards	**Other School Types**	V = Career & Tech Ed Programs
35 AIDS Education	270 Character Education	294 Accountability	Ⓐ = Alternative School	
38 Alternative/At Risk	271 Migrant Education	295 Network System	Ⓒ = Charter School	
39 Multi-Cultural Curriculum	273 Teacher Mentor	296 Title II Programs	Ⓜ = Magnet School	
30 Social Work	274 Before/After Sch	297 Webmaster	Ⓨ = Year-Round School	Personnel with email addresses are underscored

Social Media

f = Facebook

t = Twitter

New Schools are shaded
New Superintendents and Principals are bold

´Victory Preparatory Sch 110 Masters Dr, St Augustine 32084 Michelle Mauro	K-12		95		904/810-0535
Washington Classical Chrn Sch 2121 US Highway 1 S Ste 28, St Augustine 32086 Kimberly Evans	K-7		401		904/323-2911 Fax 904/797-6363

ST LUCIE COUNTY

ST LUCIE PUBLIC SCHOOLS

● **St Lucie Co School Dist** PID: 00202844   772/429-3600
501 NW University Blvd, Port St Lucie 34986   Fax 772/429-3916

> **Schools:** 45 \ **Teachers:** 2,409 \ **Students:** 44,210 \
> **Special Ed Students:** 4,843 \ **LEP Students:** 3,588 \ **College-Bound:** 92%
> \ **Ethnic:** Asian 2%, African American 31%, Hispanic 31%, Caucasian
> 36% \ **Exp:** $153 (Low) \ **Poverty:** 17% \ **Title I:** $12,413,577 \
> **Special Education:** $30,027,000 \ **Bilingual Education:** $6,542,000 \
> **Open-Close:** 08/12 - 06/02 \ **DTBP:** $196 (High) \ 🇹

Wayne Gent	1	Kim Albritton	2
Michelle Thomas	2,19	John Gilette	3
Terence O'Leary	3,5,17,71,73,76	Deborah Wuest	4
Don Carter	5	Jill Willette	6*
Latanya Greene	7,77	Dr Helen Wild	8,11,18,57,271
Kimberly Jay	9	Megan Green	10
Dr Jonathan Prince	15,69,91,294	Craig Jerome	16
Kerry Padrick	16,71,75	Aliesha Seitz	27,31
Dr Mary Huffstetter	34	Kate Ems	39
Beth Bonnie	42	Christina Worley	46
Heather Knab	49	Kimberly Coopea	50
Bill Tomlinson	58,79,83,88	Dawna Guiel	58
Debbie Hawley	67	Dr Rafael Sanchez	68
Darrell Canamas	69,294	Dr Kathleen McGinn	70
Heather Clark	79	Brian Reuther	91
Mandy Rowland	280,296	Kelly Lunt	285
Julie Kittrell	295	Jennifer Chevalier	298

Public Schs..Principal	Grd	Prgm	Enr/#Cls	SN	
Allapattah Flats Sch 12051 NW Copper Creek Dr, Port St Lucie 34987 Ana Oronoz	PK-8	T	1,044	74%	772/468-5050 Fax 772/468-5013
Bayshore Elem Sch 1661 SW Bayshore Blvd, Port St Lucie 34984 Jacqueline Lynch	PK-5	T	633 45	72%	772/340-4720 Fax 772/340-4726
Chester A Moore Elem Sch 827 N 29th St, Fort Pierce 34947 Ucola Barrett-Baxter	PK-5	T	643 32	92%	772/468-5315 Fax 772/468-5896
Ⓜ Creative Arts Acad of St Lucie 1100 Delaware Ave, Fort Pierce 34950 **Dr Lori Anne Reid**	K-8	T	329 12	71%	772/467-4278 Fax 772/247-4277
Dale Cassens Ed Complex 1905 S 11th St, Fort Pierce 34950 Ellen Harden	Spec	AT	199 17	75%	772/468-5190 Fax 772/468-5198
Dan McCarty Middle Sch 1201 Mississippi Ave, Fort Pierce 34950 Lisa Sullivan	6-8	TV	853 40	77%	772/468-5700 Fax 772/468-5737 🇹
Ⓜ Fairlawn Elem Sch 3203 Rhode Island Ave, Fort Pierce 34947 **Heather Ricksecker**	K-5	T	618 35	57%	772/468-5345 Fax 772/468-5377

Floresta Elem Sch 1501 SE Floresta Dr, Port St Lucie 34983 Marcy Luckey	K-5	T	630 35	73%	772/340-4755 Fax 772/340-4756
Forest Grove Middle Sch 3201 S 25th St, Fort Pierce 34981 **Dr Arthur Jamison**	6-8	T	870 68	68%	772/468-5885 Fax 772/595-1187
Ⓜ Frances K Sweet Elem Sch 1400 Avenue Q, Fort Pierce 34950 D'Jion Jackson-Harris	K-5	T	600 34	70%	772/468-5330 Fax 772/468-5334
Ft Pierce Central High Sch 4101 S 25th St, Fort Pierce 34981 **Monarae Buchanon**	9-12	ATV	2,602	63%	772/468-5888 Fax 772/468-5761
Ft Pierce Westwood Academy 1801 Panther Ln, Fort Pierce 34947 Joseph Lezeau	9-12	ATV	1,769 88	65%	772/468-5400 Fax 772/468-5465
Lakewood Park Elem Sch 7800 Indrio Rd, Fort Pierce 34951 **Kerri Walukiewicz**	PK-5	T	732 36	75%	772/468-5830 Fax 772/468-5833
Lawnwood Elem Sch 1900 S 23rd St, Fort Pierce 34950 Jennifer Ingersoll	PK-5	T	710 32	81%	772/468-5740 Fax 772/468-5204
Ⓜ Lincoln Park Academy 1806 Avenue I, Fort Pierce 34950 Henry Sanabria	6-12	TV	1,725 82	45%	772/468-5474 Fax 772/468-5824
Manatee K-8 Sch 1450 SW Heatherwood Blvd, Port St Lucie 34986 Lillian Beauchamp	K-8	T	1,354 47	64%	772/340-4745 Fax 772/340-4775
Mariposa Elem Sch 2620 SE Mariposa Ave, Port St Lucie 34952 R Logue	PK-5	T	665 43	74%	772/337-5960 Fax 772/337-5976
Morningside Elem Sch 2300 SE Gowin Dr, Port St Lucie 34952 Kathleen Melrose	K-5	T	581 40	64%	772/337-6730 Fax 772/337-6744
Ⓐ Mosaic Digital Academy 12051 NW Copper Creek Dr, Fort Pierce 34947 Jean Zimba	K-12		31		772/429-5504 Fax 772/429-3978
Northport K-8 Sch 250 NW Floresta Dr, Port St Lucie 34983 Glenn Rustay	PK-8	TV	1,171 62	66%	772/340-4700 Fax 772/340-4716
Oak Hammock K-8 Sch 1251 SW California Blvd, Port St Lucie 34953 **Patricia Galloway**	K-8	T	1,460	64%	772/344-4490 Fax 772/204-7211 🇹
Ⓐ Pace Ctr for Girls-Treasure 3651 Virginia Ave, Fort Pierce 34981 **Vickie Colter**	6-12		47	47%	772/595-8880 Fax 772/595-8980
© Palm PT Educ Research Sch 10680 SW Academic Way, Port St Lucie 34987 Kathleen Perez	K-8	T	1,450	49%	772/345-3245 Fax 772/345-3244
Parkway Elem Sch 7000 NW Selvitz Rd, Port St Lucie 34983 Carolyn Wilkins	PK-5	T	533 35	68%	772/340-4800 Fax 772/340-4807
Performance Based Prep Academy 2909 Delaware Ave, Fort Pierce 34947 **Susan Seal**	9-12		114	65%	772/468-5880 Fax 772/468-5795
Port St Lucie High Sch 1201 SE Jaguar Ln, Port St Lucie 34952 **Brooke Wigginton**	9-12	TV	1,754 120	62%	772/337-6770 Fax 772/337-6780
© Renaissance CS at St Lucie [133] 300 NW Cashmere Blvd, Port St Lucie 34986 Christiana Coburn	K-8	T	1,290	61%	772/344-5982 Fax 772/344-5985
© Renaissance CS-Tradition [133] 10900 SW Tradition Pkwy, Port St Lucie 34987 **Amanda Wilson**	K-8	T	1,145	44%	772/236-2180 Fax 772/236-2181
River's Edge Elem Sch 5600 NE Saint James Dr, Port St Lucie 34983 **Mrs Ingersoll**	K-5	T	631 45	69%	772/785-5600 Fax 772/785-5625

1	Superintendent	8	Curric/Instruct K-12	19	Chief Financial Officer	29	Family/Consumer Science
2	Bus/Finance/Purchasing	9	Curric/Instruct Elem	20	Art K-12	30	Adult Education
3	Buildings And Grounds	10	Curric/Instruct Sec	21	Art Elem	31	Career/Sch-to-Work K-12
4	Food Service	11	Federal Program	22	Art Sec	32	Career/Sch-to-Work Elem
5	Transportation	12	Title I	23	Music K-12	33	Career/Sch-to-Work Sec
6	Athletic	13	Title V	24	Music Elem	34	Early Childhood Ed
7	Health Services	14	Asst Superintendent	25	Music Sec	35	Health/Phys Education
		15	Instructional Media Svcs	26	Business Education	36	Guidance Services K-12
		16	Chief Operations Officer	27	Career & Tech Ed	37	Guidance Services Elem
		17	Chief Academic Officer	28	Technology Education	38	Guidance Services Sec

39	Social Studies K-12	49	English/Lang Arts Elem	59	Special Education Elem	69	Academic Assessment
40	Social Studies Elem	50	English/Lang Arts Sec	60	Special Education Sec	70	Research/Development
41	Social Studies Sec	51	Reading K-12	61	Foreign/World Lang K-12	71	Public Information
42	Science K-12	52	Reading Elem	62	Foreign/World Lang Elem	72	Summer School
43	Science Elem	53	Reading Sec	63	Foreign/World Lang Sec	73	Instructional Tech
44	Science Sec	54	Remedial Reading K-12	64	Religious Education K-12	74	Inservice Training
45	Math K-12	55	Remedial Reading Elem	65	Religious Education Elem	75	Marketing/Distributive
46	Math Elem	56	Remedial Reading Sec	66	Religious Education Sec	76	Info Systems
47	Math Sec	57	Bilingual/ELL	67	School Board President	77	Psychological Assess
48	English/Lang Arts K-12	58	Special Education K-12	68	Teacher Personnel	78	Affirmative Action

School / Address / Principal	Grd	Prgm	Enr/#Cls	SN	Phone
Samuel S Gaines Academy 2250 S Jenkins Rd, Fort Pierce 34947 Keith Davis	K-8	T	1,052	80%	772/462-8888 Fax 772/468-5004
Savanna Ridge Elem Sch 6801 SE Lennard Rd, Port St Lucie 34952 Roberto Bonsenor	PK-5	T	559 30	67%	772/460-3050 Fax 772/460-3003
© Somerset Academy St Lucie [130] 4402 SW Yamada Dr, Port St Lucie 34953 Joann Roach	K-5		468		772/281-2300
© Somerset College Prep Acad [130] 725 NW California Blvd, Port St Lucie 34986 Erika Rains	9-12		357		772/343-7028 Fax 772/343-7029
Southern Oaks Middle Sch 5500 NE Saint James Dr, Port St Lucie 34983 Bridgette Hargadine	6-8	TV	901 75	67%	772/785-5640 Fax 772/785-5660
Southport Middle Sch 2420 SE Morningside Blvd, Port St Lucie 34952 Nicole Telese	6-8	T	822 59	69%	772/337-5900 Fax 772/337-5903
St Lucie Elem Sch 2020 S 13th St, Fort Pierce 34950 Michelle Herrington	PK-5	T	720 40	87%	772/468-5213 Fax 772/468-5823
St Lucie Virtual Sch 700 SW Darwin Blvd, Port St Lucie 34953 Jeanne Ziamba	K-12		150	22%	772/429-5504 Fax 772/429-3978
St Lucie West Centennial HS 1485 SW Cashmere Blvd, Port St Lucie 34986 Andrea Popwell	9-12	TV	2,523 70	60%	772/344-4400 Fax 772/344-4406
St Lucie West K-8 Sch 1501 SW Cashmere Blvd, Port St Lucie 34986 Eldrique Gardner	K-8	TV	1,319 55	63%	772/785-6630 Fax 772/785-6632 🇹
Treasure Coast High Sch 1000 SW Darwin Blvd, Port St Lucie 34953 **Todd Smith**	9-12	T	2,823	61%	772/807-4300 Fax 772/807-4320
⊛ Village Green Elem Sch 1700 SE Lennard Rd, Port St Lucie 34952 Terrance Davis	PK-5	T	566 30	74%	772/337-6750 Fax 772/337-6764
Weatherbee Elem Sch 800 E Weatherbee Rd, Fort Pierce 34982 Kimberly Cain	PK-5	T	718 45	82%	772/468-5300 Fax 772/467-4033
West Gate K-8 Sch 1050 NW Cashmere Blvd, Port St Lucie 34986 Kristi Parker	K-8	T	1,309	55%	772/807-7600 Fax 772/807-7616
White City Elem Sch 905 W 2nd St, Fort Pierce 34982 **Alexandra Laoutas**	PK-5	T	586 34	82%	772/468-5840 Fax 772/467-4067
Windmill Point Elem Sch 700 SW Darwin Blvd, Port St Lucie 34953 Brie Lamb	PK-5	T	884 40	76%	772/336-6950 Fax 772/336-6962

ST LUCIE CATHOLIC SCHOOLS

- **Diocese of Palm Beach Ed Off** PID: 02231700
  Listing includes only schools located in this county. See District Index for location of Diocesan Offices.

Catholic Schs..Principal	Grd	Prgm	Enr/#Cls	SN	Phone
John Carroll High Sch 3402 Delaware Ave, Fort Pierce 34947 Corey Heroux	9-12		515 25		772/464-5200 Fax 772/464-5233 🇫
St Anastasia Sch 401 S 33rd St, Fort Pierce 34947 Dr Kevin Hoeffner	PK-8		535 24		772/461-2232 Fax 772/468-2037

ST LUCIE PRIVATE SCHOOLS

Private Schs..Principal	Grd	Prgm	Enr/#Cls	SN	Phone
Barnabas Christian Academy 10330 S US Highway 1, Port St Lucie 34952 Rick Corley	K-12		105 9		772/344-1643 Fax 772/344-1443
Florida State Christian Acad 5200 Oleander Ave, Fort Pierce 34982 Tamara Daniel	K-12		660		772/801-5522
Grace Christian Academy 590 NW Peacock Blvd Ste 4, Port St Lucie 34986 Cynthia Netwig	PK-12		120		772/905-8096 Fax 772/879-6975
James E Sampson Mem SDA Sch 3201 Memory Ln, Fort Pierce 34981 Sherril Davis	PK-8		45		772/465-8386 Fax 772/489-7858
Liberty Baptist Academy 3660 W Midway Rd, Fort Pierce 34981 Katherine Johnson	K-12		500		772/461-2731 Fax 772/461-2542
Morningside Academy 2180 SE Morningside Blvd, Port St Lucie 34952 Kim Adams \ Phillip Gray	K-12		320 20		772/335-3231 Fax 772/335-7323
Orange Ave Baptist Sch 100 Cyclone Dr, Fort Pierce 34945 Wanda Hart	PK-12		80 6		772/461-1225 Fax 772/461-0605
St Andrew's Episcopal Academy 210 S Indian River Dr, Fort Pierce 34950 Mandy Doss \ Suzanne Barry	PK-12		175 14		772/461-7689 Fax 772/461-4683
Sun Grove Montessori Sch 5610 Oleander Ave, Fort Pierce 34982 Terri Zuidema	PK-8		120 9		772/464-5436 Fax 772/464-0834

ST LUCIE REGIONAL CENTERS

- **FDLRS-Galaxy** PID: 04496176   772/429-4585
  1201 Mississippi Ave, Fort Pierce 34950   Fax 772/429-3622

Wayne Gent ....1 Bennett Buckles 73

SUMTER COUNTY

SUMTER PUBLIC SCHOOLS

- **Sumter Co School Dist** PID: 00203989   352/793-2315
  2680 W C 476, Bushnell 33513   Fax 352/793-4180

Schools: 10 \ **Teachers:** 545 \ **Students:** 8,500 \
Special Ed Students: 1,209 \ **LEP Students:** 256 \ **College-Bound:** 73% \ **Ethnic:** Asian 2%, African American 14%, Hispanic 15%, Caucasian 69% \ **Exp:** $118 (Low) \ **Poverty:** 24% \ **Title I:** $1,952,844 \
Special Education: $2,045,000 \ **Bilingual Education:** $46,000 \
Open-Close: 08/12 - 05/29 \ **DTBP:** $152 (High) \ 🇫

Richard Shirley	1	Deborah Smith	2
Travis Davies	3,17	William-Eric Suber	3,4,91,95,275
Michael Foote	5	Janet Connelly	7
Debbie Moffitt	8,11,16,288,298	Helen Christian	9,12
Katherine Dustin	13,57,58,77,81	Dana Williams	16,74,273

---

79 Student Personnel | 91 Safety/Security | 275 Response To Intervention | 298 Grant Writer/Ptnrships | **School Programs** | **Social Media**
80 Driver Ed/Safety | 92 Magnet School | 277 Remedial Math K-12 | 750 Chief Innovation Officer | A = Alternative Program | 🇫 = Facebook
81 Gifted/Talented | 93 Parental Involvement | 280 Literacy Coach | 751 Chief of Staff | G = Adult Classes | 🇹 = Twitter
82 Video Services | 95 Tech Prep Program | 285 STEM | 752 Social Emotional Learning | M = Magnet Program
83 Substance Abuse Prev | 97 Chief Infomation Officer | 286 Digital Learning | | T = Title I Schoolwide
84 Erate | 98 Chief Technology Officer | 288 Common Core Standards | **Other School Types** | V = Career & Tech Ed Programs
85 AIDS Education | 270 Character Education | 294 Accountability | Ⓐ = Alternative School
88 Alternative/At Risk | 271 Migrant Education | 295 Network System | Ⓒ = Charter School | New Schools are shaded
89 Multi-Cultural Curriculum | 273 Teacher Mentor | 296 Title II Programs | Ⓜ = Magnet School | New Superintendents and Principals are bold
90 Social Work | 274 Before/After Sch | 297 Webmaster | Ⓨ = Year-Round School | Personnel with email addresses are underscored

Public Schs..Principal	Grd	Prgm	Enr/#Cls	SN	
Bushnell Elem Sch 218 W Flannery Ave, Bushnell 33513 Kelly Goodwin	PK-5	T	757 50	68%	352/793-3501 Fax 352/793-1336 f
Lake Panasoffkee Elem Sch 790 County Road 482 N, Lk Panasoffke 33538 Nicole Wade	PK-5	T	592 27	74%	352/793-1093 Fax 352/568-8080
South Sumter High Sch 706 N Main St, Bushnell 33513 Christina McKinney	9-12	ATV	1,044 48	65%	352/793-3131 Fax 352/793-2992
South Sumter Middle Sch 773 NW 10th Ave, Webster 33597 Joel Camp	6-8	ATV	863 55	72%	352/793-2232 Fax 352/793-3976
Sumter Co Adult Education Ctr 1425 County Road 526A, Sumterville 33585 Christine Burk	Adult	V	75 4		352/793-5719 Fax 352/793-6508
Ⓐ Sumter Prep Academy 200 Cleveland Ave, Wildwood 34785 James Presley	6-12	T	45	96%	352/568-1113 Fax 352/568-3455
Ⓒ Villages Charter Sch 350 Tatonka Ter, The Villages 32162 Leanne Yerk \ Dr Peggy Irwin \ Dr William Zwick	PK-12	V	3,215 16	30%	352/259-2350 Fax 352/259-3850 f
Webster Elem Sch 349 S Market Blvd, Webster 33597 Teeter McMullen	PK-5	T	655 28	82%	352/793-2828 Fax 352/796-6785 f
Wildwood Elem Sch 300 Huey St, Wildwood 34785 John Temple	PK-5	T	829 30	91%	352/748-3353 Fax 352/748-4788
Wildwood Middle High Sch 700 Huey St, Wildwood 34785 Richard Hampton	6-12	ATV	743 35	80%	352/748-1314 Fax 352/748-7668 f

SUMTER PRIVATE SCHOOLS

Private Schs..Principal	Grd	Prgm	Enr/#Cls	SN	
Maranatha Christian Academy 10926 S US Highway 301, Webster 33597 Jerry Alexander	K-12	G	17 3		352/793-7224

SUWANNEE COUNTY

SUWANNEE PUBLIC SCHOOLS

● **Suwannee Co School Dist** PID: 00204098
1729 Walker Ave SW Ste 200, Live Oak 32064

386/647-4243
Fax 386/364-2635

Schools: 9 \ **Teachers:** 381 \ **Students:** 5,776 \ **Special Ed Students:** 756 \ **LEP Students:** 350 \ **College-Bound:** 70% \ **Ethnic:** Asian 1%, African American 16%, Hispanic 18%, Caucasian 65% \ **Exp:** $145 (Low) \ **Poverty:** 27% \ **Title I:** $2,322,639 \ **Special Education:** $4,176,000 \ **Bilingual Education:** $955,000 \ **Open-Close:** 08/12 - 05/29 \ **DTBP:** $161 (High)

Public Schs..Principal	Grd	Prgm	Enr/#Cls	SN	
Branford Elem Sch 26801 State Road 247, Branford 32008 Deidre McManaway	PK-5	T	667 29	63%	386/935-5700 Fax 386/935-6311
Branford High Sch 405 Reynolds St NE, Branford 32008 Terry Huddleston	6-12	TV	706 35	49%	386/935-5600 Fax 386/935-3867
Riveroak Technical Center 415 Pinewood Dr SW, Live Oak 32064 Mary Keen	Voc	G	200 17		386/647-4200 Fax 386/364-4698
Suwannee Elem Sch 1748 Ohio Ave S, Live Oak 32064 Amy Boggus	2-3	T	731	69%	386/647-4400 Fax 386/330-1215
Suwannee High Sch 1314 Pine Ave SW, Live Oak 32064 Ronald Gray	9-12	TV	1,186 75	48%	386/647-4000 Fax 386/364-2794
Suwannee Inter Sch 1419 Walker Ave SW, Live Oak 32064 Jennifer Beach	4-5	T	697 60	67%	386/647-4700 Fax 386/364-2680
Suwannee Middle Sch 1730 Walker Ave SW, Live Oak 32064 Jimmy Wilkerson	6-8	TV	1,042 56	61%	386/647-4500 Fax 386/208-1474
Suwannee Primary Sch 1625 Walker Ave SW, Live Oak 32064 Marsha Tedder	PK-1	T	829 55	73%	386/647-4300 Fax 386/364-2667
Suwannee Virtual Sch 305 Pinewood Dr SW, Live Oak 32064 Jennifer Barr	6-12		93	19%	386/647-4248 Fax 386/364-4698

SUWANNEE PRIVATE SCHOOLS

Private Schs..Principal	Grd	Prgm	Enr/#Cls	SN	
Florida Sheriff's Boys Ranch 1813 Cecil Webb Pl, Live Oak 32060 Sue Moffat	6-12	G	43 3		386/842-5555 Fax 386/842-1012

1	Superintendent	8	Curric/Instruct K-12	19	Chief Financial Officer	29	Family/Consumer Science	39	Social Studies K-12	49	English/Lang Arts Elem	59	Special Education Elem	69	Academic Assessment
2	Bus/Finance/Purchasing	9	Curric/Instruct Elem	20	Art K-12	30	Adult Education	40	Social Studies Elem	50	English/Lang Arts Sec	60	Special Education Sec	70	Research/Development
3	Buildings And Grounds	10	Curric/Instruct Sec	21	Art Elem	31	Career/Sch-to-Work K-12	41	Social Studies Sec	51	Reading K-12	61	Foreign/World Lang K-12	71	Public Information
4	Food Service	11	Federal Program	22	Art Sec	32	Career/Sch-to-Work Elem	42	Science K-12	52	Reading Elem	62	Foreign/World Lang Elem	72	Summer School
5	Transportation	12	Title I	23	Music K-12	33	Career/Sch-to-Work Sec	43	Science Elem	53	Reading Sec	63	Foreign/World Lang Sec	73	Instructional Tech
6	Athletic	13	Title V	24	Music Elem	34	Early Childhood Ed	44	Science Sec	54	Remedial Reading K-12	64	Religious Education K-12	74	Inservice Training
7	Health Services	14	Asst Superintendent	25	Music Sec	35	Health/Phys Education	45	Math K-12	55	Remedial Reading Elem	65	Religious Education Elem	75	Marketing/Distributive
		15	Asst Superintendent	26	Business Education	36	Guidance Services K-12	46	Math Elem	56	Remedial Reading Sec	66	Religious Education Sec	76	Info Systems
		16	Instructional Media Svcs	27	Career & Tech Ed	37	Guidance Services Elem	47	Math Sec	57	Bilingual/ELL	67	School Board President	77	Psychological Assess
		17	Chief Operations Officer	28	Technology Education	38	Guidance Services Sec	48	English/Lang Arts K-12	58	Special Education K-12	68	Teacher Personnel	78	Affirmative Action
		18	Chief Academic Officer												

FL—138

Melody Christian Academy 10046 US Highway 129, Live Oak 32060 Amanda Davis	PK-12	220 12	386/364-4800 Fax 386/364-1889
Tabernacle Baptist Sch 8637 Goldkist Blvd SW, Live Oak 32064 Gil Roser	K-12	35 3	386/362-7800
Westwood Christian Sch 920 11th St SW, Live Oak 32064 Bill Yanossy	PK-12	175 10	386/362-3735 Fax 386/364-6486

TAYLOR COUNTY

TAYLOR PUBLIC SCHOOLS

● **Taylor Co School Dist** PID: 00204165   850/838-2500
318 N Clark St, Perry 32347   Fax 850/838-2501

Schools: 6 \ *Teachers:* 194 \ *Students:* 2,900 \ *Special Ed Students:* 448 \ *LEP Students:* 12 \ *College-Bound:* 66% \ *Ethnic:* Asian 2%, African American 25%, Hispanic 3%, Native American: 1%, Caucasian 69% \ *Exp:* $200 (Med) \ *Poverty:* 32% \ *Title I:* $1,386,721 \ *Special Education:* $2,788,000 \ *Open-Close:* 08/12 - 05/29 \ *DTBP:* $188 (High) \

Danny Glover 1	Ashley Valentine 2,11,19,294
Dan Anderson 3	Benny Blue 4
Wendy Slaughter 5	Maurice Belcher 6,35*
Sharon Hathcock 8,12,286,288,296	Charles Finley 10*
Laurie Wynn 16,82*	Kelly Brannon 57,274*
Alicia Poole 58,69,77,81,275,752	Brenda Carlton 67
Michael Thompson ... 68,73,79,83,88,270,295	Pamela Padgett 73,76,98*
Rhonda Brooks 90*	Chris Olsen 91,298
Tim Murphy 295	

Public Schs..Principal	Grd	Prgm	Enr/#Cls	SN
Big Bend Tech Institute 3233 S Bryon Butler Pkwy, Perry 32348 Jodi Tillman	9-12	GT	65 13		850/838-2545 Fax 850/838-2546
Perry Co Primary Sch 1600 Howard St, Perry 32347 Pamela Padgett	PK-2	T	855 44	64%	850/838-2506 Fax 850/838-2556
Steinhatchee Sch 1109 1st Ave SE, Steinhatchee 32359 Marion McCray	PK-6	T	77 11	80%	352/498-3303 Fax 352/498-6050
Taylor Co Elem Sch 1600 E Green St, Perry 32347 Sabrina Lytle	3-5	T	680 40	60%	850/838-2530 Fax 850/838-1379
Taylor Co High Sch 900 N Johnson Stripling Rd, Perry 32347 Charles Finley	9-12	GT	578 56	46%	850/838-2525 Fax 850/838-2521
Taylor Co Middle Sch 601 E Lafayette St, Perry 32347 Stefani Puhl	6-8	T	559 46	62%	850/838-2516 Fax 850/838-2559

TAYLOR PRIVATE SCHOOLS

Private Schs..Principal	Grd	Prgm	Enr/#Cls	SN
Point of Grace Christian Sch 920 N Courtney Rd, Perry 32347 Eddie Pridgen	K-11		175		850/584-5445

UNION COUNTY

UNION PUBLIC SCHOOLS

● **Union Co School Dist** PID: 00204244   352/448-5051
55 SW 6th St, Lake Butler 32054   Fax 386/496-4819

Schools: 6 \ *Teachers:* 167 \ *Students:* 2,300 \ *Special Ed Students:* 407 \ *LEP Students:* 9 \ *College-Bound:* 56% \ *Ethnic:* African American 14%, Hispanic 4%, Caucasian 82% \ *Exp:* $236 (Med) \ *Poverty:* 21% \ *Title I:* $509,429 \ *Special Education:* $2,845,000 \ *Open-Close:* 08/12 - 05/22 \ *DTBP:* $350 (High)

Carlton Faulk 1	Renae Prevatt 2
Betsy Whitehead 4	Tony Raish 5
Ronny Pruitt 6*	Stacey Rimes 8,11,69,294,296*
Barry Sams 10,16,27,68,88,273	Christie Whitehead 31,36,57,58,79,85
Becky Raulerson 67	Garrett Crosby 73,286,295,297
Mary Ann Taylor 84	

Public Schs..Principal	Grd	Prgm	Enr/#Cls	SN
Ⓐ Alternative Ed 208 SE 6th St, Lake Butler 32054 Barry Sams	6-12	TV	25 3		352/448-5195
Lake Butler Elem Sch 800 SW 6th St, Lake Butler 32054 Marcie Tucker	PK-4	T	979 50	56%	352/448-5302 Fax 386/496-4395
Lake Butler Middle Sch 150 SW 6th St, Lake Butler 32054 Carolyn Parrish	5-8	ATV	754 50	47%	352/448-5153 Fax 386/496-4352
Union Co Adult Sch 208 SE 6th St, Lake Butler 32054 Barry Sams	Adult		50		352/448-5195 Fax 386/496-4919
Union Co High Sch 1000 S Lake Ave, Lake Butler 32054 Michael Ripplinger	9-12	ATV	587 45	38%	352/448-5204 Fax 386/496-4187
Ⓐ Union Juvenile Residential Sch Ⓨ 14692 NE County Road 199, Raiford 32083 Barry Sams	6-12	MV	25 2	87%	386/431-1997

---

79 Student Personnel	91 Safety/Security	275 Response To Intervention	298 Grant Writer/Ptnrships	**School Programs**	**Social Media**
80 Driver Ed/Safety	92 Magnet School	277 Remedial Math K-12	750 Chief Innovation Officer	A = Alternative Program	
81 Gifted/Talented	93 Parental Involvement	280 Literacy Coach	751 Chief of Staff	G = Adult Classes	= Facebook
82 Video Services	95 Tech Prep Program	285 STEM	752 Social Emotional Learning	M = Magnet Program	
83 Substance Abuse Prev	97 Chief Information Officer	286 Digital Learning		T = Title I Schoolwide	= Twitter
84 Erate	98 Chief Technology Officer	288 Common Core Standards	**Other School Types**	V = Career & Tech Ed Programs	
85 AIDS Education	270 Character Education	294 Accountability	Ⓐ = Alternative Program		
88 Alternative/At Risk	271 Migrant Education	295 Network System	Ⓒ = Charter School	**New Schools are shaded**	
89 Multi-Cultural Curriculum	273 Teacher Mentor	296 Title II Programs	Ⓜ = Magnet School	**New Superintendents and Principals are bold**	
90 Social Work	274 Before/After Sch	297 Webmaster	Ⓨ = Year-Round School	Personnel with email addresses are underscored	

FL—139

VOLUSIA COUNTY

VOLUSIA PUBLIC SCHOOLS

- **Volusia Co School Dist** PID: 00204294   386/734-7190
  200 N Clara Ave, Deland 32720   Fax 386/822-6790

Schools: 83 \ **Teachers:** 4,126 \ **Students:** 64,000 \
Special Ed Students: 10,599 \ **LEP Students:** 4,272 \ **College-Bound:** 93%
\ **Ethnic:** Asian 2%, African American 17%, Hispanic 20%, Caucasian
61% \ **Exp:** $120 (Low) \ **Poverty:** 22% \ **Title I:** $23,499,592 \
Special Education: $54,920,000 \ **Bilingual Education:** $6,514,000 \
Open-Close: 08/12 - 05/29 \ **DTBP:** $200 (High)

Timothy Egnor	1	Bertha Trawick	2
Deborah Mulher	2,19	Maria Kraft	2,3
Rose Pendleton	2	Sandy Higginbotham	2
Saralee Morrissey	2	Stephanie Weaver	2
Barbara Ivey	3	Greg Akin	3,17
Thomas Brown	3	Heather Demeola	4
Chris Boyer	5	Mike Frazee	5
Mitch Moyer	5	Lawrence Beal	6,88
Debbie Hinson-Fisher	7	Colleen Winburn	8
Rachel Hazel	8,18	Luanne Blankenship	11
Emma Field	12	Gianna Acevedo-Alamo	12,57,61,89,271
Jamie Haynes	12	Leslie Frazee	12
Melissa Shaw	12	Sheila Rees	12
Patricia Corr	15	Rose Roland	15
Susan Freeman	15	Kelly Amy	27
Rachel Rutledge	31	Grace Kellermeier	35
Dr Amy Hall	36	Desiree Rybinski	49,51
Kimberly Gilliland	58	Dr Mary Myers	58
Dr Rolanda Fabien	58	Carl Persis	67
Dana Paige-Pender	68	Heidi Kochis	68
Eric Holland	69,286	Dr Kati Dyer	70,74
Kelly Schulz	71	Leticia Roman	72,271,296,298
Caitlyn Distler	73	Mike Cicchetti	73,76,295
Annmarie Wrenn	78	Diane Martin-Morgan	83,90*
Richard Myers	91	Nancy Wait	93
Cherie Houser	274	Amy Monahan	285
Susy Peterson	286*	David Creech	297
Justin Lipomi	752		

Public Schs..Principal	Grd	Prgm	Enr/#Cls	SN	
Ⓐ Amikids Volusia Campus	K-12		150	33%	386/274-5786
1420 Mason Ave Ste 110, Daytona Beach 32117					Fax 386/274-5787
Nicole Barnes					
Atlantic High Sch	9-12	ATV	1,102	63%	386/322-6100
1250 Reed Canal Rd, Port Orange 32129			70		Fax 386/506-0001
Stephen Hinson					
Blue Lake Elem Sch	PK-5	T	565	86%	386/822-4070
282 N Blue Lake Ave, Deland 32724			60		Fax 386/822-6765
Scott Lifvendahl					
© Burns Science & Tech Chtr Sch	K-8	T	452	59%	386/210-4915
160 Ridge Rd, Oak Hill 32759					Fax 386/210-4922
Dr Janet McGee					
Campbell Middle Sch	6-8	TV	846	90%	386/258-4661
625 S Keech St, Daytona Beach 32114			73		Fax 386/506-5087
Dr Jerry Picott					
Champion Elem Sch	PK-5	T	630	84%	386/258-4664
921 Tournament Dr, Daytona Beach 32124			29		Fax 386/506-5072
Richard Inge					

© Chiles Academy	6-12	T	164	53%	386/322-6102
868 George W Engram Blvd, Daytona Beach 32114			8		Fax 386/258-4681
Anne Ferguson					
Chisholm Elem Sch	K-5	T	400	65%	386/424-2540
557 Ronnoc Ln, New Smyrna 32168			21		Fax 386/424-2500
Craig Zablo					
Citrus Grove Elem Sch	K-5	T	941	68%	386/626-0053
729 Hazen Rd, Deland 32720					Fax 386/626-0065
Jennifer Williams					
Coronado Beach Elem Sch	K-5	T	243	38%	386/424-2525
3550 Michigan Ave, New Smyrna 32169			14		Fax 386/424-2501
Tracy Buckner					
Creekside Middle Sch	6-8	TV	1,152	40%	386/322-6155
6801 Airport Rd, Port Orange 32128			59		Fax 386/506-0002
John Cash					
Cypress Creek Elem Sch	K-5	A	802	35%	386/322-6101
6100 S Williamson Blvd, Port Orange 32128					
Adrian Bronson					
David C Hinson Sr Middle Sch	6-8	T	1,012	58%	386/258-4682
1860 N Clyde Morris Blvd, Daytona Beach 32117					Fax 386/506-5064
William Dunnigan					
Debary Elem Sch	K-5	T	784	47%	386/575-4230
88 W Highbanks Rd, Debary 32713			45		Fax 386/968-0021
Alisa Fedigan					
Deland High Sch	9-12	ATV	2,690	55%	386/822-6909
800 N Hill Ave, Deland 32724					Fax 386/626-0056
Melissa Carr					
Deland Middle Sch	6-8	TV	1,179	68%	386/822-5678
1400 Aquarius Ave, Deland 32724			100		Fax 386/626-0057
John DeVito					
Deltona High Sch	9-12	TV	1,663	66%	386/575 4153
100 Wolf Pack Run, Deltona 32725			120		Fax 386/968-0014
Carolyn Carbonell					
Deltona Lakes Elem Sch	PK-5	T	773	81%	386/575-4115
2022 Adelia Blvd, Deltona 32725			60		Fax 386/968-0022
Ramonita Ortiz					
Deltona Middle Sch	6-8	TV	1,159	77%	386/575-4150
250 Enterprise Rd, Deltona 32725			50		Fax 386/968-0015
Kimberly Feltner					
Discovery Elem Sch	K-5	T	602	88%	386/575-4133
975 Abagail Dr, Deltona 32725					Fax 386/968-0023
Leslie McLean					
© Easter Seals Charter Sch	Spec		54		386/255-4568
1219 Dunn Ave, Daytona Beach 32114			12		Fax 386/944-7855
April Leopold					
Edgewater Public Sch	PK-5	T	570	77%	386/424-2573
801 S Old County Rd, Edgewater 32132			45		Fax 386/426-7349
Rebecca Porter					
Edith I Starke Elem Sch	PK-5	T	417	94%	386/943-9651
730 S Parsons Ave, Deland 32720			27		Fax 386/943-7957
Eilene Ahr					
Ⓐ Elearning East	9-12		62		386/506-0013
1250 Reed Canal Rd, Port Orange 32129					
Susy Peterson					
Ⓐ Elearning West	9-12		47		386/575-4076
1000 W Rhode Island Ave, Orange City 32763					
Dr Melissa Carr					
Enterprise Elem Sch	PK-5	T	580	80%	386/575-4135
211 Main St, Enterprise 32725			44		Fax 386/968-0024
Alicia Douglas					
Forest Lake Elem Sch	PK-5	T	634	77%	386/575-4166
1600 Doyle Rd, Deltona 32725			29		Fax 386/860-6623
Virginia Freeman					
Freedom Elem Sch	PK-5	T	744	56%	386/943-4375
1395 S Blue Lake Ave, Deland 32724			30		Fax 386/943-7680
Joy Boyd-Walker					

1 Superintendent	8 Curric/Instruct K-12	19 Chief Financial Officer	29 Family/Consumer Science
2 Bus/Finance/Purchasing	9 Curric/Instruct Elem	20 Art K-12	30 Adult Education
3 Buildings And Grounds	10 Curric/Instruct Sec	21 Art Elem	31 Career/Sch-to-Work K-12
4 Food Service	11 Federal Program	22 Art Sec	32 Career/Sch-to-Work Elem
5 Transportation	12 Title I	23 Music K-12	33 Career/Sch-to-Work Sec
6 Athletic	13 Title V	24 Music Elem	34 Early Childhood Ed
7 Health Services	15 Asst Superintendent	25 Music Sec	35 Health/Phys Education
	16 Instructional Media Svcs	26 Business Education	36 Guidance Services K-12
	17 Chief Operations Officer	27 Career & Tech Ed	37 Guidance Services Elem
	18 Chief Academic Officer	28 Technology Education	38 Guidance Services Sec

39 Social Studies K-12	49 English/Lang Arts Elem	59 Special Education Elem	69 Academic Assessment
40 Social Studies Elem	50 English/Lang Arts Sec	60 Special Education Sec	70 Research/Development
41 Social Studies Sec	51 Reading K-12	61 Foreign/World Lang K-12	71 Public Information
42 Science K-12	52 Reading Elem	62 Foreign/World Lang Elem	72 Summer School
43 Science Elem	53 Reading Sec	63 Foreign/World Lang Sec	73 Instructional Tech
44 Science Sec	54 Remedial Reading K-12	64 Religious Education K-12	74 Inservice Training
45 Math K-12	55 Remedial Reading Elem	65 Religious Education Elem	75 Marketing/Distributive
46 Math Elem	56 Remedial Reading Sec	66 Religious Education Sec	76 Info Systems
47 Math Sec	57 Bilingual/ELL	67 School Board President	77 Psychological Assess
48 English/Lang Arts K-12	58 Special Education K-12	68 Teacher Personnel	78 Affirmative Action

School	Grades	Type	Enroll	%	Phone
Friendship Elem Sch 2746 Fulford St, Deltona 32738 Cristina Raimundo	PK-5	T	428 	89%	386/575-4130 Fax 386/968-0029
Galaxy Middle Sch 2400 Eustace Ave, Deltona 32725 Karen Chenoweth	6-8	TV	1,035 105	75%	386/575-4144 Fax 386/968-0016
George W Marks Elem Sch 1000 N Garfield Ave, Deland 32724 Shannon Young	K-5	T	549 40	66%	386/822-6986 Fax 386/626-0059
Heritage Middle Sch 1001 Parnell Ct, Deltona 32738 Thomas Vaughan	6-8	T	1,100 85	75%	386/575-4113 Fax 407/708-0020
Ⓐ Highbanks Learning Center 336 E Highbanks Rd, Debary 32713 Dale Johns	8-12	T	30	90%	386/822-7896
Holly Hill Sch 1500 Center Ave, Holly Hill 32117 Jason Watson	PK-8	T	1,084 35	91%	386/258-4662 Fax 386/506-5073
Horizon Elem Sch 4751 Hidden Lake Dr, Port Orange 32129 Gary Harms	PK-5	T	802 50	64%	386/322-6150 Fax 386/763-3784
Indian River Elem Sch 650 Roberts Rd, Edgewater 32141 Carrie Crkvenac	PK-5	T	610 30	71%	386/424-2650 Fax 386/426-7354
Ⓒ Ivy Hawn CS of the Arts 565 S Lakeview Dr Unit 110, Lake Helen 32744 Kelly Conway	K-8	T	948	37%	386/228-3900 Fax 386/228-3901
Ⓐ Legacy Scholar Academy 51 Childrens Way, Deltona 32725 Stephanie Workman	6-12		50	41%	386/668-4774
Longstreet Elem Sch 2745 S Peninsula Dr, Daytona Beach 32118 Judith Watson	K-5	T	431 30	72%	386/322-6172 Fax 386/506-0004
Louise S McInnis Elem Sch 5715 US Hwy 17, De Leon Spgs 32130 Dr Sharon Lavallee	PK-5	T	402 23	91%	386/943-6384 Fax 386/985-6710
Mainland High Sch 1255 W Intl Speedwy Blvd, Daytona Beach 32114 Timothy Huth	9-12	TV	1,870 115	67%	386/258-4665 Fax 386/506-5069
Manatee Cove Elem Sch 734 W Ohio Ave, Orange City 32763 Michelle Sojka	PK-5	T	706	73%	386/968-0004 Fax 386/968-0017
New Smyrna Beach High Sch 1015 10th St, New Smyrna 32168 Matthew Krajewski	9-12	TV	1,954 80	49%	386/424-2555 Fax 386/424-2505
New Smyrna Beach Middle Sch 1200 S Myrtle Ave, New Smyrna 32168 Michael Leader	6-8	TV	1,179 88	60%	386/424-2550 Fax 386/424-2504
Orange City Elem Sch 555 E University Ave, Orange City 32763 Charles Bynum	PK-5	T	557 32	80%	386/575-4215 Fax 386/968-0030
Ormond Beach Elem Sch 100 Corbin Ave, Ormond Beach 32174 Shannon Hay	K-5	T	344 16	79%	386/258-4666 Fax 386/506-5075
Ormond Beach Middle Sch 151 Domicilio Ave, Ormond Beach 32174 Susan Tuten	6-8	TV	1,065 60	58%	386/258-4667 Fax 386/506-5070
Ortona Elem Sch 1265 N Grandview Ave, Daytona Beach 32118 Shantell Adkins	K-5	T	202 14	79%	386/258-4668 Fax 386/506-5076
Osceola Elem Sch 100 Osceola Ave, Ormond Beach 32176 Lynn Bruner	K-5	T	405 25	71%	386/258-4669 Fax 386/506-5077
Osteen Elem Sch 500 Doyle Rd, Osteen 32764 Jim Dambrick	K-5	T	503 44	71%	407/688-9555 Fax 407/688-9501
Pace Center for Girls-Volusia 208 Central Ave, Ormond Beach 32174 Georgia McCurdy	6-12		39	23%	386/944-1111 Fax 386/944-1112
Palm Terrace Elem Sch 1825 Dunn Ave, Daytona Beach 32114 Tucker Harris	PK-5	T	640 55	94%	386/258-4670 Fax 386/274-3448
Pathways Elem Sch 2100 Airport Rd, Ormond Beach 32174 Gregory Schwartz	PK-5	T	775 36	47%	386/258-4671 Fax 386/676-5363
Pierson Elem Sch 657 N Center St, Pierson 32180 Kimberly Hutcherson	PK-5	T	537 27	88%	386/740-0850 Fax 386/749-6870
Pine Ridge High Sch 926 Howland Blvd, Deltona 32738 Paul Nehrig	9-12	TV	1,725 90	67%	386/575-4195 Fax 407/688-9502
Pine Trail Elem Sch 300 Airport Rd, Ormond Beach 32174 Tami Fisher	K-5	T	703 34	53%	386/258-4672 Fax 386/506-5080
Port Orange Elem Sch 402 Dunlawton Ave, Port Orange 32127 Angela Polite	K-5	T	408 22	67%	386/322-6271 Fax 386/756-7117
Pride Elem Sch 1100 Learning Ln, Deltona 32738 Libby Johnson	PK-5	T	590	77%	386/968-0010
Read-Pattillo Elem Sch 400 6th St, New Smyrna 32168 Kelly Lewis	K-5	T	417 30	74%	386/424-2600 Fax 386/424-2575
Ⓒ Reading Edge Academy 2975 Enterprise Rd, Debary 32713 Margaret Comardo	K-5		294 15	7%	386/668-8911 Fax 386/668-8443
Ⓒ Richard Milburn Academy 1031 Mason Ave, Daytona Beach 32117 Artherley Sands	7-12	T	350	82%	386/304-0086 Fax 386/304-0087
Ⓒ Richard Milburn Academy West 1200 Deltona Blvd Ste 53, Deltona 32725 Earl Barnett	7-12		210		386/738-9150 Fax 386/738-9151
River Springs Middle Sch 900 W Ohio Ave, Orange City 32763 Stacy Gotlib	6-8	T	1,255	61%	386/968-0011 Fax 386/968-0018
Ⓐ Riverview Learning Center 801 N Wild Olive Ave, Daytona Beach 32118 Dale Johns	6-12	T	17 10	75%	386/258-4673 Fax 386/239-6218
Ⓒ Samsula Academy 248 N Samsula Dr, New Smyrna 32168 Peggy Comardo	K-5		242	7%	386/423-6650 Fax 386/423-6651
Seabreeze High Sch 2700 N Oleander Ave, Daytona Beach 32118 Joe Rawlings	9-12	TV	1,652 85	42%	386/258-4674 Fax 386/506-5071
Silver Sands Middle Sch 1300 Herbert St, Port Orange 32129 Amanda Wiles	6-8	TV	1,215	57%	386/322-6175 Fax 386/506-5042
South Daytona Elem Sch 600 Elizabeth Pl, South Daytona 32119 Tennille Wallace	K-5	T	852 50	81%	386/322-6180 Fax 386/506-0008
Southwestern Middle Sch 605 W New Hampshire Ave, Deland 32720 Jacquese Copeland	6-8	TV	783 48	72%	386/822-6815 Fax 386/822-6708
Spirit Elem Sch 1500 Meadowlark Dr, Deltona 32725 Carrie DeVaney	PK-5	T	693	80%	386/575-4080 Fax 386/968-0031
Spruce Creek Elem Sch 642 Taylor Rd, Port Orange 32127 Andrea Hall	PK-5	T	853 30	66%	386/322-6200 Fax 386/506-0009
Spruce Creek High Sch 801 Taylor Rd, Port Orange 32127 Todd Sparger	9-12	TV	2,567 159	38%	386/322-6272 Fax 386/506-5045

79	Student Personnel
80	Driver Ed/Safety
81	Gifted/Talented
82	Video Services
83	Substance Abuse Prev
84	Erate
85	AIDS Education
88	Alternative/At Risk
89	Multi-Cultural Curriculum
90	Social Work

91	Safety/Security
92	Magnet School
93	Parental Involvement
95	Tech Prep Program
97	Chief Infomation Officer
98	Chief Technology Officer
270	Character Education
271	Migrant Education
273	Teacher Mentor
274	Before/After Sch

275	Response To Intervention
277	Remedial Math K-12
280	Literacy Coach
285	STEM
286	Digital Learning
288	Common Core Standards
294	Accountability
295	Network System
296	Title II Programs
297	Webmaster

298	Grant Writer/Ptnrships
750	Chief Innovation Officer
751	Chief of Staff
752	Social Emotional Learning

Other School Types
Ⓐ = Alternative School
Ⓒ = Charter School
Ⓜ = Magnet School
Ⓨ = Year-Round School

School Programs
A = Alternative Program
G = Adult Classes
M = Magnet Program
T = Title I Schoolwide
V = Career & Tech Ed Programs

New Schools are shaded
New Superintendents and Principals are bold
Personnel with email addresses are underscored

Social Media
🅕 = Facebook
🅣 = Twitter

Sugar Mill Elem Sch 1101 Charles St, Port Orange 32129 Mary Speidel	PK-5	T	667 45	74%	386/322-6171 Fax 386/506-0011	
Sunrise Elem Sch 3155 Phonetia Dr, Deltona 32738 Efrain Alejandro	PK-5	T	524 37	79%	386/575-4103 Fax 407/328-5544	
Sweetwater Elem Sch 5800 Victoria Gardens Blvd, Port Orange 32127 Tamera Hopkins	K-5	T	684 43	47%	386/322-6230 Fax 386/506-0012	
Td Taylor Middle High Sch 100 E Washington Ave, Pierson 32180 Kathleen Gibbons	6-12	TV	1,149 65	79%	386/749-6800 Fax 386/749-6836	
Timbercrest Elem Sch 2401 Eustace Ave, Deltona 32725 **Lonnie Tidmarsh**	PK-5	T	784 50	67%	386/575-4221 Fax 386/626-0425	
Tomoka Elem Sch 999 Old Tomoka Rd, Ormond Beach 32174 Julie Roseboom	PK-5	T	773 64	52%	386/258-4676 Fax 386/506-5082	
Turie T Small Elem Sch 800 South St, Daytona Beach 32114 Cameron Robinson	PK-5	T	532 30	96%	386/258-4675 Fax 386/506-5084	
University High Sch 1000 W Rhode Island Ave, Orange City 32763 Dr Julian Jones	9-12	T	2,689	57%	386/968-0013 Fax 386/968-0019	
Volusia Pines Elem Sch 500 E Kicklighter Rd, Lake Helen 32744 Julie Gordon	K-5	T	567 26	80%	386/575-4125 Fax 386/968-0034	
Westside Elem Sch 1210 Jimmy Ann Dr, Daytona Beach 32117 **Dwayne Copeland**	PK-5	T	586 27	95%	386/274-3400 Fax 386/274-3417	
Woodward Avenue Elem Sch 1201 S Woodward Ave, Deland 32720 Carlos Scott	PK-5	T	639 40	76%	386/740-7910 Fax 386/626-0063	

VOLUSIA CATHOLIC SCHOOLS

• **Diocese of Orlando Ed Office** PID: 00197639
  Listing includes only schools located in this county. See District Index for location of Diocesan Offices.

Catholic Schs..Principal	Grd	Prgm	Enr/#Cls	SN
Basilica School of St Paul 317 Mullally St, Daytona Beach 32114 Ronald Pagano	PK-8		230 15	386/252-7915 Fax 386/238-7903
Father Lopez Catholic High Sch 3918 Lpga Blvd, Daytona Beach 32124 Leigh Svajko	9-12		450 20	386/253-5213 Fax 386/252-6101 f t
Lourdes Academy 1014 N Halifax Ave, Daytona Beach 32118 Stephen Dole	PK-8		278 14	386/252-0391 Fax 888/259-1201
Sacred Heart Sch 1003 Turnbull St, New Smyrna 32168 Shelley Niswonger	PK-8		246 8	386/428-4732 Fax 386/428-4087 f
St Brendan Sch 1000 Ocean Shore Blvd, Ormond Beach 32176 Philip Gorrasi	PK-8		225 11	386/441-1331 Fax 386/441-0774
St Peter Catholic Sch 421 W New York Ave, Deland 32720 Peter Randlov	PK-8		272 10	386/822-6010 Fax 386/822-6013 f

VOLUSIA PRIVATE SCHOOLS

Private Schs..Principal	Grd	Prgm	Enr/#Cls	SN
Calvary Christian Academy 1687 W Granada Blvd, Ormond Beach 32174 Barbara Philips	PK-12	V	300 30	386/672-2081 Fax 386/615-3736
Central Fellowship Chrn Acad 626 E Kicklighter Rd, Lake Helen 32744 Lamar Breedlove	K-12		4 3	386/228-2803 Fax 386/228-3661
Children's House Montessori 509 E Pennsylvania Ave, Deland 32724 Sherri Holzman	PK-8		170 5	386/736-3632 Fax 386/736-3667
Daytona Beach Christian Sch 1850 S Clyde Morris Blvd, Daytona Beach 32119 James Price	PK-12		100 10	386/760-4808 Fax 386/760-1357
Deltona Adventist Sch 1725 Catalina Blvd, Deltona 32738 Joanne Waite	PK-8		40 4	386/532-9333 Fax 386/532-9633
Deltona Christian Sch 1200 Providence Blvd, Deltona 32725 Phillip Herchenroder	PK-12		182 15	386/574-1971 Fax 386/574-1771
DuVall Home 3395 Grand Ave, Deland 32720 Steven DeVane	Spec	G	100 5	386/734-2874 Fax 386/734-5504
Esformes Hebrew Academy 1079 W Granada Blvd, Ormond Beach 32174 Selena Bowe	PK-8		70	386/672-9300
First Presby Church Day Sch 724 N Woodland Blvd, Deland 32720 Laura Carlisle	PK-PK		100 9	386/734-6214 Fax 386/736-7878
Good Shepherd Academy 750 Howland Blvd, Deltona 32738 Jared Rathje	PK-8		200	407/324-2274 Fax 407/936-2653
Grace Academy 1060A W Granada Blvd, Ormond Beach 32174 Christian Dickinson	K-8		95 11	386/673-5166 Fax 321/978-0252
Halifax Academy 275 N Williamson Blvd, Daytona Beach 32114 Joseph Dougherty	4-12		94	386/252-9557 Fax 386/252-9414
Indigo Christian Jr Academy 401 N Williamson Blvd, Daytona Beach 32114 Shannon Hagen	PK-8		38 3	386/255-5917 Fax 386/269-9997
Lighthouse Christian Academy 126 S Ridgewood Ave, Deland 32720 Elena Wallen	PK-12	V	210 28	386/734-5380 Fax 386/734-5627
Mt Calvary Academy 700 Bellevue Ave, Daytona Beach 32114 Dr Diane Potter	PK-6		120 7	386/255-8654 Fax 386/258-0456
Riverbend Academy 2080 W Granada Blvd, Ormond Beach 32174 Jason Karr	K-12		220 8	386/615-0986 Fax 386/672-7945
St Barnabas Episcopal Sch 322 W Michigan Ave, Deland 32720 Paul Garcia	PK-8		390 21	386/734-3005 Fax 386/822-9417 f t
Stetson Baptist Chrn Sch 1025 W Minnesota Ave, Deland 32720 Sheryl Jackson	PK-8		304 30	386/734-7791 Fax 386/734-7109
Trinity Christian Academy 875 Elkcam Blvd, Deltona 32725 William Henderson	PK-12		600 31	386/789-4515 Fax 386/789-0210
Victory Christian Academy 209 Adams Rd, Edgewater 32141 Wade Hinson	K-12		2 1	386/427-7115

1 Superintendent	8 Curric/Instruct K-12	19 Chief Financial Officer	29 Family/Consumer Science	39 Social Studies K-12	49 English/Lang Arts Elem	59 Special Education Elem	69 Academic Assessment
2 Bus/Finance/Purchasing	9 Curric/Instruct Elem	20 Art K-12	30 Adult Education	40 Social Studies Elem	50 English/Lang Arts Sec	60 Special Education Sec	70 Research/Development
3 Buildings And Grounds	10 Curric/Instruct Sec	21 Art Elem	31 Career/Sch-to-Work K-12	41 Social Studies Sec	51 Reading K-12	61 Foreign/World Lang K-12	71 Public Information
4 Food Service	11 Federal Program	22 Art Sec	32 Career/Sch-to-Work Elem	42 Science K-12	52 Reading Elem	62 Foreign/World Lang Elem	72 Summer School
5 Transportation	12 Title I	23 Music K-12	33 Career/Sch-to-Work Sec	43 Science Elem	53 Reading Sec	63 Foreign/World Lang Sec	73 Instructional Tech
6 Athletic	13 Title V	24 Music Elem	34 Early Childhood Ed	44 Science Sec	54 Remedial Reading K-12	64 Religious Education K-12	74 Inservice Training
7 Health Services	15 Asst Superintendent	25 Music Sec	35 Health/Phys Education	45 Math K-12	55 Remedial Reading Elem	65 Religious Education Elem	75 Marketing/Distributive
	16 Instructional Media Svcs	26 Business Education	36 Guidance Services K-12	46 Math Elem	56 Remedial Reading Sec	66 Religious Education Sec	76 Info Systems
	17 Chief Operations Officer	27 Career & Tech Ed	37 Guidance Services Elem	47 Math Sec	57 Bilingual/ELL	67 School Board President	77 Psychological Assess
	18 Chief Academic Officer	28 Technology Education	38 Guidance Services Sec	48 English/Lang Arts K-12	58 Special Education K-12	68 Teacher Personnel	78 Affirmative Action

Warner Christian Academy 1730 S Ridgewood Ave, Daytona Beach 32119 Nealy Walton	PK-12	720 55	386/767-5451 Fax 386/760-6834	
Xceed Dme Academy-Daytona 2441 Bellevue Ave, Daytona Beach 32114 Anna Gonzalez	6-12	25	386/405-4509	

WAKULLA COUNTY

WAKULLA PUBLIC SCHOOLS

● **Wakulla Co School Dist** PID: 00204854   850/926-0065
   69 Arran Rd, Crawfordville 32327   Fax 850/926-0123

Schools: 11 \ *Teachers:* 314 \ *Students:* 5,255 \
Special Ed Students: 1,063 \ *LEP Students:* 8 \ *Ethnic:* African
American 11%, Hispanic 4%, Caucasian 85% \ *Exp:* $189 (Low) \
Poverty: 16% \ *Title I:* $943,417 \ *Special Education:* $6,876,000 \
Bilingual Education: $16,000 \ *Open-Close:* 08/12 - 05/22 \ *DTBP:* $155
(High)

Robert Pearce 1	Randy Beach 2,19	
Randy Bristol 3	Lisa McCloudy 4	
Pat Jones 5	Mike Smith 6	
Tanya English 7,36,57,58,79,81,85,90	Lori Sandgren 8	
Sunny Chancey 8,13,83,285,286,288,298*	Krista Sharin 12,16,69,88,296	
Dalynda Vause 27,31*	Dodd Walker 30*	
Gregory Thomas 67	Angela Walker 68,79,91,294	
Timothy Stephens 73,76,295	Allison Barrett 76	
Jim Griner 91	Tracy Dempsey 273	

Public Schs..Principal	Grd	Prgm	Enr/#Cls	SN	
© Coast Charter Sch 48 Shell Island Rd, Saint Marks 32355 Jeffery LaChapelle	K-8	T	133 9	91%	850/925-6344 Fax 850/925-6396
Crawfordville Elem Sch 379 Arran Rd, Crawfordville 32327 Louis Hernandez	K-5	T	573 40	39%	850/926-3641 Fax 850/926-4303
Medart Elem Sch 2558 Coastal Hwy, Crawfordville 32327 Stan Ward	PK-5	T	465 46	52%	850/962-4881 Fax 850/962-3953
Riversink Elem Sch 530 Lonnie Raker Ln, Crawfordville 32327 Simeon Nelson	K-5	T	443	41%	850/926-2664 Fax 850/926-9462
Riversprings Middle Sch 800 Spring Creek Hwy, Crawfordville 32327 Sabrina Yeomans	6-8	TV	546 35	48%	850/926-2300 Fax 850/926-2111
Shadeville Elem Sch 45 Warrior Way, Crawfordville 32327 Nicholas Weaver	K-5	T	598 46	36%	850/926-7155 Fax 850/926-5044
Ⓐ Wakulla Co Alt High Sch 69 Arran Rd, Crawfordville 32327	6-12	G	40 4		850/962-0100 Fax 850/962-3572
Wakulla Co High Sch 3237 Coastal Hwy, Crawfordville 32327 Michael Barwick	9-12	TV	1,490 65	45%	850/926-7125 Fax 850/926-8571
Wakulla Educational Center 87 Andrew J Hargrett Sr Rd, Crawfordville 32327 Laura Kelley	PK-PK		241 16		850/926-8111 Fax 850/926-1694
Wakulla Middle Sch 22 Jean Dr, Crawfordville 32327 Tolar Griffin	6-8	TV	504 50	52%	850/926-7143 Fax 850/926-3752

Wakulla Virtual 7001 Sch 69 Arran Rd, Crawfordville 32327 Sunny Chancey	K-12	100	850/926-0065	

WAKULLA PRIVATE SCHOOLS

Private Schs..Principal	Grd	Prgm	Enr/#Cls	SN	
Wakulla Christian Sch 1391 Crawfordville Hwy, Crawfordville 32327 Mrs Fell	PK-9		125		850/926-5583 Fax 850/926-5186

WALTON COUNTY

WALTON PUBLIC SCHOOLS

● **Walton Co School Dist** PID: 00204907   850/892-1100
   145 S Park St Ste 3, Defuniak Spgs 32435   Fax 850/892-1190

Schools: 21 \ *Teachers:* 591 \ *Students:* 10,201 \ *Special Ed Students:* 963
\ *LEP Students:* 343 \ *College-Bound:* 75% \ *Ethnic:* Asian 1%,
African American 6%, Hispanic 12%, Caucasian 80% \ *Exp:* $301 (High)
\ *Poverty:* 25% \ *Title I:* $3,105,013 \ *Special Education:* $2,052,000 \
Bilingual Education: $122,000 \ *Open-Close:* 08/12 - 05/28 \ *DTBP:* $152
(High)

A Russell Hughes 1	Stephanie Hofheinz 2,19	
Jeff Infinger 3	Jill Smith 3	
Robert Martin 4	Dennis Grey 5	
Crystal Apple 8,16,27,34,74*	Myca Chandler 11,296	
Crystal Apple 34,81,294	Cathy Hall 57,88	
William Eddins 67	Candy Bodie 68	
Kaye Black 68	Sonya Alford 68,78	
Randy Stafford 69,77*	Henry Martin 73,76	
Michael Pinnella 73	Chris Piland 76	
Janie Griffith 84	Charlie Morse 91	
Lorie Hughes 93		

Public Schs..Principal	Grd	Prgm	Enr/#Cls	SN	
Bay Elem Sch 118 Gilmore Rd, Santa Rsa Bch 32459 Meredith Spence	K-4		511 17	23%	850/622-5050 Fax 850/622-5059
Dune Lakes Elem Sch 6565 US Highway 98 East, Santa Rsa Bch 32459 **Meredith Spence**	K-5		700		850/622-5013 Fax 850/622-5014
Emerald Coast Middle Sch 4019 US Highway 98 E, Santa Rsa Bch 32459 Todd Drake	5-8		991	28%	850/622-5026 Fax 850/622-5027
Emerald Coast Technical Clg 761 N 20th St, Defuniak Spgs 32433 Mike Davis	Voc	AGT	100 11		850/892-1240 Fax 850/892-1249 f
Freeport Elem Sch 15381 331 Business, Freeport 32439 Kristin Lewis	PK-4	T	780 50	66%	850/892-1211 Fax 850/892-1219
Freeport High Sch 12615 331 Business, Freeport 32439 Milton Hope	9-12	TV	468 28	56%	850/892-1201 Fax 850/892-1209
Freeport Middle Sch 360 Kylea Laird Dr, Freeport 32439 Joshua Harrison	5-8	T	555 12	65%	850/892-1221 Fax 850/892-1229

79 Student Personnel	91 Safety/Security	275 Response To Intervention	298 Grant Writer/Ptnrships	**School Programs**	**Social Media**
80 Driver Ed/Safety	92 Magnet School	277 Remedial Math K-12	750 Chief Innovation Officer	A = Alternative Program	
81 Gifted/Talented	93 Parental Involvement	280 Literacy Coach	751 Chief of Staff	G = Adult Classes	f = Facebook
82 Video Services	95 Tech Prep Program	285 STEM	752 Social Emotional Learning	M = Magnet Program	
83 Substance Abuse Prev	97 Chief Information Officer	286 Digital Learning		T = Title I Schoolwide	t = Twitter
84 Erate	98 Chief Technology Officer	288 Common Core Standards	**Other School Types**	V = Career & Tech Ed Programs	
85 AIDS Education	270 Character Education	294 Accountability	Ⓐ = Alternative School		
88 Alternative/At Risk	271 Migrant Education	295 Network System	© = Charter School	New Schools are shaded	
89 Multi-Cultural Curriculum	273 Teacher Mentor	296 Title II Programs	Ⓜ = Magnet School	New Superintendents and Principals are bold	
90 Social Work	274 Before/After Sch	297 Webmaster	Ⓨ = Year-Round School	Personnel with email addresses are underscored	

FL—143

	Grd	Prgm	Enr/#Cls	SN	
Maude Saunders Elem Sch 416 John Baldwin Rd, Defuniak Spgs 32433 Pamela Jones	K-5	T	544 35	88%	850/892-1260 Fax 850/892-1269
Mossy Head Sch 13270 US Highway 90 W, Defuniak Spgs 32433 Ronita Hinote	PK-5	T	427 24	81%	850/892-1290 Fax 850/892-1299
Paxton Sch 21893 US Highway 331 N, Paxton 32538 Cindy Neale	PK-12	TV	802 42	60%	850/892-1230 Fax 850/892-1239
© Seacoast Collegiate High Sch 109 Greenway Trl, Santa Rsa Bch 32459 Dr Scott O'Prey	9-12		150		850/200-4170
© Seaside Neighborhood Sch 10 Smolian Cir, Santa Rsa Bch 32459 **Kim Mixson**	5-12		357 9	4%	850/231-0396 Fax 850/231-4725
South Walton High Sch 645 Greenway Trl, Santa Rsa Bch 32459 Alexis Tibbetts	9-12		859 32	28%	850/622-5020 Fax 850/622-5039
Van R Butler Elem Sch 6694 W County Highway 30A, Santa Rsa Bch 32459 Tammy Smith	PK-4		1,038 25	31%	850/622-5041 Fax 850/622-5048
Ⓐ Walton Academy [143] © 389 Dorsey Ave, Defuniak Spgs 32435 David Schmidt	6-12	T	177 10	91%	850/892-3999 Fax 850/892-7854
Walton High Sch 449 Walton Rd, Defuniak Spgs 32433 Janet Currid	9-12	TV	746 45	64%	850/892-1270 Fax 850/892-1279
Walton Learning Center 286 Gene Hurley Rd, Defuniak Spgs 32435 **Ray Sansom**	6-12		38		850/520-4642 Fax 850/892-8584
Walton Middle Sch 605 Bruce Ave, Defuniak Spgs 32435 William Campbell	6-8	I	682 46	75%	850/892-1280 Fax 850/892-1289
Walton Virtual Sch 145 S Park St Ste 3, Defuniak Spgs 32435 Randy Stafford	6-12		13		850/892-1100
West Defuniak Elem Sch 815 Lincoln Ave, Defuniak Spgs 32435 Darlene Paul	K-5	T	704 36	70%	850/892-1250 Fax 850/892-1259
Ⓐ Wise Center 555 Walton Rd, Defuniak Spgs 32433 Tracey Dickey	9-12		86		850/892-1111 Fax 850/892-1202

WALTON PRIVATE SCHOOLS

Private Schs..Principal	Grd	Prgm	Enr/#Cls	SN
Cornerstone Church Academy 2044 State Highway 83, Defuniak Spgs 32433 Doyle Redwine	1-12		50 1	850/892-9358 Fax 850/892-7130
First Christian Academy 216 Live Oak Ave E, Defuniak Spgs 32435 Lisa Tucker	K-5		35	850/892-2722

WASHINGTON PUBLIC SCHOOLS

● **Washington Co School Dist** PID: 00205004   850/638-6222
652 3rd St, Chipley 32428   Fax 850/638-6226

Schools: 9 \ *Teachers:* 265 \ *Students:* 3,400 \ *Special Ed Students:* 578
\ *LEP Students:* 35 \ *College-Bound:* 74% \ *Ethnic:* Asian 1%,
African American 17%, Hispanic 3%, Native American: 1%, Caucasian
79% \ *Exp:* $211 (Med) \ *Poverty:* 26% \ *Title I:* $1,175,259 \
Special Education: $4,315,000 \ *Bilingual Education:* $78,000 \
Open-Close: 08/12 - 05/22 \ *DTBP:* $158 (High)

Joseph Taylor	1	Lucy Carmichael	2
Pamela Corbin	2	Kyle Newsom	3,5,74,91
Blake Wilson	6*	Gerald Tranquille	6*
Susan Saunders	8,280,285	Troy People	11,58,69,77,79,83,296,298
Dr Lou Cleveland	67	Pat Collins	68,88,275
DeWayne Geoghagan	73,286	Kimberly Register	91
Elizabeth Arnold	294		

Public Schs..Principal	Grd	Prgm	Enr/#Cls	SN	
Chipley High Sch 1545 Brickyard Rd, Chipley 32428 Kyle Newsom	9-12	T	536 40	48%	850/638-6100 Fax 850/638-6017
Kate M Smith Elem Sch 1447 South Blvd, Chipley 32428 Lesa Burdeshaw	PK-4	T	923 54	63%	850/638-6220 Fax 850/638-6279
Roulhac Middle Sch 1535 Brickyard Rd, Chipley 32428 Nancy Holley	5-8	T	411 34	62%	850/638-6170 Fax 850/638-6319
Vernon Elem Sch 3665 Roche Ave, Vernon 32462 Steve Griffin	PK-5	T	619 35	83%	850/535-2486 Fax 850/535-1437
Vernon High Sch 3232 Moss Hill Rd, Vernon 32462 Brian Riviere	9-12	T	365 40	63%	850/535-2046 Fax 850/535-9364
Vernon Middle Sch 3190 Moss Hill Rd, Vernon 32462 Kimberly Register	6-8	T	303 25	76%	850/535-2807 Fax 850/535-1683
Washington Co Virtual Sch 652 3rd St, Chipley 32428 Gail Riley	K-12		9		850/638-6222
Ⓐ Washington Inst-Specialized Ed 680 2nd St, Chipley 32428 Samuel Cox	6-12	T	50	81%	850/638-6020 Fax 850/415-5024
Wave Sch 934 Tiger Loop, Chipley 32428 Brenda Basnaw	Spec		45		850/638-6222

WASHINGTON PRIVATE SCHOOLS

Private Schs..Principal	Grd	Prgm	Enr/#Cls	SN
Washington Co Christian Sch 1405 Brickyard Rd, Chipley 32428 Jason Haddock	PK-12		145 9	850/638-9227 Fax 850/638-9234 f

1	Superintendent	8	Curric/Instruct K-12	19	Chief Financial Officer	29	Family/Consumer Science	39	Social Studies K-12	49	English/Lang Arts Elem	59	Special Education Elem	69	Academic Assessment
2	Bus/Finance/Purchasing	9	Curric/Instruct Elem	20	Art K-12	30	Adult Education	40	Social Studies Elem	50	English/Lang Arts Sec	60	Special Education Sec	70	Research/Development
3	Buildings And Grounds	10	Curric/Instruct Sec	21	Art Elem	31	Career/Sch-to-Work K-12	41	Social Studies Sec	51	Reading K-12	61	Foreign/World Lang K-12	71	Public Information
4	Food Service	11	Federal Program	22	Art Sec	32	Career/Sch-to-Work Elem	42	Science K-12	52	Reading Elem	62	Foreign/World Lang Elem	72	Summer School
5	Transportation	12	Title I	23	Music K-12	33	Career/Sch-to-Work Sec	43	Science Elem	53	Reading Sec	63	Foreign/World Lang Sec	73	Instructional Tech
6	Athletic	13	Title V	24	Music Elem	34	Early Childhood Ed	44	Science Sec	54	Remedial Reading K-12	64	Religious Education K-12	74	Inservice Training
7	Health Services	15	Asst Superintendent	25	Music Sec	35	Health/Phys Education	45	Math K-12	55	Remedial Reading Elem	65	Religious Education Elem	75	Marketing/Distributive
		16	Instructional Media Svcs	26	Business Education	36	Guidance Services K-12	46	Math Elem	56	Remedial Reading Sec	66	Religious Education Sec	76	Info Systems
FL—144		17	Chief Operations Officer	27	Career & Tech Ed	37	Guidance Services Elem	47	Math Sec	57	Bilingual/ELL	67	School Board President	77	Psychological Assess
		18	Chief Academic Officer	28	Technology Education	38	Guidance Services Sec	48	English/Lang Arts K-12	58	Special Education K-12	68	Teacher Personnel	78	Affirmative Action

WASHINGTON REGIONAL CENTERS

• **Panhandle Area Ed Consortium** PID: 04433112   850/638-6131
753 West Blvd, Chipley 32428   Fax 850/638-6134

John Selover 1   Locia Esquivel 2
Dr Maria Pouncey 8,51,74,271   Faye Yongue 58
Charles Walker 68

?9 Student Personnel	**91** Safety/Security	**275** Response To Intervention	**298** Grant Writer/Ptnrships	**School Programs**
?0 Driver Ed/Safety	**92** Magnet School	**277** Remedial Math K-12	**750** Chief Innovation Officer	**A = Alternative Program**
?1 Gifted/Talented	**93** Parental Involvement	**280** Literacy Coach	**751** Chief of Staff	**G = Adult Classes**
?2 Video Services	**95** Tech Prep Program	**285** STEM	**752** Social Emotional Learning	**M = Magnet Program**
?3 Substance Abuse Prev	**97** Chief Information Officer	**286** Digital Learning		**T = Title I Schoolwide**
?4 Erate	**98** Chief Technology Officer	**288** Common Core Standards	**Other School Types**	**V = Career & Tech Ed Programs**
?5 AIDS Education	**270** Character Education	**294** Accountability	Ⓐ = Alternative School	
?8 Alternative/At Risk	**271** Migrant Education	**295** Network System	Ⓒ = **Charter School**	**New Schools are shaded**
?9 Multi-Cultural Curriculum	**273** Teacher Mentor	**296** Title II Programs	Ⓜ = **Magnet School**	**New Superintendents and Principals are bold**
?0 Social Work	**274** Before/After Sch	**297** Webmaster	Ⓨ = **Year-Round School**	**Personnel with email addresses are underscored**

Social Media

🅕 = Facebook

🅣 = Twitter

FL—145

SCHOOL DISTRICT	NO. OF SCHOOLS	ENROLL-MENT	COUNTY	PAGE
PUBLIC SCHOOL DISTRICTS				
Alachua Co School Dist	57	26,179	Alachua	1
Baker Co School Dist	8	5,000	Baker	3
Bay Co School Dist	47	27,390	Bay	4
Bradford Co School Dist	11	3,300	Bradford	5
Brevard Co School Dist	107	77,214	Brevard	6
Brevard Co Schs-Choice			Brevard	6
Brevard Co Schs-Elementary			Brevard	7
Brevard Co Schs-Secondary			Brevard	8
Broward Co Public Charter Schs			Broward	15
Broward Co Public Schools	311	270,550	Broward	10
Calhoun Co School Dist	6	2,100	Calhoun	20
Charlotte Co Public Sch Dist	26	16,300	Charlotte	20
Citrus Co School Dist	23	15,000	Citrus	22
Clay Co School Dist	48	35,609	Clay	23
Collier Co Public School Dist	62	47,816	Collier	25
Columbia Co School Dist	16	10,000	Columbia	27
DeSoto Co School Dist	5	5,238	De Soto	28
Dixie Co School Dist	5	2,149	Dixie	28
Duval Co PSD-Elementary Region			Duval	30
Duval Co PSD-HS Alt Region			Duval	32
Duval Co PSD-Middle Schools			Duval	32
Duval Co PSD-Turnaround School			Duval	33
Duval Co Public School Dist	193	129,000	Duval	29
Escambia Co School Dist	62	42,211	Escambia	36
Flagler Co School Dist	12	12,904	Flagler	39
Florida Virtual School Dist	3	5,540	Orange	93
Franklin Co School Dist	2	1,000	Franklin	40
Gadsden Co School Dist	14	5,000	Gadsden	40
Gilchrist Co School Dist	4	2,741	Gilchrist	41
Glades Co School Dist	4	1,650	Glades	41
Gulf Co School Dist	5	1,924	Gulf	41
Hamilton Co School Dist	2	1,650	Hamilton	42
Hardee Co School Dist	8	5,276	Hardee	42
Hendry Co School Dist	15	7,500	Hendry	43
Hernando Co School Dist	27	21,790	Hernando	43
Highlands Co School Dist	19	12,300	Highlands	44
Hillsborough Co Pub Sch Dist	292	220,287	Hillsborough	45
Hillsborough Co SD-Achievement			Hillsborough	47
Hillsborough Co SD-Area 1			Hillsborough	48
Hillsborough Co SD-Area 2			Hillsborough	49
Hillsborough Co SD-Area 3			Hillsborough	50
Hillsborough Co SD-Area 4			Hillsborough	51
Hillsborough Co SD-Area 5			Hillsborough	51
Holmes Co School Dist	7	3,500	Holmes	55
Jackson Co School Dist	17	6,500	Jackson	57
Jefferson Co School Dist	1	769	Jefferson	57
Lafayette Co School Dist	3	1,300	Lafayette	58
Lake Co School Dist	54	41,590	Lake	58
Lee Co School Dist	113	94,405	Lee	60
Leon Co School Dist	51	34,500	Leon	64
Levy Co School Dist	12	6,100	Levy	66
Liberty Co School Dist	5	1,373	Liberty	67
Madison Co School Dist	7	2,500	Madison	67
Manatee Co School Dist	68	49,200	Manatee	68
Marion Co Public Schools	57	42,624	Marion	70
Martin Co School Dist	29	19,244	Martin	72
Miami-Dade Co Public Sch Dist	467	350,101	Miami-Dade	74
Miami-Dade-Central Region			Miami-Dade	74
Miami-Dade-North Region			Miami-Dade	78
Miami-Dade-South Region			Miami-Dade	81
Monroe Co School Dist	19	8,849	Monroe	89
Nassau Co School Dist	18	12,000	Nassau	90
Okaloosa Co School Dist	46	30,638	Okaloosa	91
Okeechobee Co School Dist	11	6,200	Okeechobee	93
Orange Co PSD-Transformation			Orange	95
Orange Co Public School Dist	251	215,703	Orange	94
Orange Co Public SD-Dep Supt			Orange	95
Orange Co Public SD-East			Orange	96
Orange Co Public SD-High Sch			Orange	97
Orange Co Public SD-North			Orange	97
Orange Co Public SD-Southeast			Orange	98
Orange Co Public SD-Southwest			Orange	98
Orange Co Public SD-West			Orange	99
Osceola Co School Dist	77	67,709	Osceola	102
Palm Beach Co School Dist	223	195,455	Palm Beach	105
Palm Beach Co SD-Ctl Region			Palm Beach	106
Palm Beach Co SD-Glades Region			Palm Beach	107
Palm Beach Co SD-North Region			Palm Beach	108
Palm Beach Co SD-South Region			Palm Beach	109
Pasco Co School Dist	97	75,001	Pasco	112
Pasco CSD-Elementary Schools			Pasco	113
Pasco CSD-High Schools			Pasco	114
Pasco CSD-Middle Schools			Pasco	114
Pinellas Co School Dist	152	101,427	Pinellas	116
Pinellas Co Schools-Area 1			Pinellas	116
Pinellas Co Schools-Area 2			Pinellas	117
Pinellas Co Schools-Area 3			Pinellas	118
Pinellas Co Schools-Area 4			Pinellas	119
Polk Co School Dist	156	105,000	Polk	121
Polk Co SD-Four Regions HS			Polk	122
Polk Co SD-Four Regions MS			Polk	122
Polk Co SD-Multiple Pathways			Polk	123
Polk Co SD-NE & SE			Polk	124
Polk Co SD-School Improvement			Polk	124
Polk Co SD-W & N Ctrl			Polk	125
Putnam Co School Dist	21	11,000	Putnam	126
Santa Rosa Co School Dist	37	29,089	Santa Rosa	127
Sarasota Co School Dist	59	43,150	Sarasota	129
School Dist of Indian River Co	29	17,500	Indian River	55
Seminole Co Public School Dist	68	68,000	Seminole	131
St Johns Co School Dist	44	42,222	St Johns	134
St Lucie Co School Dist	45	44,210	St Lucie	136
Sumter Co School Dist	10	8,500	Sumter	137
Suwannee Co School Dist	9	5,776	Suwannee	138
Taylor Co School Dist	6	2,900	Taylor	139
Union Co School Dist	6	2,300	Union	139
Volusia Co School Dist	83	64,000	Volusia	140
Wakulla Co School Dist	11	5,255	Wakulla	143
Walton Co School Dist	21	10,201	Walton	143
Washington Co School Dist	9	3,400	Washington	144
CATHOLIC DIOCESE				
Archdiocese of Miami Ed Office	60	35,000	Miami-Dade	85
Diocese of Orlando Ed Office	37	14,673	Orange	100
Diocese of Palm Beach Ed Off	19	6,300	Palm Beach	110
Diocese of Venice Ed Office	15	4,350	Sarasota	131
Diocese Pensacola-Tallahassee	9	2,400	Escambia	38
Diocese St Augustine Ed Office	29	10,603	Duval	34
Diocese St Petersburg Ed Off	41	12,000	Pinellas	120
REGIONAL CENTERS				
FDLRS-Action			Orange	102
FDLRS-Alpha			Palm Beach	112
FDLRS-Crown			Duval	36
FDLRS-East Brevard			Brevard	10
FDLRS-Galaxy			St Lucie	137
FDLRS-Gateway			Hamilton	42
FDLRS-Gulfcoast			Pinellas	121
FDLRS-Heartland			Highlands	45
FDLRS-Hillsborough			Hillsborough	55
FDLRS-Island Coast			Lee	64
FDLRS-Miccosukee			Leon	66
FDLRS-Nefec			Putnam	127
FDLRS-Reach			Broward	20
FDLRS-South			Miami-Dade	89
FDLRS-Springs			Marion	72
FDLRS-Suncoast			Sarasota	131

SCHOOL DISTRICT	NO. OF SCHOOLS	ENROLL-MENT	COUNTY	PAGE	SCHOOL DISTRICT	NO. OF SCHOOLS	ENROLL-MENT	COUNTY	PAGE
FDLRS-Sunrise			Polk	126					
FDLRS-Westgate			Escambia	39					
Panhandle Area Ed Consortium			Washington	145					

NAME/District	JOB FUNCTIONS	PAGE
A		
Abbatinozzi, Paul/*St Johns Co School Dist*	6,88	134
Abrahams, Jacqueline/*Diocese of Orlando Ed Office*	2,11	100
Abrahante, Magaly, Dr/*Miami-Dade Co Public Sch Dist*	12,15,34,72	74
Acevedo-Alamo, Gianna/*Volusia Co School Dist*	12,57,61,89,271	140
Adams, Kay/*Sarasota Co School Dist*	76	129
Adams, Ryan/*Osceola Co School Dist*	6,80	102
Adams, Sean/*Columbia Co School Dist*	58	27
Aday, Silvia/*Miami-Dade Co Public Sch Dist*	47	74
Adkins, Gregory, Dr/*Lee Co School Dist*	1	60
Adkins, Joe/*Columbia Co School Dist*	11	27
Aemisegger, Sherry/*Pinellas Co School Dist*	68	116
Aemisegger, Shery/*FDLRS-Gulfcoast*	1,11	121
Agarwal, Deepak/*Palm Beach Co School Dist*	71,76,97	105
Aguilar, Margie/*Diocese of Orlando Ed Office*	73	100
Ajrab, Mina/*Sarasota Co School Dist*	71,297	129
Akes, Michael, Dr/*Polk Co School Dist*	8,15,18,74	122
Akin, Greg/*Volusia Co School Dist*	3,17	140
Alaback, Brian/*Escambia Co School Dist*	74	36
Alberts, Sonia/*Sarasota Co School Dist*	34,79,81	129
Albritton, Kim/*St Lucie Co School Dist*	2	136
Albritton, Laurie/*DeSoto Co School Dist*	2	28
Alege, Yinka/*Hillsborough Co SD-Achievement*	15	47
Alexander, Kristi/*Sarasota Co School Dist*	70	129
Alexander, Timothy/*Dixie Co School Dist*	67	29
Alexander, Todd/*Sarasota Co School Dist*	73	129
Alfano, Janet/*Hernando Co School Dist*	2	43
Alford, Sonya/*Walton Co School Dist*	68,78	143
Algazi, Louis, Dr/*Florida Virtual School Dist*	1	93
Allbritton, Danny/*Leon Co School Dist*	3	64
Allen, Darby/*Gilchrist Co School Dist*	9,280	41
Allen, Michael/*Osceola Co School Dist*	10	102
Allen, Tommy/*St Johns Co School Dist*	67	134
Allison, Kim/*Columbia Co School Dist*	7	27
Alonso, Melissa/*Hillsborough Co Pub Sch Dist*	52	46
Alonso, Orlando/*Miami-Dade Co Public Sch Dist*	5	74
Alt, Dawn/*Santa Rosa Co School Dist*	34	127
Alvarez, Sherree/*Bradford Co School Dist*	8,12,296	5
Alvarez, Tammy/*Marion Co Public Schools*	4	70
Alves, Lissette/*Miami-Dade Co Pub Sch Dist*	15,288	74
Amato, Joseph/*Hernando Co School Dist*	73,76	43
Amburgey, Steve/*Clay Co School Dist*	76,294	23
Amy, Kelly/*Volusia Co School Dist*	27	140
Anderson, Amy/*Manatee Co School Dist*	3	68
Anderson, Dan/*Taylor Co School Dist*	3	139
Anderson, Debbie/*Santa Rosa Co School Dist*	58	127
Anderson, Lakesha/*Duval Co Public School Dist*	5	29
Anderson, Nancy/*Flagler Co School Dist*	3	39
Anderson, Stephen/*Okaloosa Co School Dist*	4	91
Anderson, Terri/*Leon Co School Dist*	7	64
Androski, Kathy/*Citrus Co School Dist*	16,73,82,286,295	22
Ang, Cheng, Dr/*Collier Co Public School Dist*	69,76,294	25
Appelquist, Nicole/*St Johns Co School Dist*	12,13,296	134
Apple, Crystal/*Walton Co School Dist*	8,16,27,34,74	143
Apple, Crystal/*Walton Co School Dist*	34,81,294	143
Arbulu, Marianne/*Jefferson Co School Dist*	1	57
Archer, Stephanie/*Brevard Co School Dist*	15	6
Archer, Stephanie/*Brevard Co Schs-Choice*	15	6
Ardila, Suzanne/*Manatee Co School Dist*	88	68
Armbruster, Michael, Dr/*Orange Co Public School Dist*	15,27	94
Armstrong, Cynthia/*Pasco Co School Dist*	67	112
Arnette, Cherie/*Escambia Co School Dist*	39	36
Arnold, Elizabeth/*Washington Co School Dist*	294	144
Arnold, Sean/*Hernando Co School Dist*	3	43
Arnott, Jeff/*Brevard Co School Dist*	30	6
Artime, Carlos/*Collier Co Public School Dist*	27,31	25
Asplen, Brennan/*St Johns Co School Dist*	78	134
Aulakh, Pamela/*Brevard Co School Dist*	286	6
Aune, Peggy/*Collier Co Public School Dist*	8,15	25
Austin, Laura/*Santa Rosa Co School Dist*	88,286	127
Austin, Leigh/*Orange Co Public School Dist*	58,81	94
Avery-Moore, Angela/*Palm Beach Co SD-Glades Region*	1	107
Axford, Theresa/*Monroe Co School Dist*	35,83	89
Ayres, Van/*Hillsborough Co Pub Sch Dist*	8,15	46

NAME/District	JOB FUNCTIONS	PAGE
B		
Baker, Cecil/*Alachua Co School Dist*	4	1
Baker, Chris/*Clay Co School Dist*	76	23
Baker, Eugene/*Miami-Dade Co Public Sch Dist*	73,76,295	74
Baker, Mike/*St Johns Co School Dist*	2,3,4	134
Baker, Shirley/*Bay Co School Dist*	68,78	4
Balsamo, Joanne/*School Dist of Indian River Co*	298	55
Banks, Alexandria/*Marion Co Public Schools*	294	70
Banks, Kim/*Leon Co School Dist*	19	64
Barber, Elaine/*Calhoun Co School Dist*	2	20
Barber, Karen, Dr/*Santa Rosa Co School Dist*	11,271	127
Barber, Mike/*Manatee Co School Dist*	71	68
Barberi, Angela/*Escambia Co School Dist*	20,23	36
Barbieri, Frank/*Palm Beach Co School Dist*	67	105
Barch, Fred/*Palm Beach Co School Dist*	30	105
Barker, Dewey/*Escambia Co School Dist*	3	36
Barkholz, David/*Osceola Co School Dist*	3	102
Barmoha, Guy/*Broward Co Public Schools*	10	10
Barner, Angela/*Osceola Co School Dist*	69	102
Barnes, Patricia/*Polk Co SD-School Improvement*	15	124
Barratt, Evelyn/*Gilchrist Co School Dist*	76	41
Barrett, Allison/*Wakulla Co School Dist*	76	143
Barrett, Brian/*Okeechobee Co School Dist*	3,91	93
Barrett, Cynthia/*Brevard Co School Dist*	4	6
Barrett, Denise, Dr/*Florida Dept of Education*	81,280	1
Barrios, Tina/*Polk Co School Dist*	15,76,286	122
Barrow, Jeff/*Monroe Co School Dist*	3	89
Barrs, Jennifer/*Suwannee Co School Dist*	9,34	138
Bartholomew, Patrick/*Manatee Co School Dist*	91	68
Barton, Tammy/*Escambia Co School Dist*	45	36
Basilotto, James/*Sarasota Co School Dist*	5	129
Bass, Donna/*Diocese Pensacola-Tallahassee*	68,74	38
Bass, Renee/*Suwannee Co School Dist*	69,294	138
Bass, Scott/*Glades Co School Dist*	1	41
Battell, Kelly/*St Johns Co School Dist*	79,274	134
Bauer, Laurie/*Alachua Co School Dist*	68	1
Bauguss, Jeff/*Santa Rosa Co School Dist*	42,45	127
Baum, Richard/*Broward Co Public Schools*	69,70	10
Baumer, Steven/*Citrus Co School Dist*	68	22
Baxley, Melissa/*Holmes Co School Dist*	16,71,73,82,84,286,295	55
Baysura, Kelly/*School Dist of Indian River Co*	9	55
Beach, Randy/*Wakulla Co School Dist*	2,19	143
Beagle, James/*Escambia Co School Dist*	3	36
Beal, Lawrence/*Volusia Co School Dist*	6,88	140
Beeker, Tracey/*Sarasota Co School Dist*	71	129
Beekman, James/*Hillsborough Co Pub Sch Dist*	5	46
Beers, Ed/*Marion Co Public Schools*	295	70
Beers, Lynn/*Charlotte Co Public Sch Dist*	69	21
Begley, Michelle/*Duval Co Public School Dist*	2,19	29
Belcher, Maurice/*Taylor Co School Dist*	6,35	139
Belcher, Vaughn/*Polk Co School Dist*	5	122
Belinski, Joseph, Dr/*Diocese of Orlando Ed Office*	70	100
Bell, Donald/*Clay Co School Dist*	3	23
Bell, Leslie/*Santa Rosa Co School Dist*	4	127
Bell, Lisa/*Okeechobee Co School Dist*	4	93
Bell, Lisa/*St Johns Co School Dist*	58,77,81	134
Benbow, Sheena/*Hardee Co School Dist*	68	42
Bender, Barbara/*Collier Co Public School Dist*	5	25
Bender, Brian/*School Dist of Indian River Co*	91	55
Bennett, Al/*Pinellas Co School Dist*	6,35,80	116
Bennett, Deelynn/*Charlotte Co Public Sch Dist*	27	21
Bennett, Morgan/*Levy Co School Dist*	76	66
Bennett, Vivian/*Glades Co School Dist*	58,79,270,275	41
Benson, Amy/*Manatee Co School Dist*	4	68
Bentolila, Jacques, Dr/*Miami-Dade-Central Region*	2,73	74
Benvenuti, Richard/*Miami-Dade Co Public Sch Dist*	16	74
Berg, Lisa/*Manatee Co School Dist*	73	68
Berntsen, Nita/*Alachua Co School Dist*	2	1
Berryhill, Tammy/*Pasco Co School Dist*	15	112
Bertram, MacKenzie/*Osceola Co School Dist*	74	102
Berube, Brenda/*Osceola Co School Dist*	27,30,31	102
Bess, Angela, Dr/*Palm Beach Co School Dist*	88	105
Bible, Billiejo/*Gilchrist Co School Dist*	68	41
Billon, Fernand/*Collier Co Public School Dist*	57,61	25
Binder, Nicole/*Hillsborough Co Pub Sch Dist*	69,294	46

1 Superintendent	16 Instructional Media Svcs	30 Adult Education	44 Science Sec	58 Special Education K-12	72 Summer School	88 Alternative/At Risk	277 Remedial Math K-12
2 Bus/Finance/Purchasing	17 Chief Operations Officer	31 Career/Sch-to-Work K-12	45 Math K-12	59 Special Education Elem	73 Instructional Tech	89 Multi-Cultural Curriculum	280 Literacy Coach
3 Buildings And Grounds	18 Chief Academic Officer	32 Career/Sch-to-Work Elem	46 Math Elem	60 Special Education Sec	74 Inservice Training	90 Social Work	285 STEM
4 Food Service	19 Chief Financial Officer	33 Career/Sch-to-Work Sec	47 Math Sec	61 Foreign/World Lang K-12	75 Marketing/Distributive	91 Safety/Security	286 Digital Learning
5 Transportation	20 Art K-12	34 Early Childhood Ed	48 English/Lang Arts K-12	62 Foreign/World Lang Elem	76 Info Systems	92 Magnet School	288 Common Core Standards
6 Athletic	21 Art Elem	35 Health/Phys Education	49 English/Lang Arts Elem	63 Foreign/World Lang Sec	77 Psychological Assess	93 Parental Involvement	294 Accountability
7 Health Services	22 Art Sec	36 Guidance Services K-12	50 English/Lang Arts Sec	64 Religious Education K-12	78 Affirmative Action	95 Tech Prep Program	295 Network System
8 Curric/Instruct K-12	23 Music K-12	37 Guidance Services Elem	51 Reading K-12	65 Religious Education Elem	79 Student Personnel	97 Chief Information Officer	296 Title II Programs
9 Curric/Instruct Elem	24 Music Elem	38 Guidance Services Sec	52 Reading Elem	66 Religious Education Sec	80 Driver Ed/Safety	98 Chief Technology Officer	297 Webmaster
10 Curric/Instruct Sec	25 Music Sec	39 Social Studies K-12	53 Reading Sec	67 School Board President	81 Gifted/Talented	270 Character Education	298 Grant Writer/Ptnrships
11 Federal Program	26 Business Education	40 Social Studies Elem	54 Remedial Reading K-12	68 Teacher Personnel	82 Video Services	271 Migrant Education	750 Chief Innovation Officer
12 Title I	27 Career & Tech Ed	41 Social Studies Sec	55 Remedial Reading Elem	69 Academic Assessment	83 Substance Abuse Prev	273 Teacher Mentor	751 Chief of Staff
13 Title V	28 Technology Education	42 Science K-12	56 Remedial Reading Sec	70 Research/Development	84 Erate	274 Before/After Sch	752 Social Emotional Learning
15 Asst Superintendent	29 Family/Consumer Science	43 Science Elem	57 Bilingual/ELL	71 Public Information	85 AIDS Education	275 Response To Intervention	

NAME/District	JOB FUNCTIONS	PAGE
Calderone, Tina/*Seminole Co Public School Dist*	67	132
Callahan, Jessica/*FDLRS-Nefec*	73	127
Camacho, Severina/*Duval Co Public School Dist*	12	29
Campbell, Leslie/*Osceola Co School Dist*	58,296	102
Campbell, Sherie/*FDLRS-Hillsborough*	73	55
Campese, Matt/*Duval Co Public School Dist*	39,42	29
Canaday, Andi/*Okeechobee Co School Dist*	74,280	93
Canamas, Darrell/*St Lucie Co School Dist*	69,294	136
Cannady, Teri/*Lee Co School Dist*	11	60
Canning, Lori, Dr/*Broward Co Public Schools*	34,57	10
Canova, Cheryl/*Bradford Co School Dist*	67	5
Cantalupo, Denise, Dr/*Sarasota Co School Dist*	69,70,294,298	129
Cantees, Stephen/*Sarasota Co School Dist*	10,80	129
Capley, Mark/*Martin Co School Dist*	73,295	72
Caraker, Tammy, Dr/*Collier Co Public School Dist*	15	25
Caravello, Ralph/*Seminole Co Public School Dist*	2	131
Cardenas, Tracey/*FDLRS-Suncoast*	1	131
Cardenas, Tracey/*Sarasota Co School Dist*	79	129
Cardona, Minnie/*Seminole Co Public School Dist*	57,61,89	132
Caren, Ethan/*Clay Co School Dist*	295	23
Carias, Ingrid/*Duval Co Public School Dist*	57	29
Carlin, Denise, Dr/*Lee Co School Dist*	71	60
Carlson, Teresa/*Clay Co School Dist*	58	23
Carlton, Brenda/*Taylor Co School Dist*	67	139
Carmichael, Lucy/*Washington Co School Dist*	2	144
Carnley, Conni/*Santa Rosa Co School Dist*	15,68,78	127
Carr, Bill/*Gulf Co School Dist*	2,4,15,68,71	41
Carr, John/*Lake Co School Dist*	3,5,15,91	58
Carr, Mary/*Sarasota Co School Dist*	2	129
Carranza, Cristian/*Miami-Dade Co Public Sch Dist*	285	74
Carroll, Kristin/*Putnam Co School Dist*	68	127
Carswell, Lex/*Columbia Co School Dist*	1	27
Carter, Don/*St Lucie Co School Dist*	5	136
Carter, Michael/*Bay Co School Dist*	5	4
Carvalho, Alberto/*Miami-Dade Co Public Sch Dist*	1	74
Carver, Jeffrey/*School Dist of Indian River Co*	2	55
Carver, Mark/*Suwannee Co School Dist*	3,91	138
Cason, Robyn/*Gilchrist Co School Dist*	82	41
Cassels, Tammy/*Sarasota Co School Dist*	58	129
Cassidy, Micha/*Hamilton Co School Dist*	73,76,295	42
Castro, Joyce/*Miami-Dade Co Public Sch Dist*	15,68	74
Caudill, Debbie/*Seminole Co Public School Dist*	58	132
Caudle, Everett/*Alachua Co School Dist*	11,296,298	1
Causseaux, Derek/*Liberty Co School Dist*	6	67
Cavinee, Mark/*Osceola Co School Dist*	3	102
Cedeno, Barbara/*Lee Co School Dist*	3	60
Cells, Frances/*Lake Co School Dist*	27,31	58
Cernich, Cherise/*Citrus Co School Dist*	7,68,91	22
Cerra, Shawn/*Broward Co Public Schools*	6	10
Cespedes, Argely/*Hernando Co School Dist*	3	43
Chambers, Marcus/*Okaloosa Co School Dist*	1	91
Champion, Linda/*Florida Dept of Education*	2,15	1
Chancey, Sunny/*Wakulla Co School Dist*	8,13,83,285,286,288,298	143
Chandler, Myca/*Walton Co School Dist*	11,296	143
Chapman, Shari/*Manatee Co School Dist*	58	68
Chapp, Tom/*Nassau Co School Dist*	4	90
Charbonnet, Jeffry/*Alachua Co School Dist*	69,70	1
Charles, Rob, Dr/*Bradford Co School Dist*	10	5
Chason, Jenna/*Liberty Co School Dist*	76	67
Chastain, Evelyn/*Bradford Co School Dist*	9	5
Chastain, Evelyn/*Clay Co School Dist*	9,12	23
Chatman, Steve/*Okaloosa Co School Dist*	78	91
Cheatham, Russell/*Brevard Co School Dist*	15,73,76,95,97,295	6
Cherry, Melissa/*Madison Co School Dist*	90	67
Chesley, Chad/*Seminole Co Public School Dist*	4	131
Chesser, Amalia/*Dixie Co School Dist*	38	29
Chevalier, Jennifer/*St Lucie Co School Dist*	298	136
Chichitano, Peter/*Flagler Co School Dist*	3	39
Childers, Vince/*Escambia Co School Dist*	3	36
Christian, Helen/*Sumter Co School Dist*	9,12	137
Christian, Jessica/*Sumter Co School Dist*	280	138
Christian, Kevin/*Marion Co Public Schools*	71	70
Churchwell, Lisa/*Bay Co School Dist*	296	4
Cicchetti, Mike/*Volusia Co School Dist*	73,76,295	140
Clark, Anthony/*Marion Co Public Schools*	73	70
Clark, Gina/*Brevard Co School Dist*	82	6

NAME/District	JOB FUNCTIONS	PAGE
Clark, Heather/*School Dist of Indian River Co*	58	55
Clark, Heather/*St Lucie Co School Dist*	79	136
Clark, James/*Sarasota Co School Dist*	35	129
Clark, Michael/*St Johns Co School Dist*	297	134
Clark, Paula/*Hernando Co School Dist*	11,74,296	43
Clark, Scott/*Osceola Co School Dist*	16,27,73,82,84	102
Clark, Stephen/*Sarasota Co School Dist*	3	129
Clark, Willie/*Manatee Co School Dist*	7,77	68
Clarke, John/*Diocese of Palm Beach Ed Off*	8,15	110
Clarke, Karen/*Alachua Co School Dist*	1	1
Clarke, Teresa/*Sarasota Co School Dist*	3,5	129
Class, James/*Pasco Co School Dist*	2	112
Cleveland, Lou, Dr/*Washington Co School Dist*	67	144
Clinch, Marc/*Osceola Co School Dist*	3,17	102
Cline, Adrian/*DeSoto Co School Dist*	1	28
Cline, Jane/*Brevard Co School Dist*	9,12,15,16,34,93,280	6
Cline, Jane/*Brevard Co Schs-Elementary*	15	7
Coates, Chuck/*Flagler Co School Dist*	3	39
Cobb, Neda/*Hardee Co School Dist*	76	42
Cobbe, Linda/*Pasco Co School Dist*	71	112
Cochrane, Steven/*Polk Co SD-Multiple Pathways*	15	123
Cockcroft, Amy/*Lake Co School Dist*	8,69,74	58
Cockrell, Danica/*Pasco Co School Dist*	90	112
Codelia, Annette/*Manatee Co School Dist*	9	68
Codie, Robert/*Lee Co School Dist*	5	60
Coker, Amanda/*Sarasota Co School Dist*	295	129
Coker, Wendy/*Okeechobee Co School Dist*	58,77,81,85,90,275	93
Cole, James/*Leon Co School Dist*	5	64
Coleman, Camille, Dr/*Palm Beach Co SD-North Region*	1	108
Coleman, Tiffanie/*Santa Rosa Co School Dist*	58	127
Collins, Megan/*Florida Dept of Education*	71	1
Collins, Pat/*Washington Co School Dist*	68,88,275	144
Collins, Sandra/*FDLRS-Action*	1,11	102
Collins, Tracy/*Polk Co SD-Four Regions MS*	15	122
Colo, Laura, Dr/*Escambia Co School Dist*	12	36
Combs, Amy/*Liberty Co School Dist*	4,69,286	67
Combs, Courtney/*Escambia Co School Dist*	68	36
Combs, Karen/*Osceola Co School Dist*	88	102
Compton Twist, Jill/*Highlands Co School Dist*	67	45
Conage, Mary/*Pinellas Co School Dist*	298	116
Conbass, Chris/*Hamilton Co School Dist*	91	42
Cone, Steffond/*Miami-Dade Co Public Sch Dist*	15	74
Connell, Jim/*Clay Co School Dist*	3	23
Connelly, Janet/*Sumter Co School Dist*	7	137
Connor, Terry/*Clay Co School Dist*	8,18	23
Conte, Tony/*Charlotte Co Public Sch Dist*	5	21
Conway, Deacon Scott/*Diocese St Augustine Ed Office*	1	34
Conway, La Cheron/*Hardee Co School Dist*	4	42
Cook, Deborah/*Hillsborough Co Pub Sch Dist*	8,18,288	46
Cook, Kerry/*Marion Co Public Schools*	3	70
Coomer, Judith/*Sarasota Co School Dist*	4	129
Coon, Alicia/*Santa Rosa Co School Dist*	23	127
Coopea, Kimberly/*St Lucie Co School Dist*	50	136
Copa, Juan/*Florida Dept of Education*	15,70,294	1
Cope-Otterson, Tammy/*Osceola Co School Dist*	68	102
Copeman, Kim/*School Dist of Indian River Co*	2	55
Coppock, Angela/*Columbia Co School Dist*	30,31	27
Corbett, William, Dr/*Pinellas Co School Dist*	15	116
Corbin, Pamela/*Washington Co School Dist*	2	144
Corcoran, Mitsi/*Sarasota Co School Dist*	2,15,19	129
Corcoran, Richard/*Florida Dept of Education*	1	1
Corkin, Jennifer/*Martin Co School Dist*	34	72
Corr, Patricia/*Volusia Co School Dist*	15	140
Corkin, William/...		
Cory, Jackie/*Clay Co School Dist*	68	23
Cote, Anna Marie, Dr/*Seminole Co Public School Dist*	15,78	132
Coudella, Kristin/*Monroe Co School Dist*	16	89
Coughlin, Madonna/*Columbia Co School Dist*	4	27
Coupe, Joe/*Manatee Co School Dist*	295	68
Cowart, Tom/*Alachua Co School Dist*	3	1
Cox-McKimmey, Jennifer/*Charlotte Co Public Sch Dist*	7,83,85	21
Cox, Alan, Dr/*Leon Co School Dist*	7,15	64
Cox, Joe/*Bradford Co School Dist*	3	5
Cox, Nicole/*Manatee Co School Dist*	58	68
Craft, Tracey/*Sarasota Co School DIST*	295	129
Craig, Pamela, Dr/*Manatee Co School Dist*	74,270,285	68
Crawford, David/*Baker Co School Dist*	91	3

1	Superintendent	16	Instructional Media Svcs	30	Adult Education	44	Science Sec	58	Special Education K-12	72	Summer School	88	Alternative/At Risk	277	Remedial Math K-12
2	Bus/Finance/Purchasing	17	Chief Operations Officer	31	Career/Sch-to-Work K-12	45	Math K-12	59	Special Education Elem	73	Instructional Tech	89	Multi-Cultural Curriculum	280	Literacy Coach
3	Buildings And Grounds	18	Chief Academic Officer	32	Career/Sch-to-Work Elem	46	Math Elem	60	Special Education Sec	74	Inservice Training	90	Social Work	285	STEM
4	Food Service	19	Chief Financial Officer	33	Career/Sch-to-Work Sec	47	Math Sec	61	Foreign/World Lang K-12	75	Marketing/Distributive	91	Safety/Security	286	Digital Learning
5	Transportation	20	Art K-12	34	Early Childhood Ed	48	English/Lang Arts K-12	62	Foreign/World Lang Elem	76	Info Systems	92	Magnet School	288	Common Core Standards
6	Athletic	21	Art Elem	35	Health/Phys Education	49	English/Lang Arts Elem	63	Foreign/World Lang Sec	77	Psychological Assess	93	Parental Involvement	294	Accountability
7	Health Services	22	Art Sec	36	Guidance Services K-12	50	English/Lang Arts Sec	64	Religious Education K-12	78	Affirmative Action	95	Tech Prep Program	295	Network System
8	Curric/Instruct K-12	23	Music K-12	37	Guidance Services Elem	51	Reading K-12	65	Religious Education Elem	79	Student Personnel	97	Chief Information Officer	296	Title II Programs
9	Curric/Instruct Elem	24	Music Elem	38	Guidance Services Sec	52	Reading Elem	66	Religious Education Sec	80	Driver Ed/Safety	98	Chief Technology Officer	297	Webmaster
10	Curric/Instruct Sec	25	Music Sec	39	Social Studies K-12	53	Reading Sec	67	School Board President	81	Gifted/Talented	270	Character Education	298	Grant Writer/Ptnrships
11	Federal Program	26	Business Education	40	Social Studies Elem	54	Remedial Reading K-12	68	Teacher Personnel	82	Video Services	271	Migrant Education	750	Chief Innovation Officer
12	Title I	27	Career & Tech Ed	41	Social Studies Sec	55	Remedial Reading Elem	69	Academic Assessment	83	Substance Abuse Prev	273	Teacher Mentor	751	Chief of Staff
13	Title V	28	Technology Education	42	Science K-12	56	Remedial Reading Sec	70	Research/Development	84	Erate	274	Before/After Sch	752	Social Emotional Learning
15	Asst Superintendent	29	Family/Consumer Science	43	Science Elem	57	Bilingual/ELL	71	Public Information	85	AIDS Education	275	Response To Intervention		

NAME/District	JOB FUNCTIONS	PAGE
Dustin, Katherine/*Sumter Co School Dist*	13,57,58,77,81	137
Duval, Susan/*Hernando Co School Dist*	67	43
Dyer, Diane/*Flagler Co School Dist*	8,16,31,285,288,296,298	39
Dyer, Kati, Dr/*Volusia Co School Dist*	70,74	140
Dykes, Diana/*Gulf Co School Dist*	5	41

E

NAME/District	JOB FUNCTIONS	PAGE
Eakins, Jeff/*Hillsborough Co Pub Sch Dist*	1	45
Eastmon, Brandon/*Levy Co School Dist*	2	66
Ebersole, Raymond/*Sarasota Co School Dist*	295	129
Echevarria, Ana/*Collier Co Public School Dist*	5	25
Eddins, William/*Walton Co School Dist*	67	143
Edison, Jeff/*Levy Co School Dist*	1	66
Edwards, Brenda/*Duval Co Public School Dist*	91	29
Edwards, Cheryl/*Charlotte Co Public Sch Dist*	10,288	21
Edwards, Donald, Dr/*Archdiocese of Miami Ed Office*	15	85
Edwards, Kimberley/*Bay Co School Dist*	58	4
Edwards, Robert/*Lafayette Co School Dist*	1	58
Egley, Robert/*Hendry Co School Dist*	8,13,15,16,45,51,286,288	43
Egnor, Timothy/*Volusia Co School Dist*	1	140
Elder, Krista/*FDLRS-Sunrise*	73	126
Eldon, Darryl/*Lee Co School Dist*	84	60
Ellers, David/*Marion Co Public Schools*	77,79,81,90	70
Ellington, Kelly/*Sarasota Co School Dist*	74,296	129
Elliott, Brian/*St Johns Co School Dist*	76	134
Elliott, Jeff/*Escambia Co School Dist*	76	36
Ellis, Bryce/*Clay Co School Dist*	3	23
Ellis, Tami/*Okaloosa Co School Dist*	42,285	91
Ellison, Karla/*Sarasota Co School Dist*	4	129
Elwood, Amy/*Seminole Co Public School Dist*	58	132
Embry, Debi/*Brevard Co School Dist*	274	6
Emerson, Bill/*Santa Rosa Co School Dist*	8,15,69,71	127
Ems, Kate/*St Lucie Co School Dist*	39	136
England, Becca/*St Johns Co School Dist*	49	134
English, Tanya/*Wakulla Co School Dist*	7,36,57,58,79,81,85,90	143
Enos, Colin/*Sarasota Co School Dist*	73	129
Eplin, Chane/*Florida Dept of Education*	57	1
Esposito, Sonia, Dr/*Osceola Co School Dist*	92	102
Esquivel, Locia/*Panhandle Area Ed Consortium*	2	145
Estes, Debra/*Manatee Co School Dist*	57	68
Etheridge, Brad/*Levy Co School Dist*	67	66
Etter, Carol/*Osceola Co School Dist*	16,73	102
Eubanks, Pamela/*Marion Co Public Schools*	274	70
Eunice, Maria/*Alachua Co School Dist*	4	1
Evans, Dan, Dr/*Pinellas Co School Dist*	69,70,294	116
Evans, Jerry/*Dixie Co School Dist*	3,73,91	28
Evans, Scott/*Orange Co Public School Dist*	20,23	94
Everett, Ann/*Polk Co School Dist*	51	122
Everette, Chris/*Escambia Co School Dist*	92,286	36
Eversdyke, Melissa/*Martin Co School Dist*	30	72

F

NAME/District	JOB FUNCTIONS	PAGE
Fabal, Randy/*Monroe Co School Dist*	5	89
Faber, Debbie/*Charlotte Co Public Sch Dist*	2	21
Fabien, Rolanda, Dr/*Volusia Co School Dist*	58	140
Fagan, Ronald/*Duval Co Public School Dist*	2	29
Faggione, James/*Monroe Co School Dist*	4	89
Faircloth, Leon/*Bay Co School Dist*	73,286	4
Faramo, Dianne/*Collier Co Public School Dist*	49,52	25
Farkas, Chris/*Hillsborough Co Pub Sch Dist*	3,5,17	46
Farmer, Bill/*Manatee Co School Dist*	3	68
Farmer, Susan/*Nassau Co School Dist*	2	90
Farnsworth, Chad/*Lake Co School Dist*	15,68	58
Farrar, Suzanne/*Bay Co School Dist*	10	4
Faulk, Carlton/*Union Co School Dist*	1	139
Faulkner, Melanie/*Hillsborough Co Pub Sch Dist*	21,24	46
Fazzino, Tabitha/*Miami Dade Co Public Sch Dist*	294	74
Fealey, James/*Hendry Co School Dist*	68	43
Featherstone, Ginger, Dr/*Martin Co School Dist*	15	72
Fedderman, Diane/*Palm Beach Co School Dist*	8,15	105
Feild, Gisela/*Miami-Dade Co Public Sch Dist*	69,70	74
Fennoy, Donald, Dr/*Palm Beach Co School Dist*	1	105
Fenske, Taryn/*Florida Dept of Education*	71	1
Ferguson, Casey/*Sumter Co School Dist*	31	138
Fernandez, Donna/*Sarasota Co School Dist*	76	129
Fernandez, Lissette/*Manatee Co School Dist*	11	68

NAME/District	JOB FUNCTIONS	PAGE
Fernandez, Patricia/*Miami-Dade Co Public Sch Dist*	15,68	74
Ferrante, Victor/*Miami-Dade Co Public Sch Dist*	274	74
Ferrara, James/*Sarasota Co School Dist*	295	129
Ferren, Michelle/*Seminole Co Public School Dist*	58	132
Field, Emma/*Volusia Co School Dist*	12	140
Figgett, Katrina/*Florida Dept of Education*	42,45,73	1
Figueroa, Maria/*Hardee Co School Dist*	76	42
Finley, Beverly/*Alachua Co School Dist*	68	1
Finley, Charles/*Taylor Co School Dist*	10	139
Firlik, Genele/*Hernando Co School Dist*	3	43
Fitzgerald, Michelle/*Hillsborough Co SD-Achievement*	1	47
Fitzpatrick, Don/*Alachua Co School Dist*	57	1
Fitzpatrick, Janene/*Suwannee Co School Dist*	8,15	138
Fitzpatrick, Tommy/*Clay Co School Dist*	5	23
Flanagan, Ana/*Okaloosa Co School Dist*	51	91
Flanigan, Jacquelyn, Dr/*Diocese of Orlando Ed Office*	15	100
Flannery, Katrina/*Nassau Co School Dist*	4	90
Flecha, Shanna/*Lee Co School Dist*	74,79	60
Flenniken, Amber/*Okaloosa Co School Dist*	4	91
Fletcher, Jane/*Florida Dept of Education*	15,294	1
Fletcher, Sandra/*Madison Co School Dist*	2	67
Flock, James/*Lee Co School Dist*	3	60
Flood, Brooke/*School Dist of Indian River Co*	34	55
Flores, Yolanda/*Collier Co Public School Dist*	30	25
Flowers, Renee/*Pinellas Co School Dist*	67	116
Fontan, Patricia/*FDLRS-East Brevard*	11	10
Fontana, Mimi/*Collier Co Public School Dist*	76	25
Foote, Michael/*Sumter Co School Dist*	5	137
Ford, Joy/*Seminole Co Public School Dist*	3	131
Forde, Gerie/*Levy Co School Dist*	285,298	66
Forfar, Justin/*St Johns Co School Dist*	295	134
Forhand, Carol/*Dixie Co School Dist*	12,271	29
Forson, Tim/*St Johns Co School Dist*	1	134
Forsythe, Cindy/*Columbia Co School Dist*	16,28,73,286	27
Fortier, Henry/*Diocese of Orlando Ed Office*	1	100
Fortner, Valdenora/*Alachua Co School Dist*	12	1
Fossa, James/*Clay Co School Dist*	3	23
Foster, Janice/*Glades Co School Dist*	36	41
Fowler, Janet/*Dixie Co School Dist*	11,84,298	29
Fox, Mark/*Pasco Co School Dist*	3	112
Frakes, Russell/*Okaloosa Co School Dist*	88	91
France, Laura/*Putnam Co School Dist*	8,15,34,54,74,288	127
Franceschi, Janice/*Osceola Co School Dist*	74	102
Francis, Philip/*Hillsborough Co Pub Sch Dist*	37	46
Francis, Rick/*Seminole Co Public School Dist*	91	132
Frangella, Frank/*Martin Co School Dist*	91	73
Frank, Serena/*Florida Virtual School Dist*	73,76,295	93
Franklin, Chris/*Jackson Co School Dist*	8,285,288,296	57
Frazee, Leslie/*Volusia Co School Dist*	12	140
Frazee, Mike/*Volusia Co School Dist*	5	140
Frazier, Derrick/*Alachua Co School Dist*	8,47	1
Frazier, Scott/*Collier Co Public School Dist*	71	25
Freck, Richard/*Sarasota Co School Dist*	295	129
Freeman, Chauncey/*Alachua Co School Dist*	68	1
Freeman, Cheryl/*St Johns Co School Dist*	93	134
Freeman, Dave/*Flagler Co School Dist*	3	39
Freeman, Sherri, Dr/*Lee Co School Dist*	74,79	60
Freeman, Susan/*Volusia Co School Dist*	15	140
Freeman, Valerie/*Alachua Co School Dist*	78	1
Friedman, Sid/*Sarasota Co School Dist*	79	129
Friedt, Matti/*Polk Co School Dist*	34	122
Fritz, Scott, Dr/*Osceola Co School Dist*	15,751	102
Fritzler, Patricia/*Orange Co Public SD-West*	1	99
Frontz, Charles/*Collier Co Public School Dist*	8	25
Fuller, Carrie/*DeSoto Co School Dist*	8,16,83,273,285	28
Fuller, Dan/*Bay Co School Dist*	2	4
Fulton-Collins, Donte/*Broward Co Public Charter Schs*	15	15
Fussell, Debbie/*Escambia Co School Dist*	2	36
Futch, Amanda/*Bradford Co School Dist*	752	5

G

NAME/District	JOB FUNCTIONS	PAGE
Gabrowski, Garrett/*Martin Co School Dist*	3	72
Gadd, Ray/*Pasco Co School Dist*	15	112
Gaines, Michelle/*Florida Dept of Education*	35	1
Galbraith, Channah/*Lafayette Co School Dist*	16	58
Gann, Sheila/*Clay Co School Dist*	68	23

NAME/District	JOB FUNCTIONS	PAGE
Gannon, Sandy/Sarasota Co School Dist	2	129
Ganus, Karen/Dixie Co School Dist	76,297	29
Garbacz, Darci/Palm Beach Co School Dist	2,298	105
Garcia, Candy/Clay Co School Dist	76,294	23
Garcia, Elena/Manatee Co School Dist	296,298	68
Gard-Harrold, Shawn/Seminole Co Public School Dist	8,296	132
Gardner, Charlotte/Jackson Co School Dist	67	57
Gardner, Stephanie/Citrus Co School Dist	76	22
Garnes, Deirdre/Seminole Co Public School Dist	83,88	132
Gartin, Linda/Gilchrist Co School Dist	10,13,56,285	41
Gary, Dawana/Marion Co Public Schools	78	70
Garza, Martha/Hardee Co School Dist	3	42
Gatzke, Charlene/Lake Co School Dist	4	58
Gavilan, Deborah, Dr/Broward Co Public Schools	274	10
Gay, Gerald/Gadsden Co School Dist	5	40
Gayle, Michelle, Dr/Leon Co School Dist	15,70	64
Gaylord, Fred/Columbia Co School Dist	3	27
Gaylord, Laurie/Martin Co School Dist	1	72
Gaynes, Lisa/Diocese of Palm Beach Ed Off	74	110
Geeting, Renee/Okeechobee Co School Dist	15	93
Geist, Lynnanne/Pinellas Co School Dist	4	116
Gelo, Gary/Diocese of Palm Beach Ed Off	1	110
Gent, Wayne/FDLRS-Galaxy	1	137
Gent, Wayne/St Lucie Co School Dist	1	136
Gentilli, Sally/Bay Co School Dist	57	4
Geoghagan, DeWayne/Washington Co School Dist	73,286	144
Gergora, Georgann/School Dist of Indian River Co	7	55
Gerlach, Holly/Marion Co Public Schools	280,285	70
Ghandour, Tarek/Duval Co Public School Dist	3	29
Giacolone, Debra/Sarasota Co School Dist	79	129
Gibbs, Gregory/Escambia Co School Dist	3	36
Giblin, Jennifer/Flagler Co School Dist	36	39
Gibowski, Vicki/Escambia Co School Dist	10	36
Gibson, Carol/Madison Co School Dist	67	67
Gibson, Shirin, Dr/Manatee Co School Dist	8,70	68
Gilbert, Kimberly/Orange Co Public School Dist	11	94
Gilbert, Lora/Orange Co Public School Dist	4	94
Gilette, John/St Lucie Co School Dist	3	136
Gilliland, Kimberly/Volusia Co School Dist	58	140
Gillis, Leslie/Sarasota Co School Dist	2	129
Gillit, Cary/Sarasota Co School Dist	295	129
Girard, Beverly, Dr/Sarasota Co School Dist	4	129
Gittens, Gwynetta/Lee Co School Dist	67	60
Gleason, Virginia/Brevard Co School Dist	275	6
Glendenning, Bruce/FDLRS-Crown	73	36
Glenn, Elizabeth, Dr/Leon Co School Dist	11	64
Glover, Danny/Taylor Co School Dist	1	139
Glover, Susie/Clay Co School Dist	4	23
Goff, Reginald/Manatee Co School Dist	3	68
Gohl, Dan/Broward Co Public Schools	8,18	10
Goldman, Ava/Miami-Dade Co Public Sch Dist	58,77	74
Gombos, Melanie/Sarasota Co School Dist	3	129
Gonzalez-Diego, Daisy/Miami-Dade Co Public Sch Dist	71	74
Gooch, Heidi, Dr/Seminole Co Public School Dist	273	132
Gooch, Nancy/Sarasota Co School Dist	4	129
Goodman, Allen/Okaloosa Co School Dist	4	91
Goodson, Eileen/Sumter Co School Dist	36,69,79,83,85,88,270	138
Goodwin, Jane/Sarasota Co School Dist	67	129
Gordon, Carly/Sarasota Co School Dist	70	129
Gordon, Judith/Osceola Co School Dist	4	102
Gornto, Robert/Miami-Dade Co Public Sch Dist	15,30	74
Gorokhovsky, Oleg/Broward Co Public Schools	2	10
Goyette, Isaac/Madison Co School Dist	295	67
Graber, Sarah/Osceola Co School Dist	2,19	102
Grabowski, Garrett/Martin Co School Dist	3	72
Grammatis, Lori/Charlotte Co Public Sch Dist	2	21
Grant, Felita, Dr/Pinellas Co School Dist	12	116

NAME/District	JOB FUNCTIONS	PAGE
Grant, Tashonia, Dr/Duval Co Public School Dist	71	29
Grant, William/Sarasota Co School Dist	3	129
Grantham, Jonathan, Dr/Marion Co Public Schools	15,286,288	70
Gravier, Mike/Seminole Co Public School Dist	2	131
Greco, Jennifer/Citrus Co School Dist	58	22
Green, David/Hardee Co School Dist	73	42
Green, Megan/St Lucie Co School Dist	10	136
Green, Mike/Baker Co School Dist	36,58,81,83,85,90	3
Greene, Diana, Dr/Duval Co Public School Dist	1	29
Greene, Latanya/St Lucie Co School Dist	7,77	136
Grego, Michael, Dr/Pinellas Co School Dist	1	116
Gregory, Gillian/Leon Co School Dist	15,16,74,271	64
Grey, Dennis/Walton Co School Dist	5	143
Grey, Mary/Pasco Co School Dist	274	112
Griffin, Carlisle/Santa Rosa Co School Dist	69	127
Griffin, Cynthia/Alachua Co School Dist	5	1
Griffin, Dean/Baker Co School Dist	67	3
Griffin, Rhonda/Franklin Co School Dist	288	40
Griffin, Walt, Dr/Seminole Co Public School Dist	1	131
Griffis, Mike/Clay Co School Dist	73	23
Griffith, Janie/Walton Co School Dist	84	143
Grimaldo, Mildred/Broward Co Public Schools	280	10
Griner, Greg/Charlotte Co Public Sch Dist	2,19	21
Griner, Jim/Wakulla Co School Dist	91	143
Grohowski, Paul/Sarasota Co School Dist	91	129
Grooms, Cindy, Dr/Nassau Co School Dist	79	90
Gross, Lisa/Flagler Co School Dist	68	39
Gruett, Ruth/Manatee Co School Dist	2	68
Guck, George/Sarasota Co School Dist	295	129
Guiel, Dawna/St Lucie Co School Dist	58	136
Gunthorpe, Pamela/Brevard Co School Dist	298	6
Gurcan, Ertac/Sarasota Co School Dist	295	129
Guthrie, Lynn/Liberty Co School Dist	73,84,295	67

H

NAME/District	JOB FUNCTIONS	PAGE
Hackett, Wayne/Alachua Co School Dist	2	1
Hahn, Daniel/Santa Rosa Co School Dist	91	127
Haley, Meg/Columbia Co School Dist	81	27
Haley, Michael/Highlands Co School Dist	91	45
Hall, Amy, Dr/Volusia Co School Dist	36	140
Hall, Cathy/Walton Co School Dist	57,88	143
Hall, Chris/Martin Co School Dist	295	73
Hall, Eric/Florida Dept of Education	750	1
Hall, Rosalind/Levy Co School Dist	7,58,83,85,88,90	66
Hall, Sheila/Liberty Co School Dist	2	67
Hall, Theresa/Hardee Co School Dist	8,11,57,69,89,271,294,296	42
Hamby, Kendra/Marion Co Public Schools	34	70
Hamilton, Casey/Alachua Co School Dist	91	1
Hampton, Don/Sarasota Co School Dist	3	129
Hancock, Lisa/Lafayette Co School Dist	69	58
Hancock, Ray/Lafayette Co School Dist	35,83,85,88	58
Hann, Susan/Brevard Co School Dist	3,15	6
Hanna, Martha/Escambia Co School Dist	7,85	36
Hanna, Rocky/Leon Co School Dist	1	64
Hans, Phil/Clay Co School Dist	3	23
Hansen, Nicole/Charlotte Co Public Sch Dist	34	21
Hansen, Scott/Manatee Co School Dist	98	68
Hantman, Perla/Miami-Dade Co Public Sch Dist	67	74
Hardee, Kathleen/Nassau Co School Dist	58,81	90
Harden, Carolyn/Gadsden Co School Dist	34	40
Hardesty, Cathy/Highlands Co School Dist	39,42	45
Harper, Tim, Dr/Seminole Co Public School Dist	71,73,76,97,98	132
Harrell, Joey/Santa Rosa Co School Dist	15	127
Harrell, Kirk/Bay Co School Dist	6	4
Harrell, Renee/Calhoun Co School Dist	84	20
Harrell, Steven/Escambia Co School Dist	5	36
Harrelson, Greg/Hardee Co School Dist	2	42

1	Superintendent	16	Instructional Media Svcs	30	Adult Education	44	Science Sec	58	Special Education K-12	72	Summer School	88	Alternative/At Risk	277	Remedial Math K-12
2	Bus/Finance/Purchasing	17	Chief Operations Officer	31	Career/Sch-to-Work K-12	45	Math K-12	59	Special Education Elem	73	Instructional Tech	89	Multi-Cultural Curriculum	280	Literacy Coach
3	Buildings And Grounds	18	Chief Academic Officer	32	Career/Sch-to-Work Elem	46	Math Elem	60	Special Education Sec	74	Inservice Training	90	Social Work	285	STEM
4	Food Service	19	Chief Financial Officer	33	Career/Sch-to-Work Sec	47	Math Sec	61	Foreign/World Lang K-12	75	Marketing/Distributive	91	Safety/Security	286	Digital Learning
5	Transportation	20	Art K-12	34	Early Childhood Ed	48	English/Lang Arts K-12	62	Foreign/World Lang Elem	76	Info Systems	92	Magnet School	288	Common Core Standards
6	Athletic	21	Art Elem	35	Health/Phys Education	49	English/Lang Arts Elem	63	Foreign/World Lang Sec	77	Psychological Assess	95	Tech Prep Program	294	Accountability
7	Health Services	22	Art Sec	36	Guidance Services K-12	50	English/Lang Arts Sec	64	Religious Education K-12	79	Affirmative Action	97	Chief Information Officer	295	Network System
8	Curric/Instruct K-12	23	Music K-12	37	Guidance Services Elem	51	Reading K-12	65	Religious Education Elem	79	Student Personnel	98	Chief Technology Officer	296	Title II Programs
9	Curric/Instruct Elem	24	Music Elem	38	Guidance Services Sec	52	Reading Elem	66	Religious Education Sec	80	Driver Ed/Safety	270	Character Education	297	Webmaster
10	Curric/Instruct Sec	25	Music Sec	39	Social Studies K-12	53	Reading Sec	67	School Board President	81	Gifted/Talented	271	Migrant Education	298	Grant Writer/Ptnrships
11	Federal Program	26	Business Education	40	Social Studies Elem	54	Remedial Reading K-12	68	Teacher Personnel	82	Video Services	273	Teacher Mentor	750	Chief Innovation Officer
12	Title I	27	Career & Tech Ed	41	Social Studies Sec	55	Remedial Reading Elem	69	Academic Assessment	83	Substance Abuse Prev	274	Before/After Sch	751	Chief of Staff
13	Title V	28	Technology Education	42	Science K-12	56	Remedial Reading Sec	70	Research/Development	84	Erate	275	Response To Intervention	752	Social Emotional Learning
15	Asst Superintendent	29	Family/Consumer Science	43	Science Elem	57	Bilingual/ELL	71	Public Information	85	AIDS Education				

NAME/District	JOB FUNCTIONS	PAGE
Harris-Lively, Jeanne/*Sumter Co School Dist*	34,90	138
Harris, Abria/*Gadsden Co School Dist*	42,45	40
Harris, David/*Bradford Co School Dist*	15	5
Harris, Janet/*Glades Co School Dist*	8,11,76,83,88,296,298	41
Harris, Jason/*Manatee Co School Dist*	5	68
Harris, Loretta, Dr/*Lake Co School Dist*	16	58
Harris, Lyn/*FDLRS-Westgate*	1,11	39
Harris, Penny/*Escambia Co School Dist*	76,295	36
Harris, Theresa/*Charlotte Co Public Sch Dist*	68	21
Harrison, Emily/*St Johns Co School Dist*	27,31,57	134
Hart, Tara/*Lake Co School Dist*	58,81	58
Hartvigsen, Angela/*Sarasota Co School Dist*	20,23	129
Harvey, Lenon/*Putnam Co School Dist*	71	127
Hatcher, Keith/*Columbia Co School Dist*	2	27
Hathcock, Sharon/*Taylor Co School Dist*	8,12,286,288,296	139
Haugabrook, Letizia/*Lake Co School Dist*	11	58
Havee, Nicole/*Okeechobee Co School Dist*	5	93
Hawk, David/*Seminole Co Public School Dist*	3	131
Hawley, Debbie/*St Lucie Co School Dist*	67	136
Hawthorne, Nicole/*Putnam Co School Dist*	4	127
Hayes, Chandra/*Florida Dept of Education*	271	1
Hayes, Daryl/*Liberty Co School Dist*	67	67
Hayes, Renee/*Sarasota Co School Dist*	2	129
Haynes, Jamie/*Volusia Co School Dist*	12	140
Hays, Virginia/*Duval Co Public School Dist*	69	29
Haywood, Barbara/*Highlands Co School Dist*	4	45
Hazel, Rachel/*Volusia Co School Dist*	8,18	140
Hazewinkel, Nate/*Escambia Co School Dist*	69	36
Heaven, Stawania/*Manatee Co School Dist*	5	68
Hebert, Scott/*Citrus Co School Dist*	9,18,72,296	22
Hedine, Julie/*Pasco Co School Dist*	4	112
Henderson, Adam/*Nassau Co School Dist*	84,295	90
Henderson, Deborah/*Polk Co SD-W & N Ctrl*	15	125
Hendrick, Kevin/*Pinellas Co School Dist*	8,15,288	116
Henkins, Jerry/*Seminole Co Public School Dist*	3	131
Henninger, Michelle/*Osceola Co School Dist*	74	102
Henry, Michael/*Duval Co PSD-Middle Schools*	1	32
Henson, Todd/*Manatee Co School Dist*	3	68
Herbic, Clint/*Pinellas Co School Dist*	3,5,15	116
Herlean, Greg/*Charlotte Co Public Sch Dist*	2	21
Hernandez, Beatrice/*Collier Co Public School Dist*	68	25
Herrell, Lynn/*Lee Co School Dist*	68	60
Herron, Ron/*Hardee Co School Dist*	5	42
Hershey, Lori/*Duval Co Public School Dist*	67	29
Hewett, Melissa/*Lafayette Co School Dist*	36	58
Hickman, Amanda/*Lafayette Co School Dist*	67	58
Hickman, Antoine, Dr/*Broward Co Public Schools*	58,81	10
Hiers, Marla/*Levy Co School Dist*	68,74,273	66
Higginbotham, Sandy/*Volusia Co School Dist*	2	140
Higgins, James/*Escambia Co School Dist*	3	36
Higgins, Thomas/*Sarasota Co School Dist*	5	129
Highsmith, Robert/*Monroe Co School Dist*	67	89
Hightower, Patty/*Escambia Co School Dist*	67	36
Hill, Cherry/*Columbia Co School Dist*	9,15,296	27
Hill, John/*Polk Co School Dist*	15	122
Hill, Robin/*Madison Co School Dist*	8,11,83,93,288,296,298	67
Hill, Sondra/*Escambia Co School Dist*	58	36
Hilton, Terry/*Franklin Co School Dist*	4	40
Hilton, Vanessa/*Pasco Co School Dist*	8,12,15,18	112
Himmel, Sandra/*Citrus Co School Dist*	1	22
Hingson, Alissa/*Lafayette Co School Dist*	8,298	58
Hinkejohnathan, Johnathan/*Putnam Co School Dist*	8	127
Hinson-Fisher, Debbie/*Volusia Co School Dist*	7	140
Hires, Barbara, Dr/*Pinellas Co Schools-Area 2*	15	117
Hite, Monica/*Lake Co School Dist*	79	58
Hoaglin, Vince/*Manatee Co School Dist*	295	68
Hodgens, Jenna/*Hillsborough Co Pub Sch Dist*	92	46
Hofheinz, Stephanie/*Walton Co School Dist*	2,19	143
Hogan, Don/*Lake Co School Dist*	6	58
Hogarth, Thomas/*Palm Beach Co School Dist*	3	105
Hogue, Myra/*Hillsborough Co Pub Sch Dist*	69,90	46
Hogue, Tamra/*Bay Co School Dist*	16,73,82	4
Holanchock, Mary/*St Johns Co School Dist*	34	134
Holcomb, Jill/*Okeechobee Co School Dist*	67	93
Holden, Diana/*Collier Co Public School Dist*	298	25
Hollan, Carrie/*Escambia Co School Dist*	68	36

NAME/District	JOB FUNCTIONS	PAGE
Holland, Eric/*Volusia Co School Dist*	69,286	140
Hollimon, Shameka/*DeSoto Co School Dist*	88	28
Holmes, Bryan/*Orange Co Public School Dist*	91	94
Holmes, Russell/*Osceola Co School Dist*	73	102
Holnebel, Laura/*Martin Co School Dist*	4	72
Holt, Dennis, Dr/*Hillsborough Co Pub Sch Dist*	41	46
Hood, Cheryl/*Osceola Co School Dist*	2	102
Hope, Paul/*Dixie Co School Dist*	5	29
Hope, Ted/*Hillsborough Co Pub Sch Dist*	10,25	46
Hoppenstedt, Michele/*Lake Co School Dist*	68	58
Horne, Shana/*Marion Co Public Schools*	74	70
Horsley, Mike/*Manatee Co School Dist*	3	68
Horton, Steve/*Okaloosa Co School Dist*	15,16,71,76	91
Houchens, Paul/*Palm Beach Co School Dist*	69,70	105
Houchin, Lori/*Lee Co School Dist*	7,10,35	60
Hough, Renee/*Putnam Co School Dist*	27,30,31,73,95	127
Houser, Cherie/*Volusia Co School Dist*	274	140
Howard, Allyn/*FDLRS-Miccosukee*	73	66
Howard, Danielle/*School Dist of Indian River Co*	68	55
Howard, Michele/*Suwannee Co School Dist*	7,36	138
Howat, Scott/*Orange Co Public School Dist*	71	94
Howcroft, James/*Leon Co School Dist*	4	64
Howell, Kiwana/*Palm Beach Co School Dist*	274	105
Howell, Tonya/*Dixie Co School Dist*	2,15	28
Howell, Wayne/*Baker Co School Dist*	295,297	3
Howes, Harry/*Highlands Co School Dist*	76,295	45
Howser, Nancy/*Brevard Co School Dist*	81	6
Hudson, Camilla/*Bay Co School Dist*	69,294	4
Hudson, Mickey/*Holmes Co School Dist*	3,6,78,92	55
Huene-Johnson, Shari, Dr/*Collier Co Public School Dist*	74	25
Huff, Brian/*Sumter Co School Dist*	295	138
Huff, R Bryan/*Sumter Co School Dist*	76	138
Huff, Richard/*School Dist of Indian River Co*	3	55
Huffstetter, Mary, Dr/*St Lucie Co School Dist*	34	136
Hughes, A Russell/*Walton Co School Dist*	1	143
Hughes, Beverly/*Osceola Co School Dist*	91	102
Hughes, Lorie/*Walton Co School Dist*	93	143
Hull, Sally/*Manatee Co School Dist*	91	68
Humbaugh, Kit/*Citrus Co School Dist*	79	22
Humphrey, Brian/*Okaloosa Co School Dist*	6,35,83,91	91
Hunkiar, John/*Leon Co School Dist*	91	64
Hunt, Chloe/*Levy Co School Dist*	8,11,16,271,274,296	66
Hunt, Mark/*Pinellas Co School Dist*	27,30,31	116
Hunter, William/*Gadsden Co School Dist*	3	40
Hurley, Andrew/*St Johns Co School Dist*	294	134
Hurley, Shirley/*Manatee Co School Dist*	36	68
Hurst, Sandra/*Hernando Co School Dist*	77,752	43
Husfelt, William/*Bay Co School Dist*	1	4
Husted, James/*FDLRS-Springs*	1	72
Hutchins, Cathy/*St Johns Co School Dist*	15,68	134
Hutchins, Kimberly/*Lee Co School Dist*	2	60
Hyatt, Robert/*Alachua Co School Dist*	67	1

I

NAME/District	JOB FUNCTIONS	PAGE
Iannone, Jamie/*Clay Co School Dist*	57,74,273	23
Idlette, Jennifer/*School Dist of Indian River Co*	5	55
Iftikhar, Maria/*Seminole Co Public School Dist*	71	132
Ilse, Monica, Dr/*Pasco CSD-High Schools*	15	114
Infinger, Jeff/*Walton Co School Dist*	3	143
Infinger, Jennifer/*Florida Dept of Education*	20,23	1
Ingram, Mark/*Marion Co Public Schools*	57	70
Ingram, Tom/*Escambia Co School Dist*	73,76,82,295	36
Irvine, Linda/*Madison Co School Dist*	68	67
Ismail, Salah/*Seminole Co Public School Dist*	4	131
Itzen, Richard, Dr/*Lee Co School Dist*	69,70,294	60
Iuliucci, Theresa/*Martin Co School Dist*	79	73
Iverson, Sheerynne/*DeSoto Co School Dist*	4	28
Ivey, Barbara/*Volusia Co School Dist*	3	140
Izquierdo, Maria/*Miami-Dade Co Public Sch Dist*	8,18,69,294	74

J

NAME/District	JOB FUNCTIONS	PAGE
Jackson, Beverly/*Jackson Co School Dist*	2	57
Jackson, Jason/*Miami-Dade-Central Region*	44	74
Jackson, Josephine/*Duval Co Public School Dist*	78	29
Jackson, Sylvia, Dr/*Gadsden Co School Dist*	10,27,30,42,45	40
Jacobs, Johnnie/*Baker Co School Dist*	5	3

NAME/*District*	JOB FUNCTIONS	PAGE
Jacobs, Teresa/*Orange Co Public School Dist*	67	94
Jaimes, Abel/*Collier Co Public School Dist*	12,271,298	25
James, Bruce/*Gadsden Co School Dist*	91	40
Jamison, Lynn/*Columbia Co School Dist*	58,79	27
Jamison, Scott/*Alachua Co School Dist*	2	1
Jankowski, Leonard/*School Dist of Indian River Co*	6	55
Jarrett, Michelle/*Osceola Co School Dist*	16,73	102
Jay, Kimberly/*St Lucie Co School Dist*	9	136
Jenkins, Barbara, Dr/*Orange Co Public School Dist*	1	94
Jenkins, Heather/*Manatee Co School Dist*	19	68
Jenkins, Vicky/*Martin Co School Dist*	58	72
Jennings, Tripp/*Sarasota Co School Dist*	27	129
Jensen, Tina/*Martin Co School Dist*	4	72
Jernigan, Hope/*Columbia Co School Dist*	9	27
Jerome, Craig/*St Lucie Co School Dist*	16	136
Joanos, Manny/*Leon Co School Dist*	5	64
Joe, Cheryl/*Polk Co School Dist*	74	122
Joens, Kristie/*DeSoto Co School Dist*	73	28
Johns, Barbara/*Bradford Co School Dist*	57,58,79	5
Johnson, Earl, Dr/*Flagler Co School Dist*	74	39
Johnson, Ivan/*Madison Co School Dist*	5	67
Johnson, Jackie/*Alachua Co School Dist*	71	1
Johnson, Jewel/*St Johns Co School Dist*	68,90	134
Johnson, Kristy/*Charlotte Co Public Sch Dist*	58,81,296	21
Johnson, Marva/*Florida Dept of Education*	67	1
Johnson, Megan/*Manatee Co School Dist*	12	68
Johnson, Robert/*Clay Co School Dist*	2	23
Johnson, Vicki/*Gadsden Co School Dist*	93	40
Johnson, Wayne/*Sarasota Co School Dist*	95,295	129
Jones, Analynn, Dr/*Seminole Co Public School Dist*	34	132
Jones, Carol/*Levy Co School Dist*	27,280	66
Jones, Donna/*Alachua Co School Dist*	15	1
Jones, Edward/*Osceola Co School Dist*	5	102
Jones, Kristy/*Charlotte Co Public Sch Dist*	295	21
Jones, Lauren, Dr/*Nassau Co School Dist*	4	90
Jones, Michael/*Bay Co School Dist*	91	4
Jones, Pat/*Wakulla Co School Dist*	5	143
Jones, Peggy, Dr/*Pasco Co School Dist*	70,294	112
Jones, Rahin/*Orange Co Public SD-North*	1	97
Jones, Rashan/*Okeechobee Co School Dist*	295	93
Jordan, Gregory/*Gulf Co School Dist*	6	41
Jordan, Karen/*Hernando Co School Dist*	71	43
Joseph, Auden/*Seminole Co Public School Dist*	4	131
Joseph, Scott/*Escambia Co School Dist*	3	36
Joseph, Shirley/*Madison Co School Dist*	1	67
Joyner, Kathy/*Sumter Co School Dist*	67	138
Joyner, Lisa, Dr/*Escambia Co School Dist*	36,79	36
Judkins, Sonya/*Columbia Co School Dist*	8	27
Juhas, Michael/*Diocese Pensacola-Tallahassee*	1	38

K

Kaczmarski, Jenna/*Polk Co School Dist*	4	122
Kamm, Grayson/*Hillsborough Co Pub Sch Dist*	71	46
Karac, Natasa, Dr/*Pinellas Co School Dist*	57	116
Karns, Boyd/*Seminole Co Public School Dist*	68	132
Kasselakis, Angie/*Miami-Dade Co Public Sch Dist*	4	74
Katz, Brian/*Broward Co Public Schools*	91	10
Keck, Kathleen/*Lee Co School Dist*	298	61
Keegan, Patrick/*Charlotte Co Pub Sch Dist*	68,78	21
Keenan, Harry/*Pasco Co School Dist*	3	112
Kellermeier, Grace/*Volusia Co School Dist*	35	140
Kelley, Bill/*Manatee Co School Dist*	3,68	68
Kelley, Denise/*Bay Co School Dist*	9,15,30,77,90	4
Kelley, Lucinda/*Hendry Co School Dist*	15,69	43
Kelly, Dale/*Orange Co Public School Dist*	2,19	94
Kelly, Damien/*Florida Dept of Education*	91	1
Kelly, George/*Hardee Co School Dist*	68	42

NAME/*District*	JOB FUNCTIONS	PAGE
Kelly, J Alex/*Florida Dept of Education*	751	1
Kelly, Martin/*Florida Virtual School Dist*	8	93
Kelly, Patricia/*Nassau Co School Dist*	58	90
Kelly, William/*Seminole Co Public School Dist*	2,19	131
Kemp, Michael/*Clay Co School Dist*	3,15	23
Kennedy, Angela/*Hernando Co School Dist*	11,57	43
Kennedy, Thomas/*Citrus Co School Dist*	67	22
Kennedy, Trevor/*Nassau Co School Dist*	4	90
Kennedy, Ward/*Pinellas Co Schools-Area 1*	15	116
Kennon, Tina/*St Johns Co School Dist*	58	134
Kenworthy, Ken/*Okeechobee Co School Dist*	1	93
Keough, Patrick/*Hernando Co School Dist*	71	43
Kerekes, Janice/*Clay Co School Dist*	67	23
Kerekes, Michael/*Clay Co School Dist*	71	23
Kern, Lisa/*Pasco Co School Dist*	7	112
Khalil, Enas/*Collier Co Public School Dist*	2	25
Khanal, Sheila/*Martin Co School Dist*	12,57,271	72
Kidwell, Donna/*Alachua Co School Dist*	58,81	1
Kilts, Michael/*Jackson Co School Dist*	11,57,286,298	57
Kincaid, Jennifer/*Collier Co Public School Dist*	9	25
King, Bethany/*Sarasota Co School Dist*	88,93	129
King, Kelly/*Marion Co Public Schools*	67	70
King, Tim/*Flagler Co School Dist*	58,81,93	39
Kingsley, Laura, Dr/*Sarasota Co School Dist*	8,15,18	129
Kinsey, Terri, Dr/*Lee Co School Dist*	298	61
Kirby, Lynne/*Citrus Co School Dist*	34,58,77	22
Kirkreit, Christine/*Seminole Co Public School Dist*	58	132
Kirsch, Lauri, Dr/*Hillsborough Co Pub Sch Dist*	81	46
Kirvin, Stacy/*Franklin Co School Dist*	67	40
Kisiday, Carmel/*Charlotte Co Pub Sch Dist*	9,274	21
Kittrell, Julie/*St Lucie Co School Dist*	295	136
Kledzik, Thaddeus/*Pasco Co School Dist*	5	112
Klemont, Raymond/*DeSoto Co School Dist*	68	28
Klingensmith, Karen/*Hernando Co School Dist*	84	43
Klock, Laura/*Levy Co School Dist*	34,79	66
Knab, Heather/*St Lucie Co School Dist*	49	136
Knight, Charlin/*Santa Rosa Co School Dist*	27,30,31	127
Knight, Robert/*Marion Co Public Schools*	3	70
Knight, Sarah/*Gadsden Co School Dist*	51	40
Knowles, Reathea/*Jefferson Co School Dist*	4	57
Knust, Heather/*Palm Beach Co School Dist*	2	105
Koch, Kathy/*Broward Co Public Schools*	71	10
Kochis, Heidi/*Volusia Co School Dist*	68	140
Kohler, Traci, Dr/*Collier Co Public School Dist*	74	25
Kolosey, Connie/*Pinellas Co School Dist*	16,286	116
Kolp, Kris/*Leon Co School Dist*	69	64
Konopelko, Douglas/*Martin Co School Dist*	286	73
Konraidy, Tara/*Sarasota Co School Dist*	11	129
Kopp, Robert/*Sarasota Co School Dist*	5	129
Kornegay, Diane/*Lake Co School Dist*	1	58
Kosek, Shannah/*Clay Co School Dist*	30	23
Kovalsky, Sandie/*Sarasota Co School Dist*	5	129
Kraft, Amanda/*Osceola Co School Dist*	2,7	102
Kraft, Maria/*Volusia Co School Dist*	2,3	140
Krahl, Rob/*Hardee Co School Dist*	3,91	42
Kramer, David/*Nassau Co School Dist*	3	90
Kriznar, Dana, Dr/*Duval Co Public School Dist*	15,751	29
Krostag, Kelly/*Escambia Co School Dist*	68	36
Kuhn, Betsy/*Pasco Co School Dist*	15	112
Kuras, Jenifer/*Palm Beach Co School Dist*	74	105
Kutz, Tim/*Collier Co Public School Dist*	91	25

L

La Fountain, Jeanne/*Lee Co School Dist*	12,271,275	60
La-Cava, Gonzalo, Dr/*Palm Beach Co School Dist*	68	105
Labo, Timothy/*Diocese of Orlando Ed Office*	67	100
Laing, Richard/*Santa Rosa Co School Dist*	3	127

1	Superintendent	16	Instructional Media Svcs	30	Adult Education	44	Science Sec	58	Special Education K-12	72	Summer School	88	Alternative/At Risk	277	Remedial Math K-12
2	Bus/Finance/Purchasing	17	Chief Operations Officer	31	Career/Sch-to-Work K-12	45	Math K-12	59	Special Education Elem	73	Instructional Tech	89	Multi-Cultural Curriculum	280	Literacy Coach
3	Buildings And Grounds	18	Chief Academic Officer	32	Career/Sch-to-Work Elem	46	Math Elem	60	Special Education Sec	74	Inservice Training	90	Social Work	285	STEM
4	Food Service	19	Chief Financial Officer	33	Career/Sch-to-Work Sec	47	Math Sec	61	Foreign/World Lang K-12	75	Marketing/Distributive	91	Safety/Security	286	Digital Learning
5	Transportation	20	Art K-12	34	Early Childhood Ed	48	English/Lang Arts K-12	62	Foreign/World Lang Elem	76	Info Systems	92	Magnet School	288	Common Core Standards
6	Athletic	21	Art Elem	35	Health/Phys Education	49	English/Lang Arts Elem	63	Foreign/World Lang Sec	77	Psychological Assess	93	Parental Involvement	294	Accountability
7	Health Services	22	Art Sec	36	Guidance Services K-12	50	English/Lang Arts Sec	64	Religious Education K-12	78	Affirmative Action	95	Tech Prep Program	295	Network System
8	Curric/Instruct K-12	23	Music K-12	37	Guidance Services Elem	51	Reading K-12	65	Religious Education Elem	79	Student Personnel	97	Chief Information Officer	296	Title II Programs
9	Curric/Instruct Elem	24	Music Elem	38	Guidance Services Sec	52	Reading Elem	66	Religious Education Sec	80	Driver Ed/Safety	98	Chief Technology Officer	297	Webmaster
10	Curric/Instruct Sec	25	Music Sec	39	Social Studies K-12	53	Reading Sec	67	School Board President	81	Gifted/Talented	270	Character Education	298	Grant Writer/Ptnrships
11	Federal Program	26	Business Education	40	Social Studies Elem	54	Remedial Reading K-12	68	Teacher Personnel	82	Video Services	271	Migrant Education	750	Chief Innovation Officer
12	Title I	27	Career & Tech Ed	41	Social Studies Sec	55	Remedial Reading Elem	69	Academic Assessment	83	Substance Abuse Prev	273	Teacher Mentor	751	Chief of Staff
13	Title V	28	Technology Education	42	Science K-12	56	Remedial Reading Sec	70	Research/Development	84	Erate	274	Before/After Sch	752	Social Emotional Learning
15	Asst Superintendent	29	Family/Consumer Science	43	Science Elem	57	Bilingual/ELL	71	Public Information	85	AIDS Education	275	Response To Intervention		

NAME/District	JOB FUNCTIONS	PAGE	NAME/District	JOB FUNCTIONS	PAGE
Lake, Kimberly/*Levy Co School Dist*	2	66	Lott, John/*Levy Co School Dist*	8,36,54,277,286,288,294	66
Lamoreaux, Renee/*Putnam Co School Dist*	69	127	Love, Laura/*Sarasota Co School Dist*	4	129
Lancaster, Barbara/*Highlands Co School Dist*	76	45	Lovett, Jamie/*Alachua Co School Dist*	4	1
Lancaster, Deen/*Gilchrist Co School Dist*	67	41	Lowe, Kim/*Hardee Co School Dist*	58	42
Land, Debbie/*Suwannee Co School Dist*	58,79	138	Lowe, Mike/*Manatee Co School Dist*	3	68
Landry, Dena/*Collier Co Public School Dist*	79	25	Loyed, Jim/*Bay Co School Dist*	2,19	4
Landry, Kristine/*Lake Co School Dist*	7,36,77,79,90	58	Lozano, Beth/*Collier Co Public School Dist*	5	25
Lane, Chad/*School Dist of Indian River Co*	3	55	Luke, Stephanie/*Lake Co School Dist*	67	58
Laneau, Richard/*Hillsborough Co Pub Sch Dist*	73	46	Lundy, Leslie/*Okeechobee Co School Dist*	12,298	93
Langston, Christina/*St Johns Co School Dist*	71,97	134	Lunt, Kelly/*St Lucie Co School Dist*	285	136
Langston, Clarissa/*Collier Co Public School Dist*	74	25	Lupinetti, David/*Charlotte Co Public Sch Dist*	91	21
Lanier, Pamela/*Highlands Co School Dist*	34,58,78,81	45	Lyford, Melissa/*Lake Co School Dist*	58	58
Larkin, Shawn/*Jackson Co School Dist*	58,81	57	Lyles, John/*Broward Co Public Schools*	5	10
Larroque, Jessica/*Marion Co Public Schools*	81	70	Lynch, Lisa/*Osceola Co School Dist*	2	102
Larsen, James/*Orange Co Public SD-Southwest*	1	98	Lynch, Nikki/*St Johns Co School Dist*	11	134
Larson, Michelle/*Clay Co School Dist*	2	23			
Lathem-Walters, Jennifer/*Bay Co School Dist*	34	4	**M**		
Laudato, Mia/*FDLRS-Action*	73	102	Mabee, Brian/*Manatee Co School Dist*	3	68
Lawrence, Kathryn/*Clay Co School Dist*	58	23	Maclemale, Richard/*Pasco Co School Dist*	297	112
Lawrence, Michael/*Seminole Co Public School Dist*	71	132	Maggi, Valerie/*Sarasota Co School Dist*	2	129
Laws, Greg/*Martin Co School Dist*	69	72	Magloire, Judith/*Brevard Co School Dist*	57,89	6
Lawson, David/*Sarasota Co School Dist*	295	129	Maier, Heidi, Dr/*Marion Co Public Schools*	1	70
Layfield, Darrell/*Highlands Co School Dist*	16,69,73,76,286,294	45	Majeski, Mark, Dr/*Diocese St Petersburg Ed Off*	8,76	120
Layson, Steve/*Martin Co School Dist*	45	72	Malay, Susan/*Lee Co School Dist*	2,4	60
Leath, Ralph/*Hernando Co School Dist*	5	43	Malham, Mark/*Martin Co School Dist*	41	72
Leathers, Tia/*Duval Co Public School Dist*	93	29	Maliniak, Gina/*Manatee Co School Dist*	2	68
Leavins, Kelly/*Holmes Co School Dist*	2	55	Malits, Karen/*School Dist of Indian River Co*	11,57,296	55
LeBlanc, Richard/*Seminole Co Public School Dist*	3	131	Mancini, Nicole, Dr/*Broward Co Public Schools*	9	10
Lechner, Tom/*Pinellas Co School Dist*	15,76,295	116	Mandell, Erin/*Seminole Co Public School Dist*	58	132
Lee, Douglas/*Bay Co School Dist*	3,15	4	Manin, Max/*Glades Co School Dist*	6	41
Lee, Joseph, Dr/*Palm Beach Co SD-North Region*	10	108	Manke, Doug/*Glades Co School Dist*	5	41
Lee, Susan/*Florida Dept of Education*	69	1	Mankie, Don/*Sarasota Co School Dist*	4	129
Lefere, Patrick/*Monroe Co School Dist*	3,91	89	Manoogian, Robert/*Sarasota Co School Dist*	16	129
Legutko, Susan, Dr/*Clay Co School Dist*	2,15	23	Mansberger, Flavia/*Collier Co Public School Dist*	11,271	25
Lehtinen, Justin/*Putnam Co School Dist*	76,84	127	Marcanio, Steve/*Escambia Co School Dist*	8,15	36
Lemond, Brent/*Nassau Co School Dist*	27,30,88	90	Marchese, Tracy/*Sarasota Co School Dist*	4	129
Leonard, Keith/*Escambia Co School Dist*	68	36	Marchica, Anthony/*Diocese of Palm Beach Ed Off*	64	110
Leslie, Robert/*Clay Co School Dist*	295	23	Marines, Sandra/*Manatee Co School Dist*	5	68
Letcher, Kelly/*Lee Co School Dist*	2	60	Markel, Todd/*Hardee Co School Dist*	16,73,84,295	42
Lethbridge, Andrew/*Highlands Co School Dist*	15,68,71,74,79,273	45	Marsh, Giselle/*Leon Co School Dist*	294	64
Leto, Brenda/*Bradford Co School Dist*	76	5	Marsh, Melissa/*Escambia Co School Dist*	51,54	36
Leutwyler, Lori/*Charlotte Co Public Sch Dist*	68	21	Marshall, Mary/*Collier Co Public School Dist*	42	25
Levine, Michael/*FDLRS-Hillsborough*	1,11	55	Marte, Judith/*Broward Co Public Schools*	2,19	10
Lewis, Anne/*Baker Co School Dist*	83	3	Martin Ventura, Manuel/*Sarasota Co School Dist*	2	129
Lewis, Carol/*Manatee Co School Dist*	95	68	Martin-Morgan, Diane/*Volusia Co School Dist*	83,90	140
Lewis, Gay/*Liberty Co School Dist*	8,11,57,275,285,288,294,296	67	Martin, April/*Santa Rosa Co School Dist*	9,274,298	127
Lewis, Glenda/*DeSoto Co School Dist*	88	28	Martin, Dexter/*Leon Co School Dist*	78	64
Lewis, Kate/*Escambia Co School Dist*	91	36	Martin, Donna/*Nassau Co School Dist*	67	90
Libersat, Mary/*Seminole Co Public School Dist*	68	132	Martin, Heather/*Hernando Co School Dist*	15	43
Licata, Peter//*Palm Beach Co SD-South Region*	1	109	Martin, Helen/*Lee Co School Dist*	74	60
Licata, Peter, Dr/*Palm Beach Co School Dist*	15,27,31	105	Martin, Henry/*Walton Co School Dist*	73,76	143
Lightbourne, Shelia/*Okaloosa Co School Dist*	10,15,69	91	Martin, John/*Hernando Co School Dist*	3	43
Lindsay, Anne, Dr/*Highlands Co School Dist*	9,89,288	45	Martin, Robert/*Okaloosa Co School Dist*	80	91
Linton, Betty/*FDLRS-Gateway*	58	42	Martin, Robert/*Walton Co School Dist*	4	143
Linton, Betty/*Hamilton Co School Dist*	27,58,81,275	42	Martin, Ronald/*Martin Co School Dist*	3	72
Lipomi, Justin/*Volusia Co School Dist*	752	140	Martinez, Gladys/*FDLRS-Reach*	16	20
Lipscomb, Gwen/*FDLRS-Reach*	1,11	20	Martinez, Lillian, Dr/*School Dist of Indian River Co*	58,79,83,88,90,275	55
Liroberts, Christia/*Martin Co School Dist*	67	72	Martinez, Sandy/*Collier Co Public School Dist*	5	25
Lisa, Karen/*Citrus Co School Dist*	298	22	Maschhoff, Caroline/*School Dist of Indian River Co*	7	55
Lisenko, Dan/*Manatee Co School Dist*	3	68	Masters, Gary/*Levy Co School Dist*	5	66
Little, Brenda/*Bradford Co School Dist*	73,286	5	Mastoridis, George/*St Johns Co School Dist*	68	134
Little, Robert/*Seminole Co Public School Dist*	3	131	Mate, Julia/*Palm Beach Co School Dist*	285	105
Littleton, Ginger/*Bay Co School Dist*	67	4	Mathieu, Yvette/*Collier Co Public School Dist*	5	25
Lively, Lori/*Marion Co Public Schools*	83,88	70	Mathis, Cheryl/*Manatee Co School Dist*	58	68
Lloyd, Robert/*Jefferson Co School Dist*	2	57	Mathis, Kathy/*FDLRS-Heartland*	1	45
Lloyd, Roger/*Lee Co School Dist*	3,5	60	Mathis, Leslie/*Hendry Co School Dist*	73,74,76,295	43
Lockhart, John/*Putnam Co School Dist*	295	127	Mathis, Misty/*Nassau Co School Dist*	58,81	90
Lombardo, Michael/*Seminole Co Public School Dist*	4	131	Mathis, Vickie/*Escambia Co School Dist*	88	36
Londrie, Angel/*Alachua Co School Dist*	274	1	Mattox, Lori/*Lake Co School Dist*	3	58
Long, Deborah, Dr/*School Dist of Indian River Co*	78	55	Matway, Lori/*Pinellas Co School Dist*	15,79	116
Longa, Maria/*Polk Co School Dist*	11,296	122	Maultsby, Jeff/*Sarasota Co School Dist*	3,15,17	129
Longoria, Roberto/*Manatee Co School Dist*	3	68	Maund, Tammi/*Lafayette Co School Dist*	2	58
Longshore, Brenda, Dr/*Highlands Co School Dist*	1	44	Maxwell, James/*Polk Co School Dist*	79	122
Lopez, Alfred/*Florida Virtual School Dist*	68	93	May, Maryann, Dr/*Broward Co Public Schools*	3	10
Lopez, Edwin/*Miami-Dade Co Public Sch Dist*	91	74	May, Shawna/*Okeechobee Co School Dist*	73,76	93
Lorenzo, Julia/*Collier Co Public School Dist*	16	25	Mayo, Roger/*Escambia Co School Dist*	6	36

NAME/District	JOB FUNCTIONS	PAGE
Mays, Laclarence/*Gadsden Co School Dist*	2	40
Maznicki, Frank/*Glades Co School Dist*	73	41
McArthur, Jo/*Escambia Co School Dist*	93	36
McAuley, Michael/*Clay Co School Dist*	15	23
McBride, Rick/*Pinellas Co School Dist*	5	116
McCann, Mike/*Manatee Co School Dist*	83,88	68
McCants, Theresa/*Escambia Co School Dist*	2	36
McCarthy, Kevin/*Hendry Co School Dist*	3,5	43
McClellan, Angela/*Nassau Co School Dist*	275	90
McCloudy, Lisa/*Wakulla Co School Dist*	4	143
McCole, Susan/*Santa Rosa Co School Dist*	2,15	127
McCormack, Karen/*Sarasota Co School Dist*	7	129
McCormick, Kevin/*Palm Beach Co School Dist*	58	105
McCoy, Pat/*Okeechobee Co School Dist*	8,11,15,16	93
McCray, Christina/*DeSoto Co School Dist*	58	28
McCurdy, Katie/*Bay Co School Dist*	42	4
McCutchen, Angela/*School Dist of Indian River Co*	5	55
McDaniel, Cheryl/*Jackson Co School Dist*	4,15,71,294	57
McDaniel, Eileen/*Florida Dept of Education*	74	1
McDonald, Juliene/*Seminole Co Public School Dist*	58	132
McDonald, Stephanie/*Manatee Co School Dist*	4	68
McElhone, Brian/*St Johns Co School Dist*	34	134
McElroy, Bill/*Alachua Co School Dist*	31	1
McEntyre, Joyce/*Hernando Co School Dist*	2	43
McFadden, Stephen/*Collier Co Public School Dist*	37	25
McFarland, Chris/*Escambia Co School Dist*	92	36
McFarland, Duane/*Gulf Co School Dist*	8,30,88	41
McFatten, Dennis/*Marion Co Public Schools*	91	70
McGeever, Erin/*Diocese St Augustine Ed Office*	30,64	34
McGinn, Kathleen, Dr/*St Lucie Co School Dist*	70	136
McGonagle, Jim/*Seminole Co Public School Dist*	4	131
McGovern, Maria/*Flagler Co School Dist*	73	39
McGowan, Jonathan/*Marion Co Public Schools*	36,77	70
McGriff, Tammy/*Gadsden Co School Dist*	9	40
McGriff, Tammy/*Jefferson Co School Dist*	11	57
McGuinness, Paul/*Martin Co School Dist*	73,76	73
McInnis, Jay/*Okaloosa Co School Dist*	5	91
McKay, Kathy/*Clay Co School Dist*	2	23
McKeever, Cheryl, Dr/*Palm Beach Co School Dist*	69	105
McKenna, Eunshil/*Alachua Co School Dist*	4	1
McKenzie, Tiffany/*School Dist of Indian River Co*	286	55
McKeon, Karen/*St Johns Co School Dist*	69	134
McKie, Evelyn/*Nassau Co School Dist*	5	90
McKinnon, Caroline/*Gadsden Co School Dist*	69	40
McKinzie, Stan/*Seminole Co Public School Dist*	5	132
McKnight, Patti/*Santa Rosa Co School Dist*	48,280	127
McLaughlin, Denise/*Okaloosa Co School Dist*	74	91
McMahon, Tabatha/*Columbia Co School Dist*	27	27
McManus, Tricia/*Hillsborough Co Pub Sch Dist*	15,750	46
McNaughton, Joseph/*Polk Co School Dist*	45	122
McNeal, Ronald/*Alachua Co School Dist*	3	1
McNeeley, Paul/*Okaloosa Co School Dist*	82	91
McPartland, Peter/*Diocese of Venice Ed Office*	2	131
McRea, Shaylia/*Hillsborough Co SD-Achievement*	15	47
McSwain, Sonya/*Duval Co Public School Dist*	34	29
McTier, Moneek, Dr/*Palm Beach Co SD-Glades Region*	8	107
Mears, Terry/*Holmes Co School Dist*	1	55
Mecusker, Emilee/*Bradford Co School Dist*	68,273	5
Medina-Graham, Adalia/*School Dist of Indian River Co*	68	55
Medina, Harold/*Manatee Co School Dist*	271	68
Medina, Jose/*Orange Co Public School Dist*	57,271	94
Mela, Carol, Dr/*Brevard Co School Dist*	12	6
Mellow, Travis/*Flagler Co School Dist*	3	39
Mendez-Cartaya, Iraida/*Miami-Dade Co Public Sch Dist*	11,15,298	74
Mendizabal, Barbara/*Miami-Dade-South Region*	1	81
Mendoza, Ivette/*Hernando Co School Dist*	93	43
Mercado, Meri-De/*School Dist of Indian River Co*	2	55
Merritt, Janice/*Sarasota Co School Dist*	7	129
Meserve, Wendy/*Okaloosa Co School Dist*	76	91
Messer, Jim/*Clay Co School Dist*	2,19	23
Messina, Diana/*Sarasota Co School Dist*	76	129
Messina, Michele/*Manatee Co School Dist*	79	68
Metz, Mke/*Flagler Co School Dist*	3	39
Meyers, David/*Lake Co School Dist*	68	58
Meyers, Yvonne/*Alachua Co School Dist*	46,74	1
Michalicka, Gina/*Hernando Co School Dist*	8,31,285	43
Michalik, Sharon/*Bay Co School Dist*	71	4
Michaud, Michael/*Monroe Co School Dist*	76	89
Micheau, Nicole/*Duval Co Public School Dist*	11,296	29
Mickler, Martha/*St Johns Co School Dist*	15,285	134
Miedona, Shelly/*Florida Dept of Education*	46	1
Mika, Stephen/*Okaloosa Co School Dist*	4	91
Milenkovic, Lisa, Dr/*Broward Co Public Schools*	285	10
Miles, Richard/*Seminole Co Public School Dist*	4	131
Millen, Carlene/*Palm Beach Co School Dist*	74	105
Miller, Adam/*Florida Dept of Education*	92	1
Miller, Adam, Dr/*Palm Beach Co School Dist*	73	105
Miller, Brandon/*Sarasota Co School Dist*	295	129
Miller, Daniel/*Hardee Co School Dist*	73	42
Miller, Gina/*Manatee Co School Dist*	5	68
Miller, Jean/*Manatee Co School Dist*	73	68
Miller, Neva/*Calhoun Co School Dist*	68,91	20
Miller, Pam/*Manatee Co School Dist*	3	68
Miller, Tracey, Dr/*Martin Co School Dist*	8,13,18,288,296	72
Milliken, Linda/*Lake Co School Dist*	4	58
Mills, Alexa/*Dixie Co School Dist*	34,58,69,79,81,275	29
Milstead, Darrell/*Charlotte Co Public Sch Dist*	28,71,73,295,297	21
Milton, Carol/*Hamilton Co School Dist*	296,208	42
Milton, Paula/*Gadsden Co School Dist*	4	40
Milton, Roger/*Gadsden Co School Dist*	1	40
Miner, Dave/*Manatee Co School Dist*	67	68
Minnetto, Jamee/*Seminole Co Public School Dist*	11,298	132
Mitchell, Daniela/*Orange Co Public School Dist*	16,73	94
Mitchell, Eric/*Okaloosa Co School Dist*	73,76,84,295	91
Mitchell, Lea/*Pasco Co School Dist*	20,35,39,44,74	112
Mitchell, Mark/*Palm Beach Co School Dist*	68	105
Mitchell, Patrick/*Columbia Co School Dist*	73	27
Mitchell, Rex/*FDLRS-Gateway*	1	42
Mitchell, Rex/*Hamilton Co School Dist*	1	42
Mittelstadt, Cathy/*St Johns Co School Dist*	3,15	134
Mobley, Robin/*Baker Co School Dist*	15,68,78,273	3
Mock, Thomas/*Lake Co School Dist*	2	58
Moeller, Katie/*Clay Co School Dist*	57,74	23
Moeller, Susanne/*FDLRS-Gulfcoast*	58	121
Moffitt, Debbie/*Sumter Co School Dist*	8,11,16,288,298	137
Molinaris, Carmen/*FDLRS-South*	8	89
Monahan, Amy/*Volusia Co School Dist*	285	140
Monbleau, Allison/*Palm Beach Co School Dist*	4	105
Moncada, Fernando/*Collier Co Public School Dist*	5	25
Monier, Ashley/*Charlotte Co Public Sch Dist*	11,298	21
Monk, Natalie/*St Johns Co School Dist*	2	134
Monteleone, Joe/*Charlotte Co Public Sch Dist*	76	21
Montijo, Alicia/*Pasco Co School Dist*	57,61	112
Montilla, Deborah/*Miami-Dade Co Public Sch Dist*	79	74
Moore, Benjamin H, Dr/*Diocese of Venice Ed Office*	1	131
Moore, Christine/*Brevard Co School Dist*	12,15,34,271	6
Moore, David, Dr/*Miami-Dade Co Public Sch Dist*	8,15	74
Moore, Frank/*Columbia Co School Dist*	68,74,273	27
Moore, Jane/*Seminole Co Public School Dist*	280	132
Moore, Joyce/*Seminole Co Public School Dist*	69	132
Moore, Larry/*Jackson Co School Dist*	1	57
Moore, Tom/*Clay Co School Dist*	71,97	23
Moquin, Jeffrey/*Broward Co Public Schools*	15,751	10
Mora, Marc/*Lee Co School Dist*	2	60

1 Superintendent	16 Instructional Media Svcs	30 Adult Education	44 Science Sec	58 Special Education K-12	72 Summer School	88 Alternative/At Risk	277 Remedial Math K-12
2 Bus/Finance/Purchasing	17 Chief Operations Officer	31 Career/Sch-to-Work K-12	45 Math K-12	59 Special Education Elem	73 Instructional Tech	89 Multi-Cultural Curriculum	280 Literacy Coach
3 Buildings And Grounds	18 Chief Academic Officer	32 Career/Sch-to-Work Elem	46 Math Elem	60 Special Education Sec	74 Inservice Training	90 Social Work	285 STEM
4 Food Service	19 Chief Financial Officer	33 Career/Sch-to-Work Sec	47 Math Sec	61 Foreign/World Lang K-12	75 Marketing/Distributive	91 Safety/Security	286 Digital Learning
5 Transportation	20 Art K-12	34 Early Childhood Ed	48 English/Lang Arts K-12	62 Foreign/World Lang Elem	76 Info Systems	92 Magnet School	288 Common Core Standards
6 Athletic	21 Art Elem	35 Health/Phys Education	49 English/Lang Arts Elem	63 Foreign/World Lang Sec	77 Psychological Assess	93 Parental Involvement	294 Accountability
7 Health Services	22 Art Sec	36 Guidance Services K-12	50 English/Lang Arts Sec	64 Religious Education K-12	78 Affirmative Action	95 Tech Prep Program	295 Network System
8 Curric/Instruct K-12	23 Music K-12	37 Guidance Services Elem	51 Reading K-12	65 Religious Education Elem	79 Student Personnel	97 Chief Information Officer	296 Title II Programs
9 Curric/Instruct Elem	24 Music Elem	38 Guidance Services Sec	52 Reading Elem	66 Religious Education Sec	80 Driver Ed/Safety	98 Chief Technology Officer	297 Webmaster
10 Curric/Instruct Sec	25 Music Sec	39 Social Studies K-12	53 Reading Sec	67 School Board President	81 Gifted/Talented	270 Character Education	298 Grant Writer/Ptnrships
11 Federal Program	26 Business Education	40 Social Studies Elem	54 Remedial Reading K-12	68 Teacher Personnel	82 Video Services	271 Migrant Education	750 Chief Innovation Officer
12 Title I	27 Career & Tech Ed	41 Social Studies Sec	55 Remedial Reading Elem	69 Academic Assessment	83 Substance Abuse Prev	273 Teacher Mentor	751 Chief of Staff
13 Title V	28 Technology Education	42 Science K-12	56 Remedial Reading Sec	70 Research/Development	84 Erate	274 Before/After Sch	752 Social Emotional Learning
15 Asst Superintendent	29 Family/Consumer Science	43 Science Elem	57 Bilingual/ELL	71 Public Information	85 AIDS Education	275 Response To Intervention	

FL-T10

NAME/District	JOB FUNCTIONS	PAGE
Morales, Mabel/*Miami-Dade Co Public Sch Dist*	20	74
Morell, David/*St Johns Co School Dist*	275	134
Morgado, Melissa/*Hillsborough Co Pub Sch Dist*	61	46
Morgan, Beryl/*Monroe Co School Dist*	11,57	89
Morgan, Brian/*St Johns Co School Dist*	39,57,61	134
Morgan, Lesa/*Escambia Co School Dist*	10	36
Morris, John/*Orange Co Public School Dist*	3	94
Morris, Sharon/*Hillsborough Co SD-Area 5*	1	51
Morris, Sonya/*Florida Dept of Education*	11,271	1
Morrissey, Saralee/*Volusia Co School Dist*	2	140
Morse, Charlie/*Walton Co School Dist*	91	143
Morse, Scott/*Charlotte Co Public Sch Dist*	295	21
Moses, Traci/*Franklin Co School Dist*	1	40
Mosley, Kelly/*Clay Co School Dist*	27	23
Mosley, Mitch/*Escambia Co School Dist*	3	36
Moxley, Susan, Dr/*School Dist of Indian River Co*	1	55
Moyer, Mitch/*Volusia Co School Dist*	5	140
Mulder, Mary/*Broward Co Public Schools*	4	10
Muldoon, Mike/*Manatee Co School Dist*	58	68
Mulher, Deborah/*Volusia Co School Dist*	2,19	140
Mulkusky, Kara/*Bay Co School Dist*	36,79	4
Mullen, John/*Citrus Co School Dist*	76	22
Mullen, Michael/*Citrus Co School Dist*	3,5,15	22
Mullins, Mark/*FDLRS-East Brevard*	1	10
Mullins, Mark, Dr/*Brevard Co School Dist*	1	6
Mundy, Barbara/*Hendry Co School Dist*	57,271,296	43
Mungillo, Wendy/*Manatee Co School Dist*	68	68
Mungin, Tanya/*Nassau Co School Dist*	83,91,275	90
Muniz, Karen, Sr/*Archdiocese of Miami Ed Office*	64	85
Murdock, Trudi/*Seminole Co Public School Dist*	2	131
Murillo, Marco/*Hillsborough Co SD-Area 2*	1	49
Murphy, David/*Monroe Co School Dist*	69,294	89
Murphy, David/*Monroe Co School Dist*	69,294	89
Murphy, Julie/*Seminole Co Public School Dist*	5	132
Murphy, Tim/*Taylor Co School Dist*	295	139
Murray, Patrick/*Martin Co School Dist*	274	73
Musselwhite, Barbara/*School Dist of Indian River Co*	274	55
Musselwhite, Melissa/*Pasco Co School Dist*	34,36,58,81,88	112
Myers, Carol/*Escambia Co School Dist*	42	36
Myers, Lauren/*Okeechobee Co School Dist*	79	93
Myers, Mary, Dr/*Volusia Co School Dist*	58	140
Myers, Richard/*Volusia Co School Dist*	91	140

N

NAME/District	JOB FUNCTIONS	PAGE
Naidu, Felicia/*Seminole Co Public School Dist*	58	132
Nalefski, James/*Sarasota Co School Dist*	73	129
Nara, David/*Collier Co Public School Dist*	2	25
Narvaez, Julio/*Bay Co School Dist*	4	4
Negron, Carlos/*Lee Co School Dist*	57	60
Nelson, Don/*Duval Co Public School Dist*	3,5,15,17	29
Nelson, Simon/*Sarasota Co School Dist*	5	129
Nettles, Marcy/*Pasco Co School Dist*	15	112
Nettles, Marcy/*Pasco CSD-Middle Schools*	15	114
New, Toni/*Santa Rosa Co School Dist*	21	127
Newman, John/*Hillsborough Co Pub Sch Dist*	91	46
Newsom, Kyle/*Washington Co School Dist*	3,5,74,91	144
Newsome, Craig/*Hamilton Co School Dist*	3	42
Nguyen, Catherine/*Orange Co Public School Dist*	2	94
Nichols, Elayne/*Seminole Co Public School Dist*	2	131
Nicholson, Mary/*Leon Co School Dist*	68	64
Nicoleau, Carl/*Miami-Dade Co Public Sch Dist*	3,15	74
Nielsen, Cassie/*Florida Virtual School Dist*	71	93
Niles, Linda/*Bradford Co School Dist*	295	5
Nimmons, William/*Leon Co School Dist*	73,76	64
Nobles, Kathy/*Florida Dept of Education*	15	1
Noles, Anthony/*Escambia Co School Dist*	3	36
Norris, Jessica/*Manatee Co School Dist*	294	68
Norris, Natalie/*Alachua Co School Dist*	12,271	1
Norton, Jim/*Gulf Co School Dist*	1	41
Nottage, Laquieria/*Polk Co School Dist*	38	122
Novelli, Robin/*Brevard Co School Dist*	5,7,15,36	6
Nulisch, Joy/*Monroe Co School Dist*	73,95	89
Nunez, George/*Miami-Dade Co Public Sch Dist*	6	74

O

NAME/District	JOB FUNCTIONS	PAGE
O'Hara-Morris, Greta/*Manatee Co School Dist*	68	68

NAME/District	JOB FUNCTIONS	PAGE
O'Keefe, Sean/*Sarasota Co School Dist*	295	129
O'Leary, Terence/*St Lucie Co School Dist*	3,5,17,71,73,76	136
O'Steen, Wendy/*Gilchrist Co School Dist*	57	41
O'Toole, Sara/*Pinellas Co School Dist*	7	116
Oakes, Elizabeth/*Escambia Co School Dist*	68	36
Oberst, Julie/*Levy Co School Dist*	4	66
Ocasio, Melissa/*Marion Co Public Schools*	76	70
Odom, Rhonda/*Putnam Co School Dist*	2,15,19	126
Oh, Won/*Manatee Co School Dist*	5	68
Olguin, Oscar/*Lee Co School Dist*	275	60
Olivo, Jerry/*Charlotte Co Public Sch Dist*	15,79	21
Olsen, Chris/*Taylor Co School Dist*	91,298	139
Olson, Cheryl/*Seminole Co Public School Dist*	2	131
Ortiz, Alfredo/*Orange Co Public School Dist*	298	94
Oswald, Keith/*Palm Beach Co School Dist*	8,15,18	105
Osypian, Benjamin/*Flagler Co School Dist*	68	39
Overton, Lisa/*Osceola Co School Dist*	58	102
Owens, Sherri/*Lake Co School Dist*	71	58
Owens, Shirley/*Holmes Co School Dist*	67	55
Owens, Stacy/*Putnam Co School Dist*	27	127

P

NAME/District	JOB FUNCTIONS	PAGE
Pace, Debra, Dr/*Osceola Co School Dist*	1	102
Pace, John/*Miami-Dade-Central Region*	1	74
Pacheco, Robert/*Orange Co Public School Dist*	3,17	94
Padgett, Heather/*Martin Co School Dist*	74	73
Padgett, Pamela/*Taylor Co School Dist*	73,76,98	139
Padgett, Toni/*Clay Co School Dist*	2	23
Padrick, Kerry/*St Lucie Co School Dist*	16,71,75	136
Paige-Pender, Dana/*Volusia Co School Dist*	68	140
Palelis, Ashley/*Florida Dept of Education*	73	1
Palmer, Jeff/*Okaloosa Co School Dist*	9	91
Palmer, Mark/*Lake Co School Dist*	91	58
Pantano, Al/*St Johns Co School Dist*	5	134
Papaemanuel, Vicki/*Pasco Co School Dist*	752	112
Pardee, Skip/*Collier Co Public School Dist*	20,23	25
Pardo, Vivian/*Miami-Dade Co Public Sch Dist*	15	74
Parfitt, Ricahrd/*Lee Co School Dist*	91	60
Parker, Edward/*Osceola Co School Dist*	2	102
Parrish, Ronda/*Gilchrist Co School Dist*	7,8,15,51,69,83,288,294	41
Parsons, Elia/*Martin Co School Dist*	27	72
Pascarella, Simonetta/*Sarasota Co School Dist*	91	129
Paschke, Walter/*Hernando Co School Dist*	295	43
Pastura, Christopher/*Diocese St Petersburg Ed Off*	1,11	120
Patrick, Sharon/*Santa Rosa Co School Dist*	275	127
Patton, Kamela, Dr/*Collier Co Public School Dist*	1	25
Paul, Wanda/*Palm Beach Co School Dist*	3,17	105
Pauline, Tiffanie/*Miami-Dade Co Public Sch Dist*	15	74
Paulk, Alice/*Clay Co School Dist*	27	23
Pavelchak, John/*Florida Virtual School Dist*	2,19	93
Pawlowski, Roberta/*FDLRS-Gulfcoast*	73	121
Payne, Airen/*Clay Co School Dist*	7	23
Pearce, Robert/*Wakulla Co School Dist*	1	143
Pearsall, Sherry/*Lee Co School Dist*	2	60
Pearson, Joey/*Lafayette Co School Dist*	3,4,5,6	58
Pearson, Kati Rose/*Lake Co School Dist*	57,69,275	58
Pearson, Melissa/*Lafayette Co School Dist*	7	58
Pearson, Phyllis, Dr/*Flagler Co School Dist*	7	39
Peddie, Karen/*Franklin Co School Dist*	68	40
Peddiferd, Barbara/*Madison Co School Dist*	69,294	67
Peek, Karen/*Okaloosa Co School Dist*	68,273,296	91
Peek, Sharwonda/*Duval Co Public School Dist*	15	29
Pegg, Jeffrey/*Palm Beach Co SD-South Region*	9	109
Peirce, Linda/*Hernando Co School Dist*	69,294	43
Pejot, Christine/*Pasco Co School Dist*	68	112
Pendleton, Rose/*Volusia Co School Dist*	2	140
People, Troy/*Washington Co School Dist*	11,58,69,77,79,83,296,298	144
Perez, Carlos/*Martin Co School Dist*	68	72
Perez, Mary Ann/*Osceola Co School Dist*	34,274	102
Perez, Raul/*Miami-Dade Co Public Sch Dist*	15	74
Perez, Ronald/*Levy Co School Dist*	76,84	66
Perez, San Janita/*Hendry Co School Dist*	4	43
Perkins, Lakysha/*Gadsden Co School Dist*	34	40
Perkins, Rich/*Clay Co School Dist*	295	23
Perrone, Ivan/*Broward Co Public Schools*	2	10
Perrone, Michael/*Polk Co School Dist*	2,15,19	122

1 Superintendent	16 Instructional Media Svcs	30 Adult Education	44 Science Sec	58 Special Education K-12	72 Summer School	88 Alternative/At Risk	277 Remedial Math K-12
2 Bus/Finance/Purchasing	17 Chief Operations Officer	31 Career/Sch-to-Work K-12	45 Math K-12	59 Special Education Elem	73 Instructional Tech	89 Multi-Cultural Curriculum	280 Literacy Coach
3 Buildings And Grounds	18 Chief Academic Officer	32 Career/Sch-to-Work Elem	46 Math Elem	60 Special Education Sec	74 Inservice Training	90 Social Work	285 STEM
4 Food Service	19 Chief Financial Officer	33 Career/Sch-to-Work Sec	47 Math Sec	61 Foreign/World Lang K-12	75 Marketing/Distributive	91 Safety/Security	286 Digital Learning
5 Transportation	20 Art K-12	34 Early Childhood Ed	48 English/Lang Arts K-12	62 Foreign/World Lang Elem	76 Info Systems	92 Magnet School	288 Common Core Standards
6 Athletic	21 Art Elem	35 Health/Phys Education	49 English/Lang Arts Elem	63 Foreign/World Lang Sec	77 Psychological Assess	93 Parental Involvement	294 Accountability
7 Health Services	22 Art Sec	36 Guidance Services K-12	50 English/Lang Arts Sec	64 Religious Education K-12	78 Affirmative Action	95 Tech Prep Program	295 Network System
8 Curric/Instruct K-12	23 Music K-12	37 Guidance Services Elem	51 Reading K-12	65 Religious Education Elem	79 Student Personnel	97 Chief Information Officer	296 Title II Programs
9 Curric/Instruct Elem	24 Music Elem	38 Guidance Services Sec	52 Reading Elem	66 Religious Education Sec	80 Driver Ed/Safety	98 Chief Technology Officer	297 Webmaster
10 Curric/Instruct Sec	25 Music Sec	39 Social Studies K-12	53 Reading Sec	67 School Board President	81 Gifted/Talented	270 Character Education	298 Grant Writer/Ptnrships
11 Federal Program	26 Business Education	40 Social Studies Elem	54 Remedial Reading K-12	68 Teacher Personnel	82 Video Services	271 Migrant Education	750 Chief Innovation Officer
12 Title I	27 Career & Tech Ed	41 Social Studies Sec	55 Remedial Reading Elem	69 Academic Assessment	83 Substance Abuse Prev	273 Teacher Mentor	751 Chief of Staff
13 Title V	28 Technology Education	42 Science K-12	56 Remedial Reading Sec	70 Research/Development	84 Erate	274 Before/After Sch	752 Social Emotional Learning
15 Asst Superintendent	29 Family/Consumer Science	43 Science Elem	57 Bilingual/ELL	71 Public Information	85 AIDS Education	275 Response To Intervention	

NAME/District	JOB FUNCTIONS	PAGE
Roberts, Mike/*DeSoto Co School Dist*	76	28
Robey, Mike/*Marion Co Public Schools*	3	70
Robinson, Chanda/*Highlands Co School Dist*	5	45
Robinson, Eugenia/*Bay Co School Dist*	11,93	4
Robinson, Kecia/*Suwannee Co School Dist*	11	138
Robinson, Lanness/*Hillsborough Co Pub Sch Dist*	6	46
Robinson, Sandra/*Gadsden Co School Dist*	68	40
Robinson, Senita/*Sarasota Co School Dist*	5	129
Robinson, Tuuli/*Okeechobee Co School Dist*	30,69,294	93
Roderick, Lisa/*Madison Co School Dist*	11	67
Rodgers, Kathleen/*Leon Co School Dist*	15,78,83,275	64
Rodriguez, Jamie/*Sarasota Co School Dist*	57,271	129
Rodriguez, Lisette, Dr/*Miami-Dade Co Public Sch Dist*	81	74
Rodriguez, Mary/*Lee Co School Dist*	36	60
Rodriguez, Penny/*Collier Co Public School Dist*	5	25
Rodriguez, Yesicca/*Collier Co Public School Dist*	5	25
Rodriguez, Zuzel/*Broward Co Public Schools*	81	10
Rogers, Kimberly, Dr/*Brevard Co School Dist*	88	6
Rogers, Sheryl, Dr/*Collier Co Public School Dist*	74	25
Roland, David/*Citrus Co School Dist*	10,285	22
Roland, Rose/*Volusia Co School Dist*	15	140
Roland, Shane/*Madison Co School Dist*	73,76,295	67
Rollison, Melody/*Dixie Co School Dist*	4	28
Rollo, Diana/*Alachua Co School Dist*	20,23,61,89,92	1
Roman, Leticia/*Volusia Co School Dist*	72,271,296,298	140
Romano, Lori/*Pasco Co School Dist*	298	112
Rora, Rebecca/*Marion Co Public Schools*	5	70
Rosales, Ava, Dr/*Miami-Dade Co Public Sch Dist*	44	74
Rosario, Sandra/*Hillsborough Co Pub Sch Dist*	57	46
Rose, Jackie/*DeSoto Co School Dist*	57,271	28
Rose, Karen/*Sarasota Co School Dist*	10,72	129
Rose, Rhonda/*Diocese St Augustine Ed Office*	8,15	34
Rosenaw, Kaitlyn/*Collier Co Public School Dist*	68	25
Rosenbalm, Mark/*Collier Co Public School Dist*	6	25
Ross, Duscha/*Okaloosa Co School Dist*	76	91
Ross, Laura, Dr/*Seminole Co Public School Dist*	18	132
Ross, Norman/*Escambia Co School Dist*	15	36
Roston, Cassandra/*Marion Co Public Schools*	11,298	70
Roth, Terry/*Clay Co School Dist*	36,77,79,81,83	23
Rothenberg, Will/*Lee Co School Dist*	68	60
Rouleau, Marc/*Collier Co Public School Dist*	3	25
Roush, Ted/*Suwannee Co School Dist*	1	138
Rowell, Cylle/*Bay Co School Dist*	45	4
Rowell, Jessica/*Escambia Co School Dist*	48	36
Rowland, Mandy/*St Lucie Co School Dist*	280,296	136
Rudd, Jill/*Franklin Co School Dist*	28,29,34,57,58,73,77,296	40
Runcie, Robert/*Broward Co Public Schools*	1	10
Runions, Sheina/*Sarasota Co School Dist*	2	129
Russell, Christina/*Hillsborough Co Pub Sch Dist*	73,286	46
Russell, Marla/*Monroe Co School Dist*	34	89
Russell, Marla/*Monroe Co School Dist*	34	89
Russo, Dennis/*Pinellas Co School Dist*	91	116
Russo, Domenick/*Archdiocese of Miami Ed Office*	68	85
Rutledge, Rachel/*Volusia Co School Dist*	31	140
Ryals, Danny/*Calhoun Co School Dist*	67	20
Ryan, Chris/*Clay Co School Dist*	58	23
Rybinski, Desiree/*Volusia Co School Dist*	49,51	140

S

NAME/District	JOB FUNCTIONS	PAGE
Saari, Joan/*Sarasota Co School Dist*	2	129
Saba, Kevin/*Collier Co Public School Dist*	10	25
Sage, Justin/*Martin Co School Dist*	2	72
Salcedo, Octavio/*Pinellas Co School Dist*	69,70,294	116
Saldala, Victoria/*Broward Co Public Schools*	57	10
Sallas, Greg/*Holmes Co School Dist*	91,752	55
Saltmarsh, Mark/*Flagler Co School Dist*	73,76	39
Samala, Michael, Dr/*Escambia Co School Dist*	270	36
Sams, Barry/*Union Co School Dist*	10,16,27,68,88,273	139
Samson, Jerry/*Okaloosa Co School Dist*	31	91
Samuels, Paul/*Hardee Co School Dist*	67	42
Sanchez, Rafael/*St Lucie Co School Dist*	68	136
Sanchez, Sandra/*Collier Co Public School Dist*	4	25
Sanchez, Shawn/*Orange Co Public School Dist*	93	94
Sancho, Teresa/*Florida Dept of Education*	8,288	1
Sanders, Jennifer/*Palm Beach Co SD-Ctl Region*	9	106
Sanders, Jim/*School Dist of Indian River Co*	3	55

NAME/District	JOB FUNCTIONS	PAGE
Sanders, Kathy/*Leon Co School Dist*	2	64
Sandgren, Lori/*Wakulla Co School Dist*	8	143
Santiago, Mabel/*Manatee Co School Dist*	5	68
Santiago, Mark/*Lee Co School Dist*	2	60
Santini, Douglas, Dr/*Lee Co School Dist*	79	60
Sapp, Dawn/*St Johns Co School Dist*	8	134
Sasser, Jennifer/*Orange Co Public School Dist*	15,70,294,298	94
Sauer, Dawn/*Manatee Co School Dist*	92,93	68
Sauer, Don/*Manatee Co School Dist*	286	68
Saunders, Cynthia/*Manatee Co School Dist*	1	68
Saunders, Gretchen/*Hillsborough Co Pub Sch Dist*	2	45
Saunders, Lynsey/*Monroe Co School Dist*	71,297	89
Saunders, Susan/*Washington Co School Dist*	8,280,285	144
Scallan, Rita/*Okaloosa Co School Dist*	2,19	91
Scanga, David/*Pasco Co School Dist*	15	112
Scanlan, Maureen/*Seminole Co Public School Dist*	8	132
Schaaf, P/*Martin Co School Dist*	4	72
Schafer, Dana Lee/*Osceola Co School Dist*	71	102
Scheuer, Mark/*Osceola Co School Dist*	3	102
Schlabach, Susan/*Sarasota Co School Dist*	5	129
Schmitges, Henry/*FDLRS-Crown*	1,11	36
Schofield, Buddy/*Dixie Co School Dist*	8,27,30,31,83,294,296	29
Scholz, Janice/*Brevard Co School Dist*	27	6
Schrier, George/*Manatee Co School Dist*	88	68
Schroder-King, Linda/*Osceola Co School Dist*	58	102
Schroder, Terry/*Okaloosa Co School Dist*	77	91
Schroeder, Matthew/*Broward Co Public Schools*	80	10
Schultz, Jason/*Florida Virtual School Dist*	8	93
Schultz, Scott/*Clay Co School Dist*	2	23
Schultz, Victoria/*Duval Co Public School Dist*	15,68	29
Schulz, Kelly/*Volusia Co School Dist*	71	140
Schumacher, Sara/*Osceola Co School Dist*	36	102
Schuster, John/*Miami-Dade Co Public Sch Dist*	71	74
Schwanemann, Bill/*Manatee Co School Dist*	3	68
Schwied, Danielle/*Sarasota Co School Dist*	68	129
Scott, Alan, Dr/*Escambia Co School Dist*	15,68	36
Scott, Antonio/*St Johns Co School Dist*	20,23	134
Scott, Ashley/*Leon Co School Dist*	12,298	64
Scott, Ken/*Leon Co School Dist*	79	64
Scott, Leslie/*Escambia Co School Dist*	4	36
Scott, Nakita/*Polk Co School Dist*	90	122
Scott, Sherry/*Polk Co School Dist*	77	122
Scott, Steve/*Gadsden Co School Dist*	67	40
Sealy, James/*Hendry Co School Dist*	68	43
Sears, Tony/*School Dist of Indian River Co*	5,91	55
Sechrist, Mark/*Martin Co School Dist*	3	72
See, Jennifer/*Jackson Co School Dist*	6,10,13,16,72,76	57
Seeds, Cathy/*Florida Dept of Education*	16	1
Segur, Robert/*Charlotte Co Public Sch Dist*	67	21
Seibel, Linda/*Sarasota Co School Dist*	76	129
Seis, Todd/*Seminole Co Public School Dist*	2	131
Seitz, Aliesha/*St Lucie Co School Dist*	27,31	136
Selover, John/*Panhandle Area Ed Consortium*	1	145
Sennoy, Donald, Dr/*FDLRS-Alpha*	1	112
Sessa, Julie/*Martin Co School Dist*	2	72
Seth, Kim/*FDLRS-Suncoast*	74	131
Severson, Kathy/*DeSoto Co School Dist*	11,54,57,296,298	28
Sexmour, Jill/*Polk Co School Dist*	91	122
Shamburger, Tamara/*Hillsborough Co Pub Sch Dist*	67	46
Shankar, Uma/*Alachua Co School Dist*	16,73,82	1
Shapiro, Daniel, Dr/*Broward Co Public Schools*	37	10
Sharin, Krista/*Wakulla Co School Dist*	12,16,69,88,296	143
Sharman, Katie/*St Johns Co School Dist*	69	134
Shaw, Melissa/*Volusia Co School Dist*	12	140
Shayman, Robert/*Hardee Co School Dist*	1	42
Sheets, Richard/*Alachua Co School Dist*	39	1
Sheffield, Glenda/*Palm Beach Co SD-South Region*	10	109
Shelar, Michele/*Alachua Co School Dist*	7	1
Sheppard, Camaille, Dr/*Seminole Co Public School Dist*	274	132
Shibley, Kevin/*Pasco Co School Dist*	15,68,69	112
Shields, Cathy/*Leon Co School Dist*	58	64
Shields, Christi/*School Dist of Indian River Co*	30	55
Shirley, Richard/*Sumter Co School Dist*	1	137
Shoemaker, William/*Monroe Co School Dist*	3	89
Shores, Tanya, Dr/*Seminole Co Public School Dist*	58	132
Short, James, Dr/*Lee Co School Dist*	295	60

1 Superintendent	16 Instructional Media Svcs	30 Adult Education	44 Science Sec	58 Special Education K-12	72 Summer School	88 Alternative/At Risk	277 Remedial Math K-12
2 Bus/Finance/Purchasing	17 Chief Operations Officer	31 Career/Sch-to-Work K-12	45 Math K-12	59 Special Education Elem	73 Instructional Tech	89 Multi-Cultural Curriculum	280 Literacy Coach
3 Buildings And Grounds	18 Chief Academic Officer	32 Career/Sch-to-Work Elem	46 Math Elem	60 Special Education Sec	74 Inservice Training	90 Social Work	285 STEM
4 Food Service	19 Chief Financial Officer	33 Career/Sch-to-Work Sec	47 Math Sec	61 Foreign/World Lang K-12	75 Marketing/Distributive	91 Safety/Security	286 Digital Learning
5 Transportation	20 Art K-12	34 Early Childhood Ed	48 English/Lang Arts K-12	62 Foreign/World Lang Elem	76 Info Systems	92 Magnet School	288 Common Core Standards
6 Athletic	21 Art Elem	35 Health/Phys Education	49 English/Lang Arts Elem	63 Foreign/World Lang Sec	77 Psychological Assess	93 Parental Involvement	294 Accountability
7 Health Services	22 Art Sec	36 Guidance Services K-12	50 English/Lang Arts Sec	64 Religious Education K-12	78 Affirmative Action	95 Tech Prep Program	295 Network System
8 Curric/Instruct K-12	23 Music K-12	37 Guidance Services Elem	51 Reading K-12	65 Religious Education Elem	79 Student Personnel	97 Chief Infomation Officer	296 Title II Programs
9 Curric/Instruct Elem	24 Music Elem	38 Guidance Services Sec	52 Reading Elem	66 Religious Education Sec	80 Driver Ed/Safety	98 Chief Technology Officer	297 Webmaster
10 Curric/Instruct Sec	25 Music Sec	39 Social Studies K-12	53 Reading Sec	67 School Board President	81 Gifted/Talented	270 Character Education	298 Grant Writer/Ptnrships
11 Federal Program	26 Business Education	40 Social Studies Elem	54 Remedial Reading K-12	68 Teacher Personnel	82 Video Services	271 Migrant Education	750 Chief Innovation Officer
12 Title I	27 Career & Tech Ed	41 Social Studies Sec	55 Remedial Reading Elem	69 Academic Assessment	83 Substance Abuse Prev	273 Teacher Mentor	751 Chief of Staff
13 Title V	28 Technology Education	42 Science K-12	56 Remedial Reading Sec	70 Research/Development	84 Erate	274 Before/After Sch	752 Social Emotional Learning
15 Asst Superintendent	29 Family/Consumer Science	43 Science Elem	57 Bilingual/ELL	71 Public Information	85 AIDS Education	275 Response To Intervention	

NAME/District	JOB FUNCTIONS	PAGE
T		
Taggert, James/*Flagler Co School Dist*	1	39
Takacs, Nancy/*Okaloosa Co School Dist*	27	91
Talbot, Dan/*Polk Co School Dist*	6,80	122
Talley, Tammie/*Duval Co Public School Dist*	6	29
Tanner, Elizabeth/*Hillsborough Co Pub Sch Dist*	752	46
Tanner, Leanna/*Alachua Co School Dist*	4	1
Tant, Tom/*Flagler Co School Dist*	2,19	39
Tarte, Tonya/*Baker Co School Dist*	4	3
Tatem, Judy/*Columbia Co School Dist*	83,85,88	27
Taylor-Allen, Jennifer/*Alachua Co School Dist*	36,79	1
Taylor, Chris/*School Dist of Indian River Co*	69,294	55
Taylor, Daniel/*Columbia Co School Dist*	5	27
Taylor, Diane/*Polk Co School Dist*	58,81	122
Taylor, Joseph/*Washington Co School Dist*	1	144
Taylor, Mary Ann/*Union Co School Dist*	84	139
Taylor, Michelle, Dr/*Escambia Co School Dist*	74	36
Taylor, Penny/*Florida Dept of Education*	7	1
Taylor, Tammy/*Manatee Co School Dist*	2	68
Taylor, Tracie/*Calhoun Co School Dist*	8,69,74,271,273,294	20
Tellone, Michael/*Sarasota Co School Dist*	5	129
Terembes, Barbara/*Palm Beach Co School Dist*	15,294	105
Terrell, Kerry/*Hardee Co School Dist*	58	42
Terry, Roy/*Collier Co Public School Dist*	67	25
Teske, John/*School Dist of Indian River Co*	3,15	55
Texel, Paula/*Pinellas Co School Dist*	15,68,78	116
Thedy, Beth, Dr/*Brevard Co School Dist*	15,68	6
Thetford, Stephanie/*Okaloosa Co School Dist*	45,277	91
Thigpen, Kelly/*St Johns Co School Dist*	270	134
Thoma, Regina/*Manatee Co School Dist*	4	68
Thomas, Dale/*Holmes Co School Dist*	295	55
Thomas, Dwan/*Marion Co Public Schools*	58	70
Thomas, Gregory/*Wakulla Co School Dist*	67	143
Thomas, Joanette/*Gadsden Co School Dist*	12	40
Thomas, John/*Gadsden Co School Dist*	295	40
Thomas, Malcom/*Escambia Co School Dist*	1	36
Thomas, Michelle/*St Lucie Co School Dist*	2,19	136
Thomas, Mike/*Dixie Co School Dist*	1	28
Thomas, Patti, Dr/*Escambia Co School Dist*	9	36
Thomas, Reginald/*Alachua Co School Dist*	5	1
Thomas, Sabrina/*Clay Co School Dist*	69	23
Thomas, Sharon/*Gadsden Co School Dist*	81	40
Thomas, Tameka/*Florida Dept of Education*	88	1
Thompson, Beth/*Escambia Co School Dist*	68	36
Thompson, Carol/*St Johns Co School Dist*	88	134
Thompson, Kelly/*Seminole Co Public School Dist*	69,70,294	132
Thompson, Laurel, Dr/*Broward Co Public Schools*	79	10
Thompson, Lesley, Dr/*Monroe Co School Dist*	58,79	89
Thompson, Linda, Dr/*St Johns Co School Dist*	16,88,280	134
Thompson, Michael/*Taylor Co School Dist*	68,73,79,83,88,270,295	139
Thompson, Robin, Dr/*Manatee Co School Dist*	34	68
Thompson, Terry/*Gulf Co School Dist*	73,295	41
Thorne, Peter/*Osceola Co School Dist*	71	102
Thornton, Janna/*Clay Co School Dist*	2	23
Thornton, Kevin/*Brevard Co School Dist*	4	6
Thorpe, Mike/*Santa Rosa Co School Dist*	16,73,74	127
Tierney, Edward/*Palm Beach Co SD-Ctl Region*	10	106
Tillman, Poinsetta/*FDLRS-Sunrise*	1,11	126
Tinajero, Anjelica/*Highlands Co School Dist*	2	44
Tirado, Shana/*Hillsborough Co Pub Sch Dist*	285	46
Tolentino, Julia/*Seminole Co Public School Dist*	4	131
Tomlinson, Bill/*St Lucie Co School Dist*	58,79,83,88	136
Topping, Michelle/*Pinellas Co School Dist*	88	116
Torrence, Marian, Dr/*Escambia Co School Dist*	78	36
Torrens, Jaime/*Miami-Dade Co Public Sch Dist*	3	74
Torres, Ana/*FDLRS-South*	1,11	89
Torres, Leah, Dr/*Osceola Co School Dist*	69,70,294	102
Tourney, Julie/*FDLRS-Westgate*	73	39
Tovine, William/*Orange Co Public School Dist*	88	94
Townley, Michelle/*Polk Co SD-NE & SE*	15	124
Townsend, Anne/*Hillsborough Co Pub Sch Dist*	17,36,77	46
Tracey, Kathleen/*Santa Rosa Co School Dist*	22	127
Tracy, Dana/*Collier Co Public School Dist*	50,53	25
Trammel, Richard/*School Dist of Indian River Co*	5	55
Tranquille, Gerald/*Washington Co School Dist*	6	144

NAME/District	JOB FUNCTIONS	PAGE
Trawick, Bertha/*Volusia Co School Dist*	2	140
Trevino, Janie/*Collier Co Public School Dist*	68	25
Trick, Dave/*Sumter Co School Dist*	73,84	138
Tricquet, Eydie/*FDLRS-Miccosukee*	1	66
Tritto, Danny/*Broward Co Public Schools*	38	10
Troutman, Brenda/*Clay Co School Dist*	68	23
Tubbs, Travis/*Hardee Co School Dist*	6	42
Tuck, Andy/*Florida Virtual School Dist*	67	93
Tucker, Lisa/*Okaloosa Co School Dist*	275	91
Tucker, Trevor/*Flagler Co School Dist*	67	39
Turchetta, Greg/*Collier Co Public School Dist*	71	25
Tyler, Trevor/*Monroe Co School Dist*	27,30	89
Tyre, John/*Okaloosa Co School Dist*	4	91
U		
Underwood, Lynn/*Hillsborough Co Pub Sch Dist*	280	46
Upchurch, Jessica/*School Dist of Indian River Co*	6	55
Urban, Lisa/*Leon Co School Dist*	57	64
Usher, Angela/*Polk Co School Dist*	3,15	122
V		
Vaccaro, Terrence, Dr/*Miami-Dade Co Public Sch Dist*	275	74
Vacchio, Erin/*Orange Co Public School Dist*	69	94
Valdez, Enid/*Broward Co Public Schools*	27,30	10
Valentine, Ashley/*Taylor Co School Dist*	2,11,19,294	139
Valentine, Joshua/*Jefferson Co School Dist*	57	57
Valinski, John/*Bradford Co School Dist*	2	5
Vallejo, Ansberto/*Hillsborough Co Pub Sch Dist*	33	46
Vanoer, Steve/*Hillsborough Co Pub Sch Dist*	35,85	46
Vargas, Edward/*Sarasota Co School Dist*	5	129
Vasquez, Maria/*Orange Co Public School Dist*	15	94
Vasquez, Rita/*Pinellas Co School Dist*	10	116
Vattell, Kelly/*St Johns Co School Dist*	288	134
Vause, Dalynda/*Wakulla Co School Dist*	27,31	143
Vazquez, Ulysses/*Osceola Co School Dist*	76,97	102
Veatch, Sheila/*St Johns Co School Dist*	280	134
Venable, Shannon/*Franklin Co School Dist*	2	40
Verges, Vince/*Florida Dept of Education*	15,69,70,294	1
Verra-Tirado, Monica, Dr/*Florida Dept of Education*	58	1
Vester, Richard/*Hamilton Co School Dist*	6	42
Vianello, Mark/*Marion Co Public Schools*	27,30,31,75	70
Vickers, Patricia/*Osceola Co School Dist*	79	102
Vickery, Kyle/*Manatee Co School Dist*	3	68
Villalba, Pamela/*Orange Co Public School Dist*	10	94
Villani, Lou/*Collier Co Public School Dist*	4	25
Villwock, Michelle/*Martin Co School Dist*	79,286	73
Vincent, Mike/*Manatee Co School Dist*	3	68
Vinson, Jamey/*Clay Co School Dist*	295	23
Vinson, Michael/*Hamilton Co School Dist*	19	42
Vislocky, Karen/*Osceola Co School Dist*	74	102
Vogel Gesang, Tom/*Jefferson Co School Dist*	16,69,73,76,82,286,295	57
Vollmer, Elizabeth/*DeSoto Co School Dist*	2	28
Von Suskil, Natalie/*Sarasota Co School Dist*	4	129
Voorhees, Susan/*Baker Co School Dist*	11,54,57,69,294	3
Vreuis, Julie/*Sarasota Co School Dist*	275	129
W		
Wagner, Doug/*Manatee Co School Dist*	2,15	68
Wagner, Nathan/*Clay Co School Dist*	295	23
Wain, Joseph/*Levy Co School Dist*	5	66
Wait, Nancy/*Volusia Co School Dist*	93	140
Walden, Elizabeth/*Jackson Co School Dist*	84,295,297	57
Walker, Adam/*Lafayette Co School Dist*	73,84,286,295	58
Walker, Angela/*Wakulla Co School Dist*	68,79,91,294	143
Walker, Charles/*Panhandle Area Ed Consortium*	68	145
Walker, Dodd/*Wakulla Co School Dist*	30	143
Walker, Donna/*Santa Rosa Co School Dist*	57	127
Walker, Ida, Dr/*Gadsden Co School Dist*	74,273	40
Walker, Orenthia/*Manatee Co School Dist*	5	68
Wallace, Lisa/*Sarasota Co School Dist*	5	129
Waller, Casandra/*Escambia Co School Dist*	35,80,83	36
Walsh, Michelle, Dr/*Seminole Co Public School Dist*	58,77,81	132
Walters, Andrew/*Brevard Co School Dist*	91	6
Walters, Lee/*Bay Co School Dist*	3	4
Wanbaugh, Joshua/*Manatee Co School Dist*	5	68
Wanza, Valerie, Dr/*Broward Co Public Schools*	294	10

1	Superintendent	16	Instructional Media Svcs	30	Adult Education
2	Bus/Finance/Purchasing	17	Chief Operations Officer	31	Career/Sch-to-Work K-12
3	Buildings And Grounds	18	Chief Academic Officer	32	Career/Sch-to-Work Elem
4	Food Service	19	Chief Financial Officer	33	Career/Sch-to-Work Sec
5	Transportation	20	Art K-12	34	Early Childhood Ed
6	Athletic	21	Art Elem	35	Health/Phys Education
7	Health Services	22	Art Sec	36	Guidance Services K-12
8	Curric/Instruct K-12	23	Music K-12	37	Guidance Services Elem
9	Curric/Instruct Elem	24	Music Elem	38	Guidance Services Sec
10	Curric/Instruct Sec	25	Music Sec	39	Social Studies K-12
11	Federal Program	26	Business Education	40	Social Studies Elem
12	Title I	27	Career & Tech Ed	41	Social Studies Sec
13	Title V	28	Technology Education	42	Science K-12
15	Asst Superintendent	29	Family/Consumer Science	43	Science Elem

44	Science Sec	58	Special Education K-12	72	Summer School
45	Math K-12	59	Special Education Elem	73	Instructional Tech
46	Math Elem	60	Special Education Sec	74	Inservice Training
47	Math Sec	61	Foreign/World Lang K-12	75	Marketing/Distributive
48	English/Lang Arts K-12	62	Foreign/World Lang Elem	76	Info Systems
49	English/Lang Arts Elem	63	Foreign/World Lang Sec	77	Psychological Assess
50	English/Lang Arts Sec	64	Religious Education K-12	78	Affirmative Action
51	Reading K-12	65	Religious Education Elem	79	Student Personnel
52	Reading Elem	66	Religious Education Sec	80	Driver Ed/Safety
53	Reading Sec	67	School Board President	81	Gifted/Talented
54	Remedial Reading K-12	68	Teacher Personnel	82	Video Services
55	Remedial Reading Elem	69	Academic/Assessment	83	Substance Abuse Prev
56	Remedial Reading Sec	70	Research/Development	84	Erate
57	Bilingual/ELL	71	Public Information	85	AIDS Education

88	Alternative/At Risk	277	Remedial Math K-12
89	Multi-Cultural Curriculum	280	Literacy Coach
90	Social Work	285	STEM
91	Safety/Security	286	Digital Learning
92	Magnet School	288	Common Core Standards
93	Parental Involvement	294	Accountability
95	Tech Prep Program	295	Network System
97	Chief Infomation Officer	296	Title II Programs
98	Chief Technology Officer	297	Webmaster
270	Character Education	298	Grant Writer/Ptnrships
271	Migrant Education	750	Chief Innovation Officer
273	Teacher Mentor	751	Chief of Staff
274	Before/After Sch	752	Social Emotional Learning
275	Response To Intervention		

NAME/District	JOB FUNCTIONS	PAGE
Wright, Corey/*Duval Co PSD-HS Alt Region*	1	32
Wright, John/*Orange Co Public SD-Dep Supt*	1	95
Wright, John, Dr/*Orange Co Public School Dist*	15,71	94
Wright, Kathleen/*Polk Co School Dist*	35,85	122
Wright, Kevin/*Seminole Co Public School Dist*	3	131
Wright, Patricia/*Pinellas Co Schools-Area 4*	15	119
Wright, Ramona/*Escambia Co School Dist*	57,271	36
Wright, Samantha/*Clay Co School Dist*	68	23
Wuest, Deborah/*St Lucie Co School Dist*	4	136
Wulff, Mary/*Martin Co School Dist*	2	72
Wynn, Iris/*Madison Co School Dist*	4	67
Wynn, Laurie/*Taylor Co School Dist*	16,82	139
Wyrosdick, Tim/*Santa Rosa Co School Dist*	1	127

X

Xenick, Angelique/*Hillsborough Co Pub Sch Dist*	38	46

Y

Yanosik, Michael/*Hendry Co School Dist*	2,19	43
Yavalar, Melissa/*Sarasota Co School Dist*	3	129
Yeates, Lester/*Osceola Co School Dist*	91	102
Yoder, Ralph/*Calhoun Co School Dist*	1	20
Yongue, Faye/*Panhandle Area Ed Consortium*	58	145
York, Wendy/*Sarasota Co School Dist*	5	129
Yorke, Tammy/*Flagler Co School Dist*	11	39
Yost, Lisa/*Hillsborough Co SD-Area 1*	1	48
Youmans, Darlean/*Gadsden Co School Dist*	16,76,286	40
Young, Andrea/*Brevard Co School Dist*	297	6
Young, Marcy/*Levy Co School Dist*	58,77	66
Young, Nicole/*Clay Co School Dist*	71	23
Young, Owen/*Hillsborough Co SD-Area 4*	1	51
Youngblood, Clark/*Santa Rosa Co School Dist*	39	127

Z

Zentko, Jane/*Duval Co Public School Dist*	4	29
Zerega, John/*Orange Co Public School Dist*	7	94
Zinser, Leanne/*Collier Co Public School Dist*	71	25
Zipperer, Ksena/*Florida Dept of Education*	85	1
Zmach, Courtney, Dr/*Collier Co Public School Dist*	298	25
Zorc, Laura/*School Dist of Indian River Co*	67	55
Zorovich-Godek, Dana, Dr/*Palm Beach Co School Dist*	11	105
Zuercher, Pennie/*Brevard Co School Dist*	2,11,19	6
Zuloaga-Haines, Valerie/*Palm Beach Co SD-Ctl Region*	1	106

NAME/*School*	PAGE	NAME/*School*	PAGE
McMandon, Sandra/*Valley Ridge Academy*	135	Miles, Daphne/*Pinellas Central Elem Sch*	119
McMeen, Dave/*P J Sullivan Partnership Sch*	48	Miles, Sheila/*Trinity Lutheran Sch*	105
McMillan, Kelly/*Apollo Beach Elem Sch*	51	Milford, James/*MacLay Sch*	66
McMullen, Teeter/*Webster Elem Sch*	138	Millard, William/*Buck Lake Elem Sch*	64
McNally, Gina/*Waller Elem Sch*	5	Miller, Adam/*Kings Academy*	111
McNeal, Crystal/*Oscar Patterson Elem Sch*	5	Miller, Christina/*Millhopper Montessori Sch*	3
McNealy, Tiffany/*Bethel SDA Elem Sch*	86	Miller, Christopher/*R Bruce Wagner Elem Sch*	125
McNeill, Lynn/*High Springs Community Sch*	2	**Miller, Craig**/*Shoal River Middle Sch*	92
McNerney, Stacy/*St Joseph Sch*	73	Miller, Dawn/*Orangewood Christian Sch*	101
McNichols, Deborah/*Greenacres Elem Sch*	107	Miller, Dina/*Somerset Academy CS-Davie [130]*	17
McNichols, Scott/*Forest Hill Elem Sch*	107	**Miller, Donald**/*Lake Co Virtual Sch*	59
McNulty, Maureen/*Little Flower Sch*	18	Miller, Eric, Dr/*Banyan Elem Sch*	10
McPherson, Christina/*Horace O'Bryant Sch*	89	Miller, Jodi/*Paladin Academy*	19
McPherson, Wendelynn/*Marathon Middle High Sch*	89	Miller, Keith/*Advantage Academy-Hillsborough [132]*	46
McSparren, Camellia/*Shalimar Elem Sch*	92	Miller, Krista/*Astronaut High Sch*	8
McWhite, Charles/*Tiger Academy*	30	Miller, Linda/*Lake Minneola High Sch*	59
McWilliams, Aaron/*Keystone Heights Jr Sr HS*	23	**Miller, Lukeshia**/*Wheatley Elem Sch*	95
McWilliams, Kathy/*Beaches Chapel Sch*	34	Miller, Marcus/*Brownsville Middle Sch*	75
Mealor, Michelle, Dr/*Palmetto Elem Sch*	69	Miller, Randy/*Palm Grove Mennonite Sch*	131
Mears, Stuart/*Adult Education Center*	105	Miller, Ruthann/*Benoist Farms Elem Sch*	106
Mearsheimer, Laurie, Dr/*Manatee Elem Sch*	26	Miller, Sharon/*Ben Gamla Charter -N Broward [130]*	16
Mederios, Matthew/*Varsity Lakes Middle Sch*	63	Miller, William/*Montclair Elem Sch*	24
Medina-Maestre, Janet/*Chickasaw Elem Sch*	96	Milliken, Randy/*North Miami Beach Sr High Sch*	80
Medina, Maria/*Miami Lakes Middle Sch*	80	Milliner, Smith/*J E B Stuart Middle Sch*	32
Meechin, Michael/*Neocity Academy*	103	Millins, Thomas/*N Ft Myers Academy for Arts*	62
Megara, Peter/*Progress Village Magnet Sch*	52	Mills, Aaron/*Calvary Christian Academy*	18
Mehr, Lisa/*Woodville K-8 Sch*	65	Mills, Deshuan/*Providence Sch*	35
Mejia, Marta/*Ojus Elem Sch*	80	Mills, Genell/*School of Success Academy*	30
Mekler, Jennifer/*Brooker Creek Elem Sch*	116	Mills, Janice/*Spectrum Jr Sr High Sch*	73
Melian, Ileana/*Mater Acad of Int'l Studies [130]*	77	Mills, Karen/*Sara Scott Harllee Ctr-Sable*	69
Melian, Ileana/*Mater International Prep Acad*	77	Mills, Steve/*Deerlake Middle Sch*	64
Mellin, Fredric/*Land O'Lakes High Sch*	114	Millson, Whitney/*Broach School-Orange Park*	24
Melosh, Geri, Dr/*Childrens Reading Center CS*	127	Milne, Jack/*Bolles School-Bartram*	34
Melrose, Kathleen/*Morningside Elem Sch*	136	Miranda, Enrique/*Masters Prep Sch*	87
Melvin, Debra/*Baker Co Virtual Sch*	4	Miranda, Michael/*Orange Grove Mag Sch the Arts*	51
Memmer-Novak, Dianne/*Hobe Sound Elem Sch*	73	Miret, Humberto/*Miami Southridge Sr High Sch*	83
Menard, Lynne/*Robert H Prine Elem Sch*	69	**Mirhaj, Afshin**/*Archimedean Middle Conserv Sch*	81
Mendez, Lori/*Watkins Elem Sch*	15	**Mirhaj, Afshin**/*Archimedean Upper Conserv Sch*	81
Mendez, Marisol/*Meadow Woods Middle Sch*	98	Misas, Alba/*Royal Green Elem Sch*	84
Mendez, Orestes/*Colson Elem Sch*	51	Miser, Kati/*St Michael Lutheran Sch*	64
Mendez, Priscilla/*Renaissance CS at Goldenrod [133]*	95	**Misty, Cruz**/*Liberty High Sch*	103
Mendoza, Kathryn, Dr/*Creative Learning Sch*	9	Mitchell, Amber/*Woodland Hall Academy*	66
Mendoza, Mario/*William H Bashaw Elem Sch*	69	Mitchell, Kathleen/*St Luke Early Chldhd Center*	120
Mendoza, Melody/*High Point Elem Sch*	118	Mitchell, Kelly/*Spring Lake Elem Sch*	133
Menendez, Maria/*Hollywood Park Elem Sch*	12	Mitchell, Melvern/*Ft Myers Christian Sch*	63
Menendez, Teresa/*Nuestra Senora De Lourdes Sch*	88	**Mitchell, Nishira**/*Adams Middle Sch*	50
Menger, Lori/*San Jose Episcopal Day Sch*	36	Mitchell, Rayann/*James M Marlowe Elem Sch*	113
Menken, Ivy/*Warfield Elem Sch*	73	Mitchell, Ronald/*Sneads High Sch*	57
Mennes, James/*Virgil Mills Elem Sch*	69	Mitchell, Rosanne/*Bethlehem Sch*	55
Menocal, Georgette, Dr/*Ludlam Elem Sch*	76	**Mitchell, Samone, Dr**/*Dunbar Cmty Sch*	61
Mentis, Christine/*Eagles Nest Charter Academy*	16	Mitchell, Scott/*Watergrass Elem Sch*	114
Mercier, Carol/*Palm Harbor Montessori Academy*	121	Mitchell, Tonya/*Clearwater Intermediate Sch*	117
Merhar, Rebecca, Dr/*Corkscrew Elem Sch*	25	Mitidieri, Bethany/*Wards Creek Elem Sch*	135
Merrick, Lindsey/*SAS at the Center*	65	Mitkevicius, Maria/*Montessori Sch of Pensacola*	38
Merrill, Bradley/*Rockledge High Sch*	9	**Mixson, Kim**/*Seaside Neighborhood Sch*	144
Mesa, Melissa/*N Edelcup-Sunny Isles Bch K-8*	80	Mobley, Dawn/*North Marion Middle Sch*	71
Mesa, Melissa/*North County K-8 Center*	80	Mobley, Denise/*Pinecrest Elem Sch*	52
Metz, Melissa/*Bayview Elem Sch*	30	Mobley, Robin/*Tyrone Middle Sch*	119
Metz, Starla/*St Petersburg Collegiate HS*	116	Mock, Jonilyn/*Port St Joe Elem Sch*	41
Meyer, Grant/*Destin Middle Sch*	92	Moenning, Debbie/*First Baptist Academy*	35
Meyers, Dart/*Frostproof Elem Sch*	124	Moffat, Sue/*Florida Sheriff's Boys Ranch*	138
Meyers, Robin/*Lake Hills Sch*	59	Mohamed, Shaikh/*Danul-Uloom Islamic Inst*	19
Micensky, Paul/*Tequesta Trace Middle Sch*	15	Mohammed, Judy/*Nur Ul Islam Academy*	19
Michaud, Shelley/*Ocean Breeze Elem Sch*	8	Mohler, Barbara/*St Edward's Sch*	56
Michel, Thomas/*Mariner High Sch*	62	Moldovan, Seth/*Verde Elem Sch*	110
Michna, Yvonne/*Longwood Elem Sch*	92	Moloney, Matt/*Holy Family Catholic Sch*	34
Middleto, Marina/*Lyndon B Johnson Middle Sch*	9	Moltisanti, Deborah/*Hortense Mintz Elem Sch*	52
Mielke, Aimee/*Sports Ldrshp Management Acad [130]*	47	Moncilovich, Thomas/*Sheridan Tech High Sch*	14
Mielke, Sarah, Dr/*Community Christian Sch*	21	Monod, Kelly/*State Clg of FL Collegiate Sch*	69
Migliore, Lori/*Roy Allen Elem Sch*	8	**Monod, Kelly**/*State Clg of FL Collegiate Sch*	130
Mijuskovic, Sylvia/*Space Coast Jr Sr High Sch*	9	Montano, Carrie/*Pinecrest Glades Academy*	84
Mikell, Tiffaney/*Frost Elem Sch*	48	Monte, Robyn/*Palm City Elem Sch*	73
Mikulski, Joseph/*Gulf Coast High Sch*	25	Monteagudo, Omar, Dr/*School Adv Studies-Homestead*	84

School/City/County DISTRICT/CITY/COUNTY	PID	TELEPHONE NUMBER	PAGE
A			
A Crawford Mosley High Sch/*Lynn Haven*/Bay	00181549	850/767-4400	4
A D Henderson Univ Sch/*Boca Raton*/ Palm Beach	02048060	561/297-3970	1
A K Suter Elem Sch/*Pensacola*/Escambia	00190289	850/595-6810	36
A L Mebane Middle Sch/*Alachua*/Alachua	00181111	386/462-1648	1
A Philip Randolph Career Acad/*Jacksonville*/ Duval	01843453	904/924-3011	32
A Quinn Jones Center/*Gainesville*/Alachua	00181381	352/955-6840	1
Abels Academy/*Clermont*/Lake	12225767	352/223-1999	60
Abess Park Elem Sch/*Jacksonville*/Duval	04756768	904/220-1260	30
Abraham Lincoln Middle Sch/*Gainesville*/ Alachua	00181290	352/955-6711	1
Abundant Life Chrn Academy/*Margate*/Broward	03413274	954/979-2665	18
Acad of Environmental Science/*Crystal River*/ Citrus	04870950	352/795-8793	22
Academic Achievement Center/*Seffner*/ Hillsborough	01436713	813/654-4198	53
Academic Connection Excellence/*Key West*/ Monroe	11621716	305/293-1400	89
Academic High Sch/*Boca Raton*/Palm Beach	04999908	561/929-0333	111
Academic Solutions Academy-A/*Ft Lauderdale*/ Broward	12169864	954/572-6600	15
Academic Solutions High Sch/*Ft Lauderdale*/ Broward	11922675	954/572-6600	15
Academie Da Vinci Charter Sch/*Dunedin*/ Pinellas	04757504	727/298-2778	116
Academir Charter Sch Prep/*Miami*/Miami-Dade	12262806	305/964-7542	81
Academir Charter School Middle/*Miami*/ Miami-Dade	11829712	305/967-8492	81
Academir Charter School-West/*Miami*/ Miami-Dade	11561386	305/485-9911	81
Academir Preparatory Academy/*Miami*/ Miami-Dade	12114857	305/967-8492	81
Academy at Ocean Reef/*Key Largo*/Monroe	03535418	305/367-2409	90
Academy at the Farm/*Dade City*/Pasco	05194797	352/588-9737	112
Academy at the Lakes/*Land O Lakes*/Pasco	04898079	813/948-2133	115
Academy at Youth Care Lane/*Sebring*/ Highlands	05345142	863/471-5457	45
Academy for Autism/*Orlando*/Orange	11463734	407/852-9922	100
Academy for Love & Learning/*St Petersburg*/ Pinellas	11815321	727/865-3962	120
Academy for Positive Learning/*Lake Worth*/ Palm Beach	05348481	561/585-6104	105
Academy Int'l Education CS/*Miami Springs*/ Miami-Dade	11719569	305/883-3900	74
Academy of the Holy Names/*Tampa*/ Hillsborough	00200731	813/839-5371	53
Academy Prep Center for Educ/*St Petersburg*/ Pinellas	11236983	727/322-0800	120
Academy Prep Center of Tampa/*Tampa*/ Hillsborough	11134323	813/248-5600	53
Acceleration East High Sch/*Orlando*/Orange	11452802	407/992-0917	94
Acceleration West High Sch/*Orlando*/Orange	11820601	407/521-2358	94
Access Charter Sch/*Orlando*/Orange	11820675	321/319-0640	94
Achieve Center at Pasco/*Spring Hill*/Pasco	12234990	813/346-2000	114
Achieve Center at Richey/*New Prt Rchy*/ Pasco	12235009	727/774-7860	113
Achievement Acad-Bartow/*Bartow*/Polk	10007296	863/533-0690	123
Achievement Acad-Lakeland/*Lakeland*/Polk	02400119	863/683-6504	123
Achievement Acad-Winter Haven/*Winter Haven*/ Polk	10007284	863/683-6504	123
Achievement Center/*Sarasota*/Sarasota	04336033	941/504-7547	131
Acreage Pines Elem Sch/*Loxahatchee*/ Palm Beach	03402500	561/904-9500	108
ADA Merritt K-8 Center/*Miami*/Miami-Dade	05278501	305/326-0791	74
Adams Middle Sch/*Tampa*/Hillsborough	00191817	813/975-7665	50
Addie R Lewis Elem Sch/*Valparaiso*/Okaloosa	00196130	850/833-4130	91
Addison Mizner Elem Sch/*Boca Raton*/ Palm Beach	00198712	561/362-3100	109
Admiral Farragut Academy/*St Petersburg*/ Pinellas	01834373	727/384-5501	120
Adom Virtual Sch/*Miami Gardens*/Miami-Dade	12306189	305/508-5556	85
Adult & Cmty Education/*Tallahassee*/Leon	04033748	850/717-2020	64
Adult and Career Center/*Fort Myers*/Lee	11718436	239/939-6310	61
Adult Education Center/*West Palm Bch*/ Palm Beach	01811620	561/616-7800	105
Adult Lrng Center Osceola/*Kissimmee*/ Osceola	04291081	407/518-8140	102

School/City/County DISTRICT/CITY/COUNTY	PID	TELEPHONE NUMBER	PAGE
Advanced Technology College/*Daytona Beach*/ Volusia	05010531	386/506-4100	1
Advantage Acad-Math & Sci/*Homestead*/ Miami-Dade	11719624	305/248-6206	81
Advantage Academy-Hillsborough/*Plant City*/ Hillsborough	11447948	813/567-0801	46
Advent Lutheran Sch/*Boca Raton*/Palm Beach	01404394	561/395-3623	111
Adventist Christian Academy/*Tallahassee*/ Leon	03406881	850/597-7825	65
Adventure Christian Academy/*Tavares*/Lake	11222061	352/742-4543	60
Advoserv-Carlton Palms Sch/*Mount Dora*/Lake	03191189	352/735-0588	60
Agape Christian Academy/*Orlando*/Orange	05147328	407/298-1111	100
Agenoria Paschal-Olinda ES/*Miami*/ Miami-Dade	00186240	305/633-0308	75
Air Base K-8 Ctr for Int'l Ed/*Homestead*/ Miami-Dade	00187268	305/258-3676	81
Al-Furqan Academy/*Jacksonville*/Duval	04983038	904/645-0810	34
ALACHUA CO SCH DIST/*GAINESVILLE*/ **ALACHUA**	00181094	352/955-7300	1
Alachua Elem Sch/*Alachua*/Alachua	00181135	386/462-1841	1
Alachua Eschool/*Gainesville*/Alachua	11924831	352/955-7584	1
Alachua Learning Academy ES/*Alachua*/ Alachua	04874669	386/418-2080	1
Alachua Learning Academy MS/*Alachua*/ Alachua	11744629	386/418-2080	1
Alafia Elem Sch/*Valrico*/Hillsborough	03006508	813/744-8190	51
Alazhar Sch/*Tamarac*/Broward	05286974	954/722-1555	18
Alden Road Excptnl Student Ctr/*Jacksonville*/ Duval	01397856	904/565-2722	32
Alee Academy Chtr Sch-Umatilla/*Eustis*/Lake	04876978	352/357-9426	58
Alethia Christian Academy/*Pensacola*/ Escambia	04328153	850/969-0088	38
Alex W Dreyfoos Jr Sch of Arts/*West Palm Bch*/ Palm Beach	03337125	561/802-6000	108
Alexander Elem Sch/*Tampa*/Hillsborough	00191831	813/872-5395	49
Alexander Montessori Sch/*Miami*/Miami-Dade	01527104	305/665-6274	86
Alexander Sch/*Miami*/Miami-Dade	03016498	305/235-3995	86
Alfred Adler Elem Sch/*St Petersburg*/ Pinellas	11103568	727/329-9545	116
Alfred I DuPont Middle Sch/*Jacksonville*/ Duval	00188781	904/739-5200	32
Alhambra Height Challenger Sch/*Miami*/ Miami-Dade	12229957	786/553-8555	86
Alice B Landrum Middle Sch/*Ponte Vedra*/ St Johns	03394501	904/547-8410	134
Alimacani Elem Sch/*Jacksonville*/Duval	03329465	904/221-7101	30
All Angels Academy/*Miami Springs*/ Miami-Dade	11235551	305/888-9483	86
All Saints Acad-Bostick Campus/*Winter Haven*/ Polk	04937936	863/293-5980	126
All Saints Acad-Hampton Campus/*Winter Haven*/ Polk	00202179	863/293-5980	126
All Saints Catholic Sch/*Jupiter*/Palm Beach	05280724	561/748-8994	110
All Saints Catholic Sch/*Sunrise*/Broward	11737236	954/742-4842	18
All Souls Catholic Sch/*Sanford*/Seminole	00197641	407/322-7090	133
Allamanda Elem Sch/*Palm Bch Gdns*/ Palm Beach	00198499	561/803-7200	108
Allapattah Flats Sch/*Port St Lucie*/ St Lucie	10914302	772/468-5050	136
Allen D Nease High Sch/*Ponte Vedra*/ St Johns	02127525	904/547-8300	134
Allen Park Elem Sch/*Fort Myers*/Lee	00194091	239/936-1459	61
Allison Academy/*N Miami Beach*/Miami-Dade	03130305	305/940-3922	86
Aloma Charter High Sch/*Winter Park*/Orange	11452852	407/657-4343	94
Aloma Elem Sch/*Winter Park*/Orange	00196570	407/672-3100	96
Alonso High Sch/*Tampa*/Hillsborough	04950914	813/356-1525	49
Alonzo & Tracy Mourning Sr HS/*N Miami Beach*/ Miami-Dade	11453430	305/919-2000	78
Alpha Charter Sch-Excellence/*Miami*/ Miami-Dade	11822233	305/643-2132	75
Alpha International Academy/*Hollywood*/ Broward	11822271	954/505-7974	16
Alpha Learning Academy/*Orlando*/Orange	05252583	407/422-6941	100
Alta Vista Elem Sch/*Haines City*/Polk	00201503	863/421-3235	124
Alta Vista Elem Sch/*Sarasota*/Sarasota	00203240	941/361-6400	129
Altamonte Christian Sch/*Altamonte SPG*/ Seminole	00203953	407/831-0950	133
Altamonte Elem Sch/*Altamonte SPG*/Seminole	00203587	407/746-2950	132
Alternative Choices Edu Acad/*Altamonte SPG*/ Seminole	11221419	407/339-6632	133
Alternative Ctr for Education/*Vero Beach*/ Indian River	04808385	772/564-6240	55

School/City/County DISTRICT/CITY/COUNTY	PID	TELEPHONE NUMBER	PAGE
Alternative Ed/*Lake Butler*/Union	04887599	352/448-5195	139
Altha Public Sch/*Altha*/Calhoun	00184369	850/762-3121	20
Altoona Sch/*Altoona*/Lake	05348003	352/669-3444	58
Alturas Elem Sch/*Alturas*/Polk	00201967	863/519-3917	124
Alva Sch/*Alva*/Lee	00194106	239/728-2494	61
Ambassador Christian Sch/*Merritt Is*/ Brevard	12235815	321/305-6931	9
Ambleside School of Ocala/*Ocala*/Marion	11728479	352/694-1635	72
Amelia Earhart Elem Sch/*Hialeah*/Miami-Dade	00185519	305/688-9619	78
Amelia Island Mont Sch/*Fernandina*/Nassau	02383236	904/261-6610	91
American Christian Sch/*Hialeah*/Miami-Dade	12313431	305/827-6544	86
American Global Sch/*Jacksonville*/Duval	12364856	888/242-4262	34
American Heritage Sch/*Plantation*/Broward	01434698	954/472-0022	18
American Heritage-Boca Delray/*Delray Beach*/ Palm Beach	04211691	561/495-7272	111
American High School Academy/*Miami*/ Miami-Dade	12242208	305/270-1440	86
American Preparatory Academy/*Davie*/Broward	11735848	954/434-8936	18
American Senior High Sch/*Hialeah*/ Miami-Dade	01526978	305/557-3770	78
American Youth Academy/*Tampa*/Hillsborough	04329913	813/987-9282	53
AMI Kids Crossroads Hope Acad/*Punta Gorda*/ Charlotte	11932280	941/575-5790	21
AMI Kids Emerald Coast/*Ft Walton Bch*/ Okaloosa	05280384	850/244-2711	91
AMI Kids Greater Ft Lauderdale/*Ft Lauderdale*/ Broward	02182604	954/764-2733	18
AMI Kids Pinellas/*Pinellas Park*/Pinellas	01827136	727/471-0390	120
AMI Kids School-Jacksonville/*Jacksonville*/ Duval	02234908	904/223-1121	34
AMI Kids Tallahassee/*Tallahassee*/Leon	04334401	850/921-1250	65
AMI Kids Tampa/*Tampa*/Hillsborough	02235017	813/248-5091	53
AMI Kids-Orlando Sch/*Apopka*/Orange	11713591	407/886-5405	94
Amikids Volusia Campus/*Daytona Beach*/ Volusia	11715587	386/274-5786	140
Amos P Godby High Sch/*Tallahassee*/Leon	00194481	850/617-4700	64
Anclote Elem Sch/*New Prt Rchy*/Pasco	00199168	727/774-3200	113
Anclote High Sch/*Holiday*/Pasco	11452058	727/246-3000	114
Anderson Elem Sch/*Rockledge*/Brevard	00182206	321/633-3610	7
Anderson Elem Sch/*Tampa*/Hillsborough	00192378	813/272-3075	48
Andover Elem Sch/*Orlando*/Orange	10002038	407/658-6800	98
Andover Middle Sch/*Miami*/Miami-Dade	11128245	305/654-2727	78
Andrew A Robinson Elem Sch/*Jacksonville*/ Duval	03401350	904/630-6550	30
Andrew Jackson High Sch/*Jacksonville*/Duval	00188793	904/630-6950	32
Andrew Jackson Middle Sch/*Titusville*/ Brevard	00181989	321/269-1812	8
Andrews High School-N Broward/*Pompano Beach*/ Broward	11716402	954/944-4123	16
Ann Storck Center/*Ft Lauderdale*/Broward	02359077	954/584-8000	18
Anna Maria Elem Sch/*Holmes Beach*/Manatee	00195045	941/708-5525	68
Annabel C Perry Elem Sch/*Miramar*/Broward	00183901	754/323-7050	10
Annette P Edwins Elem Sch/*Ft Walton Bch*/ Okaloosa	00196142	850/833-3333	91
Annie Lucy Williams Elem Sch/*Parrish*/ Manatee	10913530	941/776-4040	68
Annie R Morgan Elem Sch/*Jacksonville*/Duval	00188808	904/381-3970	30
Annunciation Catholic Academy/*Altamonte SPG*/ Seminole	04471425	407/774-2801	133
Annunciation Catholic Sch/*Hollywood*/ Broward	00187878	954/989-8287	18
Annunciation Catholic Sch/*Middleburg*/Clay	04145212	904/282-0504	24
Anona Elem Sch/*Largo*/Pinellas	00199443	727/588-4730	117
Anthony Elem Sch/*Anthony*/Marion	00195356	352/671-6000	70
Antioch Elem Sch/*Crestview*/Okaloosa	04750568	850/683-7540	91
Apalachee Tapestry Sch of Arts/*Tallahassee*/ Leon	00194493	850/488-7110	64
Apalachicola Bay Charter Sch/*Apalachicola*/ Franklin	05010488	850/653-1222	40
Aparicio-Levy Technical Center/*Tampa*/ Hillsborough	10003068	813/740-4884	46
Apollo Beach Elem Sch/*Apollo Beach*/ Hillsborough	02180694	813/671-5172	51
Apollo Elem Sch/*Titusville*/Brevard	00181991	321/267-7890	7
Apollo Middle Sch/*Hollywood*/Broward	00183913	754/323-2900	10
Apopka Christian Academy/*Apopka*/Orange	12106472	407/889-7288	100
Apopka Elem Sch/*Apopka*/Orange	01527204	407/884-2200	97
Apopka High Sch/*Apopka*/Orange	01397947	407/905-5500	97
Apopka Middle Sch/*Apopka*/Orange	00196582	407/884-2208	97
Apple Tree Montessori Sch/*Sw Ranches*/ Broward	04983870	954/252-9250	18
Arbor Ridge Sch/*Orlando*/Orange	03250591	407/672-3110	95

School/City/County DISTRICT/CITY/COUNTY	PID	TELEPHONE NUMBER	PAGE
Arch Creek Elem Sch/*North Miami*/Miami-Dade	11128207	305/892-4000	78
Archbishop Carroll Catholic HS/*Miami*/ Miami-Dade	04926925	305/388-6700	85
Archbishop Edward McCarthy HS/*Sw Ranches*/ Broward	04815481	954/434-8820	18
ARCHDIOCESE OF MIAMI ED OFFICE/ **MIAMI SHORES/MIAMI-DADE**	00187854	305/757-6241	85
Archer Elem Sch/*Archer*/Alachua	00181147	352/495-2111	1
Archimedean Academy/*Miami*/Miami-Dade	05194802	305/279-6572	81
Archimedean Middle Conserv Sch/*Miami*/ Miami-Dade	11453533	305/279-6572	81
Archimedean Upper Conserv Sch/*Miami*/ Miami-Dade	11469879	305/279-6572	81
Arcola Lake Elem Sch/*Miami*/Miami-Dade	00185911	305/836-2820	75
Argonauta Preschool/*St Petersburg*/Pinellas	05374557	727/347-8783	120
Argyle Elem Sch/*Orange Park*/Clay	10001515	904/336-0375	23
Arlington Community Academy/*Jacksonville*/ Duval	12225183	904/717-1590	34
Arlington Elem Sch/*Jacksonville*/Duval	00188822	904/745-4900	30
Arlington Heights Elem Sch/*Jacksonville*/ Duval	00188834	904/745-4923	33
Arlington Middle Sch/*Jacksonville*/Duval	00188846	904/720-1680	33
Armwood Senior High Sch/*Seffner*/ Hillsborough	02226884	813/744-8040	47
Arthur I Meyer Jewish Academy/*Palm BCH GDNS*/ Palm Beach	01559808	561/686-6520	111
Arts Academy of Excellence/*Opa Locka*/ Miami-Dade	12263094	786/534-4528	74
Arvida Middle Sch/*Miami*/Miami-Dade	01526992	305/385-7144	81
Asbury Christian Sch/*Hialeah*/Miami-Dade	02234790	305/823-5313	86
Ascend Career Academy/*Pompano Beach*/ Broward	12162426	954/978-4555	16
Ascension Catholic Sch/*Melbourne*/Brevard	00197653	321/254-5495	9
Ashton Elem Sch/*Sarasota*/Sarasota	01527324	941/361-6440	129
Aspire Charter Academy/*Orlando*/Orange	11820625	407/297-9955	94
Assumption Catholic Sch/*Jacksonville*/Duval	00202545	904/398-1774	34
Assurance Christian Academy/*Rockledge*/ Brevard	11728936	321/638-0985	9
Astatula Elem Sch/*Astatula*/Lake	04871320	352/343-1334	58
Astoria Park Elem Sch/*Tallahassee*/Leon	00194508	850/488-4673	64
Astronaut High Sch/*Titusville*/Brevard	00182115	321/264-3000	8
Atala Montessori Sch/*Homestead*/Miami-Dade	12089434	786/738-1210	86
Athenian Acad-Tech & Arts/*New Prt Rchy*/ Pasco	10030164	727/372-0200	112
Athenian Academy Charter Sch/*Clearwater*/ Pinellas	04931281	727/298-2718	116
Atlantic Beach Elem Sch/*Atlantic Bch*/Duval	00188858	904/247-5924	30
Atlantic Christian Academy/*West Palm Bch*/ Palm Beach	00199120	561/686-8081	111
Atlantic Cmty High Sch/*Delray Beach*/ Palm Beach	00198724	561/243-1500	109
Atlantic Coast High Sch/*Jacksonville*/Duval	11560605	904/538-5120	32
Atlantic High Sch/*Port Orange*/Volusia	04287389	386/322-6100	140
Atlantic Mont Chtr Sch West/*Ft Lauderdale*/ Broward	12115112	954/423-9704	16
Atlantic Montessori Chtr Sch/*Pembroke Pnes*/ Broward	11820194	754/263-2700	16
Atlantic Technical High Sch/*Coconut Creek*/ Broward	00182749	754/321-5100	10
Atlantic West Elem Sch/*Margate*/Broward	00182901	754/322-5300	10
Atlantis Academy/*Coral Springs*/Broward	04420567	954/752-7571	18
Atlantis Academy/*Miami*/Miami-Dade	01772854	305/271-9771	86
Atlantis Academy/*West Palm Bch*/Palm Beach	01437133	561/642-3100	111
Atlantis Elem Sch/*Cocoa*/Brevard	03336705	321/633-6143	7
Attucks Middle Sch/*Hollywood*/Broward	00183482	754/323-3000	10
Atwater Elem Sch/*North Port*/Sarasota	11445160	941/257-2317	129
Auburndale Central Elem Sch/*Auburndale*/ Polk	00201711	863/965-5450	125
Auburndale Elem Sch/*Miami*/Miami-Dade	00186393	305/445-3587	75
Auburndale High Sch/*Auburndale*/Polk	00201759	863/965-6200	122
Aucilla Christian Academy/*Monticello*/ Jefferson	00193671	850/997-3597	58
Audubon Elem Sch/*Merritt Is*/Brevard	00182579	321/452-2085	7
Audubon Park K-8 Sch/*Orlando*/Orange	12311433	407/317-5829	95
Augusta Raa Middle Sch/*Tallahassee*/Leon	00194510	850/488-6287	64
Aukela Christian Military Acad/*Hollywood*/ Broward	04983569	954/929-7010	18
Avalon Elem Sch/*Naples*/Collier	00184826	239/377-6200	25
Avalon Elem Sch/*Orlando*/Orange	04945347	407/207-3825	95
Avalon Middle Sch/*Milton*/Santa Rosa	00203202	850/983-5540	128
Avalon Middle Sch/*Orlando*/Orange	10024402	407/207-7839	95
Avalon Sch/*Orlando*/Orange	01775208	407/297-4353	100

School/City/County DISTRICT/CITY/COUNTY	PID	TELEPHONE NUMBER	PAGE
Avalon Tech Center/*Orlando*/Orange	11562029	407/281-5155	94
Avant Garde Academy/*Hollywood*/Broward	12115124	754/816-6153	16
Avant Garde Academy/*Kissimmee*/Osceola	12167921	407/944-4464	102
Avant Garde Academy of Osceola/*Kissimmee*/ Osceola	11931975	321/697-3800	102
Avant Garde Academy Westchase/*Tampa*/ Hillsborough	12231625	813/551-2144	46
Aventura City of Excellence CS/*Aventura*/ Miami-Dade	05262124	305/466-1499	78
Aventura Waterways K-8 Center/*Miami*/ Miami-Dade	11128271	305/933-5200	78
Avocado Elem Sch/*Homestead*/Miami-Dade	00187270	305/247-4942	81
Avon Elem Sch/*Avon Park*/Highlands	01170476	863/452-4355	45
Avon Park High Sch/*Avon Park*/Highlands	00191726	863/452-4311	45
Avon Park Middle Sch/*Avon Park*/Highlands	00191738	863/452-4333	45
Azalea Elem Sch/*St Petersburg*/Pinellas	00199455	727/893-2187	118
Azalea Middle Sch/*St Petersburg*/Pinellas	00199467	727/893-2606	118
Azalea Park Baptist Sch/*Orlando*/Orange	01437092	407/277-4056	100
Azalea Park Elem Sch/*Orlando*/Orange	00196611	407/249-6280	96

B

School/City/County DISTRICT/CITY/COUNTY	PID	TELEPHONE NUMBER	PAGE
B C Graham Elem Sch/*Tampa*/Hillsborough	00191843	813/276-5408	47
B D Gullett Elem Sch/*Bradenton*/Manatee	10913528	941/727-2067	68
Babcock Neighborhood Sch/*Punta Gorda*/ Charlotte	12230724	850/727-4985	21
Bacot Academy/*Panama City*/Bay	12037314	850/215-2614	5
Bagdad Elem Sch/*Milton*/Santa Rosa	00203020	850/983-5680	128
Bailey Elem Sch/*Dover*/Hillsborough	11447924	813/707-7531	51
Bair Middle Sch/*Sunrise*/Broward	00183119	754/322-2900	10
Bak Middle School of Art/*West Palm Bch*/ Palm Beach	04810481	561/882-3870	108
Baker Co Adult Ed Center/*Macclenny*/Baker	11718357	904/259-0403	3
Baker Co High Sch/*Glen St Mary*/Baker	00181496	904/259-6286	3
Baker Co Middle Sch/*Macclenny*/Baker	00181501	904/259-2226	4
Baker Co PK & Kindergarten Ctr/*Macclenny*/ Baker	10011156	904/259-0405	4
BAKER CO SCH DIST/**MACCLENNY**/ **BAKER**	00181484	904/259-6251	3
Baker Co Virtual Sch/*Macclenny*/Baker	11589637	904/259-7825	4
Baker Head Start/*Punta Gorda*/Charlotte	00184486	941/575-5470	21
Baker Sch/*Baker*/Okaloosa	00196154	850/689-7279	91
Baldwin Academy/*Ft Lauderdale*/Broward	05267784	954/730-7855	18
Baldwin Academy South/*Ft Lauderdale*/ Broward	12240169	954/909-5906	18
Baldwin Middle Senior High Sch/*Baldwin*/ Duval	00188860	904/266-1200	32
Baldwin Park Elem Sch/*Orlando*/Orange	00196609	407/897-6400	96
Baldwin Preparatory Sch/*N Palm Beach*/ Palm Beach	11233759	561/844-7700	111
Ballard Elem Sch/*Bradenton*/Manatee	00195057	941/708-8400	68
Ballast Point Elem Sch/*Tampa*/Hillsborough	00191855	813/272-3070	48
Banyan Creek Elem Sch/*Delray Beach*/ Palm Beach	00198803	561/894-7100	109
Banyan Elem Sch/*Miami*/Miami-Dade	00186848	305/221-4011	75
Banyan Elem Sch/*Sunrise*/Broward	02042119	754/322-5350	10
Baptist Temple Sch/*Orlando*/Orange	01437078	407/293-2772	100
Barbara Goleman Sr High Sch/*Miami Lakes*/ Miami-Dade	04365369	305/362-0676	78
Barbara Harvey Elem Sch/*Parrish*/Manatee	12365903	941/803-9340	68
Barbara Hawkins Elem Sch/*Miami Gardens*/ Miami-Dade	00185739	305/624-2615	78
Bardmoor Elem Sch/*Seminole*/Pinellas	00199479	727/547-7824	117
Barnabas Christian Academy/*Port St Lucie*/ St Lucie	04984630	772/344-1643	137
Barrington Middle Sch/*Lithia*/Hillsborough	11447912	813/657-7266	51
Barron G Collier High Sch/*Naples*/Collier	01827045	239/377-1200	25
Barton Elem Sch/*Lake Worth*/Palm Beach	00198736	561/540-9100	106
Bartow Elem Academy/*Bartow*/Polk	00201979	863/534-7410	124
Bartow Int'l Baccalaureat HS/*Bartow*/Polk	04756548	863/534-0194	122
Bartow Middle Sch/*Bartow*/Polk	00201981	863/534-7415	122
Bartow Senior High Sch/*Bartow*/Polk	00202002	863/534-0194	122
Bartram Springs Elem Sch/*Jacksonville*/ Duval	11446190	904/260-5860	30
Bartram Trail High Sch/*Saint Johns*/ St Johns	04918526	904/547-8340	134
Basilica School of St Paul/*Daytona Beach*/ Volusia	00197938	386/252-7915	142
Basilica School St Mary/*Key West*/Monroe	00188535	305/294-1031	90
Bauder Elem Sch/*Seminole*/Pinellas	00199481	727/547-7829	118
Baudhuin Pre-School/*Ft Lauderdale*/Broward	01434789	954/262-7100	18
Bauers Triple D's Chrn Acad/*Pensacola*/ Escambia	04968040	850/492-4873	38

School/City/County DISTRICT/CITY/COUNTY	PID	TELEPHONE NUMBER	PAGE
BAY CO SCH DIST/**PANAMA CITY**/**BAY**	00181537	850/767-4100	4
Bay Crest Elem Sch/*Tampa*/Hillsborough	00191867	813/872-5382	49
Bay Elem Sch/*Santa Rsa Bch*/Walton	05273587	850/622-5050	143
Bay Haven Charter Academy/*Panama City*/Bay	04950146	850/248-3500	4
Bay Haven School Basics Plus/*Sarasota*/ Sarasota	00203252	941/359-5800	129
Bay High Sch/*Panama City*/Bay	00181563	850/767-4600	4
Bay Lake Elem Sch/*Windermere*/Orange	12168913	407/217-7960	98
Bay Meadows Elem Sch/*Orlando*/Orange	03333650	407/876-7500	98
Bay Pines Lutheran Sch/*Seminole*/Pinellas	01404459	727/397-3204	120
Bay Point Elem Sch/*St Petersburg*/Pinellas	00199493	727/552-1449	118
Bay Point Middle Sch/*St Petersburg*/ Pinellas	00199508	727/893-1153	118
Bay Virtual Sch/*Panama City*/Bay	11589857	850/767-4377	4
Bay Vista Fundamental Sch/*St Petersburg*/ Pinellas	00199510	727/893-2335	118
Baymeadows Christian Academy/*Jacksonville*/ Duval	12044379	904/733-3400	34
Bayonet Point Middle Sch/*New Prt Rchy*/ Pasco	00199170	727/774-7400	114
Bayshore Christian Sch/*Tampa*/Hillsborough	01404227	813/839-4297	53
Bayshore Elem Sch/*Bradenton*/Manatee	00195069	941/751-7000	68
Bayshore Elem Sch/*N Ft Myers*/Lee	00194120	239/543-3663	61
Bayshore Elem Sch/*Port St Lucie*/St Lucie	03052703	772/340-4720	136
Bayshore High Sch/*Bradenton*/Manatee	01170488	941/751-7004	68
Bayside High Sch/*Clearwater*/Pinellas	05346926	727/507-4730	117
Bayside High Sch/*Palm Bay*/Brevard	04809365	321/956-5000	8
Bayview Elem Sch/*Ft Lauderdale*/Broward	00183121	754/322-5400	10
Bayview Elem Sch/*Jacksonville*/Duval	00188872	904/381-3920	30
Beach Park Sch/*Tampa*/Hillsborough	01436696	813/289-3747	53
Beaches Chapel Sch/*Neptune Beach*/Duval	01773913	904/241-4211	34
Beaches Episcopal Sch/*Jax Bch*/Duval	00190239	904/246-2466	34
Beaches Sch/*Neptune Beach*/Duval	11237080	904/249-0905	34
Beachland Elem Sch/*Vero Beach*/Indian River	00193346	772/564-3300	55
Beachside Montessori Vlg Sch/*Hollywood*/ Broward	11554670	754/323-8050	10
Beacon College Prep Sch/*Opa Locka*/ Miami-Dade	12032730	786/353-6109	75
Beacon Cove Interm Sch/*Jupiter*/Palm Beach	04947266	561/366-6400	108
Beacon High School-Naples/*Naples*/Collier	12045115	239/377-1059	25
Beacon Hill Preparatory Sch/*Miami Gardens*/ Miami-Dade	01435305	305/624-1600	86
Beacon Hill Sch/*Hollywood*/Broward	01772153	954/963-2600	18
Beacon of Hope Chrn Sch/*St Augustine*/ St Johns	11234002	904/797-6996	135
Bear Creek Elem Sch/*St Petersburg*/Pinellas	00199522	727/893-2332	118
Bear Lake Elem Sch/*Apopka*/Seminole	00203599	407/746-5550	132
Bear Lakes Middle Sch/*West Palm Bch*/ Palm Beach	03253505	561/615-7700	108
Beauclerc Elem Sch/*Jacksonville*/Duval	00188884	904/739-5226	30
Beeman Park Preparatory Sch/*Orlando*/Orange	02235718	407/894-5121	100
Bel-Aire Elem Sch/*Cutler Bay*/Miami-Dade	00187282	305/233-5401	81
Belcher Elem Sch/*Clearwater*/Pinellas	00199534	727/538-7437	117
Belen Jesuit Preparatory Sch/*Miami*/ Miami-Dade	00187892	305/223-8600	85
Believers Academy/*West Palm Bch*/Palm Beach	10023343	561/340-2507	105
Believers Christian Academy/*Clermont*/Lake	12224084	352/404-7717	60
Bell Creek Academy/*Riverview*/Hillsborough	11925536	813/793-6075	46
Bell Creek High School Academy/*Riverview*/ Hillsborough	11925524	813/793-6075	46
Bell Elem Sch/*Bell*/Gilchrist	04289909	352/463-3275	41
Bell Middle High Sch/*Bell*/Gilchrist	00191271	352/463-3232	41
Bell Shoals Baptist Academy/*Brandon*/ Hillsborough	02375629	813/689-9183	53
Bellalago Charter Academy/*Kissimmee*/ Osceola	05346524	407/933-1690	102
Bellamy Elem Sch/*Tampa*/Hillsborough	00191879	813/872-5387	49
Belle Glade Elem Sch/*Belle Glade*/ Palm Beach	00198360	561/829-4800	107
Belle Terre Elem Sch/*Palm Coast*/Flagler	10004751	386/447-1500	39
Belleair Elem Sch/*Clearwater*/Pinellas	00199546	727/469-5983	117
Belleview Christian Academy/*Belleview*/ Marion	11223900	352/245-6151	72
Belleview Elem Sch/*Belleview*/Marion	00195368	352/671-6100	70
Belleview High Sch/*Belleview*/Marion	04285032	352/671-6210	70
Belleview Middle Sch/*Belleview*/Marion	04029474	352/671-6235	70
Belleview-Santos Elem Sch/*Belleview*/Marion	00195370	352/671-6260	70
Bellview Elem Sch/*Pensacola*/Escambia	00190368	850/941-6060	36
Bellview Middle Sch/*Pensacola*/Escambia	00190370	850/941-6080	36
Belmont Academy/*Lake City*/Columbia	11919551	386/487-0487	27
Belvedere Elem Sch/*West Palm Bch*/ Palm Beach	00198097	561/838-5900	106

School/City/County DISTRICT/CITY/COUNTY	PID	TELEPHONE NUMBER	PAGE
Ben Gamla Charter -N Broward/*Hollywood*/ Broward	10907189	954/342-4064	16
Ben Gamla Charter Palm Beach/*Boynton Beach*/ Palm Beach	11717004	561/742-8017	105
Ben Gamla Charter Sch/*Miami*/Miami-Dade	11735654	305/596-6266	81
Ben Gamla CS-South Broward/*Sunrise*/Broward	11551472	954/587-8348	16
Ben Gamla Preparatory Chtr Sch/*Hollywood*/ Broward	12115136	954/924-6495	16
Ben Hill Griffin Jr Elem Sch/*Frostproof*/ Polk	04036283	863/635-7820	124
Ben Sheppard Elem Sch/*Hialeah*/Miami-Dade	03038202	305/556-2204	78
Benjamin Franklin K-8 Ctr/*North Miami*/ Miami-Dade	00185923	305/681-3547	75
Benjamin Sch/*N Palm Beach*/Palm Beach	02085343	561/626-3747	111
Bennett C Russell Elem Sch/*Milton*/ Santa Rosa	10908963	850/983-7000	128
Bennett Elem Sch/*Ft Lauderdale*/Broward	00183133	754/322-5450	11
Benoist Farms Elem Sch/*West Palm Bch*/ Palm Beach	05102342	561/681-2250	106
Bent Tree Elem Sch/*Miami*/Miami-Dade	02199748	305/221-0461	81
Bentley Elem Sch/*Sanford*/Seminole	04944276	407/871-9950	132
Berean Christian Academy/*Jacksonville*/ Duval	02876867	904/264-5333	34
Berean Christian Sch/*West Palm Bch*/ Palm Beach	05325659	561/798-9300	111
Berkeley Preparatory Sch/*Tampa*/ Hillsborough	00193229	813/885-1673	53
Berkley Accelerated Middle Sch/*Auburndale*/ Polk	05346689	863/984-2400	123
Berkley Charter Elem Sch/*Auburndale*/Polk	04921999	863/968-5024	123
Berkshire Elem Sch/*West Palm Bch*/ Palm Beach	00198102	561/304-2000	106
Berryhill Elem Sch/*Milton*/Santa Rosa	00203032	850/983-5690	128
Beryl Wisdom Adventist Sch/*Orlando*/Orange	04983428	407/291-3073	100
Bessey Creek Elem Sch/*Palm City*/Martin	04455134	772/219-1500	73
Best Academy/*Brooksville*/Hernando	11918296	352/544-2373	43
Best Chance North/*Crestview*/Okaloosa	11557880	850/689-5535	91
Betesda Christian Sch/*Opa Locka*/Miami-Dade	11234791	305/685-7566	86
Beth Emet Elem Sch/*Cooper City*/Broward	11228871	954/680-1882	18
Beth Jacob High Sch/*Miami*/Miami-Dade	04983703	305/957-1670	86
Beth Shields Middle Sch/*Ruskin*/ Hillsborough	05351165	813/672-5338	47
Bethany Christian Sch/*Ft Lauderdale*/ Broward	02182666	954/522-2554	18
Bethany Christian Sch/*W Melbourne*/Brevard	01434569	321/727-2038	9
Bethel Christian Academy/*Tallahassee*/Leon	04929226	850/222-6605	65
Bethel Holiness Academy/*Jacksonville*/Duval	04983014	904/781-5400	34
Bethel Junior Academy/*Riviera Beach*/ Palm Beach	11824164	561/881-0130	111
Bethel SDA Elem Sch/*Florida City*/ Miami-Dade	11735800	305/248-4973	86
Bethlehem Sch/*Bonifay*/Holmes	00193267	850/547-3621	55
Bethune Academy/*Haines City*/Polk	00201527	863/421-3334	124
Betton Hills Preparatory Sch/*Tallahassee*/ Leon	04329236	850/422-2464	66
Betton Hills Sch/*Tallahassee*/Leon	11233905	850/656-9211	66
Beulah Academy of Science/*Pensacola*/ Escambia	04807575	850/944-2822	36
Beulah Elem Sch/*Pensacola*/Escambia	00190382	850/941-6180	37
Beulah Middle Sch/*Pensacola*/Escambia	00190411	850/316-3800	37
Beverly Shores Elem Sch/*Leesburg*/Lake	00193724	352/787-4175	58
Bexley Elem Sch/*Land O Lakes*/Pasco	12234988	813/346-4300	113
Bible Truth Ministry Academy/*Tampa*/ Hillsborough	05011561	813/231-9177	53
Big Bend Tech Institute/*Perry*/Taylor	00204232	850/838-2545	139
Big Cypress Elem Sch/*Naples*/Collier	02888638	239/377-6300	25
Big Pine Academy/*Big Pine Key*/Monroe	05070775	305/872-1266	89
Bill Duncan Opportunity Center/*Lakeland*/ Polk	01340231	863/499-2860	123
Biltmore Elem Sch/*Jacksonville*/Duval	00188901	904/693-7969	33
Biltmore Sch/*Miami*/Miami-Dade	10967256	305/266-4666	86
Binks Forest Elem Sch/*Wellington*/ Palm Beach	04878665	561/904-9800	106
Biotech-Richmond Heights HS/*Miami*/ Miami-Dade	12045050	786/573-5353	81
Biscayne Elem Sch/*Jacksonville*/Duval	05274141	904/714-4650	30
Biscayne Elem Sch/*Miami Beach*/Miami-Dade	00185181	305/868-7727	78
Biscayne Gardens Elem Sch/*Miami*/Miami-Dade	00185193	305/681-5721	78
Biscayne High Sch/*Jacksonville*/Duval	11920275	904/252-6311	29
Bishop John J Snyder High Sch/*Jacksonville*/ Duval	05098052	904/771-1029	34
Bishop Kenny High Sch/*Jacksonville*/Duval	00202557	904/398-7545	34

School/City/County DISTRICT/CITY/COUNTY	PID	TELEPHONE NUMBER	PAGE
Bishop Larkin Sch/*Port Richey*/Pasco	03266136	727/862-6981	115
Bishop McLaughlin Catholic HS/*Spring Hill*/ Pasco	05280748	727/857-2600	115
Bishop Moore High Sch/*Orlando*/Orange	00197665	407/293-7561	100
Bishop Verot High Sch/*Fort Myers*/Lee	00200767	239/274-6700	63
Blackburn Elem Sch/*Palmetto*/Manatee	00195124	941/723-4800	68
Blake High Sch/*Tampa*/Hillsborough	04754978	813/272-3422	48
Blake Sch/*Plantation*/Broward	01772165	954/584-6816	18
Blanche Ely High Sch/*Pompano Beach*/Broward	00182751	754/322-0950	11
Blankner Sch/*Orlando*/Orange	00196867	407/245-1720	95
Blanton Elem Sch/*St Petersburg*/Pinellas	00199558	727/547-7820	119
Blessed Sacrament Cath Sch/*Seminole*/ Pinellas	00200779	727/391-4060	120
Blessed Star Montessori Sch/*Pensacola*/ Escambia	02373669	850/476-9208	38
Blessed Trinity Cath Sch/*Ocala*/Marion	00197677	352/622-5808	72
Blessed Trinity Catholic Sch/*Jacksonville*/ Duval	11396662	904/641-6458	34
Blessed Trinity Sch/*Miami*/Miami-Dade	00187907	305/871-5766	85
Bloomingdale High Sch/*Valrico*/Hillsborough	03006510	813/744-8018	51
Blossom Montessori Sch-Deaf/*Clearwater*/ Pinellas	11616644	727/539-7879	120
Blountstown Elem Sch/*Blountstown*/Calhoun	00184371	850/674-8169	20
Blountstown Middle Sch/*Blountstown*/Calhoun	00184395	850/674-8234	20
Blountstown Senior High Sch/*Blountstown*/ Calhoun	00184383	850/674-5724	20
Blue Angels Elem Sch/*Pensacola*/Escambia	04922632	850/457-6356	37
Blue Lake Elem Sch/*Deland*/Volusia	02200672	386/822-4070	140
Blue Lakes Elem Sch/*Miami*/Miami-Dade	00186850	305/271-7411	81
Bluewater Elem Sch/*Niceville*/Okaloosa	03336341	850/833-4240	91
Bob Graham Education Center/*Miami Lakes*/ Miami-Dade	05101336	305/557-3303	78
Bob Sikes Elem Sch/*Crestview*/Okaloosa	00196166	850/689-7268	91
Boca Ciega High Sch/*Gulfport*/Pinellas	00199560	727/893-2780	118
Boca Prep International Sch/*Boca Raton*/ Palm Beach	04912560	561/852-1410	111
Boca Raton Christian Sch/*Boca Raton*/ Palm Beach	01775351	561/391-2727	111
Boca Raton Cmty High Sch/*Boca Raton*/ Palm Beach	00198762	561/338-1400	109
Boca Raton Cmty Middle Sch/*Boca Raton*/ Palm Beach	00198750	561/416-8700	109
Boca Raton Elem Sch/*Boca Raton*/Palm Beach	00198748	561/544-1700	109
Boggy Creek Elem Sch/*Kissimmee*/Osceola	02201896	407/344-5060	102
Bolles School- San Jose/*Jacksonville*/Duval	00190174	904/733-9292	34
Bolles School-Bartram/*Jacksonville*/Duval	04486121	904/732-5700	34
Bolles School-Ponte Vedra/*Ponte Vedra*/ St Johns	03419682	904/285-4658	135
Bond Elem Sch/*Tallahassee*/Leon	00194687	850/488-7676	64
Bonifay K-8 Sch/*Bonifay*/Holmes	00193279	850/547-3631	55
Bonita Spring High Sch/*Bonita Spgs*/Lee	12229969	239/495-3022	61
Bonita Springs Charter Sch/*Bonita Spgs*/Lee	05101221	239/992-6932	61
Bonita Springs Elem Sch/*Bonita Spgs*/Lee	00194132	239/992-0801	61
Bonita Springs MS for the Arts/*Bonita Spgs*/ Lee	01527178	239/992-4422	61
Bonneville Elem Sch/*Orlando*/Orange	00196623	407/249-6290	96
Booker High Sch/*Sarasota*/Sarasota	00203264	941/355-2967	129
Booker Middle Sch/*Sarasota*/Sarasota	00203276	941/359-5824	129
Booker T Washington Elem Sch/*Tampa*/ Hillsborough	05351127	813/233-3720	47
Booker T Washington SHS/*Miami*/Miami-Dade	04876447	305/324-8900	75
Boone High Sch/*Orlando*/Orange	00196635	407/893-7200	97
Boulevard Heights Elem Sch/*Hollywood*/ Broward	00183925	754/323-4950	11
Boulware Springs Charter Sch/*Gainesville*/ Alachua	12032948	352/244-9732	1
Bowers-Whitley Career Center/*Tampa*/ Hillsborough	05351141	813/558-1750	51
Bowling Green Elem Sch/*Bowling Green*/ Hardee	00191489	863/375-2288	42
Bowman-Ashe-Doolin K-8 Acad/*Miami*/ Miami-Dade	03412024	305/386-6667	81
Boyd H Anderson High Sch/*Laud Lakes*/ Broward	00183145	754/322-0200	11
Boyette Springs Elem Sch/*Riverview*/ Hillsborough	04017263	813/671-5060	51
Boynton Beach Cmty High Sch/*Boynton Beach*/ Palm Beach	04947230	561/752-1200	109
Braden River Elem Sch/*Bradenton*/Manatee	03050767	941/751-7012	68
Braden River High Sch/*Bradenton*/Manatee	10009464	941/751-8230	68
Braden River Middle Sch/*Bradenton*/Manatee	03396638	941/751-7080	68
Bradenton Christian Sch/*Bradenton*/Manatee	01404318	941/792-5454	70

School/City/County DISTRICT/CITY/COUNTY	PID	TELEPHONE NUMBER	PAGE
Bradenton Early Learning Acad/*Bradenton*/			
Manatee	11750836	941/216-3305	70
Bradford Christian Academy/*Starke*/Bradford	04982876	904/964-9619	6
BRADFORD CO SCH DIST/**STARKE**/			
BRADFORD	00181874	904/966-6800	5
Bradford High Sch/*Starke*/Bradford	00181898	904/966-6075	6
Bradford Intervention Center/*Starke*/			
Bradford	11829645	904/966-6004	6
Bradford Middle Sch/*Starke*/Bradford	00181903	904/966-6705	6
Bradford Virtual Elem Sch/*Starke*/Bradford	11589869	904/966-6010	6
Bradford Virtual High Sch/*Starke*/Bradford	11589871	904/966-6860	6
Brandon Academy/*Brandon*/Hillsborough	01436751	813/689-1952	53
Brandon Epic3/*Seffner*/Hillsborough	05351218	813/651-2165	51
Brandon Senior High Sch/*Brandon*/			
Hillsborough	00191922	813/744-8120	51
Branford Elem Sch/*Branford*/Suwannee	04914465	386/935-5700	138
Branford High Sch/*Branford*/Suwannee	00204103	386/935-5600	138
Bratt Elem Sch/*Century*/Escambia	00190394	850/761-6200	37
Brauser Maimonides Academy/*Ft Lauderdale*/			
Broward	01434571	954/989-6886	18
Breakfast Point Academy/*P C Beach*/Bay	11071862	850/767-1190	4
Brentwood Elem Sch/*Jacksonville*/Duval	03401362	904/630-6630	33
Brentwood Elem Sch/*Miami Gardens*/			
Miami-Dade	00185521	305/624-2657	78
Brentwood Elem Sch/*Pensacola*/Escambia	00190409	850/595-6800	37
Brentwood Elem Sch/*Sarasota*/Sarasota	00203290	941/361-6230	129
Brentwood Sch/*Gainesville*/Alachua	01771862	352/373-3222	3
Brevard Adult Education Cocoa/*Cocoa*/			
Brevard	04915512	321/633-3575	6
Brevard Adventist Chrn Acad/*Cocoa*/Brevard	11828225	321/636-2551	9
Brevard Co Adult Sch-Titusvile/*Titusville*/			
Brevard	04915536	321/264-3088	6
BREVARD CO SCH DIST/**VIERA**/			
BREVARD	00181965	321/633-1000	6
BREVARD CO SCHS-CHOICE/**MELBOURNE**/			
BREVARD	12234885	321/633-1000	6
BREVARD CO SCHS-ELEMENTARY/			
MELBOURNE/**BREVARD**	12234861	321/633-1000	7
BREVARD CO SCHS-SECONDARY/			
MELBOURNE/**BREVARD**	12234873	321/633-1000	8
Brevard Private Academy/*Merritt Is*/Brevard	11735082	321/459-3466	9
Brevard Virtual Elem Sch/*Cocoa*/Brevard	11745910	321/633-3660	6
Brevard Virtual High Sch/*Cocoa*/Brevard	11745922	321/633-3660	6
Brewster Tech & Adult Center/*Tampa*/			
Hillsborough	00191934	813/276-5448	46
Brickhouse Academy/*Sarasota*/Sarasota	11236945	941/924-7681	131
Bridge to Success Acad HS/*Jacksonville*/			
Duval	12368814	904/924-3470	32
Bridge to Success Acad MS/*Jacksonville*/			
Duval	12368826	904/630-6592	33
Bridgeprep Acad Broward Co/*Tamarac*/Broward	12233506	954/271-0090	16
Bridgeprep Acad Greater Miami/*Miami*/			
Miami-Dade	11719662	786/477-4372	75
Bridgeprep Acad Hollywd Hills/*Hollywood*/			
Broward	12032754	954/362-8268	16
Bridgeprep Acad Interamerican/*Miami*/			
Miami-Dade	11825314	305/643-4833	75
Bridgeprep Acad of Riverview/*Riverview*/			
Hillsborough	12231675	813/370-1910	46
Bridgeprep Acad-N Miami Beach/*Miami*/			
Miami-Dade	12233702	305/570-4048	75
Bridgeprep Academy Duval/*Jacksonville*/			
Duval	12233489	904/694-2660	29
Bridgeprep Academy of Collier/*Naples*/			
Collier	12310051	239/747-1016	25
Bridgeprep Academy Orange/*Orlando*/Orange	12168949	321/775-2119	94
Bridgeprep Academy Osceola/*Kissimmee*/			
Osceola	12308905	407/603-3890	102
Bridgeprep Academy South/*Miami*/Miami-Dade	11559931	305/271-3109	81
Bridgeprep Academy-Palm Beach/*Delray Beach*/			
Palm Beach	12241448	561/406-0709	105
Bridgeprep Academy-Tampa/*Tampa*/			
Hillsborough	12034348	813/258-5652	46
Bridgeprep Academy-Vlg Green/*Miami*/			
Miami-Dade	11719650	305/253-8775	82
Bridges Montessori Sch/*Stuart*/Martin	04336526	772/221-9490	73
Bridgewater Middle Sch/*Winter Garden*/			
Orange	10902505	407/905-3710	99
Bright Futures Acad Riverside/*Palm Bch Gdns*/			
Palm Beach	04950562	561/253-7504	105
Bright Horizons Sch/*Pompano Beach*/Broward	00183004	754/321-6400	11

School/City/County DISTRICT/CITY/COUNTY	PID	TELEPHONE NUMBER	PAGE
Bright Learning-Cyber High Sch/*Winter Park*/			
Orange	11727437	407/455-0622	100
Brighton Prep Sch/*St Petersburg*/Pinellas	03419486	727/327-1454	120
Brito Miami Private Sch/*Miami*/Miami-Dade	01436024	305/448-1463	86
Broach School-Orange Park/*Orange Park*/Clay	11230264	904/637-0300	24
Broach School-South/*Jacksonville*/Duval	11816533	904/674-0900	34
Broach School-West Campus/*Jacksonville*/			
Duval	02148529	904/389-5106	34
Broadmoor Elem Sch/*Miami*/Miami-Dade	00185935	305/691-0861	75
Broadview Elem Sch/*N Lauderdale*/Broward	00182763	754/322-5500	11
Bronson Elem Sch/*Bronson*/Levy	02225074	352/486-5281	66
Bronson Middle High Sch/*Bronson*/Levy	00194819	352/486-5261	66
Brooker Creek Elem Sch/*Tarpon Spgs*/			
Pinellas	04757516	727/943-4600	116
Brooker Elem Sch/*Brandon*/Hillsborough	00192330	813/744-8184	51
Brooker Elem Sch/*Brooker*/Bradford	00181915	352/485-1812	6
Brooks Debartolo Collegiate HS/*Tampa*/			
Hillsborough	10902622	813/971-5600	46
Brookshire Elem Sch/*Winter Park*/Orange	00196647	407/623-1400	96
Brookside Middle Sch/*Sarasota*/Sarasota	00203305	941/361-6472	129
Brooksville Elem Sch/*Brooksville*/Hernando	00191647	352/797-7014	43
Brookview Elem Sch/*Jacksonville*/Duval	00188925	904/565-2720	30
Broward Children's Ctr North/*Pompano Beach*/			
Broward	04500882	954/946-7503	18
BROWARD CO PUBLIC CHARTER SCHS/			
FT LAUDERDALE/**BROWARD**	11818828	754/321-2135	15
BROWARD CO PUBLIC SCHOOLS/			
FT LAUDERDALE/**BROWARD**	00182725	754/321-0000	10
Broward Elem Sch/*Tampa*/Hillsborough	00191946	813/276-5592	47
Broward Estates Elem Sch/*Lauderhill*/			
Broward	00183494	754/322-5550	11
Broward Jr Academy/*Plantation*/Broward	11237200	954/316-8301	18
Broward Math & Science Schools/*Margate*/			
Broward	11820235	954/969-8488	16
Broward Virtual Sch/*Coconut Creek*/Broward	11554682	754/321-6050	11
Brown-Barge Middle Sch/*Pensacola*/Escambia	00190423	850/494-5640	37
Browning Pearce Elem Sch/*San Mateo*/Putnam	00202210	386/329-0557	127
Brownsville Middle Sch/*Miami*/Miami-Dade	00186422	305/633-1481	75
Brucie Ball Education Center/*Miami*/			
Miami-Dade	00186678	305/514-5100	82
Brush Arbor Christian Sch/*Orlando*/Orange	02235732	407/671-9774	100
Bryan Plant City Elem Sch/*Plant City*/			
Hillsborough	01843544	813/757-9300	47
Bryceville Elem Sch/*Bryceville*/Nassau	01340190	904/266-9241	90
Buchanan Middle Sch/*Tampa*/Hillsborough	00191960	813/975-7600	50
Buck Lake Elem Sch/*Tallahassee*/Leon	03251337	850/488-6133	64
Buckhorn Elem Sch/*Valrico*/Hillsborough	02042157	813/744-8240	51
Buckingham Exceptional Center/*Fort Myers*/			
Lee	02226963	239/693-1233	61
Buddy Taylor Middle Sch/*Palm Coast*/Flagler	02130704	386/446-6700	39
Buffalo Creek Middle Sch/*Palmetto*/Manatee	10913542	941/721-2260	68
Bunche Park Elem Sch/*Miami Gardens*/			
Miami-Dade	00185533	305/621-1469	78
Bunnell Elem Sch/*Bunnell*/Flagler	00191013	386/437-7533	39
Burns Middle Sch/*Brandon*/Hillsborough	03011199	813/744-8383	51
Burns Science & Tech Chtr Sch/*Oak Hill*/			
Volusia	11709394	386/210-4915	140
Bushnell Elem Sch/*Bushnell*/Sumter	00203991	352/793-3501	138
Byrneville Elem Sch/*Century*/Escambia	00190459	850/256-6350	37
C			
C A Weis Elem Sch/*Pensacola*/Escambia	00190461	850/595-6888	37
C C Washington Academy/*Panama City*/Bay	11559826	850/767-5576	4
C G Bethel High Sch/*N Miami Beach*/			
Miami-Dade	11453428	786/629-7053	78
C H Price Middle Sch/*Interlachen*/Putnam	00202258	386/684-2113	127
C L Overturf Jr 6th Grade Ctr/*Palatka*/			
Putnam	00202325	386/329-0569	127
C O Taylor-Kirklane Elem Sch/*Palm Springs*/			
Palm Beach	00198188	561/804-3500	106
C W Norton Elem Sch/*Gainesville*/Alachua	04017172	352/955-6765	2
C W Ruckel Middle Sch/*Niceville*/Okaloosa	00196178	850/833-4142	91
Calhoun Co Adult Sch/*Blountstown*/Calhoun	01485506	850/674-8734	20
CALHOUN CO SCH DIST/**BLOUNTSTOWN**/			
CALHOUN	00184357	850/674-5927	20
Callahan Elem Sch/*Callahan*/Nassau	00196025	904/879-2121	90
Callahan Intermediate Sch/*Callahan*/Nassau	01487671	904/879-1114	90
Callahan Middle Sch/*Callahan*/Nassau	00196037	904/879-3606	90
Callaway Elem Sch/*Panama City*/Bay	00181575	850/767-1241	4
Caloosa Elem Sch/*Cape Coral*/Lee	00194144	239/574-3113	61
Caloosa Middle Sch/*Cape Coral*/Lee	01340140	239/574-3232	61
Calusa Elem Sch/*Boca Raton*/Palm Beach	03006883	561/989-7500	109

School/City/County DISTRICT/CITY/COUNTY	PID	TELEPHONE NUMBER	PAGE
Calusa Elem Sch/*Miami*/Miami-Dade	02130003	305/385-0589	82
Calusa Elem Sch/*New Prt Rchy*/Pasco	01877997	727/774-3700	113
Calusa Park Elem Sch/*Naples*/Collier	05026205	239/377-6400	25
Calusa Prep Sch/*Miami*/Miami-Dade	03253517	305/596-3787	86
Calvary Academy/*Mulberry*/Polk	11704497	863/428-2071	126
Calvary Chapel Academy/*Melbourne*/Brevard	10003551	321/729-9922	9
Calvary Chapel Sch/*Sarasota*/Sarasota	11228833	941/366-6522	131
Calvary Christian Academy/*Ft Lauderdale*/ Broward	00184266	954/905-5100	18
Calvary Christian Academy/*Ft Walton Bch*/ Okaloosa	00196491	850/862-1414	93
Calvary Christian Academy/*Hollywood*/ Broward	12362248	954/322-4375	18
Calvary Christian Academy/*Ormond Beach*/ Volusia	02980212	386/672-2081	142
Calvary Christian High Sch/*Clearwater*/ Pinellas	10018609	727/449-2247	120
Calvary City Chrn Acad & PS/*Orlando*/Orange	12259976	407/581-6120	101
Calvin Hunsinger Sch/*Clearwater*/Pinellas	03337060	727/469-4260	117
Cambridge Christian Sch/*Tampa*/Hillsborough	01559755	813/872-6744	53
Cambridge Elem Sch/*Cocoa*/Brevard	00182153	321/633-3550	7
Camelot Academy/*Pensacola*/Escambia	11717157	850/497-6692	37
Camelot Elem Sch/*Orlando*/Orange	04945359	407/207-3875	96
Caminiti Exceptional Center/*Tampa*/ Hillsborough	03006730	813/975-7611	48
Campbell Drive K-8 Center/*Homestead*/ Miami-Dade	01527049	305/245-0270	82
Campbell Middle Sch/*Daytona Beach*/Volusia	00204323	386/258-4661	140
Campbell Park Elem Sch/*St Petersburg*/ Pinellas	00199572	727/893-2650	119
Candlelight Christian Academy/*Lake Wales*/ Polk	05282019	863/676-0049	126
Cannella Elem Sch/*Tampa*/Hillsborough	04020521	813/975-6941	49
Canoe Creek Charter Academy/*Saint Cloud*/ Osceola	05097905	407/891-7320	103
Canopy Oaks Elem Sch/*Tallahassee*/Leon	04809860	850/488-3301	64
Canterbury Sch/*Fort Myers*/Lee	00194431	239/481-4323	63
Canterbury School of Flordia/*St Petersburg*/ Pinellas	11835486	727/521-5925	120
Canterbury School of Florida/*St Petersburg*/ Pinellas	00200602	727/525-1419	120
Cape Academy/*Cape Coral*/Lee	11226378	239/573-8668	63
Cape Coral Charter Sch/*Cape Coral*/Lee	05348388	239/995-0904	61
Cape Coral Christian Sch/*Cape Coral*/Lee	02379766	239/574-3707	63
Cape Coral High Sch/*Cape Coral*/Lee	01880683	239/574-6766	61
Cape Coral Technical College/*Cape Coral*/ Lee	04034156	239/574-4440	61
Cape Elem Sch/*Cape Coral*/Lee	00194156	239/542-3551	61
Cape View Elem Sch/*Cpe Canaveral*/Brevard	00182581	321/784-0284	7
Capital Preparatory/*Tallahassee*/Leon	12320666	850/402-9711	66
Capstone Acad Milton Campus/*Milton*/ Santa Rosa	11527603	850/626-3091	128
Capstone Academy/*Pensacola*/Escambia	05358319	850/458-7735	37
Cardinal Gibbons High Sch/*Ft Lauderdale*/ Broward	00187919	954/491-2900	18
Cardinal Mooney High Sch/*Sarasota*/Sarasota	00200781	941/371-4917	131
Cardinal Newman High Sch/*West Palm Bch*/ Palm Beach	00187921	561/683-6266	110
Care Elem Sch/*Miami*/Miami-Dade	12230669	305/572-2072	86
Career Quest Ed Center/*Pt Charlotte*/ Charlotte	01543639	941/255-7614	21
Caribbean K-8 Center/*Miami*/Miami-Dade	00187309	305/233-7131	82
Carillon Elem Sch/*Oviedo*/Seminole	04455873	407/320-4650	132
Caring & Sharing Learning Sch/*Gainesville*/ Alachua	04819786	352/372-1004	2
Carlos E Haile Middle Sch/*Bradenton*/ Manatee	04755386	941/714-7240	68
Carlton Palmore Elem Sch/*Lakeland*/Polk	00201216	863/648-3510	125
Carol City Elem Sch/*Miami Gardens*/ Miami-Dade	00185545	305/621-0509	78
Carol City Middle Sch/*Miami Gardens*/ Miami-Dade	00185557	305/624-2652	78
Carr Elem & Middle Sch/*Clarksville*/Calhoun	00184400	850/674-5395	20
Carrie P Meek-Westview K-8 Ctr/*Miami*/ Miami-Dade	00186331	305/688-9641	75
Carrollton Sch of Sacred Heart/*Miami*/ Miami-Dade	00187945	305/446-5673	86
Carrollwood Day Sch/*Tampa*/Hillsborough	02375796	813/920-2288	53
Carrollwood Elem Sch/*Tampa*/Hillsborough	00191984	813/975-7640	50
Carter G Woodson Elem Sch/*Jacksonville*/ Duval	03401374	904/924-3004	33
Carter-Parramore Academy/*Quincy*/Gadsden	01811072	850/627-6030	40

School/City/County DISTRICT/CITY/COUNTY	PID	TELEPHONE NUMBER	PAGE
Carver Cmty Middle Sch/*Delray Beach*/ Palm Beach	00198798	561/638-2100	109
Carver Exceptional Center/*Tampa*/ Hillsborough	02200426	813/236-3500	51
Carver Middle Sch/*Leesburg*/Lake	00193853	352/787-7868	58
Carver Middle Sch/*Orlando*/Orange	00196659	407/296-5110	95
Carwise Middle Sch/*Palm Harbor*/Pinellas	04036300	727/724-1442	116
Casa Dei Bambini Mont Sch/*Miami Beach*/ Miami-Dade	04927929	305/534-8911	86
Casselberry Elem Sch/*Casselberry*/Seminole	00203604	407/746-2550	132
Cassels Christian Academy/*Starke*/Bradford	11821904	904/368-9907	6
Castle Creek Elem Sch/*Orlando*/Orange	10024397	407/207-7428	96
Castle Hill Elem Sch/*Lauderhill*/Broward	00183157	754/322-5600	11
Castleview Elem Sch/*Orlando*/Orange	12367975	407/250-6290	98
Catalina Elem Sch/*Orlando*/Orange	00196661	407/245-1735	99
Cathedral Parish Early Ed Ctr/*St Augustine*/ St Johns	03381554	904/829-2933	135
Cathedral Parish Sch/*St Augustine*/St Johns	00202571	904/824-2861	135
Cecile E Gray Middle Sch/*Groveland*/Lake	01827112	352/429-3322	58
Cedar Creek Christian Sch/*Jacksonville*/ Duval	12165507	904/781-9151	34
Cedar Grove Elem Sch/*Panama City*/Bay	00181587	850/767-4550	4
Cedar Hills Bapt Chrn Sch/*Jacksonville*/ Duval	01436244	904/772-0812	34
Cedar Hills Elem Sch/*Jacksonville*/Duval	00188951	904/573-1050	33
Cedar Key Sch/*Cedar Key*/Levy	00194821	352/543-5223	66
Celebration High Sch/*Celebration*/Osceola	05274490	321/939-6600	103
Celebration Sch/*Celebration*/Osceola	04455720	407/566-2300	103
Centennial Elem Sch/*Dade City*/Pasco	03011022	352/524-5000	113
Centennial Middle Sch/*Dade City*/Pasco	04946212	352/524-9700	114
Center Academy/*Coral Springs*/Broward	11228558	954/575-1231	19
Center Academy/*Jacksonville*/Duval	04886179	904/448-1956	35
Center Academy/*Jacksonville*/Duval	05153377	904/645-5366	35
Center Academy/*Lutz*/Hillsborough	02148622	813/909-9442	53
Center Academy/*Maitland*/Orange	04983284	407/772-8727	101
Center Academy/*Pinellas Park*/Pinellas	02149016	727/541-5716	120
Center Academy/*Riverview*/Hillsborough	11233981	813/677-7777	53
Center Academy Sch/*Palm Harbor*/Pinellas	04309365	727/781-2986	120
Center Montessori Sch/*Bradenton*/Manatee	02197738	941/753-4987	70
Centerpoint Christian Academy/*Middleburg*/ Clay	11734909	904/291-1875	24
Central Ave Elem Sch/*Kissimmee*/Osceola	04941975	407/343-7330	103
Central Baptist Christian Sch/*Brandon*/ Hillsborough	03352682	813/689-6133	53
Central Charter Sch/*Ft Lauderdale*/Broward	04756873	954/735-6295	16
Central Christian Academy/*Winter Park*/ Orange	04021185	407/332-6988	101
Central Elem Sch/*Clewiston*/Hendry	03251210	863/983-1550	43
Central Elem Sch/*Okeechobee*/Okeechobee	00196544	863/462-5077	93
Central Fellowship Chrn Acad/*Lake Helen*/ Volusia	04336576	386/228-2803	142
Central Florida Chrn Academy/*Orlando*/ Orange	01775284	407/293-8062	101
Central Florida Ldrshp Academy/*Orlando*/ Orange	11557763	407/480-2352	94
Central Florida Prep Sch/*Gotha*/Orange	03417828	407/290-8073	101
Central High Sch/*Brooksville*/Hernando	03052650	352/797-7020	43
Central High Sch/*Panama City*/Bay	12115289	850/866-4148	4
Central Middle Sch/*W Melbourne*/Brevard	00182294	321/722-4150	8
Central Park Elem Sch/*Plantation*/Broward	03252367	754/322-5700	11
Central Ridge Elem Sch/*Citrus Spgs*/Citrus	11079319	352/344-3833	22
Central Riverside Elem Sch/*Jacksonville*/ Duval	00188963	904/381-7495	30
Central Sch/*Milton*/Santa Rosa	00203018	850/983-5640	128
Chaffee Trail Elem Sch/*Jacksonville*/Duval	10910497	904/693-7510	30
Chain of Lakes Collegiate HS/*Winter Haven*/ Polk	10027765	863/298-6800	123
Chain of Lakes Elem Sch/*Winter Haven*/Polk	10007260	863/326-5388	124
Chain of Lakes Middle Sch/*Orlando*/Orange	04869793	407/909-5400	99
Chaires Elem Sch/*Tallahassee*/Leon	00194558	850/488-5977	64
Challenger 7 Elem Sch/*Cocoa*/Brevard	02896984	321/636-5801	7
Challenger Elem Sch/*Tamarac*/Broward	04946963	754/322-5750	11
Challenger Middle Sch/*Cape Coral*/Lee	10030114	239/242-4341	61
Challenger Sch of Sci & Math/*Spring Hill*/ Hernando	10007557	352/797-7024	43
Chamberlain Senior High Sch/*Tampa*/ Hillsborough	00192005	813/975-7677	47
Chambers High Sch/*Homestead*/Miami-Dade	11453466	305/909-6307	82
Chaminade Madonna College Prep/*Hollywood*/ Broward	00187969	954/989-5150	18
Champagnat Catholic Sch/*Hialeah*/Miami-Dade	02234659	305/888-3760	86
Champion Elem Sch/*Daytona Beach*/Volusia	00204816	386/258-4664	140

School/City/County DISTRICT/CITY/COUNTY	PID	TELEPHONE NUMBER	PAGE
Championship Acad W Broward/*Sunrise*/ Broward	12233491	954/514-7323	16
Championship Acad-Davie/*Hollywood*/Broward	11743704	954/362-3415	16
Championship Academy-Hollywood/*Hollywood*/ Broward	10006565	954/924-8006	16
Championship Distinction HS/*Ft Lauderdale*/ Broward	12169876	954/924-8006	16
Championship Distinction MS/*Hollywood*/ Broward	12169840	954/924-8006	16
Chancery Charter High Sch/*Orlando*/Orange	11452864	407/850-9791	94
Changing Lives Academy/*Orlando*/Orange	12225585	407/613-2445	101
Channelside Acad of Math & Sci/*Tampa*/ Hillsborough	11716268	813/579-9649	46
Channelside Academy Middle Sch/*Tampa*/ Hillsborough	11830022	813/579-9649	46
Chapel Trail Elem Sch/*Pembroke Pnes*/ Broward	04364561	754/323-5000	11
Chapman Partnership ECC North/*Miami*/ Miami-Dade	11829994	305/329-3057	74
Chapman Partnership ECC South/*Homestead*/ Miami-Dade	11830008	877/994-4357	74
Character Private Sch/*Cross City*/Dixie	12225602	352/440-1420	29
Charles D Wyche Elem Sch/*Miami Gardens*/ Miami-Dade	04494984	305/628-5776	78
Charles Drew Elem Sch/*Pompano Beach*/ Broward	00182787	754/322-6250	11
Charles E Bennett Elem Sch/*Green Cv Spgs*/ Clay	00184668	904/336-0475	23
Charles R Drew K-8 Center/*Miami*/Miami-Dade	00185959	305/691-8021	75
Charles R Hadley Elem Sch/*Miami*/Miami-Dade	02949098	305/261-3719	75
Charles S Rushe Middle Sch/*Land O Lakes*/ Pasco	10904084	813/346-1200	114
Charles W Flanagan High Sch/*Pembroke Pnes*/ Broward	04457118	754/323-0650	11
CHARLOTTE CO PUBLIC SCH DIST/ **PT CHARLOTTE**/**CHARLOTTE**	00184412	941/255-0808	20
Charlotte Harbor Sch/*Pt Charlotte*/ Charlotte	02112324	941/255-7440	21
Charlotte High Sch/*Punta Gorda*/Charlotte	00184424	941/575-5450	21
Charlotte Preparatory Sch/*Pt Charlotte*/ Charlotte	04984343	941/764-7673	21
Charlotte Technical College/*Pt Charlotte*/ Charlotte	02112271	941/255-7500	21
Charlotte Virtual Sch/*Pt Charlotte*/ Charlotte	11712597	941/255-7545	21
Charter HS of the Americas/*Miami*/ Miami-Dade	12362171	305/643-4888	75
Chasco Elem Sch/*Port Richey*/Pasco	04916554	727/774-1200	113
Chasco Middle Sch/*Port Richey*/Pasco	04946200	727/774-1300	114
Chattahoochee Elem Sch/*Chattahoochee*/ Gadsden	00191104	850/662-2080	40
Chautauqua Lrn & Srv Chtr Sch/*Panama City*/ Bay	10017758	850/785-5056	4
Cheney Elem Sch/*Orlando*/Orange	00196673	407/672-3120	96
Cherokee Sch/*Orlando*/Orange	02042224	407/897-6440	99
Chester A Moore Elem Sch/*Fort Pierce*/ St Lucie	00202856	772/468-5315	136
Chester Shell Elem Sch/*Hawthorne*/Alachua	00181393	352/481-1901	2
Chester W Taylor Elem Sch/*Zephyrhills*/ Pasco	04749090	813/794-6900	113
Chestnut ES-Sci & Engineering/*Kissimmee*/ Osceola	10007624	407/870-4862	103
Chets Creek Elem Sch/*Jacksonville*/Duval	04807965	904/992-6390	30
CHI CHI Rodriguez Academy/*Clearwater*/ Pinellas	11103556	727/791-3522	117
Chiaramonte Elem Sch/*Tampa*/Hillsborough	00192017	813/272-3066	48
Chickasaw Elem Sch/*Orlando*/Orange	00196697	407/249-6300	96
Chiefland Elem Sch/*Chiefland*/Levy	00194833	352/493-6040	66
Chiefland Middle High Sch/*Chiefland*/Levy	00194845	352/493-6000	66
Children's Academy/*Miami*/Miami-Dade	01435068	305/947-1731	86
Children's House Montessori/*Deland*/Volusia	02402961	386/736-3632	142
Childrens Reading Center CS/*Palatka*/Putnam	05274555	386/328-9990	127
Chiles Academy/*Daytona Beach*/Volusia	05092266	386/322-6102	140
Chimney Lakes Elem Sch/*Jacksonville*/Duval	03329489	904/573-1100	30
Chipley High Sch/*Chipley*/Washington	00205016	850/638-6100	144
Chisholm Elem Sch/*New Smyrna*/Volusia	00204438	386/424-2540	140
Chocachatti Elem Sch/*Brooksville*/Hernando	04870912	352/797-7067	44
Choctawhatchee Senior High Sch/*Ft Walton Bch*/ Okaloosa	00196207	850/833-3614	92
Choice High & Tech Center/*Ft Walton Bch*/ Okaloosa	01395858	850/833-3500	92
Choices In Learning Chtr Sch/*Winter Spgs*/ Seminole	04950627	407/302-1005	132
Cholee Lake Elem Sch/*Greenacres*/Palm Beach	05102354	561/681-1417	106
Christ Church Academy/*Jacksonville*/Duval	04983052	904/268-8667	35
Christ Church Sch/*Ft Lauderdale*/Broward	01772218	954/771-7700	19
Christ Classical Academy/*Tallahassee*/Leon	10030308	850/656-2373	66
Christ Fellowship Academy/*Palmetto Bay*/ Miami-Dade	01865190	305/238-1833	86
Christ Sch/*Orlando*/Orange	04928571	407/849-1665	101
Christ the King Catholic Sch/*Jacksonville*/ Duval	00202583	904/724-2954	34
Christ the King Luthrn CH Sch/*Palm Coast*/ Flagler	11165217	386/447-7979	39
Christ the King Sch/*Tampa*/Hillsborough	00200793	813/876-8770	53
Christ-Mar Sch/*Hialeah*/Miami-Dade	02195235	305/823-6515	86
Christa McAuliffe Charter ES/*Cape Coral*/ Lee	10024050	239/283-4511	61
Christa McAuliffe Elem Sch/*Palm Bay*/ Brevard	02896996	321/768-0465	7
Christa McAuliffe Middle Sch/*Boynton Beach*/ Palm Beach	02948604	561/374-6600	109
Christian Crossings Academy/*Odessa*/ Hillsborough	12303149	813/792-9070	53
Christian Heritage Academy/*Jacksonville*/ Duval	01773975	904/733-4722	35
Christian Learning Academy/*Apopka*/Orange	12033174	407/410-0049	101
Christian Life Academy/*Gainesville*/Alachua	04983234	352/495-3040	3
Christina M Eve Elem Sch/*Miami*/Miami-Dade	04876459	305/383-9392	82
Christopher Columbus High Sch/*Miami*/ Miami-Dade	00187971	305/223-5650	85
Chumuckla Elem Sch/*Jay*/Santa Rosa	00203044	850/995-3690	128
Cimino Elem Sch/*Valrico*/Hillsborough	05097369	813/740-4450	51
Circle Christian Sch/*Winter Park*/Orange	11548592	407/740-8877	101
Citrus Co Renaissance Center/*Lecanto*/ Citrus	04752085	352/527-4567	22
CITRUS CO SCH DIST/**INVERNESS**/ **CITRUS**	00184527	352/726-1931	22
Citrus Cove Elem Sch/*Boynton Beach*/ Palm Beach	03253531	561/292-7000	109
Citrus Elem Sch/*Ocoee*/Orange	04919788	407/445-5475	99
Citrus Elem Sch/*Vero Beach*/Indian River	00193358	772/978-8350	56
Citrus Grove Elem Sch/*Deland*/Volusia	11715551	386/626-0053	140
Citrus Grove Elem Sch/*Miami*/Miami-Dade	00186446	305/642-4141	75
Citrus Grove Elem Sch/*Palm City*/Martin	11134294	772/223-2513	73
Citrus Grove Middle Sch/*Miami*/Miami-Dade	00186458	305/642-5055	75
Citrus High Sch/*Inverness*/Citrus	00184541	352/726-2241	22
Citrus Park Christian Sch/*Tampa*/ Hillsborough	03063908	813/920-3960	53
Citrus Park Elem Sch/*Tampa*/Hillsborough	00192029	813/558-5356	49
Citrus Ridge A Civic Academy/*Davenport*/ Polk	12168042	863/259-4001	122
Citrus Springs Elem Sch/*Dunnellon*/Citrus	02890526	352/344-4079	22
Citrus Springs Middle Sch/*Citrus Spgs*/ Citrus	04291407	352/344-2244	22
City of Hialeah Educ Academy/*Hialeah*/ Miami-Dade	11128233	305/362-4006	78
City of Life Christian Academy/*Kissimmee*/ Osceola	04331356	407/847-5184	104
City of Palms Charter HS/*Fort Myers*/Lee	10024048	239/561-6611	61
City of Pembroke Pines MS-West/*Pembroke Pnes*/ Broward	04875481	954/443-4847	16
Citygate University Sch/*Miami*/Miami-Dade	12230645	786/802-3240	86
Clair Mel Elem Sch/*Tampa*/Hillsborough	00192031	813/744-8080	47
Clarence Boswell Elem Sch/*Auburndale*/Polk	02126179	863/499-2990	125
Clark Advanced Learning Ctr/*Stuart*/Martin	05380790	772/419-5750	73
Clarke School-Jacksonvile/*Jacksonville*/ Duval	11982455	904/880-9001	35
Classical Academy of Sarasota/*Sarasota*/ Sarasota	12109113	941/925-2153	131
Classical Christian Academy/*N Ft Myers*/Lee	11397410	239/543-1532	63
Classical Christian Sch Arts/*Pinellas Park*/ Pinellas	11228766	727/547-6820	120
Classical Preparatory Sch/*Spring Hill*/ Pasco	12045127	813/803-7903	112
Claude Pepper Elem Sch/*Miami*/Miami-Dade	03395244	305/386-5244	82
Clay Charter Academy/*Middleburg*/Clay	12103729	904/406-1607	23
Clay Co Center Adult & Cmty Ed/*Orange Park*/ Clay	01810743	904/336-4450	23
CLAY CO SCH DIST/**GREEN CV SPGS**/ **CLAY**	00184656	904/336-6500	23
Clay High Sch/*Green Cv Spgs*/Clay	00184670	904/336-7175	23
Clay Hill Elem Sch/*Jacksonville*/Clay	02228064	904/336-0775	23

School/City/County DISTRICT/CITY/COUNTY	PID	TELEPHONE NUMBER	PAGE
Clay Springs Elem Sch/*Apopka*/Orange	03400045	407/884-2275	97
Clay Virtual Academy/*Orange Park*/Clay	11635523	904/336-9875	23
Claywell Elem Sch/*Tampa*/Hillsborough	02180682	813/975-7300	50
Clearview Adult Education Ctr/*St Petersburg*/Pinellas	04918631	727/221-5395	116
Clearwater Academy Int'l/*Clearwater*/Pinellas	03419462	727/446-1722	120
Clearwater Adult Ed Center/*Clearwater*/Pinellas	11823005	727/469-5817	116
Clearwater Ctrl Cath High Sch/*Clearwater*/Pinellas	00200808	727/531-1449	120
Clearwater Fundamental Mid Sch/*Clearwater*/Pinellas	00199821	727/298-1609	116
Clearwater High Sch/*Clearwater*/Pinellas	00199637	727/298-1620	117
Clearwater Intermediate Sch/*Clearwater*/Pinellas	00199613	727/298-1616	117
Clermont Elem Sch/*Clermont*/Lake	00193736	352/394-2706	58
Clermont Middle Sch/*Clermont*/Lake	05100966	352/243-2460	58
Cleveland Court Elem Sch/*Lakeland*/Polk	00201230	863/499-2929	125
Cleveland Elem Sch/*Tampa*/Hillsborough	00192043	813/276-5583	47
Clever Oaks Montesorri Sch/*Plantation*/Broward	02148000	954/473-4400	19
Clewiston Adult Sch/*Clewiston*/Hendry	01485568	863/983-1511	43
Clewiston Christian Sch/*Clewiston*/Hendry	11824920	863/983-5388	43
Clewiston High Sch/*Clewiston*/Hendry	00191568	863/983-1520	43
Clewiston Middle Sch/*Clewiston*/Hendry	00191570	863/983-1530	43
Clewiston Youth Dev Academy/*Clewiston*/Hendry	04448662	863/902-4216	43
Clifford Meigs Middle Sch/*Shalimar*/Okaloosa	00196362	850/833-4301	92
Cmty Charter Sch of Excellence/*Tampa*/Hillsborough	11076795	813/971-5500	46
Coast Charter Sch/*Saint Marks*/Wakulla	04876928	850/925-6344	143
Coastal Middle Sr High Sch/*Lake Park*/Palm Beach	02086488	561/842-6349	111
Cocoa Beach Jr Sr High Sch/*Cocoa Beach*/Brevard	00182593	321/783-1776	8
Cocoa Jr Sr High Sch/*Cocoa*/Brevard	00182177	321/632-5300	8
Coconut Creek Elem Sch/*Coconut Creek*/Broward	00182799	754/322-5800	11
Coconut Creek High Sch/*Coconut Creek*/Broward	00182804	754/322-0350	11
Coconut Grove Elem Sch/*Miami*/Miami-Dade	00186460	305/445-7876	75
Coconut Palm Elem Sch/*Miramar*/Broward	04946999	754/323-5050	11
Coconut Palm K-8 Academy/*Homestead*/Miami-Dade	11128350	305/257-0500	82
Colbert Museum Magnet/*Hollywood*/Broward	00183951	754/323-5100	11
Coleman Middle Sch/*Tampa*/Hillsborough	00192055	813/872-5335	49
Collaboratory Prep Academy/*Tampa*/Hillsborough	12231716	813/586-3172	46
Colleen Bevis Elem Sch/*Lithia*/Hillsborough	04920945	813/740-4000	51
College Academy at BC/*Davie*/Broward	05101506	754/321-6900	11
College Park Elem Sch/*Ocala*/Marion	00195394	352/291-4040	70
College Park Middle Sch/*Orlando*/Orange	00197342	407/245-1800	97
Collier Charter Academy/*Naples*/Collier	12262650	239/330-3810	25
COLLIER CO PUBLIC SCH DIST/ **NAPLES/COLLIER**	00184814	239/377-0001	25
Collier Virtual Sch/*Naples*/Collier	11717339	239/377-1050	25
Collins Elem Sch/*Dania Beach*/Broward	00183509	754/323-5150	11
Collins Elem Sch/*Riverview*/Hillsborough	10003094	813/672-5400	52
Colonial Christian Sch/*Homestead*/Miami-Dade	04764557	305/246-8608	86
Colonial Drive Elem Sch/*Miami*/Miami-Dade	00187311	305/238-2392	82
Colonial Elem Sch/*Fort Myers*/Lee	03396169	239/939-2242	61
Colonial High 9th Grade Ctr/*Orlando*/Orange	03008489	407/249-6369	97
Colonial High Sch/*Orlando*/Orange	00196702	407/482-6300	97
Colson Elem Sch/*Seffner*/Hillsborough	04017287	813/744-8031	51
Columbia City Elem Sch/*Lake City*/Columbia	04285020	386/758-4850	27
Columbia Co Adult Ed Sch/*Lake City*/Columbia	01810779	386/755-8190	27
COLUMBIA CO SCH DIST/LAKE CITY/ **COLUMBIA**	00185040	386/755-8000	27
Columbia Elem Sch/*Orlando*/Orange	00196714	407/568-2921	96
Columbia Elem Sch/*Palm Bay*/Brevard	02897005	321/676-1319	7
Columbia High Sch/*Lake City*/Columbia	00185052	386/755-8080	27
Combee Acad of Design & Eng/*Lakeland*/Polk	00201242	863/499-2960	124
Community Christian Academy/*Stuart*/Martin	02825428	772/288-7227	73
Community Christian Sch/*Bradenton*/Manatee	01436907	941/756-8748	70
Community Christian Sch/*Melbourne*/Brevard	02977538	321/259-1590	9
Community Christian Sch/*Pt Charlotte*/Charlotte	02825478	941/625-8977	21
Community Christian Sch/*Tallahassee*/Leon	02086323	850/893-6628	66
Community Haven Center/*Sarasota*/Sarasota	01776161	941/355-8808	131
Community Leadership Academy/*Tallahassee*/Leon	12209189	850/597-9124	66
Community School-Naples/*Naples*/Collier	02204549	239/597-7575	27
Compass Charter Middle Sch/*Bartow*/Polk	05101570	863/519-8701	123
Comstock Elem Sch/*Miami*/Miami-Dade	00186472	305/635-7341	75
Conchita Espinoza Academy/*Miami*/Miami-Dade	01865097	305/227-1149	86
Congregational Holiness Sch/*Green Cv Spgs*/Clay	04982785	904/529-1798	24
Congress Middle Sch/*Boynton Beach*/Palm Beach	00198786	561/374-5600	109
Conley Elem Sch/*Tallahassee*/Leon	11077141	850/414-5610	64
Connections Education Center/*West Palm Bch*/Palm Beach	12172330	561/328-6044	105
Connerton Elem Sch/*Land O Lakes*/Pasco	00199340	813/346-1800	113
Conniston Cmty Middle Sch/*West Palm Bch*/Palm Beach	00198114	561/802-5400	106
Conservative Christian Academy/*Jacksonville*/Duval	11237119	904/268-7778	35
Conway Elem Sch/*Orlando*/Orange	00196726	407/249-6310	98
Conway Middle Sch/*Orlando*/Orange	00196738	407/249-6420	98
Cooper City Elem Sch/*Cooper City*/Broward	00183511	754/323-5200	11
Cooper City High Sch/*Cooper City*/Broward	00183523	754/323-0200	11
Cope Center North/*Miami*/Miami-Dade	00185947	305/836-3300	74
Coppergate Elem Sch/*Middleburg*/Clay	10904034	904/336-0675	23
Coquina Elem Sch/*Titusville*/Brevard	00182000	321/264-3060	7
Coral Cove Elem Sch/*Miramar*/Broward	05350032	754/323-7950	11
Coral Gables Preparatory Acad/*Coral Gables*/Miami-Dade	00186484	305/448-1731	75
Coral Gables Sr High Sch/*Coral Gables*/Miami-Dade	00186496	305/443-4871	75
Coral Glades High Sch/*Coral Springs*/Broward	05347035	754/322-1250	11
Coral Park Christian Academy/*Miami*/Miami-Dade	11814949	305/559-9409	86
Coral Park Elem Sch/*Coral Springs*/Broward	03007552	754/322-5850	11
Coral Park Elem Sch/*Miami*/Miami-Dade	00186862	305/221-5632	75
Coral Reef Elem Sch/*Lake Worth*/Palm Beach	04875508	561/804-3700	109
Coral Reef Elem Sch/*Palmetto Bay*/Miami-Dade	00187323	305/235-1464	82
Coral Reef Montesorri Acad CS/*Miami*/Miami-Dade	04811590	305/255-0064	82
Coral Reef Senior High Sch/*Miami*/Miami-Dade	04755001	305/232-2044	82
Coral Shores High Sch/*Tavernier*/Monroe	00195851	305/853-3222	89
Coral Springs Charter Sch/*Coral Springs*/Broward	04875479	954/340-4100	16
Coral Springs Elem Sch/*Coral Springs*/Broward	00182816	754/322-5900	11
Coral Springs High Sch/*Coral Springs*/Broward	01413307	754/322-0500	11
Coral Springs Middle Sch/*Coral Springs*/Broward	01413319	754/322-3000	11
Coral Sunset Elem Sch/*Boca Raton*/Palm Beach	02856142	561/477-2100	109
Coral Terrace Elem Sch/*Miami*/Miami-Dade	00186874	305/262-8300	75
Coral Way K-8 Center/*Miami*/Miami-Dade	00186501	305/854-0515	75
Coram Deo Academy/*Jupiter*/Palm Beach	11746691	561/401-0754	111
Corbett Preparatory Sch/*Tampa*/Hillsborough	00193231	813/961-3087	53
Cordova Park Elem Sch/*Pensacola*/Escambia	00190502	850/595-6830	37
Corinth Christian Academy/*Jasper*/Hamilton	05270274	386/938-2270	42
Cork Elem Sch/*Plant City*/Hillsborough	00192067	813/757-9353	52
Corkscrew Baptist Sch/*Naples*/Collier	03112121	239/348-8855	27
Corkscrew Elem Sch/*Naples*/Collier	04882472	239/377-6500	25
Corkscrew Middle Sch/*Naples*/Collier	04913954	239/377-3400	25
Corner Lake Middle Sch/*Orlando*/Orange	04806296	407/568-0510	96
Cornerstone Academy/*Gainesville*/Alachua	05000483	352/378-9337	3
Cornerstone Charter Acad/*Belle Isle*/Orange	11557799	407/608-7171	94
Cornerstone Christian Academy/*Avon Park*/Highlands	11930608	863/453-0894	45
Cornerstone Christian Sch/*Jacksonville*/Duval	10014691	904/730-5500	35
Cornerstone Church Academy/*Defuniak Spgs*/Walton	04336540	850/892-9358	144
Cornerstone Learning Community/*Tallahassee*/Leon	11850113	850/386-5550	66
Cornerstone Sch/*Ocala*/Marion	02236255	352/351-8840	72
Coronado Beach Elem Sch/*New Smyrna*/Volusia	00204347	386/424-2525	140
Coronado High Sch/*Fort Myers*/Lee	11422039	239/337-9140	61
Corpus Christi Catholic Sch/*Tampa*/Hillsborough	00200810	813/988-1722	53
Corr Elem Sch/*Gibsonton*/Hillsborough	05351153	813/672-5345	52

School/City/County DISTRICT/CITY/COUNTY	PID	TELEPHONE NUMBER	PAGE
Cotee River Elem Sch/New Prt Rchy/Pasco	04289026	727/774-3000	113
Cottondale Elem Sch/Cottondale/Jackson	00193516	850/482-9820	57
Cottondale High Sch/Cottondale/Jackson	01600550	850/482-9821	57
Country Club Middle Sch/Hialeah/Miami-Dade	10024610	305/820-8800	79
Country Day Sch/Largo/Pinellas	02149028	727/596-1902	120
Country Hills Elem Sch/Coral Springs/ Broward	03252214	754/322-5950	11
Country Isles Elem Sch/Weston/Broward	03007485	754/323-5250	11
Country Oaks Elem Sch/Labelle/Hendry	02823860	863/674-4140	43
Countryside Christian Academy/Clearwater/ Pinellas	10017899	727/799-1618	120
Countryside Christian Sch/Gainesville/ Alachua	01864902	352/332-9731	3
Countryside High Sch/Clearwater/Pinellas	02042262	727/725-7956	116
Countryside Montessori Academy/Land O Lakes/ Pasco	05194838	813/996-0991	112
Covenant Academy/Pinellas Park/Pinellas	12315386	727/542-6294	121
Covenant Christian Sch/Palm Bay/Brevard	04322977	321/727-2661	9
Covenant Christian Sch/Panama City/Bay	02193251	850/769-7448	5
Cracker Trail Elem Sch/Sebring/Highlands	03400540	863/471-5777	45
Cranberry Elem Sch/North Port/Sarasota	05269885	941/480-3400	129
Cranium Clubhouse Sch/Winter Garden/Orange	11826277	407/347-5021	101
Crawfordville Elem Sch/Crawfordville/ Wakulla	00204866	850/926-3641	143
Creative Arts Acad of St Lucie/Fort Pierce/ St Lucie	04806404	772/467-4278	136
Creative Inspiration Journey/Saint Cloud/ Osceola	12362183	877/244-8562	103
Creative Learning Academy/Pensacola/ Escambia	01774163	850/432-1768	38
Creative Learning Sch/Cocoa/Brevard	10000107	321/633-5511	9
Creekside Charter Academy/Riverview/ Hillsborough	12308084	813/419-5340	46
Creekside Christian Sch/Otter Creek/Levy	05082182	352/486-2112	67
Creekside High Sch/Saint Johns/St Johns	11130420	904/547-7300	134
Creekside Middle Sch/Port Orange/Volusia	04946169	386/322-6155	140
Crenshaw School Florida/Gotha/Orange	11815826	407/757-2241	101
Crescent City High Sch/Crescent City/ Putnam	00202222	386/698-1629	127
Crest Sch/Lecanto/Citrus	00184632	352/527-0303	22
Cresthaven Elem Sch/Pompano Beach/Broward	00182828	754/322-6000	11
Crestview Elem Sch/Miami Gardens/ Miami-Dade	00185569	305/624-1495	79
Crestview High Sch/Crestview/Okaloosa	00196259	850/689-7177	92
Crestwood Elem Sch/Tampa/Hillsborough	00192079	813/872-5374	49
Crestwood Middle Sch/West Palm Bch/ Palm Beach	02176057	561/753-5000	106
Crews Lake Middle Sch/Spring Hill/Pasco	11130987	727/246-1600	115
Cristo Rey Tampa High Sch/Tampa/ Hillsborough	12179912	813/621-8300	54
Croissant Park Elem Sch/Ft Lauderdale/ Broward	00183535	754/323-5300	11
Crooms Academy of Info Tech/Sanford/ Seminole	00203616	407/320-5750	132
Cross Bayou Elem Sch/Pinellas Park/ Pinellas	00199649	727/547-7834	117
Cross Creek Sch/Pompano Beach/Broward	03006742	754/321-6450	11
Crosspointe Academy/Fort Myers/Lee	11928954	239/225-1502	63
Crosspointe Elem Sch/Boynton Beach/ Palm Beach	05102316	561/292-4100	109
Crossroad Academy/Quincy/Gadsden	04806557	850/875-9626	40
Crossroads Academy/Belle Glade/Palm Beach	11103659	561/993-8400	105
Crossroads Lakeland Sch/Lakeland/Polk	11221548	863/859-0848	126
Croton Elem Sch/Melbourne/Brevard	00182309	321/259-3818	7
Crown Point Elem Sch/Jacksonville/Duval	02130089	904/260-5808	30
Crystal Lake Cmty Middle Sch/Pompano Beach/ Broward	00182830	754/322-3100	11
Crystal Lake Elem Sch/Lake Mary/Seminole	10028185	407/871-8150	132
Crystal Lake Elem Sch/Lakeland/Polk	00201324	863/499-2966	124
Crystal Lake Elem Sch/Stuart/Martin	03318064	772/219-1525	73
Crystal Lake Middle Sch/Lakeland/Polk	00201266	863/499-2970	124
Crystal Lakes Elem Sch/Boynton Beach/ Palm Beach	03401271	561/292-6600	109
Crystal River High Sch/Crystal River/ Citrus	00184553	352/795-4641	22
Crystal River Middle Sch/Crystal River/ Citrus	00184565	352/795-2116	22
Crystal River Primary Sch/Crystal River/ Citrus	00184577	352/795-2211	22
Crystal Springs Elem Sch/Jacksonville/ Duval	03014531	904/693-7645	30

School/City/County DISTRICT/CITY/COUNTY	PID	TELEPHONE NUMBER	PAGE
CS of Excellence-Davie/Pembroke Pnes/ Broward	11076915	954/433-8838	16
CS of Excellence-Ft Lauderdale/Ft Lauderdale/ Broward	04756574	954/522-2997	16
Ctr for Int'l Educ-Cambridge/Homestead/ Miami-Dade	12038667	305/248-7911	82
Cunningham Creek Elem Sch/Saint Johns/ St Johns	04369731	904/547-7860	134
Curlew Creek Elem Sch/Palm Harbor/Pinellas	02202072	727/724-1423	117
Curtis Fundamental Elem Sch/Dunedin/ Pinellas	00199651	727/738-6483	117
Cutler Bay Middle Sch/Miami/Miami-Dade	00187347	305/235-4761	82
Cutler Bay Senior High Sch/Cutler Bay/ Miami-Dade	01527063	305/235-1581	82
Cutler Ridge Christian Academy/Miami/ Miami-Dade	00187634	305/251-1534	86
Cutler Ridge Elem Sch/Miami/Miami-Dade	00187335	305/235-4611	82
Cypress Bay High Sch/Weston/Broward	05099408	754/323-0350	11
Cypress Creek Academy/Lecanto/Citrus	04752073	352/527-3091	22
Cypress Creek Elem Sch/Port Orange/Volusia	10912500	386/322-6101	140
Cypress Creek Elem Sch/Ruskin/Hillsborough	03395725	813/671-5167	52
Cypress Creek High Sch/Orlando/Orange	04020430	407/852-3400	97
Cypress Creek Middle High Sch/Wesley Chapel/ Pasco	12235011	813/346-4400	114
Cypress Elem Sch/Kissimmee/Osceola	04013774	407/344-5000	103
Cypress Elem Sch/New Prt Rchy/Pasco	00199182	727/774-4500	113
Cypress Elem Sch/Pompano Beach/Broward	00182842	754/322-6050	11
Cypress Junction Mont Sch/Winter Haven/ Polk	12168066	863/259-1490	123
Cypress K-8 Center/Miami/Miami-Dade	00186886	305/271-1611	82
Cypress Lake HS for the Arts/Fort Myers/ Lee	00194168	239/481-2233	61
Cypress Lake Middle Sch/Fort Myers/Lee	00194170	239/481-1533	61
Cypress Palm Middle Sch/Naples/Collier	10902127	239/377-5200	25
Cypress Ridge Elem Sch/Clermont/Lake	04452778	352/394-6633	58
Cypress Run Education Center/Pompano Beach/ Broward	00182919	754/321-6500	11
Cypress Springs Elem Sch/Orlando/Orange	04366208	407/249-6950	96
Cypress Trails Elem Sch/West Palm Bch/ Palm Beach	03253581	561/904-9000	106
Cypress Woods Elem Sch/Palm Harbor/ Pinellas	02854833	727/538-7325	117

D

School/City/County DISTRICT/CITY/COUNTY	PID	TELEPHONE NUMBER	PAGE
D A Dorsey Technical College/Miami/ Miami-Dade	01340047	305/693-2490	75
D S Parrott Middle Sch/Brooksville/ Hernando	00191623	352/797-7075	44
D W Waters Career Center/Tampa/ Hillsborough	04920919	813/233-2655	52
Dade Christian Sch/Hialeah/Miami-Dade	00187646	305/822-7690	86
Dale Cassens Ed Complex/Fort Pierce/ St Lucie	03253036	772/468-5190	136
Dale R Fair Babson Park ES/Babson Park/ Polk	00201515	863/678-4664	123
Dan McCarty Middle Sch/Fort Pierce/ St Lucie	00202868	772/468-5700	136
Dania Elem Sch/Dania Beach/Broward	00183547	754/323-5510	11
Daniel Jenkins Academy/Haines City/Polk	04922175	863/421-3267	122
Dante B Fascell Elem Sch/Miami/Miami-Dade	04454415	305/380-1901	82
Danul-Uloom Islamic Inst/Pembroke Pnes/ Broward	11237195	954/963-9514	19
Darnell-Cookman Middle Sch/Jacksonville/ Duval	03401702	904/630-6805	32
Daughter of Zion Jr Academy/Delray Beach/ Palm Beach	04930495	561/243-0715	111
Daughtrey Prep Sch Arts & Sci/Bradenton/ Manatee	00195083	941/751-7023	68
Dave Thomas Educ Ctr-East/Pompano Beach/ Broward	11922687	754/321-6750	11
Dave Thomas Educ Ctr-W/Coconut Creek/ Broward	01827021	754/321-6800	11
Davenport School of the Arts/Davenport/ Polk	00201541	863/420-2557	122
David C Hinson Sr Middle Sch/Daytona Beach/ Volusia	10006917	386/258-4682	140
David Fairchild Elem Sch/Miami/Miami-Dade	00186898	305/665-5483	75
David Lawrence Jr K-8 Center/North Miami/ Miami-Dade	10021448	305/354-2600	79
David Posnack Jewish Day Sch/Davie/Broward	01559614	954/583-6100	19
Davidsen Middle Sch/Tampa/Hillsborough	04920921	813/558-5300	49
Davidson Middle Sch/Crestview/Okaloosa	04750570	850/683-7500	92

School/City/County DISTRICT/CITY/COUNTY	PID	TELEPHONE NUMBER	PAGE
Davie Elem Sch/*Davie*/Broward	01827033	754/323-5400	11
Dawson Elem Sch/*Riverview*/Hillsborough	12231601	813/442-7396	52
Dayspring Academy Elem Sch/*Port Richey*/ Pasco	04915990	727/862-8600	113
Dayspring Academy Sec Sch/*Port Richey*/ Pasco	11555973	727/847-9003	113
Dayspring Christian Academy/*Marianna*/ Jackson	04762690	850/526-4919	57
Daytona Beach Christian Sch/*Daytona Beach*/ Volusia	01776379	386/760-4808	142
Deane Bozeman Sch/*Panama City*/Bay	04918136	850/767-1300	4
Debary Elem Sch/*Debary*/Volusia	04453916	386/575-4230	140
Deep Creek Elem Sch/*Punta Gorda*/Charlotte	03329532	941/255-7535	21
Deer Park Elem Sch/*New Prt Rchy*/Pasco	03250668	727/774-8900	113
Deer Park Elem Sch/*Tampa*/Hillsborough	10019744	813/854-6031	49
Deer Point Elem Sch/*Panama City*/Bay	11548530	850/767-5462	4
Deerfield Beach Elem Sch/*Deerfield Bch*/ Broward	00182854	754/322-6100	11
Deerfield Beach High Sch/*Deerfield Bch*/ Broward	00182866	754/322-0650	11
Deerfield Beach Middle Sch/*Deerfield Bch*/ Broward	00182878	754/322-3300	11
Deerfield Park Elem Sch/*Deerfield Bch*/ Broward	00182880	754/322-6150	12
Deerlake Middle Sch/*Tallahassee*/Leon	03327247	850/922-6545	64
Deerwood Elem Sch/*Kissimmee*/Osceola	03393131	407/870-2400	103
Deerwood Elem Sch/*Orlando*/Orange	02226224	407/249-6320	96
Del Prado Elem Sch/*Boca Raton*/Palm Beach	03253567	561/544-1800	109
Deland High Sch/*Deland*/Volusia	00204359	386/822-6909	140
Deland Middle Sch/*Deland*/Volusia	00204361	386/822-5678	140
DeLaura Middle Sch/*Satellite Bch*/Brevard	00182311	321/773-7581	8
Deliverance Tabernacle Center/*Pensacola*/ Escambia	11929984	850/479-1500	38
Delphi Academy/*Clearwater*/Pinellas	03419709	727/447-6385	121
Delray Full Service Center/*Delray Beach*/ Palm Beach	11717016	561/266-1200	105
Deltona Adventist Sch/*Deltona*/Volusia	03406817	386/532-9333	142
Deltona Christian Sch/*Deltona*/Volusia	01776381	386/574-1971	142
Deltona Elem Sch/*Spring Hill*/Hernando	03319680	352/797-7040	44
Deltona High Sch/*Deltona*/Volusia	03056199	386/575-4153	140
Deltona Lakes Elem Sch/*Deltona*/Volusia	02179061	386/575-4115	140
Deltona Middle Sch/*Deltona*/Volusia	00204373	386/575-4150	140
Denham Oaks Elem Sch/*Lutz*/Pasco	04366595	813/794-1600	113
Denison Middle Sch/*Winter Haven*/Polk	00201761	863/291-5353	124
Denn John Middle Sch/*Kissimmee*/Osceola	00197988	407/935-3560	103
DePaul Sch/*Clearwater*/Pinellas	04335974	727/796-7679	121
DePaul School of NE Florida/*Jacksonville*/ Duval	03138486	904/223-3391	35
Deseret Academy/*Satsuma*/Putnam	04982967	386/649-4978	127
Design & Architecture Sr HS/*Miami*/ Miami-Dade	03338428	305/573-7135	75
DeSoto Co High Sch/*Arcadia*/De Soto	01810951	863/494-3434	28
DESOTO CO SCH DIST/**ARCADIA**/ **DE SOTO**	00188664	863/494-4222	28
DeSoto Elem Sch/*Tampa*/Hillsborough	00192108	813/276-5779	49
DeSoto Middle Sch/*Arcadia*/De Soto	00188688	863/494-4133	28
DeSoto Trail Elem Sch/*Tallahassee*/Leon	03251325	850/488-4511	64
Destin Elem Sch/*Destin*/Okaloosa	00196221	850/833-4360	92
Destin Middle Sch/*Destin*/Okaloosa	04750582	850/833-7655	92
Devereux Sch/*Viera*/Brevard	03268718	321/242-9100	9
Devon Aire K-8 Center/*Miami*/Miami-Dade	02110247	305/274-7100	82
Diamond View Elem Sch/*Greenacres*/ Palm Beach	05282057	561/304-4200	109
Dickenson Elem Sch/*Tampa*/Hillsborough	00192122	813/873-4732	49
Dillard Elem Sch/*Ft Lauderdale*/Broward	00183183	754/322-6200	12
Dillard High Sch/*Ft Lauderdale*/Broward	00183195	754/322-0800	12
Dillard Street Elem Sch/*Winter Garden*/ Orange	00196764	407/877-5000	99
Dimensions 3 Academy/*Jacksonville*/Duval	12110875	904/389-6166	35
Dinsmore Elem Sch/*Jacksonville*/Duval	00188987	904/924-3126	30
DIOCESE OF ORLANDO ED OFFICE/ **ORLANDO**/**ORANGE**	00197639	407/246-4900	100
DIOCESE OF PALM BEACH ED OFF/ **PALM BCH GDNS**/**PALM BEACH**	02231700	561/775-9547	110
DIOCESE OF VENICE ED OFFICE/ **VENICE**/**SARASOTA**	02231695	941/484-9543	131
DIOCESE PENSACOLA-TALLAHASSEE/ **PENSACOLA**/**ESCAMBIA**	01483467	850/435-3500	38
DIOCESE ST AUGUSTINE ED OFFICE/ **JACKSONVILLE**/**DUVAL**	00202533	904/262-3200	34
DIOCESE ST PETERSBURG ED OFF/ **ST PETERSBURG**/**PINELLAS**	00200729	727/344-1611	120
Diplomat Elem Sch/*Cape Coral*/Lee	03396949	239/458-0033	61
Diplomat Middle Sch/*Cape Coral*/Lee	04922280	239/574-5257	61
Discovery Acad of Lake Alfred/*Lake Alfred*/ Polk	04452730	863/295-5955	123
Discovery Academy of Science/*Dunedin*/ Pinellas	11925574	727/330-2424	116
Discovery Day Academy-Bonita/*Bonita Spgs*/ Lee	11773814	239/201-4678	63
Discovery Elem Sch/*Deltona*/Volusia	03056187	386/575-4133	140
Discovery Elem Sch/*Palm Bay*/Brevard	03055262	321/951-4920	7
Discovery Elem Sch/*Sunrise*/Broward	11449867	754/322-9100	12
Discovery High Sch/*Lake Alfred*/Polk	12168054	863/268-7178	123
Discovery Intermediate Sch/*Kissimmee*/ Osceola	04875431	407/343-7300	103
Discovery Key Elem Sch/*Lake Worth*/ Palm Beach	05102380	561/491-8200	106
Discovery Middle Sch/*Orlando*/Orange	03456032	407/384-1555	95
Discovery Oaks Elem Sch/*Orange Park*/Clay	12311768	904/336-4275	23
Disston Academy for P & E/*Gulfport*/ Pinellas	03337072	727/893-1115	117
Divine Mercy Catholic Sch/*Merritt Is*/ Brevard	00197691	321/452-0263	9
Divine Savior Academy/*Doral*/Miami-Dade	11209057	305/597-4545	86
Dixie Co High Sch/*Cross City*/Dixie	00188743	352/541-6252	29
DIXIE CO SCH DIST/**CROSS CITY**/ **DIXIE**	00188731	352/541-6250	28
Dixie Hollins Adult Ed Ctr/*St Petersburg*/ Pinellas	11822647	727/547-7872	116
Dixie Hollins High Sch/*St Petersburg*/ Pinellas	00199675	727/547-7876	118
Dixieland Elem Sch/*Lakeland*/Polk	00201278	863/499-2930	125
Doby Elem Sch/*Apollo Beach*/Hillsborough	10019756	813/672-5388	52
Doctors CS of Miami Shores/*Miami Shores*/ Miami-Dade	04756861	305/754-2381	79
Doctors Inlet Elem Sch/*Middleburg*/Clay	00184682	904/336-0975	23
Dodgertown Elem Sch/*Vero Beach*/ Indian River	00193360	772/564-4100	56
Dolphin Bay Elem Sch/*Miramar*/Broward	10011845	754/323-8000	12
Dommerich Elem Sch/*Maitland*/Orange	00196776	407/623-1407	96
Don Brewer Elem Sch/*Jacksonville*/Duval	05101829	904/745-4990	30
Don Estridge High Tech Mid Sch/*Boca Raton*/ Palm Beach	05348510	561/989-7800	109
Don Giunta Middle Sch/*Riverview*/ Hillsborough	10003070	813/740-4888	52
Don Soffer Aventura High Sch/*Aventura*/ Miami-Dade	12362169	786/481-3032	74
Donald E Woods Opportunity Ctr/*Dundee*/Polk	04452728	863/421-3325	123
Donna J Beasley Technical Acad/*Lehigh Acres*/ Lee	11923588	239/491-6822	61
Donna Klein Jewish Academy/*Boca Raton*/ Palm Beach	02197740	561/852-3300	111
Doral Academy Charter Elem Sch/*Doral*/ Miami-Dade	04881260	305/597-9999	79
Doral Academy Charter High Sch/*Doral*/ Miami-Dade	04948040	305/597-9950	75
Doral Academy Charter Mid Sch/*Doral*/ Miami-Dade	05278484	305/591-0020	75
Doral Academy K-8-Technology/*Doral*/ Miami-Dade	11719557	305/591-0020	75
Doral Int'l Acad Math & Sci/*Miami*/ Miami-Dade	12262820	786/270-2088	79
Doral Perf Arts & Ent Academy/*Doral*/ Miami-Dade	10024684	305/591-0020	75
Doris A Sanders Learning Ctr/*Lakeland*/Polk	00201395	863/499-2980	123
Dorothy M Wallace Cope Center/*Miami*/ Miami-Dade	00187294	305/233-1044	74
Dorothy Thomas Sch/*Tampa*/Hillsborough	00192134	813/975-7355	50
Double Branch Elem Sch/*Wesley Chapel*/Pasco	10904096	813/346-0400	113
Double R Private Sch/*Chuluota*/Seminole	11237781	407/365-6856	133
Douglas Anderson Sch of Arts/*Jacksonville*/ Duval	00188999	904/346-5620	32
Douglas L Jamerson Elem Sch/*St Petersburg*/ Pinellas	05273915	727/552-1703	118
Dove Vocational Academy/*Graceville*/Jackson	11223637	850/263-7550	57
Dover Elem Sch/*Dover*/Hillsborough	00192146	813/757-9457	47
Dover Shores Elem Sch/*Orlando*/Orange	00196788	407/249-6330	99
Dowdell Middle Sch/*Tampa*/Hillsborough	00192158	813/744-8322	51
Downey Christian Sch/*Orlando*/Orange	01775179	407/275-0340	101
Downtown Doral Chart Upper Sch/*Miami*/ Miami-Dade	12323022	305/569-2223	75
Downtown Doral Charter ES/*Miami*/Miami-Dade	12114869	305/569-2223	75

School/City/County DISTRICT/CITY/COUNTY	PID	TELEPHONE NUMBER	PAGE
Downtown Miami Charter Sch/*Miami*/ Miami-Dade	05101374	305/579-2112	75
Dr C D Robinson Littleton ES/*N Ft Myers*/ Lee	04020789	239/995-3800	61
Dr Carlos J Finlay Elem Sch/*Miami*/ Miami-Dade	04920880	305/552-7122	82
Dr David L Anderson Middle Sch/*Stuart*/ Martin	10027545	772/221-7100	73
Dr DD Brown Academy of Hope/*Ocala*/Marion	12260389	352/351-5464	72
Dr Edward Whigham Elem Sch/*Miami*/ Miami-Dade	04494879	305/234-4840	82
Dr Frederica Wilson-Skyway ES/*Miami Gardens*/ Miami-Dade	00185882	305/621-5838	79
Dr Gilbert L Porter Elem Sch/*Miami*/ Miami-Dade	03346322	305/382-0792	82
Dr H W Mack-W Little River K-8/*Miami*/ Miami-Dade	00186329	305/691-6491	75
Dr Henry E Perrine Acad/*Palmetto Bay*/ Miami-Dade	00187488	305/235-2442	82
Dr John A McKinney Chrn Acad/*Miami*/ Miami-Dade	11078078	786/318-3818	86
Dr John Long Middle Sch/*Wesley Chapel*/ Pasco	10020030	813/346-6200	115
Dr Kiran C Patel High Sch/*Tampa*/ Hillsborough	12362028		46
Dr Lennard High Sch/*Ruskin*/Hillsborough	10020602	813/641-5611	52
Dr Manuel Barreiro Elem Sch/*Miami*/ Miami-Dade	11128300	305/229-4800	82
Dr Marvin Dunn Acad Cmty Educ/*Miami*/ Miami-Dade	04036257	305/756-2100	74
Dr Mary Giella Elem Sch/*Spring Hill*/Pasco	03328605	727/774-5800	113
Dr Mary McLeod Bethune ES/*Riviera Beach*/ Palm Beach	04920830	561/882-7600	108
Dr Michael M Krop Sr High Sch/*Miami*/ Miami-Dade	04809597	305/652-6808	79
Dr Mona Jain Middle Sch/*Bradenton*/Manatee	12365898	941/727-4747	68
Dr N E Roberts Elem Sch/*Lakeland*/Polk	05096133	863/815-6633	125
Dr N H Jones Elem Sch/*Ocala*/Marion	00195576	352/671-7260	70
Dr Phillips Elem Sch/*Orlando*/Orange	02042212	407/354-2600	99
Dr Phillips High Sch/*Orlando*/Orange	03008491	407/355-3200	97
Dr Robert B Ingram Elem Sch/*Opa Locka*/ Miami-Dade	00185791	305/688-4605	79
Dr Rolando Espinosa K-8 Center/*Doral*/ Miami-Dade	11128219	305/889-5757	75
Dr Toni Bilbao Prep Academy/*Doral*/ Miami-Dade	12231730	305/863-5750	75
Dr W J Creel Elem Sch/*Melbourne*/Brevard	00182555	321/259-3233	7
Dr William A Chapman Elem Sch/*Homestead*/ Miami-Dade	01557082	305/245-1055	82
Dream Lake Elem Sch/*Apopka*/Orange	00196790	407/884-2227	97
Dreams Are Free-Nevins Acad/*Sarasota*/ Sarasota	04954568	941/366-4010	131
Driftwood Elem Sch/*Hollywood*/Broward	00183963	754/323-5450	12
Driftwood Middle Sch/*Hollywood*/Broward	00183975	754/323-3100	12
Dunbar Cmty Sch/*Fort Myers*/Lee	03050731	239/334-2941	61
Dunbar High Sch/*Fort Myers*/Lee	04920115	239/461-5322	61
Dunbar Magnet Sch/*Tampa*/Hillsborough	00192160	813/276-5677	47
Duncan U Fletcher High Sch/*Neptune Beach*/ Duval	00189072	904/247-5905	32
Duncan U Fletcher Middle Sch/*Jax Bch*/Duval	00189060	904/247-5929	32
Dundee Elem Academy/*Dundee*/Polk	00201553	863/421-3316	124
Dundee Ridge Middle Academy/*Dundee*/Polk	00201539	863/419-3088	122
Dune Lakes Elem Sch/*Santa Rsa Bch*/Walton	12364741	850/622-5013	143
Dunedin Academy & Day Sch/*Dunedin*/Pinellas	01437327	727/580-2042	121
Dunedin Elem Sch/*Dunedin*/Pinellas	00199687	727/738-2990	117
Dunedin High Sch/*Dunedin*/Pinellas	00199704	727/469-4100	117
Dunedin Highland Middle Sch/*Dunedin*/ Pinellas	00199699	727/469-4112	117
Dunnellon Christian Academy/*Dunnellon*/ Marion	02235445	352/489-7716	72
Dunnellon Elem Sch/*Dunnellon*/Marion	00195411	352/465-6710	70
Dunnellon High Sch/*Dunnellon*/Marion	00195423	352/465-6745	70
Dunnellon Middle Sch/*Dunnellon*/Marion	00195435	352/465-6720	70
Durant High Sch/*Plant City*/Hillsborough	04369169	813/757-9075	52
Durbin Creek Elem Sch/*Saint Johns*/St Johns	05273367	904/547-3880	134
Duval Charter HS-Baymeadows/*Jacksonville*/ Duval	11718058	904/271-4127	29
Duval Charter Sch at Westside/*Jacksonville*/ Duval	11928916	904/421-0250	29
Duval Charter Sch Baymeadows/*Jacksonville*/ Duval	11736892	904/638-7947	29

School/City/County DISTRICT/CITY/COUNTY	PID	TELEPHONE NUMBER	PAGE
Duval Charter Sch Flagler Ctr/*Jacksonville*/ Duval	12103705	904/899-1010	29
Duval Charter Sch Mandarin/*Jacksonville*/ Duval	12100363	904/440-2901	29
Duval Charter Scholars Academy/*Jacksonville*/ Duval	11560655	904/724-1536	29
Duval Charter School Coastal/*Jacksonville*/ Duval	12262662	904/512-6757	29
Duval Charter School-Southside/*Jacksonville*/ Duval	12037663	904/423-5348	29
DUVAL CO PSD-ELEMENTARY REGION/ **JACKSONVILLE/DUVAL**	12036475	904/348-7866	30
DUVAL CO PSD-HS ALT REGION/ **JACKSONVILLE/DUVAL**	12036516	904/348-7866	32
DUVAL CO PSD-MIDDLE SCHOOLS/ **JACKSONVILLE/DUVAL**	12036504		32
DUVAL CO PSD-TURNAROUND SCHOOL/ **JACKSONVILLE/DUVAL**	12232679	904/924-3722	33
DUVAL CO PUBLIC SCH DIST/ **JACKSONVILLE/DUVAL**	00188779	904/390-2000	29
Duval Early Learning Academy/*Gainesville*/ Alachua	00181161	352/955-6703	2
Duval Virtual Instruction Acad/*Jacksonville*/ Duval	11690808	904/390-2037	32
DuVall Home/*Deland*/Volusia	01776355	386/734-2874	142
Dwight D Eisenhower Elem Sch/*Palm Bch Gdns*/ Palm Beach	00198504	561/366-6000	108

E

School/City/County DISTRICT/CITY/COUNTY	PID	TELEPHONE NUMBER	PAGE
E L Bing Elem Sch/*Tampa*/Hillsborough	03395713	813/744-8088	47
E W F Stirrup Elem Sch/*Miami*/Miami-Dade	01527001	305/226-7001	75
Eagle Creek Elem Sch/*Orlando*/Orange	12108535	407/930-5592	98
Eagle Lake Elem Sch/*Eagle Lake*/Polk	00201773	863/291-5357	124
Eagle Point Elem Sch/*Weston*/Broward	04290350	754/323-5500	12
Eagle Ridge Elem Sch/*Coral Springs*/Broward	04364535	754/322-6300	12
Eagle's Nest Elem Sch/*Orlando*/Orange	05352664	407/521-2795	99
Eagle's View Academy/*Jacksonville*/Duval	04983002	904/786-1411	35
Eagles Landing Middle Sch/*Boca Raton*/ Palm Beach	04810467	561/470-7000	109
Eagles Nest Charter Academy/*Lauderhill*/ Broward	10006539	954/635-2308	16
Eagles Nest Charter Middle Sch/*Coral Springs*/ Broward	10006541	954/341-5550	16
Earlington Hgts Elem Sch/*Miami*/Miami-Dade	00186549	305/635-7505	75
Early Beginnings Acad-Civic CT/*Miami*/ Miami-Dade	10024737	305/325-1080	75
Early Beginnings Acad-N Shore/*Miami*/ Miami-Dade	10024749	305/835-9006	75
Early Childhood Learning Ctr/*Fort Myers*/ Lee	11923590	239/332-2512	61
Early Years Academy/*Hialeah*/Miami-Dade	05015696	305/824-3500	86
East Area Adult & Cmty Sch/*Auburndale*/Polk	03251600	863/965-5475	123
East Bay Senior High Sch/*Gibsonton*/ Hillsborough	00192184	813/671-5134	52
East Elem Sch/*Punta Gorda*/Charlotte	00184436	941/575-5475	21
East Hill Christian Sch/*Pensacola*/Escambia	00190942	850/438-7746	38
East Lake Elem Sch/*Kissimmee*/Osceola	11554852	407/943-8450	103
East Lake Elem Sch/*Orlando*/Orange	10002014	407/658-6825	96
East Lake High Sch/*Tarpon Spgs*/Pinellas	03011840	727/942-5419	117
East Lake MS-Acad Engineering/*Tarpon Spgs*/ Pinellas	12032857	727/940-7624	117
East Lee Co High Sch/*Lehigh Acres*/Lee	10007129	239/369-2932	61
East Marion Elem Sch/*Silver Spgs*/Marion	00195447	352/671-4810	71
East Milton Elem Sch/*Milton*/Santa Rosa	00203056	850/983-5620	128
East Naples Middle Sch/*Naples*/Collier	00184840	239/377-3600	25
East Pasco Adventist Academy/*Dade City*/ Pasco	02847141	352/567-3646	115
East Ridge High Sch/*Clermont*/Lake	05100978	352/242-2080	59
East Ridge Middle Sch/*Clermont*/Lake	11128075	352/536-8020	59
East River High Sch/*Orlando*/Orange	11452826	407/956-8550	97
East Tampa Academy/*Tampa*/Hillsborough	12231687	813/816-2100	46
Eastbrook Elem Sch/*Winter Park*/Seminole	00203628	407/746-7950	132
Easter Seal Academy/*Miami*/Miami-Dade	01773080	305/325-0470	86
Easter Seals Charter Sch/*Daytona Beach*/ Volusia	10024074	386/255-4568	140
Eastland Christian Sch/*Orlando*/Orange	01404368	407/277-5858	101
Eastside Baptist Church Sch/*Gainesville*/ Alachua	01771850	352/373-5639	3
Eastside Elem Sch/*Brooksville*/Hernando	00191659	352/797-7045	44
Eastside Elem Sch/*Clewiston*/Hendry	03251222	863/983-1560	43
Eastside Elem Sch/*Haines City*/Polk	00201565	863/421-3254	124
Eastside Elem Sch/*Lake City*/Columbia	00185064	386/755-8220	27

School/City/County DISTRICT/CITY/COUNTY	PID	TELEPHONE NUMBER	PAGE
Eastside High Sch/*Gainesville*/Alachua	00181173	352/955-6704	2
Eau Gallie High Sch/*Melbourne*/Brevard	00182323	321/242-6400	8
Ebenezer Christian Academy/*Miami*/ Miami-Dade	12313390	305/573-2867	86
Eccleston Elem Sch/*Orlando*/Orange	00196817	407/296-6400	99
Econ River High Sch/*Orlando*/Orange	12168963	407/641-1062	94
Ed Venture Charter Sch/*Hypoluxo*/Palm Beach	04810455	561/582-1454	105
Eden Christian Sch/*Brooksville*/Hernando	01404203	352/796-1619	44
Eden Park Elem Sch/*Immokalee*/Collier	11079694	239/377-9200	25
Edgar L Padgett Elem Sch/*Lakeland*/Polk	00201280	863/853-6044	125
Edge Elem Sch/*Niceville*/Okaloosa	00196336	850/833-4138	92
Edgewater High Sch/*Orlando*/Orange	00196829	407/835-4900	97
Edgewater Public Sch/*Edgewater*/Volusia	00204402	386/424-2573	140
Edgewood Academy Sch/*Fort Myers*/Lee	00194209	239/334-6205	61
Edgewood Jr Sr High Sch/*Merritt Is*/Brevard	00182608	321/454-1030	8
Edison Academics/*Bradenton*/Manatee	11233797	941/792-7500	70
Edison Elem Sch/*Tampa*/Hillsborough	00192976	813/276-5579	47
Edison Park Arts Sch/*Fort Myers*/Lee	00194211	239/334-6232	61
Edison Park K-8 Center/*Miami*/Miami-Dade	00185985	305/758-3658	75
Edison Private Sch/*Hialeah*/Miami-Dade	01436141	305/824-0303	86
Edith I Starke Elem Sch/*Deland*/Volusia	00204397	386/943-9651	140
Educational Horizons Chtr Sch/*W Melbourne*/ Brevard	05181166	321/729-0786	6
Edward A Upthegrove Elem Sch/*Labelle*/ Hendry	05101946	863/612-0750	43
Edward H White High Sch/*Jacksonville*/Duval	00189010	904/693-7620	32
Edward W Bok Academy/*Lake Wales*/Polk	11130896	863/638-1010	123
Edward W Bok Academy North/*Lake Wales*/Polk	12322963	863/232-4665	123
Eglin Elem Sch/*Eglin Afb*/Okaloosa	00196192	850/833-4320	92
Egret Lake Elem Sch/*West Palm Bch*/ Palm Beach	04369298	561/616-7900	106
Egypt Lake Elem Sch/*Tampa*/Hillsborough	00192190	813/872-5225	49
Eighth Street Elem Sch/*Ocala*/Marion	00195459	352/671-7125	71
Einstein Montessori Academy/*Cocoa*/Brevard	05344423	321/631-9876	9
Einstein Sch/*Gainesville*/Alachua	04874633	352/335-4321	2
Eisenhower Elem Sch/*Clearwater*/Pinellas	00199716	727/725-7978	117
Eisenhower Middle Sch/*Gibsonton*/ Hillsborough	00192201	813/671-5121	52
El Bethel Christian Academy/*Orlando*/Orange	11237016	407/648-1978	101
El-Bethel Apos Tab & Bible Sch/*North Port*/ Sarasota	10004919	941/429-2127	131
Elbert Elem Sch/*Winter Haven*/Polk	00201785	863/291-5364	124
Elbridge Gale Elem Sch/*Wellington*/ Palm Beach	10016053	561/422-9300	106
Eleanor H Miller Sch/*Palatka*/Putnam	02126105	386/329-0595	127
Elearning East/*Port Orange*/Volusia	11073731	386/506-0013	140
Elearning West/*Orange City*/Volusia	11073729	386/575-4076	140
Electa Arcott Lee Magnet MS/*Bradenton*/ Manatee	04915445	941/727-6500	68
Elevation Academy High Sch/*Sarasota*/ Sarasota	11730288	941/371-0462	131
Elfers Christian Sch/*New Prt Rchy*/Pasco	03419371	727/845-0235	115
Elim Jr Academy/*St Petersburg*/Pinellas	03016395	727/289-7089	121
Elisa Nelson Elem Sch/*Palm Harbor*/Pinellas	12366373	727/298-2788	117
Elizabeth Cobb Middle Sch/*Tallahassee*/Leon	00194572	850/488-3364	64
Ellen Meade Sch Creative Lrng/*Bradenton*/ Manatee	04984410	941/755-1757	70
Elliott Point Elem Sch/*Ft Walton Bch*/ Okaloosa	00196233	850/833-3355	92
Embassy Creek Elem Sch/*Hollywood*/Broward	04018683	754/323-5550	12
Emerald Coast Middle Sch/*Santa Rsa Bch*/ Walton	10011297	850/622-5026	143
Emerald Coast Technical Clg/*Defuniak Spgs*/ Walton	04017536	850/892-1240	143
Emerald Cove Middle Sch/*Wellington*/ Palm Beach	10902581	561/803-8000	106
Emerald Hills Private Sch/*Hollywood*/ Broward	11237183	954/964-9163	19
Emerald Shores Elem Sch/*Ocala*/Marion	03251193	352/671-4800	71
Emerson Elem Sch/*Miami*/Miami-Dade	00186903	305/264-5757	76
Emma E Booker Elem Sch/*Sarasota*/Sarasota	00203288	941/361-6480	129
Emma Jewel Charter Sch/*Cocoa*/Brevard	11918557	321/634-5462	6
Emma Love Hardee Elem Sch/*Fernandina*/ Nassau	00196049	904/491-7936	90
Emmanuel Christian Sch/*Opa Locka*/ Miami-Dade	04938227	305/474-0658	87
Endeavor Academy/*Brooksville*/Hernando	04806583	352/797-7013	44
Endeavor Elem Sch/*Orlando*/Orange	04919776	407/251-2560	99
Endeavor Sch/*Lake Mary*/Seminole	00203848	407/320-3350	132
Endeavour Elem Sch/*Cocoa*/Brevard	00182220	321/633-3545	7
Endeavour Prim Learning Center/*Lauderhill*/ Broward	05099460	754/321-6600	12

School/City/County DISTRICT/CITY/COUNTY	PID	TELEPHONE NUMBER	PAGE
Eneida Massas Hartner Elem Sch/*Miami*/ Miami-Dade	00186434	305/573-8181	76
Engelwood Elem Sch/*Orlando*/Orange	00196831	407/249-6340	96
Englewood Elem Sch/*Englewood*/Sarasota	00203331	941/474-3247	129
Englewood Elem Sch/*Jacksonville*/Duval	00189022	904/739-5280	30
Englewood High Sch/*Jacksonville*/Duval	00189034	904/739-5212	32
English Estates Elem Sch/*Fern Park*/ Seminole	00203630	407/746-2850	132
Ensley Elem Sch/*Pensacola*/Escambia	00190538	850/494-5600	37
Enterprise Elem Sch/*Cocoa*/Brevard	04289973	321/633-3434	7
Enterprise Elem Sch/*Enterprise*/Volusia	00204414	386/575-4135	140
Enterprise High Sch/*Clearwater*/Pinellas	11103570	727/474-1237	116
Enterprise Learning Academy/*Jacksonville*/ Duval	04807989	904/573-3260	30
Ephesus Junior Academy/*Jacksonville*/Duval	01436165	904/765-3225	35
Epiphany Cathedral Sch/*Venice*/Sarasota	00200822	941/488-2215	131
Epiphany Sch/*Lake City*/Columbia	00202595	386/752-2320	28
Epiphany Sch/*Miami*/Miami-Dade	00187995	305/667-5251	85
Episcopal Day Sch-Christ Chrh/*Pensacola*/ Escambia	00190992	850/434-3685	38
Episcopal School-Jacksonville/*Jacksonville*/ Duval	00190186	904/396-5751	35
Equestrian Trails Elem Sch/*Wellington*/ Palm Beach	05272806	561/904-9600	106
Ernest R Graham K-8 Center/*Hialeah*/ Miami-Dade	04021276	305/825-2122	79
Ernest Ward Middle Sch/*Walnut Hill*/ Escambia	00190540	850/761-6300	37
Erwin Technical Center/*Tampa*/Hillsborough	02113172	813/769-5180	46
Escambia Christian Sch/*Pensacola*/Escambia	01436488	850/433-8476	38
ESCAMBIA CO SCH DIST/**PENSACOLA**/ **ESCAMBIA**	00190265	850/432-6121	36
Escambia High Sch/*Pensacola*/Escambia	00190552	850/453-3221	37
Escambia Virtual Academy/*Pensacola*/ Escambia	11717171	850/469-5443	37
Escambia Westgate Sch/*Pensacola*/Escambia	02042145	850/494-5700	37
Esformes Hebrew Academy/*Ormond Beach*/ Volusia	11824736	386/672-9300	142
Espiritu Santo Catholic Sch/*Safety Harbor*/ Pinellas	03409728	727/812-4650	120
Essrig Elem Sch/*Tampa*/Hillsborough	02897146	813/975-7307	50
Estates Elem Sch/*Naples*/Collier	05347906	239/377-6600	25
Esteem Academy/*Winter Garden*/Orange	12305991	407/656-2399	94
Estero High Sch/*Estero*/Lee	03011307	239/947-9400	61
Esther Burney Elem Sch/*Plant City*/ Hillsborough	04369743	813/707-7334	48
Esther's School Kissimmee/*Kissimmee*/ Osceola	12239287	407/873-2235	104
Ethel Beckford-Richmond Plc/*Miami*/ Miami-Dade	00187543	305/238-5194	74
Ethel K Beckham Elem Sch/*Miami*/Miami-Dade	04454386	305/222-8161	82
Ethline R Williams Prep Sch/*Tampa*/ Hillsborough	11237054	813/374-9139	54
Eugene Gregory Mem Youth Acad/*Sanford*/ Seminole	12036451	407/708-7673	132
Eugenia B Thomas K-8 Center/*Doral*/ Miami-Dade	05101362	305/592-7914	76
Eustis Elem Sch/*Eustis*/Lake	00193774	352/357-2779	59
Eustis Heights Elem Sch/*Eustis*/Lake	00193786	352/357-2447	59
Eustis High Sch/*Eustis*/Lake	00193798	352/357-4147	59
Eustis High School-Curtright/*Eustis*/Lake	11562445	352/589-1510	59
Eustis Middle Sch/*Eustis*/Lake	00193803	352/357-3366	59
Evangelical Christian Sch/*Fort Myers*/Lee	00194443	239/936-3319	63
Evans Elem Sch/*Oviedo*/Seminole	04915146	407/320-9850	132
Evans High Sch/*Orlando*/Orange	04020442	407/552-3400	97
Everest Charter Sch/*Tamarac*/Broward	11820211	954/532-3015	16
Everglade City Sch/*Everglades*/Collier	00184852	239/377-9800	25
Everglades Elem Sch/*Okeechobee*/Okeechobee	03047801	863/462-5108	93
Everglades Elem Sch/*West Palm Bch*/ Palm Beach	11555155	561/792-9500	106
Everglades Elem Sch/*Weston*/Broward	04809341	754/323-5600	12
Everglades High Sch/*Miramar*/Broward	05280085	754/323-0500	12
Everglades K-8 Center/*Miami*/Miami-Dade	00186915	305/264-4154	76
Everglades Preparatory Academy/*Pahokee*/ Palm Beach	05102263	561/924-3002	105
Everglades Preparatory Academy/*Homestead*/ Miami-Dade	11822221	786/601-1969	82
Evergreen Elem Sch/*Ocala*/Marion	03334006	352/671-4925	71
Everitt Middle Sch/*Panama City*/Bay	00181616	850/767-3776	4
Excel Christian Academy/*Lakeland*/Polk	05325673	863/853-9235	126
Excelsior Charter Academy/*Miami Gardens*/ Miami-Dade	11546075	786/565-9188	79

School/City/County DISTRICT/CITY/COUNTY	PID	TELEPHONE NUMBER	PAGE
Excelsior Charter Sch Broward/*Ft Lauderdale*/ Broward	12311196	754/701-1192	16
Excelsior Lang Acad of Hialeah/*Hialeah*/ Miami-Dade	11128178	305/879-9004	79
Excelsior Prep Charter Sch/*Tampa*/ Hillsborough	12231637	813/644-9060	46
Explorer K-8 Sch/*Spring Hill*/Hernando	11079876	352/797-7094	44
Expressions Lrng Arts Academy/*Gainesville*/ Alachua	04874645	352/373-5223	2

F

School/City/County DISTRICT/CITY/COUNTY	PID	TELEPHONE NUMBER	PAGE
F K Marchman Tech Ed Center/*New Prt Rchy*/ Pasco	02227369	727/774-1700	114
F W Buchholz High Sch/*Gainesville*/Alachua	00181159	352/955-6702	2
Fairglen Elem Sch/*Cocoa*/Brevard	00182189	321/631-1993	7
Fairlawn Elem Sch/*Fort Pierce*/St Lucie	00202870	772/468-5345	136
Fairlawn Elem Sch/*Miami*/Miami-Dade	00186927	305/261-8880	76
Fairmount Park Elem Sch/*St Petersburg*/ Pinellas	00199730	727/893-2132	119
Fairview Middle Sch/*Tallahassee*/Leon	00194584	850/488-6880	64
Fairway Elem Sch/*Miramar*/Broward	00183987	754/323-5650	12
Faith Christian Academy/*Fernandina*/Nassau	04982773	904/321-2137	91
Faith Christian Academy/*Orlando*/Orange	02384486	407/275-8031	101
Faith Christian Sch/*Port St Joe*/Gulf	01774319	850/229-6707	42
Faith Lutheran Sch/*Eustis*/Lake	01559767	352/589-5683	60
Faith Lutheran Sch/*Hialeah*/Miami-Dade	02085953	305/885-2845	87
Faith Outreach Academy/*Tampa*/Hillsborough	03419591	813/887-5546	54
Falcon Cove Middle Sch/*Weston*/Broward	04923791	754/323-3200	12
Family Christian Academy/*Orlando*/Orange	11827609	407/568-9837	101
Family Christian Sch/*Winter Garden*/Orange	11735355	407/656-7904	101
Family Life Academy/*Archer*/Alachua	10019471	352/495-3409	3
Family Life Community Sch/*Palmetto*/Manatee	11825340	941/792-7911	70
Family of Christ Christian Sch/*Tampa*/ Hillsborough	05012292	813/558-9343	54
Famud Research Sch/*Tallahassee*/Leon	12177433	850/412-5930	1
Farnell Middle Sch/*Tampa*/Hillsborough	05097319	813/356-1640	49
Father Lopez Catholic High Sch/*Daytona Beach*/ Volusia	00197706	386/253-5213	142
Father's Harbor Academy/*Jacksonville*/Duval	11223704	904/306-9579	35
Fau High Sch/*Boca Raton*/Palm Beach	11917486	561/297-3970	111
FDLRS-ACTION/ORLANDO/ORANGE	04496205	407/317-3660	102
FDLRS-ALPHA/WEST PALM BCH/ PALM BEACH	04498241	561/434-8626	112
FDLRS-CROWN/JACKSONVILLE/DUVAL	04496243	904/346-4601	36
FDLRS-EAST BREVARD/MELBOURNE/ BREVARD	04496188	321/633-1000	10
FDLRS-GALAXY/FORT PIERCE/ ST LUCIE	04496176	772/429-4585	137
FDLRS-GATEWAY/JASPER/HAMILTON	04496229	386/792-2877	42
FDLRS-GULFCOAST/CLEARWATER/ PINELLAS	04496152	727/793-2723	121
FDLRS-HEARTLAND/LAKE PLACID/ HIGHLANDS	04496114	863/531-0444	45
FDLRS-HILLSBOROUGH/TAMPA/ HILLSBOROUGH	04498239	813/837-7777	55
FDLRS-ISLAND COAST/FORT MYERS/ LEE	10915370	239/337-8363	64
FDLRS-MICCOSUKEE/TALLAHASSEE/ LEON	04498253	850/487-2630	66
FDLRS-NEFEC/PALATKA/PUTNAM	04433148	386/329-3800	127
FDLRS-REACH/FT LAUDERDALE/ BROWARD	04498265	754/321-2205	20
FDLRS-SOUTH/MIAMI/MIAMI-DADE	04496085	305/274-3501	89
FDLRS-SPRINGS/REDDICK/MARION	04496217	352/671-6051	72
FDLRS-SUNCOAST/SARASOTA/SARASOTA	04496126	941/927-9000	131
FDLRS-SUNRISE/BARTOW/POLK	04496140	863/647-4258	126
FDLRS-WESTGATE/PENSACOLA/ ESCAMBIA	04496061	850/469-5423	39
Fearnside Family Services Ctr/*Gainesville*/ Alachua	04904733	352/955-6875	2
Felix A Williams Elem Sch/*Stuart*/Martin	04287858	772/219-1640	73
Felix Varela Sr High Sch/*Miami*/Miami-Dade	04920892	305/752-7900	82
Fellowship Baptist Academy/*New Prt Rchy*/ Pasco	04836526	727/848-4593	115
Fellsmere Elem Sch/*Fellsmere*/Indian River	00193384	772/564-5970	56
Fernandina Bch Christian Acad/*Fernandina*/ Nassau	12169436	904/491-5664	91
Fernandina Beach High Sch/*Fernandina*/ Nassau	00196051	904/491-7937	90
Fernandina Beach Middle Sch/*Fernandina*/ Nassau	00196063	904/491-7938	90

School/City/County DISTRICT/CITY/COUNTY	PID	TELEPHONE NUMBER	PAGE
Ferrell Girls Prep Academy/*Tampa*/ Hillsborough	00192586	813/276-5608	51
Ferry Pass ES Math & Science/*Pensacola*/ Escambia	00190576	850/494-5605	37
Ferry Pass Middle Sch/*Pensacola*/Escambia	00190588	850/494-5650	37
Fessenden Elem Sch/*Ocala*/Marion	00195473	352/671-4935	71
Fieldston Preparatory Sch/*Titusville*/ Brevard	10024232	321/268-3664	6
Fienberg-Fisher K-8 Center/*Miami Beach*/ Miami-Dade	00185272	305/531-0419	79
First Academy/*Lake City*/Columbia	11455555	386/466-7034	28
First Academy/*Leesburg*/Lake	04938019	352/787-7762	60
First Assembly Christian Sch/*Ocala*/Marion	04984501	352/351-1913	72
First Baptist Academy/*Jacksonville*/Duval	11824865	904/265-7474	35
First Baptist Academy/*Naples*/Collier	04984408	239/597-2233	27
First Baptist Christian Acad/*Bunnell*/ Flagler	11165190	386/446-0094	39
First Baptist Christian Sch/*Apalachicola*/ Franklin	03061780	850/653-9540	40
First Baptist Christian Sch/*Stuart*/Martin	01774967	772/287-5161	73
First Christian Academy/*Defuniak Spgs*/ Walton	11749069	850/892-2722	144
First Christian Academy/*High Springs*/ Alachua	02357706	386/454-1641	3
First Christian Academy/*New Prt Rchy*/Pasco	04935251	727/943-7411	115
First Coast Academy/*Jacksonville*/Duval	11230379	904/381-1935	35
First Coast Christian Sch/*Jacksonville*/ Duval	02193213	904/777-3040	35
First Coast High Sch/*Jacksonville*/Duval	03329520	904/757-0080	32
First Lutheran Sch/*Clearwater*/Pinellas	01865578	727/461-3444	121
First Methodist Sch/*Bartow*/Polk	02197178	863/533-0905	126
First Presby Church Day Sch/*Deland*/Volusia	01776393	386/734-6214	142
First Um Christian Sch/*Homestead*/ Miami-Dade	12177407	305/248-7992	87
First United Methodist Sch/*Brooksville*/ Hernando	02234934	352/796-3496	44
First United Methodist Sch/*Kissimmee*/ Osceola	02386185	407/847-8805	104
Fishhawk Creek Elem Sch/*Lithia*/ Hillsborough	05351177	813/651-2150	52
Fishweir Elem Sch/*Jacksonville*/Duval	00189058	904/381-3910	30
Fivay High Sch/*Hudson*/Pasco	11555997	727/246-4000	114
Five Points Elem Sch/*Lake City*/Columbia	00185076	386/755-8230	27
FL HS Accelerated Lrng-North/*Cape Coral*/ Lee	11127978	239/242-4230	1
FL HS Accelerated Lrng-South/*Fort Myers*/ Lee	11127980	239/337-9140	1
Flagami Elem Sch/*Miami*/Miami-Dade	00186939	305/261-2031	76
Flagler Christian Academy/*Bunnell*/Flagler	04982917	386/437-5242	39
FLAGLER CO SCH DIST/BUNNELL/ FLAGLER	00191001	386/437-7526	39
Flagler Co Tech & Adult Ed/*Palm Coast*/ Flagler	01485532	386/447-4345	39
Flagler Palm Coast High Sch/*Palm Coast*/ Flagler	00191025	386/437-7540	39
Flamingo Elem Sch/*Davie*/Broward	00183602	754/323-5700	12
Flamingo Elem Sch/*Hialeah*/Miami-Dade	00185571	305/691-5531	79
Flcca Clay Co/*Jacksonville*/Clay	12162880	904/247-3268	23
Fleming Island Elem Sch/*Orange Park*/Clay	04447888	904/336-1075	23
Fleming Island High Sch/*Orange Park*/Clay	05272521	904/336-7500	23
Flora Ridge Elem Sch/*Kissimmee*/Osceola	10907024	407/933-3999	103
Floral Ave Elem Sch/*Bartow*/Polk	00202014	863/534-7420	124
Floral City Elem Sch/*Floral City*/Citrus	00184589	352/726-1554	22
Floranada Elem Sch/*Ft Lauderdale*/Broward	00182892	754/322-6350	12
Floresta Elem Sch/*Port St Lucie*/St Lucie	02177142	772/340-4755	136
Florida A & M Dev Research Sch/*Tallahassee*/ Leon	02048022	850/412-5930	1
Florida Autism Ctr Excellence/*Tampa*/ Hillsborough	10902634	813/985-3223	46
Florida Christian Sch/*Miami*/Miami-Dade	00187660	305/226-8152	87
Florida City Elem Sch/*Florida City*/ Miami-Dade	00187359	305/247-4676	82
Florida College Academy/*Tampa*/Hillsborough	01436672	813/899-6800	54
Florida Connections Academy/*Tampa*/ Hillsborough	12323008	855/741-5127	46
Florida Cyber Charter Academy/*Jacksonville*/ Hillsborough	12034324	904/247-3268	46
Florida Cyber CS Acad Osceola/*Jacksonville*/ Osceola	12262844	904/247-3268	103
FLORIDA DEPT OF EDUCATION/ TALLAHASSEE/LEON	00181082	850/245-0505	1

School/City/County DISTRICT/CITY/COUNTY	PID	TELEPHONE NUMBER	PAGE
Florida Futures Academy/*West Palm Bch*/ Palm Beach	12162098	561/215-0933	105
Florida Inst for Neuro Rehab/*Wauchula*/ Hardee	04328191	863/773-2857	42
Florida Preparatory Academy/*Melbourne*/ Brevard	01404033	321/723-3211	9
Florida School-Deaf & Blind/*St Augustine*/ St Johns	02048072	904/827-2200	1
Florida Sheriff's Boys Ranch/*Live Oak*/ Suwannee	01865700	386/842-5555	138
Florida Sia Tech Charter Sch/*Gainesville*/ Alachua	05274751	352/333-7952	2
Florida Southwest Clg HS/*Fort Myers*/Lee	11557282	239/432-6767	61
Florida State Christian Acad/*Fort Pierce*/ St Lucie	11225623	772/801-5522	137
Florida State Univ Sch/*Tallahassee*/Leon	02048010	850/245-3700	1
Florida Virtual Acad Osceola/*Kissimmee*/ Osceola	11821136	407/870-1445	103
Florida Virtual Academy-Duval/*Jacksonville*/ Duval	11932254	904/476-5526	29
Florida Virtual Academy-Pasco/*Jacksonville*/ Pasco	11925756	904/247-3268	113
Florida Virtual Elem Sch/*Orlando*/Orange	11830125	407/857-6588	93
Florida Virtual High Sch/*Orlando*/Orange	11830137	407/857-6588	93
Florida Virtual Middle Sch/*Orlando*/Orange	12366024	407/857-6588	93
FLORIDA VIRTUAL SCH DIST/ **ORLANDO/ORANGE**	11830113	407/513-3627	93
Florida Youth Challenge Acad/*Starke*/Clay	11714739	866/276-9304	23
Florine J Abel Elem Sch/*Sarasota*/Manatee	02112128	941/751-7040	68
Florosa Elem Sch/*Mary Esther*/Okaloosa	00196245	850/833-4381	92
Focus Academy/*Temple Terr*/Hillsborough	11931846	813/443-5558	46
Folsom Elem Sch/*Thonotosassa*/Hillsborough	04020533	813/987-6755	48
Forest City Adventist Sch/*Orlando*/Orange	03404223	407/299-0703	101
Forest City Elem Sch/*Altamonte SPG*/ Seminole	00203642	407/746-1050	132
Forest Glen Middle Sch/*Coral Springs*/ Broward	03007564	754/322-3400	12
Forest Grove Middle Sch/*Fort Pierce*/ St Lucie	03392943	772/468-5885	136
Forest High Sch/*Ocala*/Marion	00195485	352/671-4700	71
Forest Hill Cmty High Sch/*West Palm Bch*/ Palm Beach	00198138	561/540-2400	107
Forest Hill Elem Sch/*West Palm Bch*/ Palm Beach	00198126	561/432-2300	107
Forest Hills Elem Sch/*Coral Springs*/ Broward	01339983	754/322-6400	12
Forest Hills Elem Sch/*Tampa*/Hillsborough	00192225	813/975-7633	48
Forest Lake Academy/*Apopka*/Orange	01865671	407/862-8411	101
Forest Lake Education Center/*Longwood*/ Seminole	01437030	407/862-7688	133
Forest Lake Elem Sch/*Deltona*/Volusia	04453928	386/575-4166	140
Forest Lakes Elem Sch/*Oldsmar*/Pinellas	04290130	813/891-0785	117
Forest Park Elem Sch/*Boynton Beach*/ Palm Beach	00198815	561/292-6900	109
Forest Ridge Elem Sch/*Hernando*/Citrus	04926470	352/527-1808	22
Forest Trail Academy/*Wellington*/Palm Beach	11736555	800/890-6269	111
Forsyth Woods Elem Sch/*Orlando*/Orange	11713577	407/207-7495	96
Fort White Elem Sch/*Fort White*/Columbia	00185088	386/344-6301	27
Foster Elem Sch/*Tampa*/Hillsborough	00192914	813/276-5573	48
Foundation Academy/*Jacksonville*/Duval	03419606	904/493-7300	35
Foundation Academy-North/*Winter Garden*/ Orange	03417816	407/656-3677	101
Foundation Academy-South/*Winter Garden*/ Orange	11461970	407/877-2744	101
Foundation Christian Academy/*Valrico*/ Hillsborough	10974857	813/654-2969	54
Four Corners Charter Sch/*Davenport*/Osceola	04918772	407/787-4300	103
Four Corners Upper Sch/*Davenport*/Osceola	12161874	407/589-4600	103
Fox Chapel Middle Sch/*Spring Hill*/Hernando	04754655	352/797-7025	44
Fox Hollow Elem Sch/*Port Richey*/Pasco	03394977	727/774-7600	113
Fox Trail Elem Sch/*Davie*/Broward	04809353	754/323-5800	12
Frances K Sweet Elem Sch/*Fort Pierce*/ St Lucie	00202882	772/468-5330	136
Frances Marion Military Acad/*Ocala*/Marion	11071185	352/245-6600	71
Frances S Tucker Elem Sch/*Miami*/Miami-Dade	00186563	305/567-3533	76
Frangus Elem Sch/*Orlando*/Orange	04018607	407/296-6469	99
Frank C Martin K-8 Center/*Miami*/Miami-Dade	00186941	305/238-8882	82
Frank E Brigham Academy/*Winter Haven*/Polk	00201797	863/291-5300	124
Frank Hartsfield Elem Sch/*Tallahassee*/Leon	00194596	850/488-7322	64
Frank M Golson Elem Sch/*Marianna*/Jackson	00193528	850/482-9607	57
Frank Peterson Academy of Tech/*Jacksonville*/ Duval	01843441	904/573-1150	32
Frank W Springstead High Sch/*Spring Hill*/ Hernando	01397923	352/797-7010	44
Franklin Acad Palm Beach Gdns/*Palm BCH GDNS*/ Palm Beach	12035251	561/348-2525	105
Franklin Acad Pembroke Pines/*Ft Lauderdale*/ Broward	12115148	954/315-0770	16
Franklin Acad Pembroke Pines/*Pembroke Pnes*/ Broward	11716414	954/703-2294	16
Franklin Academy/*Tallahassee*/Leon	04983088	850/575-4826	66
Franklin Academy Cooper City/*Cooper City*/ Broward	11922625	954/780-5533	16
Franklin Academy K-12/*Ft Lauderdale*/ Broward	11922613	954/315-0770	16
Franklin Academy Sunrise/*Sunrise*/Broward	11820297	754/206-0850	16
Franklin Academy-Boynton Beach/*Lake Worth*/ Palm Beach	11919941	561/767-4700	105
Franklin Boys Prep Academy/*Tampa*/ Hillsborough	00192237	813/744-8108	51
Franklin Co Sch/*Eastpoint*/Franklin	00191051	850/670-2800	40
FRANKLIN CO SCH DIST/**EASTPOINT**/ **FRANKLIN**	00191037	850/670-2810	40
Franklin Park Elem Sch/*Fort Myers*/Lee	00194223	239/332-1969	61
Fred G Garner Elem Sch/*Winter Haven*/Polk	00201802	863/965-5455	124
Fred Wild Elem Sch/*Sebring*/Highlands	00191740	863/471-5400	45
Frederick Douglass Elem Sch/*Miami*/ Miami-Dade	00186525	305/371-4687	76
Freedom 7 Elem Sch/*Cocoa Beach*/Brevard	04915574	321/868-6610	7
Freedom Academy/*Brandon*/Hillsborough	12312671	813/654-0836	54
Freedom Crossing Academy/*Saint Johns*/ St Johns	12309923	904/547-4230	134
Freedom Elem Sch/*Bradenton*/Manatee	05272052	941/708-4990	68
Freedom Elem Sch/*Deland*/Volusia	04918497	386/943-4375	140
Freedom High Sch/*Orlando*/Orange	05286405	407/816-5600	97
Freedom High Sch/*Tampa*/Hillsborough	05097333	813/558-1185	50
Freedom Middle Sch/*Orlando*/Orange	10002002	407/858-6130	99
Freedom Shores Elem Sch/*Boynton Beach*/ Palm Beach	05102328	561/804-3100	109
Freeport Elem Sch/*Freeport*/Walton	03047019	850/892-1211	143
Freeport High Sch/*Freeport*/Walton	00204933	850/892-1201	143
Freeport Middle Sch/*Freeport*/Walton	04941573	850/892-1221	143
French American Sch of Miami/*Miami*/ Miami-Dade	04983715	786/268-1914	87
Friendship Christian Academy/*Tampa*/ Hillsborough	04329937	813/932-8767	54
Friendship Elem Sch/*Deltona*/Volusia	04035617	386/575-4130	141
Frontier Elem Sch/*Clearwater*/Pinellas	04290142	727/538-7335	117
Frontier Elem Sch/*Loxahatchee*/Palm Beach	04947254	561/904-9900	108
Frost Elem Sch/*Riverview*/Hillsborough	10003082	813/740-4900	48
Frostproof Elem Sch/*Frostproof*/Polk	00201577	863/635-7802	124
Frostproof Middle Sr High Sch/*Frostproof*/ Polk	00201589	863/635-7809	122
Fruit Cove Middle Sch/*Saint Johns*/St Johns	04944161	904/547-7880	134
Fruitland Park Elem Sch/*Fruitland Pk*/Lake	00193815	352/787-2693	59
Fruitville Elem Sch/*Sarasota*/Sarasota	00203343	941/361-6200	129
Fsw Collegiate High Sch/*Punta Gorda*/ Charlotte	11447065	941/637-5673	21
Ft Braden Sch/*Tallahassee*/Leon	00194601	850/488-9374	64
Ft Caroline Elem Sch/*Jacksonville*/Duval	00189096	904/745-4904	30
Ft Caroline Middle Sch/*Jacksonville*/Duval	00189101	904/745-4927	32
Ft Clarke Middle Sch/*Gainesville*/Alachua	00181185	352/333-2800	2
Ft King Middle Sch/*Ocala*/Marion	00195497	352/671-4725	71
Ft Lauderdale High Sch/*Ft Lauderdale*/ Broward	00183212	754/322-1100	12
Ft Lauderdale Preparatory Sch/*Ft Lauderdale*/ Broward	03106990	954/485-7500	19
Ft McCoy Sch/*Fort Mc Coy*/Marion	00195502	352/671-6325	71
Ft Meade Middle Senior HS/*Fort Meade*/Polk	00202026	863/285-1180	122
Ft Myers Beach Elem Sch/*Ft Myers Bch*/Lee	00194235	239/463-6356	61
Ft Myers Christian Sch/*Fort Myers*/Lee	02148672	239/939-4642	63
Ft Myers High Sch/*Fort Myers*/Lee	00194247	239/334-2167	61
Ft Myers Middle Academy/*Fort Myers*/Lee	00194259	239/936-1759	61
Ft Myers Technical College/*Fort Myers*/Lee	00194285	239/334-4544	61
Ft Pierce Central High Sch/*Fort Pierce*/ St Lucie	00202894	772/468-5888	136
Ft Pierce Westwood Academy/*Fort Pierce*/ St Lucie	01542207	772/468-5400	136
Ft Walton Beach High Sch/*Ft Walton Bch*/ Okaloosa	00196257	850/833-3300	92
Ft White High Sch/*Fort White*/Columbia	04923856	386/319-7272	27
Fuguitt Elem Sch/*Largo*/Pinellas	00199754	727/588-3576	117
Fulford Christian Day Care Ctr/*Uleta*/ Miami-Dade	02365686	786/916-2135	87

School/City/County DISTRICT/CITY/COUNTY	PID	TELEPHONE NUMBER	PAGE
Fulford Elem Sch/*N Miami Beach*/Miami-Dade	00185208	305/949-3425	79
Fusion Academy-Boca Raton/*Boca Raton*/ Palm Beach	12312073	561/953-9365	111
Fusion Academy-Miami/*Miami*/Miami-Dade	12312085	305/831-0041	87
G			
G Holmes Braddock Sr High Sch/*Miami*/ Miami-Dade	03340055	305/225-9729	82
G K Edelman-Sabal Palm ES/*Miami*/Miami-Dade	00185466	305/651-2411	79
G Weaver Hipps Elem Sch/*Lehigh Acres*/Lee	11446293	239/368-7042	61
G-Star School of the Arts/*West Palm Bch*/ Palm Beach	05272741	561/967-2023	105
Gadsden Central Academy/*Quincy*/Gadsden	10027727	850/875-7249	40
Gadsden Co High Sch/*Havana*/Gadsden	00191192	850/662-2300	40
GADSDEN CO SCH DIST/**QUINCY**/ **GADSDEN**	00191087	850/627-9651	40
Gadsden Elem Magnet Sch/*Quincy*/Gadsden	04917936	850/627-7557	40
Gadsden Technical Institute/*Quincy*/Gadsden	00191128	850/875-8324	40
Gadsden Virtual Sch/*Quincy*/Gadsden	11925055	866/339-8784	40
Gaines Alt Ctr-Hamblen/*St Augustine*/ St Johns	04285343	904/547-8560	134
Gainesville Country Day Sch/*Gainesville*/ Alachua	02234489	352/332-7783	3
Gainesville High Sch/*Gainesville*/Alachua	00181197	352/955-6707	2
Gaither Senior High Sch/*Tampa*/Hillsborough	02228600	813/975-7340	50
Galaxy Elem Sch/*Boynton Beach*/Palm Beach	01530931	561/739-5600	109
Galaxy Middle Sch/*Deltona*/Volusia	03396846	386/575-4144	141
Galileo CS for Gifted Learning/*Sanford*/ Seminole	11722164	321/249-9221	132
Gamble Rogers Middle Sch/*St Augustine*/ St Johns	04285355	904/547-8700	134
Garden City Elem Sch/*Jacksonville*/Duval	00189113	904/924-3130	30
Garden Elem Sch/*Venice*/Sarasota	00203355	941/486-2110	129
Garden Grove Elem Sch/*Winter Haven*/Polk	01524310	863/291-5396	124
Garden of Sahaba Academy/*Boca Raton*/ Palm Beach	11233436	561/395-3011	111
Gardens School-Technology Arts/*Palm BCH GDNS*/ Palm Beach	11717030	561/290-7661	105
Garrison-Jones Elem Sch/*Dunedin*/Pinellas	03337278	727/469-5716	117
Gary Adult Education Center/*Tampa*/ Hillsborough	10003109	813/740-7660	46
Gateway Academy/*Bonifay*/Holmes	04983155	850/547-9011	55
Gateway Charter Elem Sch/*Fort Myers*/Lee	11818438	239/768-5048	61
Gateway Charter High Sch/*Fort Myers*/Lee	05348390	239/768-3350	61
Gateway Charter Interm Sch/*Fort Myers*/Lee	05275250	239/768-2491	61
Gateway Christian Academy/*Ft Lauderdale*/ Broward	11230355	954/485-7012	19
Gateway Christian Academy/*Tampa*/ Hillsborough	11615834	813/964-9800	54
Gateway Elem Sch/*Fort Myers*/Lee	04020777	239/768-3737	62
Gateway Environmental K-8 LC/*Homestead*/ Miami-Dade	11453521	305/257-6000	82
Gateway High Sch/*Kissimmee*/Osceola	02855784	407/935-3600	103
Gateway Sch/*Orlando*/Orange	00196879	407/296-6449	97
Gator Run Elem Sch/*Weston*/Broward	04809303	754/323-5850	12
Gause Academy of Leadership/*Bartow*/Polk	03050224	863/534-7425	123
Gemini Elem Sch/*Melbourne Bch*/Brevard	00182335	321/727-3090	7
Gene Witt Elem Sch/*Bradenton*/Manatee	04286397	941/741-3628	68
Genesis Christian Academy/*Clearwater*/ Pinellas	12038590	727/738-1656	121
Genesis Christian Sch/*Pt Charlotte*/ Charlotte	04984331	941/627-4849	21
Genesis Preparatory Sch/*Gainesville*/ Alachua	04920579	352/379-1188	2
Genesis Preparatory Sch/*New Prt Rchy*/Pasco	10750699	727/846-8407	115
Genesis Sch/*New Prt Rchy*/Pasco	02198031	727/845-1111	115
Genesis Sch/*New Prt Rchy*/Pasco	04984575	727/372-9333	115
Geneva Classical Academy/*Lakeland*/Polk	11236969	863/644-1408	126
Geneva Elem Sch/*Geneva*/Seminole	00203666	407/320-4950	132
George C Miller Middle Sch/*Crescent City*/ Putnam	01540508	386/698-1360	127
George Jenkins High Sch/*Lakeland*/Polk	04036271	863/648-3566	122
George Munroe Elem Sch/*Quincy*/Gadsden	00191130	850/875-8800	40
George Stone Technical Ctr/*Pensacola*/ Escambia	00190617	850/941-6200	37
George T Baker Aviation Sch/*Miami*/ Miami-Dade	01810781	305/871-3143	74
George W Carver Elem Sch/*Coral Gables*/ Miami-Dade	00186575	305/443-5286	76
George W Carver Elem Sch/*Jacksonville*/ Duval	03402172	904/924-3122	33

School/City/County DISTRICT/CITY/COUNTY	PID	TELEPHONE NUMBER	PAGE
George W Carver Middle Sch/*Miami*/ Miami-Dade	00186587	305/444-7388	76
George W Marks Elem Sch/*Deland*/Volusia	00204440	386/822-6986	141
Georgia Jones-Ayers Mid Sch/*Miami*/ Miami-Dade	00186381	305/634-9787	76
Gerald Adams Elem Sch/*Key West*/Monroe	01540481	305/293-1609	89
Gibbons St Pre-Sch Center/*Bartow*/Polk	00202040	863/535-6489	124
Gibbs High Sch/*St Petersburg*/Pinellas	00199766	727/893-5452	119
Gibsonton Elem Sch/*Gibsonton*/Hillsborough	00192263	813/671-5100	48
Gifford Middle Sch/*Vero Beach*/Indian River	00193396	772/564-3550	56
GILCHRIST CO SCH DIST/**TRENTON**/ **GILCHRIST**	00191269	352/463-3200	41
Gilchrist Elem Sch/*Tallahassee*/Leon	00194766	850/487-4310	64
Glade View Elem Sch/*Belle Glade*/Palm Beach	00198401	561/993-8800	107
Glades Academy/*Pahokee*/Palm Beach	04950548	561/924-9402	105
Glades Central Cmty High Sch/*Belle Glade*/ Palm Beach	00198396	561/993-4403	107
Glades Christian Academy/*Coral Springs*/ Broward	11234076	954/755-6405	19
GLADES CO SCH DIST/**MOORE HAVEN**/ **GLADES**	00191300	863/946-2083	41
Glades Day Sch/*Belle Glade*/Palm Beach	00199003	561/996-6769	111
Glades Middle Sch/*Miami*/Miami-Dade	00186953	305/271-3342	82
Glades Middle Sch/*Miramar*/Broward	05347047	754/323-4600	12
Gladeview Christian Sch/*Miami*/Miami-Dade	02366329	305/226-1414	87
Glen Springs Elem Sch/*Gainesville*/Alachua	00181202	352/955-6708	2
Glenallen Elem Sch/*North Port*/Sarasota	02226377	941/426-9517	129
Glendale Christian Sch/*Vero Beach*/ Indian River	02148658	772/569-1095	56
Glendale Elem Sch/*Vero Beach*/Indian River	03012387	772/978-8050	56
Glenridge Middle Sch/*Orlando*/Orange	00196881	407/623-1415	96
Global Learning Academy/*Pensacola*/Escambia	11710214	850/430-7560	37
Global Outreach Charter Acad/*Jacksonville*/ Duval	11446231	904/551-7104	29
Gloria Dei Lutheran Academy/*Davie*/Broward	02210835	954/475-8584	19
Gloria M Floyd Elem Sch/*Miami*/Miami-Dade	02046139	305/255-3934	82
Glory of God Sch/*Hialeah*/Miami-Dade	01773248	305/884-4000	87
Gocio Elem Sch/*Sarasota*/Sarasota	00203367	941/361-6405	129
God Little Creation Preschool/*Ft Lauderdale*/ Broward	02359687	954/973-1129	19
Gold Coast Junior Academy/*Boynton Beach*/ Palm Beach	02847127	561/364-7388	111
Golden Gate Elem Sch/*Naples*/Collier	00184864	239/377-6900	25
Golden Gate High Sch/*Naples*/Collier	05347920	239/377-1600	25
Golden Gate Middle Sch/*Naples*/Collier	02177087	239/377-3800	25
Golden Glades Elem Sch/*Miami Gardens*/ Miami-Dade	00185583	305/624-9641	79
Golden Grove Elem Sch/*West Palm Bch*/ Palm Beach	04755582	561/904-9700	108
Golden Terrace Elem Sch/*Naples*/Collier	03251167	239/377-7000	25
Goldsboro Elem Magnet Sch/*Sanford*/Seminole	00203678	407/320-5850	132
Golfview Elem Sch/*Rockledge*/Brevard	00182191	321/633-3570	7
Good Shepard Day Sch/*Punta Gorda*/Charlotte	11461982	941/575-2139	21
Good Shepard Lutheran Sch/*Sarasota*/ Sarasota	02210809	941/922-8164	131
Good Shepherd Academy/*Deltona*/Volusia	05013521	407/324-2274	142
Good Shepherd Cath Sch/*Orlando*/Orange	00197718	407/277-3973	100
Good Shepherd Catholic Sch/*Miami*/ Miami-Dade	04778613	305/385-7002	85
Good Shepherd Episcopal Sch/*Tequesta*/ Palm Beach	04234617	561/746-5507	111
Good Shepherd Lutheran Sch/*Gulf Breeze*/ Santa Rosa	11230757	850/932-9127	128
Good Shepherd Lutheran Sch/*N Ft Myers*/Lee	01404277	239/995-7711	63
Gordon Burnett Middle Sch/*Seffner*/ Hillsborough	04452314	813/744-6745	51
Gordon Day Sch/*Miami*/Miami-Dade	11238333	305/854-3282	87
Gorrie Elem Sch/*Tampa*/Hillsborough	00192275	813/276-5673	49
Gospel Baptist Christian Sch/*Bonita Spgs*/ Lee	03061869	239/947-1285	64
Gotha Middle Sch/*Windermere*/Orange	04295192	407/521-2360	99
Goulds Elem Sch/*Homestead*/Miami-Dade	10907713	305/257-4400	82
Gove Elem Sch/*Belle Glade*/Palm Beach	00198413	561/993-8700	107
Governor's Charter Academy/*Tallahassee*/ Leon	11825687	850/391-5259	64
Grace Academy/*Ormond Beach*/Volusia	03419620	386/673-5166	142
Grace Baptist Academy/*Miami*/Miami-Dade	02825167	305/238-7332	87
Grace Christian Academy/*Hollywood*/Broward	11237121	954/983-6497	19
Grace Christian Academy/*Orlando*/Orange	02235653	407/617-8833	101
Grace Christian Academy/*Port St Lucie*/ St Lucie	11235006	772/905-8096	137
Grace Christian Prep Sch/*Miami*/Miami-Dade	11727176	305/259-1929	87

School/City/County DISTRICT/CITY/COUNTY	PID	TELEPHONE NUMBER	PAGE
Grace Christian Sch/*Hudson*/Pasco	02149523	727/863-1825	115
Grace Christian Sch/*Ocala*/Marion	00195693	352/629-2312	72
Grace Christian Sch/*Valrico*/Hillsborough	01865308	813/689-8815	54
Grace Community Sch/*Cape Coral*/Lee	04984290	239/549-7411	64
Grace Community Sch/*Naples*/Collier	03063465	239/455-4520	27
Grace Community Sch/*Pt Charlotte*/Charlotte	04984379	941/625-7011	21
Grace Episcopal Day Sch/*Orange Park*/Clay	11734911	904/269-3718	24
Grace Lutheran Sch/*Jacksonville*/Duval	04930457	904/928-9136	35
Grace Lutheran Sch/*St Petersburg*/Pinellas	00200640	727/527-6213	121
Grace Lutheran Sch/*Winter Haven*/Polk	00202131	863/293-9744	126
Gracepointe Academy/*Summerfield*/Marion	12102050	352/897-0822	72
Graceville Elem Sch/*Graceville*/Jackson	01340126	850/263-4402	57
Graceville High Sch/*Graceville*/Jackson	00193530	850/263-4451	57
Graceway Academy & Preschool/*Ocala*/Marion	10783115	352/629-4523	72
Grady Elem Sch/*Tampa*/Hillsborough	00192304	813/872-5325	49
Grand Park Career Center/*Jacksonville*/ Duval	01397870	904/630-6894	32
Grand Ridge Sch/*Grand Ridge*/Jackson	00193542	850/482-1273	57
Grandview Preparatory Sch/*Boca Raton*/ Palm Beach	04760408	561/416-9737	111
Grant Career & Tech Ed Ctr/*Winter Haven*/ Polk	12361402	863/875-2785	126
Grasp Academy/*Jacksonville*/Duval	00189371	904/745-4909	30
Grassroots Free Sch/*Tallahassee*/Leon	01774840	850/656-3629	66
Grassy Lake Elem Sch/*Minneola*/Lake	10909113	352/242-0313	59
Grassy Waters Elem Sch/*West Palm Bch*/ Palm Beach	05348572	561/383-9000	107
Gratigny Elem Sch/*Miami*/Miami-Dade	00185210	305/681-6685	79
Great Heights Academy/*Miami*/Miami-Dade	12225418	786/773-2285	87
Great Strides Sch/*Jacksonville*/Duval	12043246	904/886-3228	35
Greater Miami Adventist Acad/*Miami*/ Miami Dade	01435898	305/220-5955	87
Greco Middle Sch/*Temple Terr*/Hillsborough	00192287	813/987-6926	48
Green Cove Springs Jr High Sch/*Green Cv Spgs*/ Clay	00184694	904/336-5175	23
Green Springs High Sch/*Miami*/Miami-Dade	11719739	305/720-2996	76
Greenacres Christian Academy/*Lake Worth*/ Palm Beach	04331203	561/965-0363	111
Greenacres Elem Sch/*Greenacres*/Palm Beach	00198150	561/649-7200	107
Greenfield Elem Sch/*Jacksonville*/Duval	00189149	904/739-5249	30
Greenglade Elem Sch/*Miami*/Miami-Dade	00186965	305/223-5330	82
Greenland Pines Elem Sch/*Jacksonville*/ Duval	03401324	904/260-5450	30
Greensboro Elem Sch/*Quincy*/Gadsden	00191142	850/442-6327	40
Greentree Prep Charter Sch/*Ft Lauderdale*/ Broward	12030823	954/780-8733	16
Greenville Elem Sch/*Greenville*/Madison	00194962	850/973-5033	67
Greenway Elem Sch/*Ocala*/Marion	04749349	352/671-4845	71
Greenwood Lakes Middle Sch/*Lake Mary*/ Seminole	02896180	407/320-7650	132
Greenwood Sch/*Jacksonville*/Duval	03138565	904/726-5000	35
Gregory Drive Elem Sch/*Jacksonville*/Duval	00189163	904/573-1190	33
Gretchen Everhart Sch/*Tallahassee*/Leon	00194613	850/488-5785	65
Greynolds Park Elem Sch/*N Miami Beach*/ Miami-Dade	00185222	305/949-2129	79
Griffin Elem Sch/*Cooper City*/Broward	02107903	754/323-5900	12
Griffin Elem Sch/*Lakeland*/Polk	00201292	863/853-6020	124
Griffin Middle Sch/*Tallahassee*/Leon	00194625	850/617-5353	65
Grove Park Elem Sch/*Orange Park*/Clay	00184711	904/336-1275	23
Grove Park Elem Sch/*Palm Bch Gdns*/ Palm Beach	00198516	561/904-7700	108
Groveland Elem Sch/*Groveland*/Lake	01827100	352/429-2472	59
Guardian Angels Catholic Sch/*Clearwater*/ Pinellas	03409716	727/799-6724	120
Guardian Catholic Sch/*Jacksonville*/Duval	00202600	904/765-6522	34
Guidepost Mont-Hollywood Beach/*Hollywood*/ Broward	12361464	954/923-7100	19
Gulf Beaches Elem Sch/*St Petersburg*/ Pinellas	12032089	727/893-2630	118
Gulf Breeze Elem Sch/*Gulf Breeze*/ Santa Rosa	00203070	850/934-5185	128
Gulf Breeze Elementary/*Gulf Breeze*/ Santa Rosa	11222724	850/934-0180	128
Gulf Breeze High Sch/*Gulf Breeze*/ Santa Rosa	00203082	850/916-4100	128
Gulf Breeze Middle Sch/*Gulf Breeze*/ Santa Rosa	00203094	850/934-4080	128
Gulf Co Adult Sch/*Port St Joe*/Gulf	00191348	850/227-1744	41
GULF CO SCH DIST/**PORT ST JOE**/ **GULF**	00191336	850/229-8256	41
Gulf Coast Acad Science Tech/*Spring Hill*/ Hernando	05344124	352/688-5092	44

School/City/County DISTRICT/CITY/COUNTY	PID	TELEPHONE NUMBER	PAGE
Gulf Coast Charter Acad South/*Naples*/ Collier	11918416	239/784-1539	25
Gulf Coast High Sch/*Naples*/Collier	04808206	239/377-1400	25
Gulf Coast Middle Sch/*Spring Hill*/Hernando	11918284	352/666-5790	44
Gulf Elem Sch/*Cape Coral*/Lee	02200634	239/549-2726	62
Gulf Gate Elem Sch/*Sarasota*/Sarasota	00203379	941/361-6499	129
Gulf High Sch/*New Prt Rchy*/Pasco	00199235	727/774-3300	114
Gulf Highlands Elem Sch/*Port Richey*/Pasco	10021943	727/774-7700	113
Gulf Middle Sch/*Cape Coral*/Lee	02177104	239/549-0606	62
Gulf Middle Sch/*New Prt Rchy*/Pasco	00199223	727/774-8000	115
Gulf Stream Sch/*Gulf Stream*/Palm Beach	00198970	561/276-5225	111
Gulf Trace Elem Sch/*Holiday*/Pasco	10904113	727/246-3600	113
Gulfcoast Christian Academy/*Bradenton*/ Manatee	04984422	941/755-0332	70
Gulfcoast SDA Sch/*St Petersburg*/Pinellas	01437420	727/345-2141	121
Gulfport Elem Montessori Acad/*Gulfport*/ Pinellas	00199792	727/893-2643	118
Gulfside Elem Sch/*Holiday*/Pasco	01540493	727/774-6000	113
Gulfstream Acad Hallandale Bch/*Hallandale*/ Broward	00183999	754/323-5950	12
Gulfstream Elem Sch/*Miami*/Miami-Dade	00187373	305/235-6811	82
Gulfstream Goodwill Life Acad/*Boynton Beach*/ Palm Beach	10002789	561/259-1000	105
Gulfview Middle Sch/*Naples*/Collier	00184876	239/377-4000	25
Gulliver Acad-Montgomery/*Pinecrest*/ Miami-Dade	04936281	305/238-3424	87
Gulliver Academy/*Coral Gables*/Miami-Dade	02122680	305/665-3593	87
Gulliver Preparatory Sch/*Miami*/Miami-Dade	00187672	305/666-7937	87
Gulliver School-Miller Drive/*Miami*/ Miami-Dade	05011171	305/274-9535	87

H

School/City/County DISTRICT/CITY/COUNTY	PID	TELEPHONE NUMBER	PAGE
H L Johnson Elem Sch/*West Palm Bch*/ Palm Beach	02200024	561/904-9300	107
H S Moody Elem Sch/*Bradenton*/Manatee	01397935	941/741-3170	68
Hagen Road Elem Sch/*Boynton Beach*/ Palm Beach	00198827	561/292-6700	109
Hagerty High Sch/*Oviedo*/Seminole	10002088	407/871-0750	132
Haines City High Sch/*Haines City*/Polk	02112166	863/421-3281	122
Haines City High School-IB/*Haines City*/ Polk	11435751	863/419-3371	122
Halifax Academy/*Daytona Beach*/Volusia	04982943	386/252-9557	142
Hallandale High Sch/*Hallandale*/Broward	01340011	754/323-0900	12
Hamilton Co Elem Sch/*Jasper*/Hamilton	12231869	386/792-8000	42
Hamilton Co High Sch/*Jasper*/Hamilton	00191439	386/792-8100	42
HAMILTON CO SCH DIST/**JASPER**/ **HAMILTON**	00191403	386/792-7800	42
Hamilton Elem Sch/*Sanford*/Seminole	02225359	407/320-6050	132
Hammett Bowen Jr Elem Sch/*Ocala*/Marion	10030138	352/291-7900	71
Hammock Pointe Elem Sch/*Boca Raton*/ Palm Beach	03401295	561/477-2200	109
Hammocks Middle Sch/*Miami*/Miami-Dade	02227565	305/385-0896	82
Hammond Elem Sch/*Odessa*/Hillsborough	10902610	813/792-5120	49
Hampden Dubose Academy/*Zellwood*/Orange	01404382	407/880-4321	101
Hampton Elem Sch/*Starke*/Bradford	00181927	352/468-1212	6
Hancock Creek Elem Sch/*N Ft Myers*/Lee	04039041	239/995-3600	62
Harbor City Elem Sch/*Melbourne*/Brevard	00182347	321/254-5534	7
Harbordale Elem Sch/*Ft Lauderdale*/Broward	00183614	754/323-6050	12
Harbour View Elem Sch/*Summerfield*/Marion	03334032	352/671-6110	71
HARDEE CO SCH DIST/**WAUCHULA**/ **HARDEE**	00191477	863/773-9058	42
Hardee Junior High Sch/*Wauchula*/Hardee	00191518	863/773-3147	42
Hardee Senior High Sch/*Wauchula*/Hardee	00191506	863/773-3181	42
Harlem Heights Cmty CS/*Fort Myers*/Lee	12169319	239/482-7706	62
Harmony Community Sch/*Harmony*/Osceola	11073664	407/892-1655	103
Harmony High Sch/*Saint Cloud*/Osceola	05346512	407/933-9900	103
Harmony Middle Sch/*Saint Cloud*/Osceola	12365769	407/593-0416	103
Harns Marsh Elem Sch/*Lehigh Acres*/Lee	10007088	239/690-1249	62
Harns Marsh Middle Sch/*Lehigh Acres*/Lee	11816791	239/690-2025	62
Harrold Clark Elem Sch/*Tampa*/Hillsborough	04810106	813/631-4333	50
Harry Schwettman Ed Center/*New Prt Rchy*/ Pasco	01536569	727/774-0000	114
Hart 2 Hart Academy/*Lake City*/Columbia	11621091	386/466-1114	28
Hartridge Academy/*Winter Haven*/Polk	04951009	863/956-4434	123
Harvest Christian Academy/*Jacksonville*/ Duval	02148531	904/724-8223	35
Harvest Community Sch/*Jacksonville*/Duval	11818737	904/997-1882	35
Havana Magnet Sch/*Havana*/Gadsden	00191180	850/662-2750	40
Haverhill Baptist Day Sch/*Haverhill*/ Palm Beach	01404409	561/683-1780	111
Hawkes Bluff Elem Sch/*Davie*/Broward	03252240	754/323-6100	12

School/City/County DISTRICT/CITY/COUNTY	PID	TELEPHONE NUMBER	PAGE
Hawks Rise Elem Sch/*Tallahassee*/Leon	04368543	850/487-4733	65
Hawthorne Middle/High Sch/*Hawthorne*/ Alachua	00181226	352/481-1900	2
Healthy Learning Academy/*Jonesville*/ Alachua	10027818	352/372-2279	2
Heart to Heart Christian Acad/*Jacksonville*/ Duval	11719870	904/783-8631	35
Heartland Christian Academy/*Sebring*/ Highlands	02234958	863/385-3850	45
Heathrow Elem Sch/*Lake Mary*/Seminole	03395141	407/320-6850	132
Hebrew Academy Community Sch/*Margate*/ Broward	03015949	954/978-6341	19
Hebrew Academy of Tampa Bay/*Tampa*/ Hillsborough	03313480	813/963-0706	54
Hebrew Academy-Greater Miami/*Miami Beach*/ Miami-Dade	00199405	305/532-6421	87
Hector A Cafferata Jr Elem Sch/*Cape Coral*/ Lee	10007076	239/458-7391	62
Heights Elem Sch/*Fort Myers*/Lee	00194261	239/481-1761	62
Helen A Davis Elem Sch/*Tampa*/Hillsborough	05351139	813/854-6010	49
Hellen Caro Elem Sch/*Pensacola*/Escambia	03399381	850/492-0531	37
Henderson Hammock Charter Sch/*Tampa*/ Hillsborough	11830046	813/739-6633	46
Hendricks Avenue Elem Sch/*Jacksonville*/ Duval	00189187	904/346-5610	30
HENDRY CO SCH DIST/**LABELLE**/ **HENDRY**	00191544	863/674-4642	43
Henry F Kite Elem Sch/*Jacksonville*/Duval	00189199	904/924-3031	30
Henry H Filer Middle Sch/*Hialeah*/ Miami-Dade	00185595	305/822-6601	79
Henry M Flagler Elem Sch/*Miami*/Miami-Dade	00186599	305/443-2529	76
Henry S Reeves Elem Sch/*Miami*/Miami-Dade	04454362	305/953-7243	76
Henry S West Laboratory Sch/*Miami*/ Miami-Dade	00186824	305/661-7661	76
Herbert A Ammons Middle Sch/*Miami*/ Miami-Dade	04754992	305/971-0158	82
Herbert C Hoover Middle Sch/*Indialantic*/ Brevard	00182359	321/727-1611	8
Heritage Christian Academy/*Fleming Isle*/ Clay	01774022	904/269-2405	24
Heritage Christian Academy/*Winter Haven*/ Polk	11233955	863/293-0012	126
Heritage Christian Sch/*Kissimmee*/Osceola	01865451	407/847-4087	104
Heritage Elem Sch/*Greenacres*/Palm Beach	04920751	561/804-3200	107
Heritage Elem Sch/*Tampa*/Hillsborough	05262265	813/740-4580	50
Heritage High Sch/*Palm Bay*/Brevard	11447883	321/722-4178	8
Heritage Middle Sch/*Deltona*/Volusia	04873067	386/575-4113	141
Heritage Preparatory/*Orlando*/Orange	01775193	407/295-3086	101
Heritage Trails Cmty Sch/*Tallahassee*/Leon	11236828	850/488-8927	65
Hernando Christian Academy/*Brooksville*/ Hernando	02148567	352/796-0616	44
HERNANDO CO SCH DIST/**BROOKSVILLE**/ **HERNANDO**	00191611	352/797-7000	43
Hernando Elem Sch/*Hernando*/Citrus	00184591	352/726-1833	22
Hernando Eschool/*Brooksville*/Hernando	11714014	352/797-7072	44
Hernando High Sch/*Brooksville*/Hernando	00191673	352/797-7015	44
Heron Creek Middle Sch/*North Port*/Sarasota	05269897	941/480-3371	129
Heron Heights Elem Sch/*Parkland*/Broward	11449855	754/322-9150	12
Hershorin Schiff Comm Day Sch/*Sarasota*/ Sarasota	04867458	941/552-2770	131
Hialeah Elem Sch/*Hialeah*/Miami-Dade	00186018	305/888-6709	76
Hialeah Gardens Elem Sch/*Hialeah GDNS*/ Miami-Dade	04303256	305/827-8830	79
Hialeah Gardens Middle Sch/*Hialeah GDNS*/ Miami-Dade	11128180	305/817-0017	79
Hialeah Gardens Sr High Sch/*Hialeah*/ Miami-Dade	11435763	305/698-5000	79
Hialeah Miami Lakes Adult Ed/*Hialeah*/ Miami-Dade	10907775	305/823-1330	74
Hialeah Middle Sch/*Hialeah*/Miami-Dade	00185600	305/681-3527	79
Hialeah Senior High Sch/*Hialeah*/Miami-Dade	00185612	305/822-1500	79
Hialeah-Miami Lakes Sr HS/*Hialeah*/ Miami-Dade	00185624	305/823-1330	79
Hiawassee Elem Sch/*Orlando*/Orange	00196908	407/296-6410	99
Hibiscus Elem Sch/*Miami*/Miami-Dade	00185234	305/652-3018	79
Hickory Creek Elem Sch/*Saint Johns*/ St Johns	10005286	904/547-7450	134
Hickory Tree Elem Sch/*Saint Cloud*/Osceola	02225933	407/891-3120	103
Hidden Oak Elem Sch/*Gainesville*/Alachua	03054749	352/333-2801	2
Hidden Oaks Elem Sch/*Lake Worth*/Palm Beach	10002765	561/804-3800	109
Hidden Oaks Elem Sch/*Orlando*/Orange	03400057	407/249-6350	98
Hidden Oaks Middle Sch/*Palm City*/Martin	04012964	772/219-1655	73

School/City/County DISTRICT/CITY/COUNTY	PID	TELEPHONE NUMBER	PAGE
High Point Elem Sch/*Clearwater*/Pinellas	00199807	727/538-7440	118
High Springs Community Sch/*High Springs*/ Alachua	00181238	386/454-1958	2
Highbanks Learning Center/*Debary*/Volusia	12105246	386/822-7896	141
Highland City Elem Sch/*Highland City*/Polk	00202064	863/648-3540	124
Highland Elem Sch/*Lake Worth*/Palm Beach	00198839	561/202-0500	107
Highland Lakes Elem Sch/*Palm Harbor*/ Pinellas	03399044	727/724-1429	117
Highland Oaks Middle Sch/*Miami*/Miami-Dade	01557757	305/932-3810	79
Highlands Christian Academy/*Pompano Beach*/ Broward	01772347	954/421-1747	19
HIGHLANDS CO SCH DIST/**SEBRING**/ **HIGHLANDS**	00191702	863/471-5555	44
Highlands Elem Sch/*Immokalee*/Collier	00184888	239/377-7100	26
Highlands Elem Sch/*Jacksonville*/Duval	00189204	904/696-8754	33
Highlands Elem Sch/*Kissimmee*/Osceola	00197990	407/935-3620	103
Highlands Elem Sch/*Winter Spgs*/Seminole	04457819	407/746-6650	132
Highlands Grove Elem Sch/*Lakeland*/Polk	10902725	863/648-3002	125
Highlands Middle Sch/*Jacksonville*/Duval	00189216	904/696-8771	33
Highlands Virtual Sch/*Sebring*/Highlands	12307652	863/471-5679	45
Highpoint Academy/*Miami*/Miami-Dade	02193902	305/552-0202	87
Highpoint Christian Academy/*Orange Park*/ Clay	11850527	904/272-7949	24
Hiland Park Elem Sch/*Panama City*/Bay	00181628	850/767-4685	4
Hill Middle Sch/*Tampa*/Hillsborough	03011204	813/975-7325	50
Hill-Gustat Middle Sch/*Sebring*/Highlands	04451683	863/471-5437	45
Hillcrest Elem Sch/*Orlando*/Orange	00196910	407/245-1770	95
Hillcrest Elem Sch/*Lake Wales*/Polk	00201620	863/678-4215	123
Hillcrest Sch/*Ocala*/Marion	00195526	352/671-6800	71
Hillel Academy/*Tampa*/Hillsborough	02085393	813/963-2242	54
Hilliard Elem Sch/*Hilliard*/Nassau	01487683	904/845-4471	90
Hilliard Middle Sr High Sch/*Hilliard*/ Nassau	00196075	904/845-2171	90
Hillsborough Acad Math & Sci/*Tampa*/ Hillsborough	11925512	813/793-6085	46
Hillsborough Baptist Sch/*Seffner*/ Hillsborough	02825272	813/620-0683	54
HILLSBOROUGH CO PUB SCH DIST/ **TAMPA/HILLSBOROUGH**	00191805	813/272-4000	45
HILLSBOROUGH CO SD-ACHIEVEMENT/ **TAMPA/HILLSBOROUGH**	12309832	813/272-4000	47
HILLSBOROUGH CO SD-AREA 1/ **TAMPA/HILLSBOROUGH**	03395581	813/272-3800	48
HILLSBOROUGH CO SD-AREA 2/ **TAMPA/HILLSBOROUGH**	03395610	813/631-4050	49
HILLSBOROUGH CO SD-AREA 3/ **TAMPA/HILLSBOROUGH**	04869688	813/558-1406	50
HILLSBOROUGH CO SD-AREA 4/ **SEFFNER/HILLSBOROUGH**	03395634	813/740-3710	51
HILLSBOROUGH CO SD-AREA 5/ **PLANT CITY/HILLSBOROUGH**	04750221	813/707-7050	51
Hillsborough High Sch/*Tampa*/Hillsborough	00192316	813/276-5620	51
Hillsborough Virtual Sch/*Tampa*/ Hillsborough	11716218	813/983-7278	46
Hilltop Elem Sch/*Wauchula*/Hardee	10020339	863/773-2750	42
His Academy/Institute/*Lake Park*/Palm Beach	03419761	561/881-5412	111
His Royal Christian Academy/*Leesburg*/Lake	04336497	352/267-9525	60
Hive Preparatory Sch/*Hialeah*/Miami-Dade	11453442	305/231-4888	79
Hobe Sound Christian Academy/*Hobe Sound*/ Martin	01774979	772/546-5534	73
Hobe Sound Elem Sch/*Hobe Sound*/Martin	00195722	772/219-1540	73
Hochberg Preparatory Sch/*Miami*/Miami-Dade	02365997	305/932-2829	87
Hogan-Spring Glen Elem Sch/*Jacksonville*/ Duval	00189228	904/720-1640	31
Holiday Hill Elem Sch/*Jacksonville*/Duval	00189230	904/720-1676	31
Holley-Navarre Interm Sch/*Navarre*/ Santa Rosa	03250553	850/936-6020	128
Holley-Navarre Middle Sch/*Navarre*/ Santa Rosa	00203111	850/936-6040	128
Holley-Navarre Primary Sch/*Navarre*/ Santa Rosa	04285367	850/936-6130	128
Holly Hill Sch/*Holly Hill*/Volusia	00204476	386/258-4662	141
Hollywood Acad Arts & Sciences/*Hollywood*/ Broward	05347011	954/925-6404	16
Hollywood Central Elem Sch/*Hollywood*/ Broward	00184022	754/323-6150	12
Hollywood Hills Elem Sch/*Hollywood*/Broward	00184034	754/323-6200	12
Hollywood Hills High Sch/*Hollywood*/Broward	00183626	754/323-1050	12
Hollywood Park Elem Sch/*Hollywood*/Broward	00184046	754/323-6250	12
Holmes Co High Sch/*Bonifay*/Holmes	00193293	850/547-9000	55
HOLMES CO SCH DIST/**BONIFAY**/ **HOLMES**	00193255	850/547-6674	55

School/City/County DISTRICT/CITY/COUNTY	PID	TELEPHONE NUMBER	PAGE
Holmes Elem Sch/*Miami*/Miami-Dade	00186020	305/836-3421	76
Holy Comforter Episcopal Sch/*Tallahassee*/Leon	01404289	850/383-1007	66
Holy Cross Lutheran Academy/*Sanford*/Seminole	05013492	407/936-3636	133
Holy Cross Lutheran Sch/*North Miami*/Miami-Dade	00187684	305/893-0851	87
Holy Cross Pre-School & Center/*West Palm Bch*/Palm Beach	11708405	561/366-8026	110
Holy Family Catholic Sch/*Jacksonville*/Duval	05110129	904/645-9875	34
Holy Family Catholic Sch/*Orlando*/Orange	04471487	407/876-9344	100
Holy Family Catholic Sch/*St Petersburg*/Pinellas	00200846	727/526-8194	120
Holy Family Sch/*Miami*/Miami-Dade	00188016	305/947-6535	85
Holy Name of Jesus Sch/*Indialantic*/Brevard	00197720	321/773-1630	9
Holy Nativity Episcopal Sch/*Panama City*/Bay	00181850	850/747-0060	5
Holy Redeemer Catholic Sch/*Kissimmee*/Osceola	04304602	407/870-9055	104
Holy Spirit Catholic Sch/*Jacksonville*/Duval	03266394	904/642-9165	34
Holy Temple Christian Academy/*Ft Lauderdale*/Broward	11237169	954/467-0758	19
Holy Trinity Episcopal Academy/*Melbourne*/Brevard	00182701	321/723-8323	9
Holy Trinity Episcopal Sch/*Fruitland Pk*/Lake	04862381	352/787-8855	60
Holy Trinity Lutheran Sch/*Tampa*/Hillsborough	00193176	813/839-0665	54
Homestead Middle Sch/*Homestead*/Miami-Dade	00187385	305/247-4221	82
Homestead Senior High Sch/*Homestead*/Miami-Dade	02046127	305/245-7000	82
Homosassa Elem Sch/*Homosassa*/Citrus	00184606	352/628-2953	22
Hope Academy/*Homestead*/Miami-Dade	11932216	786/243-3390	87
Hope Center for Autism/*Stuart*/Martin	10976049	772/334-3288	73
Hope Charter Sch/*Ocoee*/Orange	04950287	407/656-4673	94
Hope Christian Academy/*Starke*/Bradford	11620102	352/473-4040	6
Hope Forest Academy/*Paisley*/Lake	12323034	352/742-6920	59
Hope Preparatory Academy/*Groveland*/Lake	12322341	352/557-4959	60
Hope Ranch Learning Academy/*Hudson*/Pasco	11831600	727/232-0119	115
Hope Rural Sch/*Indiantown*/Martin	02113029	772/597-2203	73
Hope Sch/*Marianna*/Jackson	00193554	850/482-9616	57
Hope-Centennial Elem Sch/*West Palm Bch*/Palm Beach	11449946	561/640-1200	107
Hopper Center/*Altamonte SPG*/Seminole	04751495	407/746-2650	132
Horace Mann Middle Sch/*El Portal*/Miami-Dade	00186032	305/757-9537	76
Horace O'Bryant Sch/*Key West*/Monroe	00195899	305/296-5628	89
Horeb Christian Sch/*Hialeah*/Miami-Dade	02234764	305/557-6811	87
Horizon Academy at Marion Oaks/*Ocala*/Marion	10982830	352/671-6290	71
Horizon Charter School Tampa/*Tampa*/Hillsborough	05262435	813/887-3800	46
Horizon Elem Sch/*Port Orange*/Volusia	03251181	386/322-6150	141
Horizon Elem Sch/*Sunrise*/Broward	00183303	754/322-6450	12
Horizon Middle Sch/*Kissimmee*/Osceola	04365151	407/943-7240	103
Horizon West Middle Sch/*Windermere*/Orange	12367963	407/544-1570	99
Horizons Academy/*Bradenton*/Manatee	10009440	941/714-7470	68
Horizons Elem Sch/*Davenport*/Polk	11130884	863/419-3430	124
Hortense Mintz Elem Sch/*Brandon*/Hillsborough	03395672	813/744-8353	52
Hosford Elem Jr High Sch/*Hosford*/Liberty	00194912	850/379-8480	67
House of Hope Academy/*Orlando*/Orange	04331382	407/843-8686	101
Howard D McMillan Middle Sch/*Miami*/Miami-Dade	01527013	305/385-6877	82
Howard Drive Elem Sch/*Miami*/Miami-Dade	00187397	305/235-1412	82
Howard Middle Sch/*Ocala*/Marion	00195540	352/671-7225	71
Howard Middle Sch/*Orlando*/Orange	00196922	407/245-1780	95
Howard W Bishop Middle Sch/*Gainesville*/Alachua	00181240	352/955-6701	2
Howell L Watkins Middle Sch/*Palm BCH GDNS*/Palm Beach	00198528	561/776-3600	108
Hubert O Sibley K-8 Center/*Miami*/Miami-Dade	05101350	305/953-3737	79
Hudson Elem Sch/*Hudson*/Pasco	00199247	727/774-4000	113
Hudson High Sch/*Hudson*/Pasco	00199259	727/774-4200	114
Hudson Middle Sch/*Hudson*/Pasco	02228052	727/774-8200	115
Hugo Schmidt Elem Sch/*Brandon*/Hillsborough	05262253	813/651-2110	51
Hungerford Elem Sch/*Maitland*/Orange	00196934	407/623-1430	96
Hunter's Creek Elem Sch/*Orlando*/Orange	04290257	407/858-4610	99
Hunter's Creek Middle Sch/*Orlando*/Orange	04290269	407/858-4620	96

School/City/County DISTRICT/CITY/COUNTY	PID	TELEPHONE NUMBER	PAGE
Hunter's Green Elem Sch/*Tampa*/Hillsborough	04018578	813/973-7394	50
Husky Prep Academy/*Davenport*/Polk	12225652	863/866-2017	126
Hutchison Beach Elem Sch/*P C Beach*/Bay	00181630	850/767-5195	4
Hyde Grove Elem Sch/*Jacksonville*/Duval	00189242	904/693-7562	33
Hyde Park Elem Sch/*Jacksonville*/Duval	00189254	904/381-3950	33
I Prep/*Miami*/Miami-Dade	11463746	305/523-8338	74
Ibn Seena Academy/*Orlando*/Orange	11735238	407/888-1000	101
Ican Charter Academy/*Tampa*/Hillsborough	12361995	813/563-3809	46
Ida M Stewart Elem Sch/*Bradenton*/Manatee	02112130	941/741-3176	68
Ida S Baker High Sch/*Cape Coral*/Lee	05348429	239/458-6690	62
Idyllwilde Elem Sch/*Sanford*/Seminole	00203692	407/320-3750	132
Idylwild Elem Sch/*Gainesville*/Alachua	00181252	352/955-6709	2
Iflagler Virtual Sch/*Palm Coast*/Flagler	12225298	386/447-1520	39
Imagine ES-N Lauderdle CS/*N Lauderdale*/Broward	04946949	954/973-8900	16
Imagine School at Broward/*Coral Springs*/Broward	11076953	954/255-0020	16
Imagine School at Land O'Lakes/*Land O Lakes*/Pasco	11130975	813/428-7444	113
Imagine Schools Chancellor/*Boynton Beach*/Palm Beach	05010505	561/585-1189	105
Imagine Schools Kissimmee CA/*Kissimmee*/Osceola	04924783	407/847-1400	103
Imagine Schools Lakewood Ranch/*Bradenton*/Manatee	11079395	941/750-0900	68
Imagine Schools North Manatee/*Palmetto*/Manatee	10913504	941/981-5345	68
Imagine Schools North Port ES/*North Port*/Sarasota	11077402	941/426-2050	129
Imagine Schools North Port Up/*North Port*/Sarasota	11723742	941/426-2050	130
Imagine Schools Palmer Rnch/*Sarasota*/Sarasota	11451913	941/923-1125	130
Imagine Schools Plantation/*Plantation*/Broward	11822269	954/358-4200	16
Imagine Schools S Vero/*Vero Beach*/Indian River	11219753	772/567-2728	56
Imagine Schools South Lake/*Clermont*/Lake	10007442	352/243-2960	59
Imagine Schools Town Ctr/*Palm Coast*/Flagler	11445392	386/586-0100	39
Imagine Schools W Melbourne/*W Melbourne*/Brevard	04811954	321/768-6200	6
Imagine Weston/*Weston*/Broward	04946937	954/659-3600	16
Imater Academy Elem Sch/*Hialeah*/Miami-Dade	11931559	305/884-6320	79
Imater Academy Middle Sch/*Hialeah*/Miami-Dade	11923162	305/802-5722	79
Imater Prep Academy High Sch/*Hialeah*/Miami-Dade	11923174	305/805-5722	79
Img Academy/*Bradenton*/Manatee	10966654	941/739-3964	70
Immaculata-La Salle High Sch/*Coconut Grove*/Miami-Dade	00188042	305/854-2334	85
Immaculate Conception Sch/*Hialeah*/Miami-Dade	00188054	305/822-6461	85
Immanuel Lutheran Sch/*Brandon*/Hillsborough	02194554	813/685-1978	54
Immanuel Lutheran Sch/*Winter Haven*/Polk	01404497	863/967-5145	126
Immokalee Cmty Sch/*Immokalee*/Collier	04913966	239/867-3223	26
Immokalee High Sch/*Immokalee*/Collier	00184890	239/377-1800	26
Immokalee Middle Sch/*Immokalee*/Collier	00184905	239/377-4200	26
Immokalee Technical Center/*Immokalee*/Collier	04292401	239/377-9900	26
Imperial Estates Elem Sch/*Titusville*/Brevard	00182012	321/267-1773	7
Incarnation Catholic Sch/*Sarasota*/Sarasota	00200872	941/924-8588	131
Incarnation Catholic Sch/*Tampa*/Hillsborough	00200884	813/884-4502	53
Independence Academy/*Dover*/Hillsborough	10902646	813/473-8600	46
Independence Elem Sch/*Winter Garden*/Orange	12108523	407/217-7727	99
Independence Middle Sch/*Jupiter*/Palm Beach	05102392	561/799-7500	108
Indialantic Elem Sch/*Indialantic*/Brevard	00182361	321/723-2811	7
Indian Harbour Montessori Sch/*Indn HBR Bch*/Brevard	02854170	321/777-1480	9
Indian Pines Elem Sch/*Lake Worth*/Palm Beach	00198774	561/804-3300	109
Indian Ridge Middle Sch/*Davie*/Broward	04364547	754/323-3300	12
Indian Ridge Sch/*West Palm Bch*/Palm Beach	03427407	561/681-0000	107
Indian River Academy/*Vero Beach*/Indian River	03010638	772/564-3390	56
Indian River Charter High Sch/*Vero Beach*/Indian River	04808402	772/567-6600	56

School/City/County DISTRICT/CITY/COUNTY	PID	TELEPHONE NUMBER	PAGE
Indian River Elem Sch/*Edgewater*/Volusia	03380691	386/424-2650	141
Indian River Virtual Sch/*Vero Beach*/			
Indian River	11716127	772/564-3067	56
Indian Rocks Christian Sch/*Largo*/Pinellas	03062174	727/596-4321	121
Indian Trace Elem Sch/*Weston*/Broward	03336729	754/323-6300	12
Indian Trails Middle Sch/*Palm Coast*/			
Flagler	04451748	386/446-6732	39
Indian Trails Middle Sch/*Winter Spgs*/			
Seminole	04019522	407/320-4350	132
Indiantown Adult Learning Ctr/*Indiantown*/			
Martin	11819365	772/597-3848	73
Indiantown Middle Sch/*Indiantown*/Martin	00195734	772/597-2146	73
Indigo Christian Jr Academy/*Daytona Beach*/			
Volusia	01752749	386/255-5917	142
Inlet Grove Cmty High Sch/*Riviera Beach*/			
Palm Beach	00198607	561/881-4600	105
Innovation Charter Sch/*Pompano Beach*/			
Broward	12115150	954/715-1777	16
Innovation Middle Sch/*Orlando*/Orange	12230073	407/730-4670	98
Innovation Mont High Sch/*Ocoee*/Orange	12322999	407/654-2045	94
Innovation Mont-Ocoee/*Winter Garden*/Orange	11820649	407/654-2045	94
Innovation Sch of Excellence/*Tallahassee*/			
Leon	04493681	850/575-5580	66
Innovations Middle Charter Sch/*Orlando*/			
Orange	11557787	407/440-2846	94
Int'l Studies Charter Mid Sch/*Miami*/			
Miami-Dade	11560203	305/643-2955	83
Integrated Sci Asian Cult Acad/*Miami*/			
Miami-Dade	11453519	305/863-8030	76
Interactive Educ Academy/*Valrico*/			
Hillsborough	11227188	813/689-2087	54
Interlachen Elem Sch/*Interlachen*/Putnam	00202046	386/684-2130	127
Interlachen High Sch/*Interlachen*/Putnam	01524334	386/684-2116	127
International Community Sch/*Winter Park*/			
Orange	11236933	407/645-2343	101
International Sch of Broward/*Hollywood*/			
Broward	10907191	954/987-2026	16
International Studies Chart HS/*Miami*/			
Miami-Dade	05346885	305/643-2955	76
Intl Studies Prep Academy/*Coral Gables*/			
Miami-Dade	11595753	305/663-7200	76
Inverness Christian Academy/*Inverness*/			
Citrus	11735068	352/726-3759	22
Inverness Middle Sch/*Inverness*/Citrus	00184618	352/726-1471	22
Inverness Primary Sch/*Inverness*/Citrus	00184620	352/726-2632	22
Inwood Elem Sch/*Winter Haven*/Polk	00201826	863/291-5369	124
Ippolito Elem Sch/*Riverview*/Hillsborough	05097371	813/672-5180	48
Ipreparatory Academy/*Miami*/Miami-Dade	11719715	305/995-1929	76
Irving Beatrice Peskoe K-8 Ctr/*Homestead*/			
Miami-Dade	04036269	305/242-8340	83
Island Christian Sch/*Islamorada*/Monroe	01775038	305/664-4933	90
Island Coast High Sch/*Cape Coral*/Lee	10909539	239/458-0362	62
Island Park High Sch/*Fort Myers*/Lee	12045141	239/204-5965	62
Island Prep Primary Sch/*St Augustine*/			
St Johns	11773242	904/547-2996	135
Island Village Mont Sch-Saraso/*Sarasota*/			
Sarasota	04943882	941/954-4999	130
Island Village Mont-Venice/*Venice*/Sarasota	11554979	941/484-4999	130
Itech at Thomas Edison Ed Ctr/*Miami*/			
Miami-Dade	12037211	305/762-5000	76
Ivey Lane Elem Sch/*Orlando*/Orange	00196946	407/296-6420	95
Ivy Hawn CS of the Arts/*Lake Helen*/Volusia	11715563	386/228-3900	141

J

J Allen Axson Elem Sch/*Jacksonville*/Duval	00189266	904/992-3600	31
J C Mitchell Elem Sch/*Boca Raton*/			
Palm Beach	00198841	561/750-4900	109
J Colin English Elem Sch/*N Ft Myers*/Lee	00194273	239/995-2258	62
J D Parker Math-Sci-Tech Sch/*Stuart*/Martin	00195760	772/219-1580	73
J E B Stuart Middle Sch/*Jacksonville*/Duval	00189278	904/573-1000	32
J Franklin Keller Interm Sch/*Macclenny*/			
Baker	03246461	904/259-4244	4
J J Finley Elem Sch/*Gainesville*/Alachua	00181264	352/955-6705	2
J M Tate Senior High Sch/*Cantonment*/			
Escambia	00190667	850/937-2300	37
J P Taravella High Sch/*Coral Springs*/			
Broward	02176942	754/322-2300	12
J R Arnold High Sch/*P C Beach*/Bay	04918150	850/767-3700	4
J S Robinson Elem Sch/*Plant City*/			
Hillsborough	00192342	813/757-9424	52
J W Mitchell High Sch/*New Prt Rchy*/Pasco	04916542	727/774-9200	114
Jack D Gordon Elem Sch/*Miami*/Miami-Dade	04290075	305/234-4805	83

School/City/County DISTRICT/CITY/COUNTY	PID	TELEPHONE NUMBER	PAGE
Jack R Lamb Elem Sch/*Tampa*/Hillsborough	12106305	813/605-4950	52
Jackson Alternative Sch/*Marianna*/Jackson	10022583	850/482-9666	57
Jackson Co Adult Educ Center/*Marianna*/			
Jackson	01811383	850/482-9617	57
JACKSON CO SCH DIST/**MARIANNA**/			
JACKSON	00193499	850/482-1200	57
Jackson Co Virtual Sch/*Marianna*/Jackson	11924893	866/339-8784	57
Jackson Elem Sch/*Plant City*/Hillsborough	00192926	813/757-9341	48
Jackson Heights Middle Sch/*Oviedo*/Seminole	00203707	407/320-4550	132
Jackson Middle Sch/*Orlando*/Orange	00197419	407/249-6430	98
Jacksonville Adventist Academy/*Jacksonville*/			
Duval	01436220	904/268-2433	35
Jacksonville Assem Chrn Acad/*Jacksonville*/			
Duval	12235803	904/786-1198	35
Jacksonville Beach Elem Sch/*Jax Bch*/Duval	03402158	904/247-5942	31
Jacksonville Christian Academy/*Jacksonville*/			
Duval	11237107	904/783-2818	35
Jacksonville Country Day Sch/*Jacksonville*/			
Duval	00190198	904/641-6644	35
Jacksonville Hts Elem Sch/*Jacksonville*/			
Duval	00189292	904/573-1120	31
Jacksonville School for Autism/*Jacksonville*/			
Duval	12036097	904/732-4343	35
Jacobson Tech HS at Seminole/*Seminole*/			
Pinellas	00200183	727/545-6405	118
Jacqueline Harris Prep Academy/*Pensacola*/			
Escambia	04950158	850/432-2273	37
James A Long Elem Sch/*Palatka*/Putnam	00202260	386/329-0575	127
James A Shanks Middle Sch/*Quincy*/Gadsden	00191099	850/875-8737	40
James B Sanderlin IB World Sch/*St Petersburg*/			
Pinellas	05273898	727/552-1700	118
James C Bailey Middle Sch/*Pensacola*/			
Escambia	04417857	850/492-6136	37
James E Sampson Mem SDA Sch/*Fort Pierce*/			
St Lucie	01437535	772/465-8386	137
James E Stephens Elem Sch/*Bartow*/Polk	01524322	863/534-7455	124
James Elem Sch/*Tampa*/Hillsborough	05351206	813/740-4800	48
James H Bright-J W Johnson ES/*Hialeah*/			
Miami-Dade	00186044	305/885-1683	79
James Irvin Education Center/*Dade City*/			
Pasco	04366600	352/524-5700	114
James M Anderson Elem Sch/*Cross City*/Dixie	00188755	352/541-6251	29
James M Marlowe Elem Sch/*New Prt Rchy*/			
Pasco	04872142	727/774-8600	113
James Madison Middle Sch/*Titusville*/			
Brevard	00182024	321/264-3120	8
James Madison Prep Chtr HS/*Madison*/Madison	11931925	850/253-2173	67
James Rickards High Sch/*Tallahassee*/Leon	00194637	850/488-1783	65
James Rickards Middle Sch/*Oakland Park*/			
Broward	03400277	754/322-4400	12
James S Hunt Elem Sch/*Coral Springs*/			
Broward	00182907	754/322-6500	12
James Stephens Int'l Academy/*Fort Myers*/			
Lee	00194297	239/337-1333	62
James Tillman Elem Sch/*Palmetto*/Manatee	00195136	941/723-4833	68
James W Johnson Prep Mid Sch/*Jacksonville*/			
Duval	00189307	904/693-7600	33
James W Sikes Elem Sch/*Lakeland*/Polk	02199669	863/648-3525	125
Jan Mann Opp Sch/*Opa Locka*/Miami-Dade	00185636	305/625-0855	74
Jane Roberts K-8 Center/*Miami*/Miami-Dade	03249578	305/220-8254	83
Janie Howard Wilson Elem Sch/*Lake Wales*/			
Polk	00201668	863/678-4211	123
Jay Elem Sch/*Jay*/Santa Rosa	00203123	850/359-8230	128
Jay High Sch/*Jay*/Santa Rosa	01527312	850/675-4507	128
Jeaga Middle Sch/*West Palm Bch*/Palm Beach	05272789	561/242-8000	108
Jean O'Dell Learning Center/*Bartow*/Polk	01397985	863/534-7440	123
Jean Ribault High Sch/*Jacksonville*/Duval	00189814	904/924-3092	32
Jean Ribault Middle Sch/*Jacksonville*/Duval	00189802	904/924-3062	33
JEFFERSON CO SCH DIST/**MONTICELLO**/			
JEFFERSON	00193619	850/342-0100	57
Jefferson Davis Middle Sch/*Jacksonville*/			
Duval	00189319	904/573-1060	33
Jefferson Senior High Sch/*Tampa*/			
Hillsborough	00192988	813/872-5241	49
Jefferson Somerset K-12 Sch/*Monticello*/			
Jefferson	00193645	850/997-3555	57
Jennings First Christian Sch/*Jennings*/			
Hamilton	04982797	386/938-1179	42
Jennings Middle Sch/*Seffner*/Hillsborough	05262095	813/740-4575	48
Jensen Beach Elem Sch/*Jensen Beach*/Martin	00195746	772/219-1555	73
Jensen Beach High Sch/*Jensen Beach*/Martin	05344681	772/232-3500	73

School/City/County DISTRICT/CITY/COUNTY	PID	TELEPHONE NUMBER	PAGE
Jere L Stambaugh Middle Sch/*Auburndale/* Polk	02224915	863/965-5494	122
Jerry Thomas Elem Sch/*Jupiter/*Palm Beach	02130015	561/741-9100	108
Jesse J McCrary Elem Sch/*Miami/*Miami-Dade	00186094	305/754-7531	76
Jesse Keen Elem Sch/*Lakeland/*Polk	00201307	863/499-2880	124
Jessie P Miller Elem Sch/*Bradenton/*Manatee	00195148	941/741-3300	69
Jesuit High Sch/*Tampa/*Hillsborough	00200896	813/877-5344	54
Jewett Middle Academy/*Winter Haven/*Polk	00201890	863/291-5320	122
Jewett School of the Arts/*Winter Haven/* Polk	00201840	863/291-5373	122
Jewish Academy of Orlando/*Maitland/*Orange	02181466	407/647-0713	101
Jim Allen Elem Sch/*Cantonment/*Escambia	00190679	850/937-2260	37
Jinks Middle Sch/*Panama City/*Bay	00181642	850/767-4695	4
Jitta Bug Learning Center/*Miami/*Miami-Dade	12177275	786/274-2519	87
Joe Hall Elem Sch/*Miami/*Miami-Dade	02907040	305/223-9823	83
Joella Good Elem Sch/*Hialeah/*Miami-Dade	03343318	305/625-2008	79
John A Crookshank Elem Sch/*St Augustine/* St Johns	00202375	904/547-7840	134
John A Ferguson Sr High Sch/*Miami/* Miami-Dade	05278472	305/408-2700	83
John Carroll High Sch/*Fort Pierce/*St Lucie	00197732	772/464-5200	137
John D Floyd Elem Sch/*Spring Hill/*Hernando	02892897	352/797-7055	44
John E Ford Elem Sch/*Jacksonville/*Duval	03402134	904/630-6540	31
John F Kennedy Middle Sch/*Miami/*Miami-Dade	00185260	305/947-1451	79
John F Kennedy Middle Sch/*Riviera Beach/* Palm Beach	00198554	561/845-4501	108
John F Kennedy Middle Sch/*Rockledge/* Brevard	00182218	321/633-3500	9
John F Turner Sr Elem Sch/*Palm Bay/*Brevard	02191083	321/676-5700	7
John G DuPuis Elem Sch/*Hialeah/*Miami-Dade	00185648	305/821-6361	79
John G Riley Elem Sch/*Tallahassee/*Leon	00194649	850/488-5840	65
John Hopkins Middle Sch/*St Petersburg/* Pinellas	00200353	727/893-2400	118
John I Leonard High Sch/*Greenacres/* Palm Beach	00198164	561/641-1200	107
John I Smith K-8 Center/*Miami/*Miami-Dade	04454374	305/406-0220	76
John Love Elem Sch/*Jacksonville/*Duval	00189333	904/630-6790	33
John M Sexton Elem Sch/*St Petersburg/* Pinellas	00200078	727/570-3400	119
John NC Stockton ES/*Jacksonville/*Duval	00189345	904/381-3955	31
John Paul II Catholic High Sch/*Tallahassee/* Leon	05009506	850/201-5744	65
John Snively Elem Sch/*Eloise/*Polk	00201838	863/291-5325	125
John Young Elem Sch/*Orlando/*Orange	03334513	407/858-3120	96
Jones High Sch/*Orlando/*Orange	00196958	407/835-2300	97
Jordan Glen Sch/*Archer/*Alachua	01771915	352/495-2728	3
Jorge Mas Canosa Middle Sch/*Miami/* Miami-Dade	10907737	305/252-5900	83
Jose De Diego Middle Sch/*Miami/*Miami-Dade	00186410	305/573-7229	76
Jose Marti Mast 6-12 Academy/*Hialeah/* Miami-Dade	03038197	305/557-5931	79
Jose Marti Sch/*Miami/*Miami-Dade	04983686	305/441-0565	87
Jose Marti/Little Shaver 1/*Miami/* Miami-Dade	03381011	305/856-9044	87
Joseph Finegan Elem Sch/*Atlantic Bch/*Duval	00189357	904/247-5996	31
Joseph Stilwell Middle Sch/*Jacksonville/* Duval	00189369	904/693-7523	33
Joseph Williams Elem Sch/*Gainesville/* Alachua	00181458	352/955-6719	2
Joshua Christian Academy/*Jacksonville/* Duval	04983040	904/388-2227	35
Journeys Academy/*Sanford/*Seminole	11451470	407/320-7820	132
Joy Explosion Christian Acad/*Lake City/* Columbia	11927651	386/867-0749	28
Joyce Bullock Elem Sch/*Williston/*Levy	00194857	352/528-3341	66
Jubilee Christian Academy/*Pensacola/* Escambia	04983181	850/474-9484	38
Julia Landon College Prep/*Jacksonville/* Duval	00189436	904/346-5650	33
Julington Creek Elem Sch/*Saint Johns/* St Johns	00202430	904/547-7980	134
Jupiter Academy/*Jupiter/*Palm Beach	05230664	561/747-1003	111
Jupiter Christian Sch/*Jupiter/*Palm Beach	00199027	561/746-7800	111
Jupiter Cmty High Sch/*Jupiter/*Palm Beach	00198542	561/744-7900	108
Jupiter Elem Sch/*Jupiter/*Palm Beach	00198530	561/741-5300	108
Jupiter Elem Sch/*Palm Bay/*Brevard	03398985	321/952-5990	7
Jupiter Farms Elem Sch/*Jupiter/*Palm Beach	03380914	561/741-5400	108
Jupiter Middle Sch/*Jupiter/*Palm Beach	01530929	561/745-7200	108
Just Arts/Mngmnt Charter MS/*Doral/* Miami-Dade	11829724	305/597-9999	76
Just Elem Sch/*Tampa/*Hillsborough	05351103	813/276-5708	48
Just for Girls Academy/*Bradenton/*Manatee	11816818	941/747-5757	69

School/City/County DISTRICT/CITY/COUNTY	PID	TELEPHONE NUMBER	PAGE
Juvenile Justice Center Sch/*Miami/* Miami-Dade	04036594	305/638-5054	74

K

School/City/County DISTRICT/CITY/COUNTY	PID	TELEPHONE NUMBER	PAGE
K E Cunningham-Canal Point ES/*Canal Point/* Palm Beach	00198372	561/924-9800	107
Kaleidoscope Sch of Disc/*Panama City/*Bay	11226172	850/785-7157	5
Kanapaha Middle Sch/*Gainesville/*Alachua	04452546	352/955-6960	2
Karen M Siegel Academy/*Lake Alfred/*Polk	00201814	863/965-5566	123
Kate M Smith Elem Sch/*Chipley/*Washington	00205030	850/638-6220	144
Kate Sullivan Elem Sch/*Tallahassee/*Leon	00194651	850/487-1216	65
Kathleen Elem Sch/*Lakeland/*Polk	00201321	863/853-6030	125
Kathleen High Sch/*Lakeland/*Polk	00201345	863/499-2655	122
Kathleen Middle Sch/*Lakeland/*Polk	00201333	863/853-6040	125
Katz Hillel Day Sch Boca Raton/*Boca Raton/* Palm Beach	04295219	561/470-5000	111
Katz Yeshiva HS South Florida/*Boca Raton/* Palm Beach	04983961	561/417-7422	111
Keene's Crossing Elem Sch/*Windermere/* Orange	11452797	407/654-1351	99
Keeth Elem Sch/*Winter Spgs/*Seminole	02202711	407/320-5350	132
Kelley Smith Elem Sch/*Palatka/*Putnam	00202337	386/329-0568	127
Kelsey Pharr Elem Sch/*Miami/*Miami-Dade	00186616	305/633-0429	76
Kendale Elem Sch/*Miami/*Miami-Dade	00186977	305/274-2735	83
Kendale Lakes Elem Sch/*Miami/*Miami-Dade	01527025	305/385-2575	83
Kendall Christian Sch/*Miami/*Miami-Dade	01773274	305/271-3723	87
Kendall Square K-8 Center/*Miami/*Miami-Dade	12310489	305/382-6830	83
Kenly Elem Sch/*Tampa/*Hillsborough	00192380	813/744-8074	48
Kensington Park Elem Sch/*Miami/*Miami-Dade	00186628	305/649-2811	76
Kenwood Elem Sch/*Ft Walton Bch/*Okaloosa	00196295	850/833-3570	92
Kenwood K-8 Center/*Miami/*Miami-Dade	00186989	305/271-5061	83
Kernan Middle Sch/*Jacksonville/*Duval	05101817	904/220-1350	33
Kernan Trail Elem Sch/*Jacksonville/*Duval	05101805	904/220-1310	31
Keswick Christian Sch/*St Petersburg/* Pinellas	00200652	727/393-9100	121
Ketterlinus Elem Sch/*St Augustine/*St Johns	04013700	904/547-8540	134
Key Biscayne K-8 Center/*Key Biscayne/* Miami-Dade	00186630	305/361-5418	76
Key Largo Sch/*Key Largo/*Monroe	00195904	305/453-1255	89
Key West Collegiate Sch/*Key West/*Monroe	11745984	305/296-5927	89
Key West High Sch/*Key West/*Monroe	00195916	305/293-1549	89
Keypoint Christian Academy/*Miami/* Miami-Dade	05078351	305/998-5413	87
Keys Gate Charter High Sch/*Homestead/* Miami-Dade	11719686	786/272-9600	83
Keys Gate Charter Sch/*Homestead/*Miami-Dade	05278458	786/272-9600	83
Keystone Christian Academy/*Keystone HGTS/* Clay	11829097	352/494-1829	24
Keystone Heights Elem Sch/*Keystone HGTS/* Clay	01340023	904/336-1377	23
Keystone Heights Jr Sr HS/*Keystone HGTS/* Clay	00184723	904/336-7775	23
Keystone Prep High Sch/*Odessa/*Hillsborough	12235877	813/264-4500	54
Kid's Cmty Clg Riverview South/*Riverview/* Hillsborough	10003161	813/671-1440	46
Kids Cmty Clg SE Chtr Sch/*Riverview/* Hillsborough	12028636	813/699-4600	46
Kids Cmty Clg SE Mid CS/*Riverview/* Hillsborough	12231699	813/672-0144	46
Kids Cmty Clg-Orange Co Campus/*Ocoee/* Orange	11713618	407/982-2421	94
Kids Cmty College Charter HS/*Riverview/* Hillsborough	12231663	813/699-5751	46
Killarney Elem Sch/*Winter Park/*Orange	00196984	407/623-1438	97
Killearn Lakes Elem Sch/*Tallahassee/*Leon	02848535	850/921-1265	65
Killian Oaks Academy/*Miami/*Miami-Dade	01435628	305/274-2221	87
Kimball Wiles Elem Sch/*Gainesville/*Alachua	02856790	352/955-6955	2
Kimbell Elem Sch/*Tampa/*Hillsborough	11076769	813/983-3900	48
Kinder Cub Sch/*Cross City/*Dixie	11735599	352/498-0002	29
Kindergarten Learning Center/*Sebring/* Highlands	10909955	863/314-5281	45
King of Kings Lutheran Sch/*Maitland/*Orange	01775210	407/628-5696	101
King Senior High Sch/*Tampa/*Hillsborough	00192392	813/744-8333	50
Kingdom Academy/*Miami/*Miami-Dade	10782953	305/385-3761	87
Kingdom Christian Acad & PS/*Ocala/*Marion	11619799	352/369-3119	72
Kings Academy/*West Palm Bch/*Palm Beach	00199039	561/686-4244	111
Kings Christian Sch/*Miami/*Miami-Dade	01773315	305/221-2008	87
Kings Highway Elem Sch/*Clearwater/*Pinellas	12032845	727/223-8949	118
Kings Kids Christian Academy/*Tampa/* Hillsborough	11237042	813/248-6548	54
Kings Trail Elem Sch/*Jacksonville/*Duval	00189876	904/739-5254	31

School/City/County DISTRICT/CITY/COUNTY	PID	TELEPHONE NUMBER	PAGE
Kingsfield Elem Sch/*Cantonment*/Escambia	12308400	850/937-5200	37
Kingsford Elem Sch/*Mulberry*/Polk	00202076	863/701-1054	125
Kingsway Christian Academy/*Orlando*/Orange	00197586	407/295-8901	101
Kingsway Elem Sch/*Pt Charlotte*/Charlotte	04803660	941/255-7590	21
Kingswood Elem Sch/*Brandon*/Hillsborough	00192407	813/744-8234	52
Kingswood Montessori Academy/*Homestead*/ Miami-Dade	01559638	305/248-2308	87
Kinloch Park Elem Sch/*Miami*/Miami-Dade	00186642	305/445-1351	76
Kinloch Park Middle Sch/*Miami*/Miami-Dade	00186654	305/445-5467	76
Kinnan Elem Sch/*Sarasota*/Manatee	04915433	941/358-2888	69
KIPP Impact Middle Sch/*Jacksonville*/Duval	11560629	904/683-6643	29
KIPP Jacksonville Elem Sch/*Jacksonville*/ Duval	12114833	904/683-0355	29
KIPP Sunrise Academy/*Miami*/Miami-Dade	12323010	305/694-4162	76
KIPP Voice Elem Sch/*Jacksonville*/Duval	11823562	904/683-6643	29
Kirby-Smith Middle Sch/*Jacksonville*/Duval	00189383	904/630-6600	33
Kissimmee Elem Sch/*Kissimmee*/Osceola	00197976	407/935-3640	103
Kissimmee Middle Sch/*Kissimmee*/Osceola	00198023	407/870-0857	103
Knights Elem Sch/*Plant City*/Hillsborough	00192419	813/757-9333	52
Koa Elem Sch/*Kissimmee*/Osceola	11452149	407/518-1161	103

L

School/City/County	PID	TELEPHONE NUMBER	PAGE
L A Ainger Middle Sch/*Rotonda West*/ Charlotte	02227046	941/697-5800	21
L C Swain Middle Sch/*Greenacres*/Palm Beach	10002636	561/649-6900	109
La Amistad Sch/*Maitland*/Orange	03052325	407/647-0660	101
La Progresiva Presbyterian Sch/*Miami*/ Miami-Dade	01435264	305/642-8600	87
LaBelle Adult Sch/*Labelle*/Hendry	01485582	863/674-4118	43
LaBelle Elem Sch/*Labelle*/Hendry	00191594	863/674-4150	43
LaBelle High Sch/*Labelle*/Hendry	00191609	863/674-4120	43
LaBelle Middle Sch/*Labelle*/Hendry	01521291	863/674-4646	43
LaBelle Youth Dev Academy/*Labelle*/Hendry	04802142	863/674-4590	43
Lacoochee Elem Sch/*Dade City*/Pasco	00199261	352/524-5600	113
LAFAYETTE CO SCH DIST/**MAYO**/ **LAFAYETTE**	00193683	386/294-1351	58
Lafayette Elem Sch/*Mayo*/Lafayette	01827095	386/294-2882	58
Lafayette Franchise Sch/*Mayo*/Lafayette	11647423	386/294-1351	58
Lafayette High Sch/*Mayo*/Lafayette	00193695	386/294-1701	58
Lake Academy/*Leesburg*/Lake	03191191	352/315-7890	60
Lake Alfred Elem Sch/*Lake Alfred*/Polk	00201864	863/295-5985	125
Lake Alfred Polytech Academy/*Lake Alfred*/ Polk	00201747	863/295-5988	125
Lake Asbury Elem Sch/*Green Cv Spgs*/Clay	03007411	904/336-1525	23
Lake Asbury Junior High Sch/*Green Cv Spgs*/ Clay	10001503	904/336-5375	23
Lake Brantley High Sch/*Altamonte SPG*/ Seminole	00203719	407/746-3450	132
Lake Butler Elem Sch/*Lake Butler*/Union	00204256	352/448-5302	139
Lake Butler Middle Sch/*Lake Butler*/Union	00204268	352/448-5153	139
Lake City Christian Academy/*Lake City*/ Columbia	10783725	386/758-0055	28
Lake City Middle Sch/*Lake City*/Columbia	02232003	386/758-4800	27
LAKE CO SCH DIST/**TAVARES**/**LAKE**	00193700	352/253-6500	58
Lake Co Virtual Sch/*Eustis*/Lake	11830395	352/483-4260	59
Lake Como K-8 Sch/*Orlando*/Orange	00196972	407/897-6420	99
Lake Country Elem Sch/*Lake Placid*/ Highlands	03049639	863/699-5050	45
Lake Eola Charter Sch/*Orlando*/Orange	04811667	407/246-0900	94
Lake Fern Montessori Academy/*Titusville*/ Brevard	03101952	321/268-3365	10
Lake Forest Elem Sch/*Gainesville*/Alachua	00181288	352/955-6710	2
Lake Forest Elem Sch/*Pembroke Park*/Broward	00184058	754/323-6350	12
Lake Forrest Preparatory Sch/*Maitland*/ Orange	03653773	407/331-5144	101
Lake Gem Elem Sch/*Orlando*/Orange	04806258	407/532-7900	97
Lake George Elem Sch/*Orlando*/Orange	04806260	407/737-1430	98
Lake Gibson High Sch/*Lakeland*/Polk	02046153	863/853-6100	122
Lake Gibson Middle Sch/*Lakeland*/Polk	01524308	863/853-6151	122
Lake Highland Preparatory Sch/*Orlando*/ Orange	01436983	407/206-1900	101
Lake Hills Sch/*Howey In Hls*/Lake	01527166	352/324-3175	59
Lake Howell High Sch/*Winter Park*/Seminole	00203721	407/746-9050	132
Lake Lucina Elem Sch/*Jacksonville*/Duval	00189412	904/745-4916	31
Lake Magdalene Elem Sch/*Tampa*/Hillsborough	00192421	813/975-7625	50
Lake Marion Creek Sch/*Poinciana*/Polk	10027789	863/427-1471	122
Lake Mary Elem Sch/*Lake Mary*/Seminole	00203733	407/320-5650	132
Lake Mary High Sch/*Lake Mary*/Seminole	02127367	407/320-9550	132
Lake Mary Preparatory Sch/*Lake Mary*/ Seminole	05013258	407/805-0095	134
Lake Minneola High Sch/*Minneola*/Lake	11716608	352/394-9600	59
Lake Montessori/*Leesburg*/Lake	01436816	352/787-5333	60

School/City/County	PID	TELEPHONE NUMBER	PAGE
Lake Myrtle Elem Sch/*Land O Lakes*/Pasco	02227345	813/794-1000	113
Lake Nona High Sch/*Orlando*/Orange	11445536	407/956-8300	97
Lake Nona Middle Sch/*Orlando*/Orange	11445524	407/858-5522	98
Lake Orienta Elem Sch/*Altamonte SPG*/ Seminole	01397997	407/746-2650	132
Lake Panasoffkee Elem Sch/*Lk Panasoffke*/ Sumter	03047021	352/793-1093	138
Lake Park Baptist Sch/*Lake Park*/Palm Beach	01437298	561/844-2747	111
Lake Park Elem Sch/*Lake Park*/Palm Beach	00198566	561/494-1300	108
Lake Park Elem Sch/*Naples*/Collier	00184917	239/377-7200	26
Lake Placid Elem Sch/*Lake Placid*/Highlands	00191752	863/699-5070	45
Lake Placid High Sch/*Lake Placid*/Highlands	01543641	863/699-5010	45
Lake Placid Middle Sch/*Lake Placid*/ Highlands	00191764	863/699-5030	45
Lake Region High Sch/*Eagle Lake*/Polk	04365840	863/297-3099	122
Lake Rose Christian Academy/*Orlando*/Orange	11237004	407/297-6995	101
Lake Shipp Elem Sch/*Winter Haven*/Polk	00201876	863/291-5384	125
Lake Shore Middle Sch/*Belle Glade*/ Palm Beach	00198437	561/829-1100	108
Lake Shore Middle Sch/*Jacksonville*/Duval	00189424	904/381-7440	33
Lake Silver Elem Sch/*Orlando*/Orange	00197005	407/245-1850	97
Lake St George Elem Sch/*Palm Harbor*/ Pinellas	03051759	727/669-1161	117
Lake Stevens Elem Sch/*Miami Gardens*/ Miami-Dade	00185650	305/625-6536	79
Lake Stevens Middle Sch/*Opa Locka*/ Miami-Dade	01340097	305/620-1294	79
Lake Success Academy/*Howey In Hls*/Lake	12368967	352/253-4185	59
Lake Sybelia Elem Sch/*Maitland*/Orange	00197017	407/623-1445	97
Lake Technical Center/*Eustis*/Lake	00193841	352/589-2250	59
Lake Trafford Elem Sch/*Immokalee*/Collier	00184929	239/377-7300	26
Lake Wales High Sch/*Lake Wales*/Polk	00201632	863/678-4222	123
Lake Weir High Sch/*Ocala*/Marion	01340176	352/671-4820	71
Lake Weir Middle Sch/*Summerfield*/Marion	00195552	352/671-6120	71
Lake Weston Elem Sch/*Orlando*/Orange	00197029	407/296-6430	95
Lake Whitney Elem Sch/*Winter Garden*/Orange	04757279	407/877-8888	99
Lake Worth Christian Sch/*Boynton Beach*/ Palm Beach	01527221	561/586-8216	111
Lake Worth Cmty High Sch/*Lake Worth*/ Palm Beach	00198853	561/533-6300	107
Lake Worth Cmty Middle Sch/*Lake Worth*/ Palm Beach	00198865	561/540-5500	109
Lakeland Christian Sch/*Lakeland*/Polk	00202155	863/688-2771	126
Lakeland High Sch/*Lakeland*/Polk	00201369	863/499-2900	122
Lakeland Highlands Middle Sch/*Lakeland*/ Polk	00201357	863/648-3500	122
Lakeland Mont Schoolhouse/*Lakeland*/Polk	05346718	863/413-0003	123
Lakeland Montessori Middle Sch/*Lakeland*/ Polk	11561697	863/413-0003	123
Lakemont Elem Sch/*Winter Park*/Orange	00197031	407/623-1453	96
Lakeside Christian Sch/*Clearwater*/Pinellas	01775894	727/461-3311	121
Lakeside Elem Sch/*Orange Park*/Clay	01340035	904/336-1675	23
Lakeside Elem Sch/*Pembroke Pnes*/Broward	04809315	754/323-6400	12
Lakeside Junior High Sch/*Orange Park*/Clay	00184735	904/336-5575	23
Lakeview Center Sch/*Pensacola*/Escambia	01774149	850/469-3535	37
Lakeview Christian Sch/*Lake Placid*/ Highlands	03148285	863/465-0313	45
Lakeview Elem Sch/*Miami*/Miami-Dade	00186068	305/757-1535	76
Lakeview Elem Sch/*Saint Cloud*/Osceola	03009093	407/891-3220	103
Lakeview Elem Sch/*Sarasota*/Sarasota	03011096	941/361-6571	130
Lakeview Fundamental Elem Sch/*St Petersburg*/ Pinellas	00199845	727/893-2139	118
Lakeview Middle Sch/*Winter Garden*/Orange	00197043	407/877-5010	99
Lakeville Elem Sch/*Apopka*/Orange	04806272	407/814-6110	97
Lakewood Community Adult Ctr/*St Petersburg*/ Pinellas	11822635	727/893-2955	116
Lakewood Elem Sch/*St Petersburg*/Pinellas	00199857	727/893-2196	118
Lakewood High Sch/*St Petersburg*/Pinellas	00199869	727/893-2916	118
Lakewood Park Elem Sch/*Fort Pierce*/ St Lucie	02128464	772/468-5830	136
Lakewood Ranch High Sch/*Bradenton*/Manatee	04812996	941/727-6100	69
Lamar Louise Curry Middle Sch/*Miami*/ Miami-Dade	05278460	305/222-2775	83
LaMarque Elem Sch/*North Port*/Sarasota	10024220	941/426-6371	130
Lamp Sch/*Fort Myers*/Lee	03011292	239/332-2526	62
Lancaster Elem Sch/*Orlando*/Orange	00197055	407/858-3130	98
Land O'Lakes Christian Sch/*Land O Lakes*/ Pasco	03062203	813/995-9040	115
Land O'Lakes High Sch/*Land O Lakes*/Pasco	00199273	813/794-9400	114
Land of Lakes Montessori Sch/*Clermont*/Lake	05378553	352/242-1805	60
Landmark Christian Elem Sch/*Haines City*/ Polk	11729100	863/422-2037	126

School/City/County DISTRICT/CITY/COUNTY	PID	TELEPHONE NUMBER	PAGE
Landmark Christian High Sch/Haines City/Polk	02193354	863/419-1401	126
Landmark Middle Sch/Jacksonville/Duval	03329477	904/221-7125	33
Language & Literacy Acad Lrng/Winter Haven/Polk	12312815	863/268-2903	123
Lanier Elem Sch/Tampa/Hillsborough	00192433	813/272-3060	49
Lanier James Education Center/Hallandale/Broward	03007473	754/321-7350	12
Lantana Cmty Middle Sch/Lantana/Palm Beach	00198889	561/540-3400	110
Lantana Elem Sch/Lantana/Palm Beach	00198877	561/202-0300	110
Largo High Sch/Largo/Pinellas	00199895	727/588-3758	118
Largo Middle Sch/Largo/Pinellas	00199883	727/588-4600	118
Larkdale Elem Sch/Ft Lauderdale/Broward	00183224	754/322-6600	12
Larkin Sch for Health Sciences/Miami/Miami-Dade	12362157		76
Lauderdale Lakes Middle Sch/Laud Lakes/Broward	00183236	754/322-3500	12
Lauderhill 6-12 Magnet Sch/Lauderhill/Broward	00183250	754/322-3600	13
Lauderhill P Turner Elem Sch/Lauderhill/Broward	00183262	754/322-6700	13
Laura Saunders Elem Sch/Homestead/Miami-Dade	00187256	305/247-3933	83
Laureate Park Elem Sch/Orlando/Orange	12230061	407/730-8730	98
Laurel Elem Sch/Poinciana/Polk	10902713	863/427-1375	125
Laurel Hill Sch/Laurel Hill/Okaloosa	00196312	850/652-4111	92
Laurel Oak Elem Sch/Naples/Collier	04034613	239/377-7400	26
Laurel-Nokomis Sch/Nokomis/Sarasota	00203393	941/486-2171	130
Lavilla School of Arts/Jacksonville/Duval	04917209	904/633-6069	33
Lavoy Exceptional Center/Tampa/Hillsborough	00192110	813/872-5285	49
Law Enforcomont Offr Mem HS/Miami/Miami-Dade	11453492	305/371-0400	76
Lawnwood Elem Sch/Fort Pierce/St Lucie	00202923	772/468-5740	136
Lawtey Elem Sch/Lawtey/Bradford	00181939	904/966-6795	6
Lawton Chiles Elem Sch/Orlando/Orange	04885412	407/737-1470	96
Lawton Chiles Elem Sch/Tampa/Hillsborough	04948909	813/558-5422	50
Lawton Chiles High Sch/Tallahassee/Leon	04871617	850/488-1756	65
Lawton Chiles Middle Academy/Lakeland/Polk	04017249	863/499-2742	122
Lawton Chiles Middle Sch/Hialeah/Miami-Dade	04920854	305/816-9101	79
Lawton Chiles Middle Sch/Oviedo/Seminole	04878782	407/871-7050	132
Lawton Elem Sch/Oviedo/Seminole	00203757	407/320-6350	132
Lawton M Chiles Elem Sch/Gainesville/Alachua	04874619	352/333-2825	2
Layer Elem Sch/Winter Spgs/Seminole	05347499	407/871-8050	132
Lba Const & Bus Mgt Charter HS/Hialeah GDNS/Miami-Dade	11822207	305/822-8455	79
Lead Academy/Pace/Santa Rosa	12101159	850/995-1900	128
Leaders Preparatory Sch/Orlando/Orange	04291342	407/382-9900	101
Lealman Avenue Elem Sch/St Petersburg/Pinellas	00199900	727/570-3020	119
Lealman Innovation Academy/St Petersburg/Pinellas	00199912	727/528-5802	118
Learey Technical College/Tampa/Hillsborough	04810091	813/231-1840	46
Learning Academy of Santa Rosa/Milton/Santa Rosa	04808775	850/983-3495	128
Learning Ctr-Els Ctr Excel/Jupiter/Palm Beach	04875534	561/296-1776	105
Learning Experience Sch/Miami/Miami-Dade	03130501	305/279-9811	87
Learning Gate Cmty Sch/Lutz/Hillsborough	04920907	813/948-4190	46
Learning Lodge Academy/Port Richey/Pasco	12101434	727/389-0067	113
Lecanto High Sch/Lecanto/Citrus	02226494	352/746-2334	22
Lecanto Middle Sch/Lecanto/Citrus	02125577	352/746-2050	22
Lecanto Primary Sch/Lecanto/Citrus	02042133	352/746-2220	22
Lee Academy for Gifted Ed/Tampa/Hillsborough	03148443	813/931-3316	54
LEE CO SCH DIST/FORT MYERS/LEE	00194089	239/334-1102	60
Lee Elem Mag Sch World & Tech/Tampa/Hillsborough	04036740	813/276-5405	48
Lee Elem Sch/Lee/Madison	00194986	850/973-5030	67
Lee Virtual Sch/Fort Myers/Lee	11663398	239/337-8178	62
Leesburg Elem Sch/Leesburg/Lake	05347970	352/365-6308	59
Leesburg High Sch/Leesburg/Lake	00193889	352/787-5047	59
Leewood K-8 Center/Miami/Miami-Dade	00187000	305/233-7430	83
Legacy Academy Charter Sch/Cocoa/Brevard	12262727	321/362-5601	7
Legacy Charter High Sch/Ocoee/Orange	10902543	407/656-4673	94
Legacy Elem Sch/Ocala/Marion	11926085	352/671-0800	71
Legacy Middle Sch/Orlando/Orange	10002026	407/658-5330	96
Legacy Preparatory Academy/Tampa/Hillsborough	05262409	813/253-0053	46

School/City/County DISTRICT/CITY/COUNTY	PID	TELEPHONE NUMBER	PAGE
Legacy Scholar Academy/Deltona/Volusia	12308149	386/668-4774	141
Legends Academy Charter Sch/Orlando/Orange	12114821	407/985-5195	94
Lehigh Acres Middle Sch/Lehigh Acres/Lee	02202888	239/369-6108	62
Lehigh Elem Sch/Lehigh Acres/Lee	00194302	239/369-2477	62
Lehigh Senior High Sch/Lehigh Acres/Lee	04291419	239/693-5353	62
Lehrman Community Day Sch/Miami Beach/Miami-Dade	01435434	305/866-2771	87
Leila G Davis Elem Sch/Clearwater/Pinellas	02107410	727/725-7972	117
Leisure City K-8 Center/Homestead/Miami-Dade	00187402	305/247-5431	83
Lely Elem Sch/Naples/Collier	03333181	239/377-7500	26
Lely High Sch/Naples/Collier	00184931	239/377-2000	26
Lemon Bay High Sch/Englewood/Charlotte	00184448	941/474-7702	21
Lena Vista Elem Sch/Auburndale/Polk	00201888	863/965-5464	125
Lenora Braynon Smith Elem Sch/Miami/Miami-Dade	00186379	305/635-0873	76
LEON CO SCH DIST/TALLAHASSEE/LEON	00194479	850/487-7363	64
Leon Co Virtual Sch/Tallahassee/Leon	11663415	850/561-8366	65
Leon High Sch/Tallahassee/Leon	00194675	850/617-5700	65
Leto High Sch/Tampa/Hillsborough	00192445	813/872-5300	49
LEVY CO SCH DIST/BRONSON/LEVY	00194807	352/486-5231	66
Levy My District Virtual Sch/Bronson/Levy	11831636	352/486-5231	66
Lewis Anna Woodbury Elem Sch/Fort Meade/Polk	00202088	863/285-1150	124
Lewis Carroll Elem Sch/Merritt Is/Brevard	00182634	321/452-1234	7
Lewis Elem Sch/Temple Terr/Hillsborough	02897607	813/987-6947	50
Lexington Middle Sch/Fort Myers/Lee	10007105	239/454-6130	62
Libertas Academy/Tampa/Hillsborough	11835060	813/964-1779	54
Liberty Baptist Academy/Fort Pierce/St Lucie	11734818	772/461-2731	137
Liberty Christian Prep/Tavares/Lake	03210228	352/343-0061	60
Liberty Christian Sch/Sanford/Seminole	01776317	407/323-1583	134
Liberty Christian Sch/St Petersburg/Pinellas	02394833	727/576-9635	121
Liberty City Elem Sch/Miami/Miami-Dade	00186070	305/691-8532	76
Liberty Co High Sch/Bristol/Liberty	00194924	850/643-2241	67
LIBERTY CO SCH DIST/BRISTOL/LIBERTY	00194895	850/643-2275	67
Liberty Elem Sch/Margate/Broward	05099422	754/322-6750	13
Liberty Elem Sch/Pt Charlotte/Charlotte	03011802	941/255-7515	21
Liberty High Sch/Kissimmee/Osceola	10913360	407/933-3910	103
Liberty Learning Center/Bristol/Liberty	11830400	850/643-2275	67
Liberty Magnet Elem Sch/Vero Beach/Indian River	05092773	772/564-5300	56
Liberty Middle Sch/Ocala/Marion	04915902	352/291-7930	71
Liberty Middle Sch/Orlando/Orange	01397959	407/249-6440	98
Liberty Middle Sch/Tampa/Hillsborough	05097345	813/558-1180	50
Liberty Park Elem Sch/Greenacres/Palm Beach	03337280	561/804-3400	107
Liberty Pines Academy/Saint Johns/St Johns	11130444	904/547-7900	134
Liberty Wilderness Crossroads/Sumatra/Liberty	04914362	850/379-8344	67
Life Christian Academy/Kissimmee/Osceola	11230305	407/847-8222	104
Lifeskills Academy of Orlando/Winter Spgs/Seminole	11911418	407/388-1808	134
Light of Christ Early Chld Ctr/Clearwater/Pinellas	02862074	727/442-4797	120
Lighthouse Christian Academy/Deland/Volusia	02236322	386/734-5380	142
Lighthouse Christian Academy/Mayo/Lafayette	11225180	386/294-2994	58
Lighthouse Christian Sch/Middleburg/Clay	11929611	904/406-4866	24
Lighthouse Christian Sch/Orange Park/Clay	11228883	904/272-2524	24
Lighthouse Christian Sch/Pompano Beach/Broward	11226249	954/941-7501	19
Lighthouse Christian Sch West/Jacksonville/Duval	11726495	904/854-4599	35
Lighthouse Chrn Sch-Arlington/Jacksonville/Duval	11745829	904/642-4043	35
Lighthouse Ctr-Creative Lrng/Brandon/Hillsborough	11227243	813/655-6505	54
Lighthouse Elem Sch/Jupiter/Palm Beach	03253323	561/741-9400	108
Lillian Ruediger Elem Sch/Tallahassee/Leon	00194699	850/488-1074	65
Lillian Symmes Elem Sch/Riverview/Hillsborough	04948882	813/740-4182	52
Lillie C Evans K-8 Center/Miami/Miami-Dade	00186082	305/691-4973	76
Limestone Creek Elem Sch/Jupiter/Palm Beach	03253335	561/741-9200	108
Limona Elem Sch/Brandon/Hillsborough	00192457	813/744-8200	51
Lincoln Avenue Academy/Lakeland/Polk	00201383	863/499-2955	125
Lincoln Elem Sch/Riviera Beach/Palm Beach	00198578	561/624-5175	108

School/City/County DISTRICT/CITY/COUNTY	PID	TELEPHONE NUMBER	PAGE
Lincoln High Sch/*Tallahassee*/Leon	01524267	850/487-2110	65
Lincoln Magnet Sch/*Plant City*/Hillsborough	00192469	813/757-9329	52
Lincoln Memorial Middle Sch/*Palmetto*/ Manatee	00195150	941/721-6840	69
Lincoln Park Academy/*Fort Pierce*/St Lucie	00202935	772/468-5474	136
Lincoln Park Elem Sch/*Pensacola*/Escambia	00190758	850/494-5620	37
Lincoln-Marti CHS of Americas/*Miami*/ Miami-Dade	11829736	305/325-1001	76
Lincoln-Marti CS-Hialeah/*Hialeah*/ Miami-Dade	11453404	305/827-8080	79
Lincoln-Marti CS-Intl Campus/*Florida City*/ Miami-Dade	11561415	305/242-3330	83
Lincoln-Marti CS-Little Havana/*Miami*/ Miami-Dade	11453416	305/325-1001	76
Lincoln-Marti CS-Osceola/*Kissimmee*/Osceola	12262856	407/530-5000	103
Linda Lentin K-8 Center/*Miami*/Miami-Dade	04840034	305/891-4011	79
Lindsey Hopkins Tech Ed Center/*Miami*/ Miami-Dade	01340059	305/324-6070	76
Literacy Leadership Tech Acad/*Tampa*/ Hillsborough	10003147	813/234-0940	46
Lithia Springs Elem Sch/*Valrico*/ Hillsborough	04017275	813/744-8016	52
Little Country Sch/*Jacksonville*/Duval	02235586	904/757-8200	35
Little Flower Catholic Sch/*Pensacola*/ Escambia	00202612	850/455-4851	38
Little Flower Montessori/*Wilton Manors*/ Broward	02360222	954/565-8205	19
Little Flower Sch/*Hollywood*/Broward	00188066	954/922-1217	18
Little River Elem Sch/*Orlando*/Orange	03400069	407/249-6360	96
Littlewood Elem Sch/*Gainesville*/Alachua	00181305	352/955-6712	2
Lively Technical Center/*Tallahassee*/Leon	00194704	850/487-7555	65
Living Springs Academy/*High Springs*/ Alachua	04983258	386/454-2777	3
Living Word Academy/*Orlando*/Orange	11735202	407/851-6464	101
Living Word Christian Sch/*N Ft Myers*/Lee	11237028	239/997-7702	64
Livingstone Academy/*Seffner*/Hillsborough	11825596	813/661-4200	54
Liza Jackson Preparatory Sch/*Ft Walton Bch*/ Okaloosa	04950249	850/833-3321	92
Lloyd Estates Elem Sch/*Oakland Park*/ Broward	00183286	754/322-6800	13
Lockhart Elem Sch/*Orlando*/Orange	00197067	407/296-6440	97
Lockhart Elem Sch/*Tampa*/Hillsborough	00192471	813/276-5727	51
Lockhart Middle Sch/*Orlando*/Orange	00197079	407/296-5120	97
Locklin Tech Center/*Milton*/Santa Rosa	02178940	850/983-5700	128
Lockmar Elem Sch/*Palm Bay*/Brevard	02191071	321/676-3730	7
Loggers Run Cmty Middle Sch/*Boca Raton*/ Palm Beach	02200036	561/883-8000	110
Lomax Magnet Elem Sch/*Tampa*/Hillsborough	00192495	813/276-5569	51
Lone Star Elem Sch/*Jacksonville*/Duval	00189450	904/565-2711	31
Lone Star High Sch/*Jacksonville*/Duval	11560617	904/725-5998	29
Long Branch Elem Sch/*Jacksonville*/Duval	00189462	904/630-6620	33
Longleaf Elem Sch/*Melbourne*/Brevard	04809391	321/242-4700	8
Longleaf Elem Sch/*New Prt Rchy*/Pasco	10001888	727/774-0800	113
Longleaf Elem Sch/*Pensacola*/Escambia	01395822	850/941-6110	37
Longstreet Elem Sch/*Daytona Beach*/Volusia	00204684	386/322-6172	141
Longwood Elem Sch/*Longwood*/Seminole	12233130	407/746-5250	132
Longwood Elem Sch/*Shalimar*/Okaloosa	00196324	850/833-4329	92
Lopez Elem Sch/*Seffner*/Hillsborough	02855722	813/744-8000	51
Lopez Exceptional Student Ctr/*Seffner*/ Hillsborough	11830357	813/744-8008	51
Lorah Park Elem Sch/*Miami*/Miami-Dade	00186109	305/633-1424	76
Lorenzo Walker Tech High Sch/*Naples*/ Collier	00185026	239/377-3300	26
Loretto Elem Sch/*Jacksonville*/Duval	00189474	904/260-5800	31
Lost Lake Elem Sch/*Clermont*/Lake	04871332	352/243-2433	59
Loughman Oaks Elementary/*Davenport*/Polk	04017251	863/421-3309	124
Louis Benito Middle Sch/*Tampa*/Hillsborough	04754954	813/631-4694	50
Louis Sheffield Elem Sch/*Jacksonville*/ Duval	00189486	904/696-8758	31
Louise R Johnson K-8 Sch Int'l/*Bradenton*/ Manatee	00195095	941/741-3344	69
Louise S McInnis Elem Sch/*De Leon Spgs*/ Volusia	00204529	386/943-6384	141
Lourdes Academy/*Daytona Beach*/Volusia	00197756	386/252-0391	142
Love Grove Elem Sch/*Jacksonville*/Duval	00189498	904/720-1645	31
Lovell Elem Sch/*Apopka*/Orange	00197081	407/884-2235	97
Lovely Stars Academy II/*Homestead*/ Miami-Dade	11837501	305/257-0028	87
Lower Keys Ace/*Key West*/Monroe	12323046	305/293-1549	89
Lowry Elem Sch/*Tampa*/Hillsborough	04021551	813/855-8178	49
Loxahatchee Groves Elem Sch/*Loxahatchee*/ Palm Beach	02894663	561/904-9200	107

School/City/County DISTRICT/CITY/COUNTY	PID	TELEPHONE NUMBER	PAGE
Lubavitch Educational Center/*Miami*/ Miami-Dade	00187763	305/653-8770	87
Lucille Moore Elem Sch/*Panama City*/Bay	00181654	850/767-1428	4
Lucious & Emma Nixon Acad/*Orlando*/Orange	12230114	407/412-6968	94
Ludlam Elem Sch/*South Miami*/Miami-Dade	00187012	305/667-5551	76
Luth CH of the Cross Day Sch/*St Petersburg*/ Pinellas	02394558	727/522-8331	121
Lutz K-8 Sch/*Lutz*/Hillsborough	00192500	813/949-1452	50
Lutz Preparatory Sch/*Lutz*/Hillsborough	11716256	813/428-7100	47
Lycee Franco-American Sch/*Hollywood*/ Broward	11237157	954/237-0356	19
Lyman High Sch/*Longwood*/Seminole	00203771	407/746-2050	132
Lynch Elem Sch/*St Petersburg*/Pinellas	00199924	727/570-3170	119
Lyndon B Johnson Middle Sch/*Melbourne*/ Brevard	00182373	321/242-6430	9
Lynn Haven Elem Sch/*Lynn Haven*/Bay	00181666	850/767-1454	4
Lyons Creek Middle Sch/*Coconut Creek*/ Broward	04917132	754/322-3700	13

M

School/City/County DISTRICT/CITY/COUNTY	PID	TELEPHONE NUMBER	PAGE
M K Lewis School-Millville/*Panama City*/Bay	00181707	850/767-1792	4
Mabry Elem Sch/*Tampa*/Hillsborough	00192093	813/872-5364	49
MacClenny Elem Sch/*Macclenny*/Baker	00181513	904/259-2551	4
MacFarlane Park Magnet Sch/*Tampa*/ Hillsborough	05351115	813/356-1760	49
MacLay Sch/*Tallahassee*/Leon	00194792	850/893-2138	66
Madeira Beach Fund Sch/*Madeira Beach*/ Pinellas	00199948	727/547-7697	118
Madie Ives Community Elem Sch/*N Miami Beach*/ Miami-Dade	00185284	305/651-3155	80
Madison Co Central Sch/*Madison*/Madison	00195019	850/973-5192	67
Madison Co High Sch/*Madison*/Madison	00195007	850/973-5755	67
MADISON CO SCH DIST/**MADISON**/ **MADISON**	00194948	850/973-5022	67
Madison Creative Arts Academy/*Madison*/ Madison	12170710	850/973-2529	67
Madison Middle Sch/*Miami*/Miami-Dade	00186111	305/836-2610	77
Madison Middle Sch/*Tampa*/Hillsborough	00192366	813/272-3050	49
Madison St Acad Performing Art/*Ocala*/ Marion	00195564	352/671-7250	71
Mae Walters Elem Sch/*Hialeah*/Miami-Dade	00185674	305/822-4600	80
Magnolia Montessori Academy/*Lakeland*/Polk	11923564	863/797-4991	123
Magnolia Sch/*Orlando*/Orange	00197093	407/296-6499	99
Magnolia Sch/*Tallahassee*/Leon	03191220	850/385-3834	66
Main St High Sch/*Kissimmee*/Osceola	11554840	321/250-1871	103
Mainland High Sch/*Daytona Beach*/Volusia	00204531	386/258-4665	141
Mainspring Academy/*Jacksonville*/Duval	12310439	904/503-0344	35
Maitland Middle Sch/*Maitland*/Orange	00197108	407/623-1462	96
Maitland Montessori Sch/*Maitland*/Orange	02385741	407/628-0019	101
Malone Sch/*Malone*/Jackson	00193566	850/482-9930	57
Mamie Agnes Jones Elem Sch/*Baldwin*/Duval	00189503	904/266-1214	31
Manatee Bay Elem Sch/*Weston*/Broward	05099410	754/323-6450	13
Manatee Charter Sch/*Bradenton*/Manatee	11820869	941/465-4296	69
MANATEE CO SCH DIST/**BRADENTON**/ **MANATEE**	00195033	941/708-8770	68
Manatee Cove Elem Sch/*Orange City*/Volusia	10024086	386/968-0004	141
Manatee Elem Sch/*Bradenton*/Manatee	00195174	941/741-3319	69
Manatee Elem Sch/*Fort Myers*/Lee	10910693	239/694-2097	62
Manatee Elem Sch/*Lake Worth*/Palm Beach	04290104	561/357-1800	110
Manatee Elem Sch/*Naples*/Collier	04287432	239/377-7600	26
Manatee Elem Sch/*Viera*/Brevard	05272947	321/433-0050	8
Manatee High Sch/*Bradenton*/Manatee	00195186	941/714-7300	69
Manatee K-8 Sch/*Port St Lucie*/St Lucie	04015291	772/340-4745	136
Manatee Middle Sch/*Naples*/Collier	04363969	239/377-4400	26
Manatee Sch of Arts & Science/*Bradenton*/ Manatee	04755398	941/755-5012	69
Manatee School for the Arts/*Palmetto*/ Manatee	04814384	941/721-6800	69
Manatee Technical College/*Bradenton*/ Manatee	00195162	941/751-7900	69
Manatee Virtual Sch/*Palmetto*/Manatee	11750056	941/708-4971	69
Mandarin High Sch/*Jacksonville*/Duval	03329441	904/260-3911	32
Mandarin Lakes K-8 Academy/*Homestead*/ Miami-Dade	11128348	305/257-0377	83
Mandarin Middle Sch/*Jacksonville*/Duval	03329439	904/292-0555	33
Mandarin Oaks Elem Sch/*Jacksonville*/Duval	03251466	904/260-5820	31
Mandelstam Sch/*Miami*/Miami-Dade	11734258	305/662-2736	87
Mango Elem Sch/*Seffner*/Hillsborough	00192524	813/744-8208	48
Maniscalco Elem Sch/*Lutz*/Hillsborough	03252616	813/949-0337	50
Mann Middle Sch/*Brandon*/Hillsborough	00192328	813/744-8400	51
Maplewood Elem Sch/*Coral Springs*/Broward	02107886	754/322-6850	13
Maplewood Elem Sch/*Ocala*/Marion	04017756	352/671-6820	71

School/City/County DISTRICT/CITY/COUNTY	PID	TELEPHONE NUMBER	PAGE
Maranatha Christian Academy/*Webster*/Sumter	04339657	352/793-7224	138
Marathon Middle High Sch/*Marathon*/Monroe	00195928	305/289-2480	89
Marco Island Academy/*Marco Island*/Collier	11717327	239/393-5133	26
Marco Island Charter Mid Sch/*Marco Island*/Collier	04808218	239/377-3200	26
Marcus A Milam K-8 Center/*Hialeah*/Miami-Dade	00185662	305/822-0301	80
Marcus Pointe Christian Sch/*Pensacola*/Escambia	12306220	850/479-1605	38
Margate Elem Sch/*Margate*/Broward	00182921	754/322-6900	13
Margate Middle Sch/*Margate*/Broward	00182933	754/322-3800	13
Marian Center Sch/*Miami Gardens*/Miami-Dade	00188080	305/625-8354	85
Marianna High Sch/*Marianna*/Jackson	00193580	850/482-9605	57
Marianna Middle Sch/*Marianna*/Jackson	00193578	850/482-9609	57
Marine Science Education Ctr/*Mayport*/Duval	04019273	904/247-5973	32
Mariner High Sch/*Cape Coral*/Lee	03012179	239/772-3324	62
Mariner Middle Sch/*Cape Coral*/Lee	05275274	239/772-1848	62
Marion Charter Sch/*Ocala*/Marion	04915926	352/687-2100	71
MARION CO PUBLIC SCHOOLS/ **OCALA/MARION**	00195344	352/671-7700	70
Marion Co Technical College/*Ocala*/Marion	01540479	352/671-7270	71
Marion Oaks Elem Sch/*Ocala*/Marion	11552347	352/291-7975	71
Marion Technical Institute/*Ocala*/Marion	10910071	352/671-4765	71
Mariposa Elem Sch/*Port St Lucie*/St Lucie	04015289	772/337-5960	136
Maritime & Science Tech Acad/*Miami*/Miami-Dade	03409663	305/365-6278	77
Marjorie K Rawlings Elem Sch/*Gainesville*/Alachua	00181317	352/955-6715	2
Marjorie Rawlings Elem Sch/*Pinellas Park*/Pinellas	04022347	727/547-7828	119
Marjory Stoneman Douglas ES/*Miami*/Miami Dade	03395282	305/226-4356	83
Marjory Stoneman Douglas HS/*Parkland*/Broward	03336717	754/322-2150	13
Markham Woods Middle Sch/*Lake Mary*/Seminole	10028173	407/871-1750	133
Marsh Pointe Elem Sch/*Palm BCH GDNS*/Palm Beach	11103673	561/366-6800	108
Marshall Middle Sch/*Plant City*/Hillsborough	00192548	813/757-9360	52
Martha B King Middle Sch/*Bradenton*/Manatee	01821479	941/798-6820	69
Martin Co Acceleration Academy/*Stuart*/Martin	12322951	772/924-0162	73
Martin Co High Sch/*Stuart*/Martin	00195772	772/219-1800	73
MARTIN CO SCH DIST/STUART/MARTIN	00195710	772/219-1200	72
Martin J Gottlieb Day Sch/*Jacksonville*/Duval	01436232	904/268-4200	35
Martin L King Middle Sch/*Milton*/Santa Rosa	00203147	850/983-5660	128
Martin Luther King Elem Sch/*Ft Lauderdale*/Broward	00183420	754/322-6550	13
Martin Luther King Fame Acad/*Jacksonville*/Duval	00189175	904/924-3027	33
Martinez Middle Sch/*Lutz*/Hillsborough	05097321	813/558-1190	49
Mary Bryant Elem Sch/*Tampa*/Hillsborough	05097307	813/356-1645	49
Mary Esther Elem Sch/*Mary Esther*/Okaloosa	00196348	850/833-3371	92
Mary Help of Christians Sch/*Parkland*/Broward	10013219	954/323-8006	18
Mary M Bethune Elem Sch/*Hollywood*/Broward	00183640	754/323-4900	13
Mascotte Elem Charter Sch/*Mascotte*/Lake	00193906	352/429-2294	59
Mason Classical Academy/*Naples*/Collier	12032675	239/227-2838	26
Masoret Yehudit Day Sch/*Hallandale*/Broward	12104383	954/457-3899	19
Mast-Biscayne Bay Campus/*Miami*/Miami-Dade	11929477	305/919-4450	80
Master's Academy/*Ft Lauderdale*/Broward	04471528	954/434-2960	19
Master's Academy/*Oviedo*/Seminole	03063403	407/706-2221	134
Master's Academy/*Vero Beach*/Indian River	05015488	772/794-4655	56
Masters Prep Sch/*Hialeah*/Miami-Dade	04983090	305/887-4233	87
Matanzas High Sch/*Palm Coast*/Flagler	10004763	386/447-1575	39
Mater Acad East Charter Mid HS/*Miami*/Miami-Dade	10907830	305/324-6963	77
Mater Acad of Int'l Studies/*Miami*/Miami-Dade	11453545	305/634-0445	77
Mater Acad St Cloud/*Saint Cloud*/Osceola	12308917	407/325-0762	103
Mater Academy/*Hialeah GDNS*/Miami-Dade	04811564	305/698-9900	80
Mater Academy Charter High Sch/*Hialeah GDNS*/Miami-Dade	10010059	305/828-1886	80
Mater Academy Charter Mid Sch/*Hialeah GDNS*/Miami-Dade	05101324	305/828-1886	80
Mater Academy Cutler Bay/*Cutler Bay*/Miami-Dade	12169072	305/969-5989	83
Mater Academy East Charter ES/*Miami*/Miami-Dade	04920878	305/324-4667	77
Mater Academy Lakes Mid HS/*Hialeah*/Miami-Dade	10030011	305/698-8000	80
Mater Academy-Miami Beach/*Miami Beach*/Miami-Dade	11560095	305/864-2889	80
Mater Academy-Mount Sinai/*Miami Beach*/Miami-Dade	11829750	305/604-1453	80
Mater Brighton Lakes Academy/*Kissimmee*/Osceola	12114900	407/931-0325	103
Mater Gardens Elem Mid Academy/*Hialeah*/Miami-Dade	10030035	305/512-9775	80
Mater Grove Academy/*Miami*/Miami-Dade	11719545	305/442-4992	77
Mater International Academy/*Miami*/Miami-Dade	12114871	305/638-8016	77
Mater International Prep Acad/*Miami*/Miami-Dade	12322975	305/634-0445	77
Mater Palms Academy/*Kissimmee*/Osceola	12262698	407/390-1106	103
Mater Perform Arts & Ent Acad/*Hialeah GDNS*/Miami-Dade	10907763	305/828-1886	80
Mater Preparatory Academy/*Miami*/Miami-Dade	12362080	786/648-4580	77
Mater Virtual Acad Chart MS HS/*Hialeah*/Miami-Dade	12322987	305/495-6846	80
Matthew Gilbert Middle Sch/*Jacksonville*/Duval	03401348	904/630-6700	33
Mattie Rutherford Alt Ed Ctr/*Jacksonville*/Duval	04019285	904/630-6782	32
Maude Saunders Elem Sch/*Defuniak Spgs*/Walton	00204957	850/892-1260	144
Max Bruner Jr Middle Sch/*Ft Walton Bch*/Okaloosa	00196350	850/833-3266	92
Maxey Elem Sch/*Winter Garden*/Orange	00197110	407/877-5020	99
Maximo Elem Sch/*St Petersburg*/Pinellas	00199950	727/893-2191	118
May Sands Montessori Sch/*Key West*/Monroe	12262868	305/293-1400	89
Maya Angelou Elem Sch/*Miami*/Miami-Dade	04365527	305/636-3480	77
Mayport Elem Sch/*Atlantic Bch*/Duval	00189541	904/247-5988	31
Mayport Middle Sch/*Atlantic Bch*/Duval	01555890	904/247-5977	33
Mays Conservatory of Arts/*Miami*/Miami-Dade	00187414	305/233-2300	83
McArthur Elem Sch/*Pensacola*/Escambia	01524229	850/494-5625	37
McArthur High Sch/*Hollywood*/Broward	00184060	754/323-1200	13
McCoy Elem Sch/*Orlando*/Orange	00197134	407/249-6370	98
McDonald Elem Sch/*Seffner*/Hillsborough	01524243	813/744-8154	48
McIntosh Area Sch/*Mc Intosh*/Marion	05275391	352/591-9797	71
McIntosh Middle Sch/*Sarasota*/Sarasota	00203381	941/361-6520	130
McKeel Academy of Technology/*Lakeland*/Polk	00201450	863/499-2818	123
McKeel Central Academy/*Lakeland*/Polk	05272703	863/499-1287	123
McKitrick Elem Sch/*Lutz*/Hillsborough	04948868	813/558-5427	50
McLane Middle Sch/*Brandon*/Hillsborough	00192550	813/744-8100	48
McLaughlin Mid Fine Art Acad/*Lake Wales*/Polk	00201644	863/678-4233	125
McMillan Learning Ctr/*Pensacola*/Escambia	00190629	850/595-6910	37
McMullen-Booth Elem Sch/*Clearwater*/Pinellas	04757528	727/669-1800	117
McNab Elem Sch/*Pompano Beach*/Broward	00182957	754/322-7050	13
McNair Magnet Sch/*Cocoa*/Brevard	00182244	321/633-3630	9
McNeal Elem Sch/*Bradenton*/Manatee	05272076	941/751-8165	69
McNicol Middle Sch/*Hollywood*/Broward	00184072	754/323-3400	13
Mcps Virtual Sch/*Ocala*/Marion	11714741	352/867-2137	71
McRae Elem Sch/*Keystone HGTS*/Clay	04447955	904/336-2125	24
Meadow Park Elem Sch/*Pt Charlotte*/Charlotte	00184450	941/255-7470	21
Meadow Park Elem Sch/*West Palm Bch*/Palm Beach	00198190	561/357-2800	107
Meadow Woods Elem Sch/*Orlando*/Orange	03250606	407/858-3140	98
Meadow Woods Middle Sch/*Orlando*/Orange	04806284	407/850-5180	98
Meadowbrook Academy/*Ocala*/Marion	04984513	352/861-0700	72
Meadowbrook Elem Sch/*Ft Lauderdale*/Broward	00183652	754/323-6500	13
Meadowbrook Elem Sch/*Gainesville*/Alachua	11820467	352/333-2828	2
Meadowbrook Middle Sch/*Orlando*/Orange	00197146	407/296-5130	95
Meadowlane Elem Sch/*Hialeah*/Miami-Dade	00185686	305/822-0660	80
Meadowlane Interm Elem Sch/*W Melbourne*/Brevard	10907115	321/722-5539	8
Meadowlane Primary Elem Sch/*W Melbourne*/Brevard	00182385	321/723-6354	8
Meadowlawn Middle Sch/*St Petersburg*/Pinellas	00199962	727/570-3097	119
Medart Elem Sch/*Crawfordville*/Wakulla	00204880	850/962-4881	143
Medical Acad-Science Tech/*Homestead*/Miami-Dade	11595894	305/257-4500	83
Medulla Elem Sch/*Lakeland*/Polk	00201400	863/648-3515	125
Melaleuca Elem Sch/*West Palm Bch*/Palm Beach	00198205	561/598-7300	107
Melbourne Central Catholic HS/*Melbourne*/Brevard	00197689	321/727-0793	9

School/City/County DISTRICT/CITY/COUNTY	PID	TELEPHONE NUMBER	PAGE
Melbourne High Sch/*Melbourne*/Brevard	00182397	321/952-5880	9
Mellon Elem Sch/*Palatka*/Putnam	00202284	386/329-0593	127
Melody Christian Academy/*Live Oak*/Suwannee	04336447	386/364-4800	139
Melrose Elem Sch/*Melrose*/Putnam	00202296	352/475-2060	127
Melrose Elem Sch/*Miami*/Miami-Dade	00186666	305/635-8676	77
Melrose Elem Sch/*St Petersburg*/Pinellas	00199974	727/893-2175	119
Melrose Park Elem Sch/*Lake City*/Columbia	00185117	386/755-8260	27
Memorial Elem Sch/*Arcadia*/De Soto	00188705	863/494-2736	28
Memorial Elem Sch/*Avon Park*/Highlands	11071202	863/784-0200	45
Memorial Lutheran Chapel Sch/*St Augustine*/ St Johns	03311341	904/797-8777	135
Memorial Middle Sch/*Orlando*/Orange	00197158	407/245-1810	99
Memorial Middle Sch/*Tampa*/Hillsborough	00192665	813/872-5230	48
Mendenhall Elem Sch/*Tampa*/Hillsborough	00192574	813/872-5221	51
Mendez Exceptional Center/*Tampa*/ Hillsborough	03253672	813/276-5630	51
Merriam Cherry Street Elem Sch/*Panama City*/ Bay	00181599	850/767-1480	4
Merrill Road Elem Sch/*Jacksonville*/Duval	00189553	904/745-4919	31
Merritt Brown Middle Sch/*Panama City*/Bay	03197963	850/767-3976	4
Merritt Island Christian Sch/*Merritt Is*/ Brevard	02085721	321/453-2710	10
Merritt Island High Sch/*Merritt Is*/Brevard	00182646	321/454-1000	9
MetroWest Elem Sch/*Orlando*/Orange	03051876	407/296-6450	99
Miami Arts 6-12 Zelda Glazer/*Miami*/ Miami-Dade	11435775	305/485-2323	83
Miami Arts Charter Sch/*Miami*/Miami-Dade	11453480	305/763-6257	77
Miami Beach Adult Ed/*Miami Beach*/ Miami-Dade	10907751	305/531-0451	74
Miami Beach Senior High Sch/*Miami Beach*/ Miami-Dade	00185296	305/532-4515	80
Miami Carol City Senior HS/*Miami Gardens*/ Miami-Dade	00185698	305/621-5681	80
Miami Central Sr High Sch/*Miami*/Miami-Dade	00186135	305/696-4161	77
Miami Children's Museum CS/*Miami*/ Miami-Dade	05346873	305/373-5437	80
Miami Christian Sch/*Miami*/Miami-Dade	01435460	305/221-7754	87
Miami Cmty Charter Elem Sch/*Florida City*/ Miami-Dade	05350020	305/245-2552	83
Miami Cmty Charter High Sch/*Florida City*/ Miami-Dade	11463825	786/243-9981	83
Miami Cmty Charter Middle Sch/*Florida City*/ Miami-Dade	10907816	786/243-9981	83
Miami Coral Park Sr High Sch/*Miami*/ Miami-Dade	00187024	305/226-6565	77
Miami Country Day Sch/*Miami*/Miami-Dade	01773444	305/779-7200	87
Miami Dade South/*Key Biscayne*/Miami-Dade	02234752	305/361-7934	87
Miami Edison Sr High Sch/*Miami*/Miami-Dade	00186159	305/751-7337	77
Miami Gardens Elem Sch/*Miami Gardens*/ Miami-Dade	00185703	305/625-5321	80
Miami Heights Elem Sch/*Miami*/Miami-Dade	00187426	305/238-3602	83
Miami Jackson Sr High Sch/*Miami*/Miami-Dade	00186680	305/634-2621	77
Miami Killian Sr High Sch/*Miami*/Miami-Dade	00187036	305/271-3311	83
Miami Lakes Ed Ctr & Tech Clg/*Miami Lakes*/ Miami-Dade	01340073	305/557-1100	80
Miami Lakes K-8 Center/*Miami Lakes*/ Miami-Dade	00185715	305/822-7757	80
Miami Lakes Middle Sch/*Miami Lakes*/ Miami-Dade	01526980	305/557-3900	80
Miami MacArthur South Sch/*Naranja*/ Miami-Dade	00187153	305/258-7200	74
Miami Norland Sr High Sch/*Miami*/Miami-Dade	00185313	305/653-1416	80
Miami Northwestern Sr High Sch/*Miami*/ Miami-Dade	00186161	305/836-0991	77
Miami Palmetto Sr High Sch/*Pinecrest*/ Miami-Dade	00187438	305/235-1360	83
Miami Senior High Sch/*Miami*/Miami-Dade	00186692	305/649-9800	77
Miami Shores Elem Sch/*Miami Shores*/ Miami-Dade	00186185	305/758-5525	77
Miami Shores Montessori Sch/*Miami*/ Miami-Dade	11460756	305/756-7733	87
Miami Shores Presbyterian Sch/*Miami*/ Miami-Dade	10914651	305/759-2548	88
Miami Southridge Sr High Sch/*Miami*/ Miami-Dade	01527075	305/238-6110	83
Miami Springs Adventist Sch/*Miami Springs*/ Miami-Dade	03404314	305/888-2244	88
Miami Springs Elem Sch/*Miami Springs*/ Miami-Dade	00186197	305/888-4558	77
Miami Springs Learning Center/*Miami Springs*/ Miami-Dade	01435575	305/888-1715	88
Miami Springs Middle Sch/*Miami Springs*/ Miami-Dade	02110259	305/888-6457	77
Miami Springs Sr High Sch/*Miami Springs*/ Miami-Dade	00186214	305/885-3585	77
Miami Sunset Sr High Sch/*Miami*/Miami-Dade	02110223	305/385-4255	83
Miami Union Academy/*North Miami*/Miami-Dade	01435343	305/953-9907	88
MIAMI-DADE CO PUBLIC SCH DIST/ **MIAMI/MIAMI-DADE**	00185155	305/995-1000	74
Miami-Dade Online Academy/*Miami*/Miami-Dade	11746378	305/995-1257	74
MIAMI-DADE-CENTRAL REGION/ **DORAL/MIAMI-DADE**	00186355	305/499-5050	74
MIAMI-DADE-NORTH REGION/ **HIALEAH/MIAMI-DADE**	11449960	305/572-2800	78
MIAMI-DADE-SOUTH REGION/ **MIAMI/MIAMI-DADE**	00187244	305/252-3041	81
Micanopy Academy/*Micanopy*/Alachua	05097694	352/466-1090	2
Micanopy Area Co-op Sch/*Micanopy*/Alachua	04752516	352/466-0990	2
Michigan Ave Elem Sch/*Saint Cloud*/Osceola	00198009	407/891-3140	103
Middleburg Elem Sch/*Middleburg*/Clay	00184747	904/336-1875	24
Middleburg High Sch/*Middleburg*/Clay	01877973	904/336-8075	24
Middleton High Sch/*Tampa*/Hillsborough	05097357	813/233-3360	51
Middleton-Burney Elem Sch/*Crescent City*/ Putnam	00202234	386/698-1238	127
Midtown Academy/*St Petersburg*/Pinellas	12168212	727/893-1358	119
Midway Elem Sch of Arts/*Sanford*/Seminole	00203783	407/320-5950	133
Mike Davis Elem Sch/*Naples*/Collier	11079670	239/377-9000	26
Mila Elem Sch/*Merritt Is*/Brevard	00182658	321/454-1070	8
Mildred Helms Elem Sch/*Largo*/Pinellas	00199986	727/588-3569	118
Miles Elem Sch/*Tampa*/Hillsborough	00192598	813/975-7337	48
Mill Creek Academy/*St Augustine*/St Johns	00202454	904/547-3720	134
Mill Creek Elem Sch/*Kissimmee*/Osceola	03009108	407/935-3660	103
Millennium Academy/*New Prt Rchy*/Pasco	11227360	727/845-8150	115
Millennia Elem Sch/*Orlando*/Orange	10902517	407/355-5730	99
Millennia Gardens Elem Sch/*Orlando*/Orange	12168925	407/845-0665	99
Millennium Collegiate Academy/*Tamarac*/ Broward	05099458	754/322-3900	13
Millennium Middle Sch/*Sanford*/Seminole	00203745	407/320-6550	133
Millhopper Montessori Sch/*Gainesville*/ Alachua	01771939	352/375-6773	3
Milton High Sch/*Milton*/Santa Rosa	00203159	850/983-5600	128
Milwee Middle Sch/*Longwood*/Seminole	00203795	407/746-3850	133
Mims Elem Sch/*Mims*/Brevard	00182036	321/264-3020	8
Minneola Elem Sch/*Minneola*/Lake	00193918	352/394-2600	59
Miramar Elem Sch/*Miramar*/Broward	00184084	754/323-6550	13
Miramar High Sch/*Miramar*/Broward	00184096	754/323-1350	13
Mirror Lake Elem Sch/*Plantation*/Broward	00183298	754/322-7100	13
Mirror Lakes Elem Sch/*Lehigh Acres*/Lee	04754100	239/369-2200	62
Missionary Christian Academy/*Tampa*/ Hillsborough	11226500	813/977-6513	54
Mitchell Elem Sch/*Tampa*/Hillsborough	00192603	813/872-5216	49
Mittye P Locke Elem Sch/*New Prt Rchy*/Pasco	00199211	727/774-3100	113
Molino Park Elem Sch/*Molino*/Escambia	00190693	850/754-5000	37
Mollie Ray Elem Sch/*Orlando*/Orange	00197172	407/296-6460	95
Monarch High Sch/*Coconut Creek*/Broward	05280061	754/322-1400	13
MONROE CO SCH DIST/**KEY WEST**/ **MONROE**	00195849	305/293-1400	89
Monroe Middle Sch/*Tampa*/Hillsborough	00192615	813/272-3020	49
Mont Academy Early Enrichment/*Greenacres*/ Palm Beach	10002806	561/649-0004	105
Mont Chldrn's House-Hyde Park/*Tampa*/ Hillsborough	04984070	813/354-9511	54
Montclair Elem Sch/*Orange Park*/Clay	01540467	904/336-1975	24
Montclair Elem Sch/*Pensacola*/Escambia	00190708	850/595-6969	37
Monte's Montessori Sch/*Riverview*/ Hillsborough	04838706	813/651-0653	54
Montessori Academy-East/*Pembroke Pnes*/ Broward	11711191	954/435-4622	19
Montessori Academy-Naples/*Naples*/Collier	11165982	239/597-2255	27
Montessori Achieve Ctr-Learnng/*Miami*/ Miami-Dade	11701689	305/893-5994	88
Montessori Children's House/*Miami Lakes*/ Miami-Dade	02197788	305/823-5632	88
Montessori House/*Tampa*/Hillsborough	02188191	813/884-7220	54
Montessori Ind Learning Ctr/*West Palm Bch*/ Palm Beach	02228521	561/968-2642	111
Montessori Institute-Broward/*Davie*/Broward	11037660	954/472-9620	19
Montessori Preparatory Sch/*Ocala*/Marion	11230795	352/351-3140	72
Montessori Preparatory Sch/*Tampa*/ Hillsborough	04934104	813/899-2345	54
Montessori Sch of Pensacola/*Pensacola*/ Escambia	11188001	850/433-4155	38

School/City/County DISTRICT/CITY/COUNTY	PID	TELEPHONE NUMBER	PAGE
Montessori School of Pensacola/Pensacola/ Escambia	02374297	850/469-8138	38
Montessori School-N Miami/Miami/Miami-Dade	11701677	305/893-5994	88
Montessori School-Orlando/Orlando/Orange	11845871	407/601-4247	101
Montessori Way Sch/Orlando/Orange	05015220	407/852-1997	101
Montford Middle Sch/Tallahassee/Leon	11077153	850/412-8900	65
Montura Early Learning Center/Clewiston/ Hendry	12306282	863/983-1417	43
Montverde Academy/Montverde/Lake	00194065	407/469-2561	60
Monument Christian Academy/Atlantic Bch/ Duval	05318709	904/247-0929	35
Moon Lake Elem Sch/New Prt Rchy/Pasco	02177128	727/774-4600	113
Moore Haven Elem Sch/Moore Haven/Glades	00191312	863/946-0737	41
Moore Haven Jr Sr High Sch/Moore Haven/ Glades	00191324	863/946-0811	41
Morgan Fitzgerald Middle Sch/Largo/ Pinellas	01527245	727/547-4526	119
Morgan Woods Elem Sch/Tampa/Hillsborough	00192627	813/872-5369	50
Morikami Park Elem Sch/Delray Beach/ Palm Beach	04810479	561/894-7300	110
Morning Star Sch/Jacksonville/Duval	00202624	904/721-2144	34
Morning Star Sch/Orlando/Orange	00197744	407/295-3077	100
Morning Star Sch/Pinellas Park/Pinellas	00200925	727/544-6036	120
Morning Star Sch/Tampa/Hillsborough	00200913	813/935-0232	53
Morningside Academy/Port St Lucie/St Lucie	03064483	772/335-3231	137
Morningside Elem Sch/Port St Lucie/ St Lucie	02108282	772/337-6730	136
Morningside K-8 Academy/Miami/Miami-Dade	00186226	305/758-6741	77
Morningstar Christian Sch/Keystone HGTS/ Clay	03413303	352/473-3159	24
Morrow Elem Sch/N Lauderdale/Broward	01413321	754/322-7150	13
Mort Elem Sch/Tampa/Hillsborough	00192630	813/975 7373	48
Mosaic Digital Academy/Fort Pierce/ St Lucie	11717755	772/429-5504	136
Mosi Partnership Sch/Tampa/Hillsborough	11188350	813/983-3989	47
Moss Park Elem Sch/Orlando/Orange	10902529	407/249-4747	98
Mossy Head Sch/Defuniak Spgs/Walton	11070210	850/892-1290	144
Mother of Christ Elem Sch/Miami/Miami-Dade	11008968	786/497-6111	85
Mother of Our Redeemer/Hialeah/Miami-Dade	11008970	305/829-3988	85
Mother Teresa of Calcutta CS/Lutz/ Hillsborough	00200937	813/933-4750	53
Mothers' Care and Learning Ctr/Miami/ Miami-Dade	01435032	305/696-3802	88
Moton Elem Sch/Brooksville/Hernando	01843532	352/797-7065	44
Mount Dora Christian Academy/Mount Dora/ Lake	01436804	352/383-2155	60
Mowat Middle Sch/Lynn Haven/Bay	00181680	850/767-4040	4
Msgr Edward Pace High Sch/Opa Locka/ Miami-Dade	00188121	305/623-7223	85
Mt Bethel Christian Academy/Ft Lauderdale/ Broward	04983765	954/462-0255	19
Mt Calvary Academy/Daytona Beach/Volusia	04982888	386/255-8654	142
Mt Calvary Junior Academy/Tampa/ Hillsborough	01865322	813/238-0433	54
Mt Dora High Sch/Mount Dora/Lake	00193920	352/383-2177	59
Mt Dora Middle Sch/Mount Dora/Lake	00193932	352/383-6101	59
Mt Herman Excptnl Student Ctr/Jacksonville/ Duval	02224032	904/630-6740	32
Mt Olivet Junior Academy/Ft Lauderdale/ Broward	02847153	954/792-6010	19
Mt Sinai Jr Academy/Orlando/Orange	04145937	407/298-7871	101
Mt Vernon Elem Sch/St Petersburg/Pinellas	00200004	727/893-1815	119
Mulberry Christian Academy/Mulberry/Polk	11236957	863/425-1822	126
Mulberry High Sch/Mulberry/Polk	00202105	863/701-1104	122
Mulberry Middle Sch/Mulberry/Polk	00202117	863/701-1066	122
Muller Elem Sch/Tampa/Hillsborough	05262277	813/558-1355	50
Mulrennan Middle Sch/Valrico/Hillsborough	05262083	813/651-2100	52
Murdock Middle Sch/Pt Charlotte/Charlotte	03251179	941/255-7525	21
Murray Middle Sch/Stuart/Martin	00195784	772/219-1670	73
Muslim Academy-Greater Orlando/Orlando/ Orange	11727011	407/238-0144	101
Myakka Elem Sch/Myakka City/Manatee	00195203	941/708-5515	69
Myakka River Elem Sch/Pt Charlotte/ Charlotte	03329556	941/697-7111	21
Mycroschool Charter Sch/St Petersburg/ Pinellas	11822609	727/825-3710	116
Mycroschool Jacksonville CS/Jacksonville/ Duval	11821198	904/783-3611	29
Myra Terwilliger Elem Sch/Gainesville/ Alachua	00181331	352/955-6717	2
Myrtle Grove Elem Sch/Pensacola/Escambia	00190710	850/453-7410	37

School/City/County DISTRICT/CITY/COUNTY	PID	TELEPHONE NUMBER	PAGE
Myrtle Grove K-8 Center/Opa Locka/ Miami-Dade	00185727	305/624-8431	80
N			
N B Cook Elem Sch of the Arts/Pensacola/ Escambia	00190722	850/595-6826	37
N Broward MS Acad-Excellence/N Lauderdale/ Broward	10006589	954/718-2211	16
N Central Florida Public Chart/Gainesville/ Alachua	11715874	352/379-2902	2
N Edelcup-Sunny Isles Bch K-8/Sunny Isl Bch/ Miami-Dade	11128269	305/933-6161	80
N Florida School of Special Ed/Jacksonville/ Duval	04982981	904/724-8323	35
N Ft Myers Academy for Arts/N Ft Myers/Lee	01527180	239/997-2131	62
Nap Ford Cmty Charter Sch/Orlando/Orange	04950299	407/245-8711	94
Naples Adventist Chrn Sch/Naples/Collier	02085874	239/261-6227	27
Naples Christian Academy/Naples/Collier	00185038	239/455-1087	27
Naples High Sch/Naples/Collier	00184955	239/377-2200	26
Naples Park Elem Sch/Naples/Collier	00184943	239/377-7700	26
Narcoossee Elem Sch/Saint Cloud/Osceola	11452125	407/892-6858	103
Narcoossee Middle Sch/Saint Cloud/Osceola	04875924	407/891-6600	103
Nassau Co Adult Sch/Yulee/Nassau	01811553	904/548-1750	90
NASSAU CO SCH DIST/FERNANDINA/ **NASSAU**	00196013	904/491-9900	90
Nassau Virtual Sch/Fernandina/Nassau	11712987	866/339-8784	91
Nathan B Young Elem Sch/Opa Locka/ Miami-Dade	00186238	305/685-7204	80
Nativity Catholic Sch/Brandon/Hillsborough	00200949	813/689-3395	53
Nativity Sch/Hollywood/Broward	00188133	954/983-4981	18
Natural Bridge Elem Sch/North Miami/ Miami-Dade	00185375	305/891-8649	80
Nature Coast Middle Sch/Chiefland/Levy	10022296	352/490-0700	66
Nature Coast Technical HS/Brooksville/ Hernando	05272208	352/797-7088	44
Nautilus Middle Sch/Miami Beach/Miami-Dade	00185387	305/532-3481	80
Navarre High Sch/Navarre/Santa Rosa	04449161	850/936-6080	128
Navigator Acad of Leadership/Davenport/ Polk	12362224		123
Navigator Acad of Leadership/Valrico/ Hillsborough	12362004	863/866-7566	47
Navy Point Elem Sch/Pensacola/Escambia	00190734	850/453-7415	37
NC ALC Pathways Gardendale/Merritt Is/ Brevard	04369200	321/633-3489	7
Neil A Armstrong Elem Sch/Pt Charlotte/ Charlotte	00184462	941/255-7450	21
Nelson Elem Sch/Dover/Hillsborough	05262289	813/651-2120	52
Neocity Academy/Kissimmee/Osceola	12308955	407/933-3903	103
Neptune Beach Elem Sch/Neptune Beach/Duval	02131667	904/247-5954	31
Neptune Elem Sch/Saint Cloud/Osceola	10907036	407/892-8387	103
Neptune Middle Sch/Kissimmee/Osceola	03250541	407/935-3500	103
Neva King Cooper Education Ctr/Homestead/ Miami-Dade	02853621	305/247-4307	83
New Beginings Christian Acad/Jacksonville/ Duval	04982993	904/786-3178	35
New Beginnings Education Ctr/Kissimmee/ Osceola	04455732	407/348-4466	103
New Beginnings High Sch/Winter Haven/Polk	11745996	863/298-5666	123
New Beginnings-Immokalee/Immokalee/Collier	11435804	239/377-1130	26
New Beginnings-Naples/Naples/Collier	11435799	239/377-1070	26
New Berlin Elem Sch/Jacksonville/Duval	10027260	904/714-4601	31
New Dimensions High Sch/Kissimmee/Osceola	04808311	407/870-9949	103
New Direction Academy/Haines City/Polk	12178683	863/438-7493	126
New Heights Elem Sch/St Petersburg/ Pinellas	00200509	727/521-5350	119
New Hope Christian Sch/Ft Lauderdale/ Broward	12315013	954/973-1129	19
New Hope Chrn Academy/Minneola/Lake	11222413	352/242-9750	60
New Horizon Academy/Ocala/Marion	11071771	352/694-7201	72
New Horizons/Mulberry/Polk	11923552	863/428-1520	123
New Horizons Country Day Sch/Palm Harbor/ Pinellas	02939304	727/785-8591	121
New Horizons Elem Sch/Wellington/ Palm Beach	03054062	561/651-0500	107
New Horizons Learning Center/Panama City/ Bay	04749806	850/767-1110	4
New Jerusalem Christian Acad/Miami/ Miami-Dade	11227944	305/691-1291	88
New Leaf Sch/Neptune Beach/Duval	11230410	904/246-9100	35
New Life Charter Academy/Ft Lauderdale/ Broward	12032792	954/381-5199	16

School/City/County DISTRICT/CITY/COUNTY	PID	TELEPHONE NUMBER	PAGE
New Mirawood Academy/*Hollywood*/Broward	02184212	954/983-5531	19
New Renaissance Middle Sch/*Miramar*/Broward	05099434	754/323-3500	13
New River Elem Sch/*Wesley Chapel*/Pasco	10904101	813/346-0500	113
New River Middle Sch/*Ft Lauderdale*/Broward	00183688	754/323-3600	13
New Smyrna Beach High Sch/*New Smyrna*/ Volusia	00204579	386/424-2555	141
New Smyrna Beach Middle Sch/*New Smyrna*/ Volusia	00204567	386/424-2550	141
New Springs Elem Sch/*Tampa*/Hillsborough	11714260	813/933-5025	47
New Springs Middle Sch/*Tampa*/Hillsborough	11556898	813/933-5025	47
New Testament Baptist Sch/*Cape Coral*/Lee	11440548	239/997-1020	64
New World School of the Arts/*Miami*/ Miami-Dade	03038214	305/237-3135	77
Newberry Christian Cmty Sch/*Gainesville*/ Alachua	12042058	352/363-6322	3
Newberry Elem Sch/*Newberry*/Alachua	00181343	352/472-1100	2
Newberry High Sch/*Newberry*/Alachua	00181355	352/472-1101	2
Newsome High Sch/*Lithia*/Hillsborough	05262241	813/740-4600	52
Niblack Elem Sch/*Lake City*/Columbia	04923870	386/755-8200	27
Nicaea Academy/*Naples*/Collier	11825663	239/353-9099	27
Niceville High Sch/*Niceville*/Okaloosa	00196386	850/833-4114	92
Nina Harris Sch/*Pinellas Park*/Pinellas	00200028	727/547-7850	119
Nob Hill Elem Sch/*Sunrise*/Broward	00183315	754/322-7200	13
Nocatee Elem Sch/*Arcadia*/De Soto	00188717	863/494-0755	28
Norcrest Elem Sch/*Pompano Beach*/Broward	00182983	754/322-7250	13
Norland Elem Sch/*Miami Gardens*/Miami-Dade	00185399	305/652-6074	80
Norland Middle Sch/*Miami Gardens*/ Miami-Dade	00185404	305/653-1210	80
Norma Butler Bossard Elem Sch/*Miami*/ Miami-Dade	10024581	305/254-5200	83
Normandy Village Elem Sch/*Jacksonville*/ Duval	00189618	904/693-7548	33
North Andrews Gardens Elem Sch/*Oakland Park*/ Broward	00182969	754/322-7300	13
North Bay Haven Charter ES/*Panama City*/Bay	11559814	850/248-0205	4
North Bay Haven Charter MS/*Panama City*/Bay	11589704	850/248-0801	4
North Bay Haven Chrtr Acad HS/*Panama City*/ Bay	11589716	850/248-0801	5
North Beach Elem Sch/*Miami Beach*/ Miami-Dade	00185325	305/531-7666	80
North Broward Acad Excellence/*N Lauderdale*/ Broward	04946951	954/718-2211	16
North Broward Prep Sch/*Coconut Creek*/ Broward	04838768	954/247-0011	19
North Co Charter Sch/*Vero Beach*/ Indian River	04814437	772/794-1941	56
North County K-8 Center/*Opa Locka*/ Miami-Dade	00185741	305/624-9648	80
North Dade Ctr for Modern Lang/*Miami Gardens*/ Miami-Dade	03249310	305/625-3885	80
North Dade Middle Sch/*Miami Gardens*/ Miami-Dade	00185753	305/624-8415	80
North Elem Sch/*Okeechobee*/Okeechobee	02125852	863/462-5100	93
North Florida Christian Sch/*Tallahassee*/ Leon	01404291	850/386-6327	66
North Florida Educ Inst/*Jacksonville*/Duval	11224693	904/764-0084	35
North Fork Elem Sch/*Ft Lauderdale*/Broward	00183690	754/322-7350	13
North Ft Myers High Sch/*N Ft Myers*/Lee	00194326	239/995-2117	62
North Gardens High Sch/*Miami Gardens*/ Miami-Dade	11719612	786/528-6308	80
North Glade Elem Sch/*Miami Gardens*/ Miami-Dade	00185765	305/624-3608	80
North Grade Elem Sch/*Lake Worth*/Palm Beach	00198891	561/202-9300	107
North Hialeah Elem Sch/*Hialeah*/Miami-Dade	00185777	305/681-4611	80
North Kissimmee Christian Sch/*Kissimmee*/ Osceola	04984604	407/847-2877	104
North Lakeland Elem Sch/*Lakeland*/Polk	00201412	863/499-2850	125
North Lauderdale Elem Sch/*N Lauderdale*/ Broward	00182995	754/322-7400	13
North Marion High Sch/*Citra*/Marion	00195590	352/671-6010	71
North Marion Middle Sch/*Citra*/Marion	00195605	352/671-6035	71
North Miami Beach Sr High Sch/*Miami*/ Miami-Dade	00185337	305/949-8381	80
North Miami Elem Sch/*North Miami*/ Miami-Dade	00185349	305/949-6156	80
North Miami Middle Sch/*North Miami*/ Miami-Dade	00185351	305/891-5611	80
North Miami Senior High Sch/*North Miami*/ Miami-Dade	00185363	305/891-6590	80
North Naples Middle Sch/*Naples*/Collier	05347918	239/377-4600	26
North Nicholas High Sch/*Cape Coral*/Lee	11422041	239/242-4230	62
North Park High Sch/*Opa Locka*/Miami-Dade	11719674	305/720-2995	77
North Port High Sch/*North Port*/Sarasota	04943870	941/423-8558	130
North Shore Elem Sch/*Jacksonville*/Duval	00189591	904/924-3081	31
North Shore Elem Sch/*St Petersburg*/ Pinellas	00200016	727/893-2181	119
North Side Elem Sch/*Ft Lauderdale*/Broward	00183327	754/322-7450	13
North Tampa Alt Sch/*Tampa*/Hillsborough	04810015	813/631-4426	51
North Tampa Christian Academy/*Wesley Chapel*/ Pasco	12364806	813/991-0801	115
North Technical College/*Starke*/Bradford	00181886	904/966-6764	6
North Twin Lakes Elem Sch/*Hialeah*/ Miami-Dade	00185789	305/822-0721	80
North Wauchula Elem Sch/*Wauchula*/Hardee	01555931	863/773-2183	42
Northboro Elem Sch/*West Palm Bch*/ Palm Beach	00198619	561/494-1600	108
Northdale Lutheran Sch/*Tampa*/Hillsborough	10013283	813/961-9195	54
Northeast High Sch/*Oakland Park*/Broward	00183016	754/322-1550	13
Northeast High Sch/*St Petersburg*/Pinellas	00200054	727/570-3138	119
Northern Palms Charter HS/*N Ft Myers*/Lee	12162385	239/997-9987	62
Northern Private Sch/*Lake Worth*/Palm Beach	01437224	561/585-4053	111
Northlake Park Cmty Sch/*Orlando*/Orange	04869781	407/852-3500	96
Northmore Elem Sch/*West Palm Bch*/ Palm Beach	00198621	561/494-1700	108
Northport K-8 Sch/*Port St Lucie*/St Lucie	02848494	772/340-4700	136
Northside Christian Academy/*Starke*/ Bradford	11620097	904/964-7124	6
Northside Christian Sch/*St Petersburg*/ Pinellas	11835656	727/541-7593	121
Northside Elem Sch/*Panama City*/Bay	00181692	850/767-1506	5
Northview High Sch/*Century*/Escambia	00190485	850/327-6681	37
Northwest Christian Academy/*Miami*/ Miami-Dade	01404112	305/685-8734	88
Northwest Elem Sch/*Hudson*/Pasco	00199297	727/774-4700	113
Northwest Elem Sch/*St Petersburg*/Pinellas	00200066	727/893-2147	119
Northwest Elem Sch/*Tampa*/Hillsborough	03011216	813/975-7315	50
Northwestern Middle Sch/*Jacksonville*/Duval	00189620	904/924-3100	33
Northwood Elem Sch/*Crestview*/Okaloosa	00196398	850/689-7252	92
Norwood Elem Sch/*Miami*/Miami-Dade	00185416	305/653-0068	80
Notre Dame Catholic Sch/*Spring Hill*/ Hernando	02861070	352/683-0755	44
Nova Blanche Forman Elem Sch/*Davie*/Broward	00183705	754/323-6600	13
Nova Eisenhower Elem Sch/*Davie*/Broward	00183561	754/323-6650	13
Nova High Sch/*Davie*/Broward	00183717	754/323-1650	13
Nova Middle Sch/*Davie*/Broward	00183729	754/323-3700	13
Nuestra Senora De Lourdes Sch/*Hialeah*/ Miami-Dade	03070250	305/822-2645	88
Nur Ul Islam Academy/*Cooper City*/Broward	04983856	954/434-3288	19
NW Florida Ballet Academie/*Ft Walton Bch*/ Okaloosa	05230298	850/664-7787	92
NWFSC Collegiate High Sch/*Niceville*/ Okaloosa	04916841	850/729-4949	92

O

School/City/County DISTRICT/CITY/COUNTY	PID	TELEPHONE NUMBER	PAGE
O J Semmes Elem Sch/*Pensacola*/Escambia	00190760	850/595-6975	37
Oak Creek CS of Bonita Springs/*Bonita Spgs*/ Lee	11446281	239/498-6864	62
Oak Grove Elem Sch/*N Miami Beach*/ Miami-Dade	00185428	305/945-1511	80
Oak Grove Elem Sch/*Tampa*/Hillsborough	04948870	813/356-1532	51
Oak Grove Middle Sch/*Clearwater*/Pinellas	00200080	727/524-4430	118
Oak Hall Sch/*Gainesville*/Alachua	00181472	352/332-3609	3
Oak Hammock K-8 Sch/*Port St Lucie*/St Lucie	10008056	772/344-4490	136
Oak Hammock Middle Sch/*Fort Myers*/Lee	11128013	239/693-0469	62
Oak Hill Academy/*Jacksonville*/Duval	12169888	904/573-1030	29
Oak Hill Elem Sch/*Orlando*/Orange	00197184	407/296-6470	99
Oak Park Elem Sch/*Tampa*/Hillsborough	00192677	813/740-7733	48
Oak Park Elem Sch/*Titusville*/Brevard	00182050	321/269-3252	8
Oak Park Middle Sch/*Leesburg*/Lake	00193944	352/787-3232	59
Oak Park Sch/*Sarasota*/Sarasota	00203317	941/361-6428	130
Oak Ridge Elem Sch/*Tallahassee*/Leon	00194716	850/488-3124	65
Oak Ridge High Sch/*Orlando*/Orange	00197196	407/852-3200	97
Oak View Middle Sch/*Newberry*/Alachua	04145365	352/472-1102	2
Oakcrest Elem Sch/*Ocala*/Marion	00195617	352/671-6350	71
Oakcrest Elem Sch/*Pensacola*/Escambia	00190746	850/595-6980	37
Oakhall Lower Sch/*Gainesville*/Alachua	01771927	352/332-1452	3
Oakhurst Elem Sch/*Largo*/Pinellas	00200092	727/588-6801	119
Oakland Avenue Charter Sch/*Oakland*/Orange	05286417	407/877-2039	94
Oakland Park Elem Sch/*Oakland Park*/Broward	00183339	754/322-7500	13
Oakland Terrace Elem Sch/*Panama City*/Bay	00181719	850/767-4565	5
Oakleaf High Sch/*Orange Park*/Clay	11552892	904/336-8375	24
Oakleaf Junior High Sch/*Orange Park*/Clay	10029983	904/336-5775	24
Oakleaf Village Elem Sch/*Orange Park*/Clay	11069338	904/336-2425	24
Oakridge Elem Sch/*Hollywood*/Broward	00184101	754/323-6700	13

School/City/County DISTRICT/CITY/COUNTY	PID	TELEPHONE NUMBER	PAGE
Oakridge Middle Sch/Naples/Collier	04034625	239/377-4800	26
Oakshire Elem Sch/Orlando/Orange	04885280	407/251-2500	98
Oakstead Elem Sch/Land O Lakes/Pasco	10021498	813/346-1500	113
Oasis Charter Elem Sch/Cape Coral/Lee	10007131	239/542-1577	62
Oasis Charter High Sch/Cape Coral/Lee	10024036	239/541-1167	62
Oasis Charter Middle Sch/Cape Coral/Lee	11127966	239/945-1999	62
Oasis Christian Academy/Winter Haven/Polk	02086581	863/293-0930	126
Oasis Middle Sch/Bradenton/Manatee	10913516	941/749-1979	69
Ocala Christian Academy/Ocala/Marion	01436919	352/694-4178	72
Ocala Springs Elem Sch/Ocala/Marion	02896690	352/671-6360	71
Ocali Charter Middle Sch/Ocala/Marion	12262870	352/264-9940	71
Ocean Breeze Elem Sch/Indn HBR Bch/Brevard	00182402	321/779-2040	8
Ocean Palms Elem Sch/Ponte Vedra/St Johns	04751445	904/547-3760	134
Ocean Studies Charter Sch/Tavernier/Monroe	11719765	305/852-7700	90
Oceanway Elem Sch/Jacksonville/Duval	00189668	904/696-8762	31
Oceanway Middle Sch/Jacksonville/Duval	05343936	904/714-4680	33
Ochwilla Elem Sch/Hawthorne/Putnam	04014833	352/481-0204	127
Ocoee Elem Sch/Ocoee/Orange	00197201	407/877-5027	99
Ocoee High Sch/Ocoee/Orange	10000597	407/905-3000	97
Ocoee Middle Sch/Ocoee/Orange	00197213	407/877-5035	100
Ocps Acad Ctr for Excellence/Orlando/ Orange	12230102	407/866-1280	95
Odessa Christian Sch/Odessa/Hillsborough	11221407	813/792-1825	54
Odessa Elem Sch/New Prt Rchy/Pasco	11548554	727/246-3700	113
Odyssey Charter Sch/Palm Bay/Brevard	04869640	321/733-0442	7
Odyssey Middle Sch/Orlando/Orange	04945335	407/207-3850	98
Odyssey Preparatory Academy/Palm Bay/ Brevard	11918569	321/345-4117	7
Ojus Elem Sch/Miami/Miami-Dade	00185430	305/931-4881	80
Okaloosa Acad Charter Sch/Ft Walton Bch/ Okaloosa	04468208	850/864-3133	92
OKALOOSA CO SCH DIST/FT WALTON BCH/ OKALOOSA	00196128	850/833-3100	91
Okaloosa Regional Djj Academy/Crestview/ Okaloosa	04875168	850/689-7800	92
Okaloosa Stemm Academy/Valparaiso/Okaloosa	11821411	850/833-4120	92
Okaloosa Virtual Sch/Crestview/Okaloosa	11713797	850/689-2043	92
Okaloosa Youth Academy/Crestview/Okaloosa	12313235	850/689-1984	92
Okeechobee Achievement Academy/Okeechobee/ Okeechobee	03394484	863/462-5125	93
Okeechobee Christian Academy/Okeechobee/ Okeechobee	01775129	863/763-3072	93
OKEECHOBEE CO SCH DIST/OKEECHOBEE/ OKEECHOBEE	00196506	863/462-5000	93
Okeechobee Freshman Campus/Okeechobee/ Okeechobee	04874413	863/462-5288	93
Okeechobee High Sch/Okeechobee/Okeechobee	00196520	863/462-5025	93
Okeechobee SDA Sch/Okeechobee/Okeechobee	05231280	863/763-0763	93
Okeechobee Virtual Sch/Okeechobee/ Okeechobee	12102414	863/462-5000	93
Okeeheelee Middle Sch/Greenacres/ Palm Beach	04457091	561/434-3200	110
Old Kings Elem Sch/Flagler Beach/Flagler	03318856	386/517-2060	39
Old Plank Christian Academy/Jacksonville/ Duval	11223481	904/783-4888	35
Old Town Elem Sch/Old Town/Dixie	00188767	352/541-6253	29
Oldsmar Christian Sch/Oldsmar/Pinellas	02149705	813/855-5746	121
Oldsmar Elem Sch/Oldsmar/Pinellas	00200107	813/855-7316	117
Oliver Hoover Elem Sch/Miami/Miami-Dade	02177477	305/385-4382	83
Olsen Middle Sch/Dania Beach/Broward	00183731	754/323-3800	13
Olympia Heights Elem Sch/Miami/Miami-Dade	00187048	305/221-3821	83
Olympia High Sch/Orlando/Orange	04947876	407/905-6400	97
Olympic Heights Cmty High Sch/Boca Raton/ Palm Beach	03401312	561/852-6900	110
Olympus International Academy/Boca Raton/ Palm Beach	12362195	561/900-5323	105
Omni Middle Sch/Boca Raton/Palm Beach	03337137	561/989-2800	110
One Room Elem School House/Gainesville/ Alachua	04752504	352/376-4014	2
One Room Middle Sch/Gainesville/Alachua	12262636	352/727-4373	2
One School of the Arts/Longwood/Seminole	03419400	407/774-0168	134
Oneco Elem Sch/Bradenton/Manatee	00195215	941/751-7018	69
Options Center/Key West/Monroe	11717779	305/293-1400	90
Orange Ave Baptist Sch/Fort Pierce/ St Lucie	02825686	772/461-1225	137
Orange Brook Elem Sch/Hollywood/Broward	00184113	754/323-6750	13
Orange Center Elem Sch/Orlando/Orange	00197225	407/296-6480	100
Orange City Elem Sch/Orange City/Volusia	00204593	386/575-4215	141
Orange Co Preparatory Academy/Orlando/ Orange	12102452	407/440-9293	94
ORANGE CO PSD-TRANSFORMATION/ ORLANDO/ORANGE	12367341	407/317-3244	95

School/City/County DISTRICT/CITY/COUNTY	PID	TELEPHONE NUMBER	PAGE
ORANGE CO PUBLIC SCH DIST/ ORLANDO/ORANGE	00196568	407/317-3200	94
ORANGE CO PUBLIC SD-DEP SUPT/ ORLANDO/ORANGE	12308072	407/317-3313	95
ORANGE CO PUBLIC SD-EAST/ ORLANDO/ORANGE	04803610	407/737-1490	96
ORANGE CO PUBLIC SD-HIGH SCH/ ORLANDO/ORANGE	12308060	407/317-3382	97
ORANGE CO PUBLIC SD-NORTH/ ORLANDO/ORANGE	04803608	407/532-7970	97
ORANGE CO PUBLIC SD-SOUTHEAST/ ORLANDO/ORANGE	04803581	407/317-3740	98
ORANGE CO PUBLIC SD-SOUTHWEST/ ORLANDO/ORANGE	10020444	407/318-3110	98
ORANGE CO PUBLIC SD-WEST/ WINTER GARDEN/ORANGE	04803579	407/905-3200	99
Orange County Virtual Sch/Orlando/Orange	11703259	407/317-3327	94
Orange Grove Elem Sch/Seminole/Pinellas	00200119	727/547-7845	119
Orange Grove Mag Sch the Arts/Tampa/ Hillsborough	04810118	813/276-5717	51
Orange Park Elem Sch/Orange Park/Clay	00184759	904/336-2275	24
Orange Park High Sch/Orange Park/Clay	00184773	904/336-8675	24
Orange Park Junior High Sch/Orange Park/ Clay	00184761	904/336-5975	24
Orange River Elem Sch/Fort Myers/Lee	00194338	239/694-1258	62
Orange Tech College Mid FL/Orlando/Orange	00197160	407/251-6047	94
Orange Tech College Orlando/Orlando/Orange	02127616	407/246-7060	94
Orange Youth Academy/Orlando/Orange	11550064	407/835-0111	94
Orangewood Christian Sch/Maitland/Orange	02148921	407/339-0223	101
Orangewood Elem Sch/Fort Myers/Lee	00194340	239/936-2950	62
Orchard View Elem Sch/Delray Beach/ Palm Beach	04369274	561/894-7400	110
Orchard Villa Elem Sch/Miami/Miami-Dade	00186252	305/754-0607	77
Oriole Beach Elem Sch/Gulf Breeze/ Santa Rosa	02178952	850/934-5160	128
Oriole Elem Sch/Laud Lakes/Broward	00183341	754/322-7550	13
Orlando Christian Prep/Orlando/Orange	01775246	407/823-9744	101
Orlando Gifted Academy/Orlando/Orange	12309155	407/897-6410	96
Orlando Junior Academy/Orlando/Orange	01437042	407/898-1251	101
Orlando Science Elem Sch/Orlando/Orange	11820596	407/299-6595	94
Orlando Science Middle & HS/Orlando/Orange	11076836	407/253-7304	94
Orlo Vista Elem Sch/Orlando/Orange	00197237	407/296-6490	95
Ormond Beach Elem Sch/Ormond Beach/Volusia	00204608	386/258-4666	141
Ormond Beach Middle Sch/Ormond Beach/ Volusia	00204610	386/258-4667	141
Ortega Elem Sch/Jacksonville/Duval	00189682	904/381-7460	31
Ortona Elem Sch/Daytona Beach/Volusia	00204622	386/258-4668	141
Oscar J Pope Elem Sch/Eaton Park/Polk	00201424	863/499-2992	125
Oscar Patterson Elem Sch/Panama City/Bay	00181721	850/767-4675	5
Osceola Adventist Church Sch/Kissimmee/ Osceola	03406829	407/348-2226	104
OSCEOLA CO SCH DIST/KISSIMMEE/ OSCEOLA	00197964	407/870-4600	102
Osceola County Sch for Arts/Kissimmee/ Osceola	05274505	407/931-4803	103
Osceola Creek Middle Sch/Loxahatchee/ Palm Beach	05348558	561/422-2500	108
Osceola Elem Sch/Naples/Collier	05101130	239/377-7800	26
Osceola Elem Sch/Ormond Beach/Volusia	00204634	386/258-4669	141
Osceola Elem Sch/St Augustine/St Johns	00202387	904/547-3780	134
Osceola Fundamental High Sch/Seminole/ Pinellas	02125876	727/547-7717	118
Osceola High Sch/Kissimmee/Osceola	00198011	407/518-5400	104
Osceola Magnet Sch/Vero Beach/Indian River	00193401	772/564-5821	56
Osceola Middle Sch/Ocala/Marion	00195629	352/671-7100	71
Osceola Middle Sch/Okeechobee/Okeechobee	04453021	863/462-5070	93
Osceola Middle Sch/Seminole/Pinellas	02227321	727/547-7689	118
Osceola Science Charter Sch/Kissimmee/ Osceola	12173671	407/846-0121	104
Osceola Virtual Sch/Saint Cloud/Osceola	11715721	407/870-1445	104
Oslo Middle Sch/Vero Beach/Indian River	04367800	772/564-3980	56
Osteen Elem Sch/Osteen/Volusia	00204646	407/688-9555	141
Otis A Mason Elem Sch/St Augustine/ St Johns	04013712	904/547-8440	135
Our Lady of Charity Pvt Sch/Hialeah/ Miami-Dade	03418169	305/556-5409	88
Our Lady of Holy Rosary Sch/Miami/ Miami-Dade	00188171	305/235-5442	85
Our Lady of Lourdes Academy/Miami/ Miami-Dade	00188157	305/667-1623	85
Our Lady of Lourdes Sch/Dunedin/Pinellas	00200951	727/733-3776	120
Our Lady of Lourdes Sch/Melbourne/Brevard	00197768	321/723-3631	9

School/City/County DISTRICT/CITY/COUNTY	PID	TELEPHONE NUMBER	PAGE
Palmetto Ridge High Sch/*Naples*/Collier	05347932	239/377-2400	26
Palmview Elem Sch/*Pompano Beach*/Broward	00183028	754/322-7600	13
Panacea Prep Charter Sch/*Coral Springs*/ Broward	12032807	954/341-5550	16
Panama City Advanced Sch/*Panama City*/Bay	04778962	850/784-2520	5
Panama City Marine Institute/*Panama City*/ Bay	02875992	850/872-4715	5
PANHANDLE AREA ED CONSORTIUM/ **CHIPLEY/WASHINGTON**	04433112	850/638-6131	145
Panther Run Elem Sch/*Lake Worth*/Palm Beach	03401283	561/804-3900	107
Panther Run Elem Sch/*Pembroke Pnes*/Broward	04756586	754/323-6850	13
Paragon Academy of Technology/*Hollywood*/ Broward	10006606	954/925-0155	16
Park Avenue Christian Academy/*Titusville*/ Brevard	02147953	321/267-1871	10
Park Elem Sch/*Avon Park*/Highlands	03400552	863/452-4373	45
Park Lakes Elem Sch/*Laud Lakes*/Broward	04457106	754/322-7650	14
Park Maitland Sch/*Maitland*/Orange	01775272	407/647-3038	102
Park Ridge Elem Sch/*Pompano Beach*/Broward	00183030	754/322-7700	14
Park Springs Elem Sch/*Coral Springs*/ Broward	03252197	754/322-7750	14
Park Trails Elem Sch/*Parkland*/Broward	04946987	754/322-7800	14
Park Vista Cmty High Sch/*Lake Worth*/ Palm Beach	05348534	561/491-8400	110
Parke House Academy/*Winter Park*/Orange	04882379	407/647-1121	102
Parker Elem Sch/*Panama City*/Bay	00181733	850/767-4570	5
Parkridge Christian Academy/*Coral Springs*/ Broward	11222683	954/346-0236	19
Parkside Elem Sch/*Coral Springs*/Broward	04917144	754/322-7850	14
Parkside Elem Sch/*Naples*/Collier	10913358	239/377-8900	26
Parkview Elem Sch/*Miami Gardens*/Miami-Dade	00185844	305/625-1591	81
Parkway Christian Academy/*Lakeland*/Polk	01404502	863/646 5031	126
Parkway Christian Sch/*Davie*/Broward	11827867	954/424-6425	19
Parkway Elem Sch/*Miami*/Miami-Dade	00185442	305/653-0066	81
Parkway Elem Sch/*Port St Lucie*/St Lucie	03250515	772/340-4800	136
Parkway Middle Sch/*Ft Lauderdale*/Broward	00183743	754/322-4000	14
Parkway Middle Sch/*Kissimmee*/Osceola	03050315	407/344-7000	104
Parkwood Heights Elem Sch/*Jacksonville*/ Duval	00189709	904/720-1670	31
Parkwood Preparatory Academy/*Jacksonville*/ Duval	02372421	904/721-2719	35
Parrish Charter Academy/*Parrish*/Manatee	12362066	941/545-6380	69
Parrish Cmty High Sch/*Parrish*/Manatee	12363125	941/803-9330	69
Parsons Christian Academy/*Jacksonville*/ Duval	11228235	904/745-4588	35
Partin Elem Sch/*Oviedo*/Seminole	03395153	407/320-4850	133
Partin Settlement Elem Sch/*Kissimmee*/ Osceola	05096535	407/518-2000	104
Pasadena Fundamental Elem Sch/*St Petersburg*/ Pinellas	00200169	727/893-2646	119
Pasadena Lakes Elem Sch/*Pembroke Pnes*/ Broward	00184125	754/323-6900	14
PASCO CO SCH DIST/LAND O LAKES/ **PASCO**	00199156	813/794-2000	112
PASCO CSD-ELEMENTARY SCHOOLS/ **LAND O LAKES/PASCO**	12234938	813/794-2695	113
PASCO CSD-HIGH SCHOOLS/LAND O LAKES/ **PASCO**	12234952	813/794-2753	114
PASCO CSD-MIDDLE SCHOOLS/ **LAND O LAKES/PASCO**	12234940	813/794-2753	114
Pasco E-School/*Spring Hill*/Pasco	11555985	813/346-1900	113
Pasco Elem Sch/*Dade City*/Pasco	00199314	352/524-5200	113
Pasco High Sch/*Dade City*/Pasco	00199302	352/524-5500	114
Pasco Middle Sch/*Dade City*/Pasco	00199326	352/524-8400	115
Passport Charter Sch/*Orlando*/Orange	04757360	407/658-9900	94
Pathways Academy/*Lake City*/Columbia	04941418	386/755-8296	28
Pathways at Pine Grove/*Melbourne*/Brevard	04369195	321/242-4770	7
Pathways Elem Sch/*Ormond Beach*/Volusia	04753962	386/258-4671	141
Pathways Sch/*Orlando*/Orange	04223711	407/816-2040	102
Patriot Elem Sch/*Cape Coral*/Lee	10910681	239/242-1023	62
Patriot Oaks Academy/*Saint Johns*/St Johns	12031762	904/547-4050	135
Patronis Elem Sch/*P C Beach*/Bay	04368490	850/767-5075	5
Patterson Private Sch/*Melbourne*/Brevard	04328062	321/254-9525	10
Paul B Stephens Sch/*Clearwater*/Pinellas	00199625	727/725-7982	117
Paul L Dunbar K-8 Center/*Miami*/Miami-Dade	00186537	305/573-2344	77
Paul Laurence Dunbar Mid Sch/*Fort Myers*/ Lee	00194194	239/334-1357	62
Paul R Smith Middle Sch/*Holiday*/Pasco	10020042	727/246-3200	115
Paul W Bell Middle Sch/*Miami*/Miami-Dade	04494972	305/220-2075	83
Paul Wharton High Sch/*Tampa*/Hillsborough	04754966	813/631-4710	50
Paxon School-Advanced Studies/*Jacksonville*/ Duval	00189723	904/693-7583	32

School/City/County DISTRICT/CITY/COUNTY	PID	TELEPHONE NUMBER	PAGE
Paxton Sch/*Paxton*/Walton	00204969	850/892-1230	144
Pea Ridge Elem Sch/*Pace*/Santa Rosa	02128634	850/995-3680	128
Peace Lutheran Sch/*Bradenton*/Manatee	01404320	941/747-6753	70
Peace Lutheran Sch/*Kissimmee*/Osceola	11719753	407/870-5965	104
Peace River Elem Sch/*Pt Charlotte*/ Charlotte	00184474	941/255-7622	21
Peaceforce Christian Academy/*Orlando*/ Orange	11228924	407/290-9279	102
Pedro Menendez High Sch/*St Augustine*/ St Johns	04918538	904/547-8660	135
Pelican Elem Sch/*Cape Coral*/Lee	02042171	239/549-4966	62
Pelican Island Elem Sch/*Sebastian*/ Indian River	00193425	772/564-6500	56
Pelican Marsh Elem Sch/*Naples*/Collier	04448947	239/377-7900	26
Pemayetv Emahakv Charter Sch/*Okeechobee*/ Glades	10966783	863/467-2501	41
Pembroke Lakes Elem Sch/*Pembroke Pnes*/ Broward	01413357	754/323-6950	14
Pembroke Pines Elem Sch/*Pembroke Pnes*/ Broward	00184137	754/323-7000	14
Pembroke Pines ES-Central/*Pembroke Pnes*/ Broward	05110064	954/322-3300	17
Pembroke Pines ES-East Campus/*Pembroke Pnes*/ Broward	04815194	954/443-4800	17
Pembroke Pines ES-West/*Pembroke Pnes*/ Broward	04815211	954/450-6990	17
Pembroke Pines High Sch/*Ft Lauderdale*/ Broward	04911786	954/538-3700	17
Pembroke Pines MS-Central/*Pembroke Pnes*/ Broward	11554735	954/322-3300	17
Pembroke Pines-Fsu Charter ES/*Pembroke Pnes*/ Broward	05286247	954/499-4244	1
Peniel Baptist Academy/*Palatka*/Putnam	00202351	386/328-1707	127
Pensacola Beach Charter Sch/*Pensacola Bch*/ Escambia	02125840	850/934-4020	37
Pensacola Boys Base Sch/*Pensacola*/Escambia	02047975	850/453-7521	37
Pensacola Catholic High Sch/*Pensacola*/ Escambia	00202636	850/436-6400	38
Pensacola Christian Academy/*Pensacola*/ Escambia	11840704	850/478-8496	38
Pensacola High Sch/*Pensacola*/Escambia	00190796	850/595-1500	37
Pensacola Sch of Liberal Arts/*Pensacola*/ Escambia	01865279	850/434-2294	38
Pensacola SDA Junior Academy/*Pensacola*/ Escambia	01865281	850/478-8838	38
Pentab Academy/*Miami*/Miami-Dade	11235434	305/651-9696	88
Pepin Acad-Pasco Campus/*New Prt Rchy*/Pasco	12039013	727/233-2961	113
Pepin Academies-Tampa/*Tampa*/Hillsborough	04874346	813/236-1755	47
Pepin Academy-Riverview/*Riverview*/ Hillsborough	12179156	813/533-2999	47
Performance Based Prep Academy/*Fort Pierce*/ St Lucie	12105624	772/468-5880	136
Perkins Elem Sch/*St Petersburg*/Pinellas	00200171	727/893-2117	119
Perrine SDA Sch/*Miami*/Miami-Dade	11735379	305/259-0059	88
Perry Co Primary Sch/*Perry*/Taylor	00204191	850/838-2506	139
Pershing Elem Sch/*Orlando*/Orange	00197251	407/251-2363	96
Peters Elem Sch/*Plantation*/Broward	00183353	754/322-7900	14
Philip O'Brien Elem Sch/*Lakeland*/Polk	00201371	863/499-2950	125
Philip Shore Elem Sch/*Tampa*/Hillsborough	00192706	813/276-5712	49
Phillippi Shores Elem Sch/*Sarasota*/ Sarasota	00203410	941/361-6424	130
Phillis Wheatley Elem Sch/*Miami*/Miami-Dade	00186719	305/573-2638	77
Phoenix Acad of Excellence N/*Miami*/ Miami-Dade	12323058	786/865-1346	74
Phoenix-Immokalee/*Immokalee*/Collier	12107426	239/377-1130	26
Phyl's Academy/*Margate*/Broward	03326085	954/731-7524	19
Phyllis R Miller Elem Sch/*Miami*/Miami-Dade	04021288	305/756-3800	77
Pickett Elem Sch/*Jacksonville*/Duval	00189735	904/693-7555	31
Picolata Crossing Elem Sch/*St Augustine*/ St Johns	12235267	904/547-4160	135
Piedmont Lakes Middle Sch/*Apopka*/Orange	04018619	407/884-2265	97
Pierce Hammock Elem Sch/*Loxahatchee*/ Palm Beach	05348560	561/633-4500	108
Pierce Middle Sch/*Tampa*/Hillsborough	00192718	813/872-5344	50
Pierson Elem Sch/*Pierson*/Volusia	00204658	386/740-0850	141
Pinar Elem Sch/*Orlando*/Orange	00197263	407/249-6380	98
Pine Castle Christian Academy/*Orlando*/ Orange	02825260	407/313-7222	102
Pine Crest Sch/*Ft Lauderdale*/Broward	00184230	954/492-4100	19
Pine Crest School-Boca Raton/*Boca Raton*/ Palm Beach	01865516	561/852-2800	112
Pine Estates Elem Sch/*Jacksonville*/Duval	00189747	904/696-8767	31

School/City/County DISTRICT/CITY/COUNTY	PID	TELEPHONE NUMBER	PAGE
Pine Forest High Sch/*Pensacola*/Escambia	01395834	850/941-6150	37
Pine Forest School of the Arts/*Jacksonville*/Duval	00189759	904/346-5600	31
Pine Grove Elem Sch/*Brooksville*/Hernando	03158826	352/797-7090	44
Pine Grove Elem Sch/*Delray Beach*/Palm Beach	00198906	561/266-1100	110
Pine Hills Elem Sch/*Orlando*/Orange	00197287	407/296-6500	100
Pine Island Elem Sch/*Bokeelia*/Lee	00194352	239/283-0505	62
Pine Island Montessori Sch/*Davie*/Broward	03111713	954/434-6337	19
Pine Jog Elem Sch/*West Palm Bch*/Palm Beach	11103661	561/656-5400	107
Pine Lake Elem Sch/*Miami*/Miami-Dade	01557094	305/233-7018	83
Pine Meadow Elem Sch/*Pensacola*/Escambia	00190801	850/494-5630	38
Pine Ridge Education Center/*Ft Lauderdale*/Broward	00183755	754/321-7250	14
Pine Ridge Elem Sch/*Clermont*/Lake	05278343	352/242-2223	59
Pine Ridge High Sch/*Deltona*/Volusia	04287365	386/575-4195	141
Pine Ridge Middle Sch/*Naples*/Collier	00184967	239/377-5000	26
Pine Trail Elem Sch/*Ormond Beach*/Volusia	02200115	386/258-4672	141
Pine View Elem Sch/*Land O Lakes*/Pasco	05275080	813/794-0600	113
Pine View Middle Sch/*Land O Lakes*/Pasco	01830200	813/794-4800	115
Pine View Sch/*Osprey*/Sarasota	00203422	941/486-2001	130
Pine Villa Elem Sch/*Miami*/Miami-Dade	00187490	305/258-5366	83
Pineapple Cove Classical Acad/*Palm Bay*/Brevard	12114912	321/802-9500	7
Pineapple Cove Classical Acad/*W Melbourne*/Brevard	12307353	321/499-2585	7
Pinecrest Acad ES-South Campus/*Miami*/Miami-Dade	10014550	305/386-0800	83
Pinecrest Academy/*Miami*/Miami-Dade	11455634	305/553-9762	77
Pinecrest Academy Four Corners/*Clermont*/Lake	12362030	352/978-3397	59
Pinecrest Collegiate Acad/*Orlando*/Orange	12322004	407/432-5441	94
Pinecrest Cove Academy/*Miami*/Miami-Dade	11719727	305/480-2097	83
Pinecrest Creek Academy/*Orlando*/Orange	11820637	407/757-2706	95
Pinecrest Elem Sch/*Immokalee*/Collier	00184979	239/377-8000	26
Pinecrest Elem Sch/*Lithia*/Hillsborough	00192720	813/744-8164	52
Pinecrest Elem Sch/*Pinecrest*/Miami-Dade	00187505	305/667-5579	84
Pinecrest Elem Sch/*Sanford*/Seminole	00203824	407/320-5450	133
Pinecrest Glades Academy/*Miami*/Miami-Dade	12169424	305/299-6949	84
Pinecrest Lakes Academy/*Clermont*/Lake	12232564	352/223-4482	59
Pinecrest Prep Middle/High Sch/*Miami*/Miami-Dade	11128192	305/559-8583	84
Pinecrest Preparatory Academy/*Miami*/Miami-Dade	04948052	305/207-1027	84
Pinecrest Preparatory Academy/*Orlando*/Orange	11621728	407/856-8359	95
Pinedale Elem Sch/*Jacksonville*/Duval	00189761	904/381-7490	31
Pinellas Academy Math & Sci/*Clearwater*/Pinellas	11825273	727/330-9449	116
Pinellas Central Elem Sch/*Pinellas Park*/Pinellas	00200195	727/547-7853	119
PINELLAS CO SCH DIST/LARGO/**PINELLAS**	00199429	727/588-6000	116
PINELLAS CO SCHOOLS-AREA 1/LARGO/PINELLAS	11716660	727/588-5023	116
PINELLAS CO SCHOOLS-AREA 2/LARGO/PINELLAS	01220693	727/588-5024	117
PINELLAS CO SCHOOLS-AREA 3/LARGO/PINELLAS	11716672	727/588-5020	118
PINELLAS CO SCHOOLS-AREA 4/LARGO/PINELLAS	10901501	727/588-5022	119
Pinellas Gulf Coast Academy/*Largo*/Pinellas	11925586	727/474-8836	118
Pinellas Park Elem Sch/*Pinellas Park*/Pinellas	00200200	727/547-7888	119
Pinellas Park High Sch/*Largo*/Pinellas	01527257	727/538-7410	119
Pinellas Park Middle Sch/*Pinellas Park*/Pinellas	00200212	727/545-6400	119
Pinellas Prep Academy/*Largo*/Pinellas	05194826	727/536-3600	116
Pinellas Primary Academy/*Largo*/Pinellas	11716775	727/536-3600	116
Pinellas Secondary Sch/*Pinellas Park*/Pinellas	10029103	727/549-6550	118
Pinellas Virtual Sch/*Clearwater*/Pinellas	11750824	727/588-6448	118
Pineloch Elem Sch/*Orlando*/Orange	00197209	407/245-1825	99
Pinemount Elem Sch/*Lake City*/Columbia	11445873	386/755-8179	28
Pines Lakes Elem Sch/*Pembroke Pnes*/Broward	02042121	754/323-7100	14
Pines Middle Sch/*Pembroke Pnes*/Broward	00184149	754/323-4000	14
Pinetta Elem Sch/*Pinetta*/Madison	00195021	850/973-5028	67
Pineview Elem Sch/*Tallahassee*/Leon	00194728	850/488-2819	65
Pinewood Christian Academy/*Middleburg*/Clay	04982826	904/272-6408	24
Pinewood Elem Sch/*Eagle Lake*/Polk	04922008	863/298-7977	124
Pinewood Elem Sch/*Mims*/Brevard	00182086	321/269-4530	8
Pinewood Elem Sch/*N Lauderdale*/Broward	02042107	754/322-7950	14

School/City/County DISTRICT/CITY/COUNTY	PID	TELEPHONE NUMBER	PAGE
Pinewood Elem Sch/*Orlando*/Orange	04811320	407/532-7930	97
Pinewood Elem Sch/*Stuart*/Martin	03048130	772/219-1595	73
Pinewoods Elem Sch/*Estero*/Lee	04291172	239/947-7500	62
Pioneer Career Academy/*Zolfo Springs*/Hardee	04279344	863/735-2300	42
Pioneer Middle Sch/*Cooper City*/Broward	01413345	754/323-4100	14
Pioneer Park Elem Sch/*Belle Glade*/Palm Beach	04369303	561/993-8600	108
Pioneer Sch/*St Augustine*/St Johns	12239330	904/209-5891	135
Piper High Sch/*Sunrise*/Broward	00183365	754/322-1700	14
Pivot Charter Sch/*Riverview*/Hillsborough	11716244	813/626-6724	47
Pizzo K-8 Patel Lower Campus/*Tampa*/Hillsborough	04811423	813/987-6500	48
Plant City Senior High Sch/*Plant City*/Hillsborough	00192732	813/757-9370	52
Plant Senior High Sch/*Tampa*/Hillsborough	00192299	813/272-3033	49
Plantation Elem Sch/*Plantation*/Broward	00183377	754/322-8000	14
Plantation High Sch/*Plantation*/Broward	00183389	754/322-1850	14
Plantation Key Elem Sch/*Tavernier*/Monroe	01524281	305/853-3281	90
Plantation Middle Sch/*Plantation*/Broward	00183391	754/322-4100	14
Plantation Oaks Elem Sch/*Orange Park*/Clay	11447209	904/336-2775	24
Plantation Park Elem Sch/*Plantation*/Broward	00183767	754/323-7150	14
Plato Academy Clearwater/*Clearwater*/Pinellas	05346938	727/228-9517	116
Plato Academy Largo/*Largo*/Pinellas	11557749	727/228-9952	116
Plato Academy Palm Harbor/*Palm Harbor*/Pinellas	11557737	727/228-6850	116
Plato Academy Pinellas Park/*Pinellas Park*/Pinellas	12108511	727/521-7260	116
Plato Academy Seminole/*Largo*/Pinellas	11716787	727/228-9950	116
Plato Academy St Petersburg/*St Petersburg*/Pinellas	11925562	727/521-7258	116
Plato Academy Tampa CS/*Tampa*/Hillsborough	12231651	727/205-6360	47
Plato Academy Tarpon Springs/*Tarpon Spgs*/Pinellas	11822611	727/939-6413	116
Plato Academy Trinity/*New Prt Rchy*/Pasco	12168030	727/877-2437	113
Pleasant City Elem Sch/*West Palm Bch*/Palm Beach	05102330	561/838-5800	108
Pleasant Grove Elem Sch/*Inverness*/Citrus	03048972	352/637-4400	22
Pleasant Grove Elem Sch/*Pensacola*/Escambia	00190813	850/492-0233	38
Pleasant Hill Elem Sch/*Kissimmee*/Osceola	03050303	407/935-3700	104
Plew Elem Sch/*Niceville*/Okaloosa	00196283	850/833-4100	92
Plumb Elem Sch/*Clearwater*/Pinellas	00200224	727/469-5976	118
Plumosa School of the Arts/*Delray Beach*/Palm Beach	00198918	561/330-3900	110
Poinciana Academy of Fine Arts/*Kissimmee*/Osceola	05096547	407/343-4500	104
Poinciana Elem Sch/*Boynton Beach*/Palm Beach	00198920	561/739-5700	110
Poinciana Elem Sch/*Key West*/Monroe	00195942	305/293-1630	90
Poinciana Elem Sch/*Naples*/Collier	00184981	239/377-8100	26
Poinciana High Sch/*Kissimmee*/Osceola	03393143	407/870-4860	104
Poinciana Park Elem Sch/*Miami*/Miami-Dade	00186264	305/691-5640	77
Point of Grace Christian Sch/*Perry*/Taylor	11826227	850/584-5445	139
Polk Avenue Elem Sch/*Lake Wales*/Polk	00201670	863/678-4244	123
Polk City Elem Sch/*Polk City*/Polk	00201905	863/965-6338	125
POLK CO SCH DIST/BARTOW/POLK	00201187	863/534-0500	121
POLK CO SD-FOUR REGIONS HS/LAKELAND/POLK	12036059	863/647-4810	122
POLK CO SD-FOUR REGIONS MS/BARTOW/POLK	12036047	863/519-7562	122
POLK CO SD-MULTIPLE PATHWAYS/BARTOW/POLK	12036073	863/519-8438	123
POLK CO SD-NE & SE/EAGLE LAKE/POLK	12036023	863/291-5251	124
POLK CO SD-SCHOOL IMPROVEMENT/LAKELAND/POLK	12036061	863/815-6722	124
POLK CO SD-W & N CTRL/LAKELAND/POLK	12036035	863/648-3060	125
Polk Grad Academy/*Lakeland*/Polk	12262739	863/413-2948	123
Polk Pre-Collegiate Academy/*Auburndale*/Polk	11720740	863/984-2400	123
Polk State Gateway to Clg CHS/*Lakeland*/Polk	11923538	863/669-2923	123
Polk State Lakeland Clgt HS/*Lakeland*/Polk	05346744	863/669-2322	123
Polk Virtual Sch/*Lakeland*/Polk	11745532	863/665-4538	123
Polo Park Middle Sch/*Lake Worth*/Palm Beach	04920816	561/333-5500	107
Pompano Beach Elem Sch/*Pompano Beach*/Broward	00183042	754/322-8050	14
Pompano Beach High Sch/*Pompano Beach*/Broward	04809339	754/322-2000	14

School/City/County DISTRICT/CITY/COUNTY	PID	TELEPHONE NUMBER	PAGE
Pompano Beach Middle Sch/*Pompano Beach*/			
Broward	00183066	754/322-4200	14
Ponce De Leon Elem Sch/*Clearwater*/Pinellas	00200236	727/588-3573	118
Ponce De Leon Elem Sch/*Ponce De Leon*/			
Holmes	02111186	850/836-4296	55
Ponce De Leon High Sch/*Ponce De Leon*/			
Holmes	00193308	850/836-4242	55
Ponce De Leon Middle Sch/*Coral Gables*/			
Miami-Dade	00186721	305/661-1611	77
Ponte Vedra High Sch/*Ponte Vedra*/St Johns	11130432	904/547-7350	135
Pope John Paul II High Sch/*Boca Raton*/			
Palm Beach	02113017	561/994-8998	110
Poplar Springs Sch/*Graceville*/Holmes	00193310	850/263-6260	55
Port Charlotte Adventist Sch/*Pt Charlotte*/			
Charlotte	01865011	941/625-5237	22
Port Charlotte High Sch/*Pt Charlotte*/			
Charlotte	02129547	941/255-7485	21
Port Charlotte Middle Sch/*Pt Charlotte*/			
Charlotte	00184498	941/255-7460	21
Port Malabar Elem Sch/*Palm Bay*/Brevard	02109901	321/725-0070	8
Port Orange Elem Sch/*Port Orange*/Volusia	00204672	386/322-6271	141
Port Salerno Elem Sch/*Stuart*/Martin	00195801	772/219-1610	73
Port St Joe Elem Sch/*Port St Joe*/Gulf	00191362	850/227-1221	41
Port St Joe Jr Sr High Sch/*Port St Joe*/			
Gulf	00191374	850/229-8251	41
Port St Lucie High Sch/*Port St Lucie*/			
St Lucie	03250527	772/337-6770	136
Positive Pathways Ctr/*Orlando*/Orange	10902555	407/992-0914	95
Potential Christian Academy/*Cooper City*/			
Broward	03106988	954/434-1550	19
Potentials Charter Sch/*Riviera Beach*/			
Palm Beach	04811461	561/842-3213	105
Potter Elem Sch/*Tampa*/Hillsborough	00192744	813/276-5564	48
Potters House Academy & DCC/*Orlando*/Orange	11332185	407/367-0435	102
Potters House Christian Acad/*Jacksonville*/			
Duval	11735094	904/786-0028	35
Powell Middle Sch/*Brooksville*/Hernando	02226949	352/797-7095	44
Prairie Lake Elem Sch/*Orlando*/Orange	02895150	407/884-2220	97
Praise Temple Christian Acad/*Groveland*/			
Lake	11222877	352/429-8813	60
Precious Promise Chrn Academy/*Lake Worth*/			
Palm Beach	11533195	561/540-4459	112
Prestige Christian Academy/*Miami*/			
Miami-Dade	11914795	305/836-9747	88
Prew Academy/*Sarasota*/Sarasota	01437573	941/921-7739	131
Pride Elem Sch/*Deltona*/Volusia	11073755	386/968-0010	141
Pride Elem Sch/*Tampa*/Hillsborough	04920957	813/558-5400	50
Princeton Christian Sch/*Princeton*/			
Miami-Dade	01435630	305/258-3107	88
Princeton Elem Sch/*Orlando*/Orange	00197304	407/245-1840	96
Princeton House Charter ES/*Orlando*/Orange	04813380	407/523-7121	95
Professional & Tech HS/*Kissimmee*/Osceola	04924771	407/518-5407	104
Professional Acad Mag-Loften/*Gainesville*/			
Alachua	01170464	352/955-6839	2
Progress Village Magnet Sch/*Tampa*/			
Hillsborough	00192756	813/671-5110	52
Project Compass/*Orlando*/Orange	11713620	407/745-5475	95
Promised Land Academy/*Homestead*/Miami-Dade	12225444	305/255-9561	88
Prosperitas Leadership Academy/*Orlando*/			
Orange	10976051	407/854-3945	95
Providence Academy-W Campus/*Orlando*/Orange	11574606	407/298-8699	102
Providence Christian Sch/*Cape Coral*/Lee	03014830	239/549-8024	64
Providence Christian Sch/*Riverview*/			
Hillsborough	01404253	813/661-0588	54
Providence Community Sch/*Lakewood Rch*/			
Sarasota	05256711	941/727-6860	131
Providence Sch/*Jacksonville*/Duval	04789105	904/223-5270	35
PTC-Clearwater Campus/*Clearwater*/Pinellas	05346940	727/538-7167	116
PTC-St Petersburg Campus/*St Petersburg*/			
Pinellas	01549994	727/893-2500	116
Punta Gorda Middle Sch/*Punta Gorda*/			
Charlotte	00184503	941/575-5485	21
Purcell Elem Sch/*Mulberry*/Polk	00202090	863/701-1061	125
Putman My District Virtual Sch/*Palatka*/			
Putnam	11745805	386/329-0635	127
Putnam Acad of Arts & Sciences/*Palatka*/			
Putnam	11822295	386/326-4212	127
PUTNAM CO SCH DIST/PALATKA/			
PUTNAM	00202193	386/329-0538	126
Pvpv/Rawlings Elem Sch/*Ponte Vedra*/			
St Johns	00202478	904/547-3820	135

Q

School/City/County DISTRICT/CITY/COUNTY	PID	TELEPHONE NUMBER	PAGE
Q I Roberts Jr Sr High Sch/*Florahome*/			
Putnam	05274543	386/659-1737	127
Quail Hollow Elem Sch/*Wesley Chapel*/Pasco	12105533	813/794-1100	113
Quantum High Sch/*Boynton Beach*/Palm Beach	11828653	561/293-2971	106
Queen of All Saints/*Brooksville*/Hernando	12363266	352/428-4847	44
Queen of Peace Catholic Acad/*Gainesville*/			
Alachua	11396674	352/332-8808	3
Quest Elem Sch/*Melbourne*/Brevard	05344411	321/242-1411	8
Questa-Summit Mont Middle Sch/*Ft Lauderdale*/			
Broward	04983789	954/584-3466	19
Quiet Waters Elem Sch/*Deerfield Bch*/			
Broward	03400289	754/322-8100	14

R

School/City/County DISTRICT/CITY/COUNTY	PID	TELEPHONE NUMBER	PAGE
R B Hunt Elem Sch/*St Augustine*/St Johns	00202480	904/547-7960	135
R Bruce Wagner Elem Sch/*Lakeland*/Polk	05096145	863/701-1450	125
R C Bannerman Learning Center/*Green Cv Spgs*/			
Clay	03054218	904/336-4975	24
R C Lipscomb Elem Sch/*Pensacola*/Escambia	04017988	850/494-5760	38
R Clem Churchwell Elem Sch/*Lakeland*/Polk	02846329	863/853-6011	125
R Dan Nolan Middle Sch/*Bradenton*/Manatee	05347798	941/751-8200	69
R Frank Nims Middle Sch/*Tallahassee*/Leon	00194730	850/617-6161	65
R Hobbs Middle Sch/*Milton*/Santa Rosa	00203109	850/983-5630	128
R J Hendley Christian Cmty Sch/*Riviera Beach*/			
Palm Beach	03063726	561/842-1349	112
R J Murray Middle Sch/*St Augustine*/			
St Johns	00202492	904/547-8470	135
R L Stevenson School-Arts/*Merritt Is*/			
Brevard	04915653	321/454-3550	8
R M Paterson Elem Sch/*Fleming Isle*/Clay	04013645	904/336-2575	24
R V Daniels Elem Sch/*Jacksonville*/Duval	03402043	904/630-6872	31
Radiant Life Acad & Child Care/*Orlando*/			
Orange	04983442	407/299-7460	102
Rainbow Elem Sch/*Winter Spgs*/Seminole	04033530	407/320-8450	133
Rainbow Park Elem Sch/*Opa Locka*/Miami-Dade	00185868	305/688-4631	81
Raintree Christian Academy/*New Prt Rchy*/			
Pasco	11237664	727/845-8998	115
Ralph Williams Elem Sch/*Rockledge*/Brevard	04869652	321/617-7700	8
Ramblewood Elem Sch/*Coral Springs*/Broward	01546708	754/322-8150	14
Ramblewood Middle Sch/*Coral Springs*/			
Broward	01526966	754/322-4300	14
Ramona Boulevard Elem Sch/*Jacksonville*/			
Duval	00189785	904/693-7576	33
Rampello K-8 Sch/*Tampa*/Hillsborough	04811411	813/233-2333	49
Randall Middle Sch/*Lithia*/Hillsborough	04920933	813/740-3900	52
Randazzo Sch/*Coconut Creek*/Broward	03326126	954/968-1750	19
Ransom Everglades Middle Sch/*Miami*/			
Miami-Dade	00187696	305/250-6850	88
Ransom Everglades Upper Sch/*Coconut Grove*/			
Miami-Dade	00187749	305/460-8800	88
Ransom Middle Sch/*Cantonment*/Escambia	00190825	850/937-2220	38
Ray V Pottorf Elem Sch/*Fort Myers*/Lee	10007090	239/274-3932	62
Rayma C Page Elem Sch/*Fort Myers*/Lee	10007064	239/432-2737	62
Raymond B Stewart Middle Sch/*Zephyrhills*/			
Pasco	00199209	813/794-6500	115
RCMA Leadership Academy/*Wimauma*/			
Hillsborough	11830369	813/672-5159	47
RCMA Wimauma Academy/*Wimauma*/Hillsborough	04931308	813/672-5159	47
Rcsa Elem Sch/*Jacksonville*/Duval	11560667	904/855-8010	29
Rcsa Middle High Sch/*Jacksonville*/Duval	10970679	904/855-8010	29
Rcsa-Innovation Sch/*Jacksonville*/Duval	11932084	904/855-8010	29
Rcsa-Mandarin/*Jacksonville*/Duval	12230695	904/855-8010	29
Reach Academy/*Jacksonville*/Duval	11930660	904/268-9111	36
Read-Pattillo Elem Sch/*New Smyrna*/Volusia	00204696	386/424-2600	141
Reading Edge Academy/*Debary*/Volusia	04814671	386/668-8911	141
Reagan Educational Academy/*Hialeah*/			
Miami-Dade	11817379	305/818-3044	88
Real Academy/*Lakeland*/Polk	11923576	863/413-2838	123
Real Life Christian Academy/*Clermont*/Lake	02235079	352/394-5575	60
Red Bug Elem Sch/*Casselberry*/Seminole	00203836	407/746-8350	133
Reddick Elem Sch/*Wimauma*/Hillsborough	11076757	813/634-0809	48
Reddick-Collier Elem Sch/*Reddick*/Marion	00195409	352/671-6070	71
Redeemer Christian Sch/*Ocala*/Marion	04935134	352/854-2999	72
Redeemer Lutheran Sch/*Pensacola*/Escambia	00190980	850/455-0330	38
Redeemer Lutheran Sch/*Stuart*/Martin	02148866	772/286-0932	73
Redeeming Word Pre-Sch Academy/*Ft Lauderdale*/			
Broward	11230458	954/485-1435	19
Redland Christian Academy/*Homestead*/			
Miami-Dade	02194346	305/247-7399	88
Redland Elem Sch/*Homestead*/Miami-Dade	00187517	305/247-8141	84

School/City/County DISTRICT/CITY/COUNTY	PID	TELEPHONE NUMBER	PAGE
Redland Middle Sch/*Homestead*/Miami-Dade	00187529	305/247-6112	84
Redondo Elem Sch/*Homestead*/Miami-Dade	00187531	305/247-5943	84
Reedy Creek Elem Sch/*Kissimmee*/Osceola	02126090	407/935-3580	104
Reichert House Youth Academy/*Gainesville*/ Alachua	11734105	352/334-2320	3
Reinhart Holm Elem Sch/*Pensacola*/Escambia	00190631	850/494-5610	38
Renaissance Charter ES-Pines/*Pembroke Pnes*/ Broward	12032819	954/862-1283	17
Renaissance Charter MS-Pines/*Pembroke Pnes*/ Broward	12032821	954/862-1283	17
Renaissance CS at Boggy Creek/*Kissimmee*/ Osceola	12262703	407/785-6495	104
Renaissance CS at Crown Point/*Ocoee*/Orange	12168951	321/573-1080	95
Renaissance CS at Goldenrod/*Orlando*/Orange	12103717	407/536-2952	95
Renaissance CS at St Lucie/*Port St Lucie*/ St Lucie	11456482	772/344-5982	136
Renaissance CS at Tapestry/*Kissimmee*/ Osceola	12103731	407/569-0163	104
Renaissance CS Central Palm/*Lake Worth*/ Palm Beach	12035237	561/209-7106	106
Renaissance CS Chickasaw Trail/*Orlando*/ Orange	11820651	321/206-0662	95
Renaissance CS Elem-Doral/*Doral*/Miami-Dade	04877001	305/591-2225	77
Renaissance CS Mid-Doral/*Doral*/Miami-Dade	10024701	305/728-4622	77
Renaissance CS Plantation/*Plantation*/ Broward	11716361	954/556-9700	17
Renaissance CS University/*Tamarac*/Broward	11820144	954/414-0996	17
Renaissance CS-Cooper City/*Hollywood*/ Broward	11820364	954/668-2500	17
Renaissance CS-Coral Springs/*Coral Springs*/ Broward	11716426	954/369-1179	17
Renaissance CS-Cypress/*West Palm Bch*/ Palm Beach	12035249	561/282-5860	106
Renaissance CS-Hunters Creek/*Orlando*/ Orange	11919317	321/206-3103	95
Renaissance CS-Palms West/*Loxahatchee*/ Palm Beach	11929063	561/214-6782	106
Renaissance CS-Poinciana/*Kissimmee*/Osceola	11821112	407/569-0639	104
Renaissance CS-Summit/*West Palm Bch*/ Palm Beach	11919977	561/228-5240	106
Renaissance CS-Tradition/*Port St Lucie*/ St Lucie	11929075	772/236-2180	136
Renaissance CS-W Palm Beach/*West Palm Bch*/ Palm Beach	11830486	561/839-1994	106
Renaissance CS-Wellington/*Wellington*/ Palm Beach	12035225	561/228-5242	106
Renaissance Montessori Sch/*Fort Myers*/Lee	11231218	239/275-2022	64
Resilience Charter Sch/*Gainesville*/Alachua	12167842	352/226-8675	2
Resurrection Catholic Sch/*Lakeland*/Polk	02400183	863/644-3931	126
Resurrection Christian Sch/*Brandon*/ Hillsborough	03418016	813/685-6377	54
Resurrection Early Chldhd Ctr/*Riverview*/ Hillsborough	04477730	813/672-0077	53
Resurrection Sch/*Jacksonville*/Duval	00202648	904/744-1266	34
Reynolds Lane Elem Sch/*Jacksonville*/Duval	00189797	904/381-3960	31
Rhodora J Donahue Academy/*Ave Maria*/ Collier	11712432	239/280-2450	27
Richard Brown Gifted Talented/*Jacksonville*/ Duval	03402160	904/630-6570	31
Richard L Sanders Sch/*Pinellas Park*/ Pinellas	02042303	727/547-7728	119
Richard Milburn Academy/*Daytona Beach*/ Volusia	10006905	386/304-0086	141
Richard Milburn Academy West/*Deltona*/ Volusia	11452307	386/738-9150	141
Richardson 6th Grade Academy/*Lake City*/ Columbia	04923844	386/755-8130	28
Richbourg Sch/*Crestview*/Okaloosa	11559187	850/689-5089	92
Richey Elem Sch/*New Prt Rchy*/Pasco	00199338	727/774-3500	114
Richmond Heights Middle Sch/*Miami*/ Miami-Dade	00187050	305/238-2316	84
Rideout Elem Sch/*Middleburg*/Clay	04941755	904/336-2875	24
Ridge Cmty High Sch/*Davenport*/Polk	10007272	863/419-3315	122
Ridge Technical College/*Winter Haven*/Polk	02070855	863/419-3060	123
Ridgecrest Elem Sch/*Largo*/Pinellas	00200248	727/588-3580	118
Ridgeview Elem Sch/*Orange Park*/Clay	02200062	904/336-3075	24
Ridgeview Global Studies Acad/*Davenport*/ Polk	04921987	863/419-3171	124
Ridgeview High Sch/*Orange Park*/Clay	02889838	904/336-8975	24
Ridgewood Park Elem Sch/*Orlando*/Orange	00197328	407/296-6510	97
Rimes Early Learning Center/*Leesburg*/Lake	00193877	352/787-5757	59
Rise Academy Sch-Sci & Tech/*Margate*/ Broward	11820376	954/968-7977	17
Rising Leaders Academy/*Panama City*/Bay	11819664	850/215-0844	5
River Hall Elem Sch/*Alva*/Lee	10024062	239/693-0349	63
River Ridge High Sch/*New Prt Rchy*/Pasco	03394989	727/774-7200	114
River Ridge Middle Sch/*New Prt Rchy*/Pasco	11713993	727/774-7000	115
River Springs Middle Sch/*Orange City*/ Volusia	11073743	386/968-0011	141
River's Edge Elem Sch/*Port St Lucie*/ St Lucie	00202961	772/785-5600	136
Riverbend Academy/*Ormond Beach*/Volusia	04933796	386/615-0986	142
Riverbend Academy/*Tequesta*/Martin	12311213	561/744-0211	73
Riverdale Country Sch/*Palm Bay*/Brevard	11647992	321/728-2856	7
Riverdale Elem Sch/*Orlando*/Orange	04811318	407/737-1400	96
Riverdale High Sch/*Fort Myers*/Lee	00194364	239/694-4141	63
Riverglades Elem Sch/*Parkland*/Broward	04036336	754/322-8200	14
Riverhills Elem Magnet Sch/*Temple Terr*/ Hillsborough	00192770	813/987-6911	50
Riverland Elem Sch/*Ft Lauderdale*/Broward	00183779	754/323-7200	14
Riveroak Technical Center/*Live Oak*/ Suwannee	00204153	386/647-4200	138
Riverside Elem Sch/*Coral Springs*/Broward	02897055	754/322-8250	14
Riverside Elem Sch/*Crestview*/Okaloosa	00196453	850/689-7203	92
Riverside Elem Sch/*Marianna*/Jackson	00193592	850/482-9611	57
Riverside Elem Sch/*Miami*/Miami-Dade	00186733	305/547-1520	77
Riverside Elem Sch/*Orlando*/Orange	00197330	407/296-6520	98
Riverside Presbyterian Day Sch/*Jacksonville*/ Duval	00190215	904/353-5511	36
Riversink Elem Sch/*Crawfordville*/Wakulla	11136589	850/926-2664	143
Riversprings Middle Sch/*Crawfordville*/ Wakulla	04913447	850/926-2300	143
Riverview Acad Math & Science/*Riverview*/ Hillsborough	12361983	813/412-6111	47
Riverview Elem Sch/*Riverview*/Hillsborough	00192782	813/671-5105	52
Riverview High Sch/*Riverview*/Hillsborough	04810053	813/671-5011	52
Riverview High Sch/*Sarasota*/Sarasota	00203434	941/923-1484	130
Riverview Learning Center/*Daytona Beach*/ Volusia	01527348	386/258-4673	141
Riverwalk Christian Academy/*Sanford*/ Seminole	02236346	407/321-2723	134
Riviera Beach Prep & Achv Acad/*Riviera Beach*/ Palm Beach	04950574	561/881-4740	106
Riviera Day Sch/*Coral Gables*/Miami-Dade	00187787	305/666-1856	88
Riviera Elem Sch/*Palm Bay*/Brevard	03337840	321/676-4237	8
Riviera Middle Sch/*Miami*/Miami-Dade	00187062	305/226-4286	84
Riviera Preparatory Sch/*Miami*/Miami-Dade	11736749	786/300-0300	88
Robert C Markham Elem Sch/*Pompano Beach*/ Broward	00182945	754/322-6950	14
Robert E Lee High Sch/*Jacksonville*/Duval	00189838	904/381-3930	32
Robert E Willis Elem Sch/*Bradenton*/Manatee	10028044	941/316-8245	69
Robert F Munroe Day Sch/*Quincy*/Gadsden	01436529	850/856-5500	40
Robert H Jenkins Middle Sch/*Palatka*/Putnam	00202301	386/329-0588	127
Robert H Prine Elem Sch/*Bradenton*/Manatee	00195277	941/751-7006	69
Robert J Renick Ed Center/*Miami Gardens*/ Miami-Dade	04036623	305/624-1171	81
Robert Morgan Ed Ctr/Tech Clg/*Miami*/ Miami-Dade	02046141	305/253-9920	84
Robert Russa Moton Elem Sch/*Miami*/ Miami-Dade	00187555	305/235-3612	84
Roberts Elem Sch/*Tallahassee*/Leon	04948131	850/488-0923	65
Robinson Senior High Sch/*Tampa*/ Hillsborough	00192809	813/272-3006	49
Robinswood Middle Sch/*Orlando*/Orange	00197354	407/296-5140	100
Roblanca Academy/*Hialeah*/Miami-Dade	02236384	305/557-3871	88
Robles Elem Sch/*Tampa*/Hillsborough	00192811	813/744-8033	48
Rochelle School of the Arts/*Lakeland*/Polk	00201436	863/499-2810	122
Rock Crusher Elem Sch/*Homosassa*/Citrus	03333753	352/795-2010	22
Rock Island Elem Sch/*Ft Lauderdale*/Broward	00183406	754/322-8300	14
Rock Lake Elem Sch/*Orlando*/Orange	00197366	407/245-1880	95
Rock Lake Middle Sch/*Longwood*/Seminole	02042315	407/746-9350	133
Rock Solid Christian Academy/*Okeechobee*/ Okeechobee	11713321	863/763-1847	93
Rock Springs Elem Sch/*Apopka*/Orange	03051852	407/884-2242	98
Rockledge Christian Sch/*Rockledge*/Brevard	03102009	321/632-1053	10
Rockledge High Sch/*Rockledge*/Brevard	00182268	321/636-3711	9
Rockway Elem Sch/*Miami*/Miami-Dade	00187074	305/221-1192	77
Rockway Middle Sch/*Miami*/Miami-Dade	00187086	305/221-8212	77
Rocky Bayou Christian Sch/*Niceville*/ Okaloosa	05339416	850/678-7358	93
Rodgers Middle Sch/*Riverview*/Hillsborough	04810065	813/671-5288	52
Rodney B Cox Elem Sch/*Dade City*/Pasco	00199194	352/524-5100	114

School/City/County DISTRICT/CITY/COUNTY	PID	TELEPHONE NUMBER	PAGE
Rogers Garden-Bullock Elem Sch/*Bradenton/* Manatee	11452709	941/209-7540	69
Rohr Middle Sch/*Miami*/Miami-Dade	11813701	305/947-7779	88
Roland Park Magnet Sch/*Tampa*/Hillsborough	00192823	813/872-5212	49
Rolling Green Elem Sch/*Boynton Beach/* Palm Beach	00198932	561/202-9500	107
Rolling Hills Elem Sch/*Orlando*/Orange	00197378	407/296-6530	100
Romeo Elem Sch/*Dunnellon*/Marion	04017744	352/465-6700	71
Ronald Reagan-Doral Senior HS/*Doral/* Miami-Dade	10024608	305/805-1900	77
Roosevelt Academy/*Lake Wales*/Polk	02110211	863/678-4252	124
Roosevelt Cmty Middle Sch/*West Palm Bch/* Palm Beach	00198279	561/822-0200	108
Roosevelt Elem Sch/*Tampa*/Hillsborough	00192835	813/272-3090	49
Roosevelt Elem Sch/*West Palm Bch/* Palm Beach	00198267	561/653-5100	109
Rosabelle Blake Academy/*Lakeland*/Polk	03397541	863/499-2870	122
Rosarian Academy/*West Palm Bch*/Palm Beach	00188195	561/832-5131	110
Rose Academy/*Tallahassee*/Leon	11831208	850/893-8743	66
Rosemont Elem Sch/*Orlando*/Orange	04757281	407/522-6050	95
Rosenwald Elem Sch/*South Bay*/Palm Beach	00198463	561/993-8900	108
Rosenwald High Sch/*Panama City*/Bay	00181745	850/767-4580	5
Rosewood Magnet Sch/*Vero Beach/* Indian River	00193413	772/564-3840	56
Roulhac Middle Sch/*Chipley*/Washington	00205028	850/638-6170	144
Round Lake Charter Sch/*Mount Dora*/Lake	04916308	352/385-4399	59
Rowlett Acad for Arts & Comm/*Bradenton/* Manatee	04915457	941/708-6100	69
Rowlett Middle Academy/*Bradenton*/Manatee	12262686	941/462-4001	69
Roy Allen Elem Sch/*Melbourne*/Brevard	00182426	321/242-6450	8
Royal Green Elem Sch/*Miami*/Miami-Dade	00187098	305/221-4452	84
Royal Kids Academy/*Hialeah*/Miami-Dade	04328127	305/557-5437	88
Royal Palm Academy/*Naples*/Collier	04858316	239/594-9888	27
Royal Palm Beach Cmty High Sch/*West Palm Bch/* Palm Beach	04755594	561/753-4000	107
Royal Palm Beach Elem Sch/*West Palm Bch/* Palm Beach	05102366	561/633-4400	107
Royal Palm Charter Sch/*Palm Bay*/Brevard	04915550	321/723-0650	7
Royal Palm Elem Sch/*Lauderhill*/Broward	00183418	754/322-8350	14
Royal Palm Elem Sch/*Miami*/Miami-Dade	00187103	305/221-7961	84
Royal Palm Exceptional Center/*Fort Myers/* Lee	03012155	239/337-3511	63
Royal Palm Sch/*Lantana*/Palm Beach	00198281	561/357-1900	110
Ruben Dario Middle Sch/*Miami*/Miami-Dade	03249530	305/226-0179	77
Rufus E Payne Elem Sch/*Jacksonville*/Duval	03401831	904/924-3020	33
Ruskin Christian Sch/*Ruskin*/Hillsborough	01404241	813/645-6441	54
Ruskin Elem Sch/*Ruskin*/Hillsborough	00192847	813/671-5177	48
Ruth Broad/Bay Harbor K-8 Ctr/*Bay Harbor Is/* Miami-Dade	00185179	305/865-7912	81
Ruth N Upson Elem Sch/*Jacksonville*/Duval	00189852	904/381-7485	31
Ruth Owens Kruse Center/*Miami*/Miami-Dade	04020806	305/270-8699	84
Ruth Rains Middle Sch/*Cross City*/Dixie	04287705	352/541-6254	29
Rutherford High Sch/*Panama City*/Bay	00181757	850/767-4500	5
Rutledge H Pearson Elem Sch/*Jacksonville/* Duval	03401805	904/924-3077	33
Rymfire Elem Sch/*Palm Coast*/Flagler	10031845	386/206-4600	39

S

School/City/County DISTRICT/CITY/COUNTY	PID	TELEPHONE NUMBER	PAGE
S Bryan Jennings Elem Sch/*Orange Park*/Clay	00184785	904/336-3175	24
S D Spady Elem Sch/*Delray Beach*/Palm Beach	00198944	561/454-7800	110
S P Livingston Elem Sch/*Jacksonville*/Duval	03401922	904/630-6580	33
S S Dixon Intermediate Sch/*Pace*/Santa Rosa	04285379	850/995-3650	128
S S Dixon Primary Sch/*Milton*/Santa Rosa	00203185	850/995-3660	128
S W Florida Pub Service Acad/*Fort Myers/* Lee	11718424	239/334-3897	63
Sabal Elem Sch/*Melbourne*/Brevard	00182440	321/254-7261	8
Sabal Palm Elem Sch/*Jacksonville*/Duval	03329453	904/221-7169	31
Sabal Palm Elem Sch/*Naples*/Collier	05269940	239/377-8200	26
Sabal Palm Elem Sch/*Tallahassee*/Leon	00194742	850/488-0167	65
Sabal Point Elem Sch/*Longwood*/Seminole	01340255	407/746-3050	133
Sacred Heart Cathedral Sch/*Pensacola/* Escambia	00202650	850/436-6440	38
Sacred Heart Catholic Sch/*Jacksonville/* Duval	00202662	904/771-5800	34
Sacred Heart Catholic Sch/*Pinellas Park/* Pinellas	00200975	727/544-1106	120
Sacred Heart Early Chldhd Ctr/*Dade City/* Pasco	03043178	352/588-4060	115
Sacred Heart Sch/*Lake Worth*/Palm Beach	00188212	561/582-2242	110
Sacred Heart Sch/*New Smyrna*/Volusia	00197782	386/428-4732	142
Saddlebrook Prep Sch/*Wesley Chapel*/Pasco	04835314	813/907-4300	115

School/City/County DISTRICT/CITY/COUNTY	PID	TELEPHONE NUMBER	PAGE
Saddlewood Elem Sch/*Ocala*/Marion	04871291	352/291-4075	71
Sadie Tillis Elem Sch/*Jacksonville*/Duval	00189577	904/573-1090	31
Sadler Elem Sch/*Orlando*/Orange	00197380	407/354-2620	99
Safety Harbor Elem Sch/*Safety Harbor/* Pinellas	00200274	727/724-1462	117
Safety Harbor Middle Sch/*Safety Harbor/* Pinellas	00200286	727/724-1400	118
Sagemont Lower Sch/*Weston*/Broward	05017163	954/384-5454	19
Sagemont Upper Sch/*Weston*/Broward	04927840	954/389-2454	19
Sail/*Milton*/Santa Rosa	12307793	850/983-5150	128
Sail High Sch/*Tallahassee*/Leon	01524255	850/488-2468	65
Sal Tech Charter High Sch/*Jacksonville/* Duval	05343912	904/328-5001	30
Salah-Tawfik Elem Mid Sch/*Sunrise*/Broward	10014811	954/741-8130	19
Sallie Jones Elem Sch/*Punta Gorda/* Charlotte	00184515	941/575-5440	21
Sally Ride Elem Sch/*Orlando*/Orange	00196740	407/858-3100	98
Sallye B Mathis Elem Sch/*Jacksonville/* Duval	00189084	904/924-3086	33
Samaritan Center/*Stuart*/Martin	04329200	772/287-4123	74
Samoset Elem Sch/*Bradenton*/Manatee	00195289	941/708-6400	69
Samsula Academy/*New Smyrna*/Volusia	11073767	386/423-6650	141
Samuel A Hull Elem Sch/*Jacksonville*/Duval	03401788	904/924-3136	31
Samuel S Gaines Academy/*Fort Pierce/* St Lucie	10914297	772/462-8888	137
Samuel W Wolfson High Sch/*Jacksonville/* Duval	00189888	904/739-5265	32
San Antonio Elem Sch/*Dade City*/Pasco	02126260	352/524-5300	114
San Carlos Park Elem Sch/*Fort Myers*/Lee	02042183	239/267-7177	63
San Jose Academy/*Jacksonville*/Duval	11931573	904/425-1725	30
San Jose Catholic Sch/*Jacksonville*/Duval	00202698	904/733-2313	34
San Jose Elem Sch/*Dunedin*/Pinellas	00200303	727/469-5956	117
San Jose Elem Sch/*Jacksonville*/Duval	00189890	904/739-5260	31
San Jose Episcopal Day Sch/*Jacksonville/* Duval	00190241	904/733-0352	36
San Jose Prep High Sch/*Jacksonville*/Duval	11917890	904/425-1725	30
San Juan Del Rio Catholic Sch/*Saint Johns/* St Johns	04479752	904/287-8081	135
San Mateo Elem Sch/*Jacksonville*/Duval	00189905	904/696-8750	31
San Pablo Elem Sch/*Jax Bch*/Duval	00189917	904/247-5947	31
Sancta Familia Academy/*Melbourne*/Brevard	12166381	321/259-6464	10
Sand Lake Elem Sch/*Orlando*/Orange	10030152	407/903-7400	99
Sand Pine Elem Sch/*Wesley Chapel*/Pasco	04805319	813/794-1900	114
Sandalwood High Sch/*Jacksonville*/Duval	00189929	904/646-5100	32
Sanders Memorial Elem Sch/*Land O Lakes/* Pasco	12102907	813/794-1500	114
Sanders Park Elem Sch/*Pompano Beach/* Broward	00183080	754/322-8400	14
Sandhill Elem Sch/*Haines City*/Polk	04921975	863/419-3166	124
Sandpiper Elem Sch/*Sunrise*/Broward	02897067	754/322-8450	14
Sandpiper Shores Elem Sch/*Boca Raton/* Palm Beach	03253529	561/883-4000	110
Sandy Lane Elem Sch/*Clearwater*/Pinellas	01340229	727/469-5974	118
Sanford Middle Magnet Sch/*Sanford*/Seminole	00203874	407/320-6150	133
Sanibel Sch/*Sanibel*/Lee	00194388	239/472-1617	63
Santa Clara Elem Sch/*Miami*/Miami-Dade	00186757	305/635-1417	77
Santa Fe Catholic High Sch/*Lakeland*/Polk	00197811	863/665-4188	126
Santa Fe High Sch/*Alachua*/Alachua	00181379	386/462-1125	2
Santa Rosa Adult Sch/*Milton*/Santa Rosa	02888614	850/983-5710	128
Santa Rosa Christian Sch/*Milton*/Santa Rosa	00203226	850/623-4671	128
SANTA ROSA CO SCH DIST/MILTON/ **SANTA ROSA**	00203006	850/983-5010	127
Santa Rosa High Sch/*Milton*/Santa Rosa	11930658	850/983-5710	128
Santa Rosa Online Academy/*Milton/* Santa Rosa	11831650	850/981-7860	128
Santaluces Cmty High Sch/*Lantana/* Palm Beach	02200048	561/642-6200	110
Sara Scott Harllee Ctr-Sable/*Bradenton/* Manatee	12165715	941/209-6579	69
Sarasota Academy of the Arts/*Sarasota/* Sarasota	11919408	941/377-2278	130
Sarasota Christian Sch/*Sarasota*/Sarasota	05286493	941/371-6481	131
SARASOTA CO SCH DIST/SARASOTA/ **SARASOTA**	00203238	941/927-9000	129
Sarasota Co Technical Inst/*Sarasota/* Sarasota	00203472	941/924-1365	130
Sarasota High Sch/*Sarasota*/Sarasota	00203458	941/955-0181	130
Sarasota Middle Sch/*Sarasota*/Sarasota	00203460	941/361-6464	130
Sarasota Military Academy/*Sarasota/* Sarasota	05099044	941/926-1700	130
Sarasota Military Academy Prep/*Sarasota/* Sarasota	12032302	941/877-7737	130

School/City/County DISTRICT/CITY/COUNTY	PID	TELEPHONE NUMBER	PAGE
Sarasota School-Arts & Science/*Sarasota*/ Sarasota	04810742	941/330-1855	130
Sarasota Suncoast Academy/*Sarasota*/ Sarasota	05346770	941/924-4242	130
Sarasota Virtual Sch/*Sarasota*/Sarasota	11554967	941/924-1365	130
SAS at the Center/*Tallahassee*/Leon	12161886	850/999-8267	65
SAS on Thomasville/*Tallahassee*/Leon	04876966	850/386-6566	65
Satellite High Sch/*Satellite Bch*/Brevard	00182452	321/779-2000	9
Saturn Elem Sch/*Cocoa*/Brevard	00182270	321/633-3535	8
Savanna Ridge Elem Sch/*Port St Lucie*/ St Lucie	04806430	772/460-3050	137
Sawgrass Adventist Sch/*Plantation*/Broward	02147977	954/473-4622	19
Sawgrass Bay Elem Sch/*Clermont*/Lake	10909101	352/243-1845	59
Sawgrass Elem Sch/*Sunrise*/Broward	04018712	754/322-8500	14
Sawgrass Lake Elem Sch/*St Petersburg*/ Pinellas	03399068	727/570-3121	119
Sawgrass Springs Middle Sch/*Coral Springs*/ Broward	04457900	754/322-4500	14
Scenic Heights Elem Sch/*Pensacola*/Escambia	00190837	850/494-5635	38
Scheck Hillel Community Sch/*Miami*/ Miami-Dade	01773212	305/931-2831	88
School Adv Studies-Homestead/*Homestead*/ Miami-Dade	10907749	305/237-5062	84
School Adv Studies-South/*Miami*/Miami-Dade	04290063	305/237-0510	84
School Adv Studies-Wolfson/*Miami*/ Miami-Dade	04920842	305/237-7270	84
School Advanced Studies-North/*Miami*/ Miami-Dade	04036635	305/237-1089	84
SCHOOL DIST OF INDIAN RIVER CO/ **VERO BEACH/INDIAN RIVER**	00193334	772/564-3000	55
School for Advanced Studies-W/*Doral*/ Miami-Dade	12231728	305/237-0510	84
School of Islamic Studies/*Sunrise*/Broward	11824205	954/741-8130	20
School of Success Academy/*Jacksonville*/ Duval	04757451	904/573-0880	30
School of the Kingdom/*Ocala*/Marion	04894657	352/620-0780	72
School of Virtue & Acad Excell/*Miami*/ Miami-Dade	11934898	786/220-0037	88
Schrader Elem Sch/*New Prt Rchy*/Pasco	00199352	727/774-5900	114
Schwarzkopf Elem Sch/*Lutz*/Hillsborough	04020519	813/975-6945	50
Scott Lake Elem Sch/*Lakeland*/Polk	00201448	863/648-3520	125
Scott Lake Elem Sch/*Miami*/Miami-Dade	00185870	305/624-1443	81
Scps Early Learning Center/*Sanford*/ Seminole	11932101	407/320-3940	133
Sculptor Charter Sch/*Titusville*/Brevard	04880955	321/264-4000	7
Sea Breeze Elem Sch/*Bradenton*/Manatee	03396626	941/741-3190	69
Sea Castle Elem Sch/*Miramar*/Broward	03336731	754/323-7250	14
Sea Gate Elem Sch/*Naples*/Collier	00184993	239/377-8300	26
Sea of Strengths Academy/*Sarasota*/Sarasota	12258984	941/538-6822	131
Sea Park Elem Sch/*Satellite Bch*/Brevard	00182464	321/779-2050	8
Seabreeze Elem Sch/*Jax Bch*/Duval	00189931	904/247-5900	31
Seabreeze High Sch/*Daytona Beach*/Volusia	00204737	386/258-4674	141
Seacoast Charter Academy/*Jacksonville*/ Duval	11718060	904/562-4780	30
Seacoast Christian Academy/*Jacksonville*/ Duval	03139533	904/722-1738	36
Seacoast Collegiate High Sch/*Santa Rsa Bch*/ Walton	12235906	850/200-4170	144
Seacrest Country Day Sch/*Naples*/Collier	02362361	239/793-1986	27
Seagate Christian Sch/*Naples*/Collier	01772751	239/261-0122	27
Seagull Academy of Ind Living/*West Palm Bch*/ Palm Beach	05102251	561/540-8110	106
Seagull Alternative High Sch/*Ft Lauderdale*/ Broward	00183597	754/321-7300	14
Sealey Elem Math Sci Mag Sch/*Tallahassee*/ Leon	00194754	850/488-5640	65
Seamark Ranch Sch/*Green Cv Spgs*/Clay	12115681	904/529-1951	25
Seaside Charter Sch San Jose/*Jacksonville*/ Duval	12262674	904/619-3933	30
Seaside Charter School Beaches/*Atlantic Bch*/ Duval	11932606	904/853-6287	30
Seaside Neighborhood Sch/*Santa Rsa Bch*/ Walton	04467606	850/231-0396	144
Seawind Elem Sch/*Hobe Sound*/Martin	04368361	772/219-1625	73
Sebastian Charter Jr High Sch/*Sebastian*/ Indian River	04918679	772/388-8838	56
Sebastian Elem Sch/*Sebastian*/Indian River	02848365	772/978-8200	56
Sebastian Middle Sch/*St Augustine*/St Johns	03394264	904/547-3840	135
Sebastian River High Sch/*Sebastian*/ Indian River	04285068	772/564-4170	56
Sebastian River Middle Sch/*Sebastian*/ Indian River	01546722	772/564-5111	56

School/City/County DISTRICT/CITY/COUNTY	PID	TELEPHONE NUMBER	PAGE
Sebring High Sch/*Sebring*/Highlands	00191776	863/471-5500	45
Sebring Middle Sch/*Sebring*/Highlands	00191788	863/471-5700	45
Second Chance/*Tallahassee*/Leon	11621704	850/488-2087	65
Seffner Christian Academy/*Seffner*/ Hillsborough	02234984	813/626-0001	54
Seffner Elem Sch/*Seffner*/Hillsborough	00192859	813/744-8171	51
SEMINOLE CO PUBLIC SCH DIST/ **SANFORD/SEMINOLE**	00203575	407/320-0000	131
Seminole Co Virtual Sch/*Lake Mary*/Seminole	11745817	407/871-7287	133
Seminole Elem Sch/*Miami*/Miami-Dade	00187141	305/261-7071	77
Seminole Elem Sch/*Okeechobee*/Okeechobee	03318313	863/462-5116	93
Seminole Elem Sch/*Seminole*/Pinellas	00200315	727/547-7668	119
Seminole Elem Sch/*Tampa*/Hillsborough	00192861	813/276-5556	51
Seminole Heights Charter HS/*Tampa*/ Hillsborough	11556874	813/234-0809	47
Seminole High Sch/*Sanford*/Seminole	00203886	407/320-5050	133
Seminole High Sch/*Seminole*/Pinellas	00200327	727/547-7536	119
Seminole Middle Sch/*Plantation*/Broward	00183808	754/323-4200	14
Seminole Middle Sch/*Seminole*/Pinellas	00200339	727/547-4520	119
Seminole Ridge Cmty High Sch/*Loxahatchee*/ Palm Beach	10000418	561/422-2600	109
Seminole Science Charter Sch/*Lake Mary*/ Seminole	12114807	407/268-3727	133
Seminole Springs Elem Sch/*Eustis*/Lake	03250589	352/589-1117	59
Seminole Trails Elem Sch/*West Palm Bch*/ Palm Beach	03253579	561/598-7000	107
Sessums Elem Sch/*Riverview*/Hillsborough	05262291	813/672-5230	52
Seven Bridges Sch/*Orange Park*/Clay	11234014	904/269-7377	25
Seven Oaks Elem Sch/*Wesley Chapel*/Pasco	10001876	813/794-0700	114
Seven Rivers Christian Sch/*Lecanto*/Citrus	03275046	352/746-5696	23
Seven Springs Elem Sch/*New Prt Rchy*/Pasco	03032959	727/774-9600	114
Seven Springs Middle Sch/*New Prt Rchy*/ Pasco	04446743	727/774-6700	115
Seventy-Fourth St Elem Sch/*St Petersburg*/ Pinellas	00200597	727/893-2120	119
Sgt Paul R Smith Middle Sch/*Tampa*/ Hillsborough	11076771	813/792-5125	50
Sha'Arei Bina Torah Acad-Girls/*Hollywood*/ Broward	11233199	954/927-5544	20
Shadeville Elem Sch/*Crawfordville*/Wakulla	00204878	850/926-7155	143
Shadowlawn Elem Sch/*Green Cv Spgs*/Clay	11069326	904/336-3375	24
Shadowlawn Elem Sch/*Miami*/Miami-Dade	00186290	305/758-3673	77
Shadowlawn Elem Sch/*Naples*/Collier	00185002	239/377-8400	26
Shady Hill Elem Sch/*Ocala*/Marion	02896685	352/291-4085	71
Shady Hills Elem Sch/*Spring Hill*/Pasco	12105545	727/774-4100	114
Shalimar Elem Sch/*Shalimar*/Okaloosa	00196439	850/833-4339	92
Shaw Elem Sch/*Tampa*/Hillsborough	00192873	813/975-7366	48
Sheehy Elem Sch/*Tampa*/Hillsborough	05351191	813/233-3800	48
Sheeler Charter High Sch/*Apopka*/Orange	11452876	407/886-1825	95
Shekinah Christian Academy/*Jacksonville*/ Duval	11735329	904/421-1015	36
Shelley S Boone Middle Sch/*Haines City*/ Polk	00201591	863/421-3302	125
Shelton Academy/*Doral*/Miami-Dade	11720453	305/599-9967	88
Shenandoah Elem Sch/*Miami*/Miami-Dade	00186769	305/643-4433	77
Shenandoah Elem Sch/*Orlando*/Orange	00197392	407/858-3180	98
Shenandoah Middle Sch/*Miami*/Miami-Dade	00186771	305/856-8282	77
Shepherd of God Christian Acad/*Homestead*/ Miami-Dade	12239378	786/339-8503	88
Shepherd of the Coast Chri Sch/*Ft Lauderdale*/ Broward	01772505	954/772-5468	20
Shepherd of the Woods Luth Sch/*Jacksonville*/ Duval	11397393	904/641-3393	36
Shepherd of Woods Lutheran Sch/*Jacksonville*/ Duval	11165554	904/268-6701	36
Shepherd's Hill Christian Sch/*Sarasota*/ Sarasota	04984460	941/957-3333	131
Shepherd's Sch/*Pahokee*/Palm Beach	11815838	561/924-9578	112
Sheridan Hills Christian Sch/*Hollywood*/ Broward	01772593	954/966-7995	20
Sheridan Hills Elem Sch/*Hollywood*/Broward	00184163	754/323-7300	14
Sheridan Park Elem Sch/*Hollywood*/Broward	00184175	754/323-7350	14
Sheridan Tech High Sch/*Ft Lauderdale*/ Broward	00184187	754/321-7450	14
Sherwood Elem Sch/*Melbourne*/Brevard	00182476	321/254-6424	8
Sherwood Elem Sch/*Pensacola*/Escambia	00190849	850/453-7420	38
Shiloh SDA Sch/*Ocala*/Marion	02086397	352/629-6857	72
Shiloh Youth Ranch/*Sebastian*/Indian River	01436763	772/589-4449	56
Shingle Creek Elem Sch/*Orlando*/Orange	04018592	407/354-2650	99
Shoal River Middle Sch/*Crestview*/Okaloosa	00196300	850/689-7229	92
Shore Acres Elem Sch/*St Petersburg*/ Pinellas	00200341	727/570-3173	119

School/City/County DISTRICT/CITY/COUNTY	PID	TELEPHONE NUMBER	PAGE	School/City/County DISTRICT/CITY/COUNTY	PID	TELEPHONE NUMBER	PAGE
Shorecrest Prep Sch/*St Petersburg*/Pinellas	00200690	727/522-2111	121	Somerset Academy Lakes/*West Palm Bch*/ Palm Beach	12172304	561/641-4449	106
Sidney Lanier Center/*Gainesville*/Alachua	00181408	352/955-6841	2	Somerset Academy Middle Sch/*Pembroke Pnes*/			
Sigsbee Charter Sch/*Key West*/Monroe	00195954	305/294-1861	90	Broward	05230315	954/442-0233	17
Silver Bluff Elem Sch/*Miami*/Miami-Dade	00186783	305/856-5197	78	Somerset Academy Miramar HS/*Miramar*/			
Silver Lakes Elem Sch/*Miramar*/Broward	04811899	754/323-7400	14	Broward	11820168	954/435-1570	17
Silver Lakes Middle Sch/*N Lauderdale*/				Somerset Academy Miramar MS/*Miramar*/			
Broward	02177544	754/322-4600	14	Broward	11820390	305/829-2406	17
Silver Palms Elem Sch/*Pembroke Pnes*/				Somerset Academy of the Arts/*Wellington*/			
Broward	04364573	754/323-7450	15	Palm Beach	12362200	561/421-5510	106
Silver Ridge Elem Sch/*Davie*/Broward	03007576	754/323-7500	15	Somerset Academy Palms/*Miami*/Miami-Dade	12322767	786/574-5287	84
Silver River Mentor/Instr Sch/*Ocala*/Marion	04370663	352/694-0191	71	Somerset Academy Pompano/*Pompano Beach*/			
Silver Sands Middle Sch/*Port Orange*/				Broward	11820156	954/946-4144	17
Volusia	02893334	386/322-6175	141	Somerset Academy Soho/*Homestead*/Miami-Dade	05346859	305/245-6108	84
Silver Sands Sch/*Ft Walton Bch*/Okaloosa	00196441	850/833-3364	92	Somerset Academy Soho MS/*Homestead*/			
Silver Shores Elem Sch/*Miramar*/Broward	05183528	754/323-7550	15	Miami-Dade	11453387	305/245-6108	84
Silver Trail Middle Sch/*Ft Lauderdale*/				Somerset Academy St Lucie/*Port St Lucie*/			
Broward	04364559	754/323-4300	15	St Lucie	12230619	772/281-2300	137
Simmons Career Center/*Plant City*/				Somerset Academy-Gables/*Miami*/Miami-Dade	11560215	305/442-8626	78
Hillsborough	04948894	813/707-7430	52	Somerset Academy-Miramar/*Miramar*/Broward	04756859	305/829-2406	17
Sister Clara Muhammad Sch/*Miami*/Miami-Dade	03137523	305/757-8741	88	Somerset Academy-Riverside/*Coral Springs*/			
Six Mile Charter Academy/*Fort Myers*/Lee	10007155	239/768-9375	63	Broward	12322949	954/255-9740	17
Sjb Leadership Academy/*Miami*/Miami-Dade	12102361	786/529-7750	88	Somerset Academy-Silver Palms/*Homestead*/			
Sky Academy-Englewood/*Englewood*/Sarasota	12114819	941/999-4775	130	Miami-Dade	10907804	305/257-3737	84
Sky Academy-Venice/*Venice*/Sarasota	11718723	941/244-2626	130	Somerset Academy-South Miami/*South Miami*/			
Skycrest Christian Sch/*Clearwater*/Pinellas	00200717	727/797-1186	121	Miami-Dade	11453363	305/740-0509	78
Skycrest Elem Sch/*Clearwater*/Pinellas	00200365	727/469-5987	118	Somerset Arts Conservatory HS/*Pembroke Pnes*/			
Skyline Elem Sch/*Cape Coral*/Lee	03051058	239/772-3223	63	Broward	11449908	954/442-0233	17
Skyview Elem Sch/*Pinellas Park*/Pinellas	00200377	727/547-7857	119	Somerset City Arts Academy/*Homestead*/			
Sl Jones Christian Academy/*Pensacola*/				Miami-Dade	11128324	305/246-4949	84
Escambia	11464398	850/456-2249	38	Somerset College Prep Acad/*Port St Lucie*/			
Slam Apollo/*Apollo Beach*/Hillsborough	12362016	813/773-4560	47	St Lucie	11820510	772/343-7028	137
Slam Charter School Miami/*Miami*/Miami Dade	11829748	305/326-0003	78	Somerset Oaks Academy/*Homestead*/Miami-Dade	11719698	305/247-3993	84
Slam High School Palm Beach/*West Palm Bch*/				Somerset Pines Academy/*Pompano Beach*/			
Palm Beach	12362212	561/434-2162	106	Broward	11554694	954/786-5980	17
Slam Middle Sch/*West Palm Bch*/Palm Beach	12172328	561/434-2162	106	Somerset Prep Acad Sunset/*Miami*/Miami-Dade	12114883	305/274-5696	84
Slam North Campus/*Miami*/Miami-Dade	12306268	305/333-5702	81	Somerset Prep CS Middle/*Miramar*/Broward	11716438	954/435-1570	17
Slam Osceola/*Kissimmee*/Osceola	12308929	407/569-7637	104	Somerset Prep CS-N Lauderdale/*N Lauderdale*/			
Sleepy Hill Elem Sch/*Lakeland*/Polk	10902737	863/815-6768	125	Broward	11554709	954/718-5065	17
Sleepy Hill Middle Sch/*Lakeland*/Polk	04869810	863/815-6577	122	Somerset Preparatory Academy/*Jacksonville*/			
Sligh Middle Sch/*Tampa*/Hillsborough	00192897	813/276-5596	48	Duval	11929673	904/503-0661	30
Snapper Creek Elem Sch/*Miami*/Miami-Dade	00187165	305/271-2111	84	Somerset Village Academy/*Wilton Manors*/			
Sneads Elem Sch/*Sneads*/Jackson	01527154	850/482-9003	57	Broward	11449881	954/390-0971	17
Sneads High Sch/*Sneads*/Jackson	00193607	850/482-9007	57	Somerset Village MS Acad/*Wilton Manors*/			
Socrum Elem Sch/*Lakeland*/Polk	03397527	863/853-6050	125	Broward	11589845	954/390-0971	17
Solid Rock Christian Academy/*Inverness*/				Somerset Virtual Acad Mid HS/*Homestead*/			
Citrus	11233230	352/726-9788	23	Miami-Dade	12101599	305/258-7497	78
Solid Rock Christian Sch/*Mount Dora*/Lake	04983351	352/735-5777	60	Sonshine Christian Academy/*Callahan*/Nassau	02968915	904/879-1260	91
Solid Rock Community Sch/*Tarpon Spgs*/				Sonshine Christian Academy/*Fort Myers*/Lee	02195364	239/694-8882	64
Pinellas	11734246	727/934-0909	121	Sorrento Elem Sch/*Sorrento*/Lake	11557206	352/385-1140	59
Somerset Acad -Miramar South/*Miramar*/				Souls Harbor Christian Academy/*Belleview*/			
Broward	11820405	305/829-2406	17	Marion	04885204	352/245-6252	72
Somerset Acad Canyons Mid HS/*Boynton Beach*/				South Area Cmty Adult Sch/*Melbourne*/			
Palm Beach	11919915	561/732-8252	106	Brevard	04915548	321/952-5977	7
Somerset Acad CS-Neighborhood/*Miramar*/				South Broward High Sch/*Hollywood*/Broward	00184151	754/323-1800	15
Broward	11554747	954/435-1570	17	South Broward Mont Charter Sch/*Hallandale*/			
Somerset Acad Eagle ES Campus/*Jacksonville*/				Broward	11931547	954/251-1443	17
Duval	11560631	904/551-3292	30	South Co Career Center/*Ruskin*/Hillsborough	05097383	813/233-3335	52
Somerset Acad Eagle MS Campus/*Jacksonville*/				South Creek Middle Sch/*Orlando*/Orange	10024359	407/251-2413	98
Duval	11560643	904/503-0661	30	South Dade Middle Sch/*Homestead*/Miami-Dade	10907725	305/224-5200	84
Somerset Acad ES South Campus/*Hollywood*/				South Dade Senior High Sch/*Homestead*/			
Broward	12322937	954/404-7775	17	Miami-Dade	00187567	305/247-4244	84
Somerset Acad HS Soho/*Homestead*/Miami-Dade	11719533	305/245-6108	84	South Dade Skills Center/*Homestead*/			
Somerset Acad Key Charter HS/*Deerfield Bch*/				Miami-Dade	01810808	305/247-7839	74
Broward	12169852	954/481-0602	17	South Dade Technical College/*Homestead*/			
Somerset Acad Key Charter MS/*Deerfield Bch*/				Miami-Dade	04421810	305/248-5723	74
Broward	12224361	954/481-0602	17	South Daytona Elem Sch/*South Daytona*/			
Somerset Acad-Riverside MS/*Coral Springs*/				Volusia	00204701	386/322-6180	141
Broward	11589833	954/255-9740	17	South Elem Sch/*Okeechobee*/Okeechobee	00196556	863/462-5087	93
Somerset Academy Bay Mid Sch/*Miami*/				South Florida Acad of Learning/*Coconut Creek*/			
Miami-Dade	11923198	305/274-0682	84	Broward	04983662	954/532-9110	20
Somerset Academy Boca/*Boca Raton*/				South Florida Autism Chtr Sch/*Hialeah*/			
Palm Beach	11830498	561/393-1091	106	Miami-Dade	11453399	305/823-2700	81
Somerset Academy Charter HS/*Pembroke Pnes*/				South Fork High Sch/*Stuart*/Martin	02177116	772/219-1840	73
Broward	05230327	954/442-0233	17	South Ft Myers High Sch/*Fort Myers*/Lee	10003874	239/561-0060	63
Somerset Academy CS-Dade/*Miami*/Miami-Dade	05346835	305/969-6074	84	South Grade Elem Sch/*Lake Worth*/Palm Beach	04920749	561/202-9400	107
Somerset Academy CS-Davie/*Davie*/Broward	05346976	954/584-5528	17	South Hialeah Elem Sch/*Hialeah*/Miami-Dade	00186288	305/885-4556	78
Somerset Academy East Prep/*Miramar*/Broward	11449893	954/987-7890	17	South Intensive Transition Sch/*Lake Worth*/			
Somerset Academy ES Pemb Pines/*Pembroke Pnes*/				Palm Beach	11103685	561/202-0600	106
Broward	04947802	954/442-0233	17	South Lake Elem Sch/*Titusville*/Brevard	12308163	321/264-1137	8
Somerset Academy ES-Bay/*Miami*/Miami-Dade	11923186	305/274-0682	84	South Lake High Sch/*Groveland*/Lake	00193748	352/394-2100	59
Somerset Academy JFK Chtr Sch/*Lake Worth*/				South Lake Montessori Sch/*Clermont*/Lake	05356816	352/243-0993	60
Palm Beach	05102304	561/868-6100	106				

School/City/County DISTRICT/CITY/COUNTY	PID	TELEPHONE NUMBER	PAGE
South McKeel Academy/*Lakeland*/Polk	10027777	863/510-0044	124
South Miami Heights Elem Sch/*Miami*/			
Miami-Dade	00187579	305/238-6610	84
South Miami K-8 Center/*South Miami*/			
Miami-Dade	00187115	305/667-8847	78
South Miami Middle Sch/*South Miami*/			
Miami-Dade	00187127	305/661-3481	78
South Miami Senior High Sch/*Miami*/			
Miami-Dade	00187139	305/666-5871	78
South Ocala Elem Sch/*Ocala*/Marion	00195631	352/671-4750	71
South Olive Elem Sch/*West Palm Bch*/			
Palm Beach	00198293	561/202-0200	107
South Orlando Christian Acad/*Orlando*/			
Orange	04983466	407/859-9511	102
South Plantation High Sch/*Plantation*/			
Broward	00183793	754/323-1950	15
South Pointe Elem Sch/*Miami Beach*/			
Miami-Dade	03422421	305/531-5437	81
South Seminole Middle Sch/*Casselberry*/			
Seminole	00203850	407/746-1350	133
South Sumter High Sch/*Bushnell*/Sumter	00204048	352/793-3131	138
South Sumter Middle Sch/*Webster*/Sumter	00204036	352/793-2232	138
South Tech Academy/*Boynton Beach*/			
Palm Beach	01530917	561/369-7000	106
South Tech Prep Academy/*Boynton Beach*/			
Palm Beach	11919927	561/318-8087	106
South Walton High Sch/*Santa Rsa Bch*/Walton	04806985	850/622-5020	144
South Woods Elem Sch/*Elkton*/St Johns	00202416	904/547-8610	135
Southeast High Sch/*Bradenton*/Manatee	00195306	941/741-3366	69
Southern Oak Elem Sch/*Largo*/Pinellas	03011890	727/588-4654	118
Southern Oaks Middle Sch/*Port St Lucie*/			
St Lucie	04455885	772/785-5640	137
Southland Christian Sch/*Kissimmee*/Osceola	04882628	407/201-7999	104
Southport Elem Sch/*Southport*/Bay	00181771	850/767-1636	5
Southport Middle Sch/*Port St Lucie*/			
St Lucie	03392515	772/337-5900	137
Southshore Charter Academy/*Riverview*/			
Hillsborough	12168470	813/769-1209	47
Southside Christian Sch/*St Petersburg*/			
Pinellas	04984202	727/327-2691	121
Southside Elem Sch/*Fernandina*/Nassau	00196087	904/491-7941	91
Southside Elem Sch/*Miami*/Miami-Dade	00186795	305/371-3311	78
Southside Elem Sch/*Sarasota*/Sarasota	00203484	941/361-6420	130
Southside Elem Sch/*Starke*/Bradford	00181941	904/966-6061	6
Southside Estates Elem Sch/*Jacksonville*/			
Duval	00189967	904/565-2706	31
Southside Middle Sch/*Jacksonville*/Duval	00189979	904/739-5238	33
Southside Primary Sch/*Crestview*/Okaloosa	11713785	850/689-7211	92
Southtech Siccess Center/*Boynton Beach*/			
Palm Beach	12366282	561/369-7000	106
Southwest Elem Sch/*Lakeland*/Polk	00201462	863/499-2830	125
Southwest Florida Chrn Academy/*Fort Myers*/			
Lee	04491724	239/936-8865	64
Southwest Miami Sr High Sch/*Miami*/			
Miami-Dade	00187189	305/274-0181	84
Southwest Middle Sch/*Lakeland*/Polk	00201474	863/499-2840	125
Southwest Middle Sch/*Orlando*/Orange	03400071	407/370-7200	99
Southwest Middle Sch/*Palm Bay*/Brevard	03055274	321/952-5800	9
Southwestern Middle Sch/*Deland*/Volusia	00204763	386/822-6815	141
Southwide Academy/*West Palm Bch*/Palm Beach	00199144	561/793-0657	112
Southwood Elem Sch/*Orlando*/Orange	04757358	407/858-2230	98
Southwood Middle Sch/*Palmetto Bay*/			
Miami-Dade	01527087	305/251-5361	84
Space Coast Christian Academy/*Cocoa*/			
Brevard	01535084	321/636-0883	10
Space Coast Early Intervention/*Melbourne*/			
Brevard	03174959	321/729-6858	10
Space Coast Jr Sr High Sch/*Cocoa*/Brevard	00182165	321/638-0750	9
Spanish Lake Elem Sch/*Hialeah*/Miami-Dade	10904668	305/816-0300	81
Spanish River Christian Sch/*Boca Raton*/			
Palm Beach	02204915	561/994-5006	112
Spanish River Cmty High Sch/*Boca Raton*/			
Palm Beach	02200050	561/241-2200	110
Sparr Elem Sch/*Anthony*/Marion	00195643	352/671-6060	71
Spectrum Jr Sr High Sch/*Stuart*/Martin	03318052	772/219-1870	73
Spessard L Holland Elem Sch/*Bartow*/Polk	11449128	863/648-3031	124
Spessard L Holland Elem Sch/*Satellite Bch*/			
Brevard	00182505	321/773-7591	8
Spirit Elem Sch/*Deltona*/Volusia	05342968	386/575-4080	141
Spook Hill Elem Sch/*Lake Wales*/Polk	00201694	863/678-4262	124
Sports Ldrshp Management Acad/*Tampa*/			
Hillsborough	12229995	813/920-8802	47
Spoto High Sch/*Riverview*/Hillsborough	10024270	813/672-5405	48
Spring Creek Charter Sch/*Paisley*/Lake	00193712	352/669-3275	59
Spring Creek Elem Sch/*Bonita Spgs*/Lee	02177099	239/947-0001	63
Spring Hill Christian Academy/*Spring Hill*/			
Hernando	04984549	352/683-8485	44
Spring Hill Elem Sch/*Spring Hill*/Hernando	01546710	352/797-7030	44
Spring Lake Elem Sch/*Altamonte SPG*/			
Seminole	00203903	407/746-1650	133
Spring Lake Elem Sch/*Ocoee*/Orange	00197407	407/877-5047	98
Spring Park Elem Sch/*Jacksonville*/Duval	00189981	904/346-5640	31
Spring Valley Sch/*Palm Harbor*/Pinellas	11236971	727/781-1234	121
Springfield Elem Sch/*Panama City*/Bay	00181783	850/767-4575	5
Springhead Elem Sch/*Plant City*/			
Hillsborough	00192902	813/757-9321	52
Springview Elem Sch/*Miami Springs*/			
Miami-Dade	00186305	305/885-6466	78
Springville Preparatory Acad/*Lake City*/			
Columbia	11930012	386/288-2537	28
Springwood Elem Sch/*Tallahassee*/Leon	03008726	850/488-6225	65
Spruce Creek Elem Sch/*Port Orange*/Volusia	02106454	386/322-6200	141
Spruce Creek High Sch/*Port Orange*/Volusia	00204660	386/322-6272	141
St Agatha Catholic Sch/*Miami*/Miami-Dade	02203533	305/222-8751	85
St Agnes Academy/*Key Biscayne*/Miami-Dade	00188274	305/361-3245	85
St Ambrose Sch/*Deerfield Bch*/Broward	00188286	954/427-2226	18
St Anastasia Sch/*Fort Pierce*/St Lucie	00197823	772/461-2232	137
St Andrew Catholic Sch/*Cape Coral*/Lee	03343784	239/772-3922	63
St Andrew Sch/*Coral Springs*/Broward	01534200	954/753-1280	18
St Andrew Sch/*Orlando*/Orange	00197794	407/295-4230	100
St Andrew Sch/*Panama City*/Bay	00181795	850/767-4595	5
St Andrew's Episcopal Academy/*Fort Pierce*/			
St Lucie	00202997	772/461-7689	137
St Andrew's Sch/*Boca Raton*/Palm Beach	00198968	561/210-2000	112
St Ann Catholic Sch/*West Palm Bch*/			
Palm Beach	00188298	561/832-3676	110
St Ann Sch/*Naples*/Collier	00188248	239/262-4110	27
St Anthony Catholic Sch/*San Antonio*/Pasco	00200987	352/588-3041	115
St Anthony Sch/*Ft Lauderdale*/Broward	00188303	954/467-7747	18
St Anthony Sch/*Lakeland*/Polk	04145200	863/858-0671	126
St Augustine High Sch/*St Augustine*/			
St Johns	00202507	904/547-8530	135
St Augustine Pub Mont ES/*St Augustine*/			
St Johns	11820728	904/342-5350	135
St Barnabas Episcopal Sch/*Deland*/Volusia	01404540	386/734-3005	142
St Bartholomew Sch/*Miramar*/Broward	00188315	954/431-5253	18
St Bernadette Catholic Sch/*Hollywood*/			
Broward	00188327	954/432-7022	18
St Bonaventure Catholic Sch/*Davie*/Broward	04246335	954/476-5200	18
St Brendan Elem Sch/*Miami*/Miami-Dade	00188339	305/221-2722	85
St Brendan High Sch/*Miami*/Miami-Dade	01483455	305/223-5181	85
St Brendan Sch/*Ormond Beach*/Volusia	00197809	386/441-1331	142
St Catherine Catholic Sch/*Sebring*/			
Highlands	11396650	863/873-2558	45
St Cecelia Interparochial Sch/*Clearwater*/			
Pinellas	00201008	727/461-1200	120
St Charles Borromeo Sch/*Orlando*/Orange	00197835	407/293-7691	100
St Charles Borromeo Sch/*Pt Charlotte*/			
Charlotte	00201010	941/625-5533	21
St Christopher's Mont Sch/*Key Biscayne*/			
Miami-Dade	02363054	305/361-5080	88
St Clair Evans Academy/*Jacksonville*/Duval	03401855	904/924-3035	33
St Clare Sch/*N Palm Beach*/Palm Beach	00188341	561/622-7171	110
St Clement Early Childhood Ctr/*Plant City*/			
Hillsborough	05319349	813/754-1237	53
St Cloud Elem Sch/*Saint Cloud*/Osceola	00198035	407/891-3160	104
St Cloud High Sch/*Saint Cloud*/Osceola	00198047	407/891-3100	104
St Cloud Middle Sch/*Saint Cloud*/Osceola	00198059	407/891-3200	104
St Cloud Preparatory Academy/*Saint Cloud*/			
Osceola	12045098	407/593-6601	104
St Coleman Sch/*Pompano Beach*/Broward	00188250	954/942-3500	18
St David Catholic Sch/*Davie*/Broward	02229824	954/472-7086	18
St Davids In Pine Episcopal SC/*Wellington*/			
Palm Beach	11225908	561/793-1272	112
St Edward's Sch/*Vero Beach*/Indian River	00193487	772/231-4136	56
St Elizabeth Ann Seton Cat Sch/*Palm Coast*/			
Flagler	04021513	386/445-2411	39
St Elizabeth Seton Sch/*Naples*/Collier	02137893	239/455-2262	27
St Francis Catholic Academy/*Gainesville*/			
Alachua	11014280	352/376-6545	3
St Francis Xavier Sch/*Fort Myers*/Lee	00201022	239/334-7707	63
St Gregory Sch/*Plantation*/Broward	00188391	954/473-8169	18
St Helen Catholic Sch/*Vero Beach*/			
Indian River	00197847	772/567-5457	56

School/City/County DISTRICT/CITY/COUNTY	PID	TELEPHONE NUMBER	PAGE
St Helen Sch/*Ft Lauderdale*/Broward	00188406	954/739-7094	18
St Hugh Catholic Sch/*Miami*/Miami-Dade	00188418	305/448-5602	85
St Ignatius Early Chldhd Ctr/*Tarpon Spgs*/ Pinellas	03157626	727/937-5427	120
St James Cathedral Sch/*Orlando*/Orange	00197859	407/841-4432	100
St James Sch/*North Miami*/Miami-Dade	00188420	305/681-3822	85
St Jerome Catholic Sch/*Ft Lauderdale*/ Broward	00188432	954/524-1990	18
St Jerome Early Childhood Ctr/*Largo*/ Pinellas	03344233	727/596-9491	120
St Joan of Arc Sch/*Boca Raton*/Palm Beach	00188444	561/392-7974	110
St John Lutheran Sch/*Ocala*/Marion	00195708	352/622-7275	72
St John Neumann High Sch/*Naples*/Collier	02137908	239/455-3044	27
St John Neumann Prep Cath Sch/*Miami*/ Miami-Dade	02137881	305/255-7315	85
St John Paul II Catholic Sch/*Lecanto*/ Citrus	02863846	352/746-2020	22
St John the Apostle Sch/*Hialeah*/Miami-Dade	00188468	305/888-6819	85
St John the Evangelist Sch/*Pensacola*/ Escambia	00202715	850/456-5218	38
St John Vianney Sch/*Orlando*/Orange	00197861	407/855-4660	100
St John Vianney Sch/*St Pete Beach*/Pinellas	00201034	727/360-1113	120
St John's Academy/*St Augustine*/St Johns	04982759	904/824-9224	135
St John's Country Day Sch/*Orange Park*/Clay	00184802	904/264-9572	25
St John's Episcopal Sch/*Homestead*/ Miami-Dade	02086646	305/247-5445	88
St John's Parish Lower Sch/*Tampa*/ Hillsborough	00193190	813/849-5200	54
St John's Parish Middle Sch/*Tampa*/ Hillsborough	11648697	813/849-4200	54
St John's Virtual Sch/*St Augustine*/ St Johns	11714715	904/547-8080	135
St John-Evangelist Cath Sch/*Panama City*/ Bay	00202674	850/763-1775	5
St Johns Classical Academy/*Fleming Isle*/ Clay	12262648	904/458-8240	24
St Johns Cmty Campus/*St Augustine*/St Johns	11556719	904/209-6842	135
ST JOHNS CO SCH DIST/*ST AUGUSTINE*/ **ST JOHNS**	00202363	904/547-7500	134
St Johns Technical High Sch/*St Augustine*/ St Johns	00202519	904/547-8500	135
St Joseph Academy/*Lakeland*/Polk	00197897	863/686-6415	126
St Joseph Academy/*St Augustine*/St Johns	00202727	904/824-0431	135
St Joseph Catholic Sch/*Bradenton*/Manatee	00201058	941/755-2611	70
St Joseph Catholic Sch/*Palm Bay*/Brevard	00197873	321/723-8866	9
St Joseph Catholic Sch/*Tampa*/Hillsborough	00201046	813/879-7720	53
St Joseph Catholic Sch/*Winter Haven*/Polk	02113043	863/293-3311	126
St Joseph Sch/*Stuart*/Martin	00188470	772/287-6975	73
St Joseph's Catholic Sch/*Jacksonville*/ Duval	00202741	904/268-6688	34
St Josephs Episcopal Sch/*Boynton Beach*/ Palm Beach	00199091	561/732-2045	112
St Jude Cathedral Sch/*St Petersburg*/ Pinellas	00201072	727/347-8622	120
St Jude Sch/*Boca Raton*/Palm Beach	02863054	561/392-9160	110
St Juliana Sch/*West Palm Bch*/Palm Beach	00188494	561/655-1922	111
St Kevin Catholic Sch/*Miami*/Miami-Dade	02113005	305/227-7571	85
St Lawrence Sch/*Miami*/Miami-Dade	00188509	305/932-4912	85
St Lawrence Sch/*Tampa*/Hillsborough	00201084	813/879-5090	53
St Louis Covenant Sch/*Pinecrest*/Miami-Dade	04778601	305/238-7562	85
ST LUCIE CO SCH DIST/*PORT ST LUCIE*/ **ST LUCIE**	00202844	772/429-3600	136
St Lucie Elem Sch/*Fort Pierce*/St Lucie	04457912	772/468-5213	137
St Lucie Virtual Sch/*Port St Lucie*/ St Lucie	12168169	772/429-5504	137
St Lucie West Centennial HS/*Port St Lucie*/ St Lucie	04806428	772/344-4400	137
St Lucie West K-8 Sch/*Port St Lucie*/ St Lucie	04806416	772/785-6630	137
St Luke Early Chldhd Center/*Palm Harbor*/ Pinellas	03014749	727/787-2914	120
St Luke Sch/*Palm Springs*/Palm Beach	00188511	561/965-8190	111
St Luke's Lutheran Sch/*Oviedo*/Seminole	01776329	407/365-3228	134
St Margaret Mary Sch/*Winter Park*/Orange	00197902	407/644-7537	100
St Mark Catholic Sch/*Sw Ranches*/Broward	04306181	954/434-3887	18
St Mark's Academy/*Cocoa*/Brevard	00182713	321/639-5771	10
St Mark's Episcopal Day Sch/*Jacksonville*/ Duval	00190227	904/388-2632	36
St Mark's Episcopal Sch/*Ft Lauderdale*/ Broward	00184333	954/563-4508	20
St Mark's Episcopal Sch/*Palm Bch Gdns*/ Palm Beach	02847452	561/622-1504	112
St Martha Catholic Sch/*Sarasota*/Sarasota	00201096	941/953-4181	131
St Mary Cathedral Sch/*Miami*/Miami-Dade	00188523	305/795-2000	85
St Mary Catholic Sch/*Ft Walton Bch*/ Okaloosa	00202753	850/243-8913	92
St Mary Magdalen Sch/*Altamonte SPG*/ Seminole	00197914	407/339-7301	133
St Mary's Episcopal Day Sch/*Tampa*/ Hillsborough	00193205	813/258-5508	54
St Mary's Sch/*Rockledge*/Brevard	00197926	321/636-4208	9
St Matthew Lutheran Sch/*Miami*/Miami-Dade	02236487	305/642-4177	88
St Matthew's Catholic Sch/*Jacksonville*/ Duval	00202686	904/387-4401	34
St Michael Academy/*Fernandina*/Nassau	04803830	904/321-2102	91
St Michael Lutheran Sch/*Fort Myers*/Lee	00194467	239/939-1218	64
St Michael the Archangel Sch/*Miami*/ Miami-Dade	00188559	305/642-6732	85
St Patrick Catholic Sch/*Jacksonville*/Duval	00202789	904/768-6323	34
St Patrick Catholic Sch/*Largo*/Pinellas	00201113	727/581-4865	120
St Patrick Grade Sch/*Miami Beach*/ Miami-Dade	00188573	305/534-4616	86
St Patrick Interparish Sch/*Gainesville*/ Alachua	00202777	352/376-9878	3
St Paul Catholic Sch/*Leesburg*/Lake	02180979	352/787-4657	60
St Paul Catholic Sch/*Pensacola*/Escambia	00202791	850/436-6435	38
St Paul Catholic Sch/*St Petersburg*/ Pinellas	00200999	727/823-6144	120
St Paul Child Enrichment Ctr/*Tampa*/ Hillsborough	03076785	813/264-3314	53
St Paul Lutheran Sch/*Boca Raton*/Palm Beach	00199118	561/395-8548	112
St Paul Lutheran Sch/*Lakeland*/Polk	01404473	863/644-7710	126
St Paul's Catholic Sch/*Jacksonville*/Duval	00202818	904/387-2841	34
St Paul's Sch/*Clearwater*/Pinellas	00200705	727/536-2756	121
St Paul's Sch/*Jax Bch*/Duval	02093742	904/249-5934	34
St Pauls Lutheran Sch/*Beverly Hills*/Citrus	04984496	352/489-3027	23
St Pauls Methodist Sch/*Gulf Breeze*/ Santa Rosa	11911339	850/932-0692	128
St Peter Catholic Sch/*Deland*/Volusia	00197940	386/822-6010	142
St Peter Claver Sch/*Tampa*/Hillsborough	00201125	813/224-0865	53
St Peter's Preparatory Academy/*Vero Beach*/ Indian River	04808397	772/562-1963	56
St Petersburg Cath High Sch/*St Petersburg*/ Pinellas	01483493	727/344-4065	120
St Petersburg Christian Sch/*St Petersburg*/ Pinellas	01404447	727/522-3000	121
St Petersburg Collegiate HS/*St Petersburg*/ Pinellas	05346952	727/341-4610	116
St Petersburg High Sch/*St Petersburg*/ Pinellas	00200418	727/893-1842	119
St Philip's Episcopal Sch/*Coral Gables*/ Miami-Dade	01773482	305/444-6366	88
St Raphael Catholic Sch/*St Petersburg*/ Pinellas	00201137	727/821-9663	120
St Rose of Lima Sch/*Miami Shores*/ Miami-Dade	00188585	305/751-4257	86
St Stephen Catholic Sch/*Riverview*/ Hillsborough	05008722	813/741-9203	53
St Stephen Child Care Lrng Ctr/*Jacksonville*/ Duval	05364784	904/358-2799	36
St Stephen's Episcopal Day Sch/*Miami*/ Miami-Dade	00187799	305/445-2606	88
St Stephen's Episcopal Sch/*Bradenton*/ Manatee	00195332	941/746-2121	70
St Teresa Catholic Sch/*Titusville*/Brevard	00197952	321/267-1643	9
St Theresa Catholic Sch/*Coral Gables*/ Miami-Dade	00188602	305/446-1738	86
St Thomas Aquinas Catholic Sch/*Saint Cloud*/ Osceola	03266265	407/957-1772	104
St Thomas Aquinas ECC/*New Prt Rchy*/Pasco	03014737	727/376-2330	115
St Thomas Aquinas High Sch/*Ft Lauderdale*/ Broward	00188614	954/581-0700	18
St Thomas Episcopal Sch/*Coral Gables*/ Miami-Dade	00187804	305/665-4851	88
St Thomas More Pre-School/*Boynton Beach*/ Palm Beach	05017515	561/737-3770	111
St Thomas the Apostle Sch/*Miami*/Miami-Dade	00188626	305/661-8591	86
St Timothy Early Childhood Ctr/*Lutz*/ Hillsborough	03076797	813/960-4857	53
St Timothy Parish Sch/*Miami*/Miami-Dade	00188638	305/274-8229	86
St Vincent Ferrer Sch/*Delray Beach*/ Palm Beach	00188640	561/278-3868	111
Stanley Switlik Elem Sch/*Marathon*/Monroe	00195966	305/289-2490	90

School/City/County DISTRICT/CITY/COUNTY	PID	TELEPHONE NUMBER	PAGE
Stanton College Prep Sch/Jacksonville/ Duval	00189993	904/630-6760	32
Stanton-Weirsdale Elem Sch/Weirsdale/ Marion	00195655	352/671-6150	71
Starke Christian Sch/Starke/Bradford	11222891	904/964-6100	6
Starke Elem Sch/Starke/Bradford	00181953	904/966-6045	6
Starkey Elem Sch/Seminole/Pinellas	00200420	727/547-7841	118
Starlight Cove Elem Sch/Lantana/Palm Beach	04369286	561/804-3601	107
State Clg of FL Collegiate Sch/Bradenton/ Manatee	11595416	941/752-5494	69
State Clg of FL Collegiate Sch/Venice/ Sarasota	12362236	941/408-1430	130
Steinbrenner High Sch/Lutz/Hillsborough	11447936	813/792-5131	50
Steinhatchee Sch/Steinhatchee/Taylor	00204206	352/498-3303	139
Stellar Leadership Academy/Miami/ Miami-Dade	11822219	305/693-2273	78
Stenstrom Elem Sch/Oviedo/Seminole	03161005	407/320-2450	133
Stephen Foster Elem Sch/Ft Lauderdale/ Broward	00183822	754/323-5750	15
Stephen Foster Elem Sch/Gainesville/ Alachua	00181422	352/955-6706	2
Sterling Park Elem Sch/Casselberry/ Seminole	01398006	407/746-8250	133
Stetson Baptist Chrn Sch/Deland/Volusia	01776484	386/734-7791	142
Stewart Middle Magnet Sch/Tampa/ Hillsborough	00191893	813/276-5691	49
Stewart Street Elem Sch/Quincy/Gadsden	00191257	850/627-3145	40
Stirling Elem Sch/Hollywood/Broward	00183834	754/323-7600	15
Stone Lakes Elem Sch/Orlando/Orange	10024385	407/207-7793	96
Stone Middle Sch/Melbourne/Brevard	00182517	321/723-0741	9
Stonewall Jackson Elem Sch/Jacksonville/ Duval	00190007	904/573-1020	34
Storm Grove Middle Sch/Vero Beach/ Indian River	11449374	772/564-6400	56
Stowers Elem Sch/Lithia/Hillsborough	11447900	813/657-7431	52
Stranahan High Sch/Ft Lauderdale/Broward	00183846	754/323-2100	15
Strawberry Crest High Sch/Dover/ Hillsborough	11447895	813/707-7522	52
Sts Peter & Paul Sch/Miami/Miami-Dade	00188236	305/858-3722	86
Stuart Cmty High Sch/Stuart/Martin	11819377	772/219-1296	73
Stuart Middle Sch/Stuart/Martin	00195825	772/219-1685	73
Student Leadership Academy/Venice/Sarasota	05346768	941/485-5551	130
Success Acad-Ghazvini Lrng Ctr/Tallahassee/ Leon	04033736	850/488-2087	65
Success Academy/Fort Myers/Lee	01340152	239/334-3416	63
Success Academy/Pensacola/Escambia	12311512	850/941-6100	38
Sugar Mill Elem Sch/Port Orange/Volusia	02200684	386/322-6171	142
Sugarloaf Sch/Sugarloaf Key/Monroe	00195980	305/745-3282	90
Sulphur Springs K-8 Cmty Sch/Tampa/ Hillsborough	00192938	813/975-7305	48
Summerfield Crossings Elem Sch/Riverview/ Hillsborough	10902608	813/672-5621	52
Summerfield Elem Sch/Riverview/ Hillsborough	03395737	813/671-5115	52
Summerlin Academy/Bartow/Polk	10902701	863/519-7504	122
Summers Elem Sch/Lake City/Columbia	00185143	386/755-8250	28
Summerville Advantage Academy/Homestead/ Miami-Dade	10907842	305/253-2123	84
Summit Christian Sch/Fort Myers/Lee	04984305	239/482-7007	64
Summit Questa Montessori ES/Davie/Broward	02184262	954/584-3466	20
Sumter Co Adult Education Ctr/Sumterville/ Sumter	04031996	352/793-5719	138
SUMTER CO SCH DIST/BUSHNELL/ SUMTER	00203989	352/793-2315	137
Sumter Prep Academy/Wildwood/Sumter	11820027	352/568-1113	138
Sun Academy/Bradenton/Manatee	11228522	941/752-1715	70
Sun Blaze Elem Sch/Orlando/Orange	11919305	407/203-5110	98
Sun Grove Montessori Sch/Fort Pierce/ St Lucie	02149262	772/464-5436	137
Sun'N Lake Elem Sch/Sebring/Highlands	02896415	863/471-5464	45
Suncoast Elem Sch/Spring Hill/Hernando	04286567	352/797-7085	44
Suncoast High Sch/Riviera Beach/Palm Beach	00198671	561/882-3401	109
Suncoast Innovative Studies ES/Sarasota/ Sarasota	11819224	941/953-4433	130
Suncoast Innovative Studies MS/Sarasota/ Sarasota	04811758	941/342-0963	130
Suncoast Polytechnical HS/Sarasota/ Sarasota	11077397	941/921-3981	130
Suncoast Primary Sch/Vero Beach/ Indian River	03178357	772/778-0892	56
Suncoast Waldorf Sch/Palm Harbor/Pinellas	11233278	727/786-8311	121
Suned High School-Margate/Margate/Broward	12032833	954/246-4004	17

School/City/County DISTRICT/CITY/COUNTY	PID	TELEPHONE NUMBER	PAGE
Sunfire High Sch/Oakland Park/Broward	11822283	954/678-3939	17
Sunflower Sch/Gulfport/Pinellas	01437406	727/321-7657	121
Sunflowers Academy/Miami/Miami-Dade	04480919	305/631-1284	88
Sunlake Academy of Math & Sci/Lutz/ Hillsborough	12231649	813/616-5099	47
Sunlake High Sch/Land O Lakes/Pasco	10904072	813/346-1000	114
Sunland Park Elem Sch/Ft Lauderdale/ Broward	00183432	754/322-8550	15
Sunland Sch/Marianna/Jackson	02200531	850/482-9271	57
Sunray Elem Sch/Holiday/Pasco	04916009	727/774-9100	114
Sunridge Elem Sch/Winter Garden/Orange	11816416	407/656-0809	100
Sunridge Middle Sch/Winter Garden/Orange	11816428	407/656-0794	96
Sunrise Elem Sch/Deltona/Volusia	04019027	386/575-4103	142
Sunrise Elem Sch/Kissimmee/Osceola	10007636	407/870-4866	104
Sunrise Elem Sch/Ocala/Marion	03334020	352/671-6200	71
Sunrise Elem Sch/Orlando/Orange	04757267	407/384-1585	96
Sunrise Elem Sch/Palm Bay/Brevard	10029957	321/674-6145	8
Sunrise High Sch/Ft Lauderdale/Broward	11554723	954/446-9234	17
Sunrise Middle Sch/Ft Lauderdale/Broward	00183444	754/322-4700	15
Sunrise Park Elem Sch/Boca Raton/ Palm Beach	04947228	561/477-4300	110
Sunset Elem Sch/Miami/Miami-Dade	00186800	305/661-8527	78
Sunset Hills Elem Sch/Tarpon Spgs/Pinellas	00200432	727/943-5523	117
Sunset Lakes Elem Sch/Miramar/Broward	05099446	754/323-7650	15
Sunset Palms Elem Sch/Boynton Beach/ Palm Beach	11103697	561/752-1100	110
Sunset Park Elem Sch/Miami/Miami-Dade	00187177	305/279-3222	84
Sunset Park Elem Sch/Windermere/Orange	10974405	407/905-3724	99
Sunset Preparatory Sch/Miami/Miami-Dade	01773559	305/274-5111	88
Sunshine Charter High Sch/Orlando/Orange	11820613	407/641-4156	95
Sunshine Christian Acad-Braden/Bradenton/ Manatee	03170537	941/794-3143	70
Sunshine Elem Chtr Sch/Hollywood/Broward	11076903	954/925-0155	17
Sunshine Elem Sch/Lehigh Acres/Lee	02846666	239/369-5836	63
Sunshine Elem Sch/Miramar/Broward	00184199	754/323-7700	15
Sunshine Tree Montessori Sch/Juno Beach/ Palm Beach	03654856	561/281-0085	112
Suntree Elem Sch/Melbourne/Brevard	04016051	321/242-6480	8
Superior Collegiate High Sch/Clearwater/ Pinellas	12235968	727/799-1200	121
Surfside Elem Sch/Satellite Bch/Brevard	00182531	321/773-2818	8
Surfside Middle Sch/P C Beach/Bay	03252941	850/767-5180	5
Surge Christian Academy/Clearwater/ Pinellas	12366880	727/223-4524	121
Susie E Tolbert Elem Sch/Jacksonville/ Duval	03401336	904/630-6860	34
Sutherland Elem Sch/Palm Harbor/Pinellas	02897029	727/724-1466	117
SUWANNEE CO SCH DIST/LIVE OAK/ SUWANNEE	00204098	386/647-4243	138
Suwannee Elem Sch/Live Oak/Suwannee	10030449	386/647-4400	138
Suwannee High Sch/Live Oak/Suwannee	00204127	386/647-4000	138
Suwannee Inter Sch/Live Oak/Suwannee	01811931	386/647-4700	138
Suwannee Middle Sch/Live Oak/Suwannee	00204139	386/647-4500	138
Suwannee Primary Sch/Live Oak/Suwannee	00204115	386/647-4300	138
Suwannee Virtual Sch/Live Oak/Suwannee	11830785	386/647-4248	138
Sweetwater Elem Sch/Miami/Miami-Dade	02852067	305/559-1101	78
Sweetwater Elem Sch/Port Orange/Volusia	04287377	386/322-6230	142
Sweetwater Episcopal Academy/Longwood/ Seminole	02086622	407/862-1882	134
Swift Creek Middle Sch/Tallahassee/Leon	04368555	850/414-2670	65
Swimming Pen Creek Elem Sch/Middleburg/ Clay	05346823	904/336-3475	24
Switzerland Point Middle Sch/Saint Johns/ St Johns	03394472	904/547-8650	135
Sylvania Heights Elem Sch/Miami/Miami-Dade	00187191	305/266-3511	78

T

School/City/County DISTRICT/CITY/COUNTY	PID	TELEPHONE NUMBER	PAGE
T R Jackson Pre-K Center/Milton/Santa Rosa	00203214	850/983-5720	128
T Roosevelt Elem Sch/Cocoa Beach/Brevard	00182672	321/868-6660	8
Tabernacle Baptist Academy/Lake City/ Columbia	11222437	386/752-4274	28
Tabernacle Baptist Sch/Live Oak/Suwannee	04336435	386/362-7800	139
Tabernacle Christian Ctr Acad/Davie/ Broward	11339315	954/583-4718	20
Tabernacle Christian Sch/Vero Beach/ Indian River	00193475	772/562-0720	56
Tallahassee Classical Sch/Tallahassee/Leon	12362054		65
Tallahassee Sch Math & Science/Tallahassee/ Leon	10904046	850/681-7827	65
Tallavana Christian Sch/Havana/Gadsden	01436531	850/539-5300	40
Tamarac Elem Sch/Tamarac/Broward	01339995	754/322-8600	15
Tampa Bay Blvd Elem Sch/Tampa/Hillsborough	00192952	813/872-5208	49

School/City/County DISTRICT/CITY/COUNTY	PID	TELEPHONE NUMBER	PAGE
Tampa Bay Christian Academy/*Tampa/* Hillsborough	01436646	813/343-0600	54
Tampa Bay Tech High Sch/*Tampa/*Hillsborough	00192940	813/744-8360	51
Tampa Catholic High Sch/*Tampa/*Hillsborough	00201149	813/870-0860	53
Tampa Christian Cmty Sch/*Lutz/*Hillsborough	05256709	813/949-2144	54
Tampa Day Sch/*Tampa/*Hillsborough	01436610	813/269-2100	54
Tampa Palms Elem Sch/*Tampa/*Hillsborough	03252630	813/975-7390	50
Tampa Preparatory Sch/*Tampa/*Hillsborough	01774618	813/251-8481	54
Tangelo Park Elem Sch/*Orlando/*Orange	00197421	407/354-2630	99
Tanglewood Academy/*Pembroke Pnes/*Broward	11237145	954/431-8805	20
Tanglewood Elem Sch/*Fort Myers/*Lee	00194390	239/936-0891	63
Tara Elem Sch/*Bradenton/*Manatee	04014883	941/751-7660	69
Tarpon Spgs Fundmntl Elem Sch/*Tarpon Spgs/* Pinellas	00200470	727/943-5508	117
Tarpon Springs Elem Sch/*Tarpon Spgs/* Pinellas	00200456	727/943-5500	117
Tarpon Springs High Sch/*Tarpon Spgs/* Pinellas	00200482	727/943-4900	117
Tarpon Springs Middle Sch/*Tarpon Spgs/* Pinellas	00200468	727/943-5511	117
Tatum Ridge Elem Sch/*Sarasota/*Sarasota	10006981	941/316-8188	130
Tavares Elem Sch/*Tavares/*Lake	00193970	352/343-2861	59
Tavares High Sch/*Tavares/*Lake	00193982	352/343-3007	59
Tavares Middle Sch/*Tavares/*Lake	00193994	352/343-4545	59
Taylor Co Elem Sch/*Perry/*Taylor	00204177	850/838-2530	139
Taylor Co High Sch/*Perry/*Taylor	00204218	850/838-2525	139
Taylor Co Middle Sch/*Perry/*Taylor	00204220	850/838-2516	139
TAYLOR CO SCH DIST/**PERRY/TAYLOR**	00204165	850/838-2500	139
Taylor Ranch Elem Sch/*Venice/*Sarasota	03333533	941/486-2000	130
Td Taylor Middle High Sch/*Pierson/*Volusia	00204775	386/749-6800	142
Teague Middle Sch/*Altamonte SPG/*Seminole	00203915	407/320-1550	133
Team Success Sch of Excellence/*Bradenton/* Manatee	04755403	941/714-7260	69
Tech Ctr for Career & Adult Ed/*Vero Beach/* Indian River	05342578	772/564-4970	56
Tech Ed Center-Osceola/*Kissimmee/*Osceola	04310558	407/344-5080	104
Tedder Elem Sch/*Pompano Beach/*Broward	00183092	754/322-8650	15
Tempette Learning Academy/*Jacksonville/* Duval	11620748	904/598-0078	36
Temple Beth Am Day Sch/*Miami/*Miami-Dade	01865188	305/665-6228	88
Temple Christian Sch/*N Ft Myers/*Lee	01774802	239/543-3222	64
Temple Christian Sch/*Titusville/*Brevard	04983387	321/269-2837	10
Temple Terrace Elem Sch/*Temple Terr/* Hillsborough	00192964	813/987-6903	50
Tenoroc Senior High Sch/*Lakeland/*Polk	11130872	863/614-9183	122
Tequesta Trace Middle Sch/*Weston/*Broward	03336743	754/323-4400	15
Terra Environ Research Inst/*Miami/* Miami-Dade	11445691	305/412-5800	84
Terrace Community Middle Sch/*Thonotosassa/* Hillsborough	04811435	813/987-6555	47
Terry Parker High Sch/*Jacksonville/*Duval	00190033	904/720-1650	32
Thacker Avenue Elem Sch/*Kissimmee/*Osceola	00198061	407/935-3540	104
The Academy High Sch/*Pt Charlotte/* Charlotte	04872934	941/255-7545	21
The Charter School-Waterstone/*Homestead/* Miami-Dade	10024646	305/248-6206	84
The Conservatory Sch/*N Palm Beach/* Palm Beach	00198580	561/494-1800	109
The Cushman Sch/*Miami/*Miami-Dade	00187816	305/757-1966	88
The English Center Adult Sch/*Miami/* Miami-Dade	01484538	305/445-7731	74
The First Academy/*Orlando/*Orange	03207984	407/206-8600	102
The Gap/*Bonifay/*Holmes	12172615	850/547-0470	55
The Geneva Sch/*Winter Park/*Orange	05292002	407/332-6363	102
The Greene Sch/*West Palm Bch/*Palm Beach	12177380	561/293-2888	112
The Island Sch/*Boca Grande/*Lee	04920103	941/964-8016	63
The Key to Learning/*Clermont/*Lake	12307054	352/432-1422	60
The Learning Foundation of FL/*West Palm Bch/* Palm Beach	11233709	561/795-6886	112
The Lyman Sch/*Winter Park/*Orange	12238934	407/898-7099	102
The McKay Academy/*Bradenton/*Manatee	11226689	941/840-5331	70
The Pine Sch/*Hobe Sound/*Martin	01404332	772/675-7005	74
The Quest Center/*Hollywood/*Broward	11076874	754/321-7500	15
The Rock Sch/*Gainesville/*Alachua	04328086	352/331-7625	3
The Seed School of Miami/*Miami/*Miami-Dade	12032742	855/818-7333	81
Thena Crowder Early Chldhd/*Miami/* Miami-Dade	00186276	305/836-0012	74
Theodore & Thelma Gibson CS/*Miami/* Miami-Dade	05278496	305/438-0895	78
Therapeutic Learning Center/*St Augustine/* St Johns	04931279	904/824-8932	135

School/City/County DISTRICT/CITY/COUNTY	PID	TELEPHONE NUMBER	PAGE
Thomas E Weightman Middle Sch/*Wesley Chapel/* Pasco	03394991	813/794-0200	115
Thomas Jefferson Elem Sch/*Jacksonville/* Duval	00190045	904/693-7500	31
Thomas Jefferson Middle Sch/*Merritt Is/* Brevard	00182684	321/453-5154	9
Thomas Jefferson Middle Sch/*Miami/* Miami-Dade	00185478	305/681-7481	81
Thomas Sims Middle Sch/*Pace/*Santa Rosa	04808763	850/995-3676	128
Thompson Elem Sch/*Ruskin/*Hillsborough	12034336	813/938-1203	48
Thonotosassa Elem Sch/*Thonotosassa/* Hillsborough	00192990	813/987-6987	48
Thornebrooke Elem Sch/*Ocoee/*Orange	05026217	407/909-1301	100
Three Flags Academy/*Hialeah/*Miami-Dade	03130208	305/821-5964	89
Three Oaks Elem Sch/*Fort Myers/*Lee	03050729	239/267-8020	63
Three Oaks Middle Sch/*Fort Myers/*Lee	04034144	239/267-5757	63
Three Points Elem Sch/*Orlando/*Orange	04945361	407/207-3800	98
Thunderbolt Elem Sch/*Fleming Isle/*Clay	04914934	904/336-3675	24
Thurgood Marshall Elem Sch/*Ft Lauderdale/* Broward	04364523	754/322-7000	15
Thurgood Marshall Fundmntl MS/*St Petersburg/* Pinellas	05273903	727/552-1737	119
Tice Elem Sch/*Fort Myers/*Lee	00194405	239/694-1257	63
Tiger Academy/*Jacksonville/*Duval	11446217	904/309-6840	30
Tildenville Elem Sch/*Winter Garden/*Orange	00197433	407/877-5054	100
Timber Creek High Sch/*Orlando/*Orange	04938904	321/235-7800	97
Timber Lakes Elem Sch/*Orlando/*Orange	11076812	407/249-6177	96
Timber Springs Middle Sch/*Orlando/*Orange	12230059	321/413-2201	96
Timber Trace Elem Sch/*Palm BCH GDNS/* Palm Beach	03402471	561/366-6200	109
Timbercrest Elem Sch/*Deltona/*Volusia	03342364	386/575-4221	142
Timberlin Creek Elem Sch/*St Augustine/* St Johns	10005274	904/547-7400	135
Timucuan Elem Sch/*Jacksonville/*Duval	00190057	904/573-1130	31
Tinker K-8 Sch/*Tampa/*Hillsborough	00193009	813/840-2043	49
Titusville High Sch/*Titusville/*Brevard	00182127	321/264-3100	9
Tohopekaliga High Sch/*Kissimmee/*Osceola	12308943	407/483-3685	104
Toledo Blade Elem Sch/*North Port/*Sarasota	04022335	941/426-6100	130
Tom P Haney Technical Center/*Panama City/* Bay	00181800	850/767-5500	5
Tomlin Middle Sch/*Plant City/*Hillsborough	00193011	813/757-9400	52
Tomlinson Adult Learning Ctr/*St Petersburg/* Pinellas	00200494	727/893-2723	116
Tommie Barfield Elem Sch/*Marco Island/* Collier	00185014	239/377-8500	26
Tommy Smith Elem Sch/*Panama City/*Bay	04012548	850/767-1688	5
Tomoka Elem Sch/*Ormond Beach/*Volusia	00204787	386/258-4676	142
Torah Academy of Boca Raton/*Boca Raton/* Palm Beach	11235240	561/465-2200	112
Torah Academy of Jacksonville/*Jacksonville/* Duval	11224497	904/268-7719	36
Toras Emes Academy-Miami/*N Miami Beach/* Miami-Dade	01559640	305/947-6000	89
Torchbearers' Christian Acad/*Dade City/* Pasco	01774436	352/567-3100	115
Tortuga Preserve Elem Sch/*Lehigh Acres/*Lee	11818452	239/693-5023	63
Toussaint L'Ouverture Elem Sch/*Miami/* Miami-Dade	03249528	305/758-2600	78
Toussaint L'Ouverture High Sch/*Delray Beach/* Palm Beach	04950512	561/350-9487	106
Town & Country Christian Acad/*Tampa/* Hillsborough	04329767	813/884-0971	54
Town & Country Elem Sch/*Tampa/*Hillsborough	00193023	813/871-7500	50
Tradewinds Elem Sch/*Coconut Creek/*Broward	04457883	754/322-8700	15
Tradewinds Middle Sch/*Greenacres/* Palm Beach	05348546	561/493-6400	110
Trafalgar Elem Sch/*Cape Coral/*Lee	05275262	239/283-3043	63
Trafalgar Middle Sch/*Cape Coral/*Lee	03250498	239/283-2001	63
Transition School at Hamblen/*St Augustine/* St Johns	12235255	904/547-8560	135
Transitional Learning Acad/*Orlando/*Orange	12262909	407/852-3300	95
Trapnell Elem Sch/*Plant City/*Hillsborough	00193035	813/757-9313	52
Traviss Technical College/*Lakeland/*Polk	00201199	863/499-2700	124
Treadway Elem Sch/*Leesburg/*Lake	00194003	352/742-2291	59
Treasure Coast Classical Acad/*Stuart/* Martin	12362078	772/783-3680	73
Treasure Coast Elem Sch/*Sebastian/* Indian River	10020559	772/978-8500	56
Treasure Coast High Sch/*Port St Lucie/* St Lucie	10024103	772/807-4300	137
Treasure Island Elem Sch/*North Bay Vlg/* Miami-Dade	00185480	305/865-3141	81

School/City/County DISTRICT/CITY/COUNTY	PID	TELEPHONE NUMBER	PAGE
Treasure Village Montessori CS/*Islamorada*/ Monroe	04876954	305/852-3482	90
Tree of Knowledge Lrng Academy/*Miami Beach*/ Miami-Dade	12361397	305/705-2211	89
Treeline Elem Sch/*Fort Myers*/Lee	11128001	239/768-5208	63
Trenton Elem Sch/*Trenton*/Gilchrist	03388473	352/463-3224	41
Trenton High Sch/*Trenton*/Gilchrist	00191295	352/463-3210	41
Triangle Elem Sch/*Mount Dora*/Lake	00194015	352/383-6176	59
Trilogy Sch/*Gainesville*/Alachua	11227310	352/332-8802	3
Trinitas Christian Sch/*Pensacola*/Escambia	11237274	850/484-3515	39
Trinity Catholic High Sch/*Ocala*/Marion	04924812	352/622-9025	72
Trinity Catholic Sch/*Tallahassee*/Leon	00202569	850/222-0444	65
Trinity Christ Sch-Palm Bch/*Palm Bch Gdns*/ Palm Beach	10805335	561/253-3950	112
Trinity Christian Academy/*Deltona*/Volusia	03341308	386/789-4515	142
Trinity Christian Academy/*Jacksonville*/ Duval	01404186	904/786-5320	36
Trinity Christian Academy/*Lake Worth*/ Palm Beach	05275559	561/967-1900	112
Trinity Christian Academy/*Miami*/Miami-Dade	11617868	786/888-5433	89
Trinity Christian Sch/*Apopka*/Orange	02086464	407/886-0212	102
Trinity Christian Sch/*Pompano Beach*/ Broward	11734703	954/941-8033	20
Trinity Elem Sch/*New Prt Rchy*/Pasco	04947979	727/774-9900	114
Trinity Lutheran Sch/*Delray Beach*/ Palm Beach	00199132	561/276-8458	112
Trinity Lutheran Sch/*Ft Lauderdale*/Broward	03405564	954/463-7471	20
Trinity Lutheran Sch/*Kissimmee*/Osceola	02235782	407/847-5377	105
Trinity Oaks Elem Sch/*New Prt Rchy*/Pasco	10022131	727/774-0900	114
Trinity Preparatory Sch/*Winter Park*/Orange	00197598	407/671-4140	102
Trinity School for Children/*Tampa*/ Hillsborough	04874334	813/874-2402	47
Tropic Isles Elem Sch/*N Ft Myers*/Lee	00194417	239/995-4704	63
Tropical Acres Christian Acad/*Riverview*/ Hillsborough	04329755	813/677-8036	55
Tropical Elem Sch/*Merritt Is*/Brevard	00182696	321/454-1080	8
Tropical Elem Sch/*Miami*/Miami-Dade	00187206	305/221-0284	84
Tropical Elem Sch/*Plantation*/Broward	00183860	754/323-7750	15
True North Classical Academy/*Miami*/ Miami-Dade	12114845	305/749-5725	84
Truecore Highlands Youth Acad/*Avon Park*/ Polk	12225561	863/452-3815	122
Turie T Small Elem Sch/*Daytona Beach*/ Volusia	00204799	386/258-4675	142
Turkey Creek Middle Sch/*Plant City*/ Hillsborough	00193047	813/757-9442	52
Turner-Bartels K-8 STEM/*Tampa*/Hillsborough	10003111	813/907-6801	50
Turning Point Christian Acad/*St Augustine*/ St Johns	11222449	904/824-0744	135
Turning Points Academy/*West Palm Bch*/ Palm Beach	10902593	561/681-3700	106
Turtle River Montessori/*Jupiter*/Palm Beach	04983997	561/745-1995	112
Tuskawilla Middle Sch/*Oviedo*/Seminole	00203939	407/746-8550	133
Tuskawilla Montessori Academy/*Oviedo*/ Seminole	03319460	407/678-3879	134
Tuttle Elem Sch/*Sarasota*/Sarasota	00203496	941/361-6433	130
Twin Lakes Academy Elem Sch/*Jacksonville*/ Duval	04808000	904/538-0238	32
Twin Lakes Academy Middle Sch/*Jacksonville*/ Duval	04808012	904/538-0825	33
Twin Lakes Elem Sch/*Hialeah*/Miami-Dade	00185894	305/822-0770	81
Twin Lakes Elem Sch/*Tampa*/Hillsborough	00193059	813/975-7380	50
Twin Oaks Juvenile Development/*Bristol*/ Liberty	04502892	850/643-1090	67
Tyndall Elem Sch/*Panama City*/Bay	00181812	850/767-1714	5
Tynes Elem Sch/*Middleburg*/Clay	04285202	904/336-3850	24
Tyrone Middle Sch/*St Petersburg*/Pinellas	00200511	727/893-1819	119

U

School/City/County DISTRICT/CITY/COUNTY	PID	TELEPHONE NUMBER	PAGE
U B Kinsey-Palmview Elem Sch/*West Palm Bch*/ Palm Beach	00198255	561/671-6500	107
Uco Diamond Minds Academy/*Miami*/Miami-Dade	11836478	305/623-4438	89
UCP Charter Sch-Bailes Campus/*Orlando*/ Orange	10029206	407/852-3300	95
UCP Charter Sch-West Orange/*Winter Garden*/ Orange	10029220	407/852-3300	95
UCP Charter School-Downtown/*Orlando*/Orange	02385791	407/852-3300	95
UCP Charter School-Pine Hills/*Orlando*/ Orange	10029191	407/852-3300	95
UCP of Central FL-Osceola/*Kissimmee*/ Osceola	05010517	407/852-3300	104

School/City/County DISTRICT/CITY/COUNTY	PID	TELEPHONE NUMBER	PAGE
UCP Seminole Child Dev Ctr/*Lake Mary*/ Seminole	04950615	407/852-3300	133
Umatilla Elem Sch/*Umatilla*/Lake	00194027	352/669-3181	59
Umatilla High Sch/*Umatilla*/Lake	00194039	352/669-3131	59
Umatilla Middle Sch/*Umatilla*/Lake	01877985	352/669-3171	59
Union Academy Magnet Sch/*Bartow*/Polk	00202052	863/534-7435	122
Union Co Adult Sch/*Lake Butler*/Union	11820118	352/448-5195	139
Union Co High Sch/*Lake Butler*/Union	00204282	352/448-5204	139
UNION CO SCH DIST/**LAKE BUTLER**/ **UNION**	00204244	352/448-5051	139
Union Juvenile Residential Sch/*Raiford*/ Union	04810613	386/431-1997	139
Union Park Charter Academy/*Wesley Chapel*/ Pasco	12322028	813/358-7306	113
Union Park Elem Sch/*Orlando*/Orange	00197445	407/249-6390	96
Union Park Middle Sch/*Orlando*/Orange	00197457	407/249-6309	96
Unity Chtr Sch of Cape Coral/*Cape Coral*/ Lee	11718383	239/829-5134	63
Unity Sch/*Delray Beach*/Palm Beach	01437248	561/276-4414	112
Universal Academy-Florida/*Tampa*/ Hillsborough	04984109	813/664-0695	55
Universal Education Center/*Orlando*/Orange	11713632	407/224-6634	95
University Academy/*Panama City*/Bay	11819676	850/481-4410	5
University Christian Sch/*Jacksonville*/ Duval	01404198	904/737-6330	36
University High Sch/*Orange City*/Volusia	11553468	386/968-0013	142
University High Sch/*Orlando*/Orange	03333648	407/482-8700	97
University Park Elem Sch/*Melbourne*/Brevard	00182543	321/723-2566	8
University Preparatory Academy/*West Palm Bch*/ Palm Beach	12165193	561/670-1138	106
University School-Nova SE Univ/*Ft Lauderdale*/ Broward	02203210	954/262-4400	20

V

School/City/County DISTRICT/CITY/COUNTY	PID	TELEPHONE NUMBER	PAGE
V Boone-Highland Oaks Elem Sch/*Miami*/ Miami-Dade	00185246	305/931-1770	81
Valley Ridge Academy/*Ponte Vedra*/St Johns	12031774	904/547-4090	135
Valleyview Elem Sch/*Lakeland*/Polk	03397503	863/648-3535	125
Valrico Elem Sch/*Valrico*/Hillsborough	04452326	813/744-6777	52
Valrico Lake Advantage Academy/*Riverview*/ Hillsborough	11447950	813/699-5049	47
Van E Blanton Elem Sch/*Miami*/Miami-Dade	00186317	305/696-9241	78
Van R Butler Elem Sch/*Santa Rsa Bch*/Walton	00204919	850/622-5041	144
Vanguard High Sch/*Ocala*/Marion	00195667	352/671-4900	71
Vanguard Sch/*Coconut Grove*/Miami-Dade	01435379	305/445-7992	89
Vanguard School of Lake Wales/*Lake Wales*/ Polk	01437482	863/676-6091	126
Varsity Lakes Middle Sch/*Lehigh Acres*/Lee	05348431	239/694-3464	63
Venetia Elem Sch/*Jacksonville*/Duval	00190069	904/381-3990	32
Venice Christian Sch/*Venice*/Sarasota	03139674	941/496-4411	131
Venice Elem Sch/*Venice*/Sarasota	00203501	941/486-2111	130
Venice High Sch/*Venice*/Sarasota	00203513	941/488-6726	130
Venice Middle Sch/*Venice*/Sarasota	00203525	941/486-2100	130
Ventura Elem Sch/*Kissimmee*/Osceola	03250539	407/344-5040	104
Ventura Elem Sch/*Orlando*/Orange	03008477	407/249-6400	98
Verde Elem Sch/*Boca Raton*/Palm Beach	02130027	561/218-6800	110
Verdi Ecoschool/*Melbourne*/Brevard	12317085	321/298-2501	10
Vernon Elem Sch/*Vernon*/Washington	00205042	850/535-2486	144
Vernon High Sch/*Vernon*/Washington	00205054	850/535-2046	144
Vernon Middle Sch/*Vernon*/Washington	01821481	850/535-2807	144
Vero Beach Elem Sch/*Vero Beach*/ Indian River	00193437	772/564-4560	56
Vero Beach Freshman Lrng Ctr/*Vero Beach*/ Indian River	11553834	772/564-5800	56
Vero Beach Senior High Sch/*Vero Beach*/ Indian River	00193451	772/564-5600	56
Veterans Elem Sch/*Wesley Chapel*/Pasco	11130999	813/346-1400	114
Veterans Memorial Elem Sch/*Naples*/Collier	10913334	239/377-8800	26
Veterans Park Academy for Arts/*Lehigh Acres*/ Lee	05348405	239/303-3003	63
Victory Christian Academy/*Edgewater*/ Volusia	04336552	386/427-7115	142
Victory Christian Academy/*Jacksonville*/ Duval	01436335	904/764-7781	36
Victory Christian Academy/*Lakeland*/Polk	04803543	863/859-6000	126
Victory Christian Academy/*Ocoee*/Orange	03063764	407/656-1295	102
Victory Christian Academy/*Orlando*/Orange	11231244	407/295-3332	102
Victory Christian Academy/*Sneads*/Jackson	04983167	850/593-6699	57
Victory Preparatory Sch/*St Augustine*/ St Johns	12238465	904/810-0535	136
Victory Ridge Academy/*Lake Wales*/Polk	10027753	863/679-3338	124
Viera Charter Sch/*Viera*/Brevard	11918545	321/541-1434	7

School/City/County DISTRICT/CITY/COUNTY	PID	TELEPHONE NUMBER	PAGE
Viera High Sch/*Viera*/Brevard	10020054	321/632-1770	9
Villa Lyan Sch/*Miami*/Miami-Dade	11832795	305/752-0220	89
Villa Madonna Sch/*Tampa*/Hillsborough	00201175	813/229-1322	55
Villa Preparatory Academy/*Homestead*/ Miami-Dade	11836404	305/247-5858	89
Village Academy/*Delray Beach*/Palm Beach	04920725	561/243-6100	110
Village Elem Sch/*Sunrise*/Broward	00183456	754/322-8750	15
Village Green Elem Sch/*Miami*/Miami-Dade	00187218	305/226-0441	84
Village Green Elem Sch/*Port St Lucie*/ St Lucie	02893023	772/337-6750	137
Village Oaks Elem Sch/*Immokalee*/Collier	03006182	239/377-8600	26
Village of Excellence Acad MS/*Tampa*/ Hillsborough	12101551	813/374-9422	47
Village of Excellence Academy/*Temple Terr*/ Hillsborough	04922230	813/988-8632	47
Village Pines Sch/*Miami*/Miami-Dade	01435666	305/235-6621	89
Village Sch/*Naples*/Collier	05344875	239/593-7686	27
Villages Charter Sch/*The Villages*/Sumter	04950639	352/259-2350	138
Villages Elem Sch/*Lady Lake*/Lake	04871356	352/751-0111	59
Villas Elem Sch/*Fort Myers*/Lee	00194429	239/936-3776	63
Vineland Elem Sch/*Rotonda West*/Charlotte	03009706	941/697-6600	21
Vineland K-8 Center/*Miami*/Miami-Dade	00187220	305/238-7931	84
Vineyards Elem Sch/*Naples*/Collier	03333193	239/377-8700	26
Virgil Mills Elem Sch/*Palmetto*/Manatee	05347803	941/721-2140	69
Virginia Shuman Young Elem Sch/*Ft Lauderdale*/ Broward	04289985	754/322-9050	15
Visible Men Academy/*Bradenton*/Manatee	11924817	941/758-7588	69
Vista Lakes Elem Sch/*Orlando*/Orange	10024347	407/207-4991	98
VOLUSIA CO SCH DIST/DELAND/ **VOLUSIA**	00204294	386/734-7190	140
Volusia Pines Elem Sch/*Lake Helen*/Volusia	00204505	386/575-4125	142

W

School/City/County DISTRICT/CITY/COUNTY	PID	TELEPHONE NUMBER	PAGE
W A Metcalfe Elem Sch/*Gainesville*/Alachua	00181329	352/955-6713	3
W C Pryor Middle Sch/*Ft Walton Bch*/ Okaloosa	00196477	850/833-3613	92
W D Sugg Middle Sch/*Bradenton*/Manatee	00195318	941/741-3157	69
W Douglas Hartley Elem Sch/*St Augustine*/ St Johns	02177130	904/547-8400	135
W E Cherry Elem Sch/*Orange Park*/Clay	00184797	904/336-3975	24
W H Rhodes Elem Sch/*Milton*/Santa Rosa	00203173	850/983-5670	128
W Peters Excptnl Center/*Dover*/Hillsborough	05351189	813/757-9462	53
W R Thomas Middle Sch/*Miami*/Miami-Dade	01340102	305/995-3800	85
W R Tolar Elem Middle Sch/*Bristol*/Liberty	00194900	850/643-2426	67
W W Irby Elem Sch/*Alachua*/Alachua	04017160	386/462-5002	3
Wabasso Sch/*Wabasso*/Indian River	00193463	772/978-8000	56
Wade Christian Academy/*Melbourne*/Brevard	02085745	321/259-6788	10
Wadsworth Elem Sch/*Palm Coast*/Flagler	03012105	386/446-6720	39
Wahneta Elem Sch/*Winter Haven*/Polk	00201917	863/291-5392	124
Wakulla Christian Sch/*Crawfordville*/ Wakulla	11750848	850/926-5583	143
Wakulla Co Alt High Sch/*Crawfordville*/ Wakulla	04804688	850/962-0100	143
Wakulla Co High Sch/*Crawfordville*/Wakulla	00204892	850/926-7125	143
WAKULLA CO SCH DIST/CRAWFORDVILLE/ **WAKULLA**	00204854	850/926-0065	143
Wakulla Educational Center/*Crawfordville*/ Wakulla	02178718	850/926-8111	143
Wakulla Middle Sch/*Crawfordville*/Wakulla	02125656	850/926-7143	143
Wakulla Virtual 7001 Sch/*Crawfordville*/ Wakulla	11831246	850/926-0065	143
Walden Lake Elem Sch/*Plant City*/ Hillsborough	03395684	813/757-9433	53
Walden Sch/*Gulfport*/Pinellas	04984197	727/321-7441	121
Walker Elem Sch/*Chuluota*/Seminole	05347487	407/871-7350	133
Walker Elem Sch/*Crestview*/Okaloosa	03250565	850/689-7220	92
Walker Elem Sch/*Ft Lauderdale*/Broward	00183872	754/322-8800	15
Walker Memorial Academy/*Avon Park*/ Highlands	01865293	863/453-3131	45
Walker Middle Sch/*Odessa*/Hillsborough	04754942	813/631-4726	50
Walker Middle Sch/*Orlando*/Orange	00196960	407/858-3210	98
Waller Elem Sch/*Youngstown*/Bay	00181824	850/767-4341	5
Walnut Hill Christian Sch/*Mc David*/ Escambia	01858123	850/327-4994	39
Walsingham Elem Sch/*Largo*/Pinellas	00200547	727/588-3519	118
Walter C Young Middle Sch/*Pembroke Pnes*/ Broward	03252329	754/323-4500	15
Walter Caldwell Elem Sch/*Auburndale*/Polk	00201929	863/965-5470	125
Walter Sickles High Sch/*Tampa*/Hillsborough	04754930	813/631-4742	50
Walter T Moore Elem Sch/*Tallahassee*/Leon	00194778	850/488-2858	65
Walton Academy/*Defuniak Spgs*/Walton	04931267	850/892-3999	144

School/City/County DISTRICT/CITY/COUNTY	PID	TELEPHONE NUMBER	PAGE
Walton Academy-Performing Arts/*Tampa*/ Hillsborough	05351098	813/231-9272	47
WALTON CO SCH DIST/DEFUNIAK SPGS/ **WALTON**	00204907	850/892-1100	143
Walton High Sch/*Defuniak Spgs*/Walton	00204995	850/892-1270	144
Walton Learning Center/*Defuniak Spgs*/ Walton	11712547	850/520-4642	144
Walton Middle Sch/*Defuniak Spgs*/Walton	00204983	850/892-1280	144
Walton Virtual Sch/*Defuniak Spgs*/Walton	11712535	850/892-1100	144
Ward-Highlands Elem Sch/*Ocala*/Marion	00195514	352/671-6810	72
Wards Creek Elem Sch/*St Augustine*/St Johns	10902347	904/547-8730	135
Warfield Elem Sch/*Indiantown*/Martin	00195837	772/597-2551	73
Warner Christian Academy/*Daytona Beach*/ Volusia	01404552	386/767-5451	143
Warrington Elem Sch/*Pensacola*/Escambia	00190887	850/453-7425	38
Warrington Middle Sch/*Pensacola*/Escambia	00190899	850/453-7440	38
Washington Classical Chrn Sch/*St Augustine*/ St Johns	12225640	904/323-2911	136
Washington Co Christian Sch/*Chipley*/ Washington	04927943	850/638-9227	144
Washington Co Sch/*Okeechobee*/Okeechobee	02048046	863/763-9648	93
WASHINGTON CO SCH DIST/CHIPLEY/ **WASHINGTON**	00205004	850/638-6222	144
Washington Co Virtual Sch/*Chipley*/ Washington	11745491	850/638-6222	144
Washington Elem Sch/*Riviera Beach*/ Palm Beach	00198695	561/494-1200	109
Washington High Sch/*Pensacola*/Escambia	00190904	850/475-5257	38
Washington Inst-Specialized Ed/*Chipley*/ Washington	11445885	850/638-6020	144
Washington Shores Elem Sch/*Orlando*/Orange	00197471	407/296-6540	100
Water Spring Elem Sch/*Winter Garden*/Orange	12367951	407/993-7310	100
Waterbridge Elem Sch/*Orlando*/Orange	03402299	407/858-3190	99
Waterford Elem Sch/*Orlando*/Orange	03402304	407/249-6410	96
Watergrass Elem Sch/*Wesley Chapel*/Pasco	11452060	813/346-0600	114
Waterleaf Elem Sch/*Jacksonville*/Duval	11718046	904/565-8000	32
Waters Edge Elem Sch/*Boca Raton*/Palm Beach	04457089	561/852-2400	110
Waterset Charter Sch/*Apollo Beach*/ Hillsborough	12231704	813/602-0622	47
Watkins Elem Sch/*Pembroke Park*/Broward	00184216	754/323-7800	15
Watson B Duncan Middle Sch/*Palm BCH GDNS*/ Palm Beach	03401300	561/776-3500	109
Wauchula Elem Sch/*Wauchula*/Hardee	00191520	863/773-3141	42
Wave Sch/*Chipley*/Washington	12306828	850/638-6222	144
Waverly Academy/*Jacksonville*/Duval	11718072	904/647-8552	30
Wayman Academy of the Arts/*Jacksonville*/ Duval	04916499	904/695-9995	30
Weatherbee Elem Sch/*Fort Pierce*/St Lucie	00202909	772/468-5300	137
Webb Middle Sch/*Tampa*/Hillsborough	00193114	813/872-5351	50
Webster Elem Sch/*Webster*/Sumter	00204050	352/793-2828	138
Webster Sch/*St Augustine*/St Johns	00202521	904/547-3860	135
Wedgefield Sch/*Orlando*/Orange	12172017	321/413-2989	96
Weeki Wachee High Sch/*Weeki Wachee*/ Hernando	11548578	352/797-7029	44
Weiss Sch/*Palm Bch Gdns*/Palm Beach	04012768	561/627-0740	112
Wekiva Elem Sch/*Longwood*/Seminole	01830248	407/746-3150	133
Wekiva High Sch/*Apopka*/Orange	10902531	407/297-4900	97
Welleby Elem Sch/*Sunrise*/Broward	04018724	754/322-8850	15
Wellington Cmty High Sch/*Wellington*/ Palm Beach	03054050	561/795-4900	107
Wellington Elem Sch/*Wellington*/Palm Beach	02107379	561/651-0600	107
Wellington Landings Middle Sch/*Wellington*/ Palm Beach	03007538	561/792-8100	107
Wendell Krinn Technical HS/*New Prt Rchy*/ Pasco	12307781	727/774-3900	114
Wendell Watson Elem Sch/*Lakeland*/Polk	03397539	863/853-6060	125
Wesley Chapel Elem Sch/*Wesley Chapel*/Pasco	05230547	813/794-0100	114
Wesley Chapel High Sch/*Wesley Chapel*/Pasco	04872130	813/794-8700	114
Wesley Christian Academy/*Clermont*/Lake	02379338	352/394-0191	60
Wesley Matthews Elem Sch/*Miami*/Miami-Dade	04454403	305/222-8150	85
West Area Adult & Cmty Sch/*Lakeland*/Polk	01550008	863/499-2835	124
West Bay Elem Sch/*Panama City*/Bay	12107452	850/767-1850	5
West Boca Raton Cmty High Sch/*Boca Raton*/ Palm Beach	05348522	561/672-2001	110
West Broward Academy/*Margate*/Broward	11820247	754/702-2320	17
West Broward High Sch/*Pembroke Pnes*/ Broward	11076989	754/323-2600	15
West Coast Christian Academy/*Bradenton*/ Manatee	01865396	941/755-9667	70
West Coast Christian Sch/*Crystal River*/ Citrus	02361757	352/795-2079	23
West Creek Elem Sch/*Orlando*/Orange	05352614	407/858-5920	99

School/City/County DISTRICT/CITY/COUNTY	PID	TELEPHONE NUMBER	PAGE
West Defuniak Elem Sch/*Defuniak Spgs*/ Walton	00204971	850/892-1250	144
West Elem Sch/*Arcadia*/De Soto	00188729	863/494-3155	28
West Florida Baptist Academy/*Milton*/ Santa Rosa	02148749	850/623-8984	129
West Florida HS Advanced Tech/*Pensacola*/ Escambia	05274517	850/876-7300	38
West Gadsden Middle Sch/*Quincy*/Gadsden	00191154	850/442-9500	40
West Gate Christian Sch/*Tampa*/Hillsborough	00193243	813/884-5147	55
West Gate Elem Sch/*West Palm Bch*/ Palm Beach	00198322	561/684-7100	107
West Gate K-8 Sch/*Port St Lucie*/St Lucie	10024098	772/807-7600	137
West Glades Sch/*Labelle*/Glades	05341196	863/675-3490	41
West Hernando Christian Sch/*Spring Hill*/ Hernando	04937091	352/688-9918	44
West Hernando Middle Sch/*Brooksville*/ Hernando	02110924	352/797-7035	44
West Hialeah Gardens Elem Sch/*Hialeah GDNS*/ Miami-Dade	10907787	305/818-4000	81
West Hollywood Elem Sch/*Hollywood*/Broward	00184204	754/323-7850	15
West Homestead K-8 Center/*Homestead*/ Miami-Dade	00187581	305/248-0812	85
West Lakes Preparatory Academy/*Hialeah*/ Miami-Dade	12305434	305/826-6104	81
West Meadows Baptist Academy/*Jacksonville*/ Duval	03139569	904/786-9308	36
West Melbourne Christian Acad/*Melbourne*/ Brevard	04983492	321/725-3743	10
West Melbourne ES -Science/*W Melbourne*/ Brevard	04915586	321/956-5040	8
West Miami Middle Sch/*Miami*/Miami-Dade	00187232	305/261-8383	78
West Nassau Co High Sch/*Callahan*/Nassau	00196099	904/879-3461	91
West Navarre Interm Sch/*Navarre*/Santa Rosa	04871899	850/936-6060	128
West Navarre Primary Sch/*Navarre*/ Santa Rosa	10028898	850/936-6000	128
West Oaks Academy/*Orlando*/Orange	02194542	407/292-8481	102
West Oaks Elem Sch/*Orlando*/Orange	05352640	407/532-3875	100
West Orange High Sch/*Winter Garden*/Orange	01397961	407/905-2400	97
West Palm Beach Junior Academy/*West Palm Bch*/ Palm Beach	04983911	561/689-9575	112
West Pensacola Elem Sch/*Pensacola*/Escambia	00190875	850/453-7470	38
West Port High Sch/*Ocala*/Marion	04915914	352/291-4000	72
West Riverside Elem Sch/*Jacksonville*/Duval	00190083	904/381-3900	32
West Riviera Elem Sch/*Riviera Beach*/ Palm Beach	00198683	561/494-1900	109
West Shore Elem Sch/*Tampa*/Hillsborough	00193085	813/272-3080	49
West Shore Jr Sr High Sch/*Melbourne*/ Brevard	04809389	321/242-4730	9
West Tampa Elem Sch/*Tampa*/Hillsborough	02907272	813/872-5200	49
West Technical Education Ctr/*Belle Glade*/ Palm Beach	12233520	561/829-4620	108
West University Charter HS/*Tampa*/ Hillsborough	11830383	813/774-4396	47
West Zephyrhills Elem Sch/*Zephyrhills*/ Pasco	00199388	813/794-6300	114
Westbrooke Elem Sch/*Ocoee*/Orange	11076800	407/656-6228	100
Westchase Elem Sch/*Tampa*/Hillsborough	04810041	813/631-4600	50
Westchester Elem Sch/*Coral Springs*/Broward	01340009	754/322-8900	15
Westcoast Sch-Human Dev/*Sarasota*/Sarasota	04984458	941/366-4539	131
Western Academy Charter Sch/*West Palm Bch*/ Palm Beach	05272739	561/792-4123	106
Western High Sch/*Davie*/Broward	02129999	754/323-2400	15
Western Pines Middle Sch/*West Palm Bch*/ Palm Beach	04018774	561/792-2500	109
Westgate Elem Sch/*St Petersburg*/Pinellas	00200559	727/893-2144	119
Westglades Middle Sch/*Parkland*/Broward	05158652	754/322-4800	15
Westlake Christian Sch/*Palm Harbor*/ Pinellas	04926793	727/781-3808	121
Westlake Preparatory Sch/*Hollywood*/Broward	04983820	954/236-2300	20
Westland Hialeah Sr High Sch/*Hialeah*/ Miami-Dade	11006403	305/818-3000	81
Westminster Academy/*Ft Lauderdale*/Broward	01434844	954/771-4600	20
Westminster Christian Sch/*Miami*/Miami-Dade	00187830	305/233-2030	89
Weston Christian Academy/*Weston*/Broward	04926456	954/349-9224	20
Westpine Middle Sch/*Sunrise*/Broward	04018700	754/322-4900	15
Westpointe Elem Sch/*Orlando*/Orange	12230097	407/866-1271	100
Westridge Middle Sch/*Orlando*/Orange	00197483	407/354-2640	99
Westside Christian Sch/*Largo*/Pinellas	10773990	727/517-2153	121
Westside Elem Sch/*Clewiston*/Hendry	03251208	863/983-1570	43
Westside Elem Sch/*Daytona Beach*/Volusia	00204828	386/274-3400	142
Westside Elem Sch/*Glen St Mary*/Baker	00181525	904/259-2216	4
Westside Elem Sch/*Lake City*/Columbia	04923868	386/755-8280	28

School/City/County DISTRICT/CITY/COUNTY	PID	TELEPHONE NUMBER	PAGE
Westside Elem Sch/*Palm Bay*/Brevard	04809377	321/956-5050	8
Westside Elem Sch/*Spring Hill*/Hernando	00191697	352/797-7080	44
Westside High Sch/*Jacksonville*/Duval	00189589	904/573-1170	32
Westside K-8 Sch/*Kissimmee*/Osceola	11452137	407/390-1748	104
Westside Tech Center/*Winter Garden*/Orange	01483481	407/905-2018	95
Westview Sch/*Jacksonville*/Duval	11446188	904/573-1082	33
Westward Elem Sch/*West Palm Bch*/Palm Beach	00198334	561/653-5200	109
Westwood Christian Sch/*Live Oak*/Suwannee	11234052	386/362-3735	139
Westwood Christian Sch/*Miami*/Miami-Dade	01404124	305/274-3380	89
Westwood Heights Elem Sch/*Ft Lauderdale*/ Broward	00183884	754/323-7900	15
Westwood Middle Sch/*Gainesville*/Alachua	00181446	352/955-6718	3
Westwood Middle Sch/*Winter Haven*/Polk	00201931	863/965-5484	125
Wetherbee Elem Sch/*Orlando*/Orange	11713565	407/850-5130	98
Wewahitchka Elem Sch/*Wewahitchka*/Gulf	00191386	850/639-2476	41
Wewahitchka Jr Sr High Sch/*Wewahitchka*/ Gulf	00191398	850/639-2228	41
Wheatley Elem Sch/*Apopka*/Orange	00197495	407/884-2250	95
Whiddon-Rogers Education Ctr/*Ft Lauderdale*/ Broward	02107915	754/321-7550	15
Whispering Oak Elem Sch/*Winter Garden*/ Orange	10001981	407/656-7773	100
Whispering Pines Elem Sch/*Boca Raton*/ Palm Beach	02856116	561/672-2700	110
Whispering Pines Elem Sch/*Cutler Bay*/ Miami-Dade	00187593	305/238-7382	85
Whispering Pines Sch/*Miramar*/Broward	03400291	754/321-7650	15
Whispering Winds Charter Sch/*Chiefland*/ Levy	04921303	352/490-5799	66
White City Elem Sch/*Fort Pierce*/St Lucie	00202985	772/468-5840	137
Whitehouse Elem Sch/*Jacksonville*/Duval	00190100	904/693-7542	32
Whitestone Academy/*Lakeland*/Polk	11228998	863/665-4187	126
Wicklow Elem Sch/*Sanford*/Seminole	04744375	407/320-1250	133
Wider Horizons Sch/*Spring Hill*/Hernando	03040578	352/686-1934	44
Wildlight Elem Sch/*Yulee*/Nassau	12225896	904/225-3053	91
Wildwood Elem Sch/*Wildwood*/Sumter	00204074	352/748-3353	138
Wildwood Middle High Sch/*Wildwood*/Sumter	01546746	352/748-1314	138
Wilkinson Elem Sch/*Middleburg*/Clay	03325665	904/336-4075	24
Wilkinson Elem Sch/*Sarasota*/Sarasota	00203537	941/361-6477	130
Wilkinson Junior High Sch/*Middleburg*/Clay	01540455	904/336-6175	24
William A Kirlew Jr Academy/*Miami Gardens*/ Miami-Dade	05078337	305/474-4760	89
William D Moseley Elem Sch/*Palatka*/Putnam	00202313	386/329-0562	127
William Dandy Middle Sch/*Ft Lauderdale*/ Broward	00183200	754/322-3200	15
William H Bashaw Elem Sch/*Bradenton*/ Manatee	02848561	941/741-3307	69
William J Bryan Elem Sch/*North Miami*/ Miami-Dade	00185492	305/891-0602	81
William Lehman Elem Sch/*Miami*/Miami-Dade	04365371	305/273-2140	85
William M Raines High Sch/*Jacksonville*/ Duval	00190112	904/924-3049	32
William McFatter Tech High Sch/*Davie*/ Broward	02853542	754/321-5700	15
William S Talbot Elem Sch/*Gainesville*/ Alachua	02856805	352/955-6716	3
William T Dwyer High Sch/*Palm Bch Gdns*/ Palm Beach	03402225	561/625-7800	109
Williams Magnet Middle Sch/*Tampa*/ Hillsborough	00191910	813/744-8600	51
Williston Central Christ Acad/*Williston*/ Levy	11710446	352/529-0900	67
Williston Elem Sch/*Williston*/Levy	04011453	352/528-6030	66
Williston Middle High Sch/*Williston*/Levy	00194869	352/528-3542	66
Willoughby Learning Center/*Stuart*/Martin	03011589	772/219-1515	73
Willow Sch/*Vero Beach*/Indian River	11228479	772/770-0758	56
Wilson Elem Sch/*Plant City*/Hillsborough	00193138	813/757-9307	53
Wilson Elem Sch/*Sanford*/Seminole	00203800	407/320-6950	133
Wilson Middle Sch/*Tampa*/Hillsborough	00193164	813/276-5682	49
Wilton Manors Elem Sch/*Ft Lauderdale*/ Broward	00183468	754/322-8950	15
Wimauma Elem Sch/*Wimauma*/Hillsborough	00193140	813/671-5159	53
Windermere Elem Sch/*Windermere*/Orange	00197500	407/876-7520	100
Windermere High Sch/*Windermere*/Orange	12230085	407/347-0980	97
Windermere Preparatory Sch/*Windermere*/ Orange	04937883	407/905-7737	102
Winding Waters Sch/*Weeki Wachee*/Hernando	11714026	352/797-7092	44
Windmill Point Elem Sch/*Port St Lucie*/ St Lucie	02893035	772/336-6950	137
Windsor Learning Acad-Presch/*Tampa*/ Hillsborough	04984161	813/885-3424	55

CMO No.	PID	CMO Name	Address	Phone
001	11912383	Estem Public Charter Schools	200 River Market Ave Ste 225, Little Rock AR 72201	(501) 324-9200
002	11916092	KIPP Delta Public Schools	415 Ohio, Helena AR 72342	(870) 753-9035
003	12319502	Lisa Academy Foundation	10825 Financial Centre Pkwy, Little Rock AR 72211	(501) 916-9450
004	11912826	Academy of Tucson Inc	10720 E 22nd St, Tucson AZ 85748	(520) 733-0096
005	11914305	Accelerated Learning Ctr	4105 E Shea Blvd, Phoenix AZ 85028	(602) 485-0309
006	11914288	Allen-Cochran Enterprises	1700 E Elliot Rd Ste 9, Tempe AZ 85284	(480) 632-1940
007	11914264	American Basic Schools LLC	131 E Southern Ave, Mesa AZ 85210	(480) 655-7868
008	11928033	American Leadership Acad Inc	2250 E Germann Rd Ste 14, Chandler AZ 85286	(480) 420-2101
009	11912761	Arizona Agribus&Equine Ctr Org	315 E Mulberry Dr, Phoenix AZ 85012	(602) 297-8500
010	11912759	Arizona Charter Schools	5704 E Grant Rd, Tucson AZ 85712	(520) 545-0575
011	11912723	Basis School Inc	7975 N Hayden Rd Ste B202, Scottsdale AZ 85258	(480) 289-2088
012	11914525	Benjamin Franklin Chtr Schools	690 E Warner Rd, Gilbert AZ 85296	(480) 264-3710
013	11912668	Blueprint Education	5651 W Talavi Blvd Ste 170, Glendale AZ 85306	(602) 674-5555
014	11914226	Bright Beginnings School Inc	400 N Andersen Blvd, Chandler AZ 85224	(480) 821-1404
015	11912620	CAFA Inc	4055 E Warner Rd, Gilbert AZ 85296	(480) 635-1900
016	11913387	Career Success Schools	3816 N 27th Ave, Phoenix AZ 85017	(602) 285-5525
017	11913351	Center for Academic Success	1843 Paseo San Luis, Sierra Vista AZ 85635	(520) 458-9309
018	11914173	Compass High School Inc	PO Box 17810, Tucson AZ 85731	(520) 296-4070
019	11914159	Cornerstone Charter School Inc	7107 N Black Canyon Hwy, Phoenix AZ 85021	(602) 595-2198
020	11914147	Country Gardens Educl Svcs	6313 W Southern Ave, Laveen AZ 85339	(602) 237-3741
021	11914111	Eastpointe High School Inc	8495 E Broadway Blvd, Tucson AZ 85710	(520) 731-8180
022	11914068	Educational Impact Inc	1950 E Placita Sin Nombre, Tucson AZ 85718	(520) 407-1200
023	11914044	Eduprize Schools Inc	4567 W Roberts Rd, Queen Creek AZ 85142	(480) 888-1610
024	11912395	Espiritu Community Development	4848 S 2nd St, Phoenix AZ 85040	(602) 243-7788
025	11914032	GAR LLC	8253 W Thunderbird Rd Ste 105, Peoria AZ 85381	(602) 334-4104
026	11913234	Great Hearts Academies	4801 E Washington St Ste 250, Phoenix AZ 85034	(602) 438-7045
027	11913985	Heritage Academy Inc	32 S Center St, Mesa AZ 85210	(480) 969-5641
028	11914434	Humanities & Sciences Acad US	5201 N 7th St, Phoenix AZ 85014	(602) 650-1333
029	11911781	Imagine Southwest Regional	1843 W 16th Ave, Apache Jct AZ 85120	(480) 355-0502
030	11913179	Kingman Academy of Learning	3410 N Burbank St, Kingman AZ 86409	(928) 681-2400
031	11913167	Leading Edge Charter Solutions	633 E Ray Rd Ste 132, Gilbert AZ 85296	(480) 633-0414
032	11913143	Learning Matters Educl Group	4744 W Grovers Ave, Glendale AZ 85308	(602) 439-5026
033	11913959	Legacy Traditional Schools	3125 S Gilbert Rd, Chandler AZ 85286	(480) 270-5438
034	11914599	Leona Group LLC-AZ	7878 N 16th St Ste 150, Phoenix AZ 85020	(602) 953-2933
035	11914381	Mgrm Pinnacle Education Inc	2224 W Southern Ave Ste 1, Tempe AZ 85282	(480) 755-8222
036	11913911	Montessori Schoolhouse Tucson	1301 E Fort Lowell Rd, Tucson AZ 85719	(520) 319-8668
037	11913923	Montessori Schools Flagstaff	2212 E Cedar Ave, Flagstaff AZ 86004	(928) 774-1600
038	12305874	Pima Prevention Partnership	924 N Alvernon Way, Tucson AZ 85711	(520) 791-2711
039	12306309	Plc Charter Schools	2504 S 91st Ave, Tolleson AZ 85353	(623) 474-2120
040	11912101	Pointe Educational Services	10215 N 43rd Ave, Phoenix AZ 85051	(602) 843-2014
041	11913519	PPEP and Affiliates	802 E 46th St, Tucson AZ 85713	(520) 622-3553
042	11913856	Rose Management Group	3686 W Orange Grove Rd Ste 192, Tucson AZ 85741	(520) 797-4884
043	11913832	Self Development Chtr Sch Org	1709 N Greenfield Rd, Mesa AZ 85205	(480) 641-2640
044	11913337	Sequoia Schools-Edkey Inc	1460 S Horne Bldg 6, Mesa AZ 85204	(480) 461-3200
045	11912979	Skyline Education	7450 S 40th St 7500, Phoenix AZ 85042	(877) 225-2118
046	11913349	Sonoran Schools Inc	1489 W Elliot Rd Ste 103, Gilbert AZ 85233	(480) 940-5440
047	11913806	Southern Arizona Cmty Acad Inc	2470 N Tucson Blvd, Tucson AZ 85716	(520) 319-6113
048	11912929	The Charter Foundation Inc	1150 N Country Club Rd Ste 100, Tucson AZ 85716	(520) 296-1100
049	11911901	The Edge School Inc	2555 E 1st St, Tucson AZ 85716	(520) 881-1389
050	11912890	Tucson International Academy	2700 W Broadway Blvd, Tucson AZ 85745	(520) 792-3255
051	11912802	Albert Einstein Academies	3035 Ash St, San Diego CA 92102	(619) 795-1190
052	11913686	Alliance College-Ready Pub Sch	601 S Figueroa St Fl 4, Los Angeles CA 90017	(213) 943-4930
053	12305812	Alpha Public Schools	PO Box 21366, San Jose CA 95151	(408) 455-6355
054	12262961	Alta Public Schools	2410 Broadway, Huntington Pk CA 90255	(323) 923-0383
055	11912785	American Indian Model Schools	171 12th St, Oakland CA 94607	(510) 893-8701
056	12262911	Amethod Public Schools	2101 Livingston St, Oakland CA 94606	(510) 436-0172
057	11913648	Aspire Public Schools	1001 22nd Ave Ste 100, Oakland CA 94606	(510) 434-5000
058	11912656	Bright Star Education Group	600 S La Fayette Park Pl, Los Angeles CA 90057	(323) 954-9957
059	11913404	California Montessori Projects	5330A Gibbons Dr Ste 700, Carmichael CA 95608	(916) 971-2432
060	11913399	Camino Nuevo Charter Academy	3435 W Temple St, Los Angeles CA 90026	(213) 417-3400

CMO No.	PID	CMO Name	Address	Phone
061	11912709	Ceiba Public Schools	260 W Riverside Dr, Watsonville CA 95076	(831) 740-8800
062	12260028	Citizens of the World Chtr Sch	5371 Wilshire Blvd Ste 210, Los Angeles CA 90036	(323) 634-7109
063	11912565	Civicorps Schools	101 Myrtle St, Oakland CA 94607	(510) 992-7800
064	11912539	Community Learning Center Schs	1900 3rd St, Alameda CA 94501	(510) 263-9266
065	11912527	Core-Cmty Options Resources Ed	321 16th St, Marysville CA 95901	(530) 742-2786
066	12110435	Downtown College Prep	1400 Parkmoor Ave Ste 206, San Jose CA 95126	(408) 271-8120
067	12261486	Ednovate Inc	3939 S Vermont Ave, Los Angeles CA 90037	(213) 454-0599
068	11912436	Education for Change	333 Hegenberger Rd Ste 600, Oakland CA 94621	(510) 568-7936
069	11912412	Environmental Charter Schools	2625 Manhattn Bch Blvd Ste 100, Redondo Beach CA 90278	(310) 214-3408
070	11913301	Envision Education	111 Myrtle St Ste 203, Oakland CA 94607	(510) 451-2415
071	12179015	Equitas Academy Chtr Sch Inc	1700 W Pico Blvd, Los Angeles CA 90015	(213) 201-0440
072	12305824	Fenton Charter Public Schools	8928 Sunland Blvd, Sun Valley CA 91352	(818) 962-3630
073	11912357	Five Keys Charter Schools Inc	70 Oak Grove St, San Francisco CA 94107	(415) 734-3310
074	12262935	Fortune School of Education	2890 Gateway Oaks Dr Ste 100, Sacramento CA 95833	(916) 924-8633
075	11913258	Gateway Community Charters	5112 Arnold Ave Ste A, McClellan CA 95652	(916) 286-5129
076	11912319	Golden Valley Charter Schools	3585 Maple St Ste 101, Ventura CA 93003	(805) 642-3435
077	11913595	Green Dot Public Schools	1149 S Hill St Ste 600, Los Angeles CA 90015	(323) 565-1600
078	12239598	Grimmway Schools	5080 California Ave Ste 100, Bakersfield CA 93309	(661) 432-7880
079	11912280	High Desert Partnsp Acad Excel	17500 Mana Rd, Apple Valley CA 92307	(760) 946-5414
080	11913222	High Tech High	2861 Womble Rd, San Diego CA 92106	(619) 243-5000
081	11913583	ICEF Public Schools	3855 W Slauson Ave, Los Angeles CA 90043	(323) 290-6900
082	11912266	Innovative Education Managemnt	4535 Missouri Flat Rd Ste 1A, Placerville CA 95667	(800) 979-4436
083	11913375	Isana Academies	3580 Wilshire Blvd Ste 1130, Los Angeles CA 90010	(323) 291-1211
084	11913181	King-Chavez Neighborhood Schs	415 31st St, San Diego CA 92102	(619) 525-7320
085	11916054	KIPP Bay Area Public Schools	1000 Broadway Ste 460, Oakland CA 94607	(510) 465-5477
086	11913571	KIPP Foundation	135 Main St Ste 1700, San Francisco CA 94105	(415) 399-1556
087	11916169	KIPP LA Public Schools	3601 E 1st St, Los Angeles CA 90063	(213) 489-4461
088	12115045	KIPP San Diego Clg Prep Public	1475 6th Ave, San Diego CA 92101	(619) 233-3242
089	11913155	Leadership Public Schools	99 Linden St, Oakland CA 94607	(510) 830-3780
090	12260030	Los Angeles Education Corps	3635 Atlantic Ave, Long Beach CA 90807	(562) 216-1790
091	11913557	Magnolia Ed & Research Fdn	250 E 1st St Ste 1500, Los Angeles CA 90012	(213) 628-3634
092	11912187	National Univ Academy System	2030 University Dr, Vista CA 92083	(760) 630-4080
093	12262777	Navigator Schools	650 San Benito St Ste 230, Hollister CA 95023	(831) 217-4880
094	12361373	Olive Grove Charter Schools	2353 S Broadway, Santa Maria CA 93454	(805) 623-1111
095	11935907	Opportunities for Learning	320 N Halstead St Ste 220, Pasadena CA 91107	(888) 207-1119
096	11913052	Options for Youth Inc	320 N Halstead St Ste 280, Pasadena CA 91107	(888) 389-9992
097	12262923	Pacific Charter Institute	1401 El Camino Ave Ste 510, Sacramento CA 95815	(866) 992-9033
098	11912125	Para Los Ninos PCS	5000 Hollywood Blvd, Los Angeles CA 90027	(213) 250-4800
099	11913521	Partnerships to Uplift Cmty	1405 N San Fernando Blvd 303, Burbank CA 91504	(818) 559-7699
100	11912060	Real Journey Academies	1425 W Foothill Blvd Ste 100, Upland CA 91786	(909) 888-8458
101	11912046	Roads Education Organization	2999 Cleveland Ave Ste D, Santa Rosa CA 95403	(707) 843-4676
102	11912034	Rocketship Education	350 Twin Dolphin Dr Ste 109, Redwood City CA 94065	(877) 806-0920
103	11911872	Rocklin Academy Charter Schs	2204 Plaza Dr Ste 200, Rocklin CA 95765	(916) 778-4544
104	11912008	Semillas Sociedad Civil	4736 Huntington Dr S, Los Angeles CA 90032	(323) 352-3148
105	11911987	St Hope Public Schools	PO Box 5038, Sacramento CA 95817	(916) 649-7900
106	12101381	Summit Public Schools	780 Broadway St, Redwood City CA 94063	(650) 257-9880
107	11911925	The Accelerated School	116 E Mlk Jr Blvd, Los Angeles CA 90011	(323) 235-6343
108	11911884	The Learner-Centered School	3325 Hacienda Way, Antioch CA 94509	(925) 755-7311
109	11911846	Tracy Learning Center	51 E Beverly Pl, Tracy CA 95376	(209) 290-0511
110	11911822	Value Schools	680 Wilshire Pl Ste 315, Los Angeles CA 90005	(213) 388-8676
111	12306244	Western Sierra Charter Schools	41267 Highway 41, Oakhurst CA 93644	(559) 642-1422
112	12262791	Ypi Charter Schools	10660 White Oak Ave B101, Granada Hills CA 91344	(818) 834-5805
113	12321684	Colorado Early College Network	4405 N Chestnut St Ste E, Colorado Spgs CO 80907	(719) 955-4685
114	12322432	Global Village Charter Collab	10701 Melody Dr Ste 610, Denver CO 80234	(720) 353-4113
115	11916078	KIPP Colorado	1390 Lawrence St Ste 200, Denver CO 80204	(303) 934-3245
116	12305886	Rocky Mountain Prep Schools	7808 Cherry Creek Dr S, Denver CO 80231	(720) 863-8920
117	12110356	Strive Preparatory Schools	2480 W 26th Ave Ste 360B, Denver CO 80211	(720) 772-4300
118	12322626	Tatonka Education Services	10375 Park Meadows Dr Ste 230, Lone Tree CO 80124	(303) 296-6500
119	11913090	The New America Schools Netwk	925 S Niagara St Ste 140/400, Denver CO 80224	(303) 800-0058
120	11913698	Achievement First Network	370 James St Ste 404, New Haven CT 06513	(203) 773-3223

CMO No.	PID	CMO Name	Address	Phone
121	11915414	Jumoke Academy Inc	999 Asylum Ave Ste 200, Hartford CT 06105	(860) 216-9636
122	11913650	Aspira Educl Management Org	1220 L St NW Ste 701, Washington DC 20005	(202) 835-3600
123	11913363	Center City Public Charter Sch	900 2nd St NE Ste 221, Washington DC 20002	(202) 589-0202
124	11912591	Cesar Chavez Public Chtr Schs	709 12th St SE, Washington DC 20003	(202) 547-3975
125	11912503	DC Prep	707 Edgewood St NE, Washington DC 20017	(202) 635-4590
126	11913260	Friendship Public Charter Sch	111 O St NW, Washington DC 20001	(202) 281-1700
127	11914836	KIPP DC	2600 Virginia Ave NW Ste 900, Washington DC 20037	(202) 223-4505
128	11912010	See Forever Foundation	600 Pnnsylvnia Ave SE Ste 210, Washington DC 20003	(202) 797-8250
129	11911860	The Seed Foundation	1730 Rh Isl Ave NW Ste 1102, Washington DC 20036	(202) 785-4123
130	11914680	Academica	6340 Sunset Dr, Miami FL 33143	(305) 669-2906
131	11914549	Accelerated Learning Solutions	5850 T G Lee Blvd Ste 345, Orlando FL 32822	(888) 437-9353
132	11914496	Charter School Associates Inc	5471 N University Dr, Coral Springs FL 33067	(954) 414-5767
133	11914678	Charter Schools USA	800 Corporate Dr Ste 700, Ft Lauderdale FL 33334	(954) 202-3500
134	11912541	Cmty & Eco Dev Org Gadsden Co	20 E Washington St, Quincy FL 32351	(850) 627-7656
135	11914630	Edisonlearning Inc	1 E Broward Blvd Ste 1111, Ft Lauderdale FL 33301	(877) 890-7088
136	12261709	Forza Education Management LLC	7815 111th Ter E, Parrish FL 34219	(727) 642-9319
137	11916420	Imagine South Florida Regional	13790 NW 4th St Ste 108, Sunrise FL 33325	(954) 870-5023
138	11916406	Imagine Southeast Regional	755 Town Center Blvd, Palm Coast FL 32164	(888) 709-8010
139	11916157	KIPP Jacksonville Schools	1440 McDuff Ave N, Jacksonville FL 32254	(904) 683-6643
140	12179651	Lake Wales Charter Schools	130 E Central Ave, Lake Wales FL 33853	(863) 679-6560
141	11913569	Lighthouse Academies	29140 Chapel Park Dr Bldg 5A, Wesley Chapel FL 33543	(800) 901-6943
142	11913947	LII Licensing Inc	6710 86th Ave N, Pinellas Park FL 33782	(727) 768-0989
143	11914379	Rader Group	101A Business Centre Dr, Miramar Beach FL 32550	(850) 650-3984
144	11913789	Superior Schools	861 N Hercules Ave, Clearwater FL 33765	(727) 799-1200
145	11916224	KIPP Metro Atlanta Schools	504 Fair St SW Ste 300, Atlanta GA 30313	(404) 924-6310
146	12240195	Mountain Ed Chtr High School	1963 Tom Bell Rd, Cleveland GA 30528	(706) 219-4664
147	12259990	Gem Innovation Schools	PO Box 86, Deary ID 83823	(208) 238-1388
148	11913466	Acero Charter Schools Inc	209 W Jackson Blvd Ste 500, Chicago IL 60606	(312) 637-3900
149	11913662	American Quality Schools Corp	1315 Butterfield Rd Ste 224, Chicago IL 60615	(312) 226-3355
150	11912670	Betty Shabazz Intl Chtr Sch	7822 S Dobson Ave, Chicago IL 60619	(773) 651-1221
151	11912606	Catalyst Schools	6727 S California Ave, Chicago IL 60629	(773) 295-7001
152	11912553	Civitas Education Partners	901 W Jackson Blvd Ste 205, Chicago IL 60607	(312) 733-6790
153	11913636	Concept Schools	1336 Basswood Rd, Schaumburg IL 60173	(847) 824-3380
154	11912333	Galapagos Charter	3051 Rotary Rd, Rockford IL 61109	(779) 368-0852
155	11914812	KIPP Chicago	2007 S Halsted St, Chicago IL 60608	(312) 733-8108
156	12110447	Lawndale Educ & Reg Network	3021 W Carroll Ave, Chicago IL 60612	(773) 584-4399
157	11913545	Noble Network of Charter Sch	1 N State St Ste 700, Chicago IL 60602	(312) 521-5287
158	11913038	Perspectives Charter Schools	1530 S State St Ste 200, Chicago IL 60605	(312) 604-2200
159	12260016	Regeneration Schools	1816 W Garfield Blvd, Chicago IL 60609	(773) 778-9455
160	11913246	GEO Foundation	1630 N Meridian St Ste 350, Indianapolis IN 46202	(317) 536-1027
161	12315427	Goodwill Education Initiatives	1635 W Michigan St, Indianapolis IN 46222	(317) 524-4265
162	11916145	KIPP Indy Public Schools	1740 E 30th St, Indianapolis IN 46218	(317) 547-5477
163	12179027	Tindley Accelerated Schools	3960 Meadows Dr, Indianapolis IN 46205	(317) 545-1745
164	11913430	Algiers Charter School Assoc	2401 Westbend Pkwy Ste 2001, New Orleans LA 70114	(504) 302-7001
165	12115203	Collegiate Academies	7301 Dwyer Rd, New Orleans LA 70126	(504) 503-0008
166	11930816	Crescent City Schools	3811 N Galvez St, New Orleans LA 70117	(504) 708-4136
167	11912369	Firstline Schools Inc	300 N Broad St Ste 207, New Orleans LA 70119	(504) 267-9038
168	11930725	Friends of King Schools	1617 Caffin Ave, New Orleans LA 70117	(504) 940-2243
169	12179039	Inspirenola Charter Schools	2401 Westbend Pkwy Ste 4040, New Orleans LA 70114	(504) 227-3057
170	12259213	Jcfa Charter Schools	475 Manhattan Blvd, Harvey LA 70058	(504) 410-3121
171	11916250	KIPP New Orleans Schools	1307 Oretha Castle Haley Blvd, New Orleans LA 70113	(504) 373-6269
172	11912058	Renew Schools Inc	1607 S Carrollton Ave, New Orleans LA 70118	(504) 367-3307
173	11911913	The Choice Foundation	3201 Live Oak St, New Orleans LA 70118	(504) 861-8370
174	12110411	The Einstein Group Inc	5316 Michoud Blvd, New Orleans LA 70129	(504) 324-7450
175	11913296	Excel Academy	58 Moore St, East Boston MA 02128	(617) 874-4080
176	11916171	KIPP Massachusetts Pub CH Schs	90 High Rock St, Lynn MA 01902	(781) 598-1609
177	12306086	The Community Group	190 Hampshire St Ste 2, Lawrence MA 01840	(978) 682-6628
178	12260004	Up Education Network	90 Canal St Ste 600, Boston MA 02114	(617) 307-5980
179	11913428	Baltimore Curriculum Project	2707 E Fayette St, Baltimore MD 21224	(410) 675-7000
180	11912577	City Neighbors Inc	4301 Raspe Ave, Baltimore MD 21206	(410) 325-2627

CMO No.	PID	CMO Name	Address	Phone
181	11914666	Connections Academy	10960 Grantchester Way, Columbia MD 21044	(443) 529-1000
182	11916470	Imagine Mid-Atlantic Regional	4415 Nicole Dr Ste C, Lanham MD 20706	(301) 316-1802
183	11915830	KIPP Baltimore	4701 Greenspring Ave Rm 115, Baltimore MD 21209	(410) 367-0807
184	11912228	Living Classrooms Foundation	802 S Caroline St, Baltimore MD 21231	(410) 685-0295
185	11914252	American Institutional Mgmt	5728 Schaefer Rd Ste 200, Dearborn MI 48126	(313) 624-2000
186	11914240	Bardwell Group	19800 Beech Daly Rd, Redford MI 48240	(313) 450-0642
187	11914501	Charter School Admin Services	20820 Greenfield Rd, Oak Park MI 48237	(248) 569-7787
188	11914484	Choice Schools Associates LLC	5251 Clyde Park Ave SW, Wyoming MI 49509	(616) 785-8440
189	11911858	Cornerstone Education Group	306 E 4th St, Royal Oak MI 48067	(248) 439-6228
190	11914642	CS Partners LLC	869 S Old US 23 Ste 500, Brighton MI 48114	(810) 229-5145
191	11914094	EdTec Central LLC	10 S Main St Ste 100, Mount Clemens MI 48043	(248) 582-8100
192	11914343	Education Enrichmnet Services	19236 W 11 Mile Rd, Lathrup Vlg MI 48076	(248) 905-5030
193	11914070	Education Management&Networks	27704 Franklin Rd, Southfield MI 48034	(248) 327-7673
194	11912345	Foundation for Behavioral Res	600 S Lincoln St, Augusta MI 49012	(269) 731-5796
195	11914446	Global Educational Excellence	2455 S Industrial Hwy Ste A, Ann Arbor MI 48104	(734) 369-9500
196	11914018	Hamadeh Educational Services	PO Box 1440, Dearborn MI 48121	(313) 565-0507
197	11914006	Hanley-Harper Group Inc	20542 Harper Ave, Harper Woods MI 48225	(313) 347-0026
198	11913973	Innovative Teaching Solutions	18470 W 10 Mile Rd Ste 100, Southfield MI 48075	(248) 799-2780
199	11913961	Lakeshore Educl Management	12955 Robins Ridge Rd, Charlevoix MI 49720	(231) 547-4264
200	11916597	Leona Group LLC-Midwest	2125 University Park Dr, Okemos MI 48864	(517) 333-9030
201	11912204	Midland Charter Initiative	4653 Bailey Bridge Rd, Midland MI 48640	(989) 496-2404
202	11913935	MJ Management Services Inc	PO Box 1014, Flat Rock MI 48134	(734) 675-5505
203	11914575	National Heritage Academies	3850 Broadmoor Ave SE Ste 201, Grand Rapids MI 49512	(877) 223-6402
204	11913868	PrepNet LLC	3755 36th St SE Ste 250, Grand Rapids MI 49512	(616) 726-8900
205	12038734	Promise Schools	15000 Trojan St, Detroit MI 48235	(313) 964-2339
206	11914367	Romine Group LLC	7877 Stead St Ste 100, Utica MI 48317	(586) 731-5300
207	11913818	Solid Rock Management Company	3031 W Grand Blvd Ste 524, Detroit MI 48202	(313) 873-7625
208	11913753	Technical Academy Group LLC	4801 Oakman Blvd, Dearborn MI 48126	(313) 625-4700
209	11911793	Youth Visions Solutions	1450 25th St, Detroit MI 48216	(313) 558-9022
210	12262284	Harvest Network of Schools	1300 Olson Memorial Hwy, Minneapolis MN 55411	(612) 876-4105
211	12262301	Hiawatha Academies	1611 E 46th St, Minneapolis MN 55407	(612) 455-4004
212	12115033	KIPP Minnesota Public Schools	5034 Oliver Ave N, Minneapolis MN 55430	(612) 287-9700
213	12262387	MN Transitions Charter Schs	2872 26th Ave S, Minneapolis MN 55406	(612) 722-9013
214	11914355	Sabis Educational Systems	6385 Beach Rd, Eden Prairie MN 55344	(952) 918-1850
215	12261462	Confluence Academies	611 N 10th St Ste 525, Saint Louis MO 63101	(314) 588-8554
216	12115021	KIPP Kansas City	2700 E 18th St Ste 155B, Kansas City MO 64127	(816) 241-3994
217	11916303	KIPP St Louis Public Schools	1310 Papin St Ste 203, Saint Louis MO 63103	(314) 349-1388
218	12115019	KIPP Charlotte Public Schools	931 Wilann Dr, Charlotte NC 28215	(704) 537-2044
219	11916119	KIPP Enc College Prep Pub Schs	320 Pleasant Hill Rd, Gaston NC 27832	(252) 308-6932
220	12179431	Teamcfa	9935D Rea Rd Ste 167, Charlotte NC 28277	(704) 774-3038
221	12309351	The Roger Bacon Academy	3610 Thaddeus Lott Ln NE, Leland NC 28451	(910) 655-3600
222	12306593	College Achieve Ctl CS Network	365 Emerson Ave, Plainfield NJ 07062	(908) 625-1879
223	12110332	Ilearn Schools Inc	33-00 Broadway Ste 301, Fair Lawn NJ 07410	(201) 773-9140
224	11916327	KIPP New Jersey	60 Park Pl Ste 802, Newark NJ 07102	(973) 622-0905
225	11912694	Beginning with Children Fndn	217 Havemeyer St Ste 2, Brooklyn NY 11211	(212) 750-9320
226	11912644	Brighter Choice Charter Schs	250 Central Ave, Albany NY 12206	(518) 694-4100
227	11912498	Democracy Prep Public Schools	1767 Park Ave Fl 4, New York NY 10035	(212) 281-1248
228	12262894	Excellence Community Schools	2090 7th Ave Ste 605, New York NY 10027	(212) 222-5071
229	11912371	Explore Schools Inc	20 Jay St Ste 211, Brooklyn NY 11201	(718) 989-6730
230	12161604	Great Oaks Foundation	200 Broadway 3rd Fl, New York NY 10038	(917) 239-3641
231	11912292	Harlem Village Academies	15 Penn Plz Ste 15, New York NY 10001	(646) 812-9501
232	12114986	KIPP Albany Public Schools	321 Northern Blvd, Albany NY 12210	(518) 694-9494
233	11914824	KIPP NYC Public Schools	1501 Broadway Ste 1000, New York NY 10036	(212) 991-2610
234	11912084	Public Prep Network Inc	441 E 148th St, Bronx NY 10455	(212) 346-6000
235	11912943	Success Academy Charter Schls	95 Pine St Fl 6, New York NY 10005	(646) 597-4641
236	11913478	Uncommon Schools	826 Broadway Fl 9, New York NY 10003	(212) 844-3584
237	11914563	Victory Education Partners	135 W 40 St Fl 5, New York NY 10036	(212) 786-7900
238	12179819	Accel Schools	4700 Rockside Rd Ste 345, Independence OH 44131	(216) 583-5230
239	11913416	Breakthrough Charter Schools	3615 Superior Ave E Ste 4403A, Cleveland OH 44114	(216) 456-2086
240	11912632	Buckeye on-Line School Success	119 E 5th St, E Liverpool OH 43920	(330) 385-1987

CMO No.	PID	CMO Name	Address	Phone
241	12106575	Carpe Diem Learning Systems	301 N Breiel Blvd Ste B, Middletown OH 45042	(513) 217-3400
242	11914654	Constellation Schools	5730 Broadview Rd, Parma OH 44134	(216) 712-7600
243	12319069	Educational Solutions	1500 W 3rd Ave Ste 125, Columbus OH 43212	(614) 299-1007
244	11914460	Eschool Consultants	4480 Refugee Rd, Columbus OH 43232	(614) 322-7996
245	11916509	Imagine Ohio Regional	11518 Banning Rd, Mount Vernon OH 43050	(614) 930-1184
246	11916066	KIPP Columbus	2980 Inspire Dr, Columbus OH 43224	(614) 263-6137
247	11914393	Performance Academies LLC	2 Easton Oval Ste 525, Columbus OH 43219	(614) 512-2151
248	11913480	Summit Academy Management	2791 Mogadore Rd, Akron OH 44312	(330) 670-8470
249	12363034	United Schools Network	1469 E Main St, Columbus OH 43205	(614) 299-5284
250	12305745	KIPP Okc Public Schools	PO Box 776, Oklahoma City OK 73101	(405) 425-4622
251	12115069	KIPP Tulsa Public Charter Schs	1661 E Virgin St, Tulsa OK 74106	(918) 794-8652
252	12361452	Santa Fe South Public Schools	4825 S Shields Blvd, Oklahoma City OK 73129	(405) 601-5440
253	11913117	Mastery Lrng Inst-Arthur Acad	13717 SE Division St, Portland OR 97236	(503) 762-6061
254	11914185	Charter School Management Inc	419 Avenue of the States, Chester PA 19013	(610) 447-0200
255	11912448	EdSys Inc	201 Stanwix St Ste 100, Pittsburgh PA 15222	(412) 690-2489
256	11916274	KIPP Philadelphia Public Schs	5070 Parkside Ave Ste 3500D, Philadelphia PA 19131	(215) 294-8596
257	11913129	Mastery Charter Schools	5700 Wayne Ave, Philadelphia PA 19144	(215) 866-9000
258	11914408	Omnivest Properties Management	115 Pheasant Run Ste 210, Newtown PA 18940	(215) 497-8301
259	11913026	Propel Schools	3447 E Carson St Ste 200, Pittsburgh PA 15203	(412) 325-7305
260	11912888	Universal Companies Inc	800 S 15th St, Philadelphia PA 19146	(215) 391-4161
261	12312499	Charter Institute at Erskine	1201 Main St Ste 300, Columbia SC 29201	(803) 849-2464
262	12161719	Capstone Education Group	PO Box 22569, Memphis TN 38122	(901) 416-3640
263	11914628	Chancelight Behavioral Hlth-Ed	1321 Murfreesboro Pike Ste 702, Nashville TN 37217	(615) 361-4000
264	12319629	Freedom Prep Academy Network	778 Parkrose Ave, Memphis TN 38109	(901) 881-1149
265	12038813	Gestalt Community Schools	2650 Thsnd Oaks Blvd Ste 1400, Memphis TN 38118	(901) 213-5161
266	12305850	Green Dot Pub Schs-Tennessee	4950 Fairley Rd, Memphis TN 38109	(901) 730-8160
267	11916200	KIPP Memphis Collegiate Schs	2670 Union Avenue Ext Ste 1100, Memphis TN 38112	(901) 452-2682
268	11916236	KIPP Nashville	123 Douglas Ave, Nashville TN 37207	(615) 226-4484
269	12038825	Lead Public Schools	2835 Brick Church Pike, Nashville TN 37207	(615) 815-1264
270	12110461	Republic Schools	3307 Brick Church Pike, Nashville TN 37207	(615) 921-6620
271	11911896	The Influence 1 Foundation	665 Madison Ave, Memphis TN 38103	(901) 526-1944
272	11912993	A Plus Charter Schools	8225 Bruton Rd, Dallas TX 75217	(214) 381-3226
273	12315738	Arrow Academy	PO Box 12207, College Sta TX 77842	(979) 703-8820
274	11913105	Baker-Ripley	PO Box 271389, Houston TX 77277	(713) 667-9400
275	11912618	Calvin Nelms Charter Schools	20625 Clay Rd, Katy TX 77449	(281) 398-8031
276	11912486	Democratic Schools Research	410 Bethel Ln, Bryan TX 77802	(979) 775-2152
277	11912450	East Waco Innovative Sch Dev	1020 Elm St Ste 100, Waco TX 76704	(254) 754-8000
278	11913325	Educational Leadership Inc	3333 Bering Dr Ste 200, Houston TX 77057	(713) 784-6345
279	12361414	Evolution Academy Charter Schs	1101 S Sherman St, Richardson TX 75081	(972) 907-3755
280	11913284	Faith Family Academy Chtr Schs	1608 Osprey Dr, Desoto TX 75115	(972) 224-4110
281	11912321	Golden Rule Schools Inc	2602 W Illinois Ave, Dallas TX 75233	(214) 333-9330
282	12160947	Great Hearts Texas	824 Broadway St Ste 101, San Antonio TX 78215	(210) 888-9475
283	11912307	Gulf Coast Council of La Raza	4129 Greenwood Dr, Corp Christi TX 78416	(361) 881-9988
284	11913624	Harmony Pub Schs-Cosmos Found	9321 W Sam Houston Pkwy S, Houston TX 77099	(713) 343-3333
285	11913193	Jubilee Academic Center Inc	4434 Roland Rd, San Antonio TX 78222	(210) 333-6227
286	11915828	KIPP Texas Public Schs Austin	8509 FM 969 Ste 513, Austin TX 78724	(512) 501-3643
287	11916080	KIPP Texas Public Schs Dallas	1545 S Ewing Ave, Dallas TX 75216	(972) 323-4200
288	11916133	KIPP Texas Public Schs Houston	10711 Kipp Way Dr, Houston TX 77099	(832) 328-1051
289	11916298	KIPP Texas Public Schs Sa	731 Fredericksburg Rd, San Antonio TX 78201	(210) 787-3197
290	11913131	Life School	132 E Ovilla Rd Ste 1A, Red Oak TX 75154	(469) 850-5433
291	11912163	New Frontiers Public Schools	138 Fair Ave, San Antonio TX 78223	(210) 519-3900
292	11913040	Orenda Education	2951 Williams Dr, Georgetown TX 78628	(512) 869-3020
293	11912137	Panola Charter Schools	PO Box 610, Carthage TX 75633	(903) 693-6355
294	11912096	Por Vida Inc	1135 Mission Rd, San Antonio TX 78210	(210) 532-8816
295	12113918	Priority Charter Schools	275 FM 2483, Morgans Point TX 76513	(254) 206-2013
296	11913014	Raul Yzaguirre Sch-Success Org	2950 Broadway St, Houston TX 77017	(713) 640-3700
297	12233855	Responsive Education Solutions	PO Box 292730, Lewisville TX 75029	(972) 316-3663
298	11913507	Richard Milburn Academy Inc	1263 Terminal Loop Rd, Mc Queeney TX 78123	(830) 557-6181
299	11913002	Riverwalk Education Foundation	5300 Wurzbach Rd, San Antonio TX 78238	(210) 957-1955
300	11912981	Salvaging Teens at Risk Inc	4601 N Interstate 35, Denton TX 76207	(940) 383-6655

CMO No.	PID	CMO Name	Address	Phone
301	11911999	South Texas Educ Technologies	2402 E Business 83, Weslaco TX 78596	(956) 969-3092
302	11912967	Southwest Winners Foundation	1258 Austin Hwy, San Antonio TX 78209	(210) 829-8017
303	11912955	Student Alternatives Program	PO Box 15644, San Antonio TX 78212	(210) 227-0295
304	11912931	Tekoa Academy Accel Studies	326 Thomas Blvd, Port Arthur TX 77640	(409) 982-5400
305	11913674	Texans Can Academies	325 W 12th St, Dallas TX 75208	(214) 944-1985
306	11911937	Texas Center for Arts & Acad	3901 S Hulen St, Fort Worth TX 76109	(817) 766-2390
307	11912905	Trinity Charter Schools	8305 Cross Park Dr, Austin TX 78754	(512) 706-7564
308	11911834	Two Dimensions Prep Chtr Acad	12121 Veterans Memorial Dr, Houston TX 77067	(281) 227-4700
309	11913454	Uplift Education	1825 Market Ctr Blvd Ste 500, Dallas TX 75207	(469) 621-8500
310	11911810	Varnett Public School Inc	5025 S Willow Dr, Houston TX 77035	(713) 667-4051
311	11912876	Winfree Academy Charter Schs	1555 Valwood Pkwy Ste 160, Carrollton TX 75006	(972) 869-3250
312	11912864	YES Prep Public Schools	5515 South Loop E Ste B, Houston TX 77033	(713) 967-9000
313	11914616	Imagine Schools Inc	1900 Gallows Rd Ste 250, Vienna VA 22182	(703) 527-2600
314	11914604	K12 Inc	2300 Corporate Park Dr, Herndon VA 20171	(866) 283-0300
315	12305836	Green Dot Pub Schs-Washington	4800 S 188th St Ste 250, Seatac WA 98188	(253) 382-2400
316	12306000	Seeds of Health Inc	1445 S 32nd St, Milwaukee WI 53215	(414) 672-3430